S0-BYP-548

Developing Spreadsheet-Based Decision Support Systems

Using Excel and VBA for Excel

2nd Edition

Sandra D. Ekşioğlu

Industrial and Systems Engineering
Bagley College of Engineering
Mississippi State University

Michelle M.H. Şeref

Virginia Polytechnic Institute and State University, Blacksburg

Ravindra K. Ahuja

Industrial and Systems Engineering
University of Florida, Gainesville
Innovative Scheduling, Inc., Gainesville

Wayne L. Winston

Operations and Decision Technologies
Kelly School of Business
Indiana University, Bloomington

Dynamic Ideas
Belmont, Massachusetts

Dynamic Ideas
43 Lantern Road
Belmont, Mass. 02478
U.S.A.
WWW information and orders: http://www.dynamic-ideas.com

Cover Design: Saumya Ahuja

© 2011 Dynamic Ideas
All rights reserved. No part of this book may be reproduced in any form by any electronic or mechanical means (including photocopying, recording, or information storage and retrieval) without permission in writing from the publisher.

Publisher's Cataloging-In-Publication Data

Ekşioğlu, Sandra D., Şeref, Michelle M.H., Ahuja, Ravindra K., Winston, Wayne L.
Developing Spreadsheet-Based Decision Support Systems
Includes bibliographical references and index
1. Excel. 2. VBA for Excel. 3. Decision Support Systems.

HD30.213.A37 2017

ISBN 13: 978-0-9759146-8-7

Sandra dedicates this book to her family.

Michelle dedicates this book to her parents, Magdi and Roblyn, who have always supported her in every decision she has made.

Ravi dedicates this book to his favorite decision support network: Smita, Saumya, and Shaman.

Wayne dedicates this book to his wonderful family: Vivian, Jennifer and Gregory.

Contents

Preface

Chapter OVERVIEW

Motivation

Developing Spreadsheet-Based Decision Support Systems is intended to be a textbook which describes spreadsheet functionality and modeling in Microsoft Excel, illustrates the programming basic and advanced topics in Visual Basic Applications (VBA) for Excel, and applies these techniques to build decision support systems arising in several disciplines. This book can also be used as a self-learning reference book by practitioners.

Information systems based on decision models are called Decision Support Systems (DSS). A DSS uses the data residing in spreadsheets and/or databases, models it, processes or analyzes it using problem-specific methodologies, and assists the user in the decision-making process through a graphical user interface. Industrial Engineering and Operations Research (IE/OR) and Business School graduates are frequently being employed in positions that require developing DSS. We believe that decision support systems will gain widespread popularity in the future, and knowing how to develop such systems will make our students highly desirable in the workplace.

IE/OR departments and business schools teach their students decision model-based courses that impart spreadsheet modeling, optimization and simulation skills. Most of these departments require their students to take a computer programming course, often in C++, Java or Visual Basic. Several departments require their students to take a database course as well. Thus, students acquire background in modeling, optimization, simulation, database, and programming, but there are no courses that teach students how to integrate the technologies learned in these different courses to build complete decision support systems. Students are given many components, but they are not taught how to assemble them into a complete package suitable for usage by a customer. Decision support systems combine these technologies and are ideally suited to be an integral part of the IE/OR and business school curriculum.

Developing courses that teach our students how to build decision support systems has been a demanding task so far, since it requires the availability of platforms that allow the integration of various technologies (data, models, and programming). However, in the past decade, several platforms that allow such integration have become available. One such platform is the Microsoft Excel spreadsheet package. Spreadsheets allow data analysis, mathematical modeling, optimization, and simulation, and they have emerged as one of the most popular software packages engineers and managers use in their workplace. Spreadsheet modeling courses have become standard courses in many departments, and a need is now felt for the next level follow-up course. Microsoft Excel has a built-in programming language called *Visual Basic Applications* (VBA) for Excel. Excel combined with VBA for Excel provides a complete environment for building a spreadsheet-based DSS. VBA for Excel provides a mechanism for data analysis, implementing optimization and simulation models, and building graphical user interfaces. We have developed a complete set of course material in the Excel framework for a course on Spreadsheet-Based Decision Support Systems. This textbook is a byproduct of this effort. One can alternatively build decision support systems involving databases and using more sophisticated web-enabled technologies that are the subject of another parallel effort that led to the companion book *Developing Web-Enabled Decision Support Systems,* by Abhijit A. Pol and Ravindra K. Ahuja.

DSS development skills are important to all IE/OR and business school graduates for several reasons. First, having these skills will allow them to develop simple tools that might increase their productivity. Second, many graduates will be involved in information systems development during their career, and having a better understanding of the underlying technology will allow them to play a more useful role in the development process. Third, our graduates can develop a prototype system including the techniques learned here to establish a system proof-of-concept before it is turned over to professional programmers. Fourth, several graduates are often employed in departments that are service organizations catering to the modeling and optimization needs of other departments such as manufacturing, sales, marketing, accounting, and purchasing. These departments often request decision tools to be built to meet their business needs. The users in this department are not modeling experts, and the mathematical complexity of these models becomes an impediment to their use. If our graduates are well versed in the DSS building process, they can build optimization and simulation models, and package these models within friendly interfaces so that the modeling complexity is hidden from the user. This will make modeling and optimization approaches more popular in the workplace. Finally, with data mining becoming increasingly important, companies are realizing an important need for persons who understand data, models, algorithms, and information technology; our graduates can fulfill this critical need. Our students possess modeling and algorithmic skills to analyze the data but lack information systems development skills, and providing them with these skills will make them ideally suited for this task.

Book Contents

In order for the reader to learn how to develop a spreadsheet-based decision support system, we must teach them how to use Excel functionalities and the programming language-VBA for Excel. We also need to illustrate through some practical applications how to build such decision support systems. Currently, there are no books available in the market that include all three of these topics comprehensively. Our book is intended to meet this need. There are three parts of this textbook: learning Excel functionality, learning how to program with VBA for Excel, and learning how to develop DSS applications through several case studies.

Part I—Excel Essentials: This part presents an overview of Excel basic and extended functionalities. The basic functionality topics include referencing and names, functions and formulas, charts, pivot tables, and other Excel basics. The extended functionality topics include statistical analysis, Risk Solver Platform for Education for modeling and solving optimization and simulation problems, and working with large data. The purpose of this part of the book is to give the reader an idea of the tools available in Excel which span beyond simple spreadsheet functionality to include modeling, optimization, simulation, and advanced analysis. These tools are an important component of DSS application development.

Part II—VBA for Excel: This part presents an overview of programming in VBA and manipulating Excel objects. An introduction to the visual basic environment is given and macros are explained. The programming topics discussed include variables, procedures, programming structures, and arrays. User interface development is then discussed through the explanation of user forms, form controls, and navigational buttons. In the last few chapters of this part of the book, extended Excel functionality topics are revisited to illustrate the enhancement that VBA offers: optimization and simulation using Object Oriented API in Risk Solver Platform are revisited, and working with large data in VBA is revisited. The programming topics discussed are essential to the development of DSS applications.

Part III—Case Studies: This part presents several fully developed DSS applications arising in IE/OR, business, and general engineering. The case studies are preceded by three chapters which explain the DSS development process and provide more detailed instructions on designing a good user interface and using programming principles in VBA. It is important for the reader to understand how to plan the DSS application, prepare the spreadsheet, and implement the code so that the user's objectives are met and the decision maker will truly be aided by the DSS system they will use. We have developed 25 case studies covering a variety of DSS applications; however, due to space limitation we were not able to include all of the case studies in this printed form of the book. We have included 10 case studies in this book and the remaining case studies are available on the book website: www.dssbooks.com.

This book explains all topics through classical examples selected from IE/OR, business school, and engineering curriculum. Each new concept or idea is illustrated through examples and reinforced through exercises at the end of the chapter. We have also created an extensive list and description of possible student projects, which will further enhance students' learning experience.

Required Background

We assume that the reader has some basic Excel experience. We provide some links on the book website for online tutorials on Excel for those who do not have the required experience. The book is sufficiently comprehensive in its coverage on Excel functionalities that even experienced Excel users will find the material presented educative. We have, however, not tried to cover every Excel feature as it would have taken too much space. We have covered just enough topics in just enough details so that decent decision support systems can be built.

We expect some operations research (OR) and modeling experience in Chapter 8 of the book (solver and mathematical programming). A DSS course is typically offered to junior/senior level students, and an OR/modeling course should be a prerequisite, so most students should have that background. However, we do provide several examples in this chapter so that even a reader with minimal modeling experience should be able to understand how to formulate an optimization problem in the spreadsheet and use Risk Solver Platform to find the optimal solution.

The book does not require any programming experience. We instruct the reader on how to create variables, define functions, use basic programming structures, and work with arrays in VBA. The reader will also learn how to create good graphical user interfaces in Excel through user forms and various controls. It is useful if the reader has some programming experience, but it is not required. As with *Part I* of the book for experienced Excel users, some experienced programmers may skip some chapters in *Part II* of the book. However, it is good to review the programming examples in VBA. These chapters also include several applications which may be considered as "mini" DSS applications. Therefore, even for an experienced programmer, it is useful to review these chapters to strengthen the reader's skills in using VBA in the context of developing a DSS.

We hope that after learning the Excel background and VBA material in *Parts I* and *II* of the book, the reader will be able to develop any of the case studies found in *Part III*. The case studies construct prototype decision support systems that are simple enough to be easily understood by the reader and complex enough to be reasonably accurate representatives of real-world problems. The case studies require that the reader has learned good VBA programming skills from Part II of the book.

Suggestions for Instructors

This book is primarily intended as a textbook for undergraduate and graduate students in the IE/OR and business school curriculums. This book can also be used as a self-study manual. DSS are great tools for consulting, and consultants can use the skills learnt profitably in developing their consulting practice.

As a textbook, this book can be used in a variety of ways to teach different courses. For an undergraduate-level course, instructors can cover topics at slower pace. In a graduate-level course, instructors can spend less time on Excel functionalities and cover more case studies. Instructors can offer semester-long courses (covering all the material), or half-semester/quarter courses on VBA for Excel and case studies. We present a variety of case studies from simple to complex, and the instructor can select the case studies that best suit the time frame and background of their students.

The material can also be used to supplement the courses currently taught. For example, several IE/OR departments and business schools offer spreadsheet-based Operations Research courses. The instructor can cover a module on VBA for Excel within the course and show how a simple Excel application can be easily turned into a powerful DSS. Similarly, logistics and supply-chain courses are becoming standard courses in the curriculum. The instructor can illustrate in a few class hours how to build a decision support system based on some decision problem in inventory, distribution, or transportation, and then assign student projects on building similar applications. Thus, this textbook can be used in a variety of ways, from teaching new courses to supplementing existing courses.

The spreadsheet-based DSS course may be taught in different formats including or excluding several different chapters from our text. We propose that the general structure of the course should begin by teaching Excel functionality to students to ensure they are familiar with the spreadsheet environment; then teach VBA programming to show students how to work with variables and programming structures as well as how to create a user interface; the course should then end with a full discussion of decision support systems and instructing students how to combine their acquired Excel and VBA skills to develop a DSS application. The text has been designed to follow this general course structure.

From our experience, it seems most productive to hold this course in a computer laboratory or require students to bring laptops to the class. We recommend the instructor to illustrate concepts with hands-on examples on the computer screen while students are watching and trying to do it themselves on their computers. We also recommend that there be a teaching assistant available to help students as they are doing the hands-on examples on their personal computers while the instructor illustrates the examples simultaneously at the front of the class. We have found that students learn much more in this manner as they experiment with Excel and VBA themselves along with the instructor and teaching assistant readily available to answer questions or address their difficulties.

In this suggested setting of a computer laboratory or class with laptops, we also suggest that the course be taught in two-hour sessions instead of one-hour sessions. This allows students enough time to set up their computers and instructors enough time to illustrate a full example during the class. The course material can be adjusted to teach a semester course, a half-semester module or a quarter course. The material can be covered in different rigors and at different paces and some of the material can be assigned for self-study.

We have discovered by teaching these courses over the years that students learn the most by doing course projects. Lectures teach them the technology and how to use it, but unless they apply it themselves to build complete systems, they do not assimilate the material. In addition, the process of developing a full system from conception to completion and seeing the fruits of their labor gives them tremendous satisfaction and confidence. Course projects may be done by teams of students, in which case they promote teamwork—an essential skill in any workplace. We have developed over 100 course projects from different application areas in IE/OR, business as well as engineering curriculums. These projects are available on the book website. Course projects can be assigned on an individual basis or in groups depending on the course size and course format. Students can select a project from this list or they can create their own project as long as it is sufficiently interesting and challenging. We require our students to present these projects before the entire class when completed. Many students have told us that doing these projects and building complete decision support systems was the most educative and learning experience for them in the course.

Changes Made in the Second Edition

We made two major changes to this new edition of the book. First, we feature Microsoft Excel 2010. Therefore, we have updated all of the Excel features and examples to reflect the changes made to Excel's interface and functionalities. Second, we introduce Risk Solver Platform for Education to model and solve optimization and simulation problems.

Microsoft Excel 2010 is more powerful and offers a number of additional functionalities as compared to its predecessors. This new version of Excel supports the processing of larger data sets. Excel spreadsheets now support data sets with up to 1.1 million rows and 16,000 columns. This is a large improvement compared to Excel 2003 which supported spreadsheets with up to 65,536 rows and 256 columns of data.

However, the most drastic change in Excel 2007 and 2010 as compared with prior versions of this product is the user interface. With Office 2007, Microsoft introduced an entirely new interface. Menus and toolbars are replaced with the Ribbon. Excel 2010 introduces one additional tab on the Ribbon, the File menu. Most Ribbon tabs contain commands that you use when working with your file. The File menu includes commands you use when you are finished working with the file, such as, save, open, recently used files, etc. In Chapter 2 we give an overview of the Ribbon and Quick Access Toolbar to help readers become familiar with these features and understand their functionalities. Based on our experience, the Ribbon is a user-friendly interface with many functional benefits.

Excel 2010 also provides more and better formatting options. In Chapter 2 we discuss conditional formatting and give examples of how to use new conditional formatting features such as icon sets, color scales, and in-cell bar charts. In this chapter we also discuss how to use different collections of Excel's new built-in themes to format a workbook. In Chapter 3 we discuss the new and improved charting interface of Excel and introduce Sparklines. We give a number of examples to highlight the benefits of using sparklines.

Excel 2010 also has improved capabilities for working with pivot tables. In Chapter 6 we give examples to introduce Slicers which are visual graphical filters you can use to filter the data in a pivot table. The new Excel commands now make it easier to create and modify a pivot table.

Excel 2010 also has an improved function library. The number of built-in functions available in Excel has increased to 400 as compared to 255 offered by Excel 2003. This increase is mainly due to the inclusion in Excel 2010 of about 89 functions available only to users that had access to Analysis ToolPak in earlier versions of Excel. In Chapter 4 we give an example of how to use the new IFERROR function of Excel. Excel has also improved the accuracy of some of its statistical distribution, financial, and math functions. The consistency of the function names has also been improved. For example, many of the distribution functions now include a dot in their name (NORM.DIST, NORM.S.DIST, NORM.INV, and NORM.S.INV) to distinguish between distribution and inverse distribution functions. Similarly, the change in name of statistical functions VAR, VARP, STDEV and STDEVP to VAR.S, VAR.P, STDEV.S and STDEV.P make it easier for the reader to understand their functionality. These function updates are reflected in Chapters 4 and 7.

In Chapter 10, we introduce the Official Excel Table. The new *Table* tools of Excel make the task of organizing and manipulating data in tables much easier. We give an example of how to use the tool when working with large data sets. We discuss the new *Remove Duplicates* command which removes any duplicates that may result when we combine together different sets of data.

In this new edition of the book we introduce Risk Solver Platform for Education, a trademark of Frontline Systems Inc. This is a new add-in for Excel that provides a variety of tools one can use to perform optimization, simulation, and sensitivity analysis, as well as build decision trees. Our motivation for using this product is twofold. First, Risk Solver Platform improves optimization and simulation capabilities of Excel. We can now solve larger problems faster (see Appendix A for a comparison of this product with the Standard Solver of Excel). Risk Solver Platform offers algorithms to solve linear, mixed integer, and smooth and non-smooth nonlinear programming problems. Second, the interface of Risk Solver Platform is user friendly and provides a variety of commands one can use to build a problem, solve the problem, and analyze the results.

In Chapters 8 and 9 we show how to use Risk Solver Platform to model and solve spreadsheet-based optimization and simulation problems. In Chapters 19 and 20 we discuss how to use Object Oriented API with Risk Solver Platform to modify and solve optimization and simulation models using VBA commands. We have also updated most of the case studies in Part III of the book to use Risk Solver Platform instead of the Standard Solver for solving optimization problems. The use of Risk Solver Platform has especially improved the coding efficiency and performance of the case studies that require simulation modeling and analysis; such as, Single and Multiple Server Queuing, Retirement Planning, Birthday Simulation, and Reliability Analysis. Instead of "manually" generating random problem inputs within For, Next loops in VBA to simulate a system, we now use Object Oriented API to read an existing simulation spreadsheet model, modify problem inputs, and collect a variety of statistics.

Website Contents

We have developed a website for this textbook which contains valuable resources for both students and instructors. The URL of this website is:

www.dssbooks.com

This website contains the following material:

- Excel files for the examples covered in all chapters
- Excel files for all the Hands-On Exercises covered in all chapters
- Excel files for all the 25 case studies developed by us
- Additional chapters describing the 15 case studies which were not included in the book
- PowerPoint presentations for all book chapters on Excel and VBA for Excel
- License for the educational version of Risk Solver Platform
- A booklet containing about 100 student projects
- Sample course schedules

The Solutions Manual for the book exercises is also available and will be provided to instructors offering courses using this book as the principle textbook. The website provides the email addresses for requesting the Solution Manual and giving your feedback to the book authors.

Acknowledgements

There are many people whom we would like to thank for making significant contributions to this book writing project. First and foremost, we would like to thank Dr. Donald Hearn, Chair of the Industrial and Systems Engineering Department at the University of Florida, who has been the driving force in this book-writing initiative. He motivated us to teach courses that incorporate greater levels of information technology in the IE/OR curriculum at the University of Florida. He also inspired us to write this book and provided constant encouragement throughout its evolution from concept to reality. We are truly thankful to him for his encouragement and support.

Several students helped us in the development of the book at different stages. These students included both undergraduate and graduate students of the Industrial and Systems Engineering and English Departments at the University of Florida and Mississippi State University. In particular, we would like to thank Richard Barrow, Melissa Sullivan, William Bowen, Preston Cauley and Gokçe Palak for the contributions they made in developing exercises and case studies; Carolyn Houston, Krystal Harriot, Sarah Schiff, Michael Smith, and Tamara Johnson for their copy editing of the text; and Ali Abbas, Krishna Jha, and Burak Ekşioglu for developing team projects. Our special thanks go to Ashish Nemani who assisted us in preparing the index and proofreading the book. We would also like to thank Guvenc Şahin and Onun Şeref for their feedback from teaching a DSS course using the material we developed. We are also appreciative of the feedback provided by students enrolled in these initial DSS courses. Several students, who assisted us in the book-writing project, were supported by the National Science Foundation Course Curriculum Development Grant 0341203.

Next, we would like to thank the Frontline Systems team for continuously supporting us with advice when revising several chapters of this new edition. In particular, we would like to thank Edwin Straver for never failing to respond very quickly to our questions and graciously offering his expert opinion.

Finally, we thank our families for their constant support and encouragement.

Sandra D. Ekşioğlu
Michelle M.H. Şeref
Ravindra K. Ahuja
Wayne L. Winston

CHAPTER

one Introduction

chapter **OVERVIEW**

1.1 *Introduction to Decision Support Systems*

As a new graduate, equipped with the modeling and algorithmic skills taught in a standard operations management curriculum, Susan is ready to solve real-world problems. With a knowledge and understanding of theory and applications of mathematical programming, simulation techniques, inventory management, supply-chain management, and other industrial engineering (IE) or operations research (OR) and business topics, she is ready to help her company solve distribution problems by linear programming, inventory problems by applying the economic order quantity (EOQ) model, and manpower planning problems by integer programming. However, as she works on projects with her experienced colleagues and presents results to management, she realizes that she needs more than her models and equations. The management needs Susan to help solve decision problems, but they only want to know the final results of the analysis; they have no time or interest in understanding the mathematical model for these problems. They want this decision analysis tool to be available as a software system in which they can modify parameters and see different results for various scenarios. However, Susan is clueless about how to develop such a system. She knows the right model but she does not know how to package her model and how to present it with friendly graphical user interface. She feels that her education did not impart to her the skills she needs to meet her job requirements.

Susan is not the only one facing problems in her job as an operations research or business decision analyst. This is a widely prevalent problem which is not addressed in the current IE/OR or business curriculums. As OR practitioners and business analysts, students are support staff members and are required to build systems for non-OR users. They must know how to package OR/business models so that they can be comfortably used by top managers and other co-workers. Real-life decision making often requires building interactive systems, which students must know how to design and implement. To summarize, students must learn sufficient information technology skills so that they can build intelligent information systems, alternatively, called decision support systems, which can run sophisticated models at the back-end, but are friendly enough at the front end to be used comfortably by any user.

A decision support system (DSS) gives its users access to a variety of data sources, modeling techniques, and stored domain knowledge via an easy to use graphical user interface (GUI). For example, a DSS can use the data residing in spreadsheets or databases, prepare a mathematical model using this data, solve or analyze this model using problem-specific methodologies, and can assist the user in the decision-making process through a graphical user interface. Students are frequently being employed in positions that require developing DSS which are gaining widespread popularity. As more and more companies install enterprise resource planning (ERP) packages and invest in building data warehouses, those who are able to create decision technology driven applications that interface with these systems and analyze the data they provide will become increasingly valuable. Indeed, imparting DSS development skills, which combine OR/business skills with information technology (IT) skills, will make students highly sought after in the modern workplace.

Developing courses that teach our students how to build decision support systems has been a challenging task so far since it requires the availability of platforms which allow the integration of various technologies (data, models, codes, etc.). However, in the past few years, several platforms have become available which allow such integration. One such platform is Microsoft Excel. Excel, which is the most widely used spreadsheet package among managers and engineers, allows data storage and model building. Excel also has many built-in programs as well as many add-on programs available that allow optimization and simulation of various models built in Excel. Excel also has a macro programming language, Visual Basic for Applications (VBA), which allows building GUIs and manipulating Excel objects. Thus, Excel provides a platform in which fairly sophisticated DSS applications can be built. This book imparts the skills needed to build such systems.

1.2 *Defining a Decision Support System*

A decision support system is a model-based or knowledge-based system intended to support managerial decision making in semi-structured or unstructured situations (Turban and Aronson, 2001). A DSS is not meant to replace a decision maker, but to extend his/her decision making capabilities. It uses data, provides a clear user interface, and can incorporate the decision maker's own insights. Some of the major DSS capabilities are the following:

1. A DSS brings together human judgment and computerized information for semi-structured decision situations. Such problems cannot be conveniently solved by standard quantitative techniques or computerized systems.
2. A DSS is designed to be easy to use. User friendliness, graphical capabilities, and an interactive human-machine interface greatly increase the effectiveness of a DSS.
3. A DSS usually uses models for analyzing decision-making situations and may also include a knowledge component.
4. A DSS attempts to improve the effectiveness of decision making rather than its efficiency.
5. A DSS provides support for various managerial levels from line mangers to top executives. It provides support to individuals as well as groups. It can be PC-based or web-based.

A DSS application contains five components: database, model base, knowledge base, GUI, and user (see Figure 1.1). The database stores the data, model and knowledge bases store the collections of models and knowledge, respectively, and the GUI allows the user to interact with the database, model base, and knowledge base. The database and knowledge base can be found in a basic information system. The knowledge base may contain simple search results for analyzing the data in the database. For example, the knowledge base may contain how many employees in a company database have worked at the company for over ten years. A decision support system is an intelligent information system because of the addition of the model base. The model base has the models used to perform optimization, simulation, or other algorithms for advanced calculations and analysis. These models allow the decision support system to not only supply information to the user but aid the user in making a decision. We now present a more detailed look at each of these components.

Database: The database provides the data with which decisions are made. The data may reside in spreadsheets or a data warehouse, a repository for relevant corporate decision-making data. The database allows a user to access, manipulate, and query data. Some examples of databases would include a spreadsheet containing personal banking account information or a data warehouse containing shipment records of various products.

Model Base: A model base contains statistical, financial, optimization, or simulation models that provide the analysis capabilities in a DSS. Some popular optimization models include linear programming, integer programming, and nonlinear programming. The DSS allows the ability to invoke, run, and change any model or combine multiple models. An example of a model base would be an integer programming model used to solve a capital budgeting problem.

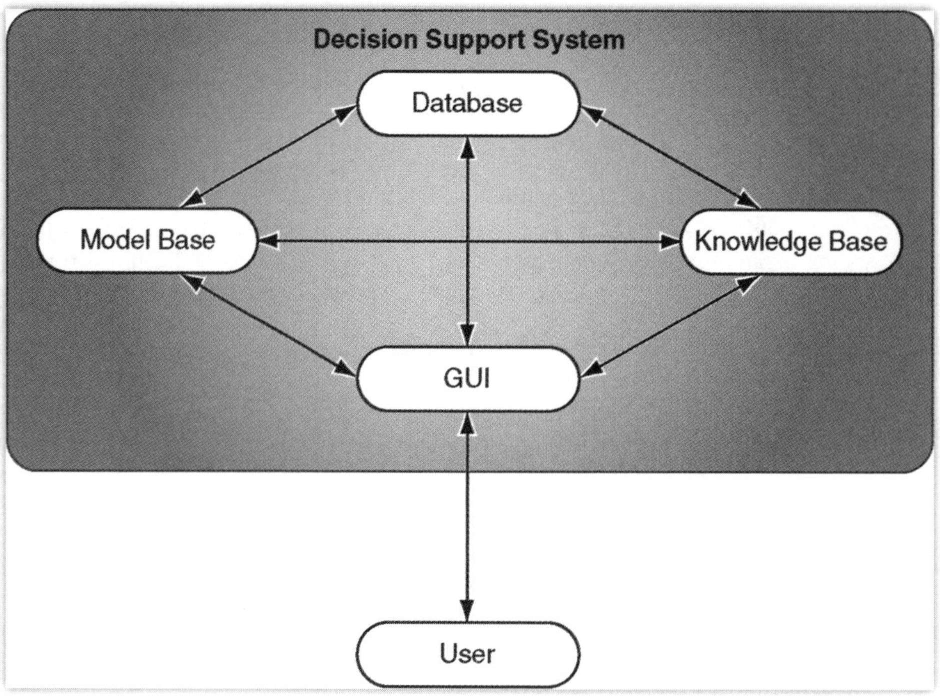

Figure 1.1 A schematic view of a decision support system.

Knowledge Base: Many managerial decision making problems are so complex that they require special expertise for their solution. The knowledge base part of a DSS allows this expertise to be stored and accessed to enhance the operation of other DSS components. For example, credit card companies use a DSS to identify credit card thefts. They store in their knowledge base the spending patterns that usually follow credit card thefts; any abnormal activity in an account would trigger checking for the presence of those patterns and a possible suspension of the account.

GUI: The graphical user interface covers all aspects of communication between a user and a DSS application. The user interface interacts with the database, model base, and knowledge base. It allows the user to enter data or update data, run the chosen model, view the results of the model, and possibly rerun the application with different data and/or model combinations. The user interface is perhaps one of the most important components of a DSS because much of the flexibility and ease of use of a DSS are derived from this component.

User: The person who uses the DSS to support the decision making process is called the user, or decision maker. A DSS has two broad classes of users: managers and staff specialists, or engineers. When designing a DSS, it is important to know for which class of users the DSS is being designed. In general, managers expect a DSS to be more user-friendly than do staff specialists.

A DSS should be distinguished from more common management information systems (MIS). An MIS can be viewed as an information system that can generate standard and exception reports and summaries for managers, provide answers to queries, and help in monitoring the performance of a system using simple data processing. A DSS can be viewed as a more sophisticated MIS where we allow the use of models and knowledge bases to process the data and perform analysis.

1.3 *Decision Support Systems Applications*

Given the above definition of a decision support system, we have developed several spreadsheet-based DSS applications in Excel. Using the spreadsheet functionality in Excel and the VBA programming capabilities, a complete decision support system can be developed. As an IE/OR or business graduate, students will discover opportunities in their careers to develop and use DSS applications. Many students who have taken DSS courses have reported that their skills of combining modeling with an information technology packaging have truly helped them be outstanding at their jobs. Let us consider two examples of DSS applications which may be found in industry.

Car Production: Consider a factory which produces cars. The manager of the factory, probably a business or IE/OR graduate, may need to make some large-scale decisions about ordering parts, hiring/firing employees, finding new suppliers, or making changes to the production process. Let us focus on a production process DSS application. The manager may be deciding where to place a new piece of equipment or how to add a new product part to the production sequence. With the use of some basic simulation and analysis tools, one could develop a DSS which allows the manager to enter the parameters to describe a possible scenario and see how it would affect production. The manager may not want to know the details of the models used, but rather what would be the affect on cost and production time and quantity if a specific change was made. This is just one example of how a DSS could be used to aid in the car production industry.

Railroad Car Management: Consider a railroad company which owns several trains on which they place several thousand railroad cars which ship to several cities in the country. A distribution manager, again with an IE/OR or business background, may need to decide which cars should go on which trains to which cities. He would benefit from using an optimization model which allows him to modify certain constraints or focus on various objectives and compare the resulting distribution plans. He may want to display the car and train plans visually, may be projected on a country map, to have a better understanding of the effects of one solution compared to another. A DSS would aid him in accomplishing this analysis and making a decision which considers all scenarios and possible outcomes.

The applications we develop are basic illustrations of decisions which are made in IE/OR and business industries. Two examples, selected from the DSS applications developed in Part III of this book, are described below.

Portfolio Management and Optimization: In this application, we allow users to create and/or edit their portfolio as well as optimize their investments. To create a portfolio, users can choose from a list of stocks in a database in Excel and add or remove them to/from their portfolio. The stocks are listed by name and category. These stocks can also be compared using their historical annual returns and changes in market price. Once users have created their portfolio, they may also edit it at any time. Users may then optimize their investment by specifying a desired return on their portfolio and the amount available for investing. The application then solves an optimization problem which minimizes users' risk on their selected portfolio. The suggested investment strategy is then displayed to the users. This application allows users to interact with the database of stock information and the knowledge base of comparative statistics. The model base for this DSS uses the Excel Solver to perform an optimization which minimizes the user's risk on the portfolio investments.

Facility Layout: In this application, we study a facility location problem which consists of placing n facilities at n locations to minimize the total handling cost. This problem is also known as the Quadratic Assignment Problem (QAP). The QAP arises in many other applications, such as the allocation of plants to candidate locations, the backboard wiring problem, design of control panels and typewriter keyboards, turbine balancing, etc. The user begins the application by providing the size of their facility. From the dimensions provided, a layout is displayed and a distance matrix is created. Random flow matrix values are generated which the user may overwrite if desired. From these two matrices, the cost matrix is derived; the total of the costs from this matrix is minimized by performing a pair-wise local search on the user's facility. The user may also opt to fix some facilities so that they cannot be moved when the local search is performed. The user may run this local search algorithm automatically or participate in the decision taken at each iteration. The final layout is then displayed to the user. The model base for this application uses an algorithm developed in the VBA code. This DSS application aids a facility designer in creating a facility layout which minimizes total handling cost. It can be used to solve typical facility layout problems which may be encountered by plant managers, school administrators, or in other applications. This DSS can also be used as a pedagogical tool in facility planning courses to illustrate the pairwise local search technique.

1.4 *Textbook Overview*

We now present an overview of the three parts of the text: Part I Excel Basics, Part II VBA for Excel, and Part III DSS Case Studies.

1.4.1 Overview of Excel

Microsoft Excel spreadsheets have become one of the most popular software packages in the business world, so much so that business schools have developed several popular Excel based courses. A spreadsheet application has functionality for storing and organizing data, performing various calculations, and using additional packages, called Add-Ins, for more advanced problem solving and analysis. *Part I* of this book discusses two aspects of Excel: basic functionality and extended functionality.

The topics we discuss on Excel basic functionality include referencing and names, functions and formulas, charts, and pivot tables. These are standard tools that may be common to most spreadsheet users. The topics we discuss on Excel extended functionality include statistical analysis, mathematical programming, simulation, and querying large data. We introduce Risk Solver Platform, an Excel add-in, to add in building simulation and optimization models. These tools are especially important for building a decision support system. The ability to model a problem and solve it or simulate it adds the model base component of the DSS we are building. There are several examples given in the chapters in this part of the book which illustrate how these tools can be applied. It is important that the reader become familiar with the capabilities of Excel so that they know what they can offer the user when developing a decision support system.

1.4.2 Overview of VBA for Excel

VBA for Excel is a programming language that allows for further manipulation of the Excel functionalities. VBA for Excel also allows the developer to create dynamic applications which can receive user input for the model base component of the DSS. VBA allows users without knowledge of Excel to be able to use spreadsheet-based DSS applications. *Part II* of this book teaches important features of VBA for Excel.

We begin the VBA part of the book by illustrating the idea of macros and the visual basic environment. Then, we discuss how to work with variables, procedures, programming structures, and arrays in VBA. VBA for Excel is an easy to understand programming language. Even if the reader has not programmed before, they should be able to program several types of applications after reading these chapters. The student will learn how to program in VBA for Excel, which will enable to them to quickly learn VBA for other Microsoft applications such as Access or Outlook as well as give them the basics for programming in any language. We then show the reader how to create a user interface in VBA. This discussion includes building user forms, working with several different form controls, using navigational functions, and designing a clear and professional application. VBA is beneficial as it places all of the complicated spreadsheet calculations and any other analysis in the background of a user-friendly system.

We then revisit some of the extended Excel functionality topics from Part I of the book. We show how VBA can enhance the modeling, simulation, and query features of Excel. Each of these chapters includes an application of a small DSS which combines the tools taught in VBA with the functionality taught in Excel. These techniques are especially important to understand in order to build complete DSS applications.

1.4.3 Overview of Case Studies

Part III of the book illustrates the relevance and importance of decision support systems in the fields of industrial and systems engineering, business, and some general engineering. We strive to accomplish this by showing how to develop DSS applications which integrate databases, models, methodologies, and user interfaces.

We have developed over 25 case studies. We have included some of these in the book and made the remaining case studies available at the website: www.dssbooks.com. Most of the case studies consist of developing a complete decision support system and are based on an important application of IE/OR or business. We have also included some simpler case studies which apply to general engineering concepts. Through these case studies, students will learn how IE/OR and business techniques apply to real-life decision problems and how those techniques can be effectively used to build DSS applications.

Some of our case studies include portfolio management and optimization, facility location, queuing systems, critical path method (or project management), and a student information system. There are also case studies on forecasting, inventory scheduling, supply chain management, and capital budgeting. These case studies are just some of the numerous case studies we may develop in order to illustrate how DSS applications can be developed by combining information technology tools with operations research and business tools to solve important decision problems. Extensions are listed for each case study for students to attempt or to use as ideas for other projects.

In this part of the book, we also propose a general DSS development process (Chapter 22). After the reader has learned how to work in the Excel spreadsheet environment (Part I) and is able to program in VBA to manipulate Excel objects and perform advanced calculations and analysis (Part II), they must then be able to combine these tools to develop a complete DSS application. Chapter 22 describes to the reader how to plan the DSS model and create an overview of the application, prepare the worksheets, create the user interface, and write the procedures so that the user's objectives are met and the decision maker will truly be aided by the DSS system they will use. In Chapter 23, we discuss how to design good graphical user interfaces and in Chapter 24, we discuss how to use good programming principles while developing a DSS. We give several examples of GUI designs to illustrate the importance of clarity and consistency when interacting with the user. The programming principles discussed will help the reader avoid errors in the DSS coding. These are both important chapters for the reader to understand before developing complete DSS applications.

1.4.4 Overview of Appendices

We have three Appendices chapters at the end of the book. The first chapter, Appendix A, gives an overview of various Excel Add-In programs. We review the Analysis Toolpak, covered in Chapters 7 and 9, and the Standard Excel Solver. We also explain how to use the Premium Solver and present a comparison between the Premium and Standard Solvers. We then give an overview of some statistical and simulation Add-Ins, namely CPLEX, @RISK, Crystal Ball, and StatTools. The next chapter, Appendix B, describes how to perform debugging and error checking in VBA for Excel. We present several methods that can be used to prevent errors and check for errors. This may be a very useful appendix to refer to while learning the VBA topics discussed in Part II of the book. In the last chapter, Appendix C, we discuss advanced programming topics. One of these topics is object-oriented programming using class modules. We describe how class modules can be used to define new objects, properties, methods, and events. Another advanced programming topic is learning how to call outside applications from within a VBA procedure. This may be useful for running more complicated software or allowing the user an external interface to a needed feature not available in Excel.

1.5 *Summary*

- Decision support systems are model-based or knowledge-based systems which support managerial decision making; they are not meant to replace a decision maker, but to extend his/her decision making capabilities.
- There are five components to a DSS: database, model base, knowledge base, GUI, and user.
- Excel is a spreadsheet application with functionality for storing and organizing data, performing various calculations, and using additional packages for more advanced problem solving and analysis.
- VBA is a programming language that allows for further manipulation of the Excel functionalities and creation of dynamic applications which can receive user input for the model base component of the DSS.
- The case studies are intended to show the reader how to develop DSS applications which integrate databases, models, methodologies, and user interfaces.

1.6 Exercises

1.6.1 Review Questions

1. What are the components of a decision support system?
2. What is the difference between an information system and a decision support system?
3. What are some industrial engineering or business problems that may use a spreadsheet application like Excel to organize data? What kind of analysis might be done with this data using Excel functionality?
4. What user interface would be necessary to communicate with a user who does not have a background in Excel or VBA programming?
5. What are some applications of industrial engineering for which a decision support system could be built?

CHAPTER

two

Excel Basics and Formatting

chapter

OVERVIEW

2.1 *Introduction*

This chapter provides a review of basic Excel functionality. It is intended for those readers who have a very brief experience with using Excel or no experience at all. It is important to be familiar with Excel's spreadsheet environment in order to increase the efficiency of developing spreadsheet-based DSS applications in Excel. The formatting techniques will be important for presenting information and results to the user as well as in developing a clear user interface.

In this chapter, the reader will learn how to:

- Work with the Excel object hierarchy.
- Perform basic data entry and data copying and pasting in cells.
- Work with the Ribbon and Quick Access toolbars.
- Customize the Ribbon and Quick Access toolbars.
- Format cells.
- Use conditional formatting.

2.2 *Defining the Set of Excel Objects*

The elements of Excel that we work with in standard spreadsheet applications and in Visual Basic for Applications (VBA) programming are called ***objects***. Some examples of Excel *objects* include the workbook, the worksheet, a range of cells, and a cell itself. A workbook, the main file that we build in Excel, can contain several worksheets (Excel spreadsheets), charts, and other advanced *objects*. Excel groups *objects* according to their order in the ***object hierarchy***. That is, the workbook *object* includes the worksheet *object*, which includes the range *object*, which includes the cell *object*. The entire system of *objects* makes up the ***object model***. We can manipulate these *objects* in any spreadsheet and especially in VBA coding.

To clarify this concept, let us use the simple example of a book. The objects of a book are parts, chapters, pages, and words. A part contains many chapters, a chapter contains many pages, and each page contains many words. Understanding the object hierarchy in Excel helps us to quickly locate objects.

Objects will become very important when using Visual Basic for Applications. Each application—Excel, Word, PowerPoint and Access—has its own object model. Therefore, in order to manipulate an object in an application, the programmer must understand the object hierarchy. For a listing of the complete Excel object hierarchy, refer to Microsoft Excel Online Help from the *Help* menu option.

Summary

Objects:	The elements manipulated in spreadsheet applications and VBA programming.
Object Hierarchy:	An ordered listing of all objects.
Object Model:	The entire system of objects.

2.3 *Entering Data into Cells*

Data entry in Excel pertains to four different types of data: numbers, text, formulas, and Boolean values (true or false). We will discuss the latter two in subsequent chapters. Numbers and text are ***simple values***. To enter this type of data into a table, we type a number or text directly in each cell. In Figure 2.1, we have typed the numbers in cells 3 through 8 of column B as shown; we have also typed the word *Data* in cell 2 of column B.

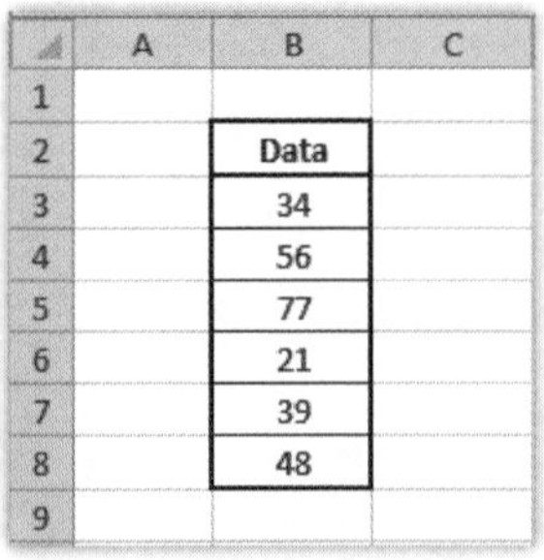

Figure 2.1 These simple values have been entered by typing directly in the cells.

To copy a cell or range of cells to surrounding cells, we click on the cell or range that we want to copy and place the cursor in the lower right-hand corner. The cursor then transforms into a small cross. Then, we ***click-and-drag*** the cursor so that a box encloses the entire area to which we would like to transfer data. In Figure 2.2, we have highlighted the set of numbers in column B and then moved the cursor to the right to copy the set into column C.

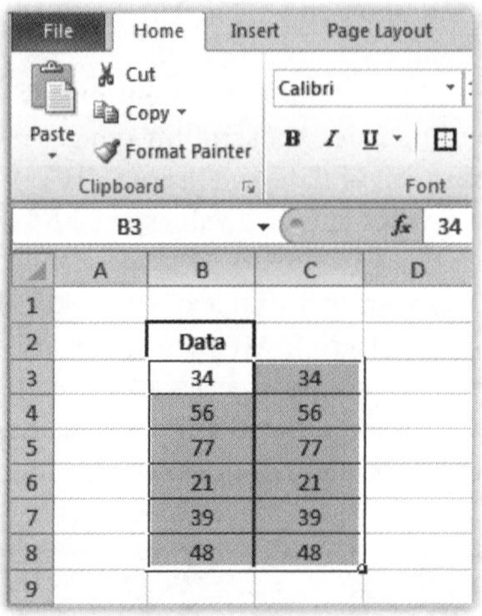

Figure 2.2 Copying a range of cells.

Excel automatically enters data if it detects a pattern. For example, if we are creating a list and numbering down a column of cells, we type "1, 2, 3" in different cells and then use the click-and-drag method described above to copy the cells to the end of the column. This time, however, Excel recognizes the numerical pattern and, instead of copying "1 2 3" again, continues the count for us (see Figure 2.3). If we are numbering by even or odd numbers only, Excel creates the same pattern.

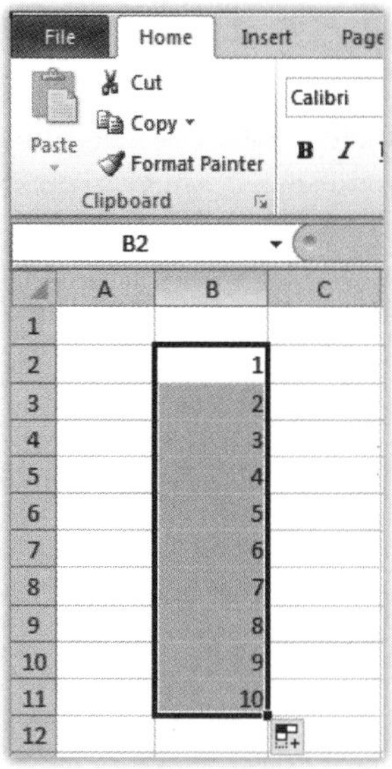

Figure 2.3 Excel automatically numbers sequentially when copying from a pattern it recognizes.

Two useful shortcuts simplify these functions. The first, a shortcut for the click-and-drag option, allows us to copy a formula to the end of a list of data. If we want to copy a formula to the end of a list of data, we can double-click on the small cross cursor on the cell/s that we want to copy. That is, in the above figure, if we have a set of data in column C for which we are assigning numbers as shown in column B, instead of clicking-and-dragging the small cross to enumerate these cells, we can highlight the cells with "1, 2, 3" and then double-click the small cross cursor. Excel then continues the enumeration, based on the pattern in column B, until the adjacent data in column C comes to an end.

The second shortcut, SHIFT+CTRL+(arrow key), highlights an entire row or column of data. That is, if we have 100 data values in a column, instead of scrolling down the worksheet to highlight all of this data, we can click on the first cell of data and press SHIFT+CTRL+(down arrow key). Excel then automatically determines when the data values end and highlights the section up to this point.

One last note on moving data in Excel: To move an entire table or even one cell, we select it and put the cursor somewhere on the border of the selection. We then see an arrow or another change in the cursor. Then, we drag-and-drop the entire section at the desired location in the worksheet. However, if we drop the selection on an area that already has data entered in the cells, Excel provides a warning that it will replace this data with the new selection.

Summary

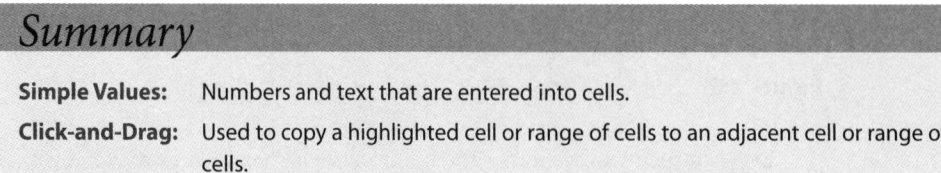

Simple Values: Numbers and text that are entered into cells.

Click-and-Drag: Used to copy a highlighted cell or range of cells to an adjacent cell or range of cells.

2.4 *Understanding the Ribbon and Quick Access Toolbar*

The Ribbon and Quick Access Toolbar create Excel's user interface. They provide options for working in the spreadsheet environment. The tabs in the ribbon and the quick access toolbar display command buttons that allow us to modify text and formulas in a spreadsheet or a diagram. Users can maximize Excel's potential by familiarizing themselves with all of the options available through this interface.

2.4.1 The Ribbon

The Excel ***Ribbon*** consists of nine main ***Tabs***: *Home, Insert, Page Layout, Formulas,* Data, Review, View, Developer and Add-Ins (Figure 2.4). Each tab includes a number of commands grouped based on their functionality. Figure 2.5 presents the ***Font*** group of the Home tab. The Ribbon also includes tabs called ***Contextual Tabs*** which are made available whenever an object (such as a chart, a table, or a SmartArt diagram) is selected. Such a tab includes specific commands for working with the selected object. See Figure 2.6 for an example of the contextual tabs that become available when working with charts.

Figure 2.4 Microsoft Excel Ribbon includes nine main tabs.

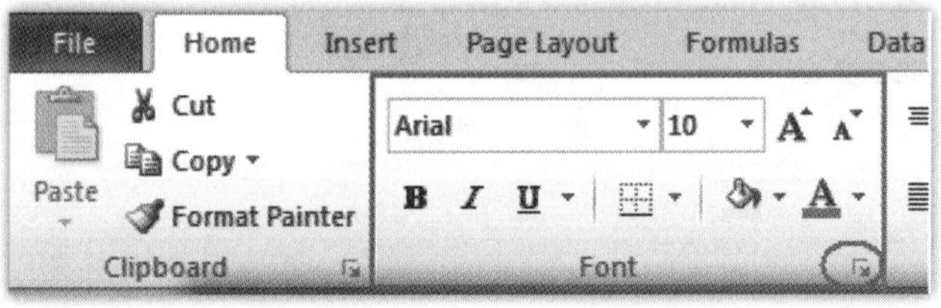

Figure 2.5 The Font Group in the Home Tab of Excel Ribbon.

The Ribbon displays commands that are most frequently used when working with Excel. To go beyond these commands click on the special symbol, the dialog launcher, on the lower-right corner of many Ribbon groups (refer to Figure 2.5). In Figure 2.7 you see a ***Dialog Box*** that displays all the commands available of the Font group in the Home tab.

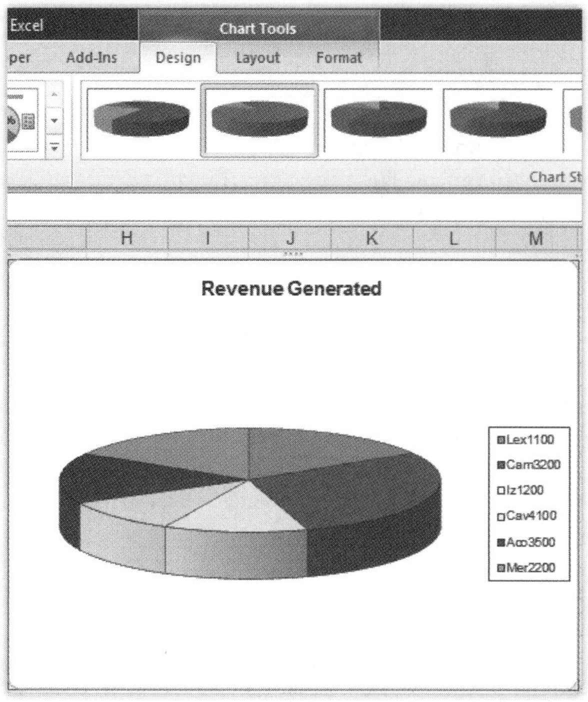

Figure 2.6 Contextual Chart Tool Tabs in Excel Ribbon.

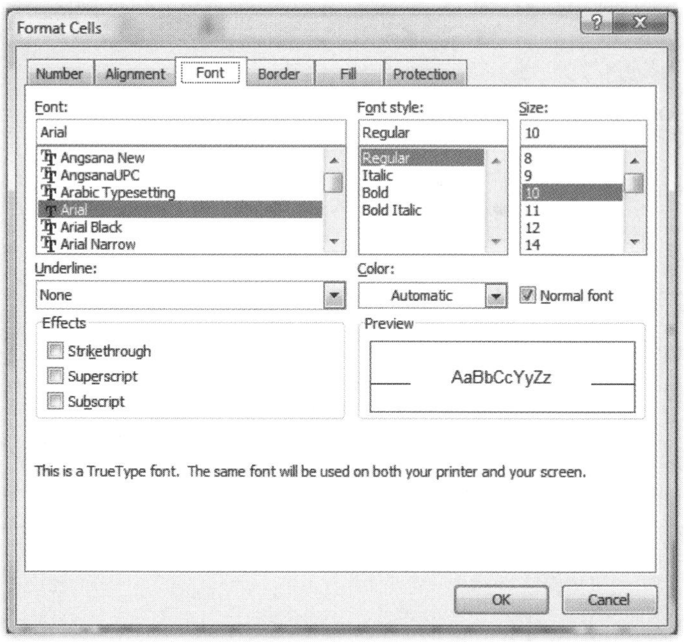

Figure 2.7 Format Cells dialog box displays commands to modify the format of a range of cells.

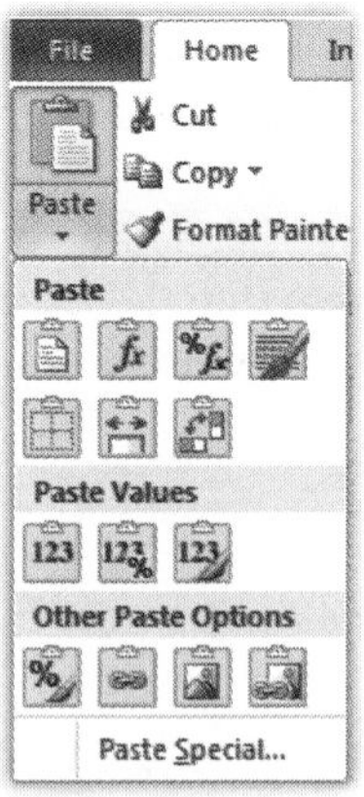

Figure 2.8 This drop-down menu lists a number of options available to paste a range of cells.

One of the commands most frequently used by Excel users is ***Paste***. The Paste command is found in the ***Clipboard*** group of the ***Home*** tab. It consists of two parts. The top part is the actual Paste command, and the bottom part is a drop-down menu offering other types of Paste commands (see Figure 2.8). ***Paste Special*** option can be used to paste *Values* alone instead of *Formulas* or *Formats*, *Formats* alone instead of *Values*, and other isolated options. *Paste Special* can also be used to ***Transpose*** data as it is pasted; in other words, we can transfer a column of data into a row of data. In Figure 2.9, we have copied the numbers in column B and pasted them using the *Paste Special* options of *Transpose* and *Values* so that the numbers are in a row instead of a column and the background color is no longer yellow.

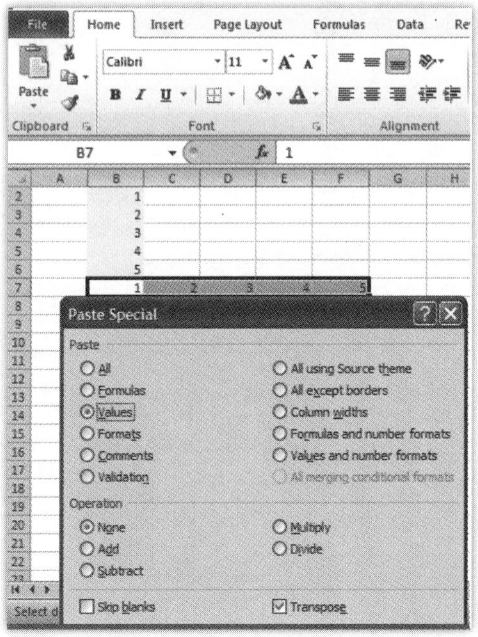

Figure 2.9 Selecting Transpose and Values in the Paste Special option.

Excel additionally offers several ***Operations*** that can be used to transform data. Say, we have a value in a cell that is separate from the range of data we wish to modify. In Figure 2.10, the value 100 is in cell D2. If we want to modify the original column of data in cells B2:B6 by multiplying each value by 100, we copy cell D2, highlight cells B2:B6, and then choose *Paste Special*. In the Paste Special dialog box, we then select *Multiply* from the Operation options and press *OK*. The resulting values, which have replaced the original column of numbers, appear in Figure 2.11.

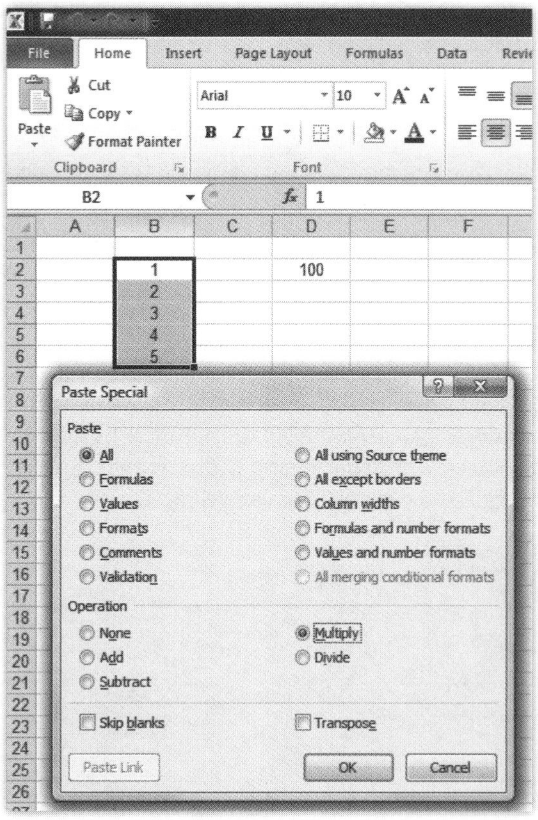

Figure 2.10 Selecting the *Multiply* operation using the value in cell D2.

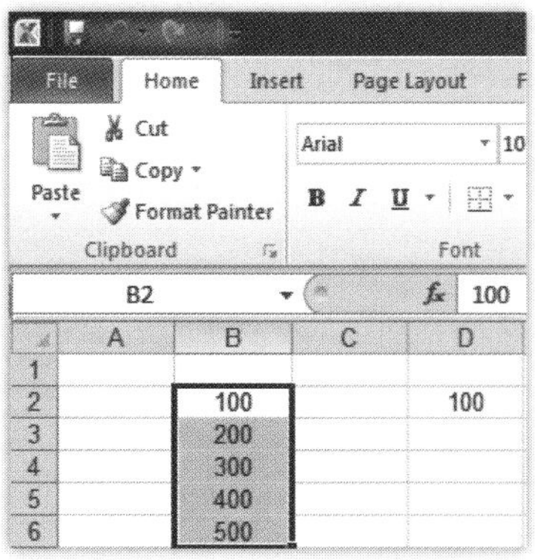

Figure 2.11 The resulting values after the Paste Special options have been selected.

Excel provides shortcut keys to simplify standard operations, such as CTRL+Z for *undoing* an operation, CTRL+C for copy, CTRL+V for paste, and CTRL+X for cut. Suppose that you use CTRL+C to copy a range of cells, and then use CTRL+V to paste. The *Paste Options* button menu appears. When you press Ctrl, a gallery of paste options is presented as shown in Figure 2.12.

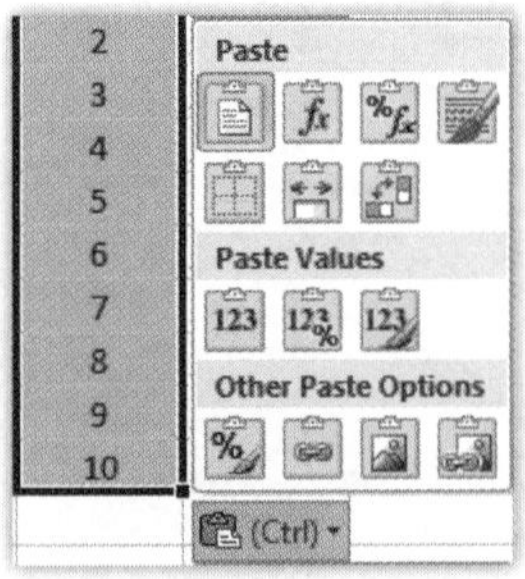

Figure 2.12 The gallery offers 14 different paste options.

2.4.2 The Quick Access Toolbar and Other Excel Interface Components

The initial location of the ***Quick Access Toolbar*** is above the left side of the ribbon. You can change its location with a right-click on the Quick Access Toolbar and select *Show Below the Ribbon* as presented in Figure 2.13.

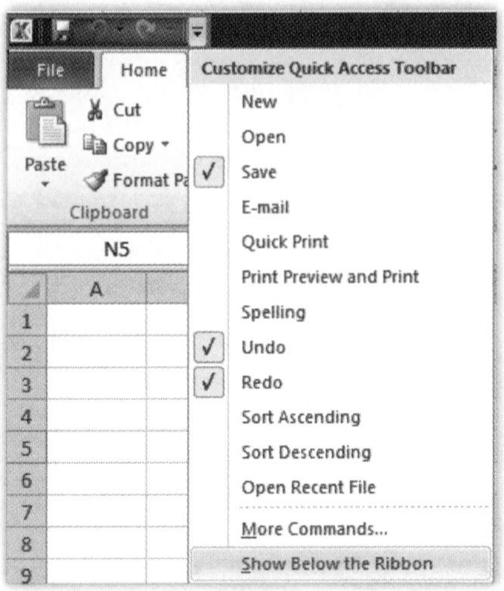

Figure 2.13 The drop-down menu offers 12 popular commands to add to Quick Access Toolbar.

The Quick Access Toolbar remains visible at all-time regardless of which tab you are working with. It is a good practice to add to Quick Access Toolbar commands that you use most frequently, so you can access them quickly without having to navigate the ribbon. The default commands of Quick Access Toolbar are *Save*, *Undo*, and *Redo*. The drop-down arrow at the right corner of the Quick Access Toolbar offers 12 popular commands that you can choose from. You can add to the Quick Access Toolbar other commands which are not available in the drop-down menu. For example, to add the *Visual Basic* command go to the *Developer* tab on the ribbon, set the mouse on top of the Visual Basic icon located at the *Code* group, right-click the mouse, and select *Add to Quick Access Toolbar* (refer to Figure 2.14).

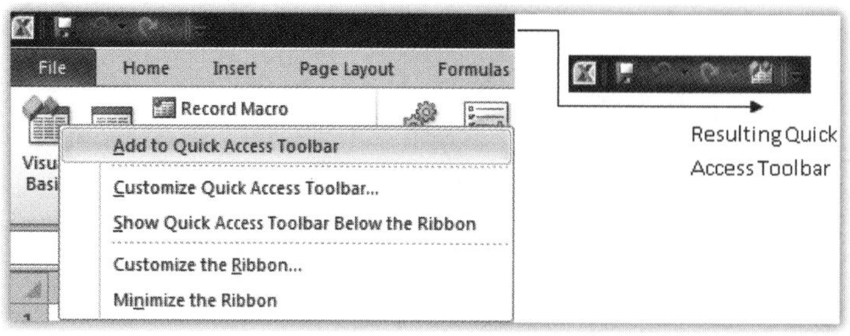

Figure 2.14 Add the Visual Basic command to the Quick Access Toolbar.

The ***File Menu*** is another important interface component which, when opened, occupies 100% of Excel window. The commands available in the File menu are not for working in a document. These commands are used after you have finished your work and are ready to do something with it, such as, *Save*, or *Print* the document. The File menu presents a number of useful commands used to *Open* and *Close* a file, locate *Recent* documents you have worked with, create a *New* document, etc.

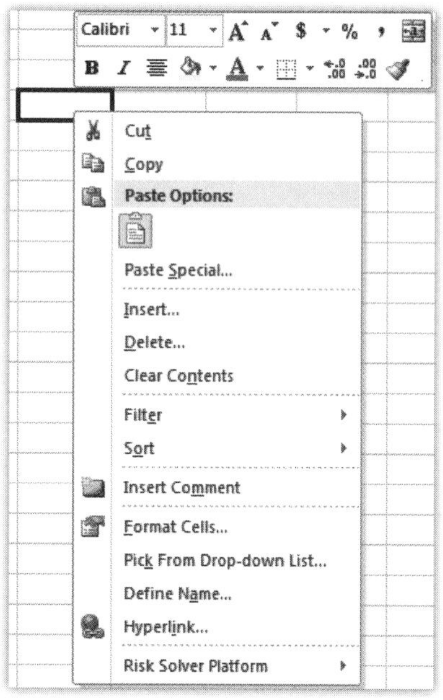

Figure 2.15 The Mini toolbar appears on the top of right-click shortcut menu.

The ***Mini Toolbar*** comes handy when working with Excel. To display the Mini toolbar, you should right-click on a cell or a range selection. The Mini toolbar appears on the top of the ***Right-Click Shortcut Menu*** as shown in Figure 2.15. The Mini toolbar displays a number of commands that can be used to format cells. The right-click shortcut menu presents frequently used commands of Excel.

Summary

Ribbon:	Consist of nine main tabs: Home, *Insert*, Page, Layout, *Formulas*, Data, *Review*, View, *Developer and Ass-Ins*.
Quick Access Toolbar:	Remains visible at all-time. *Contains most frequently used commands.*
File Menu:	Displays commands used after you are finished working with a document and want to do something with it.
Mini Toolbar:	Displays commands to format cells.
Right-Click Shortcut Menu:	Displays frequently used commands of Excel.
Dialog Box:	A separate window that provides several modifiable options on different tabs, or categories, within the box.

2.4.3 Customizing the Ribbon and Quick Access Toolbar

Excel allows us to customize the Ribbon and Quick Access Toolbar. Customization can simplify the process of accessing commands that we use frequently, or accessing commands that are not displayed on the Ribbon and Quick Access Toolbar.

You can customize the tabs and the groups within each tab of the ribbon. This is done by using the *Customize Ribbon Panel* in the *Excel Options* dialog box as presented in Figure 2.16. To access the Excel options dialog box either open the ***File Menu***, or right-click on the ribbon and select the *Customize the Ribbon* option.

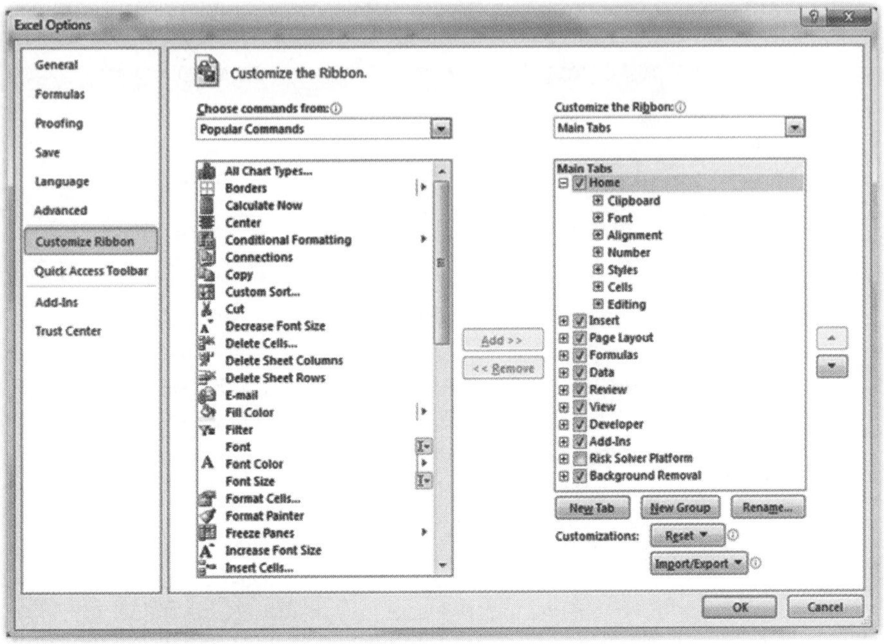

Figure 2.16 Customize Ribbon Panel in the Excel Options dialog box.

Suppose that Home and Developer are the two tabs you use most frequently when working with Excel. You would not have to bounce back and forth between these two tabs if the key commands, Visual Basic and Macros, which you use from the Developer tab, were located in the Home tab. To create a new group under the Home tab, click on the *New Group* button in the Customize Ribbon Panel. Select the *All Commands* option from the *Choose commands from* drop-down list. Next, identify the Developer commands (Visual Basic and Macros) from the list on the left and click on the *Add* button. Click on the *Rename* button to rename the *Custom group* as presented in Figure 2.17.

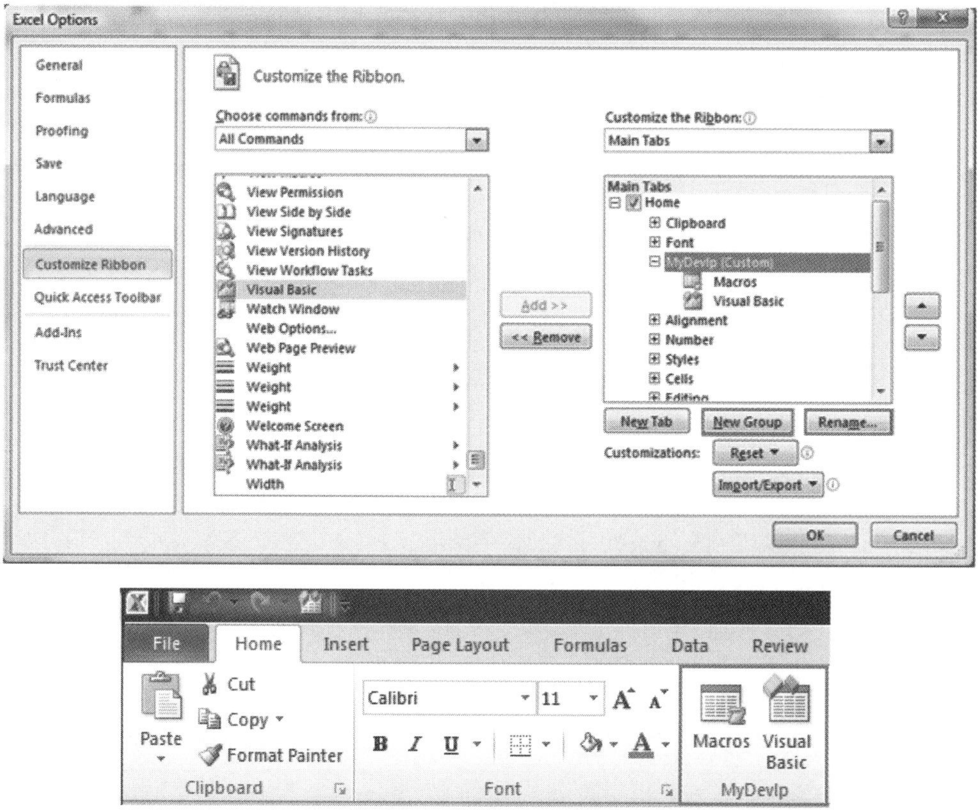

Figure 2.17 A new group, called MyDevlp, is added to the Home tab.

Suppose that Clipboard, Font, Code, and Macros are the groups that you use frequently when working with Excel. These groups of commands are located in different tabs. You can create a new tab on the Ribbon that presents just these groups of commands. To create a new tab on the Ribbon, click on the *New Tab* button located in the *Customize Ribbon Panel*. Click on the *Rename* button to name the new tab. Select the *Main Tabs* from the *Choose commands from* drop-down list. Locate the groups from the list on the left and click on the *Add* button. Figure 2.18 presents the new tab, called MyTab, which we just created. Click-on the *Reset* button in the *Customize Ribbon Panel* to remove all the customizations made.

The Quick Access Toolbar can be customized to include commands that you use frequently. Use the *Quick Access Toolbar panel* in the *Excel Options* dialog box as presented in Figure 2.19. In addition to commands, you can attach a macro to the Quick Access Toolbar, so that when you click on the icon, the macro is executed. A list of all available macros is displayed when you select *Macros* from the *Choose commands from* drop-down list. Locate the macro from the list on the left and click on the *Add* button. You can right-click on an icon and select the *Remove from the Quick Access Toolbar* option in order to remove a command from the Quick Access Toolbar.

Figure 2.18 The new tab, called MyTab, consists of Clipboard, Font, Code and Macros group.

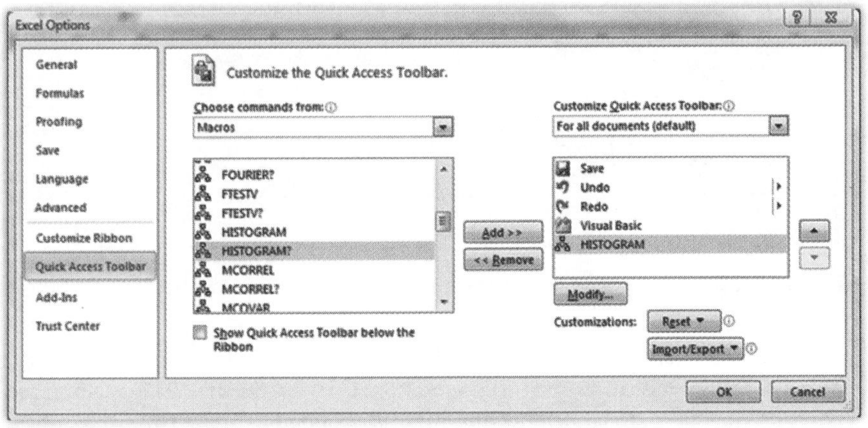

Figure 2.19 A macro is added to the Quick Access Toolbar.

2.5 *Formatting*

Excel has the incredibly helpful ability to format cells, ranges, and entire worksheets, as well as other objects.

2.5.1 Formatting Cells

To access commands available for formatting cells, you could either use the Home tab of the Ribbon, the Mini toolbar that appears when you right-click on a selection of cells, or the Format cells dialog box (refer to Figure 2.7). We will discuss only the formatting options available in the Home tab since the Mini toolbar and Format Cells dialog box have similar functionalities.

The Home tab has six groups of commands that are used to format cells. These groups are *Clipboard*, *Font*, *Alignment*, *Number*, *Styles*, and *Cells* as shown in Figure 2.20. A useful formatting tool of the *Clipboard* group is the *Format Painter* brush. This tool allows you to copy the format of a range of cells to other destination ranges. To use the Format Painter, select the range of cells you want to copy the format, click-on the Format Painter brush, then click-and-drag the mouse to select the destination range.

The *Font* group is similar to the Font options found in other Microsoft applications. You can use this group to set the font type and size as well as color and other highlighting features of a selected range of cells. In Figure 2.20, the font of a selection is set to 10-point Arial; font color is red, bold and underlined. The *Borders* drop-down menu allows you to add a variety of border styles to a cell range. The menu offers 13 frequently used border choices and 5 border drawing tools. For instance, to make the border line of a table thick and red, you first should pick the line color to be red. Set the mouse on-top of Line Color from the drop-down menu, and select the red from the flyout menu (refer to Figure 2.21). Next, select the *Thick Box Border* option from the menu. You can use the tools available in the *Draw Borders* group to customize the borders of a range of cells. The Font Color drop-down button and the Fill Color drop-down button present a number of font and cell fill-in colors you can choose from.

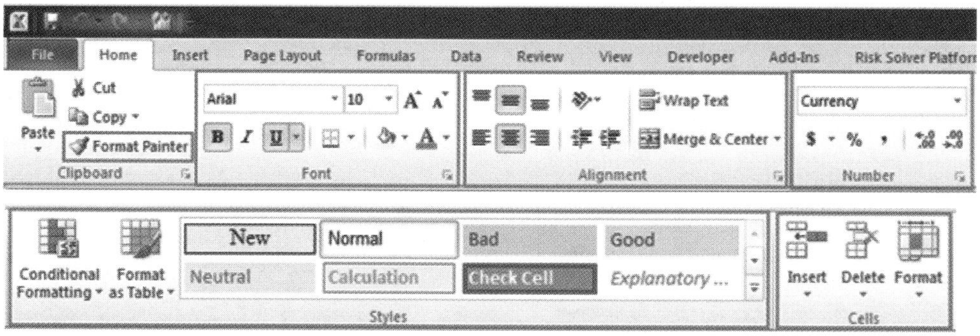

Figure 2.20 In the Home tab there are six groups of commands that support formatting.

The *Alignment* group sets the horizontal and vertical placement of a cell or range data and also determines indention and text orientation. Click on the dialog launcher in the bottom-right corner of the group to launch the *Format Cells* dialog box presented in Figure 2.22. The selection of options from the Alignment tab in the dialog box presents a format that places an entry at the center of a cell. The entry has no indentation, and appears with a 45-degree orientation. The *Text control* options reveal that the cell has been merged with one or more cells.

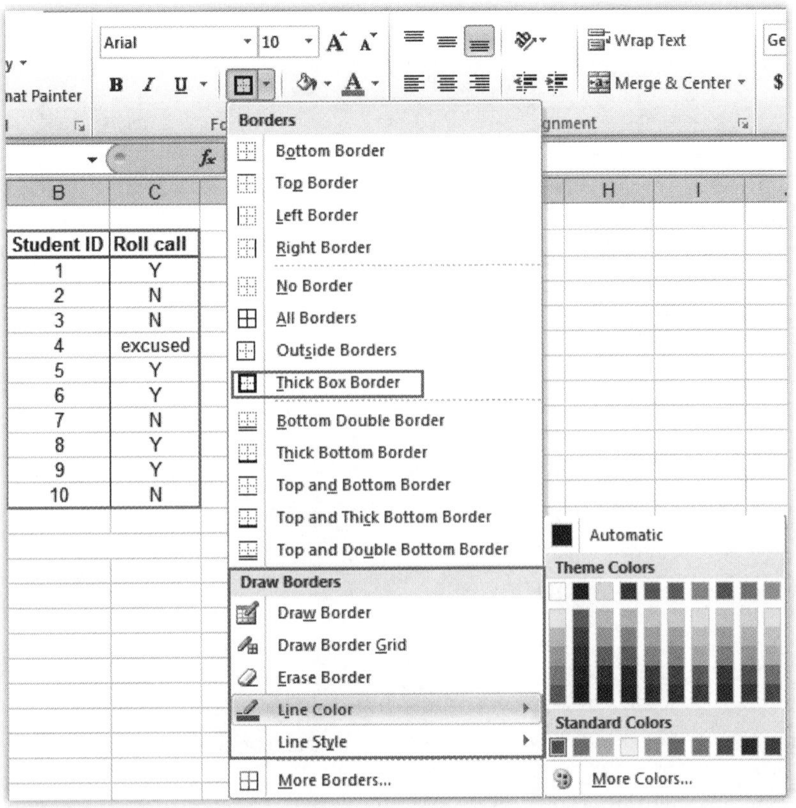

Figure 2.21 Border drawing tools available in the Font group of Home tab.

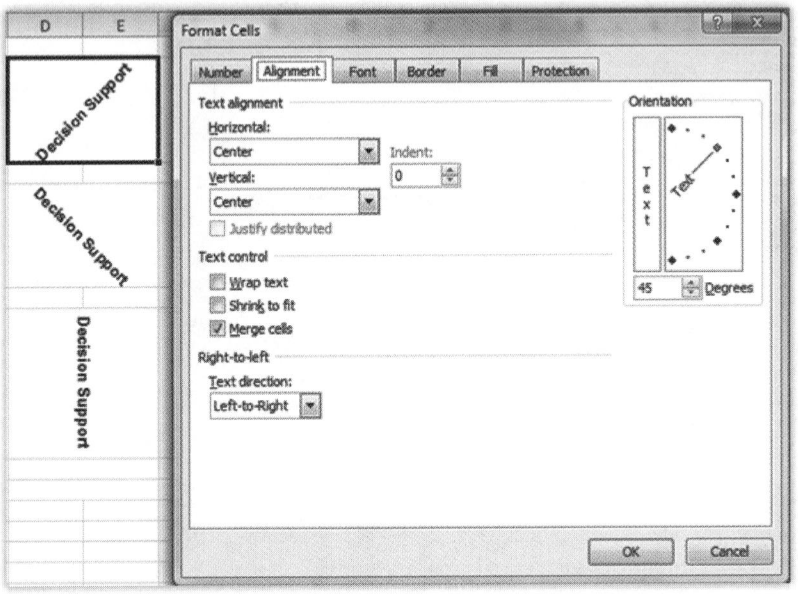

Figure 2.22 The Alignment tab of the Format Cells dialog box offers formatting options for text or other entries.

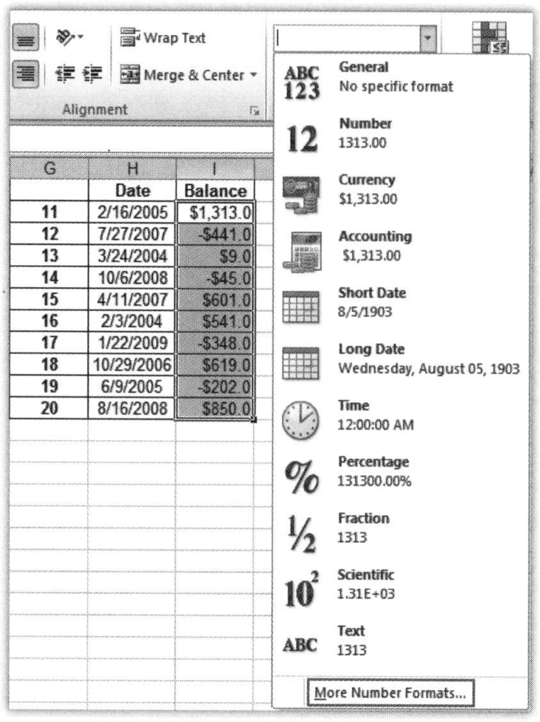

Figure 2.23 The drop-down menu in the Number group of Home tab offers 11 frequently used number styles.

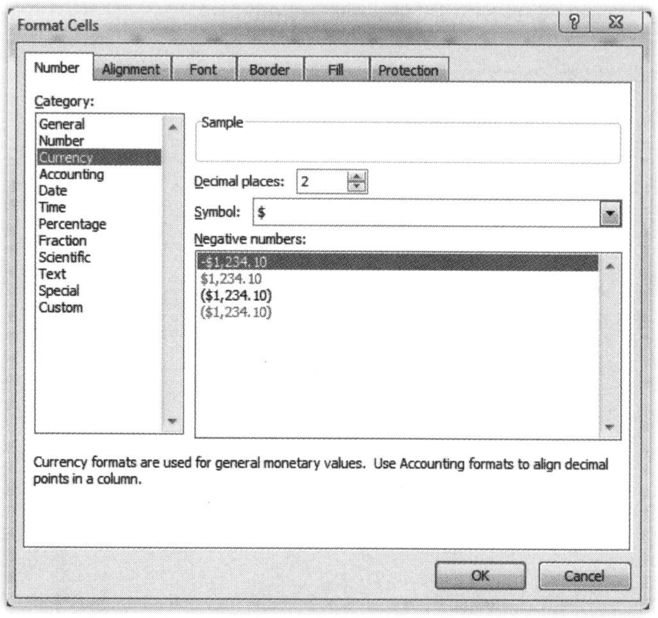

Figure 2.24 The Number tab of Format Cells dialog box lists several options for formatting numerical entries.

The *Number group* allows you to specify the type of numbers you want to use in your document. Click-on the drop-down menu for a list of frequently used number styles (see Figure 2.23). You can access all number formatting options available in Excel by selecting the *More Number Formats* button. Upon selection, the Format Cells dialog box appears. The *Number* tab is already active as shown in Figure 2.24. Suppose that you want to create a spreadsheet for financial calculations. Therefore, the entries in your spreadsheet should be formatted as *Currency* or *Accounting*, depending on the features desired. You may either wish to create a table of *Dates* or *Times* with a particular uniform format, or a table of *Numbers* with one decimal place each. The *Numbers* tab describes and lists the options available for each *Number* type. This tab also includes a *Custom* type option. By using symbols such as (), -, and #, we can define the number formatting that we want to apply to a spreadsheet. The standard format for telephone numbers, (###) ### - ####, serves as a good example of *Custom* type.

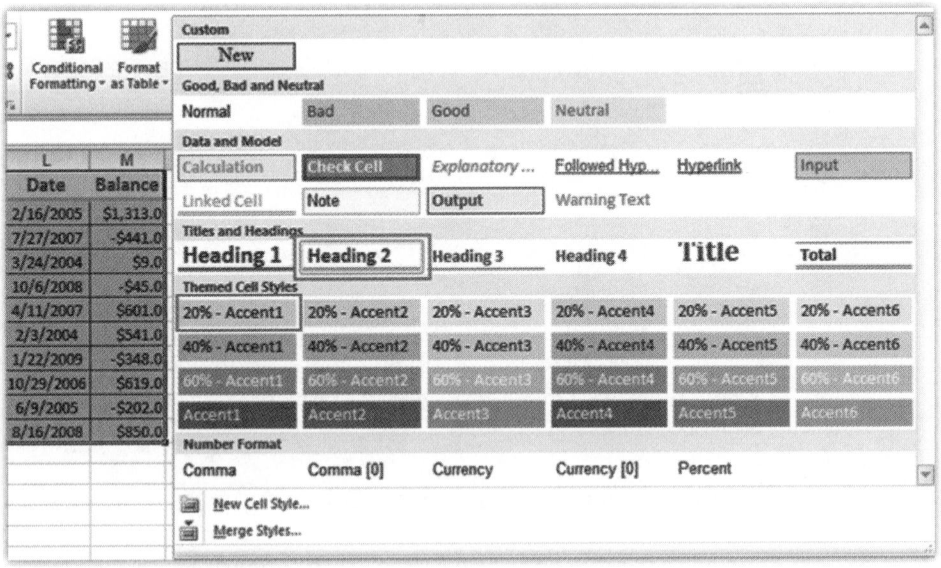

Figure 2.25 The Styles group in the Home tab offers a variety of build-in formatting styles.

The *Styles* group provides a gallery of build-in styles to use for formatting cells. The table in Figure 2.25 is formatted using the build-in styles available in Excel. The style selected for the title of the table is *Heading 2*, and the style selected for the table itself is *20% - Accent1*.

The last formatting related group on the Ribbon is the *Cells* group. The *Format* drop-down menu (see Figure 2.26) presents tools to modify cell size and visibility, as well as, organize and protect sheets. In this section we will discuss only the *Lock Cells* option on the *Protection* group. The rest of the commands of this group will be discussed in the following section. To lock cells, you should first protect your sheet using the *Protect Sheet* option from the Format drop-down menu. The *Protect Sheet* option prevents anyone from entering or changing data in locked cells. This option is beneficial when creating a form where some cells should be free for users to input information, but other informational cells should not be modified by the user. If you would like to hide from the user the formulas and functions you have used, then you should first protected the worksheet. Next, click-on the *Format Cells* option in the drop-down menu to evoke the *Format Cells* dialog box as shown in Figure 2.26. In the Protection tab select the

Hidden option box. Note that, this is only applicable when viewing the formulas in a worksheet. (We will discuss this in more detail in Chapter 4.)

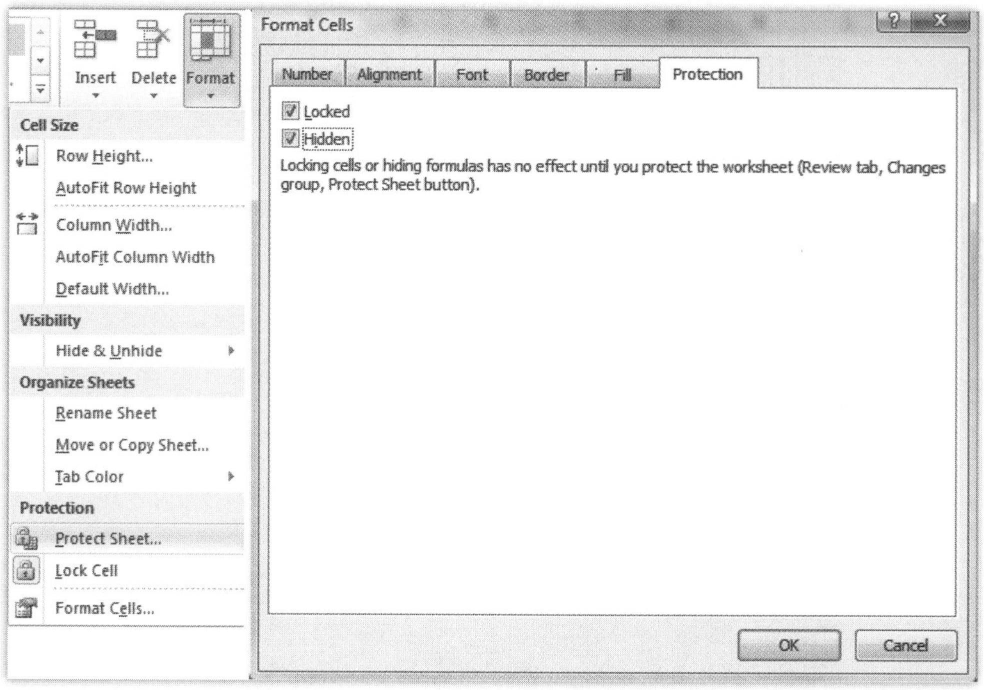

Figure 2.26 The Format drop-down menu in the Cells group of Home tab offers options to protect the content and hide formulas from the user.

After we have selected one or more cells and formatted them, we may wish to format other cells in the same fashion. To do this without repeating all of the previous formatting modifications, you could either use the *Format Painter* brush as shown above, or copy the range of cells, and evoke the Paste Special dialog box. Select *Formats* from the Paste options. The values in the selected cells will not change, only their format.

2.5.2 General Formatting

Excel offers options to format rows and columns of a worksheet, as well as the whole workbook itself. The ***Themes*** group in the ***Page Layout*** tab of the Ribbon offers a collection of build-in themes to choose from when formatting an Excel workbook (refer to Figure 2.27). A theme is a collection of colors, fonts, and effects. Upon the selection of a theme, the available gallery of colors to choose from when formatting the font and fill color of a cell, or the color of a line, etc. changes. In a similar fashion, the default font type of the workbook changes upon the selection of a style. For example, if the *Civic* theme is selected, then *Georgia* becomes the default font type of the workbook.

The ***Styles*** group of the *Home* tab presents a gallery of general formatting options (see Figure 2.25) for a selected range of cells. You can create a new style by clicking-on the ***New Cell Style*** command from Styles drop-down menu. A dialog box appears that displays the current formatting using six formatting categories as shown in Figure 2.28. Click-on the *Format* button to evoke the *Format Cells* dialog box. You can select the desired format by navigating the different tabs of the dialog box. Click-on the *OK* button to submit your changes. For example, in Figure 2.28 a style called MyStyle is presented. Its border style is ***DiagonalUp***.

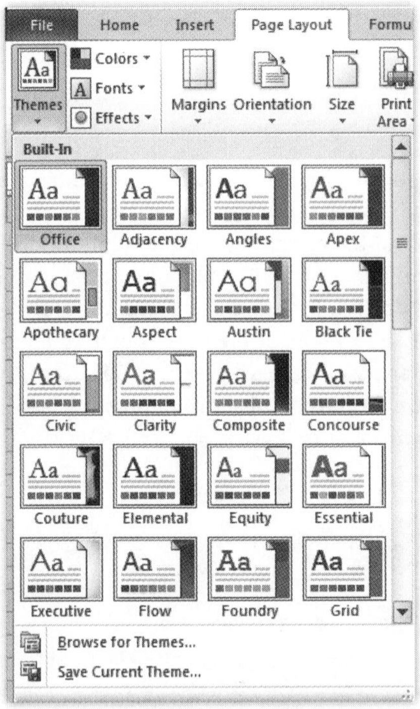

Figure 2.27 The Themes drop-down menu in the Page Layout tab of the Ribbon presents a variety of spreadsheet formatting options.

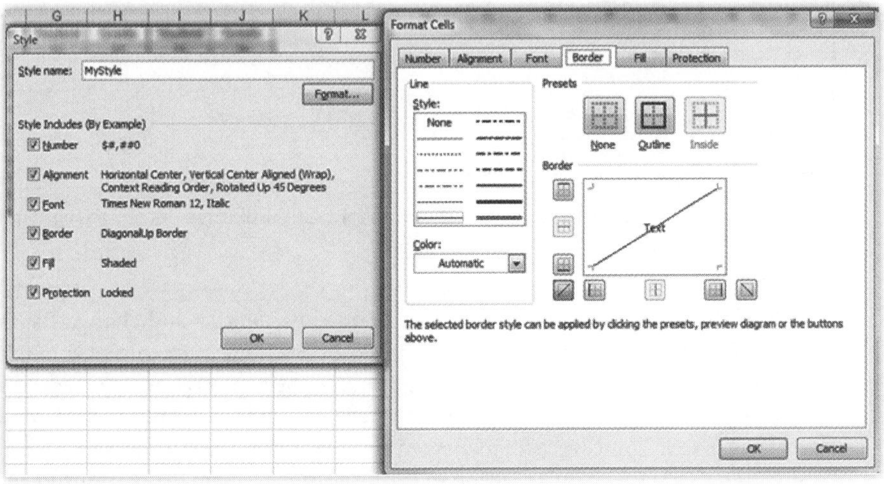

Figure 2.28 The border style of MyStyle is DiagonalUp.

The ***Format*** drop-down menu of *Cells* group in the *Home* tab presents options to format row height and column width (see Figure 2.26). The ***Auto Fit*** options alter the dimensions of rows and columns, making them as wide as necessary to show all values entered. Rows and columns can also be hid or revealed. The rest of the tools in the drop-down menu allow you to reorganize your application by renaming, moving spreadsheets, and changing the color of spreadsheet tabs.

2.5.3 Conditional Formatting

Conditional Formatting, another Excel formatting tool, is available under Styles group in the Home tab. This tool is used to format cells that meet a predetermined condition or a set of conditions. For example, suppose we want to change the format of all numbers lower than 70 to reflect a grade less than C in the Information Systems course. First, you highlight the set of numbers and then select ***Highlight Cells Rules*** from the *Conditional Formatting* drop-down menu. Select the ***Less Than*** option from the flyout menu as shown in Figure 2.29. Upon the selection of this option a dialog box appears (refer to Figure 2.30). Next, type 70 in the ***Format cells that are LESS THAN*** window on the left, select a format option from the drop-down menu on the right, and click-on the *OK* button.

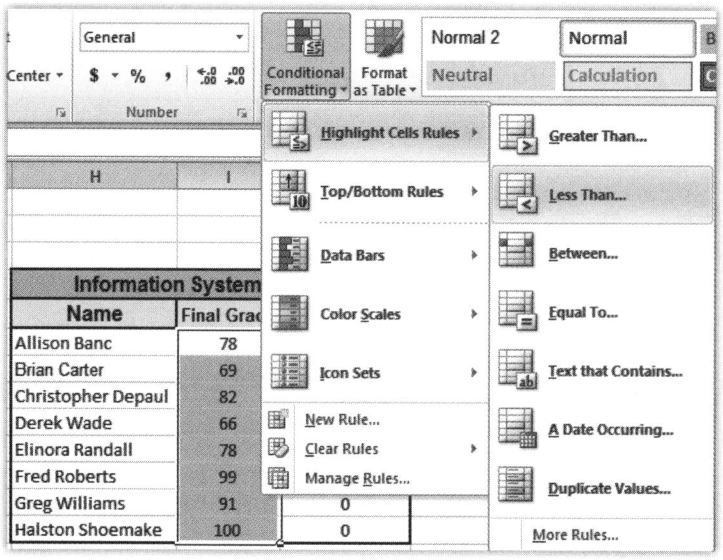

Figure 2.29 The Less Than option of the Highlight Cells Rules is selected to highlight grades less than 70.

Conditional Formatting tools allow you quickly identify and change the format of cells based on ***Top/Bottom rules***, such as the top n%, or the bottom n% of the values in the selected range are formatted. For example, in Figure 2.31 the top 10% of the grades in the selected list are bold. It is important to note that there is no limit in the number of conditions set for formatting a cell. You can easily manage the rules and set the order in which rules do apply by selecting the Manage Rules option in the *Conditional* Formatting drop-down menu. In the example presented in Figure 2.32, the *Top 10%* rule is applied first, and the *Cell Value < 70* is applied second.

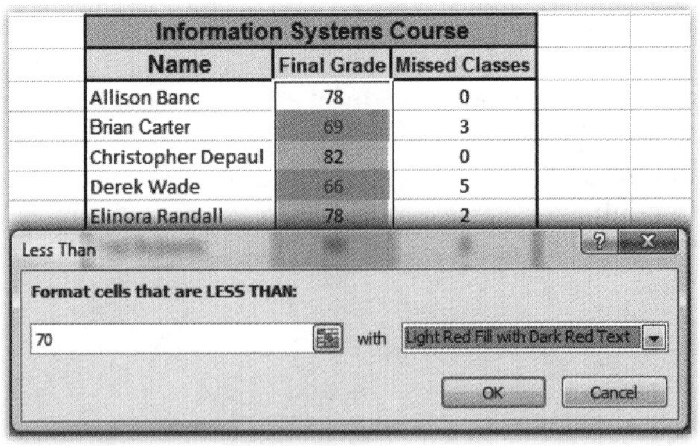

Figure 2.30 Cells which contain values less than 70 will have a light red fill with dark red text.

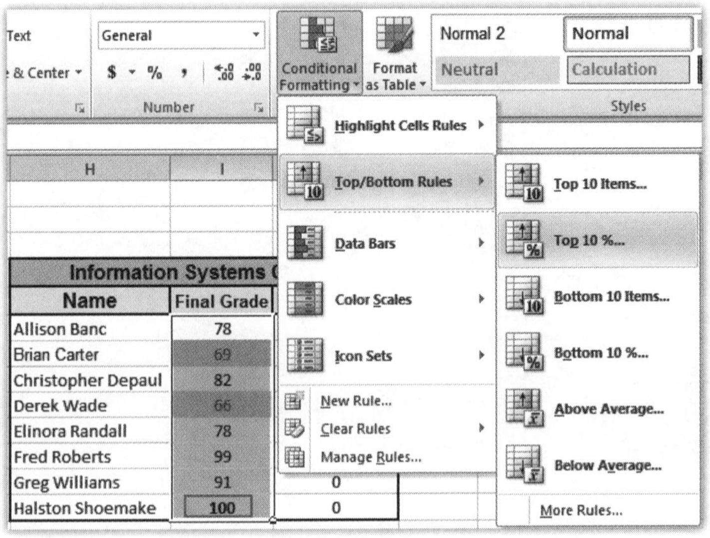

Figure 2.31 Top 10% of the grades are bold.

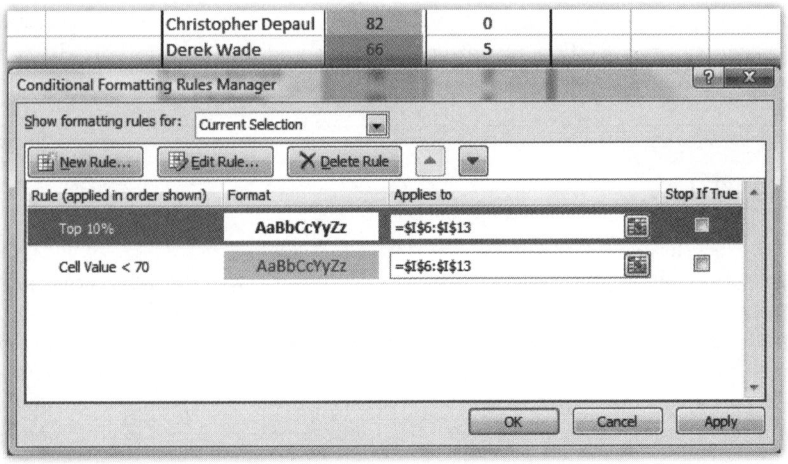

Figure 2.32 The *Top 10%* rule is applied first, and the *Cell Value < 70* is applied second.

The ***Data Bars***, ***Color Scales*** and ***Icon Sets*** option in the *Conditional Formatting* drop-down menu are powerful visualization tools. The *Data Bar* option adds tiny, in-cell bar charts based on the cell value. The *Color Scale* option adds color scales to cells based on their values. The *Icon Sets* option adds icon sets to cells based on their values. Figure 2.32 presents the results from using the ***Four Bar Ratings*** of *Icon Sets* option. The number of colored bars in each cell depends on the value of the cell. To delete a conditional format applied to a range of cells or the entire worksheet; select the ***Clear Rules*** option from the *Conditional Formatting* drop-down menu.

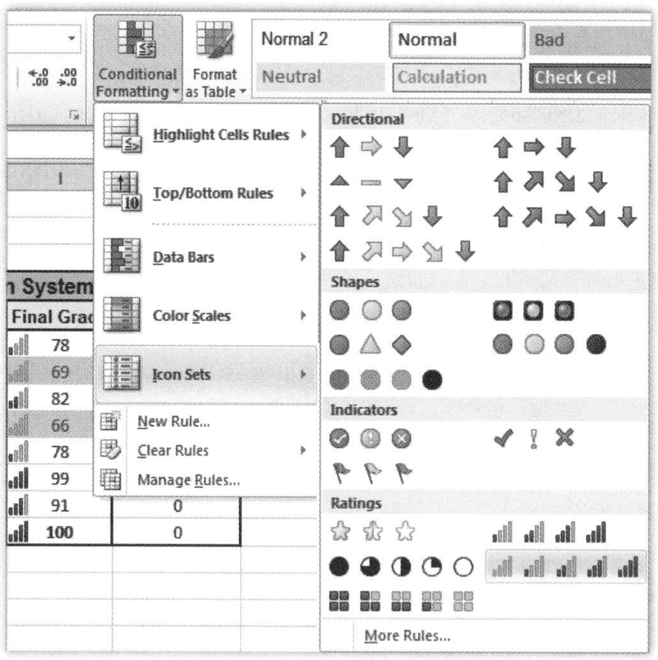

Figure 2.33 Icon Sets conditional formatting option offers a number of visualization tools.

Conditional Formatting is beneficial when we are working with large sets of data and want to distinguish certain values from others. We may be looking for particular results or patterns of data that we can specify by creating conditions and formatting them differently than the other data.

2.6 Summary

- *Excel objects* are elements that we can manipulate in spreadsheet applications and VBA programming. They follow an object hierarchy, which is an ordered listing of all the Excel objects. The object model is the entire system of objects.
- Data entry in Excel pertains to four different types of data: numbers, text, formulas, and Boolean values (true or false). Numbers and text are simple values. To enter this type of data into a table, type a number or text directly in each cell.
- The *Ribbon*, *Quick Access Toolbar*, and *File Menu* create Excel's user interface; they provide options for working in the spreadsheet environment.
- The Ribbon consists of nine main tabs: *Home*, *Insert*, *Page Layout*, *Formulas*, *Data*, *Review*, *View*, *Developer* and *Add-Ins. The commands within each tab are organized in groups based on their functionality.*

- Other *contextual tabs* are made available whenever an object (such as a chart, a table, or a SmartArt diagram) is selected.
- *Ribbon* and the *Quick Access Toolbar* is customized to simplify the process of accessing commands that are use frequently.
- You can customize the tabs and the groups within each tab of the Ribbon by using the *Customize Ribbon Panel* in the *Excel Options* dialog box.
- You can customize the Quick Access Toolbar by using the *Customize Quick Access Toolbar Panel* in the *Excel Options* dialog box. Select the commands from the list on the left side, and then click-on the *Add* button.
- The tools used to format a cell are mainly located in the following groups of the *Home* tab: *Clipboard, Font, Alignment, Number, Styles*, and *Cells.*
- Rows and columns can be formatted by setting a particular height or width, using *Auto Fit* command under the *Format* drop-down menu in the *Cells* group of *Home* tab.
- The *Styles* group of the *Home* tab offers a gallery of general formatting options for a range of selected cells.
- The *Themes* group in the *Page Layout* tab of the Ribbon offers a collection of build-in themes to choose from when formatting an Excel workbook.
- *Conditional Formatting* formats cells only if they meet a specified condition. To specify the conditions, choose from the options listed in the *Conditional Formatting* drop-down menu.

2.7 *Exercises*

2.7.1 Review Questions

1. Give four examples of Excel objects.
2. How does the object hierarchy differ from the object model?
3. List the object hierarchy for the following Excel objects:
   - The sheet titled "Price List" containing a list of office supplies, the items' purchase prices, and their selling prices.
   - The entry "$2.50" for the purchase price of a pack of pens.
   - Column B entitled "Purchase Prices."
   - The Excel file "Inventory.xls" used by an office supply company.
4. What are the main tabs of Excel Ribbon?
5. How can you customize the Quick Access Toolbar?
6. Describe the steps you would follow to create a new tab in the Ribbon.
7. Describe the steps you would follow to create a new group of commands in the Ribbon.
8. How can you change the font size of a range of cells?
9. How can you lock particular cells in a worksheet? When would this be necessary?
10. How can the width of a set of columns be automatically adjusted making them as wide as it is necessary?
11. What is the benefit of using conditional formatting?
12. Describe the use of the Data Bars option in the Conditional Formatting drop down menu.
13. What are the shortcut keys for cut, copy, and paste?
14. Which group of the Home tab includes the command to merge cells and wrap text?
15. What are four options for the data type of a cell entry?

2.7.2 Hands-On Exercises

NOTE: Please refer to the file "Chapter_02_Exercises.xlsx" for the associated worksheets noted for the hands-on exercises. The file is available at: www.dssbooks.com.

1. Use the Customize Quick Access Toolbar panel under Excel options to add frequently used commands to the Quick Access Toolbar as shown below.

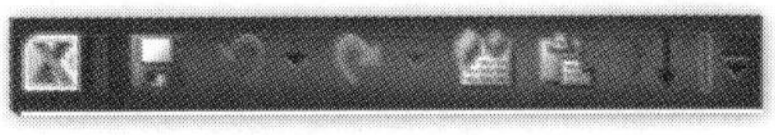

2. Use the Customize Ribbon panel under Excel options to create the tab shown below. Note that, the tab called MyGroup is a custom tab.

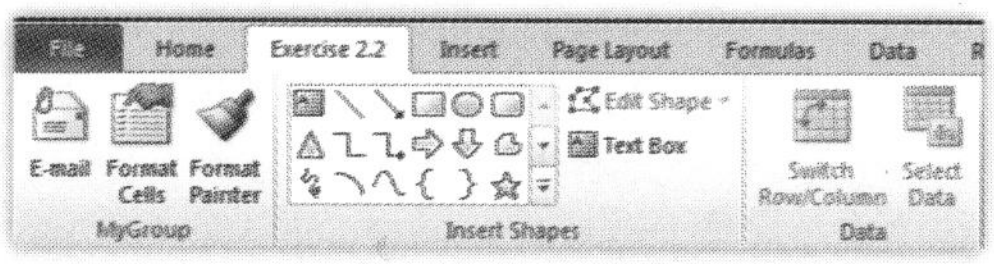

3. A professor uses the table shown in Figure A to take roll in his class. He writes a "Y" in the Roll Call column if a student is present, an "N" if a student is absent without an excuse, and "excused" if the student has an excused absence. Following Figure B, use the Conditional Formatting option to highlight all students who were not present in the class. (Refer to worksheet "2.3".)

	A	B	C	D	E	F
1						
2		Student ID	Roll call		Student ID	Roll call
3		1	Y		1	Y
4		2	N		2	N
5		3	N		3	N
6		4	excused		4	excused
7		5	Y		5	Y
8		6	Y		6	Y
9		7	N		7	N
10		8	Y		8	Y
11		9	Y		9	Y
12		10	N		10	N
13						
14		Figure A			Figure B	

4. The table in Figure A displays the amount of sales dollars earned and the percentage of returns made for three new products recently introduced onto the market. Using the options on the Formatting toolbar, enhance this table to make it resemble the table in Figure B. (Refer to worksheet "2.4".)

	A	B	C	D
1				
2			Sales	Percent Return
3		Product A	35000	0.02
4		Product B	74000	0.01
5		Product C	56000	0.03
6				
7			Figure A	
8				
9			Sales	Percent Return
10		Product A	$35,000.00	2%
11		Product B	$74,000.00	1%
12		Product C	$56,000.00	3%
13				
14			Figure B	

5. A financial analyst is comparing the following list of stock prices: 1.25, 0.35, 2.49, 3.15, 5.87, 4.63, 1.02, 0.33, 2.71, and 0.99. Enter these prices into an Excel worksheet and display them as fractions rounded to the nearest sixteenth. Use the Data Bars option from the Conditional Formatting drop-down menu to format the selected cells based on their values.

6. A chemical engineer is conducting an experiment that tests the solubility of three unknown substances (Substance A, B, and C) in water in an effort to determine the identity of the substances. If a substance remains undissolved at room temperature, she applies heat to the solution and records the temperature at which the substance does dissolve. If some of the substance remains undissolved by the time the water is boiling, she notes that the solution is supersaturated. Her initial observations include the following:

   a. 5g of substance A dissolve in 100 mL of water at room temperature.

   b. 5g of substance B dissolve in 100 mL of water at 84°C.

   c. 5g of substance C dissolve in 100 mL of water at 57°C.

   Since all of the substances dissolved, the engineer decides to create solutions that are more concentrated. Her new observations include the following:

   - 7g of substance A dissolve in 50 mL of water at 75°C.
   - 7g of substance B do not completely dissolve in 50 mL of boiling water. (Solution is supersaturated.)
   - 7g of substance C dissolve in 50 mL of water at 94°C.

   Create a table to compare the results of the two experiments by entering this data into Excel. Choose from the gallery of build-in styles presented in the Styles group of Home tab to format your table.

7. Create the following table by using the click-and-drag method.

	A	B	C	D	E	F
1						
2		1	10	1	a	Hello
3		2	9	3	b	Hello
4		3	8	5	c	Hello
5		4	7	7	a	Hello
6		5	6	9	b	Hello
7		6	5	11	c	Hello
8		7	4	13	a	Hello
9		8	3	15	b	Hello
10		9	2	17	c	Hello
11		10	1	19	a	Hello

8. A student keeps a list of his bill payment due dates, shown in Figure A. He wants to identify all the dates in October. Using conditional formatting, highlight all the dates in October and cross out all remaining dates so that the list resembles Figure B. (Refer to worksheet "2.8".)

	A	B	C	D	E	F
1						
2		10/9/02	electric		10/9/02	electric
3		12/1/02	credit card		~~12/1/02~~	credit card
4		10/26/02	ethernet		10/26/02	ethernet
5		12/13/02	water		~~12/13/02~~	water
6		10/17/02	phone		10/17/02	phone
7		9/5/02	credit card		~~9/5/02~~	credit card
8		10/15/02	water		10/15/02	water
9		9/7/02	electric		~~9/7/02~~	electric
10		11/14/02	phone		~~11/14/02~~	phone
11		10/30/02	gym		10/30/02	gym
12						
13		Figure A			Figure B	

9. A bank uses a table to record the transactions made by each of its account holders. This information is then used to prepare bank statements for the account holders. Make the statement easier for an account holder to read by using the commands under the *Number* group of the Home tab to change the number types of the cells in the following ways. (Refer to worksheet "2.9".)

a. Remove the leading zeroes from the transaction numbers.

b. Display the transaction dates in the format mm/dd/yy.

c. The account numbers are based on the account holders' social security numbers. Display these numbers as social security numbers in the format XXX-XX-XXXX.

d. Deposits and earnings result in an increase in the account balance, but withdrawals and charges result in a decrease. Show currency symbols on all monetary transactions. Display all negative transactions within parentheses.

10. A department store must predict the demand for various items of women's apparel for the upcoming months before production begins. The following table displays the forecasted demand in thousands for various items for January through June. Create this table, paying particular attention to the alignment and border formatting properties. (Refer to worksheet "2.10".)

	A	B	C	D	E	F	G	H	I
1									
2									
3			Jan	Feb	Mar	Apr	May	June	
4		coats	210	195	190	175	160	160	
5		scarves	150	150	145	135	115	110	
6		gloves	250	245	235	19	170	160	

11. The marketing department of a firm wants to create a spreadsheet of customer information so that it can plan target markets. Create a table that includes basic personal information about each customer, including address, phone number, and email. Also include demographic characteristics about each customer, such as age, gender, and any other information that may be useful for dividing the customers into various categories. Enter several mock customers into your table, and format the table with color.

12. A table gives the names, games, total points, and points per game of five basketball players (cells *A2:D7*). The column D3:D7 uses the data from cells B3:C7 to compute each player's points per game. Each cell of column D3:D7 contains a formula that divides the number of points by the number of games of each player to calculate their points per game. (Refer to worksheet "2.12".)

a. Copy the entire table, including the calculated points per game, and paste only the values to the cells *A13:D18*.

b. Copy the names from the original table and paste them in a row in cells *A20:E20*.

c. Copy the entire table and transpose it to cells *A22:F25*.

13. We are provided with a table with the annual rate of interest paid by 3-month Treasury bills for each month in 2009. To find the annual interest earned on \$1.00 invested at the current T-bill rate, we use the calculation (1 + (annual rate)/100). Therefore, it would be easier to compute earned interest if the column of annual interest rates were divided by 100. Use Paste Special Operations to transform the column of annual interest rates. (*Hint*: You will need to use a cell outside of the table.) (Refer to worksheet "2.13".)

14. In a given table given, quarterly sales for four products are displayed in columns. Copy this data to a range below so that the sales values are read as rows and not columns. (Refer to worksheet "2.14".)

15. A table contains monthly prices of the M and N stocks. Changes in stock price are also calculated. (Refer to worksheet "2.15".)

- **a.** Highlight each value at which M and N went up more than 3% in purple.
- **b.** Highlight each value at which M and N went down more than 3% in red.
- **c.** Use the Icon Sets option from the Conditional Formatting drop-down menu to format cells based on their values. Select the 4 Arrows Directional option listed under Icon Sets flyout menu.

16. A professor is reviewing her students' grades for the semester. Using conditional formatting, help her find the A's by highlighting them in red, the B's by highlighting them in yellow, and the F's by highlighting them in blue. (Refer to worksheet "2.16".) Use the Color Scales option from the Conditional Formatting drop-down menu to format cells based on their values.

17. John is trying to review his bank balance for the last several weeks. Format the data he has by changing the dates into the "mm/dd/yy" format. Then format the balance values as currency so that the negative values are red and in parentheses." (Refer to worksheet "2.17".) Use the Icon Sets option from the Conditional Formatting drop-down menu to format cells based on their values. Select the 4 Bars Rating option listed under Icon Sets flyout menu.

18. Review the quarterly sales for an office supplies company and perform the following actions. (Refer to worksheet "2.18".)

- **a.** Change the formatting of the Sales column to currency.
- **b.** Highlight the fourth quarter sales values in red.
- **c.** Make the font bold for any sales value greater than $2000.
- **d.** Use the Data Bars option from the Conditional Formatting drop-down menu to format cells based on their values.

19. Create your own accounting table. Number 20 entries using the click-and-drag method. Enter dates in "Month dd" format. Enter positive values with a "+" sign before the number. Enter negative values with a "–" sign before the number. Highlight any values greater than $1000 in yellow.

20. Create a new format style. Use the new style to format the data on the table that corresponds to Hands-On Exercise 13. The following are the features of the new style:

- **a.** Numbers are formatted as percentages with 2 decimal places.
- **b.** The text and numbers are centrally aligned.
- **c.** The font size is 12pt and the font is set to Times New Roman.
- **d.** The table has left, right, top and bottom borders.
- **e.** The table is shaded using the blue color.

CHAPTER

three Referencing and Names

chapter OVERVIEW

3.1 Introduction

This chapter discusses how to create references and names in the spreadsheet environment. These are basic but very important concepts. This chapter may be most useful for the reader who is inexperienced in Excel, but we also recommend it be reviewed by experienced users. Referencing and names will be used often in developing a DSS and these concepts should be clear to the user in Excel before they learn referencing and names in VBA.

In this chapter, the reader will learn how to:

- Reference a cell or range of cells.
- Use different types of referencing when copying cell addresses.
- Use R1C1 notation.
- Avoid circular referencing.
- Name cells using various methods.
- Create basic formulas and constants using cell names.

3.2 Referencing Cells

The address of a cell is the combination of its column letter and row number location. For example, the word "Data" in Figure 3.1 is in cell *B3*; the first number in the table, 46, is in cell *B4*; the first cell in the second column of the table, with value 31, is cell *C4*. We refer to an entire row or column of cells by listing the first and last cell separated by a colon. In Figure 3.1, the first column of the "Data" table can be referred to as *B4:B13*. The entire "Data" table can be referred to as *B4:C13*.

When typing a formula or a simple operation in a cell, we use the names of other cells to refer to the values that they contain. That is, if we want to refer to a value in cell *B3*, we type:

```
=B3
```

We can also just type an equal sign (=) in the cell and then click on cell *B3* with our cursor. This method of referencing cells is convenient when using a large range of cells in a formula. For example, we can type "=SUM(", highlight an entire range of cells to complete the formula, and then type ")". We use this method when constructing formulas to prevent making errors when referencing appropriate cells. In general, this a quicker and safer method for creating references. When typing references directly into a cell, we may risk making errors. Instead, just type "=" and then click the cells we want to refer to.

Referencing is important for using cells in formulas and in VBA code. In order to take advantage of the capabilities of organizing large data in a spreadsheet application, we must be able to refer to it properly. We can reference cells, ranges, worksheets, and workbooks in a formula or in VBA code.

3.2.1 Relative Referencing and Absolute Referencing

There are four basic ways to refer to a cell: *relative, absolute, row absolute*, and *column absolute referencing*. To express the importance of the differences between these referencing types, let's consider the following example. Figure 3.1 features two columns of data; the sums of each column are located below the "Data" table. Let's assume that we created the small "Sum" table by entering a SUM function in cell *B16*. If we want to copy the SUM function from *B16* into the adjacent cell, *C16*, to calculate the sum of the second column of data, we copy and paste the SUM function in that cell. We can also place the cursor at the bottom right-hand of cell *B16* until it transforms into a small cross, and then *click-and-drag* to the adjacent cell, using the method we discussed in Chapter 2. Excel automatically transforms the values and names of the cells in the function according to the direction of the operation. That is, if we copy to one cell below the original function, Excel automatically advances the row number by one unit. If we copy one cell to the right, as in this case, Excel automatically advances the column letter of each cell name by one unit. The functions in cell *B16* and *C16* are shown in the formulas below; we can see that Excel copied the function correctly and automatically changed the column letter by one unit.

=SUM(B4:B13) and *=SUM(C4:C13)*

Note in the figure that the format for both functions remains the same. This is an example of relative referencing. Excel automatically shifts the row and column values in the function relative to the displacement of the copy and paste action.

C16	▾		*fx*	=SUM(C4:C13)
	A	B	C	[
1				
2				
3		Data		
4		46	31	
5		25	54	
6		48	61	
7		95	48	
8		32	78	
9		85	15	
10		78	97	
11		65	35	
12		43	15	
13		91	79	
14				
15		Sum		
16		608	513	

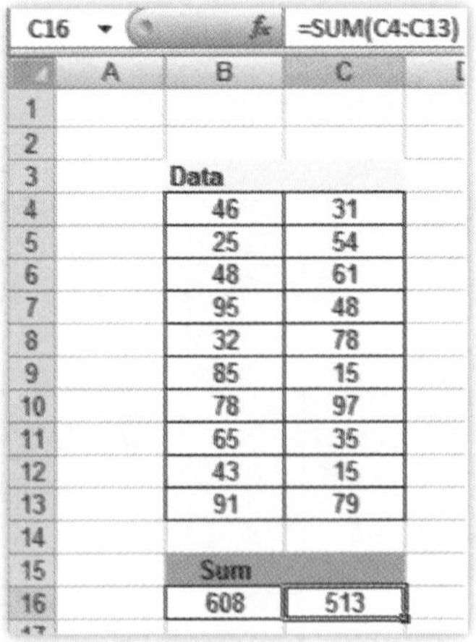

Figure 3.1   Relative referencing copies the SUM function from B16 to C16. Both the row and column values change.

Relative referencing is expressed in the following format:

column letter row number: column letter row number such as *B2:B8*

The only difference between the format of relative referencing and absolute referencing is the addition of a dollar sign. The $ implies that the value that follows cannot be changed. For absolute referencing, the format is:

$column letter $row number: $column letter $row number such as *$B$2:$B$8*

For example, using the same data columns and sums from Figure 3.1, we want to calculate a product (see Figure 3.2). We multiply both sums (from B16 and C16) by the number in cell E4 and place the result in the Product cells. We define the product operation in E11 as follows:

*=E4*B16*

Copying this formula to F11 automatically uses relative referencing to create the formula:

*=F4*C16*

However, this is not correct. We want:

*=E4*C16*

Excel detects that we are copying a function one cell to the right; as a result, it automatically increases all column letters by one unit. In this case, we need absolute referencing because we want to keep the *Multiplier* value, E4, the same in both formulas (see Figure 3.2(a)). To enforce this, we change our formula in E11 to:

*=$E$4*B16*

This way, when we copy the formula to the next product cell, F11, Excel still automatically transfers the reference to C16; however, the E4 reference will not be updated (see Figure 3.2(b)).

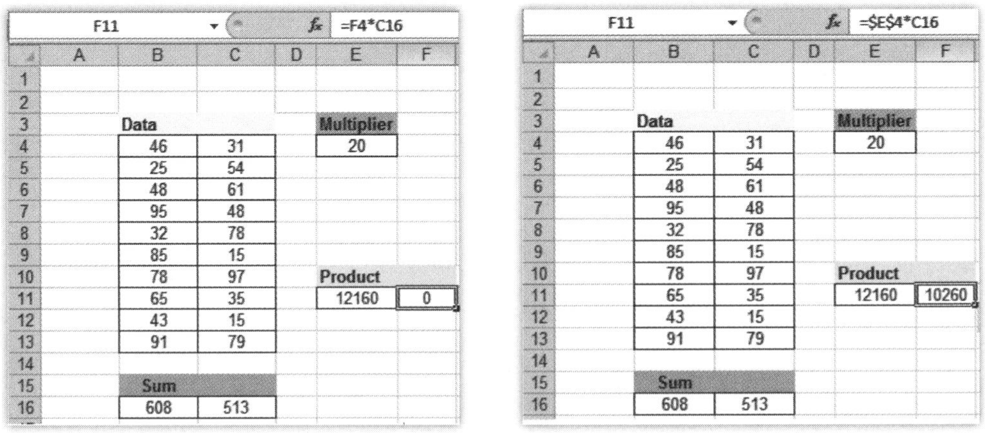

(a) **(b)**

Figure 3.2 Absolute referencing ensures that neither the row nor the column names change when copying a formula. In (a), E4 automatically changes to F4 when the default of relative referencing is assumed. Absolute referencing, (b), maintains $E$4 in both formulas.

Row absolute and column absolute referencing are similar to absolute referencing because the placement of the $ prevents the following value from changing when a formula is copied. Row absolute referencing prevents the row value from changing when a formula is copied to another cell and column absolute referencing prevents the column value from changing. (Note that the shortcut key *F4* changes the reference type; in the formula bar, select the reference that you want to change and repeatedly click *F4* to switch between relative, absolute, row absolute, and column absolute referencing.)

Consider another example. Assume we are trying to calculate a multiplication table between two sets of numbers. In Figure 3.3(a), the first set of numbers, 2 to 5, are in row 2 and the second set of numbers, also 2 to 5, are in column *A*. Instead of calculating each element individually, or even each column or row of numbers separately, we can write the multiplication operation such that it can be copied to all cells of the table and then input the correct products. To do this, we use both row absolute and column absolute referencing.

To make sure all of the first set of numbers comes from row 2 only we use row absolute referencing. We type the first number as *B$2* in the first cell, B3, so that the *$* implies this number will always come from row 2. We type the second number as *$A4* so the *$* implies this number will always come from column *A* (refer to Figure 3.3(a)). As we can see in Figure 3.3(b), when the formula in *B3* is copied to the other cells of the table, the row value is 2 for the first number and the column value is *A* for the second number. Excel automatically updates the column values for the first number and the row values for the second number; for example, *B$2* becomes *C$2*.

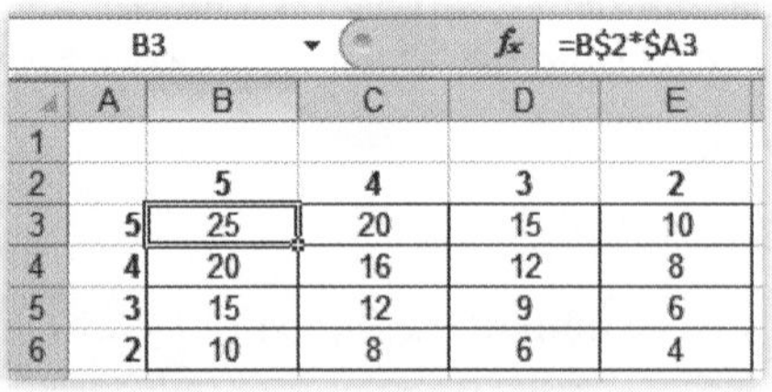

	A	B	C	D	E
1					
2		5	4	3	2
3	5	25	20	15	10
4	4	20	16	12	8
5	3	15	12	9	6
6	2	10	8	6	4

(a)

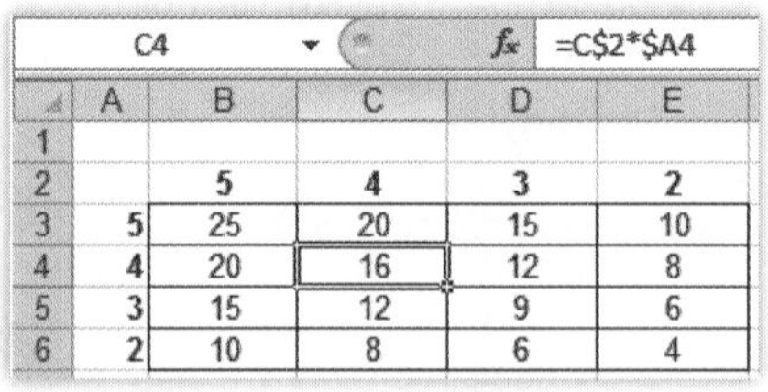

	A	B	C	D	E
1					
2		5	4	3	2
3	5	25	20	15	10
4	4	20	16	12	8
5	3	15	12	9	6
6	2	10	8	6	4

(b)

Figure 3.3 Row absolute referencing prevents the row value from changing when copying a formula to another cell. Here B$2 is transferred to C$2 in the copied formula; row 2 is constant. Column absolute referencing keeps the column value from changing when a formula is copied. The multipliers are referred to as $A3 and $A4, keeping the column name the same.

It is important to understand the differences among these common referencing types. Spreadsheet applications use several formulas that usually refer to values in many different cells. To ensure that our calculations are accurate, we check that the data cells we are referencing are correct for each instance of our formulas.

Summary

Relative Referencing: Row and column value will change (B2).

Absolute Referencing: Neither row nor column value will change ($B$2).

Row Absolute: Row value does not change, but column value will change (B$2).

Column Absolute: Column value does not change, but row value will change ($B2).

3.2.2 R1C1 Notation

There is one other type of cell referencing known as ***R1C1 notation***. Instead of referring to a cell by its row and column value, *R1C1* notation describes a cell's position relative to the cell in which the formula appears. That is, if we are inserting a formula into cell *A1*, it would be the origin cell and referred to as *R1C1*. (The address of a cell is written without brackets.) *A2* would then be *R[1]C[ ]* (or *R[1]C*) to reflect that its position is one row below *A1*, and *B3* would be *R[2]C[1]* to convey that it is two rows below and one column to the right of *A1*. It is possible to switch row and column titles to *R1C1* notation through *Excel Options* dialog box. To evoke this dialog box click on the *Options* command listed in the *File* tab of the Ribbon. In the Excel Option dialog box, select the *Formulas* tab on the left. Check *R1C1 reference style* from the list of *Working with formulas* options. Our rows and columns are now both numbered. If we enter a formula into a cell, it uses *R1C1* notation as the default referencing.

For example, if we have already transferred to *R1C1* notation and wish to perform a simple calculation by typing a formula in cell *A1*, we note the *R1C1* notation of the cells we reference. In Figure 3.4(a), we have entered the simple formula in *A1* (which is now *R1C1*):

=R[1]C[2]

This is the first value in the "Data" column, which implies that the value 95 is one row below and two columns to the right of our original cell. As another example, in Figure 3.4(b), we calculate the sum of the first two values in the "Data" column. Our origin cell is now *A2* (which is *R2C1*); to obtain the sum of 95 and 32 from the "Data" column, we use the following function:

=RC[2] + R[1]C[2]

The value 95 is in the same row, but one column to the right of *A2* (*R2C1*), and 32 is one row below and two columns to the right of *R2C1*. Note the notation *R1C1* is used to denote the address of a cell, which is based on the numbered rows and columns in the worksheet, and the notation *R[1]C[1]* is used to denote the location of a cell relative to the origin cell. In Figure 3.4(a), we can see that the address of the origin cell appears in the upper left-hand window as *R1C1*, and the formula appears in *Formula bar* located in the center top window as *=R[1]C[2]*.

Even though this type of referencing may seem tedious, it can be very useful. For example, when copying a formula using *R1C1* notation, it appears identical in each cell to which we copy it. That is, if we copy the formula from Figure 3.4(b) to the three rows below it, each time we are calculating the sum of the data value in the same row of the "Data" column and one row below it in the "Data" column. Therefore, the formula value is always the following:

=RC[2] + R[1]C[2]

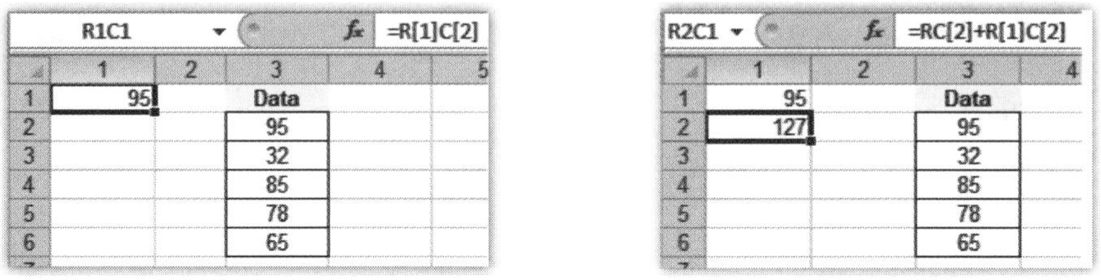

(a) (b)

Figure 3.4 R1C1 notation displays the displaced position of the referenced cell to the origin cell where the function is entered. (a) R1C1 is the name of the origin cell and R[1]C[2] is the position of the referenced cell.

This is relative to each new origin cell we copy to (see Figure 3.5). *R1C1* notation is therefore a helpful check method to ensure that we copied the formulas correctly. We can even work in the default-referencing mode (A1, A2, etc.) and then switch to *R1C1* notation just to check the formulas. (Notice that only relative referencing is used with *R1C1 Notation*.)

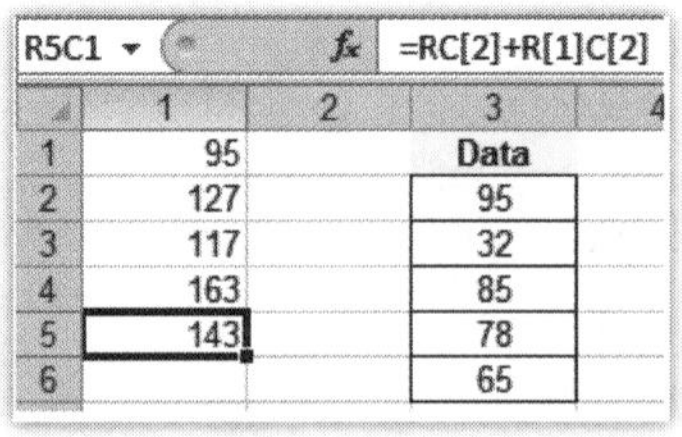

Figure 3.5 Copying formulas using R1C1 notation shows the same formula in each copied cell. Here, the formulas in R2C1 through R5C1 are all =RC[2] + R[1]C[2].

Excel offers a formula view that displays cells by their formulas instead of their calculated values. To use it, we click on the *Formulas tab* > *Formula Auditing* group > *Show Formula* command. For our example above, the screen resembles Figure 3.6. Again, the formulas in cells *R2C1* to *R5C1* are all the same.

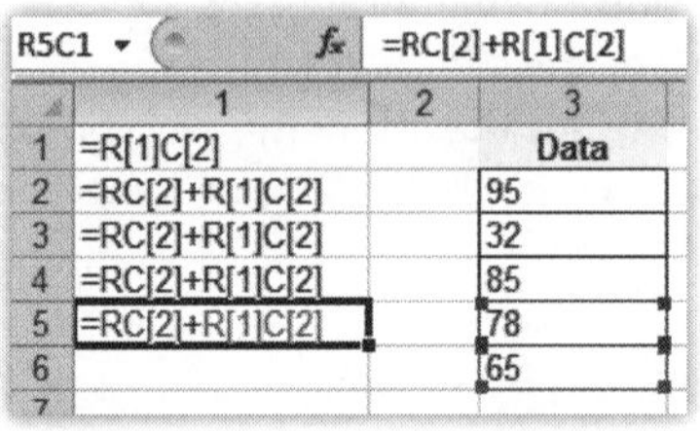

Figure 3.6 The formula view shows only the cell formulas and not the calculation results.

R1C1 notation also becomes important when working with VBA code. When writing code, *R1C1* notation is the clearest way to ensure that we are referencing cells correctly in our formulas.

Summary

R1C1 Notation: Refers to a cell's position relative to the origin cell where the formula is entered.

3.2.3 Referencing Other Worksheets and Workbooks

Formulas can also reference cells outside of the sheet in which the formula is written. To do this, we simply type the name of the sheet followed by an exclamation mark (!) in front of the cell or range name. Suppose that we have several data tables in "Sheet1" of our workbook and we keep all of our formulas in "Sheet 2." To refer to the data value in cell *A1* in "Sheet1" while typing a formula in "Sheet2," we use the format:

=Sheet1!A1

Assume we have created two sheets, "Data Sheet" and "Formula Sheet," as illustrated in Figure 3.7. In the "Data Sheet," we have two columns of data: "Data A" and "Data B." In the "Formula Sheet," we want to find the product of these two columns of data (see Figure 3.8). To reference the data in the "Data Sheet" in a formula, we must type in the "Formula Sheet." As demonstrated in the format above, we must type the name of the "Data Sheet" before we type the appropriate cell name from the "Data" columns. Notice however that these sheet names have spaces in them; if there is a space in the sheet name, we must use single quotation marks ('...') around the sheet name and before the exclamation mark. Note again that we do not have to type this or other addresses directly into a cell in order to create a reference. We can always just type "=" and then click the cells (on one or multiple sheets) which we want to reference.

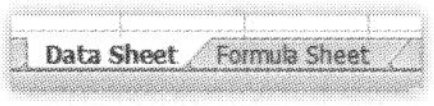

Figure 3.7   Two sheets in a workbook: one for data and the other for formulas.

Therefore, to multiply the first value of "Data A" and "Data B," which are cells *B3 and C3* respectively in the "Data Sheet," we type the following formula in the "Formula Sheet":

='Data Sheet'!B3'Data Sheet'!C3*

(See Figure 3.8(b)). We can then copy this formula to the "Product" column in the "Formula Sheet" to reference the other values from the "Data Sheet."

To refer to a cell in a different workbook, we include the title of this workbook and the sheet number in the reference. For example, if we want to refer to the data cell *A1* in the first sheet of a workbook titled "Data," we use the format:

=[Data.xlsx]Sheet1!A1

Note that if there is a space in our workbook title, for example "Collected Data," we must add single quotation marks around the workbook and worksheet name; in this case, the format is:

='[Collected Data.xlsx]Sheet1'!A1

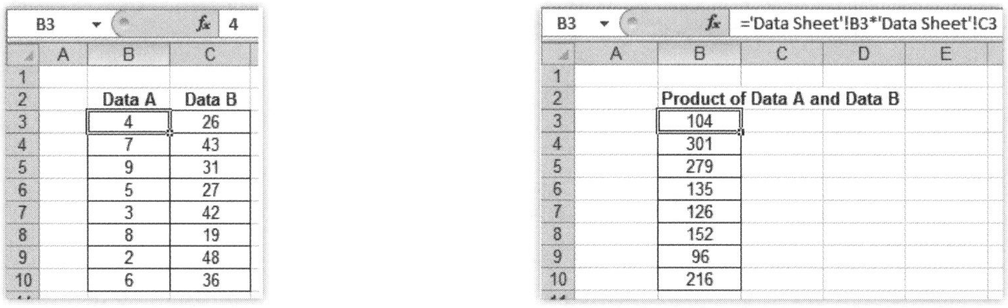

	A	B	C
1			
2		Data A	Data B
3		4	26
4		7	43
5		9	31
6		5	27
7		3	42
8		8	19
9		2	48
10		6	36

B3 ▼ *fx* 4

(a)

	A	B	C	D	E
1					
2		Product of Data A and Data B			
3		104			
4		301			
5		279			
6		135			
7		126			
8		152			
9		96			
10		216			

B3 ▼ *fx* ='Data Sheet'!B3*'Data Sheet'!C3

(b)

Figure 3.8   The formulas in the "Formula Sheet" reference the data in the "Data Sheet." (a) Two columns of data in the "Data Sheet." (b) The product of these two data columns in the "Formula Sheet."

Also note that if the workbook we are referring to is not currently open in Excel, we must type the complete path of the workbook and worksheet surrounded by single quotation marks, for example:

='C:\My Documents\Project\[Collected Data.xlsx]Sheet1'!A1

Summary

Referencing worksheets and workbooks:

Worksheet in the same workbook:	Sheet1!A1
Workbook:	[Data.xlsx]Sheet1!A1
Workbook with spaces in the title:	'[Collected Data.xlsx]Sheet1'!A1
Workbook not currently open in Excel:	'C:\My Documents\Project\[Collected Data.xlsx] Sheet1'!A1

3.2.4 Circular Referencing

A referencing loop in a spreadsheet creates a *circular reference*. A circular reference occurs, for example, if cell *A1* has the value "=B1," cell *B1* has the value "=C1," and cell *C1* has the value "=A1." This referencing loop causes an error in Excel. Circular referencing can often, but not always, be avoided. For example, we may have a formula that involves the sequential calculation of different variable values: a=2*b, c=5+a, b=c/3. If the formulas for a, b, and c are entered as references in three different cells, a circular referencing error occurs. For example, cell *A1* has value "=2*B1," cell *C1* has the value "=5+A1," and cell *B1* has the value "=C1/3."

The first possible solution to this problem requires us to rearrange our references or to modify our formula. However, if neither can be done, Excel offers another tool to aid in sequential calculations. Select *File* tab, click *Options* command, select the *Formulas* tab of *Excel Options* dialog box, and check the *Enable iterative calculations* option. Excel will then perform a specified number of iterations, or repetitions, of the calculations, to try to find a solution applicable to all equations. The values of the variables are changed by a mathematical model (the Gauss-Seidel Iteration), which converges (or stops) when the maximum change in any cell between iterations is at most .001 (or any other number specified in the *Calculations* tab), or after a maximum number of iterations has been performed.

3.3 Names for Cells, References, and Worksheets

For some formula referencing and calculations, it is more efficient to define specific names for cells and ranges, as well as constants and other formulas. Range names can be any sequence of letters and numbers that create a significant name and follow some brief rules. We cannot use spaces in range names; however, we can replace spaces with underscores (_) or periods (.). Likewise, names cannot begin with numbers or look like a cell reference (such as "A3"). Range names are not case sensitive in Excel. Single cells, ranges of cells, and non-adjacent ranges of cells can all be named. A named range is absolutely referenced; that is, if the range "Profit" is assigned to cell *B3*, it is always set to this cell unless redefined. Therefore, "Profit" is actually referenced as cell *$B$3*. Range names are unique per worksheet. If there is a range "Profit" on worksheet 1, Excel technically allows you to name another range "Profit" on worksheet 2. However, it is a good practice to use unique range names in a workbook. Ranges can be named in three different ways: using the name box; defining names; and creating names.

3.3.1 The Name Box

The easiest way to create a cell or range name is by using the ***name box***. We highlight a cell or a range of cells, we click on them and then we click in the *name box*, which appears at the upper left-hand part of the screen (just above cell *A1*), and type a name for the range. To name the first value in the table in Figure 3.9(a) as "Length," we click on cell *C3* and then enter the name in the *name box*, as illustrated in Figure 3.9(b). To see all current names in the active workbook, we simply click on the drop-down arrow next to the *name box*; F3 works as a shortcut for this operation. We can find the cell references of these range names by clicking on a name from this list; the referenced cell will then automatically be selected.

To move a range name, that is, to change the cells it references, we can simply click-and-drag the cell or range to another location. That is, if we name the cell *C3* in Figure 3.9 as "Length" and then decide to shift the data column to the right, we just click-and-drag this cell to the right so that the data cell name remains the same. The reference for the "Length" range name is now *D4*. We can work with cell references directly by using the Define option for creating names.

3.3.2 Define

To define a name in Excel, we choose *Formulas tab > Defined Names* group from the Ribbon, click on Define Name drop-down menu and select Define Name option. For example, if we have a table with some data, we can name the values with a description. In Figure 3.9(a), the default name for the first cell in the "Parameters" column is *C3*; this name appears in the upper left-hand corner of the window.

To define another name for this cell, we choose Define Name option from the Define Name drop-down menu. The screen shown in Figure 3.10 then appears. First, we check that we are naming the correct cell by looking at the bottom of the window under *Refers to*. The formula needed to name *C3* in "Sheet 1" is the following:

='Sheet1'!$C$3

(a) **(b)**

Figure 3.9 Defining a cell name. (a) The name of the cell with the value 45 is C3. (b) The name of the same cell is "Length."

If this information is correct, we then define the scope of this name. Scope allows you to duplicate names in a workbook. We can define the scope of a name to be just sheet 1 (as in Figure 3.10), or the whole workbook (as in Figure 3.12(a)). Finally, we enter a name for this cell at the top of the window next to *Name*. Excel automatically provides a name, called a natural range name, if there is an obvious reference from our spreadsheet. In this case, the name "Length" automatically appears. However, we could use a different name by typing it in this area. Now, we confirm that the name of the cell in *Sheet1!$C$3* has been changed to "Length."

Figure 3.9(b) demonstrates that the new name "Length" now appears in the upper left-hand corner for cell *C3*.

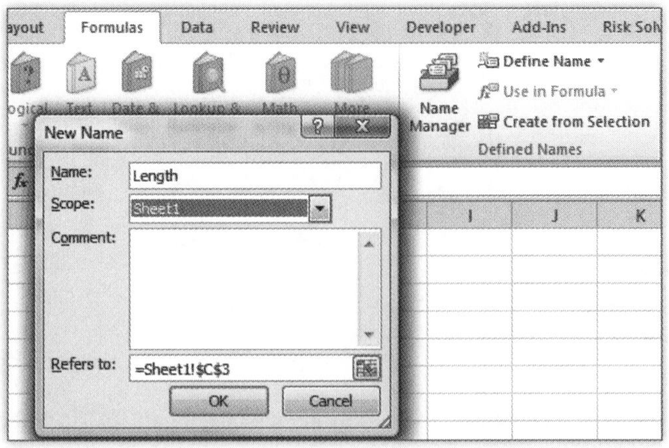

Figure 3.10 Selecting Sheet1!$C$3 as the cell to be named and entering the name "Length" in the *Name* box.

We can continue this process by naming *C4* "Width" and *C5 "Depth."* These cell names stay the same even if we change their data values. This tool is particularly useful in VBA coding when referring to cell names in calculations. The names can also be used to reference these cells in formulas. This simplifies the cell referencing options discussed in Section 3.1 so the cell name alone can refer to specific values. For example, to refer to the "Length" value, we can now type the following. (Notice no quotations are used.)

=Length

A useful shortcut key for entering cell names as a reference or as part of a formula is *F3*. The shortcut key F3 will show a small dialog box with a list of all the names created in the workbook (see Figure 3.11). That is, instead of typing "=Length", we could just type "=" and then press F3 to choose the name "Length" from the list of cell names in the workbook. This can save time, memory, and prevent errors when using cell names.

Figure 3.11 Using the F3 shortcut key can make using cell names easier and safer.

We can also name a range of cells. To do so, we highlight the entire range and again chose Define Name option from Define Name drop-down menu in the *Formula* tab of the Ribbon (see Figure 3.12(a)). We define *Sheet1!$C$3:$C$5* as the entire range (as seen at the bottom of the *New Name* dialog box) and rename this range "Parameters." When we select that range of cells in our worksheet, the name "Parameters" appears in the name box (see Figure 3.12(b)).

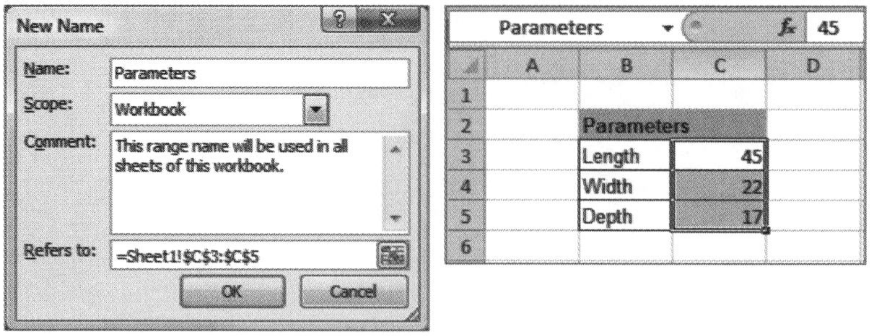

(a) **(b)**

Figure 3.12 (a) Selecting and renaming the entire range to be defined. (b) The range name "Parameters" now appears in the name box when that range is highlighted.

Name references can be modified using the *Name Manager* dialog box (see Figure 3.13.) To display this dialog box click on the *Formulas* tab > *Defined Names* group > *Name Manager* command on the *Ribbon*. From the list of names, we can select a name and then click on the *Edit* command to evoke the *Edit Name* dialog box (see Figure 3.14.) You can either change the name of an existing reference by typing the new name in the *Name* window, or you can change the reference of the selected name using the *Refers to* window. Names can also be deleted using the *Delete* button in *Name Manager* dialog box; we just select a name from the list and click *Delete*. (Note that only one name can be deleted at a time.)

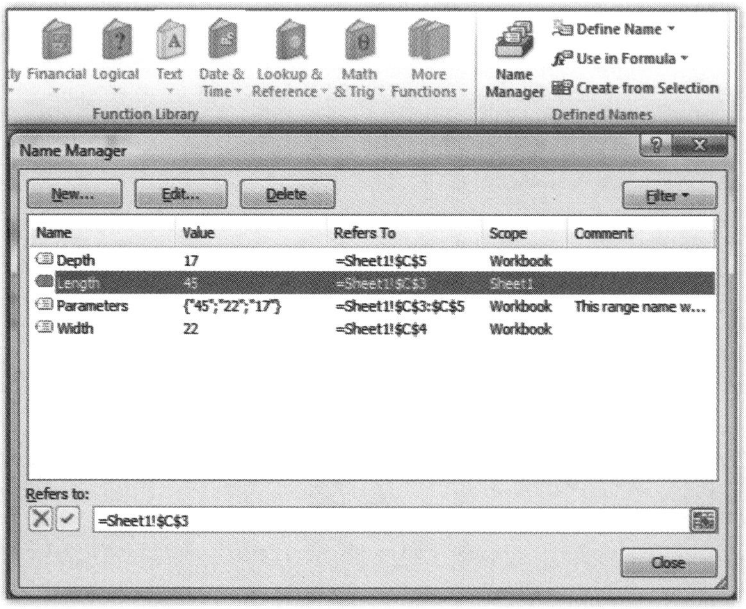

Figure 3.13 Selecting an existing name from the Name Manager dialog box.

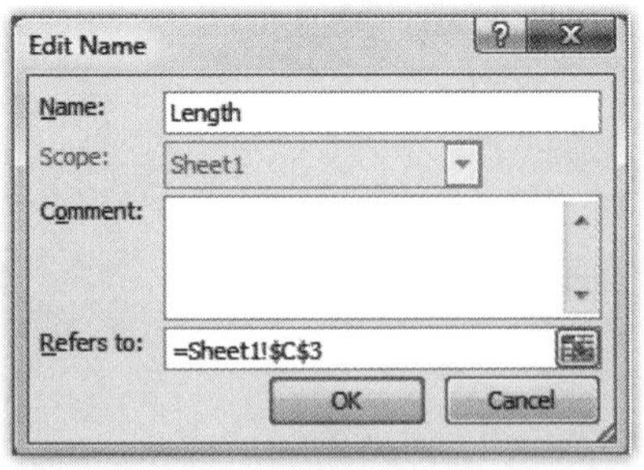

Figure 3.14 The Edit Name dialog box allows you to change the name of a cell, or change the reference cell for an existing name.

3.3.3 Apply

If we have previously referenced cells or ranges in a formula before naming them, the names will not be automatically updated. For example, in Figure 3.15 (a), "Volume" is calculated by multiplying all three data values; the formula is represented by the names of the original cells:

*=C3*C4*C5*

To update this formula with the new names, we select Formulas tab > *Defined Names* group. From the Define Name drop-down menu, select *Apply Names option.* The window in Figure 3.16 then appears. Here, we can select the names that we wish to apply and leave the default options selected. Excel then searches the worksheet for any formulas that reference these cell names and updates them. In Figure 3.15(b), Excel is updating the original formula for "Volume" to reflect the defined cell names:

*=Length*Width*Depth*

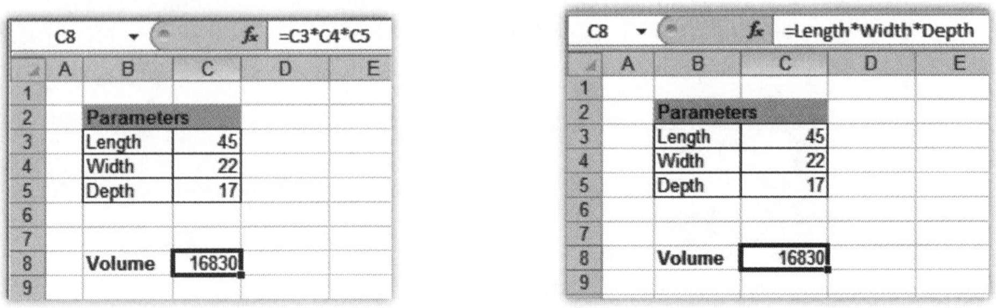

(a) **(b)**

Figure 3.15 Updating a formula so it correctly references newly named cells. (a) Even though cells C3 through C5 have been renamed, the formula previously entered still references their original names. (b) After choosing Insert > Name > Apply from the Excel menu, the formula is updated to reflect the new names of the referenced cells.

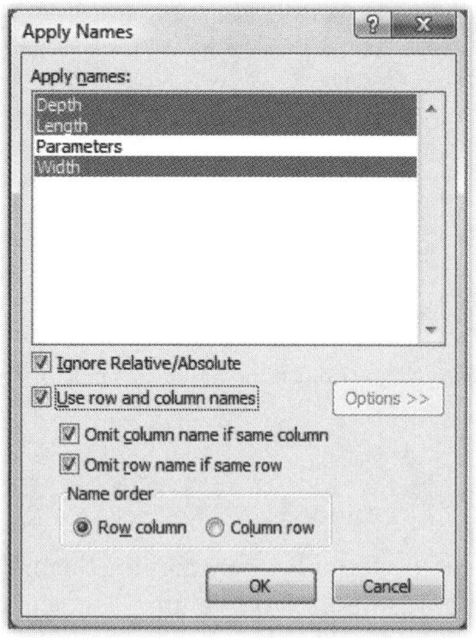

Figure 3.16 Selecting the names desired to apply to the formula cell. Other options are also shown in this screen.

3.3.4 Create

Create provides another quick way to name cells when we already have data labels in our table. Our example in Figure 3.15(b) already includes the labels "Length," "Width," and "Depth" in the table. Instead of defining each cell name separately, we can alternately highlight the entire table (labels and cell values) and select *Formulas* tab > *Defined Names* group > *Create from Selection* on the Ribbon. The dialog box in Figure 3.17(a) then appears. We select *Left column* from the *Create Names* screen to indicate that we want all of the names in the left column of the highlighted selection to be the names of the corresponding data cells. Figure 3.17(b) reveals that the names have been created for cells *C3* through *C5*. When using this method, we must remember that it is necessary to highlight the table labels before creating the range names.

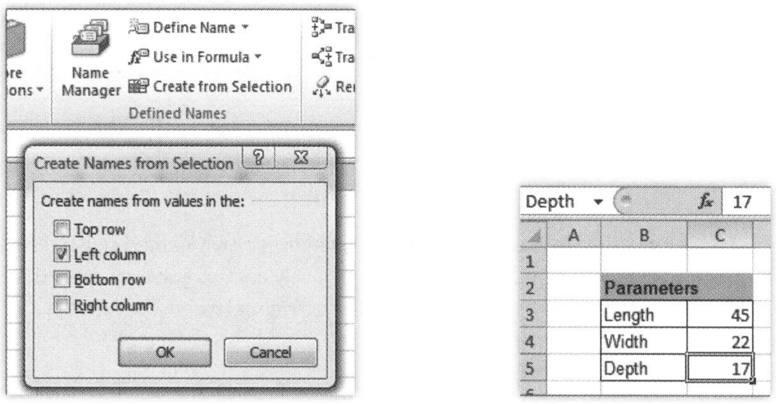

(a) (b)

Figure 3.17 Creating names by selecting a table with values and labels. (a) Choosing Left column because the cell labels are in the left column of the selected table. (b) Using the names of the labels to name the corresponding cells.

The same procedure can be followed to name an entire range of data. For example, if our "Parameters" table is expanded to include several different products, we could name each row and column of data by their labels. In Figure 3.18(a), we create range names for each row of the table by highlighting all of the rows and their table labels (*B3:E5*), choosing *Formulas* tab > *Defined Names* group > *Create from Selection*, and selecting *Left column*. We create range names for each column of the table by highlighting all of the columns and their table labels (*C2:E5*), choosing *Formulas* tab > *Defined Names* group > *Create from Selection*, and selecting names for each column by selecting *Top Row* (see Figure 3.16(b)).

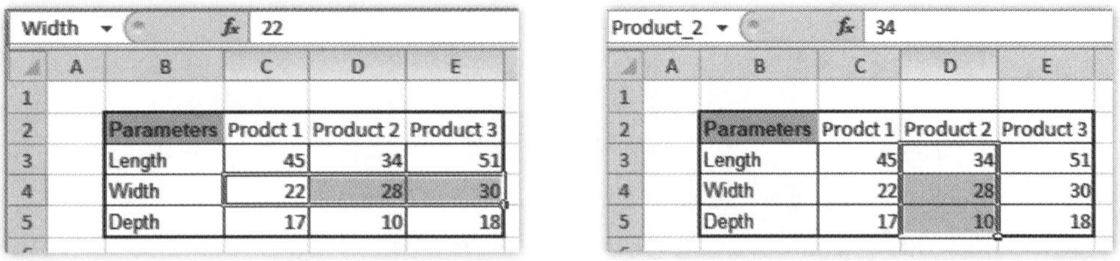

(a) (b)

Figure 3.18 Creating range names by (a) highlighting the row labels and the data cells and (b) selecting the column labels with all of the data cells.

Note that the cells do not have names now, only the same ranges. To name each element of our table completely, we must use the *Define Name* command again. We select a cell from the table (*C3:E5*), choose *Formulas* tab > *Defined Names* group > *Define Name* from the Ribbon and type an appropriate cell name in the *New Name* box. For example, in Figure 3.19(a), we select the first element of our table, *C3*, and use the method just described to go to the *New Name* dialog box. We define the name "Length_Prod1" for this cell. In Figure 3.19(b), this element is named. We continue this process to name all the other elements in the table. Alternately, we could select the entire table, and use *Formulas* tab > *Defined Names* group > *Define Name* command to give the name "Parameters_Table" to the entire range of cells. Note that we cannot use spaces when we are naming cells. Instead, we must replace a desired space with an underscore (_).

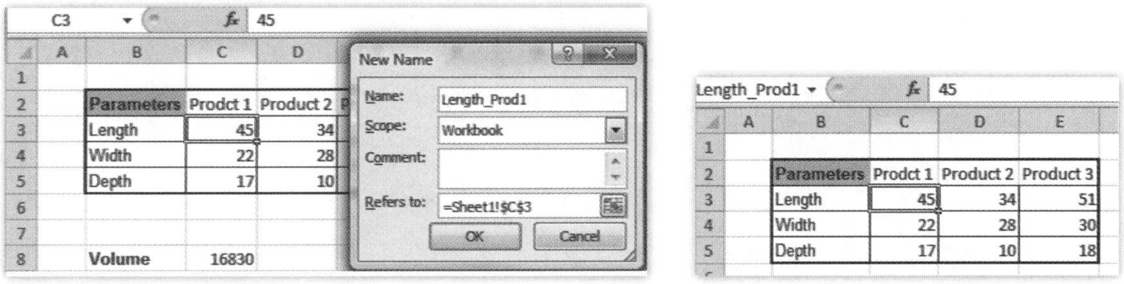

(a) (b)

Figure 3.19 Using Define Name to create names for each element. (a) Using the name "Length_Prod1" to name cell C3 in "Sheet1." (b) The name now appears for this element of the table.

3.3.5 Formulas and Constants

We can also define names for formulas and constants. Creating a name for a constant is simple. First, we select *Formulas* tab > *Defined Names* group > *Define Name* command from the Ribbon. Then, instead of selecting a cell or range, we type an "=" followed by a number value in the *Refers to* area at the bottom of the *New Name* dialog box (see Figure 3.20). This method is most helpful if we are defining multiplier values such as rates or weighted constants.

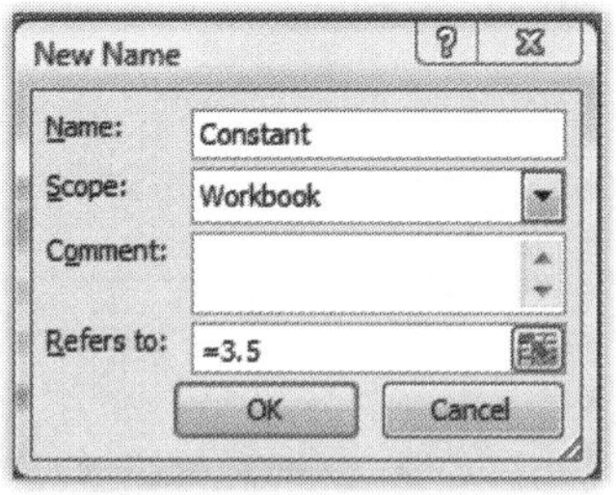

Figure 3.20 Defining a constant by the name "Constant" and giving it the value 3.5.

For example, in Figure 3.21(a), we create a formula named "product" and define this formula in the *Refers to* area:

*=Sheet1!D3*Sheet1!D4*Sheet1!D5*

The substitution of names for formulas simplifies calculations that use the results of several different formulas. For example, we may want to take the average of a product calculation and sum calculation. In Figure 3.21(b), we define the formula for sum by using the Excel function SUM. We examine functions in detail in Chapter 4; here, the function allows us to determine the sum of a given cell range:

=SUM(Sheet1!D3:D5)

To find the average of the results of these two formulas, we refer to the named formulas. We use another Excel function called AVERAGE to calculate the average value:

=AVERAGE(product, sum)

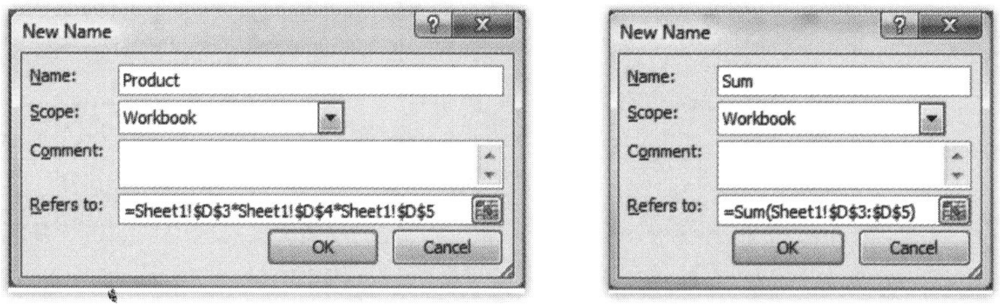

(a) **(b)**

Figure 3.21 Creating two formula names. (a) Defining the product formula as the product of cells D3 through D5. (b) Defining the sum formula as the sum of cells D3 through D5.

Again, naming constants and formulas can be very useful when using VBA code. As we will see in Part II, VBA code becomes much clearer when we use names instead of cell and range references in formulas. Naming also helps us keep data and calculations organized in a spreadsheet application.

Summary

Defining Names: Names cells, ranges, constants, and formulas.

Creating Names: Used when row and column labels are already given in a table.

Applying Names: Updates formulas with new cell and range names.

3.4 *Summary*

- There are four basic types of referencing. In relative referencing (*B2*), row and column values change. In absolute referencing (*$B$2*), neither the row nor column value changes. For row absolute (*B$2*), the row value does not change, but the column value does. For column absolute (*$B2*), the column value does not change, but the row value does.
- *R1C1* notation refers to a cell's position relative to the origin cell where the formula is entered. This type of referencing is useful in VBA coding.
- In referencing worksheets and workbooks, worksheets in the same workbook are referenced as *Sheet1!A1*. Workbooks are referenced as *[Data.xlsx]Sheet1!A1* and workbooks with spaces in the title are referenced as *'[Collected Data]Sheet1'!A1*. Workbooks not currently open in Excel must be referenced as *'C:\My Documents\Project\[Collected Data]Sheet1'!A1*.
- Circular referencing can occur when there is a referencing loop between cells. To correct this error, select *File* tab on the Ribbon, click *Options* command, select the *Formulas* tab of *Excel Options* dialog box, and check the *Enable iterative calculations* option.
- Use defining names to name cells, ranges, constants, and formulas. Use creating names when row and column labels are already given in a table. Applying names is necessary to update formulas with new cell and range names.
- Names can also be created for formulas and constants to make referencing in longer formulas clearer.
- A simpler ways to create range names are using the name window.

3.5 *Exercises*

3.5.1 Review Questions

1. What are the four basic ways to refer to a cell?
2. How can a relative reference be changed to an absolute reference? What is the shortcut key to do this?
3. Write the syntax for each of the following references:
   a. Relative reference to cell G7.
   b. Absolute reference to cell A2.
   c. Row absolute reference to cell B6.
   d. Column absolute reference to cell J12.
4. How does R1C1 notation refer to a cell?
5. How do you set R1C1 as the default notation in Excel?
6. When typing a formula in cell C2 using R1C1 notation, how do you refer to cell G5?

7. How do you refer to a cell in a different worksheet from the one in which the formula is being written?
8. Write the syntax to reference the following cells from "Sheet 1" of the workbook "Collected Data":
   a. Cell A3 on Sheet 2 of "Collected Data."
   b. Cell B5 on the sheet "New York" of open Excel book "Inventory."
9. How do you refer to cells in a workbook not currently open in Excel?
10. How do you create a cell/range name in Excel?
11. What is the use of *Scope* options in the New Name dialog box?
12. How can you update a formula when a cell or range name within that formula has been changed?
13. How is defining a constant different from naming a cell?
14. How is defining names different than creating names?
15. Give an example of circular referencing.

3.5.2 Hands-On Exercises

NOTE: Please refer to the file "Chapter_03_Exercises.xlsx" for the associated worksheets noted for the hands-on exercises. The file is available at: www.dssbooks.com.

1. A team of industrial engineers is designing a new workstation for the assembly of a product. The team plans to consider ergonomic factors in the design to minimize fatigue of the assembly personnel. To create the most ergonomic design possible, the team decided to collect information about how the current assembly personnel prefer to assemble the product. The team asked the assembly workers: whether they gather all of the parts prior to assembly or one part at a time during assembly; whether they prefer to use one or two hands; whether they prefer to stand, sit, or do both; and whether they hold the product above the table or on the table during assembly. (Refer to worksheet "3.1".)
   a. Use column headings to describe the contents of each column.
   b. Then, using the Create option, give the range of cells in each column the same name as the column heading.
   c. Finally, define a name for the whole table.
2. A materials engineer is comparing various properties of ceramics to determine the most appropriate material for use in a car engine. The ideal material will exhibit a high fracture toughness (in MPa•m$^{1/2}$), a high tensile strength (in MPa), and a low thermal conductivity (in W/m•K). The engineer tests each of the materials and obtains the following results:
   - Materials A, B, C, D, E, F, and G have fracture toughness of 3, 3.5, 3.2, 2.7, 3.9, 3.2, and 2.6 MPa•m$^{1/2}$, respectively.
   - Materials A, B, C, D, E, F, and G have tensile strengths of 270, 253, 285, 246, 279, 285, and 260 MPa, respectively.
   - Materials A, B, C, D, E, F, and G have thermal conductivities of 29, 33, 37, 41, 25, 40, and 27 W/m•K, respectively.

   Create a table of the engineer's results in an Excel spreadsheet. Define names for each row and column of your table. Also define a name for the whole table.
3. A spreadsheet is used to calculate the area of a rectangle given the parameters length and width. (Refer to worksheet "3.3".)
   a. Type the formula "=B2*B3" into cell B5 to calculate the area.
   b. Using the *Create* option, designate the contents of B2 as "Length" and B3 as "Width."
   c. Apply the names "Length" and "Width" to the spreadsheet. What is the formula now shown in cell B5?
4. A spreadsheet is used to calculate the circumference and area of a circle using the circle's radius and the constant pi. (Refer to worksheet "3.4".)
   a. Name the contents of cell B2 "Radius."
   b. Define a constant "pi" to be equal to 3.14159.
   c. Use these names to find the circumference.
   d. Use these names to find the area.
   e. Change the values in cell B2 to 10 and give the resulting circumference and area.
5. One must be very careful when using named columns or rows in a spreadsheet. Create a ten-cell column that begins in cell A1 and contains the integers 1 through 10, so that each cell contains

one integer. Define this range of integers with the name "column." Give the responses when the formula "=column" is placed in the following cells:

a. C1

b. D7

c. E11

6. A tile manufacturer uses spreadsheets to monitor the quarterly sales of each of its regional distributors. Given tables display the sales for the years 2009, 2010, and 2011 on separate worksheets. A final table is used to compile all of the sales over the three-year period. Complete this table with the regional sales for each quarter of each year by referencing the first three tables. (Refer to worksheets "3.6-2009", "3.6-2010", "3.6-2011", and "3.6-Summary".)

7. A From/To chart is used by a manufacturing plant to indicate the number of products flowing from each station A-E to another station. Create names for each row and column of data. Also define names for the formulas located in the "From Sum" column and the "To Sum" row. (*Note*: These generic formulas will be replaced with actual formulas that perform calculations in the next chapter.) (Refer to worksheet "3.7".)

8. Checking accounts at a local bank earn 4% interest annually. A table is used to compute the amount of interest earned for each account. (Refer to worksheet "3.8".)

a. Type the formula "=A2*B2" in cell C2 to compute the interest earned on the account with $5372.00. You should find that $215.00 of interest was earned.

b. Using absolute referencing to refer to the interest rate in cell A2, drag the formula in cell C2 through the remaining cells in the column to compute the interest earned on the other accounts.

9. The bank in Hands-On Exercise 8 is considering increasing the interest rates it provides to checking account holders. Revise the table you created so that earnings with interest rates of 4%, 5%, and 6% can be compared. (Refer to worksheet "3.9".)

a. Drag the formula used in cell C2 to cells D2 and E2. Modify the formulas in cells D2 and E2 so that each refers to the appropriate interest rate.

b. Using absolute referencing to refer to the appropriate interest rate, drag your formulas in cells D2 and E2 through the remaining cells in each column to compute the amount of interest earned on the other accounts at 5% and 6%.

10. A table is used to compute the velocity of a vehicle given the time and distance traveled. (Refer to worksheet "3.10".)

a. Define the names of three columns: "Time," "Distance," and "Velocity." Set worksheet "3.10" as the scope of these variables.

b. Compute the values for the "Velocity" column using the formula "=Distance/Time."

c. Copy and paste the table onto a different part of the worksheet. The values in the "Velocity" column will no longer be defined. Re-compute the values in this column using R1C1 notation.

11. Refer to the table in Chapter 2, Hands-On Exercise 9. Paste the table onto a spreadsheet so that the upper left cell, "transaction number," is located in cell A2. Then, for each transaction, give the location of the cell containing the amount of the transaction by using R1C1 notation that references cell A1.

12. A table is used to compute the force per square meter of a falling object hitting the ground. (Refer to worksheet "3.12".)

a. Define the acceleration due to gravity (9.81) as a constant called "Gravity."

b. Define the names of the columns as "Surface_Area," "Mass," "Force," and "Force_Per_Area." Set worksheet "3.12" to be the scope of these variables.

c. Compute the values of the force column with the formula "=Gravity*Mass."

d. Compute the values of the force per area column with the formula "=Force/Surface_Area."

e. Copy and paste the table onto a different part of the worksheet. Re-compute the values of the force and force per area columns using R1C1 notation.

13. A spreadsheet is used to convert a table of data in degrees Fahrenheit into degrees Celsius. The formula to perform this conversion is: *Degrees Celsius = (Degrees Fahrenheit – 32)*(5/9)*. (Refer to worksheet "3.13".)

a. Compute the values for the "Table of Degrees in Celsius" using relative referencing.
b. Compute the values for the "Table of Degrees in Celsius" using R1C1 notation.

14. A table is used to record the June retail sales of ten southeastern states. (Refer to worksheet "3.14".)
    a. Name each cell in the range B2:B12 by its corresponding state abbreviation from column A. (For example, cell B2 should be named "FL.") Set the current workbook as the scope of these names.
    b. Name the entire Monthly Sales column "Monthly Sales." Set worksheet "3.14" as the scope of this name.
    c. In cell A14, calculate the sum of the sales values using range names. (This can be done using names from part a or part b above.)
15. Perform the following operations:
    a. Create a constant named "Multiplier" that has the value 10.
    b. Multiply the first value with the constant. Create a formula that will perform this multiplication.
    c. Use relative referencing to multiply the rest of the values with the constant.
    d. Name the results from the multiplication as "New Values".
16. In a given table, two production plants have recorded the number of shipments made to three different cities. Use the *Create Names from Selection* command of *Define Names* group to name the columns and rows of this table. Use these names to find the total number of shipments made by each plant and the total number received by each city. (Refer to worksheet "3.16".)
17. A table provides a five-month documentation of beginning inventories, production, and demand. Use the *Create Names from Selection* command of *Define Names* group to name the columns and rows of this table. Use these names to calculate the values for the "Ending Inventory" column. [*End Inv = Begin Inv + Production – Demand*] (Refer to worksheet "3.17".)
18. A furniture store has $7,500 cash at the beginning of January. Cash inflow and outflow from January to May are recorded in a table. Using range names and referencing, compute the cash amount at the beginning and end of each month. (Refer to worksheet "3.18".)
19. Track the following plane route: Houston to Los Angeles to Seattle to Chicago, back to Houston. For all flight legs, each plane uses 0.1 gallons per mile. The average fuel per leg = 0.5 * (initial fuel + final fuel). In Houston, the plane begins with 1000 gallons of fuel. Using the distance of each flight leg in the given table, compute the amount of fuel left when the plane returns to Houston. (Refer to worksheet "3.19".)
20. In August, at the beginning of the semester, Mary has $500 in her savings account. At the end of each month, she earns 2% interest. Each month's interest is based on the average of the month's beginning and ending balance. Create a flow table of balances for the beginning and end of each month in the academic year (August 1 to May 1 = 9 months). Assuming that she doesn't make any withdrawals, how much money does Mary have in her savings account in May?
21. John borrowed $20,000 from the Credit Union Bank to buy a car. He will be paying this amount back in 5 equal end-of-year payments. The bank uses an APR of 2% to calculate the yearly payments.
    a. Calculate the John's yearly payments using the formula:
    b. Use range names and referencing to calculate the amount due in the beginning and end of each year and the amount of interest paid each year. Note that: Int. Paid = Beginning Balance * 0.02; End Balance = Beginning Balance – Principal Payment; Principal Payment = Yearly Payment – Int. Paid.
    c. Assume John wants to calculate the return on this investment. He plans to name the corresponding cell where the results will be stored "ROI." Will he be able to name a cell in this worksheet "ROI"? If not, explain why.
22. A distribution center is considering four possible locations for their new facility. The *x* and *y* coordinates of these locations are given in a table. The management is planning to choose the location that would minimize the total distance traveled to serve their customers. (Refer to worksheet "3.22".)
    a. Calculate the total distance traveled from each candidate location to the customers. Consider Euclidean distance between loca-

tions by referencing the customer locations. The Euclidean distance between locations A and B = $[(xB - xA)^2 + (yB - yA)^2]^{1/2}$.

b. Use the *Create Name from Selection* command of *Define Names* group to name the range of cells that presents the distances from a particular location to all customers. Use the formulas '=sum(A)' to '=sum(D)' to calculate the total distance from a candidate location to all customers.

23. "Contemporary Furniture" is a furniture store located in Houston, Texas. The company's monthly sales (in thousands) during the last year are given in a table. (Refer to worksheet "3.23".)

a. Calculate the revenues from sales during the month of January.

b. Use referencing to calculate the revenues for the rest of the months.

c. Create names for the columns: 'Price', 'Jan', . . ., 'Dec'.

d. Create names for the rows: 'Chair', 'Desk' and 'Futon'.

e. Define a name for the table.

f. Calculate the monthly revenues, the annual revenues per items and the annual revenues of the store. In calculating the revenues use the formulas: '=sum(Jan)', . . . ,'=sum(Futon)', etc.

g. The company plans to calculate the amount of tax due every month. Create a new column on your table. Name the range of cells in this column of data "Tax2010." Are you able to create this new name? If not, explain why.

24. Consider the information given in Hands-on Exercise 23. A new table presents the purchasing cost per item at "Contemporary Furniture" store. The company now wants to create a table which summarizes revenues, expenses, and profits per month. (Refer to worksheet "3.24".)

a. Copy the monthly revenues from the spreadsheet with the solution to Hands-on Exercise 23 and paste in E2:E13.

b. Calculate the monthly expenses referencing the unit costs and monthly sales presented in the Excel file (or spreadsheet) with the solution to the Hands-on Exercise 23.

c. Create names for the columns: 'Revenues', 'Expenses', and 'Profits'.

d. Define a name for the table.

e. Calculate the monthly profits using the formula Profits = Revenues – Expenses.

f. Calculate the annual profits for this business.

g. The company plans to calculate the amount of tax due. Create a new name for the cell where this amount will be stored. Name this cell "Tax2011." Are you able to create this new name? If not, explain why.

25. A health care center is considering locating their new facility either in Miami, Orlando, or Jacksonville. In making their decision, the following factors are considered: total patient miles per month, facility utilization, average time per emergency trip, expressway accessibility, land and construction costs, and employee preferences. The management evaluated each possible location using these criteria. A table gives the weight assigned to each factor and scores for each location. (Refer to worksheet "3.25".)

a. Create names for the columns: 'Weight, 'Jacksonville', 'Orlando' and 'Miami'.

b. Define a name for the table.

c. Calculate the weighted score for each location using the formula 'Weighted Score = Weight*Score'.

d. Define names for the columns that present the weighted scores for each location.

e. Identify the best location for the health care center that maximizes the total weighted score. This method of selecting among different alternatives is known as the Preference Matrix method.

CHAPTER *four*

Functions and Formulas

chapter OVERVIEW

4.1 *Introduction*

This chapter presents an overview of the many functions available in Excel. One of the strengths that Excel has to offer as a spreadsheet-based software is the many built-in functions that can be used for simple or advanced calculations. As this book focuses on the development of spreadsheet-based decision support systems, we recommend that these spreadsheet functions be incorporated into the DSS applications. In this chapter, we seek to illustrate the many functions, in various categories, available in Excel.

In this chapter, the reader will learn how to:

- Use various functions by learning the function name, arguments, and an example of its usefulness.
- Use a function not covered in this chapter by using Excel's function dialog boxes.
- Use the *Formula Is* option in conditional formatting.
- Audit formulas and functions.

4.2 *Formulas and Function Categories*

Formulas are an important topic in Excel. It is necessary to have a clear understanding of how to use formulas in spreadsheet applications and VBA programming. Formulas can be categorized into simple values, basic operators, naming and referencing, and functions. Simple values, such as numbers or text, were discussed in Chapter 2, and naming and referencing were discussed in Chapter 3.

Basic operators perform simple calculator functions such as addition, subtraction, multiplication, and division with numbers in cells. These mathematical functions used in a cell follow the order of operations. For example, if we want to enter a value into a cell that is the product of two large numbers, we can perform the calculation in the cell itself, instead of calculating and entering the solution into the cell manually. To do this, we type an "=" followed by the equation into the cell. The formula solves the calculation and displays the solution. Clicking on the cell displays the operation that we entered. In Figure 4.1, the last cell value is the result of a basic product calculation.

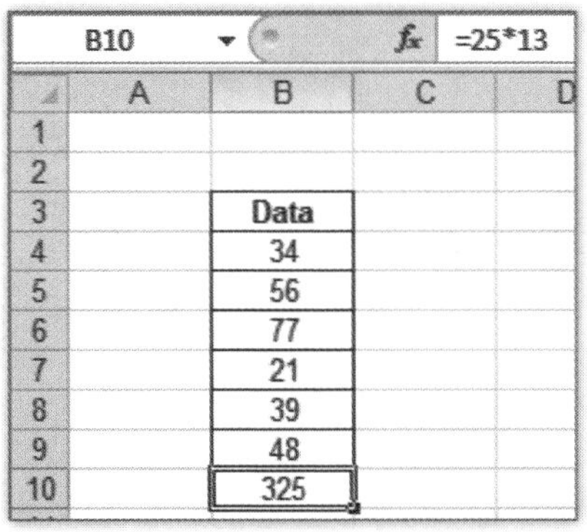

Figure 4.1 A basic operator performs simple calculations on numbers entered in a cell.

Excel has several pre-programmed functions that we can reference from the *Formulas tab* on the Ribbon. *Function Library* group in this tab lists a number of function categories: *Financial, Logical, Text, Date and Time, Lookup and Reference, and Mathematics and Trigonometry.* You can see a list of functions available for use within each category by selecting the corresponding command from the *Function Library* group. Figure 4.2 lists a number of Math & Trig functions available for use in Excel. You can also click on the *Insert Function* f_x icon from the Function Library group or from the formula bar in order to display the *Insert Function* dialog box (see Figure 4.3). You can search for a function by typing a keyword in the *Search for a function* window, and selecting the *Go* button. If you know the category the function belongs to, you can select this category from the *Select a category* drop-down list. Selecting any of these categories displays a list of corresponding functions. Selecting one of the displayed functions provides a brief description of that function at the bottom of the window (see Figure 4.3).

For example, in Figure 4.3, we have selected *Math & Trig* from the category list and SUM from the function name list. At the bottom of the dialog box, we can see the basic format and description for the SUM function. Once we select a function, the *Function Arguments* dialog box, shown in Figure 4.4, appears; it gives further instructions about how to use the function we have selected. In the bottom-left corner of these dialog boxes there is a *Help on this Function* command. If selected, it gives a detailed explanation of the function as well as an example of how to use it. The *Recently Used* command, found at the *Function Library* group of Formulas tab, shows approximately the last ten functions used. The *More Functions* command lists additional function categories such as, *Statistical, Engineering, Cube, Information* and *Compatibility* (see Figure 4.5). The *AutoSum* command lists simple, but frequently used functions of Excel, such as, SUM, AVERAGE, etc.

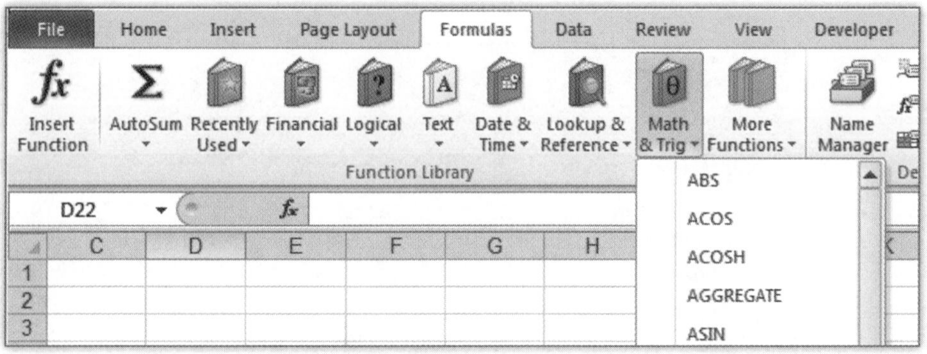

Figure 4.2 A list of Mathematics & Trigonometry functions is displayed when you select the *Math & Trig* command from the *Function Library* group.

Formula Autocomplete is a useful feature of Excel that we recommend using. Sometimes we may just remember the first letters of the name of a function. For example, there are a number of functions that we can use to sum. Since all begin with "s", we can start typing "=su" in a cell, and Excel will display a menu of all functions that begin with "su" as shown in Figure 4.6.

We will describe the most basic functions, SUM, AVERAGE, MIN, and MAX, to illustrate the common spreadsheet operations that we can perform easily with functions.

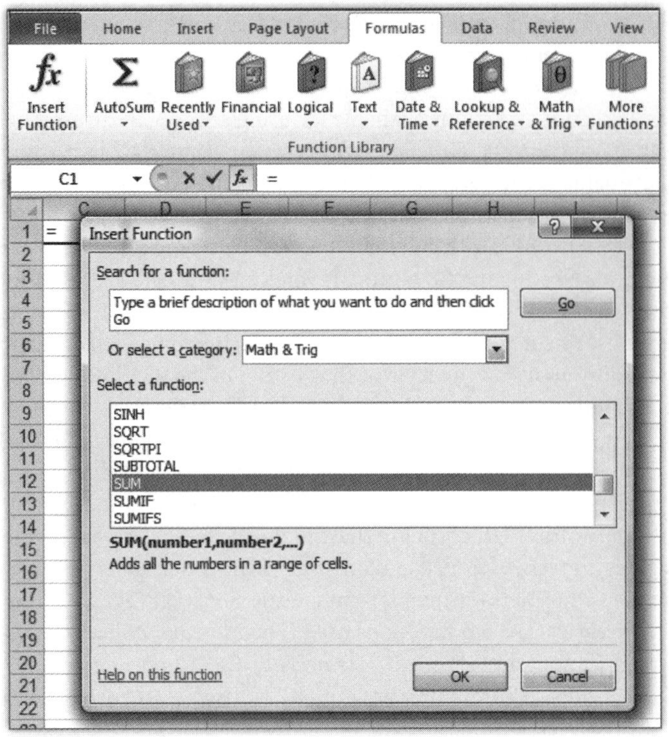

Figure 4.3 Insert Function dialog box displays the Math & Trig functions available in Excel.

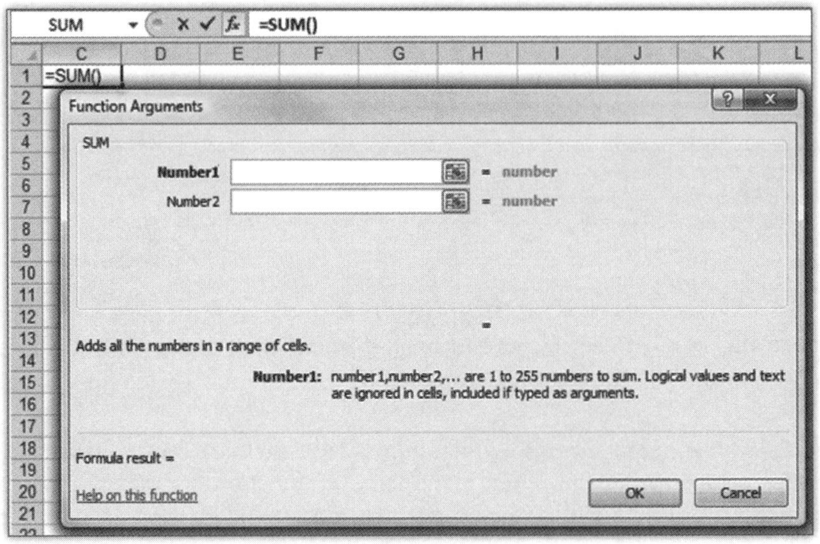

Figure 4.4 Function Arguments dialog box appear after a function is selected. The boxes allow a user to define the argument(s) of the function.

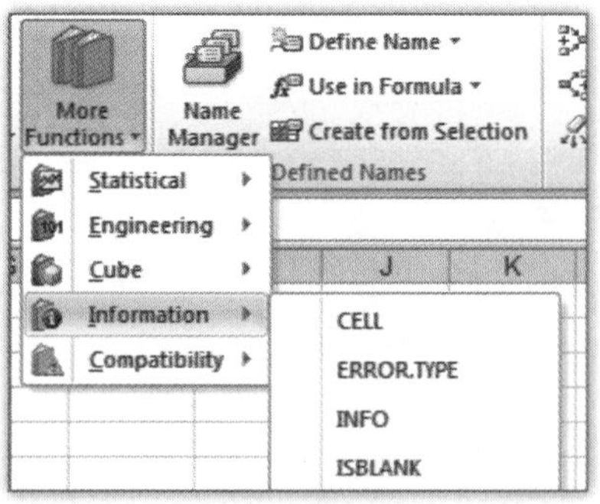

Figure 4.5 More Functions drop-down list displays five function categories. When the Information function category is selected, a flyout menu of related functions is displayed.

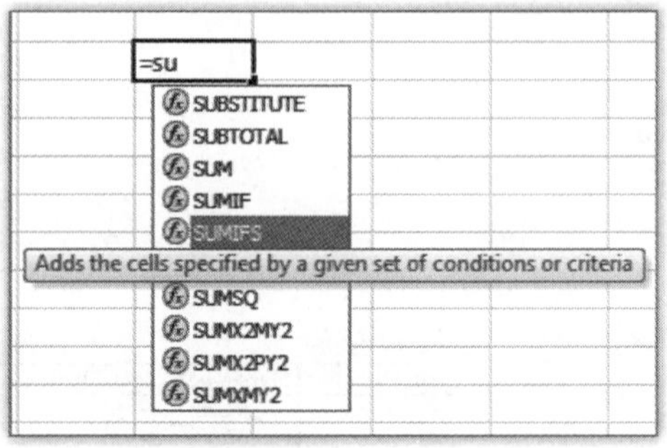

Figure 4.6 Formula Autocomplete feature of Excel displays all the functions that begin with "su".

SUM, a *Math and Trig* function, adds any range of data, including selected columns, rows, or tables of numbers. The SUM function can also be applied to non-consecutive, or non-adjacent, cells. SUM can take either of the following formats:

= *SUM(number1, number2, ...)*
= *SUM(range_name)*

The range name is the column or row of numbers of which we want to take the sum. We can also find the sum of a range of values taken from multiple rows and columns. The result of the sum calculation appears in the cell in which the formula is typed. For example, in Figure 4.7(a), each cell in the *Sum* row contains the SUM function to calculate the sum of the column above it. That is, cell *D21* has the function "=SUM(D5:D19)," which results in the value of the sum of all of the numbers in the column above.

Recall that the naming techniques discussed in Chapter 3 allow us to use created range names in formulas and functions. For example, in Figure 4.7(a), we could have named the first column "Diameter," and then entered the function in the *Sum* row as "=SUM(Diameter)."

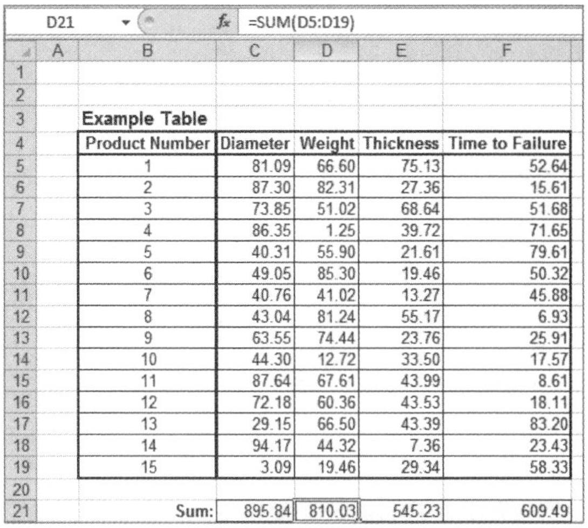

D21 =SUM(D5:D19)

	A	B	C	D	E	F
1						
2						
3		Example Table				
4		Product Number	Diameter	Weight	Thickness	Time to Failure
5		1	81.09	66.60	75.13	52.64
6		2	87.30	82.31	27.36	15.61
7		3	73.85	51.02	68.64	51.68
8		4	86.35	1.25	39.72	71.65
9		5	40.31	55.90	21.61	79.61
10		6	49.05	85.30	19.46	50.32
11		7	40.76	41.02	13.27	45.88
12		8	43.04	81.24	55.17	6.93
13		9	63.55	74.44	23.76	25.91
14		10	44.30	12.72	33.50	17.57
15		11	87.64	67.61	43.99	8.61
16		12	72.18	60.36	43.53	18.11
17		13	29.15	66.50	43.39	83.20
18		14	94.17	44.32	7.36	23.43
19		15	3.09	19.46	29.34	58.33
20						
21		Sum:	895.84	810.03	545.23	609.49

(a)

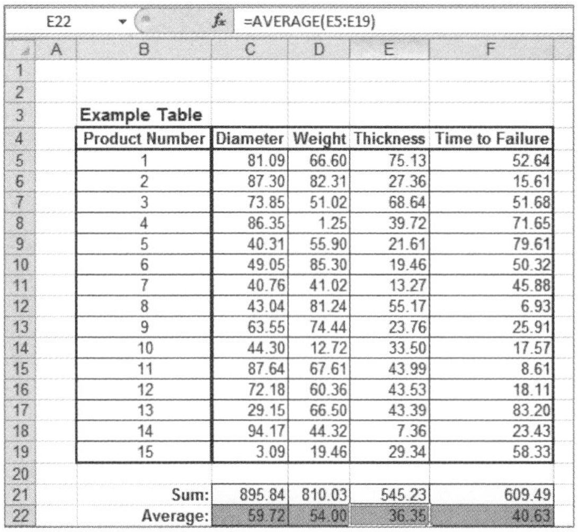

E22 =AVERAGE(E5:E19)

	A	B	C	D	E	F
1						
2						
3		Example Table				
4		Product Number	Diameter	Weight	Thickness	Time to Failure
5		1	81.09	66.60	75.13	52.64
6		2	87.30	82.31	27.36	15.61
7		3	73.85	51.02	68.64	51.68
8		4	86.35	1.25	39.72	71.65
9		5	40.31	55.90	21.61	79.61
10		6	49.05	85.30	19.46	50.32
11		7	40.76	41.02	13.27	45.88
12		8	43.04	81.24	55.17	6.93
13		9	63.55	74.44	23.76	25.91
14		10	44.30	12.72	33.50	17.57
15		11	87.64	67.61	43.99	8.61
16		12	72.18	60.36	43.53	18.11
17		13	29.15	66.50	43.39	83.20
18		14	94.17	44.32	7.36	23.43
19		15	3.09	19.46	29.34	58.33
20						
21		Sum:	895.84	810.03	545.23	609.49
22		Average:	59.72	54.00	36.35	40.63

(b)

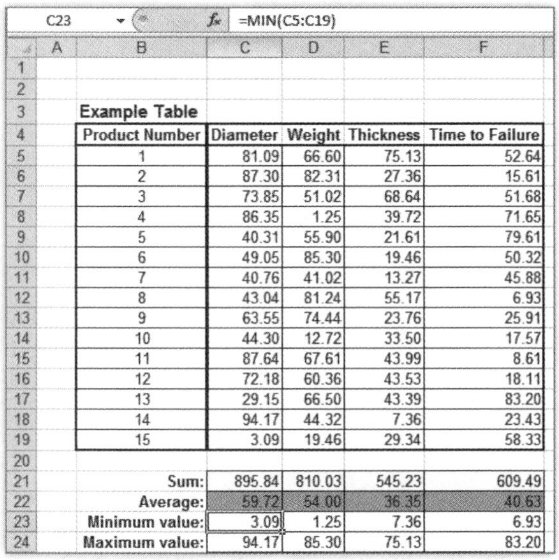

C23 =MIN(C5:C19)

	A	B	C	D	E	F
1						
2						
3		Example Table				
4		Product Number	Diameter	Weight	Thickness	Time to Failure
5		1	81.09	66.60	75.13	52.64
6		2	87.30	82.31	27.36	15.61
7		3	73.85	51.02	68.64	51.68
8		4	86.35	1.25	39.72	71.65
9		5	40.31	55.90	21.61	79.61
10		6	49.05	85.30	19.46	50.32
11		7	40.76	41.02	13.27	45.88
12		8	43.04	81.24	55.17	6.93
13		9	63.55	74.44	23.76	25.91
14		10	44.30	12.72	33.50	17.57
15		11	87.64	67.61	43.99	8.61
16		12	72.18	60.36	43.53	18.11
17		13	29.15	66.50	43.39	83.20
18		14	94.17	44.32	7.36	23.43
19		15	3.09	19.46	29.34	58.33
20						
21		Sum:	895.84	810.03	545.23	609.49
22		Average:	59.72	54.00	36.35	40.63
23		Minimum value:	3.09	1.25	7.36	6.93
24		Maximum value:	94.17	85.30	75.13	83.20

(c)

Figure 4.7 The SUM function (a) takes all of the numbers in a column (or row) and calculates their sum. The AVERAGE function (b) takes all of the numbers in a column (or row), calculates their sum, and divides by the number of cells in that column (or row). The values calculated from the MIN and MAX functions (c) shown at the bottom of the screen refer to each column of data above the cells containing the formula.

The ***AVERAGE*** function takes a range of numbers (a column or row), sums them, and then divides by the number of cells in that range. Note however, that if there are empty cells in the selected range, that is cells without numbers, these cells are not included in the count of numbers used in the dividend of this function. A *Statistical* function, AVERAGE takes one of the following formats:

= AVERAGE(range_name)

In Figure 4.7(b), cell *E22* displays the average of the column *E5:E19*, which is the range name shown in the function at the top of the window.

Two other statistical functions, ***MIN*** and ***MAX***, take all of the cell values in a range (column or row) and compare them to determine which number is the smallest or largest. The formats for the MIN and MAX functions are:

= MIN(number1, number2, ...)
= MIN(range_name)

= MAX(number1, number2, ...)
= MAX(range_name)

In Figure 4.7(c), cell *C23* is the minimum value of column *C5:C19* and cell *C24* is the maximum of this same column. Note that the range *C5:C19* appears in the MIN function formula at the top of the window.

Formulas are an important part of spreadsheet applications. They are not only necessary for basic calculations, as explained above, but they are also an integral part of VBA coding. We will now explain some of the most commonly used functions within each of the other categories.

Summary

Formula Types:

- Simple values
- Basic operators
- Naming and referencing
- Functions

4.3 *Logical and Information Functions*

The *Logical* and *Information* functions assess certain characteristics about data in a spreadsheet. Some of these functions determine whether data has certain information and displays True or False depending on whether the conditions are met. Other functions evaluate data characteristics and then perform a particular action based on the analysis of that data. Let's look at the *Logical* functions first.

4.3.1 Logical Functions

We can organize seven of the *Logical* functions, listed under *Function name* in Figure 4.8, into three pairs of related functions: TRUE/ FALSE, IF/ IFERROR/ NOT, and AND/ OR.

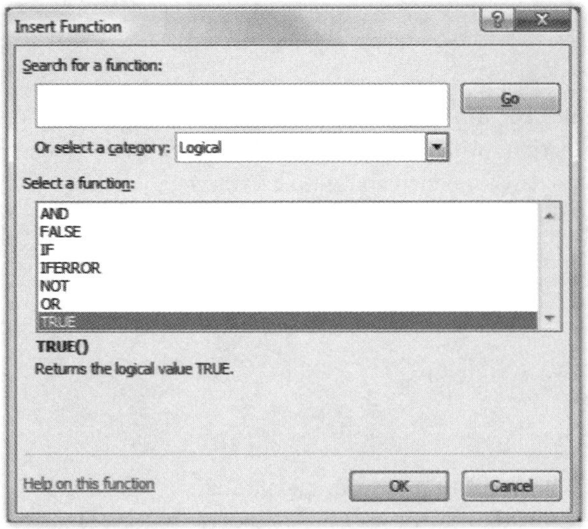

Figure 4.8 The seven Logical functions: AND, FALSE, IF, IFERROR, NOT, OR, TRUE.

The ***TRUE*** and ***FALSE*** functions simply display the Boolean values TRUE and FALSE. There are no arguments to enter for this function; we just type the function name:

= TRUE
= FALSE

We may want to use these functions in a manual evaluation of our data. For example, we want to determine which numbers are greater than 100 in the list featured in Figure 4.9. We have placed the function *=TRUE* next to each cell that contains a number larger than 100. When reviewing our list of numbers, we can immediately see which numbers are greater than 100. Alternately, we could place the FALSE function next to the cells with numbers less than 100. However, it is more likely that we want Excel to determine if something is True or False rather than entering these functions as a manual evaluation. To do this, we can use a simple formula to make an assertion and have Excel report if it is True or False. For example, in cell E4 in Figure 4.9, we could type the formula "=C4>100" and copy this formula through cell E12. Excel will then report in which instances the values in column C truly are greater than 100 by displaying TRUE.

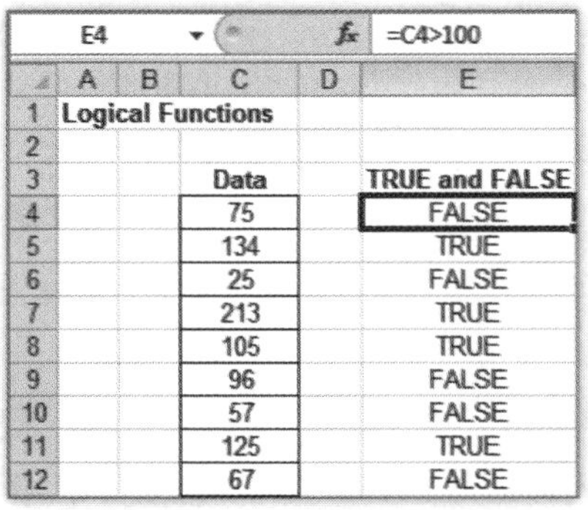
E4 fx =C4>100

	A	B	C	D	E
1	Logical Functions				
2					
3			Data		TRUE and FALSE
4			75		FALSE
5			134		TRUE
6			25		FALSE
7			213		TRUE
8			105		TRUE
9			96		FALSE
10			57		FALSE
11			125		TRUE
12			67		FALSE

Figure 4.9 The TRUE and FALSE functions display the Boolean values True and False, respectively.

The ***NOT*** function contrasts a cell with any other cell, and can be used as long as the cell that we are reviewing has a value of either *TRUE* or *FALSE*. Use the following formula to specify the opposing cell:

= *NOT(cell_address)*

So, if we place the NOT function next to every cell where we previously placed a TRUE function, we should see the result *FALSE* in each cell. Figure 4.10 illustrates that F8, with a value of *FALSE*, opposes E8, which is *TRUE*.

F8 | *fx* =NOT(E8)

	A	B	C	D	E	F
1	Logical Functions					
2						
3			Data		TRUE and FALSE	NOT
4			75		FALSE	TRUE
5			134		TRUE	FALSE
6			25		FALSE	TRUE
7			213		TRUE	FALSE
8			105		TRUE	FALSE
9			96		FALSE	TRUE
10			57		FALSE	TRUE
11			125		TRUE	FALSE
12			67		FALSE	TRUE

Figure 4.10 The NOT function displays the opposite value of a cell. Since E8 is TRUE, NOT(E8) is FALSE.

The ***IF*** function allows us to evaluate data by using a specified condition that determines whether data is true or false. An IF function requires us to specify three arguments: *condition to be met*, *return value if true*, and *return value if false*. For example:

= *IF(logical_test, value_if_true, value_if_false)*

Returning to the data in Figure 4.9, we can easily use the IF function to determine which values are greater than 100. Therefore, in Figure 4.11(a), we have added the IF function to the last column on the right. The formula for the IF function, *=IF(C5>100, TRUE, FALSE)*, directs the computer to return the value *TRUE* if C5 is greater than 100. In all other circumstances, it will return the value FALSE. We can copy this function to the entire column in order to evaluate all of the numbers in the table. Note that we can put any text or numerical value in the return arguments. For example, we could return the words "Big Number" if our number is greater than 100 and "Small Number" if it is less than 100. Likewise, we could display a "1" for all numbers greater than 100 and a "0" for all numbers less than 100. We can even display nothing by placing empty quotation marks "" in the return arguments, as displayed in Figure 4.11 (b).

The ***IFERROR*** function returns *value_if_error* if the formula is an error and the *value* of the formula itself otherwise. The format for the IFERROR function is:

=IFERROR(value, value_if_error)

Consider that we want to calculate the square root of cells I4:I12, Figure 4.9 (c). In cell J4 we type =IFERROR(SQRT(I4), "Error in Calculations"). We copy this function to the remaining of the cells in the range. This function will return the value 8.66 which is the square root of 75. However, it will return "Error in Calculations" in cell J5 since the value in I5 is not numeric.

The ***AND*** and ***OR*** functions return the values *TRUE* and *FALSE* depending on certain conditions. For the AND function, all of the conditions listed must be true in order for *TRUE* to be displayed. If any of the conditions are violated, *FALSE* is returned. The format for the AND function is:

= AND(condition1, condition2, …)

G5 =IF(C5>100, TRUE, FALSE)

	A	B	C	D	E	F	G
1	**Logical Functions**						
2							
3			**Data**		**TRUE and FALSE**	**NOT**	**IF**
4			75		FALSE	TRUE	FALSE
5			134		TRUE	FALSE	TRUE
6			25		FALSE	TRUE	FALSE
7			213		TRUE	FALSE	TRUE
8			105		TRUE	FALSE	TRUE
9			96		FALSE	TRUE	FALSE
10			57		FALSE	TRUE	FALSE
11			125		TRUE	FALSE	TRUE
12			67		FALSE	TRUE	FALSE

(a)

G5 =IF(C5>100, TRUE, "")

	A	B	C	D	E	F	G
1	**Logical Functions**						
2							
3			**Data**		**TRUE and FALSE**	**NOT**	**IF**
4			75		FALSE	TRUE	
5			134		TRUE	FALSE	TRUE
6			25		FALSE	TRUE	
7			213		TRUE	FALSE	TRUE
8			105		TRUE	FALSE	TRUE
9			96		FALSE	TRUE	
10			57		FALSE	TRUE	
11			125		TRUE	FALSE	TRUE
12			67		FALSE	TRUE	

(b)

J5 =IFERROR(SQRT(D5),"Error in Calculations")

	H	I	J	K	L	M
1						
2						
3		**Data**	**IFERROR**			
4		75	8.66			
5		A	Error in Calculations			
6		25	5.00			
7		213	14.59			
8		B	Error in Calculations			
9		96	9.80			
10		C	Error in Calculations			
11		125	11.18			
12		67	8.19			

(c)

Figure 4.11 The IF function takes three arguments: condition to be evaluated, return value if true, and return value if false. (a) In this example, TRUE is displayed if the number is greater than 100, and FALSE is displayed if it is less than or equal to 100. (b) In the second example, nothing is displayed if the condition is not true. (b) The IFERROR function return "Error in Calculations" when we try to calculate the square root of a nonnumeric value.

We can use up to 30 conditions. For the OR function, one or more of the conditions needs to be true for the result to be *TRUE*. All of the conditions would have to be violated for *FALSE* to be displayed. The OR function uses a similar format:

= OR(condition1, condition2, …)

In Figure 4.12(a), we have added the AND function to evaluate whether or not all of the numbers in our table are greater than 100. Our AND function requires every cell to be greater than 100:

= AND(C4>100, C5>100, …)

This function results in *FALSE* because some of the numbers in the data set do not match the conditions of this function. In Figure 4.12(b), by contrast, we have paired the same conditions with an OR function. Because only one of the conditions needs to be met, this function results in *TRUE*.

E14 =AND($C$4>100, $C$5>100, $C$6>100, $C$7>100, $C$8>100, $C$9>100, $C$10>100, $C$11>100, $C$12>100)

	A	B	C	D	E	F	G
1	Logical Functions						
2							
3			Data		TRUE and FALSE	NOT	IF
4			75		FALSE	TRUE	FALSE
5			134		TRUE	FALSE	TRUE
6			25		FALSE	TRUE	FALSE
7			213		TRUE	FALSE	TRUE
8			105		TRUE	FALSE	TRUE
9			96		FALSE	TRUE	FALSE
10			57		FALSE	TRUE	FALSE
11			125		TRUE	FALSE	TRUE
12			67		FALSE	TRUE	FALSE
13					AND		
14					FALSE		

(a)

F14 =OR($C$4>100, $C$5>100, $C$6>100, $C$7>100, $C$8>100, $C$9>100, $C$10>100, $C$11>100, $C$12>100)

	A	B	C	D	E	F	G
1	Logical Functions						
2							
3			Data		TRUE and FALSE	NOT	IF
4			75		FALSE	TRUE	FALSE
5			134		TRUE	FALSE	TRUE
6			25		FALSE	TRUE	FALSE
7			213		TRUE	FALSE	TRUE
8			105		TRUE	FALSE	TRUE
9			96		FALSE	TRUE	FALSE
10			57		FALSE	TRUE	FALSE
11			125		TRUE	FALSE	TRUE
12			67		FALSE	TRUE	FALSE
13					AND	OR	
14					FALSE	TRUE	

(b)

Figure 4.12 The AND and OR functions evaluate several conditions. The AND function requires all conditions to be met in order to return *TRUE*, while OR requires only one condition to be met to be *TRUE*. (a) The AND function returns *FALSE* because not every number in the table is greater than 100. (b) The OR function returns TRUE because at least one number in the table is greater than 100.

The IF, AND, and OR functions are very useful in advanced applications. For some problems, there may be several complex conditions that need to be checked. These functions can be used to evaluate data to ensure that those conditions are met and to signal which data violates those conditions.

Summary

Logical Functions:

TRUE	Returns the value True.
FALSE	Returns the value False.
NOT	Returns the opposite value.
IF	Evaluates a condition and returns one value if it is true and another value if it is false.
IFERROR	Returns value_if_error if the formula is an error and the value of the formula itself otherwise.
AND	Evaluates several conditions and returns True if all conditions are met and False if any condition is not met.
OR	Evaluates several conditions and returns True if any condition is met, and False if all conditions are not met.

4.3.2 Information Functions

There are several different *Information* functions in Excel, all of which provide some basic descriptive information about the data. Figure 4.13 lists some of these functions. One group of these functions, ***IsFunctions***, answers whether a cell value has or does not have a specified characteristic. If we do not see some of these *IsFunctions* in our list of *Information* functions, we may need to activate the *Analysis Toolpak Add-In*. To do so, we simply go to *File Menu* on the *Ribbon*, and select *Options* tab. In *Excel Options* dialog box, select *Add-Ins* from the list on the left. In the *Add-Ins* window select the *Analysis Toolpak* option and click *OK*.

The ***ISEVEN*** and ***ISODD*** functions, for example, determine whether or not a number in a cell is even or odd. We only need to specify the number itself or the name of the cell that contains the number that we are evaluating:

= ISEVEN(cell_name)	or	*=ISEVEN(number)*
= ISODD(cell_name)	or	*=ISODD(number)*

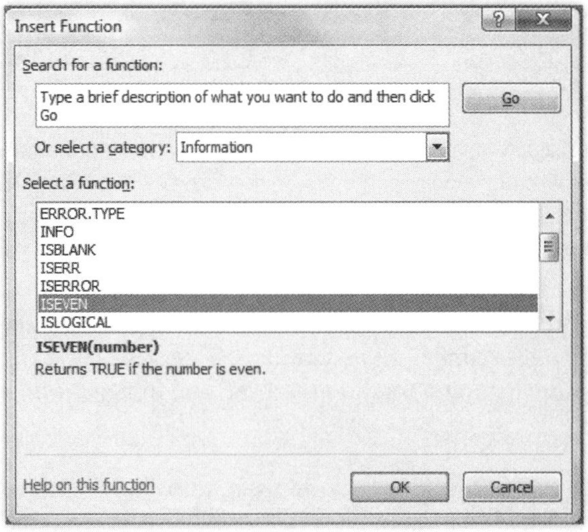

Figure 4.13 One group of *Information Functions*, which we refer to as *IsFunctions*, determines various cell qualities.

If the number is even, the ISEVEN function returns TRUE and the ISODD function returns FALSE. The opposite would occur if the number were odd.

The data table in Figure 4.14 contains both even and odd numbers. We have used the ISEVEN function in Column E to evaluate the data in Column C. So, in Figure 4.14(a), the formula for E5 determines whether or not C5 is even. In Figure 4.14(b), we have added the ISODD function in Column F. The TRUE and FALSE values in this function column are exactly the opposite of the ISEVEN values.

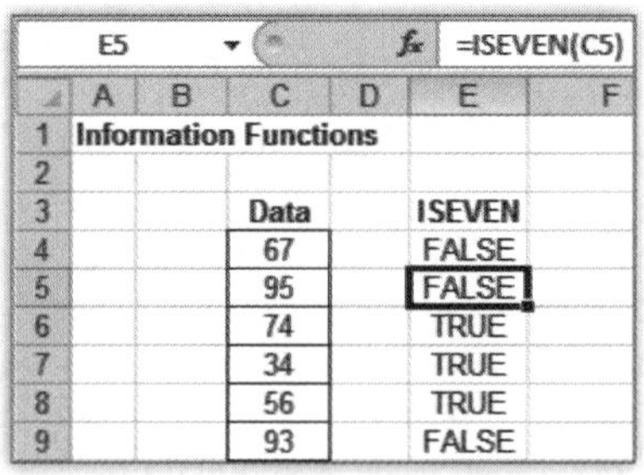

(a)

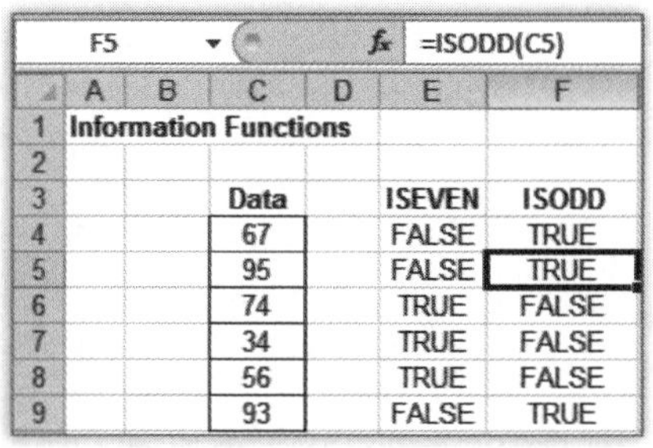

(b)

Figure 4.14 The ISEVEN and ISODD functions display TRUE if the data value is even or odd, respectively. (a) The ISEVEN function value is TRUE for even numbers and FALSE for odd numbers. (b) The ISODD function value is TRUE and FALSE for the opposite situations.

Additional examples of *IsFunctions* are the ***ISTEXT*** and ***ISNUMBER*** functions. The ISTEXT function returns *TRUE* if a cell value is text and *FALSE* if it is not. To enter a numerical value as text, we must either include it in double quotation marks or begin with a single quotation mark. Either a cell reference or a value can be used as the argument of this function:

= ISTEXT(cell_address)
= ISTEXT(value)

The ISNUMBER function returns *TRUE* if a cell value is a number and *FALSE* if it is not. The format for ISNUMBER is similarly:

= ISNUMBER(cell_address)
= ISNUMBER(value)

Column C of Figure 4.15 lists numbers 1 through 7. While some of the numbers are written as text, others are presented in numerical form. Column E evaluates the cells through the ISTEXT function, shown in Figure 4.15(a), while Column F, featured in Figure 4.15(b), displays the ISNUMBER function.

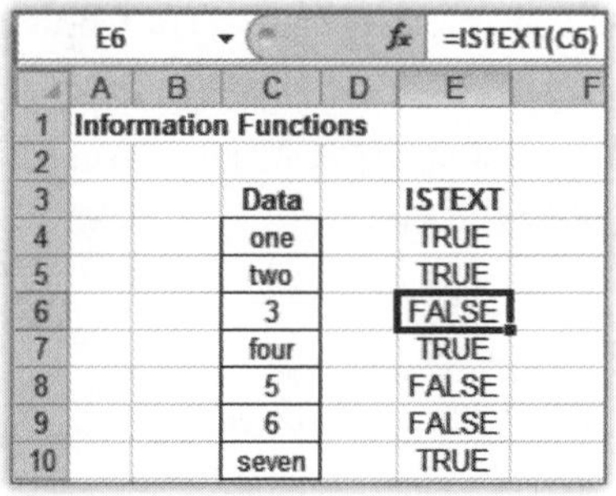

(a)

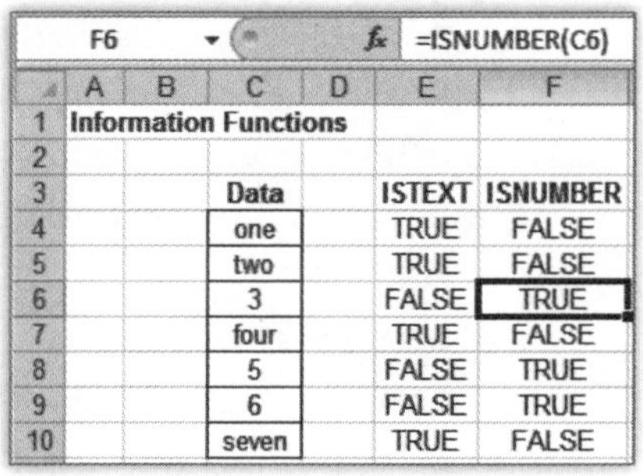

(b)

Figure 4.15 ISTEXT and ISNUMBER return TRUE if the data value is text or a number, respectively. (a) ISTEXT shows FALSE when the data is a numerical value. (b) ISNUMBER shows TRUE for the same data since it is a number.

The other *IsFunctions* are similar. If we click on the function names in the function display window, as shown in Figure 4.13, we can view a description of each function.

The ***TYPE*** function, another *Information* function, evaluates the ***data type*** of a value. Data type, a descriptive category of the different types of values possible in Excel, can take the form of number, text, or logical values. For example, let's consider the data types of number, text, and logical values. Excel uses numbers to designate each data type: the number 1 signifies a numerical data type; the number 2 signifies a text data type; and the number 4 signifies a logical value data type. The TYPE function evaluates our data and returns one of these numerical category descriptions. This function's argument is either a cell reference or a value:

= TYPE(cell_address)
= TYPE(value)

In Figure 4.16, we have examples of these three data types and the numerical results that the TYPE function returned. Data types are important when using VBA.

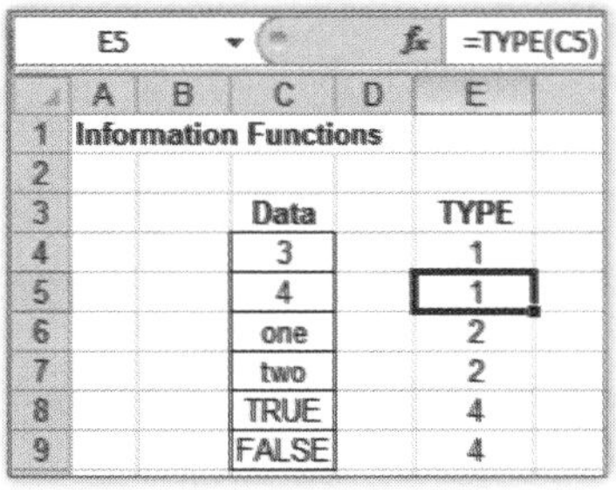

Figure 4.16 The TYPE function returns a 1 for numerical data types, a 2 for text data types, and a 4 for logical value data types.

Summary

Information Functions:

Is Functions	Checks whether or not a cell value has a specified characteristic.
ISEVEN	Returns True if the number is even, False if the number is odd.
ISODD	Returns True if the number is odd, False if the number is even.
ISTEXT	Returns True if the value is text, False if not.
ISNUMBER	Returns True if the value is a number, False if not.
Data Types	Categories of different possible values.
TYPE	Returns the numerical signifier of a data type category.

4.4 *Text and Lookup & Reference Functions*

Text and *Lookup & Reference* functions also do not involve calculations. *Text* functions, some of which are listed in Figure 4.16, manipulate text values or analyze their characteristics. *Lookup*

& Reference functions search for information within a given table of data and perform limited actions on that data. Both categories are useful for organizing data.

4.4.1 Text Functions

Excel features many different *Text* functions, but, in the interest of brevity, we will only discuss a few of those most commonly used. We will discuss some of the other functions later when explaining their applications to VBA programming.

We discuss UPPER, LOWER, CONCATENATE, and SUBSTITUTE. The first functions, ***UPPER*** and ***LOWER***, convert a cell or a range of cells with text values into all uppercase or all lowercase text. The only argument to enter in the function is the cell or range address where the text is located.

= UPPER(range_address)
= LOWER(range_address)

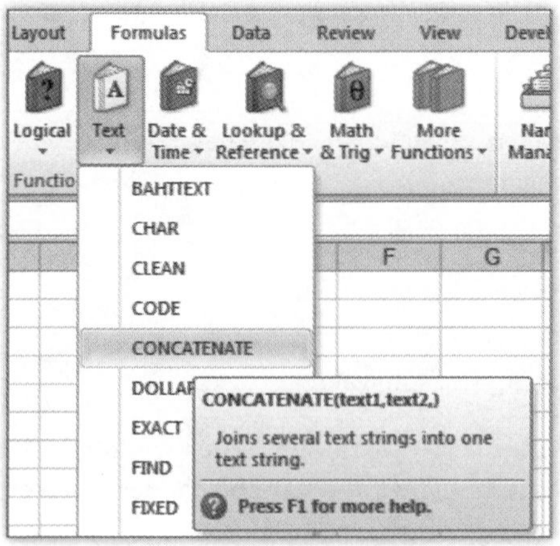

Figure 4.17 A partial listing of Text Functions.

We can use the UPPER function to convert the first sentence in Figure 4.18 (a) to all uppercase and the LOWER function to convert the sentence in Figure 4.18 (b) to all lowercase.

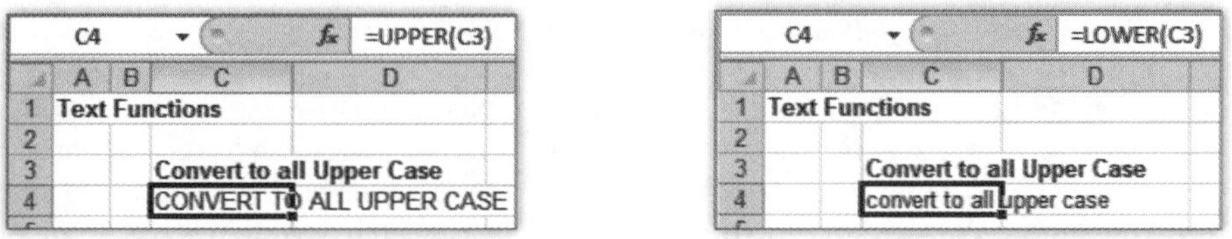

(a) **(b)**

Figure 4.18 The UPPER and LOWER functions change the case of text. (a) The UPPER function converts the text to all uppercase. (b) The LOWER function converts the text to all lowercase.

Another *Text* function, ***CONCATENATE***, joins fragments of a phrase or a sentence together by combining the text values of multiple cells. VBA programming relies heavily on concatenation, which takes the following format:

= *CONCATENATE(cell1, cell2, …)*

Figure 4.19 provides an example of how this function can be used to join several phrases into a single sentence. The arguments for this function are the locations of the fragments that we are joining. In our example, we join the words in *C3*, *D3*, *E3*, and *F3* to get a complete sentence; note that spaces are included in each group of words.

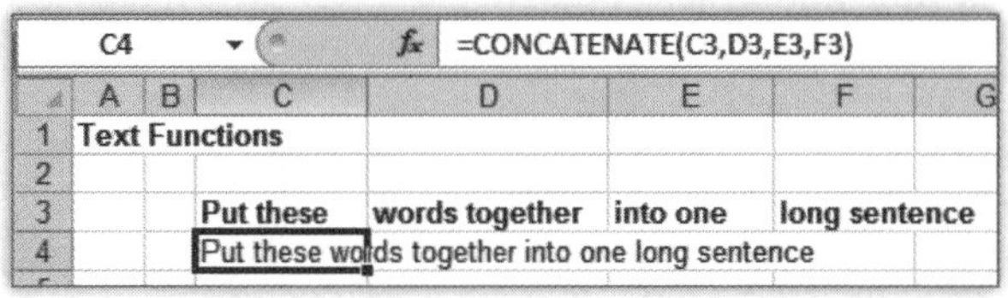

Figure 4.19 The CONCATENATE function joins text from multiple cells into one phrase or sentence.

The ampersand, "&," can also be used to concatenate text when it is placed between various values or functions in a cell. Here are some examples:

= *3 & ", " & 4* Returns: *"3, 4"*
= *"hello" & " world!"* Returns: *"hello world!"*
= *C3 & D3 & E3 & F4*Returns: (same result as Figure 4.18)
= *"sum is: " & SUM(A1:A5)* Returns: *"sum is:* (sum value)*"*

We will see the ampersand used with the IF function in a later section. In VBA, programmers frequently use the ampersand to combine text and variable values when creating output strings.

The last *Text* function we will describe, the ***SUBSTITUTE*** function, exchanges old text for new text in a cell. We can specify the cell reference, the old text, and the new text in the function arguments. We can also specify how many instances of the old text we would like to replace; if this is left blank, Excel replaces all instances of the old text with the new text. We use the following format for this function:

= *SUBSTITUTE(cell_address, old_text, new_text, instance)*

In Figure 4.20(a), we illustrate the example of substituting every "a" with an "e." Note, however, that Excel is case-sensitive and distinguishes between lower- and upper- case letters. In order to also change every "A" to an "E," we must repeat the SUBSTITUTE function, this time using the result of the first function as our text. Therefore, the substitute function refers to *C5* instead of *C4* (Figure 4.20(b)).

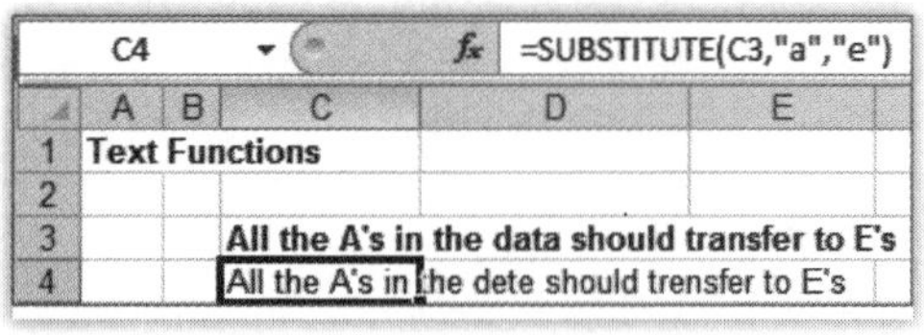

(a)

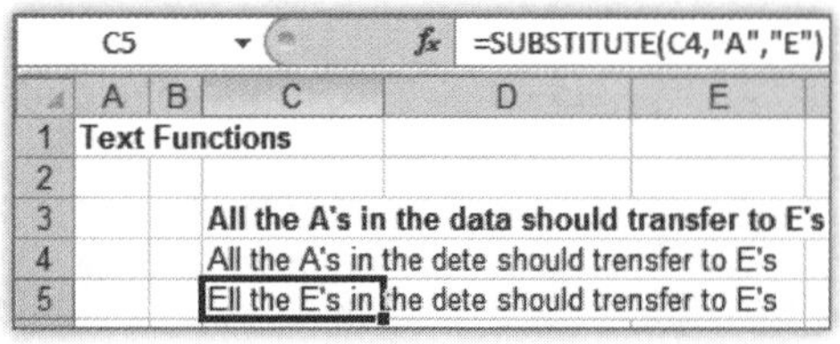

(b)

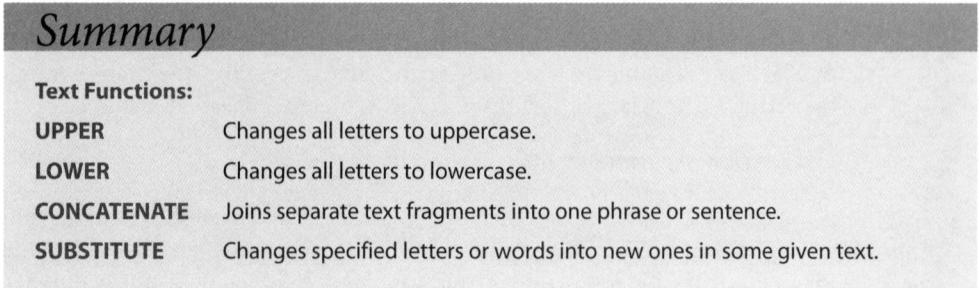

Figure 4.20 The SUBSTITUTE function changes elements in a specified block of text. (a) All of the lower case a's are changed to e's. (b) All of the uppercase A's are changed to E's.

Summary

Text Functions:

UPPER	Changes all letters to uppercase.
LOWER	Changes all letters to lowercase.
CONCATENATE	Joins separate text fragments into one phrase or sentence.
SUBSTITUTE	Changes specified letters or words into new ones in some given text.

4.4.2 Lookup & Reference Functions

Several *Lookup & Reference* functions are useful in collecting information about data. These functions will also become more important once we begin discussing VBA. For now, we would like to explain the VLOOKUP, HLOOKUP, and MATCH functions.

The ***VLOOKUP*** and ***HLOOKUP*** functions allow users to search for data in a spreadsheet. The "V" and "H" denote vertical and horizontal lookup techniques. VLOOKUP searches for a value in the left-most column of a table, finds the row that contains that value, and then returns a value from that row for a specified column. The arguments for the VLOOKUP function are as follows:

- A value in the first column of the table. This value marks the row that we will search.
- The range of cells for the target table. This range must include the first column.
- The index number, or the number of the column that we are searching.

The final argument, the *range_lookup* value, regulates the accuracy of the search for the first argument value. Therefore, if we set the *range_lookup* as *True*, the VLOOKUP finds the closest match. Setting this value to *False* results in an exact match. The default value, *True*, can be used by simply leaving the argument blank. We should designate the *range_lookup* value as *True* if the data for the first column is arranged in ascending or descending order.

= VLOOKUP(lookup_value, table_array, column_index_number, range_lookup)

Note that the titles or indices in the first column must be unique. Additionally, the index number we use for the third argument begins at one. VLOOKUP also requires that the table be sorted in ascending order by default.

Let's consider an example in which we have recorded times and distances from 3 trials of 12 products; assume that we are testing how far a product rolls and how long it takes to stop rolling. The range of cells in Figure 4.21 extends from B4 to H16 (demarcated as *B4:H16*). We include the "Product" column in the cell range because the *lookup_value* comes from this column. To find the "Time" that "Product" 5 took in trial 2, we specify our desired value by giving the "Product" value of 5 as our first argument. We have specified *B4:H16* already as our second argument and we give the value 3 for the column index of our desired data as the third argument. We can leave the *range_lookup* value blank or type *True*, since the product numbers are arranged in ascending order. As presented in Figure 4.21, our function takes the following form:

= *VLOOKUP(5, B4:H16, 3, True)*

The VLOOKUP function therefore searches the table *B4:H16* along the row whose first column value is 5 in order to find the data value in column 3 of that row. The result, *8.18* seconds, appears in E19. We could perform a similar search for the "Distance" that "Product" 5 rolled in trial 2. Our arguments here would be the same, except that the column number would be 6 instead of 3. The result for that distance, *24.53* meters, appears in E20.

= *VLOOKUP(5, B4:H16, 6, True)*

The HLOOKUP function searches in a similar fashion. However, in this function, the first and third arguments, *lookup_value* and *column_index_number*, change. HLOOKUP searches for a value in the top row of a table, finds the column that contains that value, and then returns a value from that column for a specified row. Instead of beginning with a value from the first column of the table (marking the row that we will be searching), the HLOOKUP function takes a value from the first row of the table (marking the column that we will be searching) as its first argument. Also, instead of using the index number for the column that we want to search, the HLOOKUP function uses the index number for the row that we are searching as the third argument. Note that we must also include the first row, which includes the first argument of the function, when specifying the cell range of the table. The complete format for the HLOOKUP function is:

= *HLOOKUP(lookup_value, table_array, row_index_number, range_lookup)*

E19 =VLOOKUP(5, B4:H16, 3,)

	A	B	C	D	E	F	G	H
1	**Lookup and Reference Functions**							
2								
3				**Time**			**Distance**	
4		**Product**	T 1	T 2	T 3	D 1	D 2	D 3
5		1	2.90	1.33	4.28	8.70	4.00	12.84
6		2	5.97	6.98	0.04	17.90	20.94	0.13
7		3	0.09	7.46	4.80	0.28	22.39	14.40
8		4	1.62	8.91	4.43	4.85	26.74	13.30
9		5	6.59	8.18	4.01	19.78	24.53	12.04
10		6	8.07	6.52	8.84	24.20	19.55	26.52
11		7	3.59	7.17	6.29	10.78	21.51	18.86
12		8	9.18	7.12	5.80	27.55	21.35	17.41
13		9	1.12	2.62	2.71	3.36	7.85	8.13
14		10	6.33	2.04	4.54	19.00	6.12	13.63
15		11	7.10	5.02	4.53	21.31	15.06	13.60
16		12	7.72	5.51	7.81	23.16	16.53	23.43
17								
18		**VLOOKUP**						
19		**Trial 2 Time for Product 5**			8.18			
20		**Trial 2 Distance for Product 5**			24.53			

Figure 4.21 The VLOOKUP function takes a row, specified by a value, from a table of data and returns the value from a given column.

Using the same example as before, we will now use the HLOOKUP function to find the same values. Note that we search by *T2* and *D2* instead of by "Product" 5. That is, to find the time "Product" 5 took in trial 2, we specify the text "T 2" as our first argument. We select *C4:H16* as our second argument, this time including the first row of the table instead of the first column, and we give the value 6 for the row index to denote "Product" 5 as the third argument. (Note that we could use B4:H16 as before, but the first column is unnecessary for this lookup function. If we did include column B, then we would need to adjust the search column value accordingly.) We can set the *range_lookup* value to *False*, since the values in row 4 are not in ascending order. Our function (as presented in Figure 4.21) is therefore:

= *HLOOKUP("T 2", C4:H16, 6, False)*

The HLOOKUP function searches the table *C4:H16* along the column that begins with D4 to find the data value included in row 6. The result, *8.18* seconds, appears in J19. We could perform a similar search for the "Distance" that "Product" 5 took in trial 2. Our arguments here would be the same, except that the row cell reference in our first argument would now be "*D 2*". The result for the distance is *24.53* meters. We verify that both of these functions return the same values using different search methods.

= *HLOOKUP("D 2", C4:H16, 6, False)*

When working with either of the LOOKUP functions, we may have to manipulate our table data if we are searching by a value that is not in the first row or the first column of the table and trying to find a value that is in the first row or column of the table. Suppose that we want to find the product that had a time of 8.18 in Trial 2. Because the first argument of the VLOOKUP must appear in the first column of the specified data range, we need to copy the product column to the end of the table. In this example, we copy *B4:B16* to *I4:I16*. Now we can use the LOOKUP functions as previously described, but we have to specify the range such that the first row or column is the row or column with our search data. To find the product number with a time T2 of 8.18, we move the product column to Column I and type:

= *VLOOKUP(E19, D4:I16, 6, False)*

J19 fx =HLOOKUP("T 2",C4:H16,6,FALSE)

	A	B	C	D	E	F	G	H	I	J
1	Lookup and Reference Functions									
2										
3				Time			Distance			
4		Product	T 1	T 2	T 3	D 1	D 2	D 3	Product	
5		1	2.90	1.33	4.28	8.70	4.00	12.84	1	
6		2	5.97	6.98	0.04	17.90	20.94	0.13	2	
7		3	0.09	7.46	4.80	0.28	22.39	14.40	3	
8		4	1.62	8.91	4.43	4.85	26.74	13.30	4	
9		5	6.59	8.18	4.01	19.78	24.53	12.04	5	
10		6	8.07	6.52	8.84	24.20	19.55	26.52	6	
11		7	3.59	7.17	6.29	10.78	21.51	18.86	7	
12		8	9.18	7.12	5.80	27.55	21.35	17.41	8	
13		9	1.12	2.62	2.71	3.36	7.85	8.13	9	
14		10	6.33	2.04	4.54	19.00	6.12	13.63	10	
15		11	7.10	5.02	4.53	21.31	15.06	13.60	11	
16		12	7.72	5.51	7.81	23.16	16.53	23.43	12	
17										
18		VLOOKUP					HLOOKUP			
19		Trial 2 Time for Product 5			8.18		Product 5 Time for trial 2			8.18
20		Trial 2 Distance for Product 5			24.53		Product 5 Distance for trial 2			24.53

Figure 4.22 The HLOOKUP function takes a column that is specified by a value and returns the value from a given row.

Another useful *Lookup & Reference* function, the ***MATCH*** function, searches a table of data and returns the location of a desired value. The arguments for this function are the following: the value for which we are searching, the table in which we are searching, and a code that guides the result. This code, called *match_type*, can be 0, 1, or –1. The code 0 returns the location of the first found value that is equal to the value for which we are searching. The code 1 returns the location of the largest value that is less than or equal to our specified value (given that the data is in ascending order). The code –1 returns the location of the smallest value that is greater than or equal to our value (given that the data is in descending order). We can select this argument based on the sorting order of our table to be 1 or –1 or we can search for the first matching value it finds using 0, which is the default.

= MATCH(lookup_value, table_array, match_type)

Let's consider another example. Figure 4.23 features a list of numbers in cells C3 through C12 that are arranged in ascending order. Using the MATCH function, we search for the number 50 using the three different *match_types*. Our general format is now the following:

= MATCH(50, C3:C12, match_type)

If we use *match_type* 0, the result is "N/A," which means that the number 50 is not in our data. If we use *match_type* 1, the result is 4 (see Figure 4.23(a)). This means that the largest number that is less than or equal to 50 is in the fourth row of our table: 42. If we use *match_type* –1, we must switch our table to descending order, as displayed in Figure 4.23(b), using the sort feature described in Chapter 2. The MATCH function now returns the value 6, which signifies that the smallest number that is greater than or equal to 50 is in the sixth row of our table: 56. Note that when we switch our table to descending order, the value of the MATCH function using *match_type* 1 becomes "N/A," as it requires the table to be in ascending order.

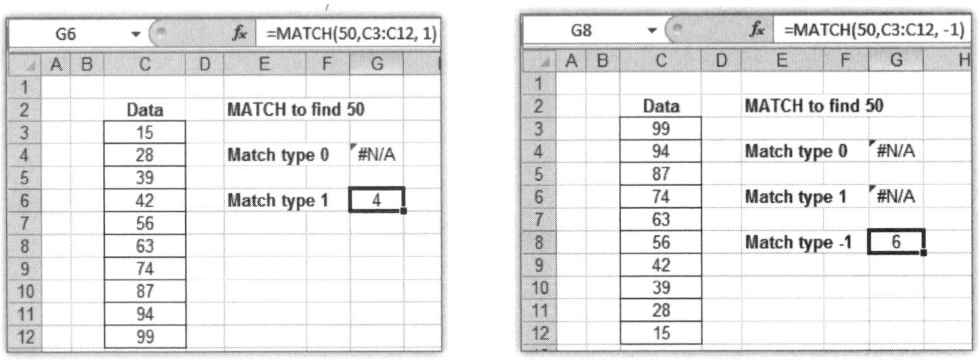

(a) (b)

Figure 4.23 The MATCH function searches for a specified value in a given table and returns its location, guided by a determined return code. (a) The return code 1 is used when the data is in ascending order and returns the location of the largest number less than or equal to the number for which we are searching. (b) Return code –1 is used when the data is in descending order and returns the location of the smallest number greater than or equal to the desired value.

In another example, we could search the rows of data in a table so that a column number is returned as the location of the desired value. In Figure 4.24, we have a row of letters. If we search for the letter "d" using return code 0, we find that it is in column 4 of our data.

= *MATCH("d", C3:G3, 0)*

E6 *fx* =MATCH("d",C3:G3,0)

	A	B	C	D	E	F	G	H
1								
2			**Data**					
3			a	b	c	d	e	
4								
5			**MATCH to find d**					
6			**Return type 0**	4				

Figure 4.24 Return code 0 is used to find the letter d, which is in column 4 of the table.

The ***INDEX*** function, like the MATCH function, allows us to find an entry in a specified row and column of a range of cells.

= *INDEX(range or range_name, row_number, column_number)*

The first column and row of a range are numbered. Let's consider an example in which this function may be useful. The table below (Figure 4.25) stores the distances between ten US cities. Since each city is numbered, we can simply use the INDEX function with these city numbers to find the distance between any two cities in the table.

	A	B	C	D	E	F	G	H	I	J	K	L
1												
2												
3		**All City Distances**										
4			Atlanta	Boston	Chicago	Denver	Phoenix	Houston	Los Angeles	Miami	New York	Seattle
5	1	Atlanta	0	1159	1255	2346	2628	1370	2719	2090	2047	2278
6	2	Boston	1159	0	827	1913	980	984	1481	2375	2215	2053
7	3	Chicago	1255	827	0	913	2236	2830	2579	515	1706	1358
8	4	Denver	2346	1913	913	0	2381	1395	1798	660	2500	2510
9	5	Phoenix	2628	980	2236	2381	0	940	2641	1556	2171	1985
10	6	Houston	1370	984	2830	1395	940	0	2667	1328	1386	1447
11	7	Los Angeles	2719	1481	2579	1798	2641	2667	0	917	898	769
12	8	Miami	2090	2375	515	660	1556	1328	917	0	2313	2978
13	9	New York	2047	2215	1706	2500	2171	1386	898	2313	0	1620
14	10	Seattle	2278	2053	1358	2510	1985	1447	769	2978	1620	0

Figure 4.25 A table of distances between 10 US Cities

For example, to find the distance between Boston and Denver, we would use the city numbers 2 and 4 in the INDEX function as follows:

= *INDEX(C5:L14, 2, 4)*

We can repeat this process to find the distances between Seattle and Miami, and Atlanta and Houston (see Figure 4.26). The range is the same for all distances; only the city numbers change. We could also name the range and use the range name with the INDEX function. For example, if we name the distance range "AllDistances," then the INDEX function to compute the distance between Boston and Denver becomes:

= *INDEX(AllDistances, 2, 4)*

We can also use the INDEX function to refer to an entire row or an entire column. To do this, we simply specify the row or column number that we want to select, and then make the column or row number 0 in the function statement. So, the first element of the table in the above example (the distance from Atlanta to Atlanta) is:

= INDEX(AllDistances, 1, 1)

C17 =INDEX(C5:L14, 2, 4)

	A	B	C	D	E	F	G
1							
2							
3		**All City Distances**					
4			Atlanta	Boston	Chicago	Denver	Phoe
5	1	Atlanta	0	1159	1255	2346	262
6	2	Boston	1159	0	827	1913	980
7	3	Chicago	1255	827	0	913	223
8	4	Denver	2346	1913	913	0	238
9	5	Phoenix	2628	980	2236	2381	0
10	6	Houston	1370	984	2830	1395	940
11	7	Los Angeles	2719	1481	2579	1798	264
12	8	Miami	2090	2375	515	660	155
13	9	New York	2047	2215	1706	2500	217
14	10	Seattle	2278	2053	1358	2510	198
15							
16		**Selected Distances**					
17		Boston-Denver	1913				
18		Seattle-Miami	2978				
19		Atlanta-Houston	1370				

Figure 4.26 Computing the distances between specific cities using the INDEX function.

The first row of the table (all the distances from Atlanta) is:

= INDEX(AllDistances, 1, 0)

And the first column of the table (all the distances to Atlanta) is:

= INDEX(AllDistances, 0, 1)

We need to enter this function into a single cell, so only the first value of the entire row or column captured by the INDEX function appears. To see all other values, we copy this function to the rest of the row or column range (see Figure 4.27).

Capturing an entire row or column of data can also be useful when we are computing calculations such as SUM, AVERAGE, MIN, or MAX. So, we can find the city farthest from Atlanta by typing:

= MAX(INDEX(AllDistances, 1, 0))

This function evaluates the entire first row of data from the table and returns the largest number. For this example, the result is 2719, which is the distance to Los Angeles. (How could we find the name, and not the distance, of the city farthest from Atlanta? *Hint*: Use a LOOKUP function with the previous example.)

Another useful *Lookup and Reference* function is the ***OFFSET*** function. The OFFSET function references a cell that is a given number of rows and columns from a specified cell, or range of cells.

= OFFSET(reference_cell, rows_to_move, columns_to_move, [height], [width])

D21 f_x =INDEX(AllDistances, 1, 0)

	A	B	C	D	E	F	G	H	
1									
2									
3		**All City Distances**							
4			Atlanta	Boston	Chicago	Denver	Phoenix	Houston	Los
5	1	Atlanta	0	1159	1255	2346	2628	1370	
6	2	Boston	1159	0	827	1913	980	984	
7	3	Chicago	1255	827	0	913	2236	2830	
8	4	Denver	2346	1913	913	0	2381	1395	
9	5	Phoenix	2628	980	2236	2381	0	940	
10	6	Houston	1370	984	2830	1395	940	0	
11	7	Los Angeles	2719	1481	2579	1798	2641	2667	
12	8	Miami	2090	2375	515	660	1556	1328	
13	9	New York	2047	2215	1706	2500	2171	1386	
14	10	Seattle	2278	2053	1358	2510	1985	1447	
15									
16		**Selected Distances**							
17		Boston-Denver	1913						
18		Seattle-Miami	2978						
19		Atlanta-Houston	1370						
20									
21		From Atlanta	0	1159	1255	2346	2628	1370	

Figure 4.27 The INDEX function captures the entire row of distances from Atlanta.

The *rows_to_move* and *columns_to_move* can be positive or negative numbers. A positive rows_to_move value implies we will offset these many rows down from the reference_cell; a negative rows_to_move value implies an upward offset. Similarly, a positive columns_to_move value implies we will offset these many columns to the right from the reference_cell; a negative columns_to_move value implies an offset to the left. If we refer to the *reference_cell* itself, the values for *rows_to_move* and *columns_to_move* are both 0. The *height* and *width* arguments are optional. They specify the height and width of the range that we want to select, beginning at the *reference_cell* plus the number of *rows_to_move* and *columns_to_move*. If these values are left blank, Excel assumes them to be the same values as the height and width of the *reference_cell*; the *reference_cell* can be a range of cells also.

Let's use the table of numbers in Figure 4.28 to demonstrate the use of the OFFSET function. First, we name the cell C2 the "RefCell" since we will reference this cell most often.

RefCell f_x 1

	A	B	C	D	E	F	G
1							
2			1	2	3	4	5
3			6	7	8	9	10
4			11	12	13	14	15

Figure 4.28 In this table of numbers, the first cell is named the "RefCell."

To find the last value in the first row of this table, we can reference the "RefCell" and look on the same row, four columns to the right. We therefore enter the OFFSET function as follows:

= *OFFSET(RefCell, 0,4)*

We have ignored the *height* and *width* arguments since we are looking for a single cell value. To find the last value in the first column, we reference the "RefCell" and look two rows down in the same column.

= OFFSET(RefCell, 2, 0)

See Figure 4.29 for the results of these examples. If we start in the last value of the first column and want to find the "RefCell" value, we type:

= OFFSET(C4, –2, 0)

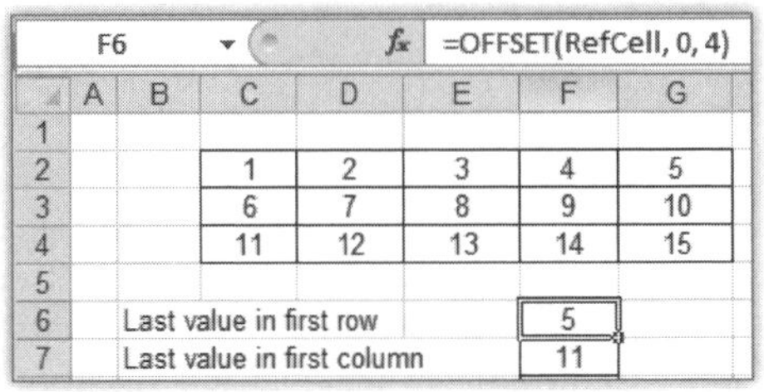

Figure 4.29 Using the OFFSET function to find the last values of the first row and the first column.

The OFFSET function can also be useful in combination with other functions. For example, to find the sum of the values in the last column of the table, we use both the SUM and OFFSET functions; this time, we also use the *height* and *width* arguments of the OFFSET function. We start at the "RefCell" and move to the last value in the first row as we did previously; now we give a *height* value of 3 and a *width* value of 1 to capture the entire column starting at the offset cell.

= SUM(OFFSET(RefCell, 0, 4, 3, 1))

Similarly, we can calculate the sum of values in the last row by typing:

= SUM(OFFSET(RefCell, 2, 0, 1, 5))

See Figure 4.30 for the results of these examples. The referencing technique used in the OFFSET function is common in VBA.

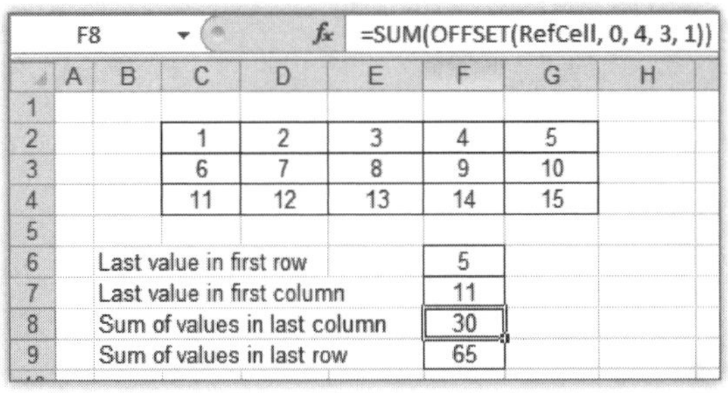

Figure 4.30 Using the SUM and OFFSET functions together.

Summary

Lookup and Reference Functions:

VLOOKUP	Looks for a given value in the first column of a table and searches the entire table along that row until it finds the value in a specified column.
HLOOKUP	Looks for a given value in the first row of a table and searches the entire table along that column until it finds the value in a specified row.
MATCH	Searches for a given value in a table and returns the location of that value dependent on the determined return code.
INDEX	Searches for a given value in a range by row and column number.
OFFSET	Find or manipulate values in a cell, or range of cells, which begin at a location a certain number of rows and columns from a referenced cell.

4.5 *Date & Time Functions*

Excel has several functions that deal specifically with manipulating dates and times. We will only discuss a few of the more relevant *Date & Time* functions from the list in Figure 4.31. Before beginning to explain these functions, we need to describe Excel's system for calculating dates and times. Excel uses a ***serial number*** to enumerate all dates and times. For dates, Excel considers January 1, 1900 as an initial starting point, which it sets to zero, and then counts each day thereafter as one unit; for time, the initial starting point is at zero hours, zero minutes, and zero seconds counting toward the current time on a 24-hour scale. For example, June 13, 2011 at 3:31 PM is equal to 40707.65 in Excel's serial number terms; here the date is 40707 and the time is 0.65. (Excel's clock is reset to zero at midnight of each day. Excel serial numbers for afternoon hours are greater than 0.50) This numerical system allows us to perform the functions in this category and will become clearer as we demonstrate some of the *Date & Time* functions.

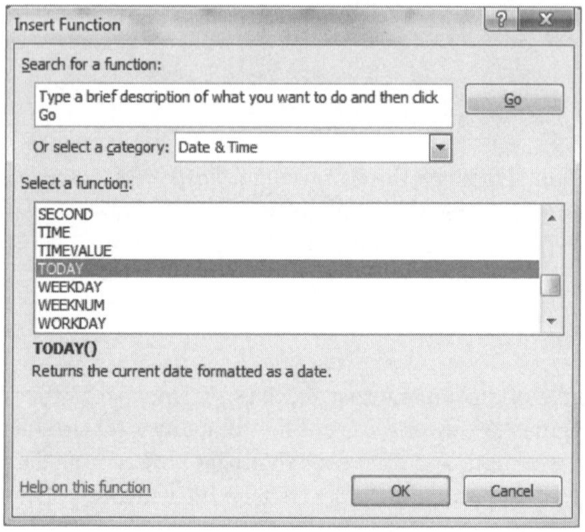

Figure 4.31 Several Date & Time Functions.

The first two functions, ***TODAY*** and ***NOW***, simply display the current date and time, respectively. There are no arguments for these functions; we simply type the following:

= *TODAY()*
= *NOW()*

Excel produces the results of these functions by using the initial starting point discussed above to determine the serial number of the current date. Note that these functions always update their results as the current day and time changes; that is, they are said to be "volatile." In Figure 4.32(a) and 4.32(b), we show how these two functions work.

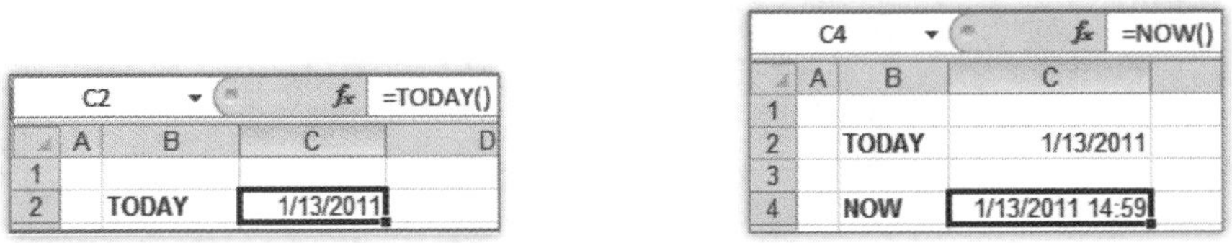

(a) **(b)**

Figure 4.32 The TODAY (a) and NOW (b) functions display the current date and time.

Three other Date & Time Functions are ***NETWORKDAYS***, ***DAYS360***, and ***YEARFRAC***. These functions calculate the workdays, total days, and fraction of a year between two dates. All three functions have a *start_date* and *end_date* as their first two arguments. The third argument for the NETWORKDAYS function is the number of *holidays* that occur between the two dates, where a holiday is any day when employees do not work. (Note that if the number of holidays is zero, this argument can be left blank.)

= *NETWORKDAYS(start_date, end_date, holidays)*

The DAYS360 function has a specified *method* as its third argument, which determines either a US standard, where the *method* is equal to *False* or left blank, or a European standard, *where the method* is equal to *True*, for counting the days. These two methods differ in that the US standard begins counting on the day after the *start_date*, while the European method includes the *start_date*.

= *DAYS360(start_date, end_date, method)*

The YEARFRAC function also has a third argument, *basis*, which specifies a counting method. For the DAYS360 and YEARFRAC functions, we recommend leaving the third argument blank unless there is a specific need to apply an alternate counting method. The general formats of these functions are the following:

= *YEARFRAC(start_date, end_date, basis)*

Let's consider an example of a company that receives shipments of office supplies each month. Given the dates in Figure 4.33, the manager of the company wants to construct a report that displays the number of workdays and total days that pass between the date the supply is shipped and when it is received. Suppose he wants to determine which supplier takes the least amount of time to transport items to his office.

	A	B	C	D
1				
2		Office Supply Shipments		
3		Incoming	Date Shipped	Date Received
4		Staplers	10/11/2010	10/17/2010
5		Paper Clips	11/15/2010	11/19/2010
6		Scissors	12/2/2010	12/5/2010
7		Pens	12/5/2010	12/10/2010
8		Pencils	12/20/2010	1/3/2011
9		Pads of Paper	1/15/2011	1/17/2011

Figure 4.33 A company's shipment figures of office supplies.

To find the number of workdays that pass between the date shipped and the date received, we enter the following function:

= NETWORKDAYS(C4, D4, 0)

As seen in Figure 4.34, we can copy this function for every supplier. However, in some cases, we must edit the third argument. For example, for "Pencils," there are two national holidays between the "Date Shipped" and "Date Received"; therefore, the function for that supplier is:

= NETWORKDAYS(C8, D8, 2)

The NETWORKDAYS function returns the total number of working days between each set of dates for each supplier.

C12 fx =NETWORKDAYS(C4,D4)

	A	B	C	D
1				
2		Office Supply Shipments		
3		Incoming	Date Shipped	Date Received
4		Staplers	10/11/2010	10/17/2010
5		Paper Clips	11/15/2010	11/19/2010
6		Scissors	12/2/2010	12/5/2010
7		Pens	12/5/2010	12/10/2010
8		Pencils	12/20/2010	1/3/2011
9		Pads of Paper	1/15/2011	1/17/2011
10				
11		Shipping Report	NETWORKDAYS	DAYS360
12		Staplers	5	6
13		Paper Clips	5	4
14		Scissors	2	3
15		Pens	5	5
16		Pencils	11	13
17		Pads of Paper	1	2

Figure 4.34 The Shipping Report calculates both the number of workdays (using NETWORKDAYS) and total days (using DAYS360) between the "Date Shipped" and the "Date Received" for the various incoming supplies.

If we now use the DAYS360 function, we receive some different results. As we have mentioned, the US method, which is the default *method* argument, begins counting on the day after the *start_date*. The NETWORKDAYS function, however, considers the *start_date* in its count. To calculate the total number of days, we use the following formula:

= *DAYS360(C4, D4,)*

We can view the results of these different counting methods in the shipment for "Paper Clips," which has more workdays than total days counted (see Figure 4.35). November 15, 2010 is a Monday (a workday) and November 19, 2010 is a Friday (also a workday). Therefore, the NETWORKDAYS function counts Monday through Friday, which is five days. However, DAYS360 begins counting on Tuesday and only counts four days.

D12 =DAYS360(C4,D4)

	A	B	C	D
1				
2		**Office Supply Shipments**		
3		**Incoming**	**Date Shipped**	**Date Received**
4		Staplers	10/11/2010	10/17/2010
5		Paper Clips	11/15/2010	11/19/2010
6		Scissors	12/2/2010	12/5/2010
7		Pens	12/5/2010	12/10/2010
8		Pencils	12/20/2010	1/3/2011
9		Pads of Paper	1/15/2011	1/17/2011
10				
11		**Shipping Report**	**NETWORKDAYS**	**DAYS360**
12		Staplers	5	6
13		Paper Clips	5	4
14		Scissors	2	3
15		Pens	5	5
16		Pencils	11	13
17		Pads of Paper	1	2

Figure 4.35 The DAYS360 function counts the total number of days between two dates starting on the day after the start_date.

The YEARFRAC function can now determine how much of a year has passed between two dates. In the report from this shipping example, the manager of the company may be interested in the shipping period he has observed. He considers the period between the first and last "Date Received":

= *YEARFRAC(D4,D9)*

Note that we have again left the third argument blank in this case. In Figure 4.36, we see that the result of this function is 0.25, which is a quarter of a year.

Other *Date & Time* functions allow us to enumerate and manipulate days and times. One of these, the ***MONTH*** function, determines the month of a given date. The months are numbered from 1 (January) through 12 (December). There is only one argument for this function, which is the date. We can actually enter a date into the function or refer to a cell that has a date as its value:

= *MONTH(date)*
= *MONTH(cell_address or range_name)*

For example, suppose the date *1/2/11* is in cell *B2* of a given table. If we type the function =*MONTH(B2)*, its result is 1, since January is the first month of the year.

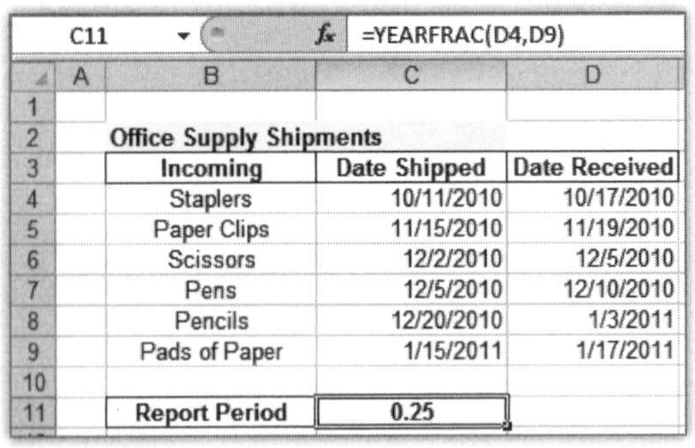

C11 | =YEARFRAC(D4,D9)

	A	B	C	D
1				
2		Office Supply Shipments		
3		Incoming	Date Shipped	Date Received
4		Staplers	10/11/2010	10/17/2010
5		Paper Clips	11/15/2010	11/19/2010
6		Scissors	12/2/2010	12/5/2010
7		Pens	12/5/2010	12/10/2010
8		Pencils	12/20/2010	1/3/2011
9		Pads of Paper	1/15/2011	1/17/2011
10				
11		Report Period	0.25	

Figure 4.36 Using YEARFRAC to compute the fraction of a year for which this report has been constructed.

Likewise, the ***WEEKDAY*** function determines the day of the week specified by a given date. There are two arguments in the WEEKDAY function: the date and the numbering method of our choice. We can enumerate Sunday as day 1 and Saturday as day 7 by entering a 1 as our second argument; this is also the default if we leave this argument blank. We can also enumerate Monday as day 1 and Sunday as day 7 by entering 2 as the argument. Finally, we can enumerate Monday as day 0 and Sunday as day 6 by entering 3 as the argument. Again, we can enter a date into the function or refer to a cell that has a date as its value.

= WEEKDAY(date, method)
= WEEKDAY(cell_address, method)

For example, if the date *1/2/11* is in cell *B2*, we type the following:

= WEEKDAY(B2, 1)

This function returns a 1, which, because we used the first numbering method, implies that this date is on a Sunday.

Let's consider an extended example to demonstrate these two functions. In Figure 4.37, we have a "Flight Sheet" with recorded flight dates and times during the last few months of the year 2010. The times are recorded as "Clock-in" and "Clock-out" times to represent the beginning and end of the flights. Suppose that the supervisor of this flight agency wants to know which flight dates correspond to which days of the week.

We need to use two functions to accomplish this task: the WEEKDAY function and the IF function, which we discussed earlier in this chapter. Using the default numbering method with Sunday as 1 and Saturday as 7, we assign words to each day of the week for each corresponding numerical result. That is, if the result of the WEEKDAY function is 1, we want to display the word "Sunday." We therefore use the IF function to check the numerical result of the WEEKDAY function and then display the corresponding day name. Our function turns out to be the following (see Figure 4.38):

= IF(WEEKDAY(C4)=1, "Sunday", IF (WEEKDAY(C4)=2, "Monday", …

Note that we do not enter our numbering method as an argument of the WEEKDAY function since option 1 is the default. Also, remember that the arguments of the IF function follow the conditions result if true, and result if false. Our result if our condition is false in this case is another IF function. That is, the above function tells Excel to display the word "Sunday" if the result of WEEKDAY is 1, "Monday" if the result is 2, and so on through the days of the week.

	A	B	C	D
1				
2		**Flight Sheet for 2010**		
3		Date	Clock-In	Clock-Out
4		8/13/2010	9:05 AM	4:00 PM
5		8/30/2010	9:00 AM	3:30 PM
6		9/14/2010	9:30 AM	5:00 PM
7		9/30/2010	9:15 AM	4:30 PM
8		10/17/2010	9:00 AM	4:30 PM
9		10/29/2010	8:55 AM	4:35 PM
10		11/19/2010	9:10 AM	4:15 PM

Figure 4.37 This Flight Sheet records the dates, clock-in, and clock-out times for the flights in the last few months of the year 2010.

E4 fx =IF(WEEKDAY(B4)=1,"Sunday",IF(WEEKDAY(B4)=2,"Monday",IF(WEEKDAY(B4)=3,"Tuesday",IF(WEEKDAY(B4)=4,"Wednesday",IF(WEEKDAY(B4)=5,"Thursday",IF(WEEKDAY(B4)=6,"Friday",IF(WEEKDAY(B4)=7,"Saturday",)))))))

	A	B	C	D	E	F	G
1							
2		**Flight Sheet for 2010**					
3		Date	Clock-In	Clock-Out	Week Day		
4		8/13/2010	9:05 AM	4:00 PM	Friday		
5		8/30/2010	9:00 AM	3:30 PM	Monday		
6		9/14/2010	9:30 AM	5:00 PM	Tuesday		
7		9/30/2010	9:15 AM	4:30 PM	Thursday		
8		10/17/2010	9:00 AM	4:30 PM	Sunday		
9		10/29/2010	8:55 AM	4:35 PM	Friday		
10		11/19/2010	9:10 AM	4:15 PM	Friday		

Figure 4.38 Using the WEEKDAY function with the IF function to display the name of the day of the week corresponding to the date in the table.

Figure 4.39 displays the name of the month for each date using the IF function again, this time with the MONTH function. We type the following:

= IF(MONTH(C4) = 1, "January", IF(MONTH(C4) = 2, "February", ...

Note in the function in Figure 4.39 that we have joined two different IF functions using the "&" sign. The "&" sign, as we have already mentioned, is another way to concatenate text, values, or formulas in a cell. We joined two IF functions in this example because an IF function can only have up to seven nested entries.

Remember that the MONTH function only has one argument, so there is no counting method signified in the function. The above function reads "If the result of MONTH is 1, display the word 'January,' otherwise check if the result of the MONTH function is 2 and display the word 'February,' otherwise check if the result of the MONTH function is 3," and so on.

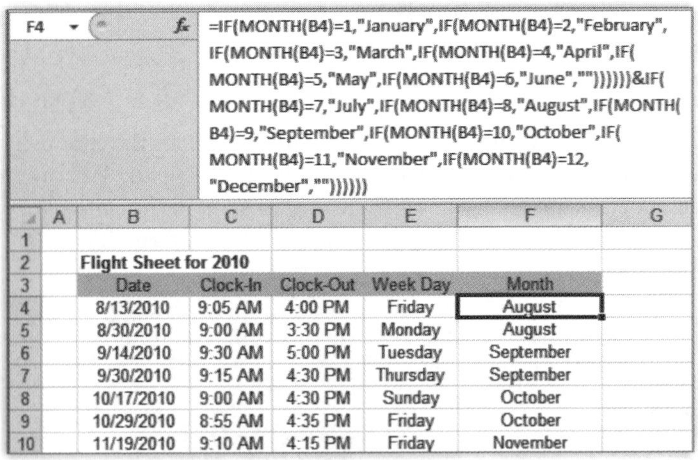

F4 =IF(MONTH(B4)=1,"January",IF(MONTH(B4)=2,"February",IF(MONTH(B4)=3,"March",IF(MONTH(B4)=4,"April",IF(MONTH(B4)=5,"May",IF(MONTH(B4)=6,"June",""))))))&IF(MONTH(B4)=7,"July",IF(MONTH(B4)=8,"August",IF(MONTH(B4)=9,"September",IF(MONTH(B4)=10,"October",IF(MONTH(B4)=11,"November",IF(MONTH(B4)=12,"December",""))))))

	A	B	C	D	E	F	G
1							
2		Flight Sheet for 2010					
3		Date	Clock-In	Clock-Out	Week Day	Month	
4		8/13/2010	9:05 AM	4:00 PM	Friday	August	
5		8/30/2010	9:00 AM	3:30 PM	Monday	August	
6		9/14/2010	9:30 AM	5:00 PM	Tuesday	September	
7		9/30/2010	9:15 AM	4:30 PM	Thursday	September	
8		10/17/2010	9:00 AM	4:30 PM	Sunday	October	
9		10/29/2010	8:55 AM	4:35 PM	Friday	October	
10		11/19/2010	9:10 AM	4:15 PM	Friday	November	

Figure 4.39 Using the MONTH function with the IF function to display the name of the month corresponding to the date in the table.

Another way to display the appropriate month names would be to use one of the LOOKUP functions. To do so, we can simply create a small table with the month numbers and names in two columns. Then, we use the VLOOKUP function in the following manner to find and display the appropriate month names in the flight table:

= VLOOKUP(MONTH(flight_table_value), month_table, column_number_with_names)

Now suppose that the supervisor needs to determine the number of hours worked each day by a pilot in order to determine her pay. We must determine the difference in times by subtracting the number of hours and minutes from the "Clock-in" and "Clock-out" times. To do so, we need two new functions: ***HOUR*** and ***MINUTE***. The function HOUR takes the time (the only argument) and returns the number of the hour to which it belongs using a numbering system from 12:00 AM as 0 to 11:00 PM as 23. The MINUTE function performs a similar operation by taking the time (again the only argument) and returning a minute number from 0 to 59. We can enter a time into the function or refer to a cell that has a time as its value. The format for these functions is:

= HOUR(time)
= HOUR(cell_address)
= MINUTE(time)
= MINUTE(cell_address)

For example, the time *4:45 AM* results in 4 for the HOUR function and 45 for the MINUTE function. *4:45 PM* results in 16 for the HOUR function and 45 for the MINUTE function.

To work with the "Clock-in" and "Clock-out" times of each flight, we first check which time has the larger hour value. For whichever is larger, we subtract the positive difference between the two values. We check these conditions using the IF function. After ensuring that these time differences are reflected correctly, we divide the minute values by 60 to show the fraction of an hour that has been worked. We then take this result with the difference in the hour values to find the total time worked for the day in terms of hours. We type the following to calculate the first time difference:

=IF(MINUTE(C4)>MINUTE(D4),HOUR(D4)-
HOUR(C4)-(MINUTE(C4)-MINUTE(D4))/60,HOUR(D4)-
HOUR(C4)+(MINUTE(D4)-MINUTE(C4))/60)

The supervisor can now easily find the total hours worked for the cumulative time of this Flight Sheet by copying the above formula for each flight and using the SUM formula to add the values in this column (refer to Figure 4.40). These are just some of the *Date and Time* functions, but the others are also useful for manipulating date and time information.

G4 fx =IF(MINUTE(C4)>MINUTE(D4),HOUR(D4)-HOUR(C4)-(MINUTE(C4)-MINUTE(D4))/60,HOUR(D4)-HOUR(C4)+(MINUTE(D4)-MINUTE(C4))/60)

	A	B	C	D	E	F	G
1							
2		Flight Sheet for 2010					
3		Date	Clock-In	Clock-Out	Week Day	Month	Hours Worked
4		8/13/2010	9:05 AM	4:00 PM	Friday	August	6.92
5		8/30/2010	9:00 AM	3:30 PM	Monday	August	6.50
6		9/14/2010	9:30 AM	5:00 PM	Tuesday	September	7.50
7		9/30/2010	9:15 AM	4:30 PM	Thursday	September	7.25
8		10/17/2010	9:00 AM	4:30 PM	Sunday	October	7.50
9		10/29/2010	8:55 AM	4:35 PM	Friday	October	7.67
10		11/19/2010	9:10 AM	4:15 PM	Friday	November	7.08
11						Total Hours in Flight =	50.42

Figure 4.40 Calculating the time worked in hours using the HOUR and MINUTE functions with the IF function.

Summary

Date and Time Functions:

TODAY Displays the current date.

NOW Displays the current time.

NETWORKDAYS Returns the difference of two dates counting only work days and discounting any holidays that the user specifies.

DAYS360 Returns the difference of two dates counting all days by the method that the user specifies.

YEARFRAC Returns the difference of two dates as a fraction of the year.

WEEKDAY Returns the number of the weekday of a date depending on the numbering method that the user specifies.

MONTH Returns the number of the month of a date.

HOUR Returns the number of the hour of a time.

MINUTE Returns the number of the minute of a time.

4.6 *Mathematics and Trigonometry Functions*

We have already discussed the more popular *Math & Trig* functions, SUM, AVERAGE, MIN, and MAX, earlier in this chapter. We would now like to introduce some more useful functions in this category.

The first function, ***ABS***, finds the absolute value of any number or expression. Its format is:

= ABS(numerical value or range or expression)

The ABS function may be used with a list of numerical values or with another function. For example, we could use the ABS function as follows:

= ABS(SUM(. . .))
= ABS(MAX(. . .))

Another function, the ***PRODUCT*** function, finds the product of several independent numbers or a range of numbers. This function, which is useful for finding the product of a large list of values, takes the following format:

= PRODUCT(numerical values or range)

Suppose that after generating this data, we determine the volume created for each set of *Height*, *Width*, and *Depth* and then sum those volumes to determine our total volume capacity from this randomly generated data. We create a new column for *Volume* and calculate the volume of each row using product operators. For example, we calculate the first value in the *Volume* column using the following:

*= C5*D5*E5*

To find the sum of these volumes, we use SUM for the values in the *Volume* column (see Figure 4.41a):

= SUM(G5:G14)

However, another function, the ***SUMPRODUCT*** function, accomplishes this same goal in one step and does not require the creation of a new table. SUMPRODUCT takes several arrays as its arguments and then finds the sum of the product of each corresponding element in these arrays.

= SUMPRODUCT(array1, array2, . . .)

Continuing with the volume example, the arrays we choose are the Height, Width, and Depth columns featured in Figure 4.41. So, our formula is:

= SUMPRODUCT(C5:C14, D5:D14, E5:E14)

Given that these are our arrays, SUMPRODUCT takes the first entry from each column and calculates the product of the three values. The SUMPRODUCT of the first row, 15.44, results from the product of 1.40, 1.78, and 6.16. SUMPRODUCT then repeats this operation for the second entry in each column and adds the two products. It finds the product of the three entries in each column and adds this value to the sum found in the previous step. This process continues until each entry in each array has been multiplied to find a product and until all of the products have been summed. We can see in Figure 4.41(b) that this function yields the same result as the more labor-intensive process of creating a new table for volumes and using the SUM function.

The SUMPRODUCT function is important to understand. We will use this function often when preparing the spreadsheet for solving optimization problems with the Solver. We discuss using this function with the Solver in Chapter 8 and Chapter 19.

G15 =SUM(G5:G14)

	A	B	C	D	E	F	G	H
1								
2								
3			Packaging Volumes					
4			Heights	Widths	Depths		Volumes	
5			1.40	1.78	6.16		15.44	
6			2.90	6.19	9.05		162.21	
7			4.89	3.32	6.35		102.99	
8			8.83	6.52	9.56		549.79	
9			5.71	8.90	2.19		111.07	
10			8.99	8.98	4.79		386.41	
11			2.68	4.96	1.92		25.50	
12			9.54	3.33	7.60		241.71	
13			8.89	1.34	5.50		65.39	
14			9.96	3.30	3.10		102.04	
15							1762.56	SUM

(a)

C16 =SUMPRODUCT(C5:C14,D5:D14,E5:E14)

	A	B	C	D	E	F
1						
2						
3			Packaging Volumes			
4			Heights	Widths	Depths	
5			1.40	1.78	6.16	
6			2.90	6.19	9.05	
7			4.89	3.32	6.35	
8			8.83	6.52	9.56	
9			5.71	8.90	2.19	
10			8.99	8.98	4.79	
11			2.68	4.96	1.92	
12			9.54	3.33	7.60	
13			8.89	1.34	5.50	
14			9.96	3.30	3.10	
15						
16			1762.56	SUMPRODUCT		

(b)

Figure 4.41 In (a), volumes are calculated for each row and the SUM function is used to total this column of volume values. The SUMPRODUCT function used in (b) multiplies the Height, Width and Depth columns and then adds the resulting volumes to arrive at the same total volume value.

The ***MMULT*** function also provides a convenient way to work with arrays. This function multiplies two matrices, or ranges, of values:

= MMULT(array1, array2)
= MMULT(range_name, range_name)

The MMULT function can only multiply two matrices if the number of columns of one matrix equals the number of rows of the other matrix. For example, in Figure 4.42, we have two matrices: one has two columns and five rows, and the other has two rows and three columns.

	A	B	C	D	E	F	G
1	Matrix Multiplication						
2							
3		1	6		2	3	2
4		2	7		3	2	3
5		3	8				
6		4	9				
7		5	10				

Figure 4.42 The number of columns of the first matrix equals the number of rows of the second matrix.

To find the matrix that results from the multiplication of these ranges, we first need to highlight a range of cells that takes the dimension of the number of rows of the longer matrix by the number of columns of the wider matrix. In the above example, the resulting matrix from the product of the two matrices shown has five rows and three columns, as shown in Figure 4.43.

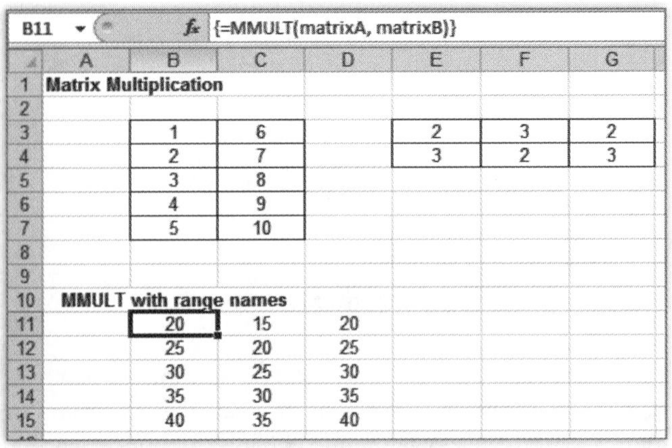

B11
{=MMULT(matrixA, matrixB)}
Matrix Multiplication
1 6
2 7
3 8
4 9
5 10
2 3 2
3 2 3
MMULT with range names
20 15 20
25 20 25
30 25 30
35 30 35
40 35 40

Figure 4.43 Hold down SHIFT and CTRL to see the entire range of values in the product matrix.

To see all values of the resulting matrix from the MMULT function, we press F2, and then hold down the SHIFT and CTRL keys while pressing ENTER. If we do not hold down SHIFT and CTRL, we will only see the upper left-hand value of the matrix product. Remember, this function can also be used with range names. For instance, instead of using B3:C7 and E3:G4 as the arrays in the above example, we could name the first matrix "matrixA" and the second "matrixB" and use these names in the MMULT function (see Figure 4.44).

Note: We will see that curly brackets ({, }) now appear around the function in the cell. These brackets indicate that this function is what is known as an "array formula." The function now becomes the value for any cell in that range. The SHIFT plus CTRL technique can be applied to fill in other formulas or functions for any range of cells.

Some other useful *Math & Trig* functions have simple arguments and are easy to use. We recommend experimenting with ***SQRT***, which finds the square root of a number. Its only argument is a number or cell reference. Some other useful functions are ***SIN***, ***COS***, and ***TAN***, which find the sine, cosine, and tangent of an angle. To use these angle functions, we need to enter an angle in radians as its argument, or refer to a cell that has an angle in radians as its value. Therefore, we also need the function ***PI***, which takes no arguments but returns the value for pi. We recommend looking through the function list in this category and use the function instructions as a guide while we experiment with data.

Two functions that are used frequently when we create spreadsheet simulation models are the ***RAND*** and ***RANDBETWEEN***. The ***RAND*** function does not have any parameters; it returns a randomly chosen real number between 0 and 1. The RAND formula is:

=RAND()

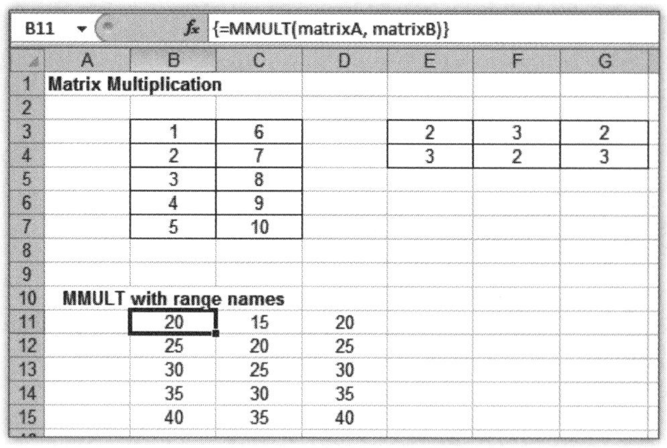
B11
{=MMULT(matrixA, matrixB)}
A B C D E F G
Matrix Multiplication
1 6
2 7
3 8
4 9
5 10
2 3 2
3 2 3
MMULT with range names
20 15 20
25 20 25
30 25 30
35 30 35
40 35 40

Figure 4.44 Range names can also be used with the MMULT function.

RAND is useful for generating test data or any data with random patterns. We can manipulate this RAND value if we want to generate values outside the interval between 0 and 1. If we want to generate numbers between a lower bound (*LB*) and an upper bound (*UB*), multiply this RAND value by (*UB* – *LB*) and add *LB*.

=RAND()(UB – LB) + LB*

We demonstrate the use of RAND in Figure 4.45. Here we want to generate heights, widths, and depths to calculate some probable packaging volumes. We type the following function to create random numbers between 1 and 10:

*=RAND()*9 + 1*

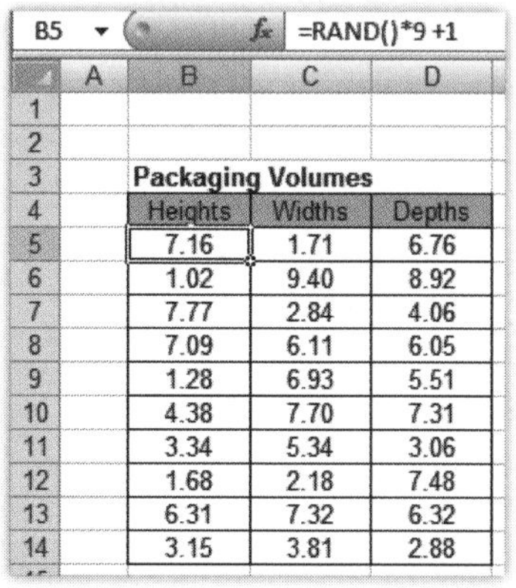
B5
=RAND()*9 +1
A B C D
Packaging Volumes
Heights Widths Depths
7.16 1.71 6.76
1.02 9.40 8.92
7.77 2.84 4.06
7.09 6.11 6.05
1.28 6.93 5.51
4.38 7.70 7.31
3.34 5.34 3.06
1.68 2.18 7.48
6.31 7.32 6.32
3.15 3.81 2.88

Figure 4.45 The RAND function can be manipulated to change the range of the random numbers produced. Here the range is changed from the default of 0 to 1, to 1 to 10.

We can convert these random numbers into random integers by changing the format of the cells in which we entered this function. Simply use the *Number* tab of the *Formatting* dialog box and set the number of decimal places to 0.

An easier way to manipulate the RAND function is to use another function called ***RANDBETWEEN***. This function takes two parameters, which are the lower and upper limits of the range. The format of this function is the following:

=RANDBETWEEN(lower_limit, upper_limit)

Note: To use the RANDBETWEEN function, we will need to ensure that the *Analysis Toolpak* has been selected as an *Add-In*. Please refer to Appendix A for more details on the *Analysis Toolpak*.

Using the same example, if we wanted to create random numbers between 1 and 10, we would type the following:

=RANDBETWEEN(1,10)

The RAND and RANDBETWEEN functions can also be used with the distribution functions discussed in Chapter 7.

Summary

Math & Trig Functions:

ABS	Finds the absolute value of a number, range of numbers, or expression.
COS	Returns the cosine value of an angle (in radians).
MMULT	Finds the matrix multiplication for two matrices.
PI	Gives the value for pi.
PRODUCT	Finds the product of several numbers or a range of numbers.
RAND	Generates random numbers between 0 and 1.
RANDBETWEEN	Generates random integers between a lower and an upper bound.
SIN	Returns the sine value of an angle (in radians).
SQRT	Returns the square root of a number.
SUMPRODUCT	Takes the product of each entry in multiply arrays and sums them.
TAN	Returns the tangent value of an angle (in radians).

4.7 *Statistical and Financial Functions*

Several *Statistical and Financial* functions are commonly used in Excel. We will describe them in detail in Chapter 7.

4.7.1 Statistical Functions

We will describe in detail such statistical functions as ***MEDIAN*** and ***STDEV*** in Chapter 7, as well as such distribution functions as ***NORM.DIST***, ***BETA.DIST***, ***CHISQ.DIST***, and ***EXPON.DIST***. At that time, we will also provide useful tools for data analysis. In Chapter 10, we will discuss the ***COUNT*** functions, ***COUNTIF*** and ***SUMIF***, with databases functions.

4.7.2 Financial Functions

Many *Financial* functions are available in Excel. We will describe six common ones and some of the depreciation functions as well. We will use a more detailed example to help us understand the applications of these functions.

Figure 4.46 presents a table of the Financial Debts and Assets for a series of machines, perhaps used in farming or manufacture. For each machine bought, we know the "Unpaid Debt," the "Monthly Loan Rate," the "Date Purchased," the number of "Payments Left," and the monthly "Payment" to be made. To begin, suppose that we do not know the number of "Payments Left" for machines B and E. To calculate this number, we can use the function ***NPER***. This function uses the rate, payment per period, and unpaid amount as arguments to calculate the total number of remaining payments. The argument *present_value* refers to the amount that remains unpaid. As we will see later, the future value can also be used as an argument. While we do not need to include both the *present_value* and *future_value* when using the NPER function, we do need to include at least one of these values. The final argument, *type*, specifies if payments are made at the beginning of the period, 0 (the default), or at the end of the period, 1.

= NPER(rate, period_payment, present_value, future_value, type)

In this example, we type the following function for Machine B. Notice that we leave the last two arguments blank since we consider our unpaid debt to be the present value of the payment and we use the default argument value for *type*.

= NPER(E5, H5, D5)

We find that if we are paying $4,000.00 per month (*period_payment*) at a loan rate of 12 percent per month (*rate*), it will take us 8.09 months (or payments) to pay the entire $-20,000 debt (*present_value*). The result for this calculation appears in G5 in Figure 4.46(a).

Likewise, if we assume that the monthly payment amounts for Machines A, C, and D are unknown, then we must calculate them. To do so, we use the function ***PMT***, which uses the arguments of rate, number of payments left, and unpaid amount to calculate the monthly payment amount. Again, the unpaid amount is entered as the present value of the payment, and the future value can be used as an argument. PMT uses the same criteria for the argument *type* as NPER:

= PMT(rate, Nper, present_value, future_value, type)

For Machine A, we type the following:

= PMT(E4, G4, D4)

We find that we must pay $1,627.45 per month to finish paying the $-10,000 debt in 10 payments (*Nper*) at a 10 percent monthly loan rate (*rate*) (see Figure 4.46(b)).

Now let's consider a record of "Investments" (see Figure 4.47). For each fund, we know the "Months Left" from which we can invest in this fund, the "Monthly Payments" we make to the fund, the "Interest Rate," and the "Ending Value" we plan to receive from the investment. If we need to calculate the "Monthly Payments" for Fund C, we could again use the function PMT. However, here we do not have an "Unpaid Debt" to pay off, but rather an "Ending Value" that we are trying to achieve. We therefore have to leave the argument of "Unpaid Debt" (or present value) blank and enter another argument for the "Ending Value" (or future value). We type the function:

= *PMT(F6, D6, , G6)*

We can see in Figure 4.47(a) that our "Monthly Payment" (or investment) amount should be $132.33 if we wish to receive $12,500.00 (*future_value*) in 30 months (*Nper*) at a 7 percent interest rate (*rate*).

G5 =NPER(E5,H5,D5)

	A	B	C	D	E	F	G	H
1								
2			Financial Debts and Assets					
3			EXPENDITURES	Unpaid Debt	Monthly Loan Rate	Date Purchased	Payments Left	Payment
4			Machine A	($10,000)	10%	Oct-00	10.00	$1,627.45
5			Machine B	($20,000)	12%	Aug-99	8.09	$4,000.00
6			Machine C	($50,000)	6%	Jan-01	30.00	$3,632.45
7			Machine D	($5,000)	20%	Apr-02	6.00	$1,503.53
8			Machine E	($17,500)	8%	Aug-98	10.67	$2,500.00

(a)

H4 =PMT(E4,G4,D4)

	A	B	C	D	E	F	G	H
1								
2			Financial Debts and Assets					
3			EXPENDITURES	Unpaid Debt	Monthly Loan Rate	Date Purchased	Payments Left	Payment
4			Machine A	($10,000)	10%	Oct-00	10.00	$1,627.45
5			Machine B	($20,000)	12%	Aug-99	8.09	$4,000.00
6			Machine C	($50,000)	6%	Jan-01	30.00	$3,632.45
7			Machine D	($5,000)	20%	Apr-02	6.00	$1,503.53
8			Machine E	($17,500)	8%	Aug-98	10.67	$2,500.00

(b)

Figure 4.46 (a) The NPER function uses the rate, monthly payment amount, and unpaid amount to calculate the number of remaining payments. (b) The PMT function uses the rate, number of payments left, and unpaid amount to calculate the amount to be paid monthly.

We can also find the "Interest Rate" if it is missing. If we know the number of "Months Left" to invest (D5), the "Monthly Payment" amount (E5), and the "Ending Value" (G5) we want to achieve for Fund B, we can enter these values as arguments in the ***RATE*** function. The arguments for this function are the number of periods, payment per period, present value or future value, and the calculation type:

= *RATE(nper, period_payment, present_value, future_value, type)*

For Fund B, then, we enter the following arguments into the function. Note that we have left the present value argument blank and used the future value instead.

= *RATE(D5, E5, ,G5)*

In Figure 4.47(b), we see that these arguments necessitate an "Interest Rate" of 5 percent.

Lastly, let's discuss how to calculate the "Ending Value." For Fund A, we can use the given "Interest Rate" (F4), "Monthly Payment" amount (E4), and number of "Months Left" (D4) to determine what value the investment will return. Here, we use the ***FV*** function to calculate the future value with these known values as our arguments:

= FV(rate, nper, period_payment, present_value, type)

In Figure 4.47(c), we have entered this function for the cells shown:

= FV(F4, D4, E4)

We conclude that investing in Fund A will return $6,590.00 at the end of 10 months.

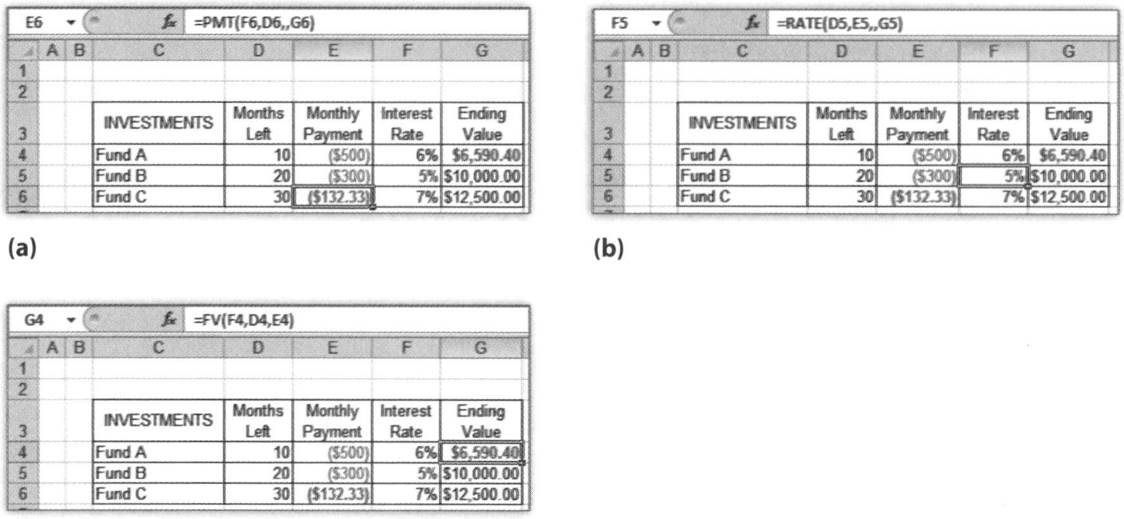

E6 =PMT(F6,D6,,G6)

INVESTMENTS	Months Left	Monthly Payment	Interest Rate	Ending Value
Fund A	10	($500)	6%	$6,590.40
Fund B	20	($300)	5%	$10,000.00
Fund C	30	($132.33)	7%	$12,500.00

(a)

F5 =RATE(D5,E5,,G5)

INVESTMENTS	Months Left	Monthly Payment	Interest Rate	Ending Value
Fund A	10	($500)	6%	$6,590.40
Fund B	20	($300)	5%	$10,000.00
Fund C	30	($132.33)	7%	$12,500.00

(b)

G4 =FV(F4,D4,E4)

INVESTMENTS	Months Left	Monthly Payment	Interest Rate	Ending Value
Fund A	10	($500)	6%	$6,590.40
Fund B	20	($300)	5%	$10,000.00
Fund C	30	($132.33)	7%	$12,500.00

(c)

Figure 4.47 (a) Using the PMT function with the future value instead of the present value to determine the monthly payments that should be made. (b) The RATE function uses the number of months, payment amount, and future value to find the interest rate. (c) The FV function calculates the future value using the other known values as arguments.

The ***NPV*** and ***IRR*** functions are two other important functions to become comfortable using. ***NPV*** calculates the net present value given the interest rate and payments each period. Unlike the above functions, ***NPV*** allows us to consider varying payment amounts per period. This function provides 30 different payment values that we can enter as arguments. If these multiple payments are kept in a range of cells, we can enter the range name as the argument:

= NPV(rate, payment1, payment2, ...)

Figure 4.48 presents a record of payments made by a manufacturing plant to five different suppliers. The 3 percent "Interest Rate" applies to all payments, listed here for each location for 5 periods. The table also records the "Salvage" value per supplier in the last period. To calculate the net present value for the Atlanta supplier, we type the NPV function with the "Interest Rate" (D3) and payment values (D6:D10) as our arguments; these payments do not include the initial investment (D5), so we add this amount to the function. Figure 4.48(a) presents the results of this function for the Atlanta data:

= D5 + NPV($D$3, D6:D10)

To determine the NPV for other suppliers, we simply apply the function to the given data.

D12 f_x =D5+NPV($D$3,D6:D10)

	A	B	C	D	E	F	G	H
1								
2			**Manufacturing Plant**					
3			**Interest Rate =**	3%				
4			Year	Atlanta GA	Orlando FL	Miami FL	Pensacola FL	Montgomery AL
5			0	-$1,000,000	-$950,000	-$1,500,000	-$750,000	-$800,000
6			1	$100,000	$90,000	$200,000	$75,000	$90,000
7			2	$250,000	$275,000	$205,000	$150,000	$185,000
8			3	$325,000	$300,000	$215,000	$200,000	$200,000
9			4	$350,000	$300,000	$300,000	$250,000	$220,000
10			5 + Salvage	$950,000	$875,000	$1,150,000	$700,000	$690,000
11			Salvage	$600,000	$550,000	$750,000	$400,000	$415,000
12			NPV	$760,606	$692,464	$342,709	$473,181	$435,454
13			FV	$881,751	$802,755	$397,293	$548,547	$504,811
14			IRR	20%	19%	9%	17%	16%

(a)

F14 f_x =IRR(F5:F10)

	A	B	C	D	E	F	G	H
1								
2			**Manufacturing Plant**					
3			**Interest Rate =**	3%				
4			Year	Atlanta GA	Orlando FL	Miami FL	Pensacola FL	Montgomery AL
5			0	-$1,000,000	-$950,000	-$1,500,000	-$750,000	-$800,000
6			1	$100,000	$90,000	$200,000	$75,000	$90,000
7			2	$250,000	$275,000	$205,000	$150,000	$185,000
8			3	$325,000	$300,000	$215,000	$200,000	$200,000
9			4	$350,000	$300,000	$300,000	$250,000	$220,000
10			5 + Salvage	$950,000	$875,000	$1,150,000	$700,000	$690,000
11			Salvage	$600,000	$550,000	$750,000	$400,000	$415,000
12			NPV	$760,606	$692,464	$342,709	$473,181	$435,454
13			FV	$881,751	$802,755	$397,293	$548,547	$504,811
14			IRR	20%	19%	9%	17%	16%

(b)

Figure 4.48 (a) Using the NPV function to calculate the net present value given the interest rate and payments per period. (b) The IRR function calculates the internal rate of return given the payments per period, including the initial investment.

If the payment periods are irregular, that is, if they occur at irregular intervals, we can still calculate the NPV using the ***XNPV*** function. Its format is:

= *XNPV(rate, payments, dates)*

The range of values should have the earliest date listed first, but other dates do not need to be sorted.

We can also calculate the internal rate of return of these payments. We do this using the ***IRR*** function, which takes the payments for all periods (including the initial investment) as a range of cells. It also has a *guess* argument used to estimate the IRR; the default value is 0.10, or 10 percent, if left blank.

= *IRR(payment_range, guess)*

In Figure 4.48(b), we have entered the following function. (Note that we left the *guess* value blank.) We can observe the IRR calculated for each location in the figure.

= *IRR(F5:F10)*

Excel also has some depreciation functions. Let's now look at the functions that perform straight-line depreciations, sum of year's digits, and fixed declining balance. The ***SLN*** function calculates the straight-line depreciation of our assets. It takes the initial cost, the salvage at the last period, and the useful life of our asset (the number of periods that our asset is worthwhile).

= *SLN(initial_cost, salvage, life)*

In Figure 4.49, we use the same data from the "Manufacturing Plant" example to calculate these depreciations. In this example, we use the SLN function to determine the straight-line depreciation of the Orlando data (Figure 4.49(a)). Notice that the initial cost is written with a negative sign:

= *SLN(−E5, E11, 5)*

For the sum of year's digits, we use the ***SYD*** function, which calculates the sum of the year's digits for a given period in the depreciation calculation. The arguments are the initial cost, the salvage at the last period, the useful life of the asset, and the period in which we are interested.

= *SYD(initial_cost, salvage, life, period)*

E17 =SLN(-E5,E11,5)

	A	B	C	D	E	F	G	H
1								
2			**Manufacturing Plant**					
3			**Interest Rate =**	3%				
4			Year	Atlanta GA	Orlando FL	Miami FL	Pensacola FL	Montgomery AL
5			0	-$1,000,000	-$950,000	-$1,500,000	-$750,000	-$800,000
6			1	$100,000	$90,000	$200,000	$75,000	$90,000
7			2	$250,000	$275,000	$205,000	$150,000	$185,000
8			3	$325,000	$300,000	$215,000	$200,000	$200,000
9			4	$350,000	$300,000	$300,000	$250,000	$220,000
10			5 + Salvage	$950,000	$875,000	$1,150,000	$700,000	$690,000
11			Salvage	$600,000	$550,000	$750,000	$400,000	$415,000
12			NPV	$760,606	$692,464	$342,709	$473,181	$435,454
13			FV	$881,751	$802,755	$397,293	$548,547	$504,811
14			IRR	20%	19%	9%	17%	16%
15								
16			Depreciation					
17			SLN	$80,000	$80,000	$150,000	$70,000	$77,000
18			SYD	$133,333	$133,333	$250,000	$116,667	$128,333
19			DB	$97,000	$98,800	$193,500	$88,500	$98,400

(a)

Figure 4.49 (a) The SLN function calculates the straight-line depreciation

F18 f_x =SYD(-F5,F11,5,1)

	A	B	C	D	E	F	G	H
1								
2			**Manufacturing Plant**					
3			**Interest Rate =**	3%				
4			Year	Atlanta GA	Orlando FL	Miami FL	Pensacola FL	Montgomery AL
5			0	-$1,000,000	-$950,000	-$1,500,000	-$750,000	-$800,000
6			1	$100,000	$90,000	$200,000	$75,000	$90,000
7			2	$250,000	$275,000	$205,000	$150,000	$185,000
8			3	$325,000	$300,000	$215,000	$200,000	$200,000
9			4	$350,000	$300,000	$300,000	$250,000	$220,000
10			5 + Salvage	$950,000	$875,000	$1,150,000	$700,000	$690,000
11			Salvage	$600,000	$550,000	$750,000	$400,000	$415,000
12			NPV	$760,606	$692,464	$342,709	$473,181	$435,454
13			FV	$881,751	$802,755	$397,293	$548,547	$504,811
14			IRR	20%	19%	9%	17%	16%
15								
16			Depreciation					
17			SLN	$80,000	$80,000	$150,000	$70,000	$77,000
18			SYD	$133,333	$133,333	$250,000	$116,667	$128,333
19			DB	$97,000	$98,800	$193,500	$88,500	$98,400

(b)

G19 f_x =DB(-G5,G11,5,1)

	A	B	C	D	E	F	G	H
1								
2			**Manufacturing Plant**					
3			**Interest Rate =**	3%				
4			Year	Atlanta GA	Orlando FL	Miami FL	Pensacola FL	Montgomery AL
5			0	-$1,000,000	-$950,000	-$1,500,000	-$750,000	-$800,000
6			1	$100,000	$90,000	$200,000	$75,000	$90,000
7			2	$250,000	$275,000	$205,000	$150,000	$185,000
8			3	$325,000	$300,000	$215,000	$200,000	$200,000
9			4	$350,000	$300,000	$300,000	$250,000	$220,000
10			5 + Salvage	$950,000	$875,000	$1,150,000	$700,000	$690,000
11			Salvage	$600,000	$550,000	$750,000	$400,000	$415,000
12			NPV	$760,606	$692,464	$342,709	$473,181	$435,454
13			FV	$881,751	$802,755	$397,293	$548,547	$504,811
14			IRR	20%	19%	9%	17%	16%
15								
16			Depreciation					
17			SLN	$80,000	$80,000	$150,000	$70,000	$77,000
18			SYD	$133,333	$133,333	$250,000	$116,667	$128,333
19			DB	$97,000	$98,800	$193,500	$88,500	$98,400

(c)

Figure 4.49 (b) The SYD function calculates the sum of year's digits for a period of interest. (c) The DB function calculates the fixed declining balance.

Figure 4.49(b) illustrates this calculation and its results for the Miami supplier. (Note again that the initial cost has a negative sign.)

= SYD(–F5, F11, 5, 1)

Like the SYD function, the fixed declining balance function ***DB*** calculates depreciation using the initial cost, the salvage at the last period, the useful life of the asset, and the period of interest as its arguments:

= DB(initial_cost, salvage, life, period)

See Figure 4.49(c) for the results of the calculations of the following DB function for the Pensacola supplier:

= DB(–G5, G11, 5, 1)

Summary

Financial Functions:

NPER	Determines the number of periods needed to pay off an unpaid amount.
PMT	Determines the payment for each period.
RATE	Calculates the interest rate.
FV	Calculates the future value of investments or payments.
NPV	Calculates the net present value of an investment.
IRR	Calculates the internal rate of return for an investment.
SLN	Finds the straight-line depreciation for assets.
SYD	Finds the sum of year's digits depreciation for a given period.
DB	Finds the fixed declining balance depreciation for assets.

4.8 *Conditional Formatting Formulas*

As we mentioned in Chapter 2, formulas can also be used with Conditional Formatting. The last option in the *Select a Rule Type* list of *New Formatting Rule* dialog box is called ***Use a formula to determine which cells to format***. This feature allows us to use formulas to create the conditions checked before a format is placed in a cell.

If we select this option, in the ***Edit the Rule Description*** window of the dialog box, a window appears where we can write a formula (see Figure 4.50).

The formulas used in Conditional Formatting are similar to those of the Logical category. For example, if we type "=E5>E4" in the formula area of the *New Formatting Rule* dialog box, Excel checks if this statement is true or false. If it is true, then the formatting specified is applied to the initially selected cell, or range of cells. Note that we cannot use absolute referencing when entering formulas here.

The ***Use a formula…*** option of Conditional Formatting allows us to format a cell, or range of cells, based not only on the value in the selected cells, but also on values in other cells. For example, Figure 4.51 displays a table of quarterly revenues for a company over a period of three years. If we want to highlight the quarters in which revenues increased from the previous quarter in purple and highlight quarters in which revenues decreased from the previous quarter in yellow, then we can use the ***Use a formula…*** option of Conditional Formatting.

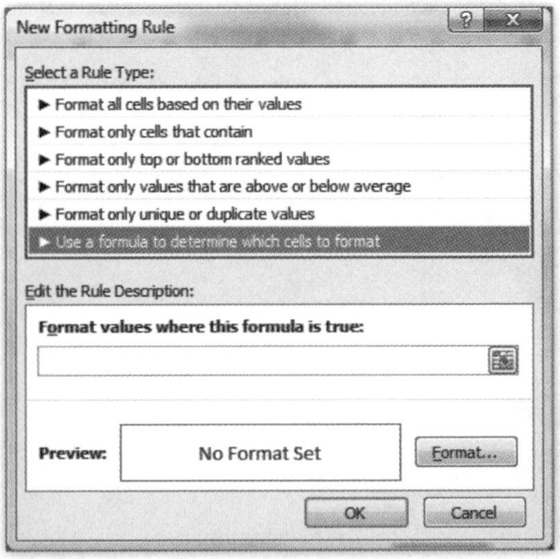

Figure 4.50 The *Use a formula to determine which cells to format* option.

	A	B	C
1			
2	**Year**	**Quarter**	**Sales**
3	2008	1	1560
4	2008	2	1354
5	2008	3	2246
6	2008	4	2094
7	2009	1	2934
8	2009	2	2908
9	2009	3	1176
10	2009	4	2325
11	2010	1	2988
12	2010	2	1109
13	2010	3	2117
14	2010	4	1236

Figure 4.51 A record of sales for each quarter over three years.

We now begin by selecting the range *B3:B14 (C3:C14)*. We select *Conditional Formatting* from the *Home* tab > *Styles* group on the *Ribbon*. From the *Conditional Formatting* drop-down list select the *New Rule* option. Select the *Use a formula ...* option, and then type the following condition (see Figure 4.52):

= *C4>C3* *Format:* purple background

You can follow similar steps as described earlier to enter the second condition for range *B3:B14 (C3:C14)*.

= *C4<C3* *Format:* yellow background

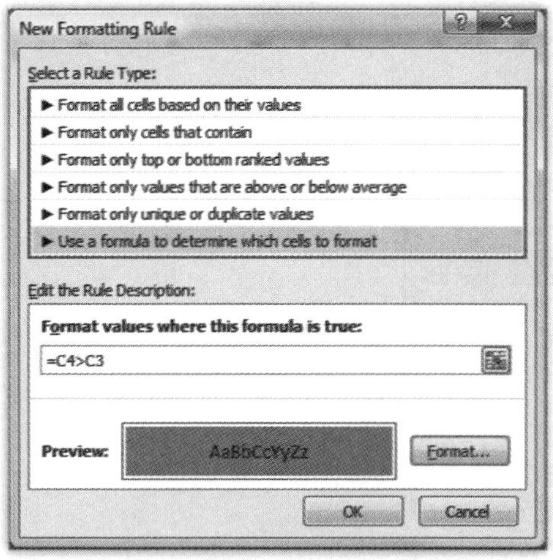

Figure 4.52 Using the *Use a formula…* option for the first condition.

To add the second condition you can also use the *Conditional Formatting Rules Manager* that is listed in the *Conditional Formatting* drop-down list. In the *Conditional Formatting Rules Manager* dialog box (see Figure 4.53) select the *New Rule* button. This button will prompt the *New Formatting Rule* dialog box (see Figure 4.52).

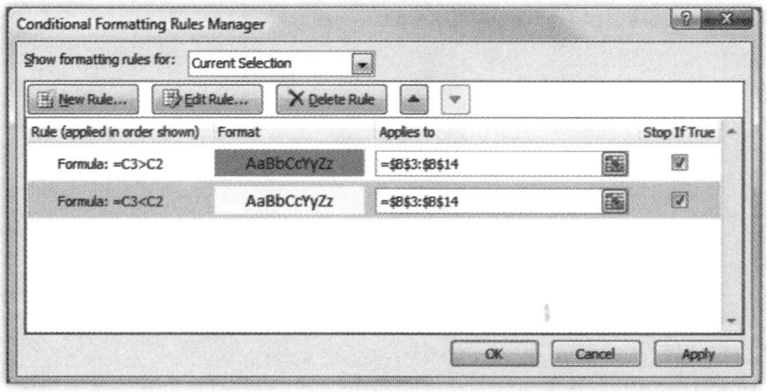

Figure 4.53 Add a new condition by selecting the New Rule command button.

	A	B	C
1			
2	Year	Quarter	Sales
3	2008	1	1560
4	2008	2	1354
5	2008	3	2246
6	2008	4	2094
7	2009	1	2934
8	2009	2	2908
9	2009	3	1176
10	2009	4	2325
11	2010	1	2988
12	2010	2	1109
13	2010	3	2117
14	2010	4	1236

Figure 4.54 The resulting table after Conditional Formatting.

4.9 Auditing

Excel's auditing feature aids in data validation and verification. Formula Auditing unveils all of the data cells involved in a function or reference. That is, if our function finds the sum of several values, auditing reveals the values from which the sum is calculated. Auditing related commands are listed in the *Formulas tab > Formula Auditing group* on the *Ribbon* (see Figure 4.55). We will use a number of these commands in the examples we are going to discuss next.

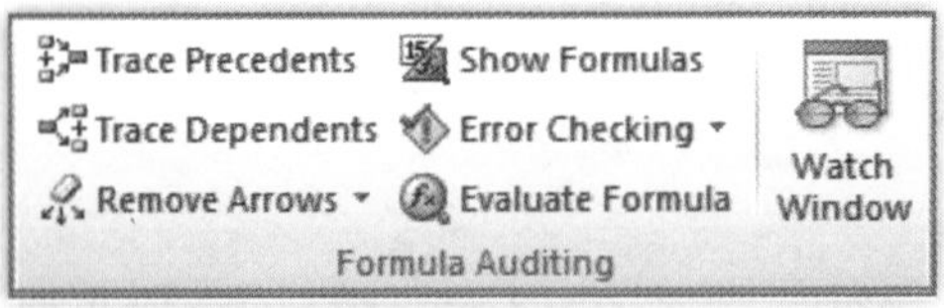

Figure 4.55 The Formula Auditing group displays all of the auditing commands.

Auditing performs two primary actions: ***tracing precedents*** and ***tracing dependents***.

Tracing a precedent of a selected cell establishes which cells provide data for a function or reference in that selected cell. For example, suppose we have used the SUM function to calculate the sum of a set of values. If we select the cell with the SUM function and click *Trace Precedents* icon on the *Formula Auditing group*, then the cells that we are summing are highlighted and an arrow points from those cells to our selected SUM cell. For example, in Figure 4.56 we have a SUM function in cell *D3* whose formula is:

= *SUM(B3:B9)*

If we click on cell *D3* and then press the *Trace Precedents* icon on the *Formula Auditing group*, the arrow shown in the figure appears. It points from the highlighted column B3:B9 to the *Sum* cell, implying that the SUM formula in the Sum cell references this column of cells. Note that we can also click on cell *D3* and then press the shortcut key F2 to highlight the cells used in its formula (however, no arrows will appear).

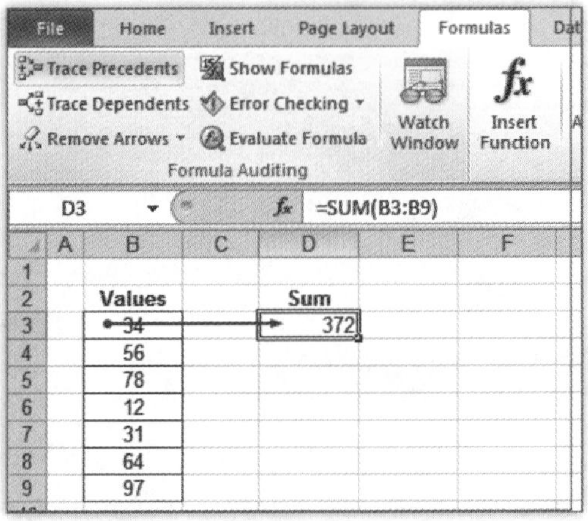

Figure 4.56 Selecting the *Sum* cell (*D3*) and choosing *Trace Precedents* from the *Formula Auditing group* displays an arrow pointing from all of the cells involved in the SUM function (*B3:B9*).

Tracing the dependents of a selected cell presents all of the cells that are dependent upon the selected cell to perform a function (see Figure 4.57). Using the same example above, if we now select one of the cells from the *Values* column, say cell *B5* (or *B3*, or *B6*), and click on *Trace Dependents*, then an arrow points from our selected cell to the *Sum* cell showing that the *Sum* cell uses this value.

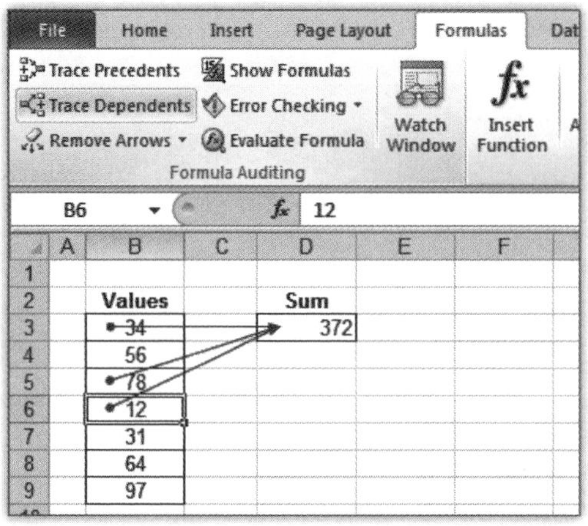

Figure 4.57 Selecting one of the *Value* cells (B3, or *B5, or B6*) and choosing *Trace Dependents* from the *Formula Auditing group* displays an arrow pointing to the *Sum* cell (*D3*), which uses the *Value* cell to perform a function.

The *Remove Arrows* drop down list in the *Formula Auditing group* (see Figure 4.58) presents options to remove all, or precedent, or dependent arrows previously created. The other commands in the *Formula Auditing* group include *show formulas (to display the formulas in each cell rather than the resulting values), error checking and tracing, formula evaluating*, and *watch window*.

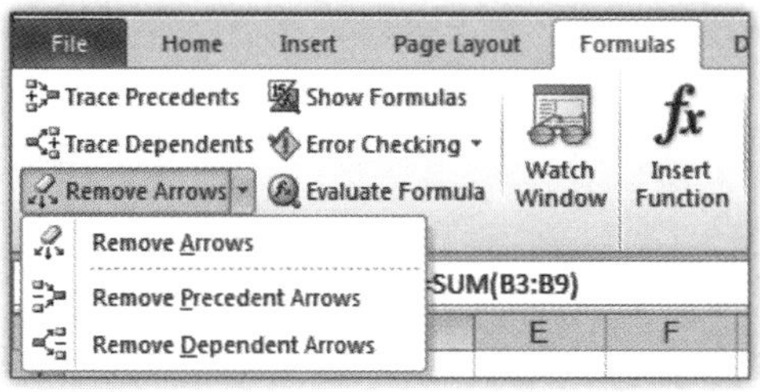

Figure 4.58 *Remove Arrows* drop-down list.

Summary

Auditing:	Unveils all of the data cells involved in a function or reference.
Tracing Precedents:	Determines which cells provide data for a function or reference in a selected cell.
Tracing Dependents:	Determines all cells that are dependent upon a selected cell to perform a function.

4.10 *Summary*

- The following are some of the function categories in Excel: *Financial, Date and Time, Mathematics and Trigonometry, Statistical, Lookup and Reference, Database, Text, Logical, Information and Engineering.*
- There are only seven *Logical* functions: TRUE, FALSE, NOT, IF, IFERROR, AND, and OR. These are important functions for determining whether certain criteria are met. The IF, AND, and OR functions are more commonly used for both spreadsheet applications and VBA programming.
- There are several different *Information* functions, all of which provide general information about data. The IsFunctions, a category of information functions, determine whether a value has a specified characteristic. The TYPE function categorizes the data type of any possible value and is an important concept to know for VBA programming.
- *Text* functions manipulate text in any cell or range. Aside from simple changes in text format, we can also CONCATENATE, or join, two or more segments of text and SUBSTITUTE specified letters or words.
- The "&" sign denotes CONCATENATE.
- *Lookup and Reference* functions search through data to find values that match certain criteria. The VLOOKUP, HLOOKUP, and MATCH are the most commonly used functions in this category. The INDEX and OFFSET functions are also very useful reference functions.
- *Date and Time* functions work with calculations involving dates and times. Nine of these functions are: TODAY, NOW, NUMWKDAYS, DAYS360, YEARFRAC, WEEKDAY, MONTH, HOUR, and MINUTE.
- There are several *Math & Trig* functions, some of which we already discussed in Chapter 2. Some other common functions in this category are RAND, RANDBETWEEN, and SUMPRODUCT. The MMULT function multiplies two matrices, or ranges, of values. We should also be familiar with SQRT, SIN, COS, TAN, and PI.
- Nine *Financial* functions we should know are NPER, PMT, RATE, FV, NPV, IRR, SLN, SYD, and DB.
- The *Use a Formula ...* option of Conditional Formatting allows we to specify conditions using logical comparisons of several cells.

4.11 *Exercises*

4.11.1 Review Questions

1. List some of the most frequently used function categories of Excel.
2. What are the seven logical functions?
3. What three arguments does the IF function require?
4. What are the three data types that can be determined with the TYPE function? Provide the number used to represent each data type.
5. What does each of the *match type* codes of the MATCH function return?
6. What is a serial number for in Excel? What are the initial starting points of the serial numbers for the date and time?
7. If you want to count the days from a Monday to the next Monday without any holidays, how many days would Excel calculate with the following functions?
   a. NETWORKDAYS
   b. DAYS360
8. What are the different options for the second argument of the WEEKDAY function and what do they represent?
9. What are two ways to generate a random number between 1 and 20?
10. What does the NPER function do and what information does it require?
11. What information is needed to calculate the sum of year's digits using Excel?
12. What are the four formula types?
13. Which tab of Ribbon presents Excel function categories?
14. How do you enter the value pi into a cell?
15. Do cells that you want to concatenate need to be neighboring each other?

16. Which Excel function returns the number of empty cells in a specified range of cells?
17. Give an example of an instance when the YEARFRAC function would be useful.
18. How does the HLOOKUP function work?
19. Compare the usefulness of the INDEX and OFFSET functions.
20. What are the requirements for the size of the arrays that can be used with the MMULT function?

4.11.2 Hands-On Exercises

NOTE: Please refer to the file "Chapter_04_Exercises.xlsx" for the associated worksheets noted for the hands-on exercises. The file is available at: www.dssbooks.com.

1. Enter the following set of numbers into an Excel spreadsheet, putting each number in a separate cell: {2, 4, 6, 8, 10, 12, 14, 16, 18, 20}.
   a. Give the results of using the MATCH function to search for the number 5 in this range of cells with each of the following *match type* codes: 1, 0, –1.
   b. Did any of the results you obtained in part (a) contain errors? If so, why did these errors occur?
2. Enter the following set of numbers defined as S into an Excel spreadsheet, putting each number in a separate cell: S = {10.1, 7.3, 1.9, 5.6, 12.7, 14.0, 4.1, 5.6, 8.9}. Then find the sum, average, minimum value, and maximum value of the set by using mathematical and statistical functions.
3. A table is used to compute the height of a cylinder given the cylinder's volume and radius. Use the following formula to compute the value of the height for each of the given radii using the volume shown: *Height = Volume/(Radius^2).* (Refer to worksheet "4.3".) Use IFERROR function that returns "Error in calculations" in case of an error when calculating Height, such as division by zero.
4. Given the following series of future cash flows, use Excel functions to determine the net present value of an investment made at an interest rate of 8%: {–$1200, $300, $450, $585, –$275, $645, $800}.
5. Wasser & Wasser Distributors, Inc. wants to find and buy a building to use as a new distribution center. The ideal building would be at least 175 feet in length, at least 100 feet in width, have a ceiling height of at least 30 feet and be no more than 5 miles from a highway. The company will pay up to $2,000,000 for a building that meets these specifications. The company will also consider buildings that are at least 165 feet in length, at least 90 feet in width, have a ceiling height of at least 25 feet and are no further than 10 miles from a highway. The company is willing to pay no more than $1,800,000 for a building that meets, but does not exceed, this second set of guidelines. (Refer to worksheet "4.5".)
   a. Using the *Create* option, define names for each column.
   b. To complete the last column of the table, use logical functions to determine which buildings are acceptable for the company to consider.
6. A statistician wishes to generate a set of "random" numbers less than 10. To do this, she plans to find twenty numbers between 0 and 10,000 and check to see if the numbers are greater than 10. If they are, she plans to take the square root of the number. She repeats this process until all values are below 10.
   a. Create a spreadsheet that duplicates this algorithm. The sheet should initially contain 20 numbers randomly distributed from 0 to 10,000. Then, it should perform repeated iterations of the algorithm above until each number in the set is less than 10.
   b. Does this appear to be a good method for gaining a sample? Why or why not?
7. A medical center must pay close attention to several health factors to determine what type of meals patients should receive. The factors to consider include the patient's age, weight, blood pressure, and cholesterol level. Patients should receive low sodium meals if their blood pressure is high and if they meet at least one of the following conditions: their age is at least 70 or their weight is at least 200. Patients should receive low cholesterol meals if their cholesterol level is high and if they meet one of the following conditions: their age is at least 70; their weight is at least 200; or their blood pressure is high. Patients may also have low sodium and low cholesterol meals if they satisfy the conditions for both the low sodium meal and the low cholesterol meal. If the

patient does not satisfy the conditions for either the low sodium meal or the low cholesterol meal, then he or she receives a regular meal. (Refer to worksheet "4.7".)

a. Create names for the columns of data.

b. Using logical functions and the names you defined, find the type of meals each patient should receive.

c. Results should be one of the following: "Regular Meal," "Low Sodium Meal," "Low Cholesterol Meal," or "Low Sodium/Low Cholesterol Meal."

8. A table is used to compute the average acceleration of a moving object given the time and velocity of the movement. Define names for each of the columns, and calculate the missing data by referring to the cells by their defined names. (Refer to worksheet "4.8".)

9. The manager of a manufacturing plant is about to place an annual order for new material handling equipment for the plant. Every year he must determine which equipment to replace and which to keep for another year. The factors involved in this decision include the cost of new equipment, the age of the current equipment, the equipment's useful life, and the salvage value of the equipment. A table displays the data for each of these factors. Any piece of equipment that is as old as its useful life must be replaced. The manager will also replace any piece of equipment with a net cost (the cost for a new piece of equipment minus the equipment's salvage value) under $250. Using logical functions and the conditions mentioned above, complete the final column of the table with a "Yes" or a "No" to indicate whether or not the equipment should be replaced. (Refer to worksheet "4.9".)

10. An electrical engineer has designed a circuit with three light emitting diodes (LEDs) placed at various points along the circuit to detect if a current is running through that section of the circuit. Two switches are also located at various points along the circuit to control the flow of the current. The engineer tries closing every combination of switches to see which LEDs will light. She obtains the following results:

- LED 1 lights as long as switch 1 is open.
- LED 2 lights as long as switch 2 is open.
- LED 3 lights as long as at least one switch is open.

The engineer creates a table to display her results. Using logical functions, show each LED as being either "On" or "Off" for each of the trials. (Refer to worksheet "4.10".)

11. Use Excel functions to determine the future value of a $5000 loan made at a 5% interest rate from the lender's perspective. Assume that the investment is made in individual payments of $1000 over the course of five periods and that all payments are made at the beginning of each period.

12. A list of values is given in a table. In a separate column, use a function to determine which cells do not contain text values. Text values should return the word "FALSE" and all other values should return the word "TRUE." (Refer to worksheet "4.12".)

13. A table containing the last name, first name, and age of various people is provided. Add an additional column that uses functions to concatenate the given data into sentences of the following form: "*First Name Last Name* is *Age* years old." For example, the first sentence should be: "Jon Henley is 39 years old." Be sure to use appropriate spacing between words. (Refer to worksheet "4.13".)

14. A payroll worker uses a table to determine the number of days an employee works during a given pay period. To do this, he must first determine the number of workdays in the pay period less any holidays given to the employees and then subtract any sick days taken by an employee. Complete the table by using functions to calculate this value. (Refer to worksheet "4.14".)

15. A college professor uses a spreadsheet to tabulate her students' grades. Each test has a maximum score of 100 points and constitutes 30% of a student's final grade. The remaining 10% of a student's grade comes from the averages of the three homework assignments, each worth a possible total of fifteen points. (Refer to worksheet "4.15".)

a. Using the VLOOKUP function, fill in the values for the Test 1 Score, Test 2 Score, Test 3 Score, and Average Homework Score located at the bottom of the spreadsheet for student number 3.

b. Use formulas to compute the Final Course Grade for student number 3.

16. A student uses an Excel spreadsheet to assist him in planning important dates in one of his courses. (Refer to worksheet "4.16".)
    a. Complete the column labeled "Days Until Next Event" with functions to calculate the number of days since the last event that the next event will occur.
    b. Then, complete the column labeled "Day of Week" with functions to determine the day of the week on which each event occurs. Display the values in this column as "Sunday," "Monday," "Tuesday," etc.

17. A clothing retailer maintains a table of information about customers who have signed up for a store credit card. These customers receive special promotional discounts, including a coupon to use during the month of their birthdays. (Refer to worksheet "4.17".)
    a. Some customers' birth dates are missing. Create a new column in the table that displays the word "TRUE" if the date of birth is missing for a particular customer.
    b. If the customer's birth date is present, create another new column in the table that displays the month of the customer's birthday.
    c. Create a final column to indicate whether a birthday coupon should be sent to a customer this month. If the month of the customer's birthday is the same as the current month, display the word "SEND" to indicate that the coupon should be sent. If the birth month is not the same as the current month, display the phrase "DO NOT SEND."

18. An airline uses a spreadsheet to track information about each of its scheduled flights. (Refer to worksheet "4.18".)
    a. After its flight from Orlando to Los Angeles, the Boeing 737 requires maintenance and is unable to fly as scheduled. A Boeing 727 will fly in its place. Use an Excel function at each instance after the Orlando to Los Angeles flight to substitute every instance of the phrase "Boeing 737" with the phrase "Boeing 727."
    b. Due to a snowstorm, all flights out of Chicago have been cancelled. Using the VLOOKUP function, return the flight number of all the cancelled flights in a cell at the bottom of the spreadsheet.
    c. The flight attendants need to know the number of minutes after the hour each flight arrives at its destination. In a new column, calculate this value for each flight based on the departure and travel times.

19. John Smith is considering advertising his company's products on a famous sports network. The ads have prices assigned to ranges. As he buys more ads, the price per ad drops; in other words, if he buys 8 ads, he pays $11,000 per ad, while if he buys 14 ads he pays $10,000 per ad. Write a formula that determines the total cost of purchasing any number of ads from 1 to 25. (Refer to worksheet "4.19".)

20. In a given table, the units sold of a particular product are stored for several countries along with the total revenue and variable cost of selling to those countries. Using OFFSET, MATCH, and LOOKUP functions, find the following. (Refer to worksheet "4.20".)
    a. The Units Sold for England.
    b. The Revenue for Germany.
    c. The Variable Cost for Spain.
    d. The largest Revenue.
    e. Now create a formula to find the Units Sold, Revenue, and Variable Cost for any given country.

21. A table displays the varying annual rates charged by a bank for varying amounts of years of money borrowed. This data can be used to interpolate the annual rate for years not recorded in the table. For example, the annual rate for borrowing money for 15 years can be calculated by noting that 15 is ° of the time between 10 years and 30 years, so the annual rate would be: $\frac{3}{4} * (9) + \frac{1}{4} * (10) = 9.25\%$. Create a formula that will find the annual rate for any period between 1 and 30 years. (Refer to worksheet "4.21".)

22. Using the distance table provided in the example for the INDEX function, find the following. (Refer to worksheet "4.22".)
    a. The distance between Los Angeles and Chicago.
    b. The distance between New York and Atlanta.
    c. The total miles traveled on a trip from Chicago to Boston to Atlanta to Miami.
    d. The city closest to New York.

e. The city farthest from Seattle.

23. A spreadsheet is used to record high and low temperatures for each month of the year. Use the OFFSET and other LOOKUP functions to determine the following. (Refer to worksheet "4.23".)

a. The month with greatest High Temperature.

b. The month with the least Low Temperature.

c. The average High Temperature for the months of June, July, and August.

d. The average Low Temperature for the months of December, January, February.

24. Using the table from Hands-On Exercise 21, determine the following by creating formulas: (Refer to worksheet "4.24".)

a. How many countries bought more than 400 units?

b. Which country had the largest Revenue?

c. Which countries had a Variable Cost between $500 and $600?

25. Using the information given in Chapter 3 Hands-On Exercise 22 calculate the Euclidean and Rectilinear distance from the candidate locations for the DC to customer locations. In calculating the distances use the Excel functions *ABS*, *SQRT*, *POWER*, and *SUM*. Present the total distance traveled from each candidate location to the customers. (Refer to worksheet "4.25".)

26. A manufacturing company is planning to buy new equipment that costs $100,000. Because of this investment, they estimate the following annual savings during the next seven years: $14,000; $17,000; $23,300; $22,000; $21,000; $18,000; $16,700. Use Excel functions to calculate the following. (Refer to worksheet "4.26".)

a. Net present value of this investment. Assume that the return in investment for this company is 5%.

b. Internal rate of return.

c. Payback period.

d. Since the APR given by a local bank is only 3%, the company is planning to borrow the money needed to buy the equipment. Identify the yearly payments the company should make to pay off the loan in five years.

27. An industrial engineer is working on a simulation project. The project simulates a manufacturing system. In order to complete his work, the engineer has to randomly generate demand, inter-arrival rate of shipments from suppliers, processing time in different machines, etc. The engineer is planning to use Excel functions to generate the input data for his model. Show what functions in Excel should be used to generate numbers from the following distributions. Generate 10 instances for each distribution.

a. Uniform distribution between 0 and 1.

b. Uniform distribution between 10 and 30.

c. Normal distribution with mean 10 and standard deviation 3.

d. Lognormal distribution with mean 10 and standard deviation 8.

e. Exponential distribution with lambda equal to 3.

f. Weibull distribution with alpha 5 and beta 6.

28. Parasol Systems sells motherboards for personal computers. They use the following model to price their products: for quantities up to 30, the company charges $325.00; for quantities between 30 and 50 they charge $300.00 for each board beyond 30; and they charge $275.00 per board for quantities beyond 50. A given table presents the last orders for motherboards. Calculate the total revenues. (Refer to worksheet "4.28".)

29. A furniture manufacturing company uses a special type of woodworking glue in the assembly of its furniture. During the last 36 weeks, the given amounts of glue (in gallons) were used by the company. (Refer to worksheet "4.29".)

a. Calculate the mean and standard deviation of this sample.

b. Consider the following class intervals for the number of gallons used each week: Less than 20; 20–27; 28–33; 34–37; 38–43; more than 43. Use Excel functions to determine the proportion of data points that fall into each interval.

c. Calculate the probability that a normal variate with the mean and standard deviation as calculated in part a. falls into the intervals specified in part b.

d. Use the Chi-Square test (in Excel) to compare the proportions calculated in part b. to the probabilities calculated in part c. (a = 5%). Is the data normally distributed?

30. Over a period of 12 consecutive production hours, samples of size 50 resulted in given proportions of defective items. (Refer to worksheet "4.30".)

a. Calculate the 3-sigma upper and lower control limits for this process. Note: (i) UCL = mean + 3*std. dev; and LCL = mean ñ 3*std. dev. (ii) the lower control limits cannot be negative.

b. Count the number of sample points that fall out of these limits.

CHAPTER

five Charts & Sparklines

chapter OVERVIEW

5.1 *Introduction*

This chapter shows the user how to create and work with charts and sparklines in Excel. This is mostly an introductory chapter for the inexperienced Excel user; however, even an experienced user may benefit from reviewing the section on dynamic charts and sparklines. Charts will be used extensively in creating DSS applications as they provide a great visual aid in displaying output to the user. A chart in a DSS may display an analysis of the user's input data, resulting output data from a simulation, or forecasted data using a mathematical model. A chart is useful if its output is clear and the user can easily analyze the chart data. A sparkline is a small chart displayed in a cell. It is a useful tool to spot trends and variations in the data without having to create a chart. Understanding dynamic charts and sparklines will be important when charts and sparklines are manipulated with VBA. Dynamic charts and sparklines will be used in simulation and other user interface for many DSS applications.

In this chapter, the reader will learn how to:

- Create a chart and a sparkline.
- Customize the chart and sparkline using various chart options.
- Create dynamic charts and sparklines.

5.2 *Creating Charts*

Charts produce graphics from data in a table and are useful for displaying data patterns or results. To create a chart, we must first have a table with data and then use the commands listed in the *Insert > Charts* group of *Excel's Ribbon* (see Figure 5.1.) Let's now work with Figure 5.2, a table of car sales for a local dealer in the year 2010, to demonstrate how to build *Charts*. The table records the numbers of various models sold as well as the total revenue generated for each model.

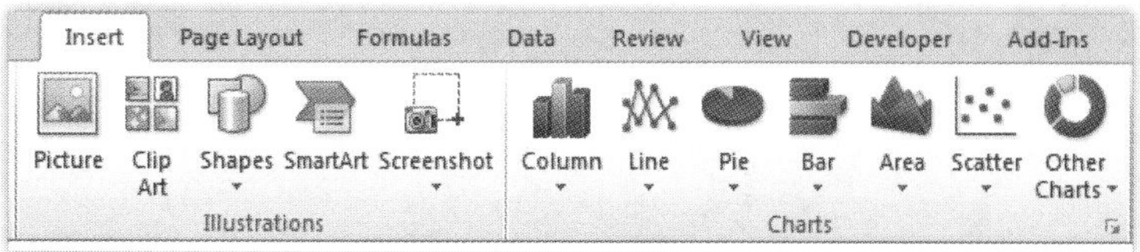

Figure 5.1 Charts commands listed on the Insert > Charts group of the Ribbon.

	A	B	C	D	E	F
1						
2						
3		Automobile Sales for Local Dealer in 2010				
4		Car Model	Year	Mileage	Number Sold	Revenue Generated
5		Lex1100	2006	78,064	3	$144,000.00
6		Cam3200	1996	81,982	8	$256,000.00
7		Iz1200	2004	97,522	6	$108,000.00
8		Cav4100	1990	68,301	7	$91,000.00
9		Aco3500	1992	81,541	10	$140,000.00
10		Mer2200	2003	82,005	3	$147,000.00
11						

Figure 5.2 Car sales for 2010 at a local dealer.

Suppose we want to find which Car Model sold the most and find which Car Model generated the most revenue. We will create two different charts to do this: a column chart and a pie chart. We begin by creating a column chart of the number sold for various models.

First, we need to highlight the data that we want to graph. In our example, we highlight the cells *B4:B10* and *E4:E10* (by holding down the CTRL key). We have highlighted the column titles so that we can label data automatically when creating the chart. To insert a *2-D Column Chart*, we could either select *Insert > Charts > Column* command from the Ribbon, or select the *Dialog Launcher* on the bottom-right corner of the *Charts* group. Upon the selection of *Column* command, a drop-down window appears (see Figure 5.3) that lists the corresponding *Chart* subtypes available in Excel.

If you use the *Dialog Launcher*, then upon selection, the *Insert Chart* dialog box appears (see Figure 5.4). The left side of the dialog box lists different types of charts available in Excel. Clicking on a *Chart type* displays all the *Chart sub-types*, which are the various display options associated with that particular *Chart type*. Deciding which chart type is best for our data depends on how we want to analyze our data. For example, comparing static values may suit a column graph best whereas comparing dynamic values may suit a scatter or line chart best. Consider who will be reading the chart and if the chart type best helps the reader analyze the data.

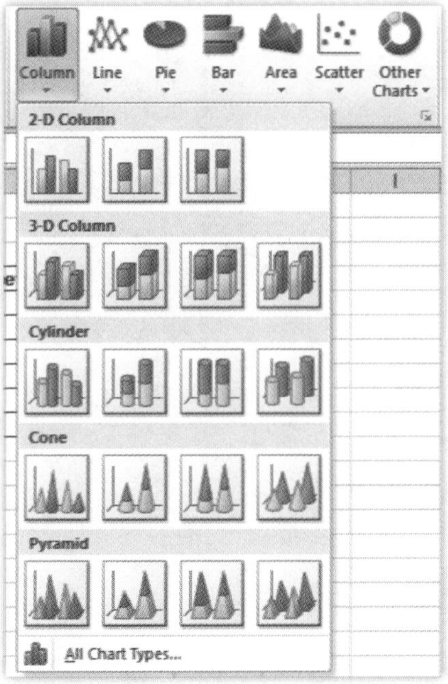

Figure 5.3 Select the Column command from Charts group to see a list of different types of column charts available in Excel.

For our example, we first want to create a vertical bar chart from our data. To do so, we select *Column* from the list of *Chart* types on the left side of *Insert Chart* dialog box (see Figure 5.4). Next, we select the top left chart from *Column* sub-type and click *OK*. The resulting column graph is in Figure 5.5. We can now follow the *same* steps again to create a pie chart of the Revenue Generated by each car model. The final chart should look like the chart shown in Figure 5.6. Here, we can see that the Cam3200 generated the most revenue.

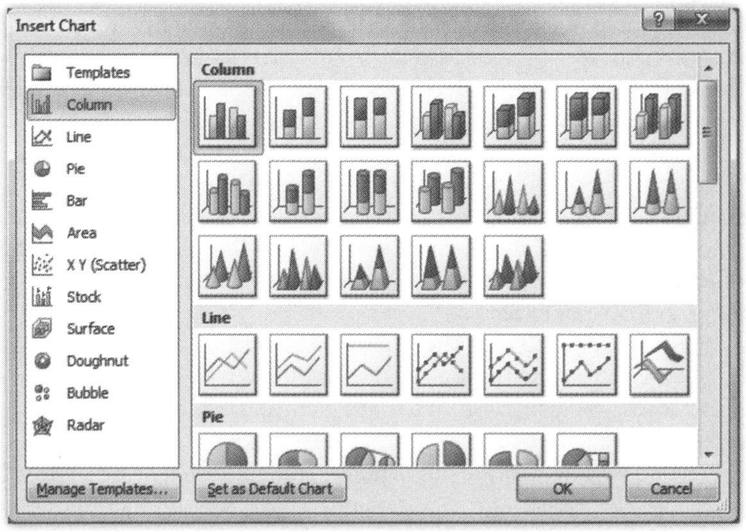

Figure 5.4 Use the chart dialog box to choose a chart type to insert.

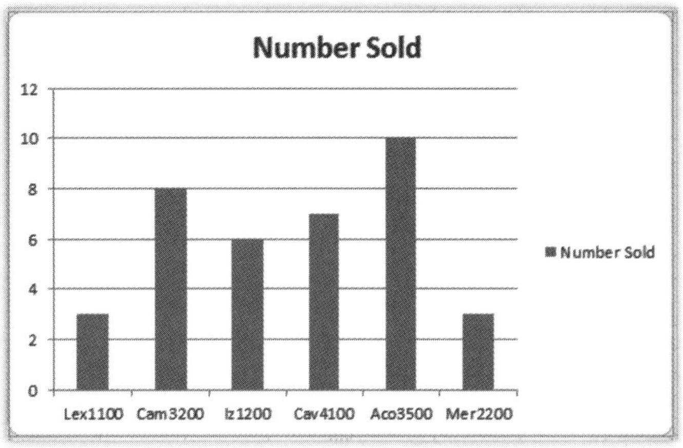

Figure 5.5 The resulting bar graph of Car Models Sold.

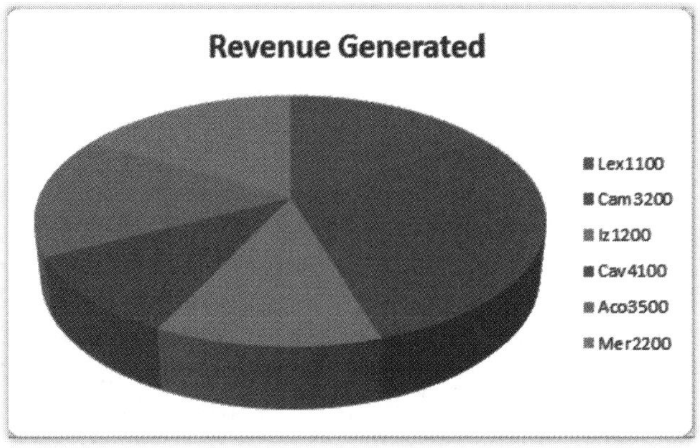

Figure 5.6 The Pie chart of Revenue Generated.

Summary

Creating a Chart

Step 1:	Select the data range.
Step 2:	Select a chart type from the list in Insert > Charts group of the Ribbon.
Step 3:	Determine the Chart Sub-type from the drop-down list.

5.3 *Working with Chart Tools*

After creating a chart, we can further customize its *Design*, *Layout* and *Format* by using the contextual *Chart Tools* tabs on the *Ribbon*. To activate these tabs we should select the chart object. A number of commands are listed within each tab to help you customize the charts you create.

The *Design* tools allow us to modify the chart type, data source, layout, style, etc. For example, we may want to change the type of our column chart in Figure 5.5 to a bar chart. To do so, we select *Design* > *Type* > *Change Chart Type* command on the Ribbon, to activate the *Change Chart Type* dialog box. From the list of chart types in the left we select the *Bar* option (see Figure 5.7). The resulting *bar Chart* is in Figure 5.8.

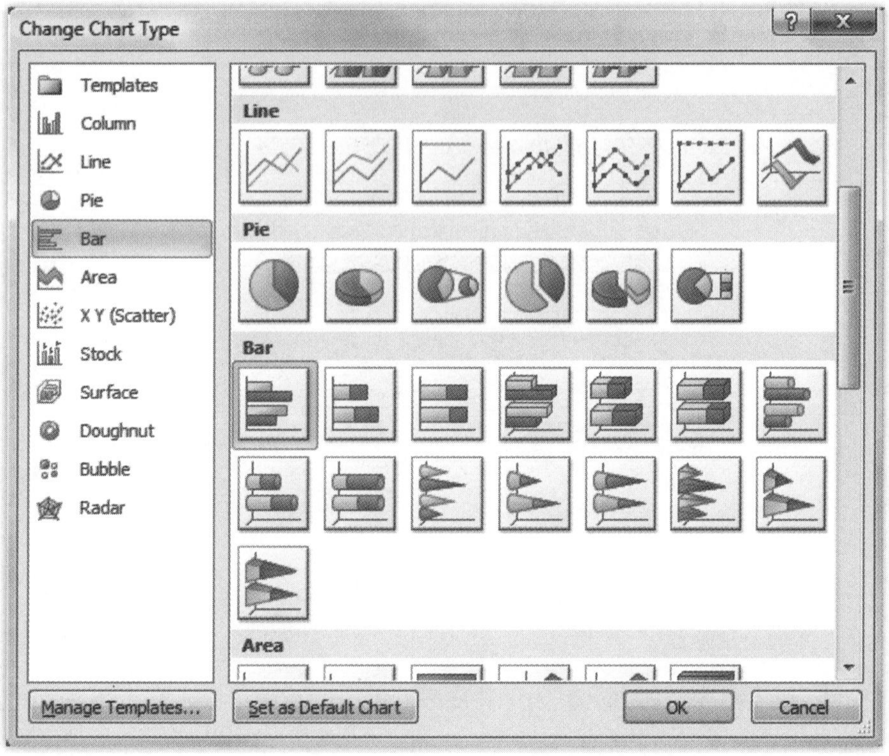

Figure 5.7 Select the Bar chart option in the Change Chat Type dialog box.

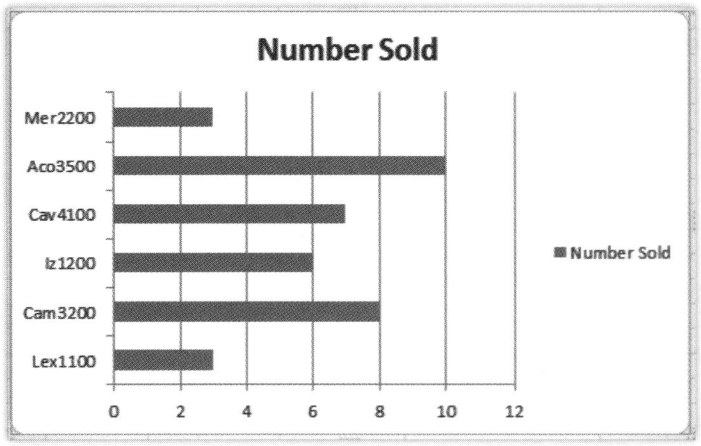

Figure 5.8 The Bar chart of Car Models Sold.

We now show how to change the data source of a chart using Design tools. For example, we want to change the data source of the Bar chart in Figure 5.8 so that it presents Mileage rather than Number Sold. We click on the *Design > Data > Select Data* command on the *Ribbon*. The *Select Data Source* dialog box appears. The Data Range of the bar chart is highlighted (see Figure 5.9). A ***Data Range*** is the range of cells that we highlight when we initially created the chart. The following is the *Data Range* of the chart:

= *'New Example'!$B$4:$B$10, 'New Example'!$E$4:$E$10*

We now change the Data Range as follows:

= *'New Example'!$B$4:$B$10, 'New Example'!$D$4:$D$10*

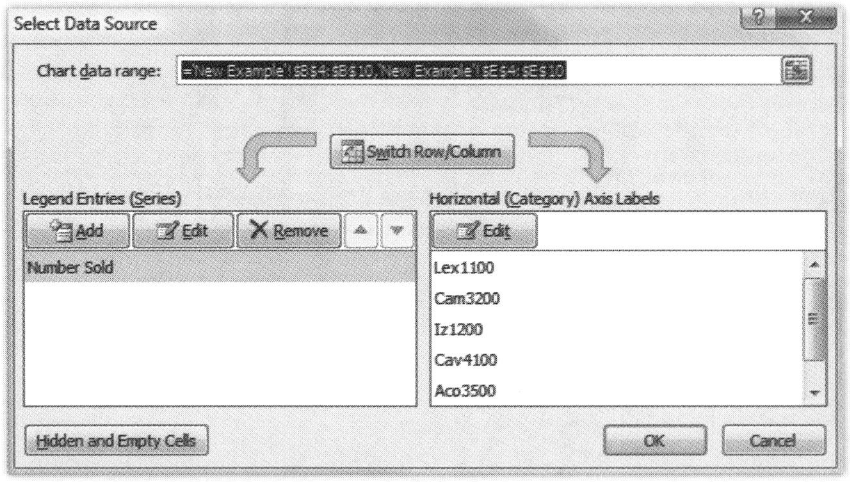

Figure 5.9 We use the Select Data Source dialog box to change the data source of our chart.

You can use the same dialog box to add or remove data ***Series*** from your chart. *Series* are various sets of data. The Series window on the left side of the dialog box lists all the series in a chart. In our chart we currently have only one series called "Number Sold." Let consider that we want to add to the same bar chart a new series of data, the revenues generated by each car model. We select the *Add* button of the *Select Data Source* dialog box. The Edit Series dialog box appears. We add a Name to the new series, and the corresponding range of data using the *Series Name* and *Values* section as in Figure 5.10. The resulting bar chart is in Figure 5.11.

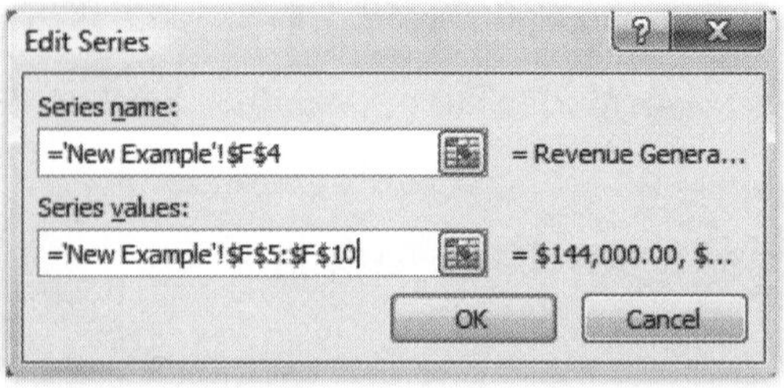

Figure 5.10 We use the Edit Series dialog box to add revenues series to the data source of the chart.

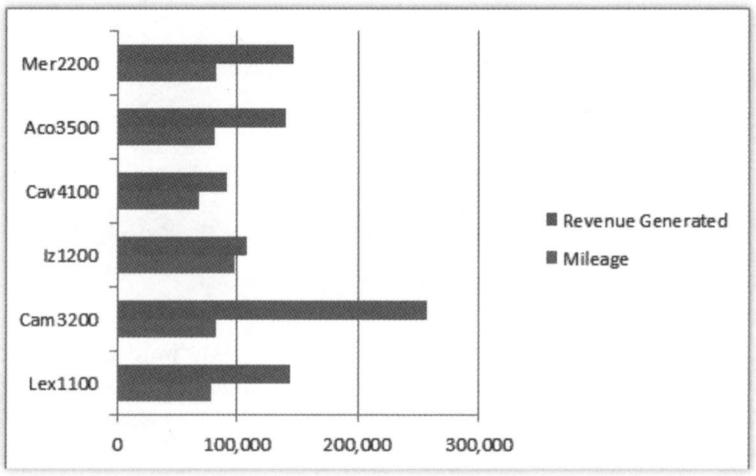

Figure 5.11 The bar chart of mileage and revenues generated per car model.

The *Layout* tools allow us to modify chart labels, axes, gridlines, background, etc. For example, the chart in Figure 5.11 does not have chart and axes title. To add axes title you select Layout > *Labels* > Axis Titles. Next, select *Primary Horizontal Axis Title* from the drop-down list. In the flyout window that appears select *Title Below Axis* option as shown in Figure 5.12. A textbox will appear in the chart where you now type "Revenue/Mileage." You can assign the title "Car Models" to the vertical axis following similar steps. You can add a title above the chart by selecting the Layout > *Labels* > *Chart Title* command on the Ribbon. Figure 5.13 presents the result of the changes made to the bar chart.

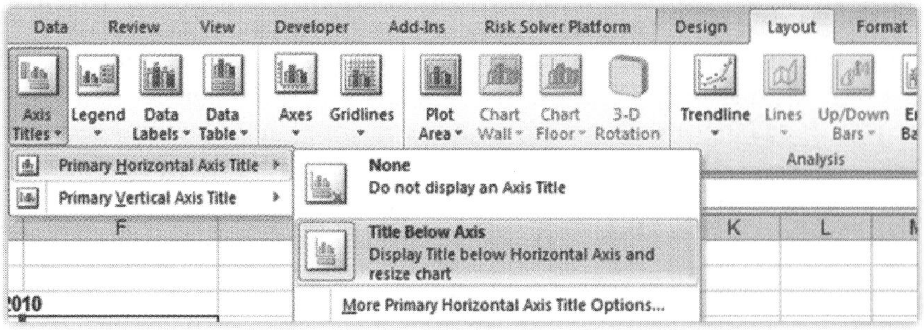

Figure 5.12 Use the Layout tab commands to add a title below the horizontal axis of the chart.

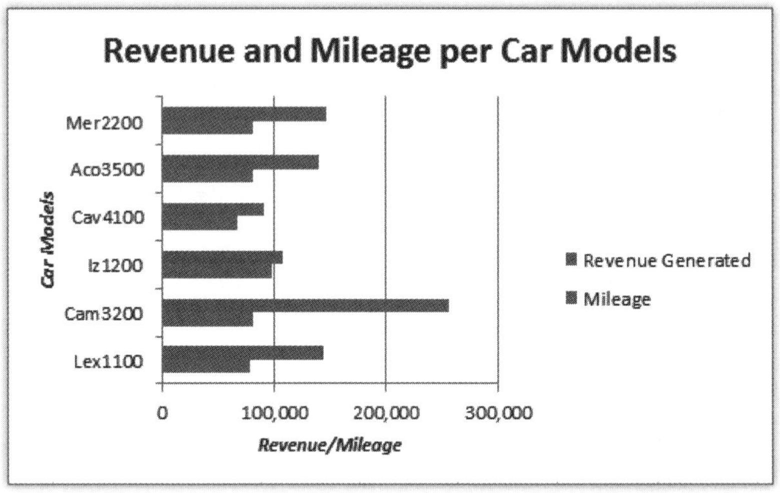

Figure 5.13 We have added chart and axes titles to the bar chart.

The *Format* tools allow us to modify chart size, shape style, word art style, etc. We can use these tools to also modify the general patterns, font, and properties of the chart. The easiest way to customize the *Format* of a chart is by double-clicking on a chart element to display the corresponding dialog box. For example, if we double-click on the main plot of the chart, the *Format Chart Area* dialog box appears (see Figure 5.14) that allows us to change chart fill color and transparency, border color, border style, etc. We can also double-click on the elements of the chart, including points, lines, and bars, axis, titles, etc. to change their existing format. For example, we can change point shapes, line styles, colors, and views of our data series. We can also right-click on the chart area to evoke the short-cut menu and mini toolbar that list options one can use to work with the chart.

To *Format Axis*, we can select the x-axis or y-axis (or z-axis if we have a 3D chart) and double-click. The dialog box that appears presents us with options to change number type, fill type, line color and style, etc. The *Axis Options* of this dialog box can be very useful if we are trying to "zoom-in" on or "zoom-out" of the data. For example, in Figure 5.15 we show how to change the maximum value of x-axis to 270,000. Gridlines can be formatted by double-clicking on any of the gridlines in the chart. The *Format Gridlines* dialog box that appears gives you options to modify line color, style etc. Remember, we can choose which gridlines to have on our chart using the options listed in Layout > Axes > Gridlines. The chart title, axis labels, legend fonts, and text can also be modified by directly clicking on them.

Figure 5.14 This dialog box appears when we double click on the chart.

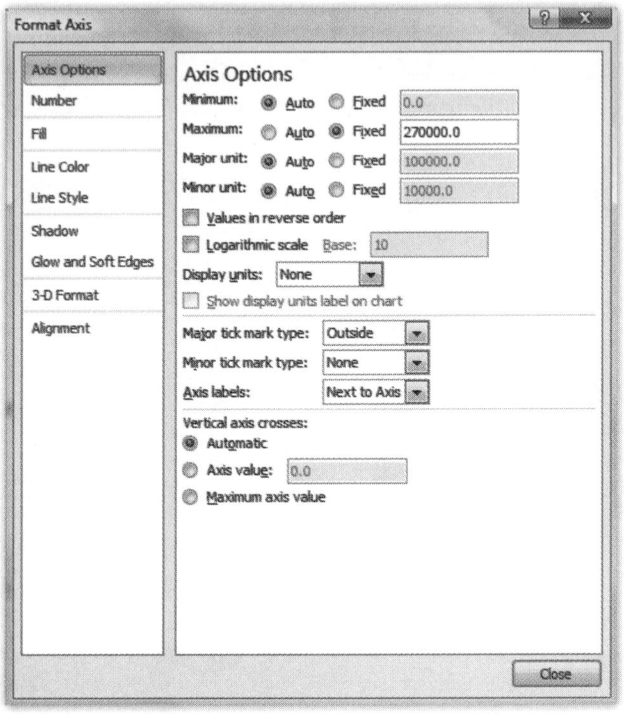

Figure 5.15 Use this dialog box to change the format of chart axis.

Chart Tools of Excel offer other options beneficial for complicated data or charting specifications. Let's look at another example to explore some of these options. Consider an experiment that measures the growth of a plant relative to the amount of minerals added to or removed from the surrounding soil. The data recorded from this experiment is provided in Figure 5.16. To graph this data, we highlight the values in *B3:C22* and click on *Insert > Charts >Scatter.*

	A	B	C
1			
2			
3		Growth	Minerals
4		-1000	-10
5		-512	-8
6		-343	-7
7		-216	-6
8		-125	-5
9		-64	-4
10		-27	-3
11		-8	-2
12		-1	-1
13		0	0
14		1	1
15		8	2
16		27	3
17		64	4
18		125	5
19		216	6
20		343	7
21		512	8
22		1000	10

Figure 5.16 The data in this table represents plant growth rates as impacted by mineral levels in the soil.

From the list of *Scatter Chart types select the Scatter with Smooth Lines and Markers option* (see Figure 5.17). Note that our *Data Range* contains our column titles as well. Therefore, our series is named automatically, and the name is listed in the legend of the chart as in Figure 5.18.

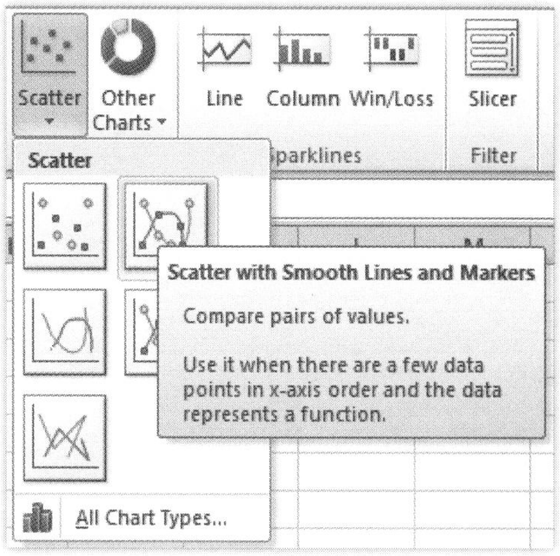

Figure 5.17 We selected a Scatter chart with smooth lines and markers connecting the data points.

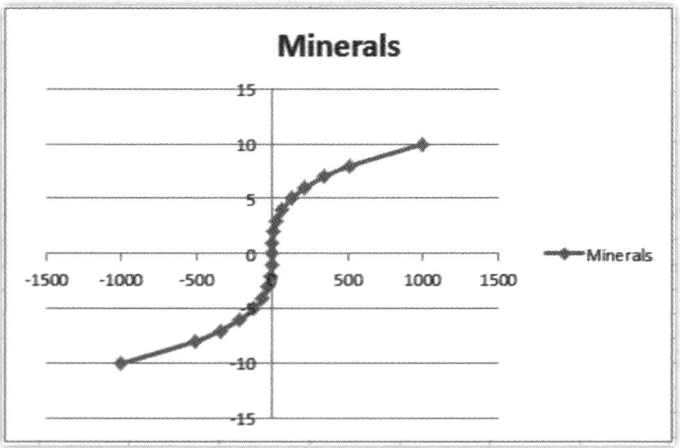

Figure 5.18 The resulting scatter chart.

We only have one series of data, the "Minerals" level, so we do not need to show this in a legend next to our graph. Therefore, we delete the legend by selecting it and clicking on the *Delete* keyboard key. We may also decide to remove all of the gridlines from the graph. We can do this by selecting *Layout > Axes > Gridlines* command from the *Ribbon*. In the flyout menu that appears upon the selection of *Vertical or Horizontal Gridlines*, select *None*, as shown in Figure 5.19.

After analyzing the data relationship shown in the graph, we may decide that the growth progress would be clearer if the mineral levels were shown as the x-values and the growth amounts were shown as the y-values. To make this switch, we select *Design > Data > Select Data* command from the *Ribbon*. In the *Select Data Source* dialog box that appears, we select "Minerals" from the list of series on the left and then click on the *Edit* button. The Edit dialog box initially presents the current data selected for the x- and y-values (see Figure 5.20a). We can redefine this data by clicking on the x-value box, highlighting the "Minerals" column from our table, and then clicking the y-value box and highlighting the "Growth" column. We have now switched the x- and y-values for the chart (see Figure 5.20b).

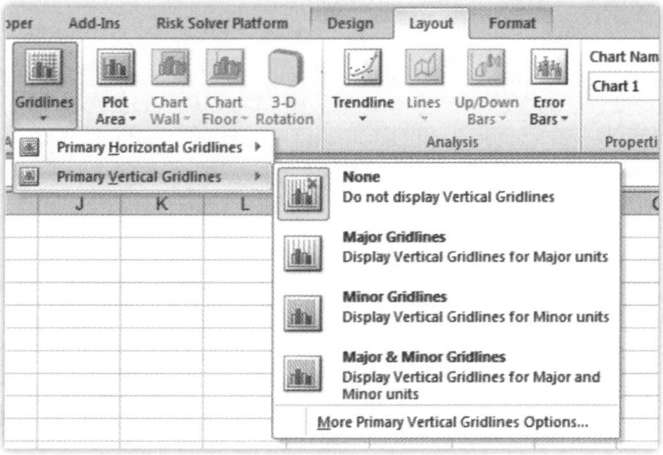

Figure 5.19 Use the options listed in the flyout menu to remove gridlines from the scatter chart.

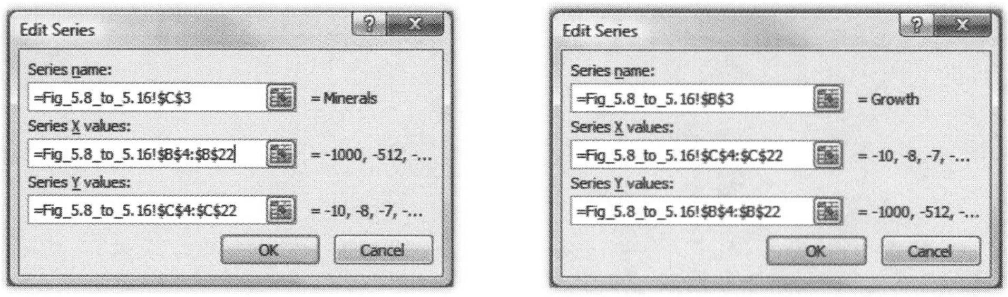

(a) **(b)**

Figure 5.20 (a) The x-values are the growth and the y-values are the mineral levels. (b) The x-values are now the mineral levels and the y-values are now the growth.

We now click *OK* and observe that Excel has updated our chart (see Figure 5.21).

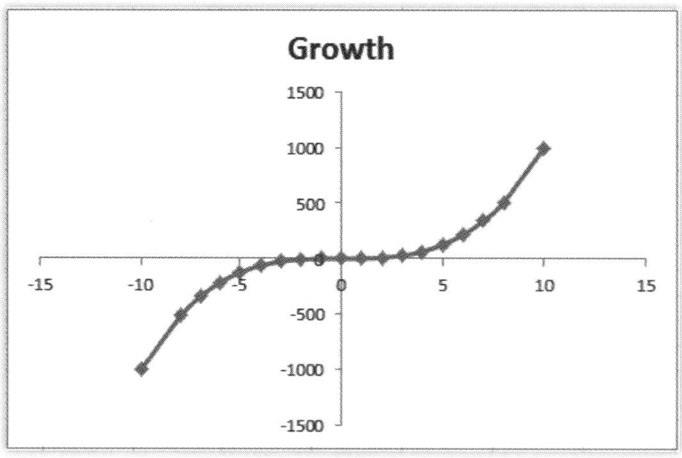

Figure 5.21 The chart is updated to reflect the new x-values as mineral levels and the new y-values as growth amounts.

The Excel *Chart Tools* allow us to define many features of a chart. It is important to make sure that we represent our data clearly so that Excel can easily conduct analysis. The chart is an important part of the spreadsheet application, and we recommend that you now familiarize yourself with all of its options.

5.4 *Creating Sparklines*

Sparklines are small charts displayed in a single cell. *Sparklines* are useful as allow you to spot trends and variations in the data without having to create a chart. The difference between a sparkline and a chart is that a sparkline uses only one series of data, and is displayed inside one single cell.

Suppose that we want to identify trends in production and sales during the last few years using the data in Figure 5.22. We first create a "Production" sparkline. We start by highlighting the cells *C4:C11*. To insert a *Column Sparkline* we select *Insert > Sparklines > Column* command from the *Ribbon*. In the *Create Sparklines* dialog box (see Figure 5.23) we select cell C13 to be the *Location Range* for the "Production" sparkline. Similarly, we highlight cells D4:D11 to create a sparkline of the unit cost, and select D13 to be the Location Range of the sparkline. The resulting sparklines are shown in Figure 5.22.

	A	B	C	D
1				
2				
3		Year	Production	Unit Cost
4		2002	64,000	$3,700
5		2003	70,000	$3,416
6		2004	100,000	$3,125
7		2005	150,000	$2,583
8		2006	175,000	$2,166
9		2007	400,000	$1,833
10		2008	785,000	$1,788
11		2009	1,000,000	$1,653
12				
13				

Figure 5.22 Column sparklines show an increase in production and decrease in unit cost in the last few years.

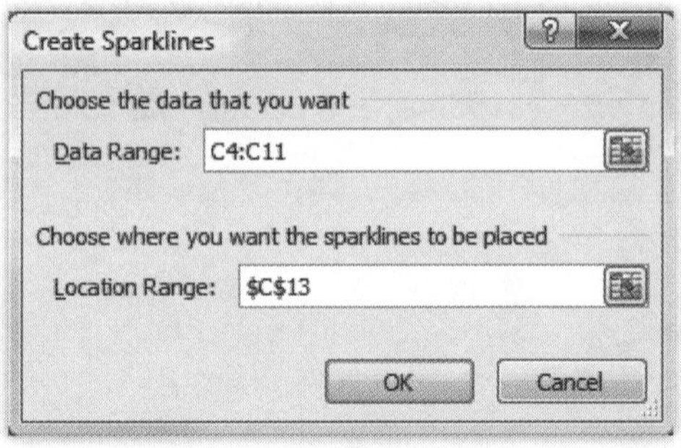

Figure 5.23 Use Location Range window to select the cell where the sparkline will be located.

The *Sparkline Design* contextual tab displays a number of commands we can use to customize a sparkline. We can change the type of the sparklines in Figure 5.22 from column to line by selecting *Sparkline Design > Type > Line* command. We can highlight the highest points of a sparkline by selecting the *Sparkline Design > Show > High Point checkbox.* We can change the color of a sparkline by selecting a color from the options listed in *Sparkline Design > Style > Sparkline Color window.* We have enlarged the size of cells C13 and D13 in Figure 5.24 so it is easy for you to see the design changes made to the sparklines.

Conditional Formatting as well offers simple tools to chart your data. The three *conditional formatting* options that display graphics (data bars, color scales and icon sets) are listed in the *Home > Styles > Conditional Formatting* drop-down menu on the *Ribbon*. For example, the *Data Bars Conditional Format* displays horizontal bars directly in a cell. The length of a bar depends on the value in the cell, relative to the values on other cells within the selected range. Suppose we want to conditional format cells C4:C11 in Figure 5.22 using Data Bars. We highlight cells C4:C11, then select Gradient Fill option of the Data Bars flyout menu (see Figure 5.25). We select the Four Bar Rating option of the Icon Sets flyout menu to format cells D4:D11.

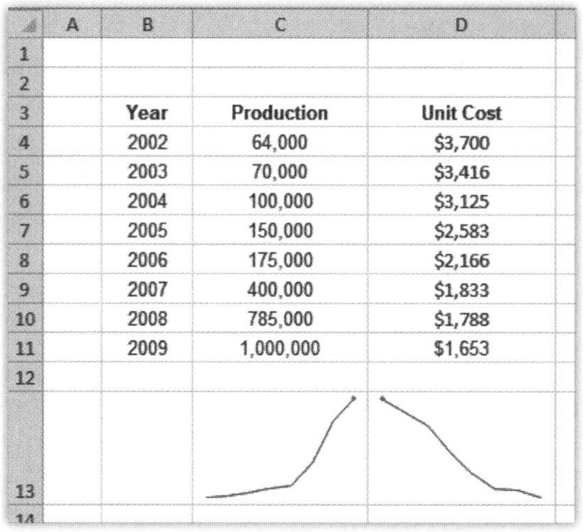

	A	B	C	D
1				
2				
3		Year	Production	Unit Cost
4		2002	64,000	$3,700
5		2003	70,000	$3,416
6		2004	100,000	$3,125
7		2005	150,000	$2,583
8		2006	175,000	$2,166
9		2007	400,000	$1,833
10		2008	785,000	$1,788
11		2009	1,000,000	$1,653
12				
13				

Figure 5.24 The highest point of these line sparklines are highlighted, and line color has changed.

As you can tell from Figures 5.24 and 5.26, sparklines and conditional formatting tools are quick alternatives to creating charts.

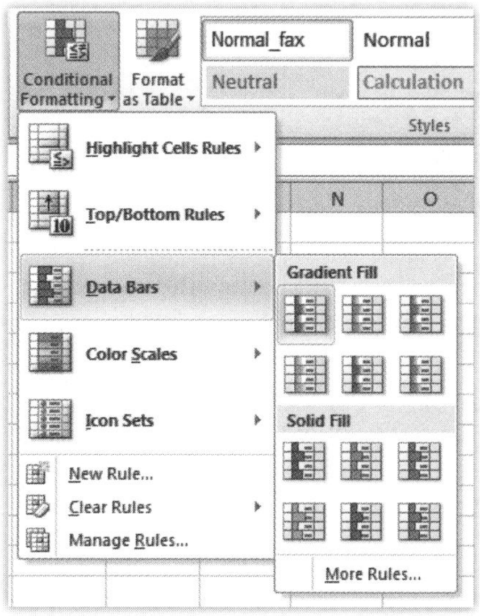

Figure 5.25 The Gradient Fill option from the Data Bars flyout menu is selected to format cells C4:C11.

	A	B	C	D
1				
2				
3		Year	Production	Unit Cost
4		2002	64,000	$3,700
5		2003	70,000	$3,416
6		2004	100,000	$3,125
7		2005	150,000	$2,583
8		2006	175,000	$2,166
9		2007	400,000	$1,833
10		2008	785,000	$1,788
11		2009	1,000,000	$1,653

Figure 5.26 The length of the data bar in each cell of column C is proportional to the production amount. The number of bars highlighted in each cell of column D is proportional to unit cost.

Summary

Creating a Line Sparkline

Step 1: Select the data range.

Step 2: Select Insert > Sparklines > Line.

Step 3: Type the address of the cell where the sparkline will be located.

5.5 *Creating Dynamic Charts and Sparklines*

A chart is linked directly to the *Data Range* specified when creating the chart. If any points in this range of data are modified, the chart is automatically updated to reflect a new corresponding data point. In reality, we could specify an empty range as the Data Range if we created the chart before the data was entered into the spreadsheet. The chart would then be updated as new data was entered. In VBA, we will see how to perform these actions automatically so that the user can observe a chart being created one data point at a time. However, before we learn any VBA coding, we should use some Excel functions we have already learned to create a ***dynamic chart***. Similarly, ***dynamic sparklines*** are automatically updated when points in the data range are modified.

We will use three main Excel concepts to create a dynamic chart and a dynamic sparkline: defining names, the OFFSET function, and the COUNT function. We will first use the OFFSET and COUNT functions to create some range names and then set the *Series* of the chart to these ***dynamic ranges***. We will use the following example to demonstrate this process. Figure 5.27 features production data that records the "Units Sold" for each month of the past year. We have created a *Scatter Chart* for this data using the *Insert > Charts > Scatter* command from the *Ribbon*. In this figure, the *Source Data* is currently linked to the range *B4:C15*. We have also created a line sparkline in cell E16 by first highlighting C4:C15 and then selecting *Insert > Sparklines > Line* command from the *Ribbon*.

Our first step is to create two dynamic ranges: one for "Months" and one for "Units Sold." By creating these dynamic ranges, we ensure that our range names include new data points as they are entered into either column of the table. We therefore use the OFFSET and COUNT functions in the following manner:

= *OFFSET(initial_data_location, 0, 0, COUNT(entire_column), 1)*

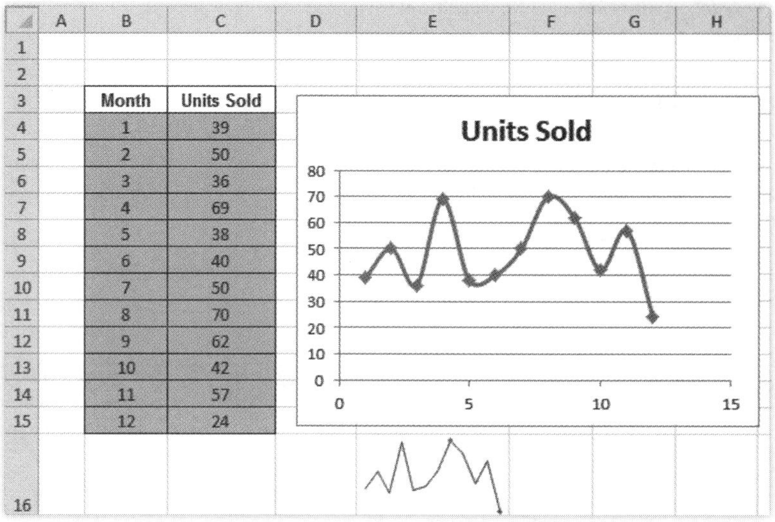

Figure 5.27 The original data, chart and sparkline (in cell E16); the chart and sparkline are currently not dynamic.

The *rows_to_move* and *columns_to_move* parameters are set to 0 because we are only interested in the column in which our *reference_cell* (= *initial_data_location*) is located. The *width* is again set to 1, since we are interested only in one column. The *height* parameter is found using the COUNT function. The COUNT function reviews the entire column of the relative data and counts how many cells have numeric values. So, the *height* of our range becomes dynamic as the amount of numeric values in the column increases.

We now create two dynamic ranges, named "Months" and "UnitsSold," with the *Define Name* command. In the *Refers To* window of this dialog box, we use the above functions as follows:

= OFFSET(B4, 0, 0, COUNT(B:B), 1) *for Month*
= OFFSET(C4, 0, 0, COUNT(C:C), 1) *for UnitsSold*

In the *New Name* dialog box, we also use sheet names and absolute referencing (see Figure 5.28).

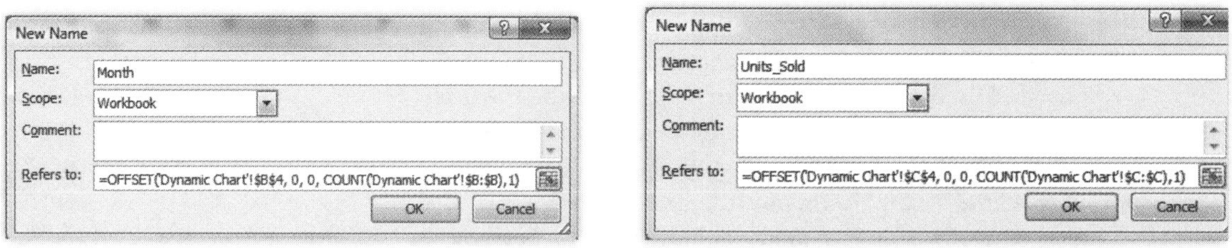

(a) **(b)**

Figure 5.28 Defining the dynamic ranges using the OFFSET and COUNT functions.

Now, we can simply use these dynamic range names to define our data range. We click on the already-created chart to activate the Chart Tools contextual tabs, and choose *Design > Data > Select Data*. We then select "Units Sold" series from the *Series* list on the left side of the dialog box, and click on the *Edit* button. In the *Edit Series* dialog box we modify the *X Values* and *Y Values* of chart series. Using the workbook name, we place the dynamic ranges in their corresponding windows as follows (see Figure 5.29):

= *WorkbookName.xlsx!Month*
= *WorkbookName.xlsx!UnitsSold*

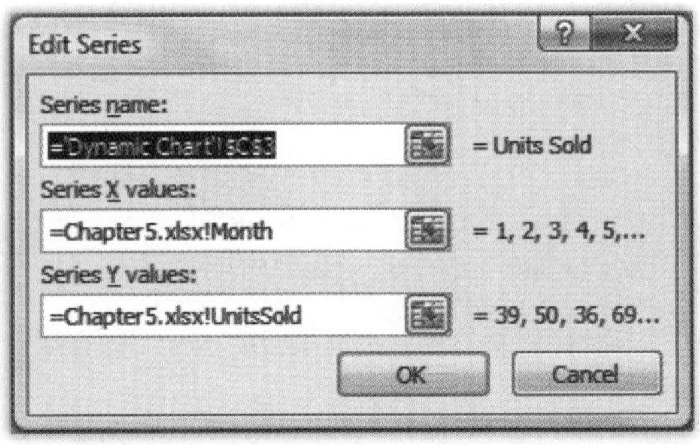

Figure 5.29 Entering the dynamic ranges as the corresponding series values of the chart.

To create the dynamic sparkline we select *Sparkline Design > Sparkline > Edit Data* command on the *Ribbon*. In the Data Range window of the dialog box that appears, we type the name of the dynamic range (see Figure 5.30).

Now, if we enter data for sequential months in the data table, the chart is updated automatically. In Figure 5.31, we have added data for months 13 to 16; without modifying the data range again, the chart and the sparkline are updated to reflect the values of these new points. We have therefore created a dynamic chart and sparkline.

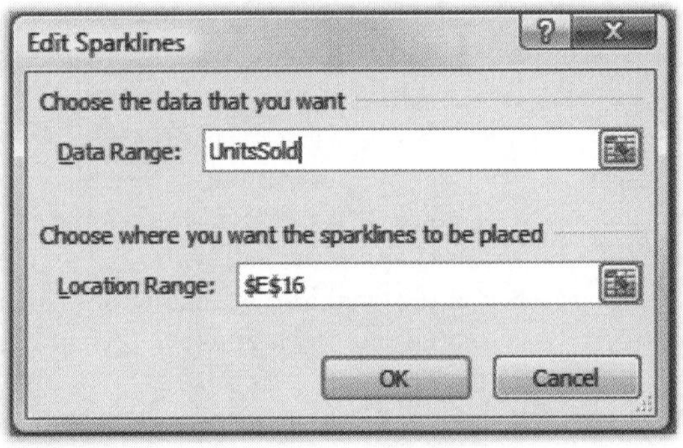

Figure 5.30 Entering the dynamic ranges as the corresponding series values of the sparkline.

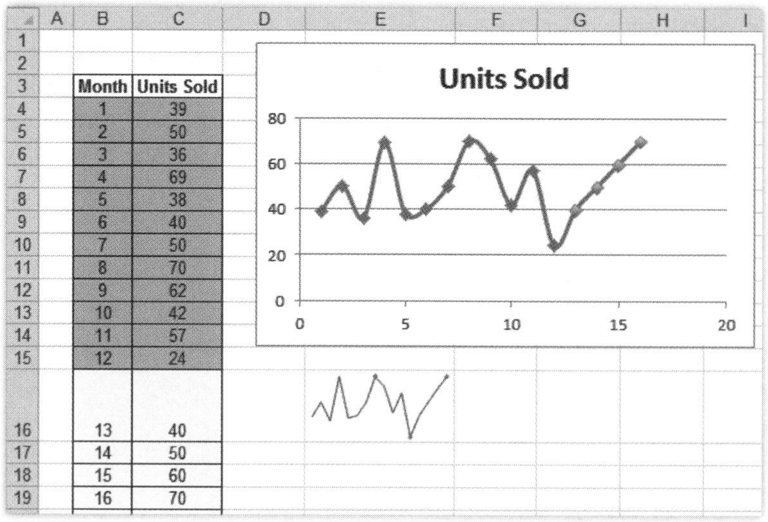

Figure 5.31 The dynamic chart and sparkline are now created. As new data values are entered, the chart and sparkline are automatically updated.

5.6 *Summary*

- Excel Charts and Sparklines allow us to illustrate data in order to perform better analysis. When using charts and sparklines, you should understand Data Ranges, Ranges, and Series.
- A Data Range is the group of cells selected to create a chart. A Range is any group of cells that forms a row, column, or area.
- Series are various sets of data. We can modify the number of series and the data sources for each series using the Select Data Source dialog Box.
- These are the basic steps to create a Chart:
  Step 1: Select the data range.
  Step 2: Select a chart type from the list in Insert > Charts group of the Ribbon.
  Step 3: Determine the Chart Sub-type from the corresponding drop-down list.
- There are two ways to modify a chart after it is created: by using the commands listed on the charts contextual tabs; and by using the dialog box that appears when double-clicking on the chart or different parts of the chart. We can change basic settings as well as formatting.
- The Data Range and Series can be modified to further manipulate the presentation of data.
- A sparkline is a small charts displayed in a single cell. *Sparklines* are useful as allow you to spot trends and variations in the data without having to create a chart.
- The difference between a sparkline and a chart is that a sparkline uses only one series of data, and is displayed inside one single cell.
- These are the basic steps to create a Line Sparkline:
  Step 1: Select the data range.
  Step 2: Select Insert > Sparklines > Line.
  Step 3: Type the address of the cell where the sparkline will be located.
- Conditional formatting options (such as, data bars, color scales and icon sets) offers simple tools to chart your data.
- A dynamic chart and sparkline can be created using the OFFSET and COUNT functions to create dynamic ranges used as *Series* in the *Source Data*.

5.7 *Exercises*

5.7.1 Review Questions

1. List ten different types of charts that can be created in Excel.
2. Why is it useful to create charts in Excel?
3. What is the Data Range of a chart?
4. How does one create a Chart in Excel?
5. What is a sparkline? Why sparklines are useful tools in Excel?
6. How many data series are needed in order to create a stock chart? In what order should the series be arranged? Give an example of when one can use this chart type.
7. What options of Conditional Formatting display graphics?
8. How can you move a chart to a new sheet?
9. How can the source data of a chart be modified after the chart has been created?
10. How is a chart different from a sparkline?
11. Can the scale of Gridlines be changed?
12. What is a dynamic chart? What is a dynamic sparkline?
13. What is a dynamic range?
14. How do you change the color of a series of data on a chart?

5.7.2 Hands-On Exercises

NOTE: *Please refer to the file "Chapter_05_Exercises.xlsx" for the associated worksheets noted for the hands-on exercises. The file is available at: www.dssbooks.com.*

1. Consider the spreadsheet created in Chapter 4, Hands-On Exercise 8. Using the Insert > Chart group on the Ribbon to create a line chart that plots velocity and average acceleration versus time. Use the commands listed in Chart Contextual Tabs to give each series an appropriate label and place the chart legend at the bottom of the table. Title the chart "Velocity and Acceleration of a Moving Object" and label the x-axis "Time (s)." Add two line sparklines to your spreadsheet, one for Velocity and one for Avg. Acceleration. (Refer to worksheet "5.1".)
2. Using the set S defined in Chapter 4, Hands-On Exercise 2, create the following series plots of the values in S: (Refer to worksheet "5.2".)
   - A scatter plot.
   - A line plot with nodes.
   - A line plot without nodes.
3. Create a table of x- and y-values for the equation $y = e^x$ using the following values for x: 0, 1, 2, 4, 6, 8, 10, 12, 14 and 16. Create a scatter chart of the data with the points connected by a smooth line. Locate the chart on the spreadsheet. (Refer to worksheet "5.3".)
   - **a.** Describe the curvature of the line. Is it convex up or convex down?
   - **b.** Change the y-axis to a logarithmic scale. Is the line concave up or concave down?
4. A table is used to monitor the performance of workers at a manufacturing plant. Create a bar chart and a scatter chart of the data in the table using the values in the "Worker Name" column as the values along the x-axis. Use Conditional Formatting > Bar Chart option to add graphics to each column of data. Also, create a line sparkline for each column of data. Try changing values in the data table and notice how the graphs, chart, and sparkline change accordingly. (Refer to worksheet "5.4".)
5. In the bar chart created in problem 4, perform the following.
   - **a.** Change the color of the data series.
   - **b.** Change the scale of the y-Axis.
   - **c.** Display all data points.
6. Using your solution to Chapter 4, Hands-On Exercise 3, plot the heights of a cylinder versus the radii for the given volume. To best depict the data, display the results in the form of cylinders of various heights. Label the x-axis: Radius (ft)″ and the series "Height." Title the chart "Height of a Cylinder with Volume = 10 ft^3." (Refer to worksheet "5.6".)
7. A materials engineer is comparing various properties of ceramics to determine which is the most appropriate for use in a car engine. The ideal material will exhibit a high fracture toughness (in MPa·$m^{1/2}$), a high tensile strength (in MPa), and a low thermal conductivity (in W/m·K). The

engineer tests each of the materials and obtains the following results. (Refer to worksheet "5.7".)

- Materials A, B, C, D, E, F, and G have a fracture toughness of 3, 3.5, 3.2, 2.7, 3.9, 3.2 and 2.6 MPa·m1/2, respectively.
- Materials A, B, C, D, E, F, and G have tensile strengths of 270, 253, 285, 246, 279, 285 and 260 MPa, respectively.
- Materials A, B, C, D, E, F, and G have thermal conductivities of 29, 33, 37, 41, 25, 40 and 27 W/m·K, respectively.

For this application, tensile strength is the most important property, followed by fracture toughness, and then thermal conductivity. Use Excel to create a chart that illustrates this data. Select the most appropriate chart type and justify your selection. Your chart should assist the engineer in making a final material selection.

8. A table displays the high, low, and closing prices for stock XYZ on the 15th of each month in the year 2011.
- Create sparklines to identify trends on the values of High Price, Low Price, and Closing Price.
- Create a stock chart to depict this information. Display the date on the x-axis and the price on the y-axis. Title the chart "Stock Prices for XYZ in 2011." Do not show a legend. (Refer to worksheet "5.8".)

9. Given that Series 1 equals the set {56, 49, 52, 45, 40, 55, 58} and Series 2 equals the set {23, 24, 32, 26, 26, 19, 29}, create the following 3-dimensional charts to plot the two series. (Refer to worksheet "5.9".)
- A surface chart
- A 3-dimensional line chart
- A stacked 3-dimensional area chart

10. In the above problem, which chart was best suited for the data? What scaling limitations, if any, did you find for different chart types? What happens if you plot by rows instead of columns?

11. Now suppose that the two series given in Hands-On Exercise 9 represent the high and low temperatures for each day of a week in February. Use sparklines and conditional formatting to depict trends within high and low temperatures, as well as between high and low temperatures. (Refer to worksheet "5.11".)

12. A team of industrial engineers is conducting a productivity study of workers at a manufacturing plant. By observing workers at random times throughout the day, the team is able to use statistical tools to estimate the percent of time the workers spend performing different activities. The categories "Direct Work," "Indirect Work," "Travel," "Breaks," and "Other" comprise the workers' activities. A table displays the team's results in terms of the percent of time workers were observed doing each activity for one week. (Refer to worksheet "5.12".)

a. Create a separate pie chart for each day of the week that depicts the percent of time workers spent doing each activity.

b. Also, create a pie chart of the overall percent of time spent doing each activity for the entire week.

c. On each chart, display data labels of the percentages represented by each section of the pie.

d. On which day was "Travel" the highest?

e. On Thursday, in which category was the most time spent?

f. When did "Direct Work" time exceed "Indirect Work" time?

13. Use sparklines to identify trends within each category of data as well as between categories of data in problem 5.12. Interpret the results.

14. The industrial engineering team in Hands-On Exercise 12 now wants to compare the types of activities done on each day of the week on a single graph. Use a doughnut graph to plot the activity distributions for each day of the week on a single graph. Determine which ring of the doughnut represents which day of the week. (Refer to worksheet "5.14".)

15. A spreadsheet is used to compare five different cities in terms of the overall population, population per square mile, and total land area occupied by the city. Create a bubble chart of this data that displays the total population on the x-axis, the population per square mile on the y-axis, and the area of the city as the size of the bubble. Title this chart "Population and Size Comparisons of Five Cities" and label the x- and y-axis appropriately. (Refer to worksheet "5.15".)

16. Plot the series of future cash flows from Chapter 4, *Hands-On Exercise 4* as a column chart. Do not show labels on the x-axis. Title the series "Cash Flow Amount" and show the legend on the left of the chart. Label the amount of each cash flow (with currency symbols) by the corresponding bar. Finally, title the chart "Cash Flow Summary." (Refer to worksheet "5.16".)

17. The manager of a production facility closely monitors the energy consumption of the facility. As the number of units produced in the facility increases, the amount of energy consumed also increases. The manager uses the forecasted demand for upcoming months to predict the number of units that will be produced and the resulting energy costs that should be included in the budget. A table is used to display her predictions for demand and energy consumption. (Refer to worksheet "5.17".)

a. Plot this data on an area chart titled "Demand-Based Predictions of Energy Consumption."

b. Display months on the x-axis and consumption on the y-axis.

c. Label the y-axis "Consumption (kWh)."

d. Display major vertical gridlines and locate the legend above the chart.

e. Format the chart so that the area under the demand curve is green, the area under the consumption curve is red, and the plot background is white.

f. Add sparklines to identify trends in units and energy consumption per month.

18. A company is comparing the expected sales figures of three different products it produces to the actual sales of those products. (Refer to worksheet "5.18".)

a. Plot this information as a line chart with nodes titled "Product Sales: Expected vs. Actual."

b. Depict each product as a separate series. The x-axis should represent the type of sales (expected or actual) and the y-axis should represent the amount of sales.

c. Label the y-axis "Sales ($)."

d. For each series, label the nodes with the appropriate values.

e. Display a legend to the right of the chart.

Which product had the highest expected sales? Which product had the lowest actual sales?

19. In a given table, the average stock returns for a portfolio are stored for various quarters. Create a chart for this data and answer the following questions. (Refer to worksheet "5.19".)

a. At what time was the portfolio value highest?

b. At what time was the portfolio value lowest?

c. What period of time (year and quarter) had the best average portfolio value?

d. Does there seem to be a trend in this data? That is, can you guess what the next quarter's value will be?

e. Do all chart types work well with this data? Can you identify a single chart type that is best suited for this data?

20. Management is trying to track a trend in sales so that each month's inventory can be better forecasted. Create a dynamic chart for the given data and enter the following new data points. (Refer to worksheet "5.20".)

What trends can be observed from this data?

21. Consider the data in problem 5.20. Create a dynamic sparkline to identify trends in monthly sales. Add new data point to your data set and observe how the sparkline changes. Do you see any difference between this sparkline and the chart created in problem 5.20?

22. Plot the following functions. (Refer to worksheet "5.21".)

a. $y = \ln(x)$ for $1 \leq x \leq 100$.

b. $y = ex$ for $1 \leq x \leq 10$.

c. $y = \sin(x)$ for $0 \leq x \leq 360$.

d. $y = \tan(x)$ for $0 \leq x \leq 360$.

23. Consider Chapter 3, Hands-On Exercise 21. Create a line chart to graph the interest payments and amount paid in the course of five years. (Refer to worksheet "5.23".)

a. Do you see any trend in the amount of interest paid in each payment?

b. Do you see any trend on the principal amount paid in each payment?

c. Title the chart and label the x-axis.

d. Place the legend in the top of the chart.

e. Name the series of data.

24. Consider Chapter 3, Hands-On Exercise 21. Create a doughnut chart to present the interest payments and amount paid in the course of five years. Each ring of the doughnut should represent a payment. Name each data series. Determine which ring of the doughnut presents a particular payment. Why do you think this chart would be useful? (Refer to worksheet "5.24".)

25. An athlete is planning to buy his daily vitamins. He is concerned about taking the right amount of vitamins C, A, E and B1. In the drug store, he found four different brand names (brand name X, Y, Z and W). Brand X contains 50% of the daily value (DV) for Vitamin C, 25% of DV for Vitamin A, 15% of DV for Vitamin E, and 20% of DV for Vitamin B1. Brand Y contains 30% of DV for Vitamin C, 20% of DV for Vitamin A, 10% of DV for Vitamin E, and 5% of DV for Vitamin B1. Brand Z contains 45% of DV for Vitamin C, 25% of DV for Vitamin A, 25% of DV for Vitamin E, and 15% of DV for Vitamin B1. Brand W contains 40% of DV for Vitamin C, 10% of DV for Vitamin A, 30% of DV for Vitamin E, and 10% of DV for Vitamin B1. Create a radar chart to identify the brand with the highest vitamin content. (Refer to worksheet "5.25".)

CHAPTER

six Pivot Tables

chapter OVERVIEW

6.1 *Introduction*

This chapter instructs the reader on how to create pivot tables and pivot charts. We have found that even experienced Excel users are not familiar with the benefits of using these tools. Pivot tables and pivot charts are a great tool for organizing large amounts of data in a format which is clearer for the user to understand. They can be useful tools for displaying large amounts of output to a user in a DSS application and enabling the user to filter this data easily. For example, in the Supply Chain Management DSS application (available in www.dssbooks.com) we use several pivot tables and pivot charts to present the output of the application to the user. The user is able to view production and shipment results for various products, factories, and customers using the filtering options available in pivot tables and pivot charts. We will also discuss how to create pivot tables and pivot charts using VBA in Chapter 21.

In this chapter, the reader will learn how to:

- Create a pivot table.
- Filter for data using slicers and other pivot table features.
- Customize a pivot table using several structural and formatting options.
- Perform advance filters using grouping, calculated fields, and the GETPIVOTDATA function.
- Transform a pivot table into a pivot chart.
- Filter data using a pivot chart.

6.2 *Pivot Tables*

Pivot tables are used to transform large amounts of data from a table or database into an organized summary report. The word "pivot" refers to the ability to rotate and reorganize the row and column headings from an original database into a new table. We will now explain the parts of a pivot table and show how to create one.

The table in Figure 6.1 contains the "Costs" for varying "Maximum Weights" and the number of "Days to Arrive" for two different "Shipping Companies." Suppose that an employee is assigned the task of comparing the performance of these shipping companies and presenting the results to his manager. The employee wants to summarize this data so that a clear comparison can be made between the "Cost" values of each company. We can observe in this table that there are three common values of "Max Weight" (*5*, *20* and, *20+*) and four common values for "Days to Arrive" (*1, 2, 4, and 8*); therefore, the "Cost" values can be compared for each of these common "Max Weight" and "Days to Arrive" values. That is, in reorganizing the table by these common values, the manager can see what the "Costs" of the varying companies are for a given combination of "Max Weight" and "Days to Arrive."

Figure 6.2 displays the final reorganized table, a pivot table. Observe that the common values for "Max Weight" are only shown once and the "Days to Arrive" values are only repeated for each of the "Max Weight" values. This arrangement allows for a higher level of organization than the repetitive nature of the original table. The costs of the two companies are shown comparatively for each combination of "Max Weight" and "Days to Arrive." The "Minimum Cost" for each row and column of data is also revealed. So, the minimum cost of the two companies for each combination of "Max Weight" and "Days to Arrive" can be found in the "Minimum Cost" column.

	A	B	C	D	E
1					
2		**Compare Shipping Companies**			
3		**Shipping Companies**	**Max Weight, lbs**	**Days to Arrive**	**Costs**
4		United Carrier	5	1	$5.00
5		United Carrier	5	2	$3.00
6		United Carrier	5	4	$1.00
7		United Carrier	5	8	$0.50
8		United Carrier	20	1	$25.00
9		United Carrier	20	2	$15.00
10		United Carrier	20	4	$10.00
11		United Carrier	20	8	$5.00
12		United Carrier	20+	1	$45.00
13		United Carrier	20+	2	$35.00
14		United Carrier	20+	4	$25.00
15		United Carrier	20+	8	$20.00
16		International Route	5	1	$4.00
17		International Route	5	2	$3.00
18		International Route	5	4	$1.00
19		International Route	5	8	$0.50
20		International Route	20	1	$23.00
21		International Route	20	2	$14.00
22		International Route	20	4	$10.00
23		International Route	20	8	$5.00
24		International Route	20+	1	$40.00
25		International Route	20+	2	$34.00
26		International Route	20+	4	$23.00
27		International Route	20+	8	$19.00

Figure 6.1 The above data can be used in a comparative experiment, but would be better organized with a pivot table.

	A	B	C	D	E
1					
2					
3	Min of Costs		Shipping Companies		
4	Max Weight, l…	Days to Arrive	International Route	United Carrier	Min Cost
5	⊟5				
6		1	$4.00	$5.00	$4.00
7		2	$3.00	$3.00	$3.00
8		4	$1.00	$1.00	$1.00
9		8	$0.50	$0.50	$0.50
10	⊟20				
11		1	$23.00	$25.00	$23.00
12		2	$14.00	$15.00	$14.00
13		4	$10.00	$10.00	$10.00
14		8	$5.00	$5.00	$5.00
15	⊟20+				
16		1	$40.00	$45.00	$40.00
17		2	$34.00	$35.00	$34.00
18		4	$23.00	$25.00	$23.00
19		8	$19.00	$20.00	$19.00
20	**Min Cost**		**$0.50**	**$0.50**	**$0.50**

Figure 6.2 The final pivot table reorganizes the data so that costs can be easily compared.

6.2.1 Terminology

In this table, "Max Weight" and "Days to Arrive" are referred to as ***Row Fields***; each value in the fields from Figure 6.1 is shown as a row in the pivot table (Figure 6.2). "Shipping Companies" is a ***Column Field***, since its values serve as column headings in the pivot table. These fields are known as category fields as they provide the parameters with which we can categorize the data. The "Cost" values that appear in cells *C6:E20* compose the ***Value Field*** that is used to create the pivot table. The value field contains the numerical data which we are seeking to analyze. The ***Report Field***, a larger category that can group all of the data in the table, would be seen at the top of the worksheet. While we have not selected a report field for this table, an example like "Shipping Regions" would work well.

The "Min Cost" column is an example of the ***Grand Totals*** feature of pivot tables, which we will discuss in more detail in a later section. These costs are computed for each row, this is a ***Row Grand Totals***. The "Min Cost" row at the bottom of the table presents minimum cost values for each column; this is a ***Column Grand Totals***. The title of the table, "Min of Costs," indicates that any *Grand Totals* would calculate minimums of the data in the *Value Field*. The ***Field Settings*** of the *Value Field* determine these data relations. *Field Settings* can also be applied to *Row* or *Column Fields* to create ***Subtotals***; we will also discuss *Subtotals* in more detail in a later section.

There is a drop-down arrow next to each field on the pivot table. In the bottom part of the drop-down dialog box we see a list of all values, called ***Items***, of the corresponding field. For example, if we click on the drop-down arrow next to "Max Weight," we see a list with the values *5*, *20*, and *20+* (see Figure 6.3(a)).

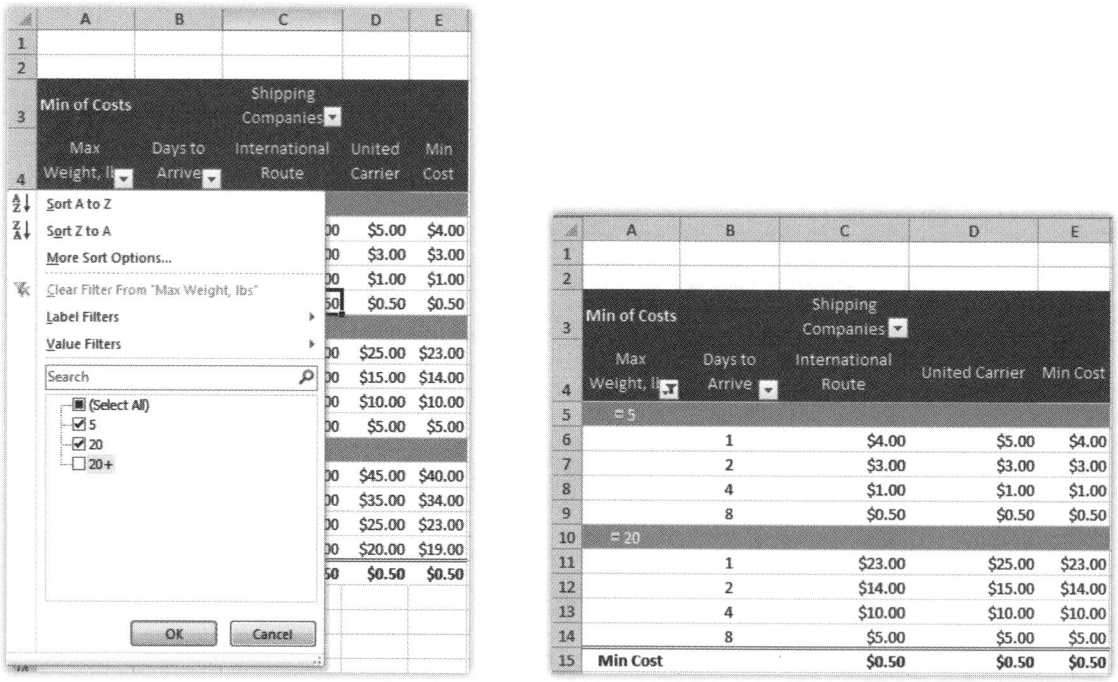

(a) (b)

Figure 6.3 The fields have drop-down lists of their corresponding values that can be selected or deselected to change the pivot table. (a) Deselecting the value 20+ from the "Max Weight" field. (b) The updated pivot table no longer displays data for the 20+ value of "Max Weight."

Using this list, we can select or deselect the values that we want to display in the pivot table. If we deselect *20+* from the drop-down list of "Max Weight" and press *OK* at the bottom of the list, the pivot table no longer displays any data associated with a "Max Weight" of *20+* (see Figure 6.3(b)). This is a great tool for filtering or searching for specific data.

Summary

Row Field	Each value, or item, in this field is shown as a row.
Column Field	Values are shown as column headings.
Report Field	A larger category that can group all data in the table.
Value Field	The main area of the table where comparative values are shown.
Grand Totals	Calculations applied to rows or columns of data in the Data Field.
Subtotals	Calculations applied to Row or Column Fields.
Field Setting	Specified calculations for Grand Totals and Subtotals.
Items	Values within a field.

6.2.2 Creating a Pivot Table

Now we will explain how to create a pivot table. First, we select *Insert > Tables > PivotTable* from the *Ribbon*. The drop-down menu lists two options: *PivotTable* and *PivotChart*. The *PivotChart option* creates a chart with filtering tools similar to those found in pivot tables. We will discuss pivot charts in more detail in a later section. For now, we will choose *the PivotTable option* so that we can recreate the pivot table from the above example. Upon the selection of *PivotTable* option, the window in Figure 6.4 appears. We need to follow three simple steps in order to create a pivot table. The steps are: specify the location of the data that we want to analyze, specify the location where the table will be placed, and create the table.

STEP 1: Data Location This step, as represented in Figure 6.4, asks us to identify the location of the data that we want to analyze. Excel lists two main data location options: *table or range*, and *external data source*. The most common data location is a *Microsoft Excel table or range*. As in the example above, our original data is in a range of cells. In the case of an *external data source*, the data is stored in another file or database, for example, if we are using a different program, such as a Microsoft Access database, to collect large amounts of data. We will discuss the use of external data in Chapter 10.

We select the data to be used in the pivot table (see Figure 6.4). If we had chosen an *external data source*, we would use the *Choose Connection ...* button to select our data. Again, we will discuss this in detail in Chapter 10. Because we have a *range of data* in this example, we can highlight the data from our worksheet that we want to use in the pivot table. From the table shown in Figure 6.1, we highlight cells *B3:E27*, the data cells and the column headings. The first row of the highlighted data must contain column headings. In Figure 6.4, the Table/*Range* we have selected is written as follows, where "Data-Shipping" is the name of our worksheet:

'Data-Shipping'!$B$3:$E$27

(**Note:** If we select the upper-left cell in the data range (B3) in the spreadsheet before we select *Insert > Tables > PivotTable* from the *Ribbon*, Excel will automatically guess what the selected data table area should be.) When using pivot tables, any changes we make to the original data source will not be updated automatically in the pivot table. We have to update the pivot table by clicking on the *PivotTable Options > Data > Refresh* button on the *Ribbon*.

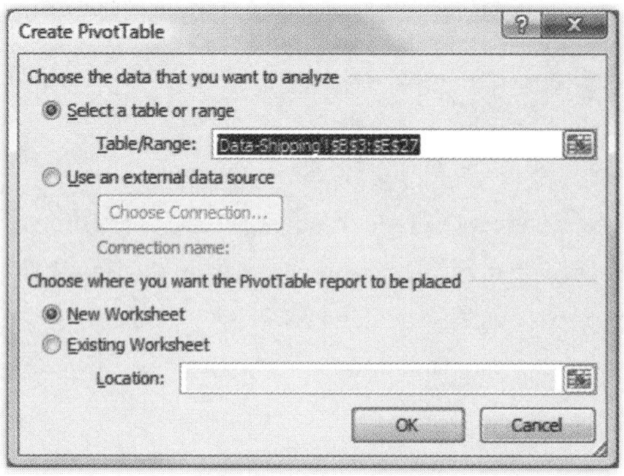

Figure 6.4 Steps 1 & 2: Specifying the location of the data and the location of the resulting pivot table.

STEP 2: Pivot Table Location In this step we specify where the pivot table will be placed. We can either place the pivot table in a new worksheet or in a particular area of the current worksheet. For this example, we have chosen to put our pivot table in a new worksheet. We click the *OK* button to proceed. Excel creates an empty pivot table and displays the *PivotTable Field List* task pane as shown in Figure 6.5. Two *PivotTable Tools* contextual tabs, *Options* and *Design*, appear on the *Ribbon*. We will use the commands in these tabs to further modify the pivot table.

STEP 3: Creating the Pivot Table This is third and most important step of creating the pivot table. In this step we specify exactly how we want to reorganize our data in the new table. We can now organize our data by determining which column heading from the original data we want to become a *Row*, *Column*, *Value*, or *Report Field*. We select one of our field names from the top of PivotTable Field List, and drag it to the corresponding areas in the bottom of the task pane. Because we want "Max Weight" to be a *Row Field*, we select and drag it to the *Row* Labels box. We select "Days to Arrive" and drag it to the same box since we also want it to be a *Row Field*. We then select "Shipping Companies" and drag it to the *Column Labels* box so that it becomes a *Column Field*. Lastly, we select and drag "Costs" to the *Values* box since this is the main data that we want to summarize and it will serve as the Value Field of the pivot table. As we make changes in the PivotTable Field List, the pivot table updates itself automatically. The resulting pivot table is in Figure 6.6. Now that we have created the pivot table, we can use the drop-down buttons to filter for specific data. We will discuss further data filtering and manipulation in the next section.

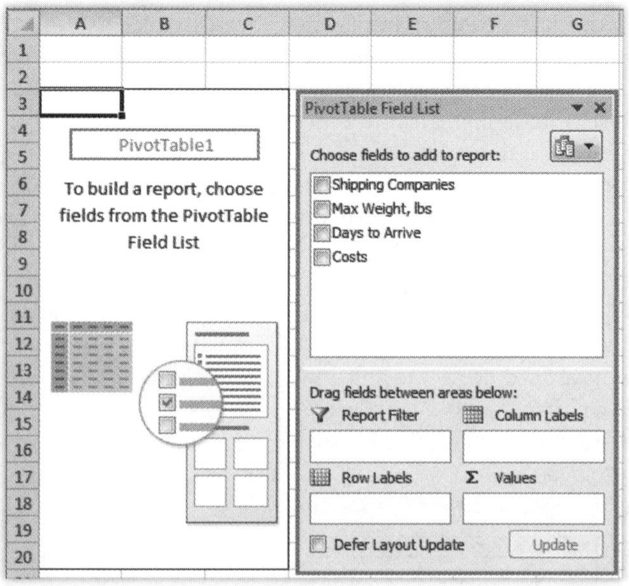

Figure 6.5 Selecting and dragging field names from the top to the boxes in the bottom of PivotTable Field List task pane determines which fields become Row Fields, Column Fields, and the Value Field. It is also possible to specify a Report Field.

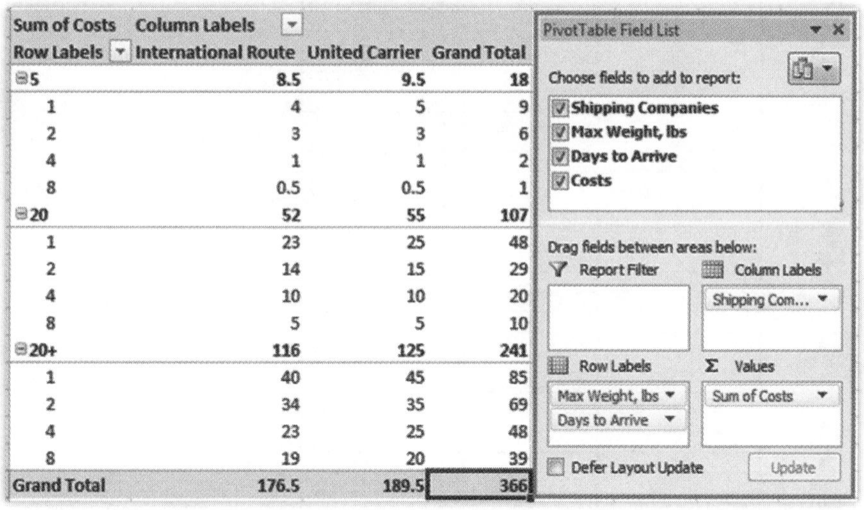

Sum of Costs	Column Labels		
Row Labels	International Route	United Carrier	Grand Total
⊟5	8.5	9.5	18
1	4	5	9
2	3	3	6
4	1	1	2
8	0.5	0.5	1
⊟20	52	55	107
1	23	25	48
2	14	15	29
4	10	10	20
8	5	5	10
⊟20+	116	125	241
1	40	45	85
2	34	35	69
4	23	25	48
8	19	20	39
Grand Total	176.5	189.5	366

Figure 6.6 The final pivot table after specifying its layout.

6.3 *Further Modifications*

6.3.1 An Example

The next example should further demonstrate the efficacy of pivot tables as we explore ways to modify or add to an already created table. The table in Figure 6.7 displays the "Units Produced" given various combinations of "Number of Operators," "Machine Number," and "Shift." To create a pivot table for this data, we choose *Insert > Tables > PivotTable* from the Ribbon, and then select *PivotTable* from the *drop-down list*. In the dialog box that appears, we indicate that our data is in an Excel worksheet and then highlight the entire table shown in the figure. Next, we determine the layout for the pivot table. We set "Number of Operators" and "Machine Number" as *Row Fields* and "Shift" as a *Column Field*. We then set "Units Produced" as our *Value Field*, since we are most interested in this value.

The pivot table summarizes the set of data included in the *Values, Row and Column Fields*. We will discuss how to modify the presentation of this data. In the table created in this example, the default *Field Setting* applied to the "Units Produced" data field is *Sum*, which can be noted by the "Sum of Units Produced" title automatically given to the table. Any *Grand Totals* or *Sub Totals* calculated would show sums of the "Units Produced" values in relative row fields or column fields. We click on *Design* > *Layout* > *Subtotal* command, and then select *Do Not Show Subtotal* option from the drop-down list to hide row subtotals. Similarly, we click on *Design* > *Layout* > *Grand Total* command, and then select *Off for Rows and Columns* option from the drop-down list to hide row grand totals (see Figure 6.8).

Number of Operators	Machine Number	Shift	Units Produced
2	1	1	50
4	1	1	58
8	1	1	33
10	1	1	58
2	2	1	32
4	2	1	32
8	2	1	44
10	2	1	41
2	3	1	48
4	3	1	43
8	3	1	34
10	3	1	45
2	1	2	49
4	1	2	43
8	1	2	53
10	1	2	38
2	2	2	56
4	2	2	59
8	2	2	59
10	2	2	59
2	3	2	58
4	3	2	54
8	3	2	60
10	3	2	49
2	1	3	57
4	1	3	49
8	1	3	30
10	1	3	47
2	2	3	60
4	2	3	55
8	2	3	42
10	2	3	42
2	3	3	40
4	3	3	48
8	3	3	46
10	3	3	50

Figure 6.7 This table records "Units Produced" for various combinations of operators, machines, and shifts.

Suppose that we want to see the *Grand Totals* for both rows and columns of the pivot table in Figure 6.8. We select *Design* > *Layout* > *Grand Total* command, and then select *On for Rows and Columns* option from the drop-down list. As a result, a new column to the right of the table features the row sums of the "Units Produced" and a new row below the table contains the column sums appear. We can now observe the total amount of "Units Produced" for each combination of "Number of Operators," "Machine Number," and "Shift" in the "Grand Total" column on the right, and the total number of "Units Produced" during each "Shift" in the "Grand Total" row below the table. (See Figure 6.9.)

Sum of Units Produced	Column Labels		
Row Labels	1	2	3
⊟2			
1	50	49	57
2	32	56	60
3	48	58	40
⊟4			
1	58	43	49
2	32	59	55
3	43	54	48
⊟8			
1	33	53	30
2	44	59	42
3	34	60	46
⊟10			
1	58	38	47
2	41	59	42
3	45	49	50

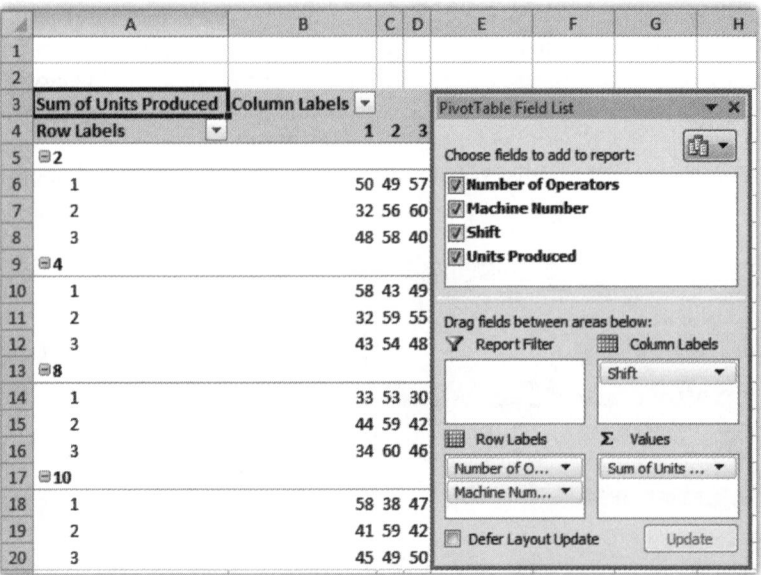

Figure 6.8 The final pivot table after specifying its layout and removing row and column total/subtotals.

Sum of Units Produced	Column Labels			
Row Labels	1	2	3	Grand Total
⊟2				
1	50	49	57	156
2	32	56	60	148
3	48	58	40	146
⊟4				
1	58	43	49	150
2	32	59	55	146
3	43	54	48	145
⊟8				
1	33	53	30	116
2	44	59	42	145
3	34	60	46	140
⊟10				
1	58	38	47	143
2	41	59	42	142
3	45	49	50	144
Grand Total	518	637	566	1721

Figure 6.9 Row and column *Grand Totals* show the sums of "Units Produced."

There are other *Value Field Setting* options aside from *Sum* (as we saw in the first example with shipping data when showing minimum costs). To modify these options we select *Options > Active Field > Field Settings* command on the *Ribbon*. The dialog box shown in Figure 6.10 then appears.

We can select any of the preset calculations in the *Summarize value field by* window in the *Summarize Value by* tab. For example, we can choose *Max* to better analyze the combination of operators, machines, and shifts that produces the most units (see Figure 6.11). With *Max*, we can clearly see the combination of "Number of Operators" and "Machine Number" that produces the most units during any "Shift." Any Grand Totals or Subtotals now display the maximum values of "Units Produced." The *Custom Name* value should automatically update depending on the summary chosen. We changed manually the name of the Grand Total column of the pivot table by typing "Max." Clicking on the *Number* Format button displays the same dialog box used to format cells. We can use this option to make values appear as currency, dates, etc.

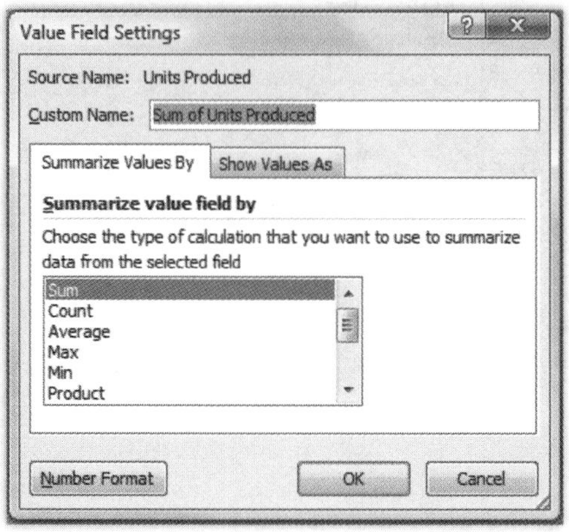

Figure 6.10 Value Field Settings for the "Units Produced" *Value Field.*

	A	B	C	D	E
1					
2					
3	**Max of Units Produced**	**Column Labels** ▾			
4	**Row Labels** ▾	**1**	**2**	**3**	**Max**
5	⊟**2**				
6	1	50	49	57	57
7	2	32	56	60	60
8	3	48	58	40	58
9	⊟**4**				
10	1	58	43	49	58
11	2	32	59	55	59
12	3	43	54	48	54
13	⊟**8**				
14	1	33	53	30	53
15	2	44	59	42	59
16	3	34	60	46	60
17	⊟**10**				
18	1	58	38	47	58
19	2	41	59	42	59
20	3	45	49	50	50
21	**Max**	**58**	**60**	**60**	**60**

Figure 6.11 The Value Field Setting on the "Units Produced" *Data Field* has now been changed to *Max*. All *Grand Totals* have been updated.

We select the *Show Values As* tab in the Value Field Setting dialog box to modify the data further after the main summarizing has been completed. For example, we can choose to show the data as a percentage of a given set of field values (see Figure 6.12).

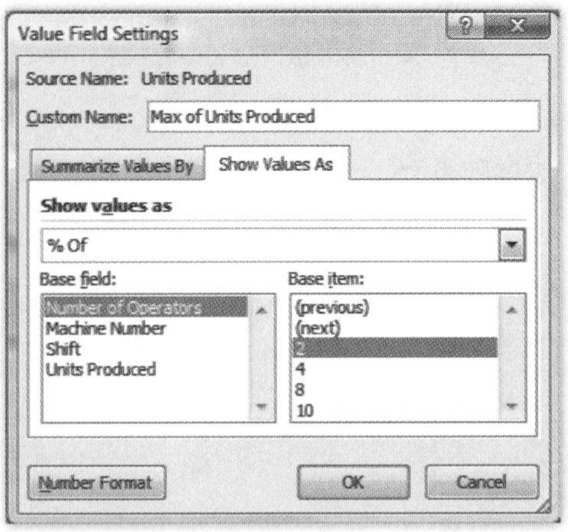

Figure 6.12 The Show Values As tab allows a user to further modify data from a selected field.

Subtotals are *Field Settings* applied to *Row* or *Column Fields*. Because totals for *Column Fields* can be calculated using *Column Grand Totals*, we will only focus on *Subtotals* of *Row Fields*. For example, to perceive the total number of "Units Produced" for each "Number of Operators" or for each "Machine Number," we add *Subtotals* to either of these fields. To do so, we simply click in one of these fields and then select the *Field Settings* option, either by right-clicking in the field name, or from the *PivotTable Tools* tabs on the Ribbon, which we will discuss later. The window in Figure 6.13 then appears. This window resembles Figure 6.10, which allows users to modify *Field Settings* for *Value Fields*. Again, we can choose from the list of *Custom* options in the *Subtotals* window.

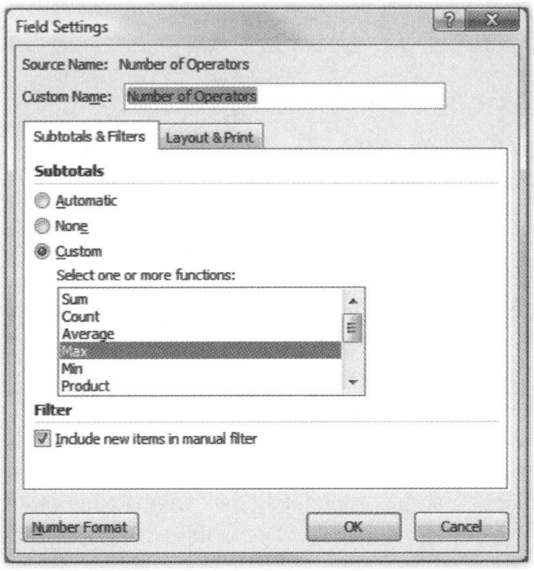

Figure 6.13 Using *Field Settings* for *Row Fields* to create *Subtotals*.

In the *Field Settings* dialog box of Figure 6.13, we have selected the *Max* subtotal option to add *Subtotals* for the "Number of Operators" *Row Field*. The Pivot Table then summarizes the maximum number of "Units Produced" for each "Number of Operators" value in separate rows (see Figure 6.14). We repeat these steps to add *Max Subtotals* for the "Machine Number" *Row Field*, which are summarized at the bottom of the table. Calculating these *Subtotals* allows us to easily find which shift had the most units produced for any number of operators or on any machine.

Max of Units Produced	Column Labels			
Row Labels	1	2	3	Max
⊟2	50	58	60	60
1	50	49	57	57
2	32	56	60	60
3	48	58	40	58
⊟4	58	59	55	59
1	58	43	49	58
2	32	59	55	59
3	43	54	48	54
⊟8	44	60	46	60
1	33	53	30	53
2	44	59	42	59
3	34	60	46	60
⊟10	58	59	50	59
1	58	38	47	58
2	41	59	42	59
3	45	49	50	50
1 Max	58	53	57	58
2 Max	44	59	60	60
3 Max	48	60	50	60
Max	58	60	60	60

Figure 6.14 Adding Subtotals for the "Number of Operators" and "Machine Number" Row Fields to the pivot table.

6.3.2 PivotTable Options and Design Tools

Using the commands listed in *PivotTable Tools* contextual tabs of the *Ribbon*, we can easily modify the pivot table after it has been created. The *Options* and *Design* tabs feature a number of related command buttons (see Figure 6.15). We can also access several of these options by right-clicking in any field of the pivot table. Note that we must select a cell in the pivot table in order to activate the *PivotTable Tools* contextual tabs.

The groups of commands listed in the *Options* tab are *PivotTable*, *Active Field*, *Group*, *Sort & Filter*, *Data*, *Actions*, *Calculations*, *Tools* and *Show*. We will discuss some useful commands within each group. You can name the pivot table we created earlier by typing "Units Produced" in the *PivotTable Name:* window within the PivotTable group. Naming your table is useful as you can refer to this table in VBA by using its name. On the click of Options > PivotTable > Options command, the dialog box in Figure 6.16 appears. You can select the *Merge and center cells with labels* checkbox (in the *Layout & Format* tab of the dialog box) to center column and row labels as in Figure 6.17. You can select the Classic PivotTable layout from the Display tab of the dialog box to change the layout of your table. The classic layout is recommended when your table has two or more row fields. For example, the table in Figure 6.14 has two row fields, "Number of Operators" and "Machine Number." These fields appear in the same column, column A. This layout, called the *Compact* view, makes the presentation of this table better. However, if you plan to reuse the results of this table, this layout is not recommended. The pivot table in Figure 6.17 has the Classic layout, where "Number of Operators" and "Machine Number" fields are presented in two different columns, columns A and B.

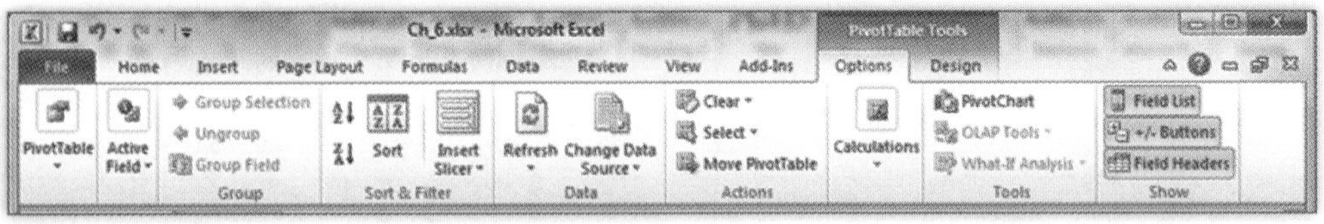

(a)

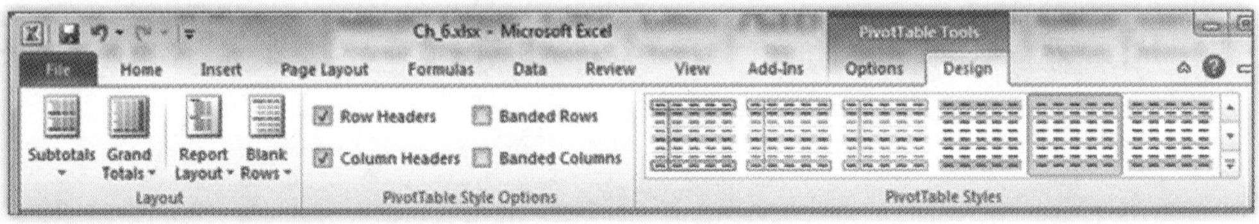

(b)

Figure 6.15 *PivotTable Tools contextual tabs of the Ribbon: (a) Options tab, and (b) Design tab.*

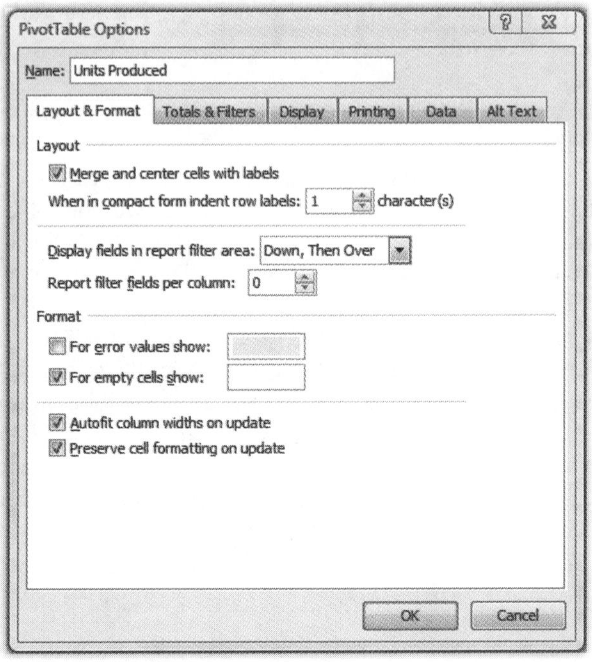

Figure 6.16 The PivotTable Options dialog box is used to change table's Layout, Format, Totals, Filters, etc.

	A	B	C	D	E	F
1						
2						
3	**Max of Units Produced**		**Shift**			
4	**Number of Operator**	**Machine Numbe**	**1**	**2**	**3**	**Max**
5		1	50	49	57	57
6	⊟ 2	2	32	56	60	60
7		3	48	58	40	58
8	**2 Max**		**50**	**58**	**60**	**60**
9		1	58	43	49	58
10	⊟ 4	2	32	59	55	59
11		3	43	54	48	54
12	**4 Max**		**58**	**59**	**55**	**59**
13		1	33	53	30	53
14	⊟ 8	2	44	59	42	59
15		3	34	60	46	60
16	**8 Max**		**44**	**60**	**46**	**60**
17		1	58	38	47	58
18	⊟ 10	2	41	59	42	59
19		3	45	49	50	50
20	**10 Max**		**58**	**59**	**50**	**59**
21		1 Max	58	53	57	58
22		2 Max	44	59	60	60
23		3 Max	48	60	50	60
24	**Max**		**58**	**60**	**60**	**60**

Figure 6.17 This is the Classic layout of our pivot table.

Field Settings command in the *Options > Active Field* group, is used frequently when working with pivot tables. Figures 6.10 and 6.12 display the two tabs of the dialog box that appears when we select this command. We have already discussed how to change the settings of a field using this dialog box.

The next group of commands in the *Options* tab is *Group*. These commands are very useful, so we discuss *them in* the following section using an example. The *Sort & Filter* group lists commands to sort the data on a table, and insert data slicer. For example, you can present the data in a decreasing order of "Number of Operators" by making "Number of Operators" the active field of the pivot table, and then selecting Options > Sort & Filter > Sort command. In the Sort (Number of Operators) dialog box that appears, select Descending option as in Figure 6.18. The resulting table is in Figure 6.19.

Slicers are visual filters of Excel. Slicers are used when you want to display only the rows of your table that meet certain criteria. This tool is useful as it allows you to organize and present your data efficiently. For example, we want to identify the number of units produced by machine 3 during the 1st and 2nd shift. We initially click on the *Insert Slicers* command. In the dialog box that appears we select two slicers as shown in Figure 6.20. Two dialog boxes appear as in Figure 6.21. From the corresponding dialog boxes select, machine number 3 and shifts 1 and 2. The selected tabs of each slicer are highlighted. Figure 6.21 presents the resulting filtered table.

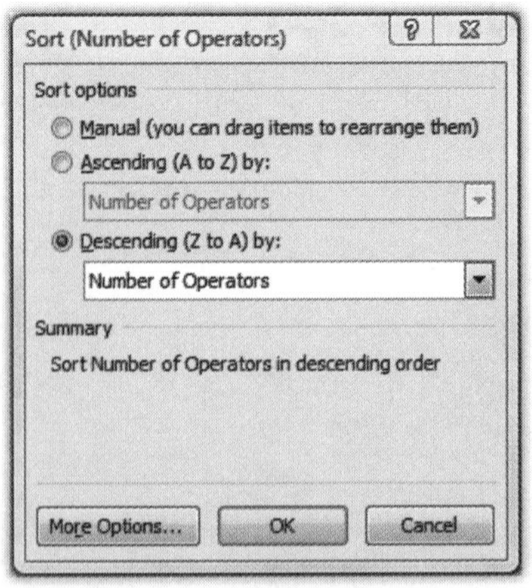

Figure 6.18 Select Descending (Z to A) by: for Number of Operators row field.

	A	B	C	D	E	F
1						
2						
3	**Max of Units Produced**		**Shift**			
4	**Number of Operator**	**Machine Number**	**1**	**2**	**3**	**Max**
5		1	58	38	47	58
6	**10**	2	41	59	42	59
7		3	45	49	50	50
8	**10 Max**		**58**	**59**	**50**	**59**
9		1	33	53	30	53
10	**8**	2	44	59	42	59
11		3	34	60	46	60
12	**8 Max**		**44**	**60**	**46**	**60**
13		1	58	43	49	58
14	**4**	2	32	59	55	59
15		3	43	54	48	54
16	**4 Max**		**58**	**59**	**55**	**59**
17		1	50	49	57	57
18	**2**	2	32	56	60	60
19		3	48	58	40	58
20	**2 Max**		**50**	**58**	**60**	**60**
21		1 Max	58	53	57	58
22		2 Max	44	59	60	60
23		3 Max	48	60	50	60
24	**Max**		**58**	**60**	**60**	**60**

Figure 6.19 This table is sorted in a descending order of "Number of Operators."

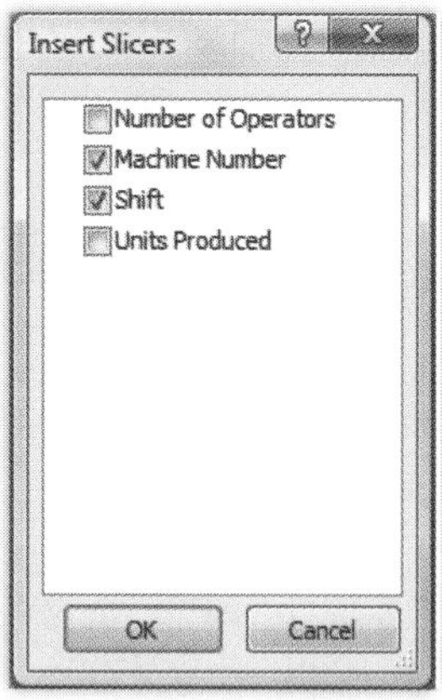

Figure 6.20 Use this dialog box to insert the "Machine Number" and "Shift" slicers.

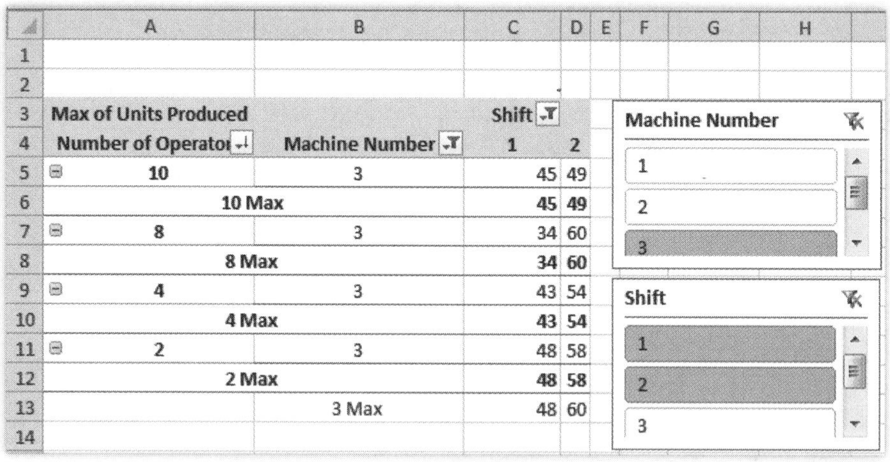

	A	B	C	D
1				
2				
3	Max of Units Produced		Shift	
4	Number of Operators	Machine Number	1	2
5	10	3	45	49
6	10 Max		45	49
7	8	3	34	60
8	8 Max		34	60
9	4	3	43	54
10	4 Max		43	54
11	2	3	48	58
12	2 Max		48	58
13		3 Max	48	60
14				

Figure 6.21 The Number of Units Produced by machine number 3 during the 1st and 2nd shift.

The *Data* group of *Options* tab contains the *Refresh* button. Note that, changes you make to the data source are not reflected automatically on the pivot table. You should click on the *Refresh* command for these changes to take effect. Use the *Options > Data > Change Data Source* command to change the source of data.

The *Actions* group lists commands that allow you to clear the content, select, and move a pivot table.

The *Summarize Values by* command in the *Calculations* group lists a number of options that you can use to summarize the value field of the pivot table. These options are similar to the ones we talked about earlier when discussed *Value Field Settings* (see Figure 6.10). The *Show Values As* command lists the same options to as the ones in Figure 6.12. The *Fields, Items & Sets* command allows you to create and manipulate calculated fields and items. This is an important topic that we will discuss in detail in the following section.

One of the commands listed in the *Tools* group is *Pivot Charts*. We will discuss this option in a later section, but, for now, note that we can create a *Pivot Chart* directly from the *Pivot Table* using this command.

The *Show* group of *Options* tab lists three commands, Field List, +/– Buttons, and Field Headers. On the click of the Field List command, the Pivot Table Field List task pane appears (see Figure 6.8). The task pane allows us to edit the layout of the pivot table. To remove a field from the table, we uncheck the field name from the list on the top of the task pane; or click on the field title listed in the corresponding area in the bottom of the task pane and drag it outside of the task pane. Suppose that we want to change the layout of our table to look similar to Figure 6.22. We select the field "Number of Operators" (that is initially located under *Row Labels* area) and drag it to *Column Labels* area. Next, we select the "Shift" field listed under *Column Labels* area, and drag it to *Row Labels* area. Figure 6.22 presents the new layout of our pivot table.

The *Options > Show > +/– Buttons* command allow you to expand or collapse items within a pivot table. For example, activate the *+/– Buttons* command, and then click on the – (minus) sign next to "Machine Number" 1 and 2. The – (minus) sign will become + (plus), and the rows corresponding to these machines will collapse. Figure 6.23 presents the resulting table. The table does not display detailed information about units produced during each shift, it only displays summary results for these two machines. You can use the *Options > Show > Field Headers* command to display or hide the column and row headers.

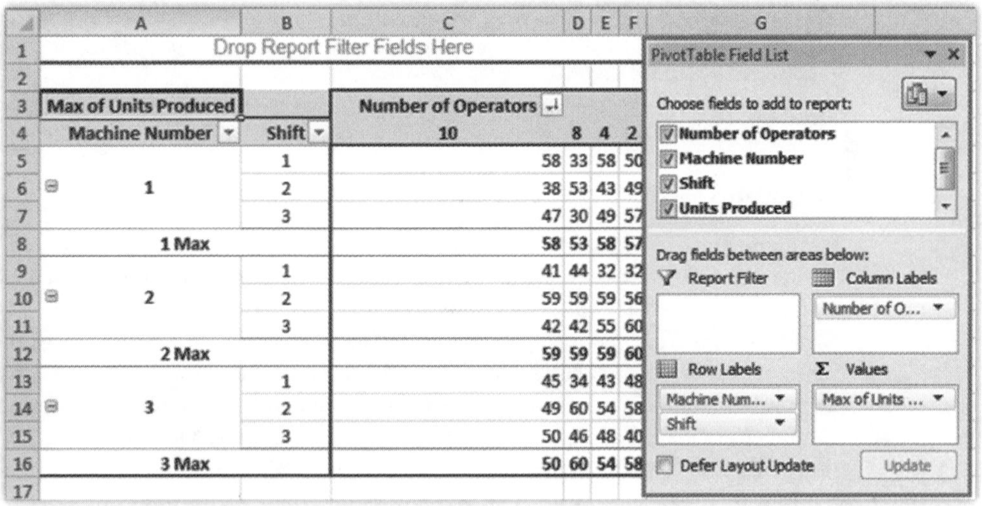

	A	B	C	D	E	F
1	Drop Report Filter Fields Here					
2						
3	Max of Units Produced		Number of Operators			
4	Machine Number	Shift	10	8	4	2
5		1	58	33	58	50
6	1	2	38	53	43	49
7		3	47	30	49	57
8	1 Max		58	53	58	57
9		1	41	44	32	32
10	2	2	59	59	59	56
11		3	42	42	55	60
12	2 Max		59	59	59	60
13		1	45	34	43	48
14	3	2	49	60	54	58
15		3	50	46	48	40
16	3 Max		50	60	54	58
17						

Figure 6.22 The pivot table is updated to reflect the new layout. We have switched the "Machine Number" and "Shift" fields.

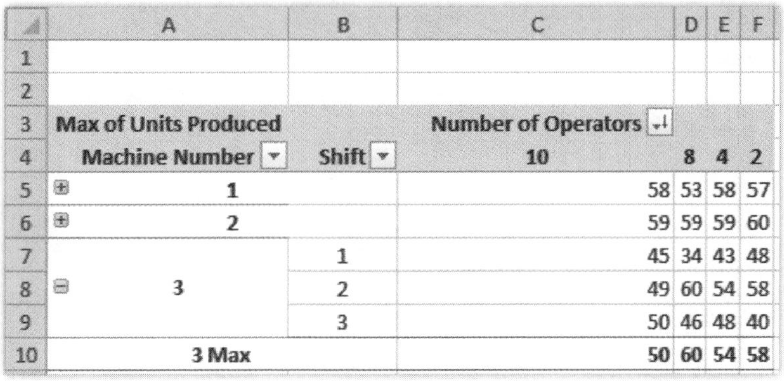

	A	B	C	D	E	F
1						
2						
3	Max of Units Produced		Number of Operators			
4	Machine Number	Shift	10	8	4	2
5	1		58	53	58	57
6	2		59	59	59	60
7		1	45	34	43	48
8	3	2	49	60	54	58
9		3	50	46	48	40
10	3 Max		50	60	54	58

Figure 6.23 The results for machines numbered 1 and 2 are collapsed.

The main groups of commands in the *Design* tab are *Layout, PivotTable Style Options, and PivotTable Styles.* The *Subtotals* and *Grand Totals* commands of the *Design > Layout* group list options you can use to change the layout of a pivot table by displaying (or not) row and column totals and subtotals. In the previous section we discussed the use of some of these commands. The *PivotTable Styles* group lists options you can use to change the format of a pivot table. We can scroll down the list to choose a PivotTable style. In Figure 6.24, the pivot table is automatically adjusting to the new style.

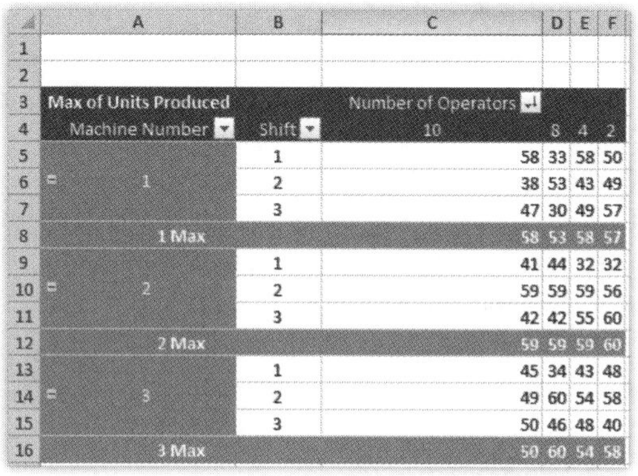

Figure 6.24 The pivot table reflects the updated style.

6.3.3 Grouping

Grouping items in a *Row* or *Column Field* allows us to further manipulate how we view or filter for data in a pivot table. To group field values, we select the field and choose *PivotTable Tools Options > Group > Group Field* command; or, we can right-click on the field and select the *Group* options from the short-cut menu that appears (see Figure 6.25). For example, suppose we want a more general analysis of how the "Number of Operators" affects production. We can form two intervals of values for this field: 2 to 5 and 6 to 10. To do so, we first select a cell in the "Number of Operators" *Row Field* and select *PivotTable Tools Options > Group > Group Selection* command. The Grouping dialog box in Figure 6.26 appears. In this dialog box, we specify the intervals that we want to create. Here, we designate 2 and 10 as our starting and ending values, and group by 4 operators. The updated pivot table is shown in Figure 6.27.

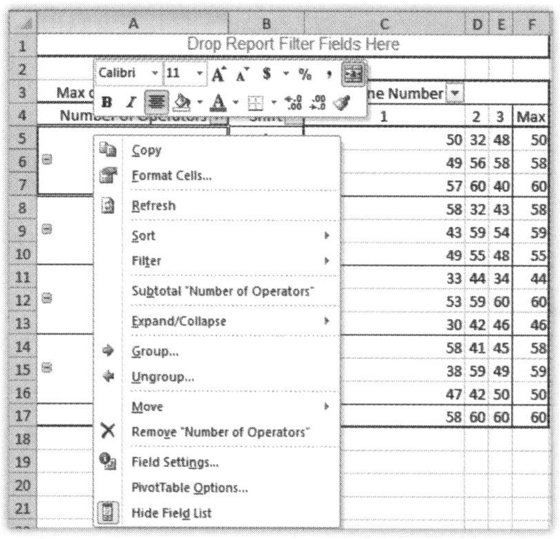

Figure 6.25 We select "Number of Operators" field, then right-click to display the short-cut menu. Select Group from the options listed in the menu.

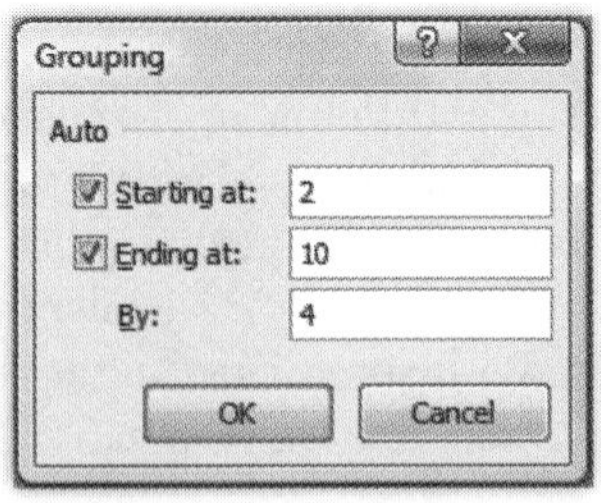

Figure 6.26 Specifying intervals in the Grouping dialog box.

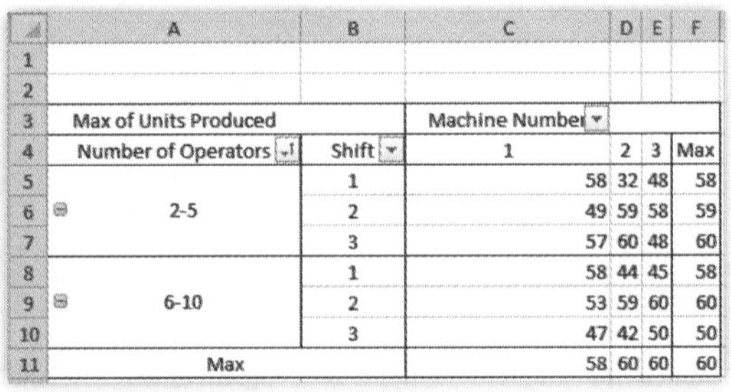

	A	B	C	D	E	F
1						
2						
3	Max of Units Produced		Machine Number			
4	Number of Operators	Shift	1	2	3	Max
5		1	58	32	48	58
6	2-5	2	49	59	58	59
7		3	57	60	48	60
8		1	58	44	45	58
9	6-10	2	53	59	60	60
10		3	47	42	50	50
11	Max		58	60	60	60

Figure 6.27 The updated pivot table now shows the values for "Number of Operators" as intervals.

We can ungroup any field by selecting *PivotTable Tools Options > Group > Ungroup.*

6.3.4 Calculated Fields and Items

To create a *Calculated Field* or *Calculated Item*, we click on *PivotTable Tools Options > Calculations > Fields, Items & Sets* from the Ribbon. From the drop-down list that appears, we select *Calculated Field* to display the window in Figure 6.28. Here, we can name and define a formula associated with the creation of a new field. This formula is stored with the pivot table. Unlike *Grand Totals* or *Subtotals*, we can enter any formula to be applied to the values in the selected field, and a new field will then be created.

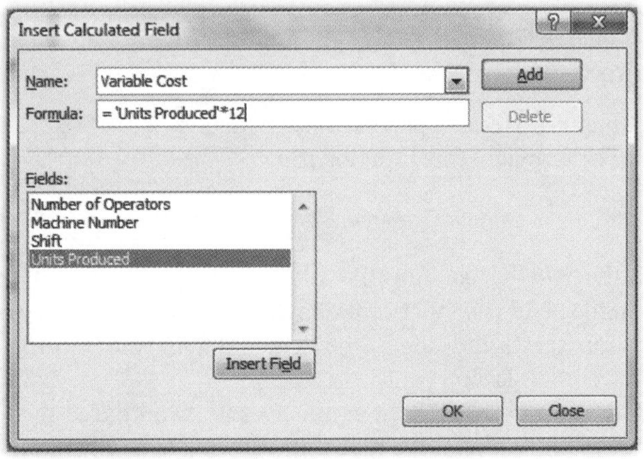

Figure 6.28 Entering a formula to create a new calculated field.

For example, say we want to determine the variable cost in every combination of operators, machines, and shifts. The variable cost is defined in terms of the number of units produced, our *Value Field*. So, we select the *PivotTable Tools Options > Calculations > Fields, Items & Sets* from the Ribbon. Select the *Calculated Field* from the list of options. In the dialog box that appears (see Figure 6.28), we create a name for the new field, "Variable Cost," and enter the formula in terms of the *Units Produced Field* listed in the *Fields* list. We assume here that the cost per unit is $12.00. A new data field called "Variable Cost" has been added to the pivot table in Figure 6.29.

	A	B	C	D	E	F	G	H
1								
2								
3			Shift	Values				
4			1		2		3	
5	Number of Operators	Machine Number	UnitsProduced	VariableCost	UnitsProduced	VariableCost	UnitsProduced	VariableCost
6		1	50	600	49	588	57	684
7	2	2	32	384	56	672	60	720
8		3	48	576	58	696	40	480
9		1	58	696	43	516	49	588
10	4	2	32	384	59	708	55	660
11		3	43	516	54	648	48	576
12		1	33	396	53	636	30	360
13	8	2	44	528	59	708	42	504
14		3	34	408	60	720	46	552
15		1	58	696	38	456	47	564
16	10	2	41	492	59	708	42	504
17		3	45	540	49	588	50	600

Figure 6.29 Adding a new Calculated Field to the pivot table.

Calculated Items create a single row rather than an entire new column of data. First, we select a *Row Field*, and then, we go to *PivotTable Tools Options > Calculations > Fields, Items, & Sets* and select *Calculated Item* from the drop-down list.

Summary

Calculated Field or Calculated Item	User-defined field or item that uses formulas.

6.3.5 GETPIVOTDATA Function

The GETPIVOTDATA function extracts a particular set of data-based values specified for each Row and Column Field. The format of this function is:

=GETPIVOTDATA(desired_field, range_of_desired_data, field1, item1, ...)

The desired_field is the field that contains the value we are filtering for. The range_of_desired_data is the range in the pivot table that contains this field. The remaining field and item values allow us to refine our search if desired. The field and item values can be listed in any order, regardless of the pivot table layout.

For example, suppose we want to find the number of units produced during Shift 2 on Machine 2 when 8 operators are working. We type the following in a cell on the worksheet:

=GETPIVOTDATA("Units Produced", C5:E19, "Shift", 2, "Machine Number", 2, "Number of Operators", 8)

The value for this search is 59 units produced (see Figure 6.30). GETPIVOTDATA can be a very useful function when pivot tables are involved in a large spreadsheet with other applications. That is, this function can be used on a "Report" sheet that refers to information searched from a pivot table. It can also be useful when a user interface is created, as we will see in applying VBA.

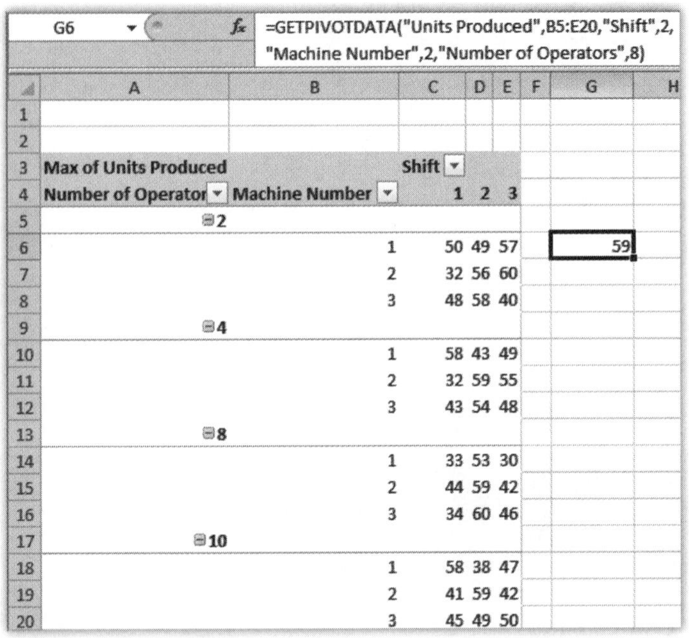

G6
=GETPIVOTDATA("Units Produced",B5:E20,"Shift",2,"Machine Number",2,"Number of Operators",8)
Max of Units Produced
Shift
Number of Operator
Machine Number
1 2 3
2
1 50 49 57
2 32 56 60
3 48 58 40
4
1 58 43 49
2 32 59 55
3 43 54 48
8
1 33 53 30
2 44 59 42
3 34 60 46
10
1 58 38 47
2 41 59 42
3 45 49 50
59

Figure 6.30 The GETPIVOTDATA function can return data for a particular field in a pivot table based on other field value criteria.

6.4 *Pivot Charts*

We can additionally create a chart that shows the data we have selected in our pivot table. To do so, we click on the *PivotTable Tools Options > Tools > PivotChart* command on the *Ribbon*. Select a chart type and subtype from the *Insert Chart* dialog box that appears. This automatically creates a chart of our pivot table (see Figure 6.31) in the same worksheet. We call this chart, which is created from a pivot table instead of directly from the original source data, a ***Pivot Chart***. Remember, we can also create a *Pivot Chart* by highlighting the source data, choosing *Insert > Tables >* PivotTable on the *Ribbon*, and then selecting *PivotChart* from the drop-down list.

Note the field names "Number of Operators" and "Machine Number" at the bottom of the chart. We can select these fields to vary the items displayed. Assume we only want to view the "Units Produced" on Machine 3. We select the field "Machine Number" and click on the drop-down arrow. In the dialog box that appears, we unselect numbers *1* and *2* (see Figure 6.32). Any change in viewing field items made to the chart is reflected in the pivot table, and likewise, any changes to the viewing field items in the pivot table are reflected in the chart. These options are useful when presenting or analyzing data.

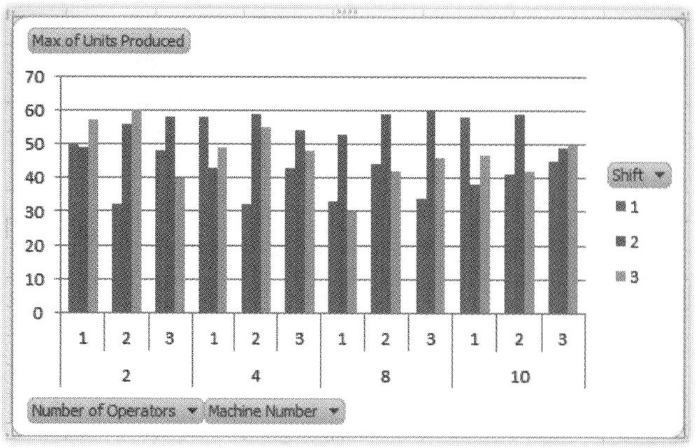

Figure 6.31 The data shown in the Pivot Chart is relative to the layout options selected in creating the pivot table.

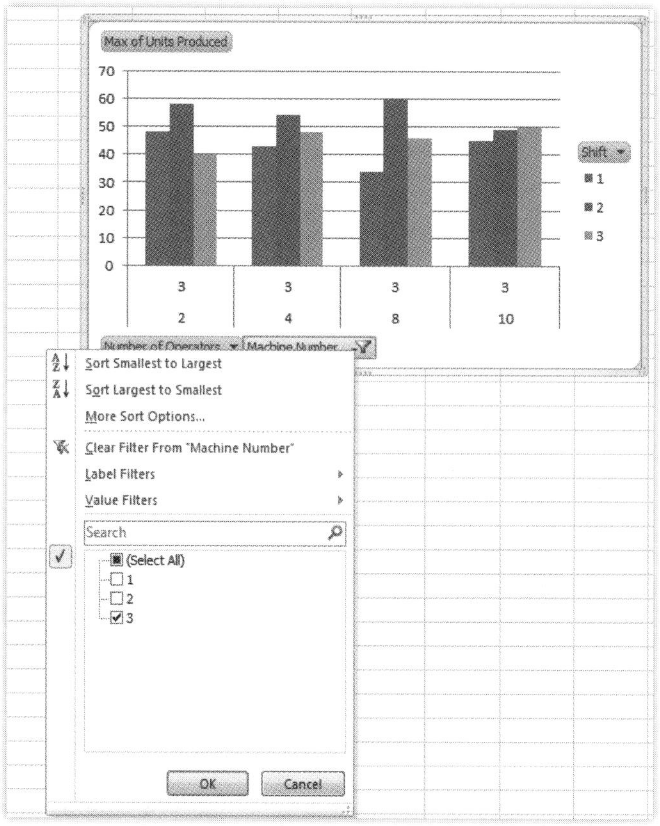

Figure 6.32 The chart is updated to show the units produced on Machine 3 only.

If we do not like the Pivot Chart format we have created, we can modify the chart design, layout, and format by using commands listed in the *PivotChart Tools* contextual tabs. For example, we can change the chart type by selecting *PivotChart Tools Design > Type > Change Chart Type* command on the *Ribbon*. From the *Change Chart Type* dialog box that appears we select a different chart type and subtype (see Figure 6.33). With the commands listed in the *PivotChart Tools* tabs, we can also modify other chart details, such as formatting. Make sure to link the Source Data to the pivot table so we can transfer the filtering capabilities to the pivot chart.

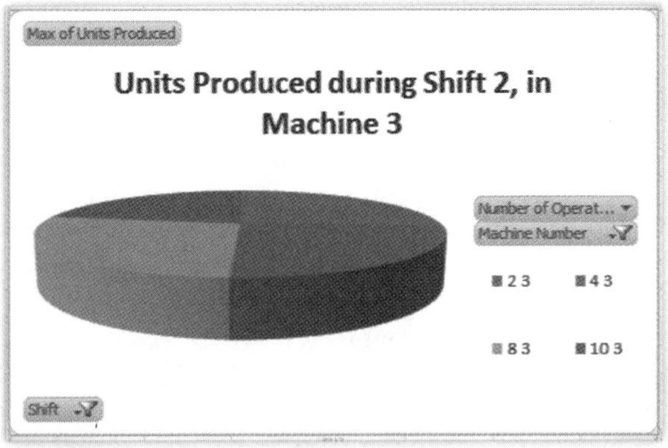

Figure 6.33 Changing the chart type from a Bar Chart to a Pie Chart. The data is filtered to show units produced by Machine 3 during Shift 2.

Summary

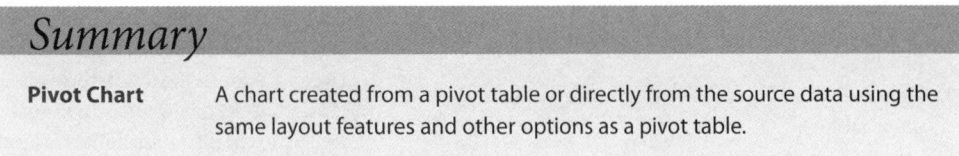

Pivot Chart A chart created from a pivot table or directly from the source data using the same layout features and other options as a pivot table.

6.5 *Summary*

- Pivot tables transform large amounts of data from a table or database into an organized summary report.
- The three steps to create a pivot table are: Data Location, Pivot Table Location, and Create Table Layout with specified options.
- From categories in our original table, select Row and Column Fields to group your data. We also choose a Value Field of comparative values. A Report Field can be created to organize the entire table by different overall categories.
- PivotTable Tools contextual tabs, Options and Design, are activated when you click inside the pivot table. Options tab includes these groups of commands: *PivotTable, Active Field, Group, Sort & Filter, Data, Actions, Calculations, Tools and Show. The Design tab includes these groups of commands: Layout, PivotTable Style Options, and PivotTable Styles.*
- Insert *Slicers* when you want to display only the rows of your table that meet certain criteria. Slicers are useful tools as they enable you to organize and present your data efficiently.
- Use *Grouping* to create intervals in field values.
- We can create Calculated Fields or Calculated Items to further analyze the data in a table. Some common formulas already constructed by Excel include SUM, MIN, and MAX. Grand Totals and Subtotals use the SUM formula to display these calculations of the row or column data.
- GETPIVOTDATA searches for data in a pivot table using field value criteria.
- *Pivot Charts* use pivot tables as their *Source Data* so that filtering options are transferred to the chart as well.

6.6 Exercises

6.6.1 Review Questions

1. What are pivot tables and how are they used?
2. What are the parts of a pivot table into which items from the original database can be placed?
3. What do the Grand Totals and Subtotals features of a pivot table do?
4. What are Slicers? Why slicers are useful tools of Excel?
5. What are the main steps in creating a pivot table?
6. What pivot table command will allow automatic updates of a pivot table when changes have been made to its data source?
7. How do you add a calculated field or item to a pivot table?
8. List four of the common pivot table fields that Excel makes available automatically.
9. What purpose do the drop-down arrows on a pivot table serve?
10. How can you apply an existing report style to a pivot table?
11. How does a pivot chart differ from a pivot table?
12. How can you create a pivot chart from the source data?
13. How do you group data?
14. Can Subtotals be created for Data Fields? How are Subtotals for Column Fields created?
15. What are the parameters of the GETPIVOTDATA function?

6.6.2 Hands-On Exercises

NOTE: Please refer to the file "Chapter_06_Exercises.xlsx" for the associated worksheets noted for the hands-on exercises. The file is available at: www.dssbooks.com.

1. A given table displays the location, store size, owner, and quarterly sales for each store owned by a particular store chain. Organize this data into a pivot table. Show quarterly average sales by store size. (Note: use store size as the row labels.) Do you notice any trends on the average sales? (Refer to worksheet "6.1".)
2. A furniture manufacturer has distribution centers in different regions of the country that supply retailers with goods to sell. A table is used to track the quantity of products shipped from a distribution center to a retailer. Create a pivot table that allows any member of the supply chain to quickly determine the following: the total number of shipments made from each distribution center; the total number of shipments received from each retailer; the average and standard deviation of distance traveled per shipments from the distribution centers. Format your table using an existing pivot table style. (Refer to worksheet "6.2".)
3. A student traveling home for the holidays is comparing flights in an effort to find a cheap flight with few connections at a desirable time. The student wishes to travel from the state of Florida to the city of Pittsburgh. There are numerous combinations of flights available to travel this route. Create a pivot table that will allow the student to quickly pull up flights between various cities to determine which flight or combination of flights is the most desirable. The table should also highlight the least expensive flight departing each city. Format your table using an existing report style. (Refer to worksheet "6.3".)
4. Refer to the soft drink bottling plant introduced in Chapter 4, Hands-on Exercise 6. In an effort to reduce the number of nonconforming bottles, the plant manager has decided to reallocate the products it offers to the bottling lines that package those products. Before doing this, the manager must be able to compare the current costs of bottling each product. Create a pivot table and add slicers to filter the data. Use the slicers to enable the manager to perform cost comparisons based on the drink type, number of fluid ounces, and material of each bottle. Format your table using an existing report style. (Refer to worksheet "6.4".)
5. Use your solution to the previous problem to create a pivot chart that compares the costs of bottling each product. What are the characteristics of the most expensive product to bottle? (Refer to worksheet "6.5".)
6. A table displays postal service rates for shipping packages. Packages can be shipped via Express, First Class, Priority, or Standard mail. Express

and First Class mail may also be certified, which means that the sender can receive verification upon delivery. The postal service charges one rate for the first ounce that a package weighs and another rate for each additional ounce. (Refer to worksheet "6.6".)

A business frequently sends out packages that weigh approximately 10 ounces. Calculate the cost of mailing a 10-oz package via each of the means shown in the table. Create a pivot table that displays the minimum cost of sending a 10-oz package via each of the shipment types. The table should also display the overall minimum cost of mailing a 10-oz package. Finally, format your table using a report style of your own creation.

7. The owner of a campus textbook store has noticed that the store's customers must wait in particularly long lines during the first few weeks of classes. Concerned about losing business to stores with speedier lines, the owner wants to analyze the length of the store's lines for comparison with lines at competing stores. To do so, she measures the following values at five random times throughout the day, every day for a week: the length of the line, the number of cashiers attending customers, and the number of idle cashiers. A table of her results is given. Create a pivot table of the information she collected that averages the store's line lengths for different times of the day and week and for different numbers of busy and idle cashiers. Apply formatting to complete your table. (Refer to worksheet "6.7".)

8. Use the pivot table you created in the previous problem to determine which hour of the day has the highest average line lengths. Then create a pivot chart to display the average line lengths for that hour of the day on each different day of the week. (Refer to worksheet "6.8".)

9. A do-it-yourself retail center sells home care products in various categories, including cleaning, gardening, and hardware. A spreadsheet is used to forecast the demand of products in each of the product categories for the next four months for each of the center's regions. Create a pivot table that totals the demand for each type and category of product for each region. Use slicers to filter the data by region and category (Refer to worksheet "6.9".)

10. A swarm of locusts is infesting the Mid-Atlantic region, so the projected insecticide demand has increased. The forecasted demand (in thousands of units) is now 85 for January, 89 for February, 87 for March, and 82 for April. Record these changes in the data table provided. Then refresh the data on the pivot table to reflect these changes. (Refer to worksheet "6.10".)

11. Sammy owns a lemonade stand and is doing some market research in an attempt to better understand his neighborhood customers. For a random sample of customers, he is given the income, gender, and number of days per week they pass by his stand. Use this information to determine how gender and income influence the frequency with which a customer buys his lemonade. Use the information given to create a pivot table. Group the data on this table based on: low, medium and high income levels (Refer to worksheet "6.11".)

12. Students at a local community college apply to study either Business or Mathematics. Determine if the college discriminates against women in admitting students to the school of their choice. Use the information given to create a pivot table. (Refer to worksheet "6.12".)

13. Jessie is the manager of a company that specializes in at-home sales. She is given data about transactions made by various salespersons for various products sold during the month of March. Use this data to create a pivot table that shows the total number of sales transactions for each salesperson. (Refer to worksheet "6.13".)

14. Using the data from Hands-On Exercise 13, create a pivot table that displays the total revenue by product for each salesperson. Use the GETPIVOTDATA function to find Danny's vacuum sales. (Refer to worksheet "6.14".)

15. Using the data from Hands-On Exercise 13, create a pivot table that displays the total revenue by salesperson for each week. (*Hint:* Use grouping.) (Refer to worksheet "6.15".)

16. A given table presents a list of recent publications by professors of a University. Create a pivot table to help the administration find the following. (Refer to worksheet "6.16".)

a. The total number of publications by department.

b. The total number of publications by department per year.

c. The total number of publications per professor within each department.

d. Use the GETPIVOTDATA function to find the total number of publications by professor Tim Frank.

17. A table of data is kept by a pharmacy. The table presents a list of medicines, their suppliers and the prices they offer. Create a pivot table that presents for each medicine, the suppliers that offers it as well as the best price offered. Use the drop-down window next to fields name to display only information about "Rapid X Min." Change the layout of the table to Tabular Format. Use the PivotTable Options dialog box to enable Excel to refresh the data of the pivot table when opening the file (Refer to worksheet "6.17".)

18. *Sun-Shine* is a real-estate company. The company has two agencies, one located in Orlando and the other in Miami, Florida. A given table presents a part of the data on home sales over a period of four months. The management is interested to compare the activity of the two agencies. (Refer to worksheet "6.18".)

Create a pivot table that presents for each month and each agency: the total number of houses sold, the average sales price, the average size, and average and standard deviation of the $/sqft.

19. Read Chapter 6 Hands-on Exercise 18. The management of the *Sun-Shine* real estate company is interested in better understanding their market. For this purpose, they wanted to know what type of house (in terms of number of bedrooms) sales best, and which city (Miami, Tampa or Orlando) has more potential buyers. (Refer to worksheet "6.19".)

Create a pivot table that presents for each house type (house with 2, 3, or 4 bedrooms) and each area: the total number of houses sold, the average sales price, the average size, and average and standard deviation of the $/sqft.

20. Read Chapter 6 Hands-on Exercise 18. The management of the *Sun-Shine* real estate company is interested in understanding how the size, age and the number of bedrooms affect the price of the house. (Refer to worksheet "6.20".)

Create a pivot table that presents for each house type (house with 2, 3, or 4 bedrooms), each age and size, the corresponding average price and standard deviation. Note that the age of the houses on the database vary from 1 to 13; and the size varies from 1,067sqft to 2,872sqft. Therefore, group the data to create the pivot table.

CHAPTER

seven Statistical Analysis with Excel

chapter OVERVIEW

7.1 *Introduction*

This chapter illustrates the tools available in Excel for performing statistical analysis. These tools include some new functions, the Data Analysis Toolpak, and some new chart features. This chapter is not intended to teach the statistical concepts which are used in Excel's analysis, but rather demonstrate to the reader that several tools are available in Excel that use these statistical functions. Statistical analysis is used often in DSS applications for analyzing input and displaying conclusive output. These tools will be used especially in applications involving simulation. Some examples of such DSS applications include the Birthday Simulation and Retirement Planning cases in Part III of the text. Other applications which rely on statistical analysis are the Queuing cases and the Reliability Analysis case. A user may want to analyze historical data for forecasting purposes, analyze the performance of a simulation to test the quality of their model and parameters, or understand the probability of some future results in order to aid in decision making. We discuss the application of statistical analysis in simulation in Chapter 9 and again in Chapter 20 with VBA.

In this chapter, the reader will learn how to:

- Perform basic statistical analysis of data using Excel functions.
- Use some of the statistical features of the Data Analysis Toolpak such as Descriptive Statistics and Histograms.
- Work with trend curves to analyze data patterns.
- Perform basic linear regression techniques in Excel.
- Work with several different distribution functions in Excel.

7.2 *Understanding Data*

Statistical analysis provides an understanding of a set of data. Using statistics, we can determine an average value, a variation of the data from this average, a range of data values, and perform other interesting analysis. We begin this analysis by using statistical Excel functions.

One of the basic statistical calculations to perform is finding the ***mean*** of a set of numbers; the mean is simply the average, which we learned how to calculate with the ***AVERAGE*** function in Chapter 4:

=AVERAGE(range or range_name)

Figure 7.1 displays a table of family incomes for a given year. We first name this range of data, cells B4:B31, as "FamIncome." We can now find the average, or *mean*, family income for that year using the AVERAGE function as follows (see Figure 7.2):

=AVERAGE(FamIncome)

The ***median*** is the "middle" value of a set of numbers. The median is the middle number in a list of sorted data. To find the median, we use the ***MEDIAN*** function, which takes a range of data as its parameter:

=MEDIAN(range or range_name)

	A	B	C
1	Yearly Family Income		
2			
3		Income	
4		$33,628	
5		$38,808	
6		$36,399	
7		$34,611	
8		$42,532	
9		$35,996	
10		$49,255	
11		$36,469	
12		$45,460	
13		$40,161	
14		$29,800	
15		$45,006	
16		$30,165	
17		$32,193	
18		$25,095	
19		$45,272	
20		$46,612	
21		$28,794	
22		$47,941	
23		$25,703	
24		$42,606	
25		$37,253	
26		$40,766	
27		$39,331	
28		$27,912	
29		$28,525	
30		$48,599	
31		$45,548	

Figure 7.1 Family incomes for a given year.

D6 *fx* =AVERAGE(FamIncome)

	A	B	C	D	E	F
1	Yearly Family Income					
2						
3		Income				
4		$33,628				
5		$38,808		Mean (Average)		
6		$36,399		$37,873		

Figure 7.2 Calculating the mean, or average, of all family incomes using the AVERAGE function.

To determine the median of the above family incomes, we enter the MEDIAN function as follows:

=MEDIAN(FamIncome)

We can check whether or not this function has returned the correct result by sorting the data and finding the middle number (refer to Chapter 10 for details on sorting). Since there are an even number of family incomes recorded in the table, we must average the two middle numbers. The result is the same (see Figure 7.3).

Another important value, ***standard deviation***, is the square root of the ***variance***, which measures the difference between the mean of the data set and the individual values. Finding the standard deviation is simple with the ***STDEV.P*** and ***STDEV.S*** functions. ***STDEV.P*** finds the standard deviation of a population, and ***STDEV.S*** finds the standard deviation of a sample. The parameter for these functions is also just the range of data for which we are calculating the standard deviation:

=STDEV.P(range or range_name) and *=STDEV.S(range or range_name)*

In Figure 7.4, we calculate the standard deviation of the family income data using the following function. Why the results from using these functions on the same range of data are different? Can you explain this mathematically?

=STDEV.S(FamIncome) and *=STDEV.P(FamIncome)*

D9 =MEDIAN(FamIncome)

	A	B	C	D	E	F
1	Yearly Family Income					
2						
3		Income				
4		$33,628				$25,095
5		$38,808		Mean (Averag		$25,703
6		$36,399		$37,873		$27,912
7		$34,611				$28,525
8		$42,532		Median		$28,794
9		$35,996		$38,031		$29,800
10		$49,255				$30,165
11		$36,469				$32,193
12		$45,460				$33,628
13		$40,161				$34,611
14		$29,800				$35,996
15		$45,006				$36,399
16		$30,165				$36,469
17		$32,193				$37,253
18		$25,095				$38,808
19		$45,272				$39,331
20		$46,612				$40,161
21		$28,794				$40,766
22		$47,941				$42,532
23		$25,703				$42,606
24		$42,606				$45,006
25		$37,253				$45,272
26		$40,766				$45,460
27		$39,331				$45,548
28		$27,912				$46,612
29		$28,525				$47,941
30		$48,599				$48,599
31		$45,548				$49,255

Figure 7.3 Using the MEDIAN function and verifying the result by sorting the data and finding the middle value.

D12 =STDEV.S(FamIncome)

	A	B	C	D	E
1	Yearly Family Income				
2					
3		Income			
4		$33,628			
5		$38,808		Mean (Average)	
6		$36,399		$37,873	
7		$34,611			
8		$42,532		Median	
9		$35,996		$38,031	
10		$49,255			
11		$36,469		Standard Deviation	
12		$45,460	Sample	$7,401	
13		$40,161	Population	$7,268	

Figure 7.4 Using the STDEV.S and STDEV.P functions.

Summary

Statistical Functions:

AVERAGE	Finds the mean of a set of data.
MEDIAN	Finds the median of a set of data.
STDEV.P	Finds the standard deviation of a set of data that represents the whole population.
STDEV.S	Finds the standard deviation of a sample of data from a population.

The ***Analysis Toolpak*** provides an additional method by which to perform statistical analysis. This Excel Add-In includes statistical analysis techniques such as *Descriptive Statistics*, *Histograms*, *Exponential Smoothing*, *Correlation*, *Covariance*, *Moving Average*, and others (see Figure 7.5). These tools automate a sequence of calculations that require much data manipulation if only Excel functions are being used. We will now discuss how to use *Descriptive Statistics* and *Histograms* in the *Analysis Toolpak*. (Refer to Appendix A for more discussion on Excel Add-Ins.)

(*Note:* Before using the *Analysis Toolpak*, you must ensure that it is installed in your computer. If it is installed, then you should see the *Data > Analysis > Data Analysis* command on the *Ribbon*. Otherwise, select *Options* from the list of options in the *File* tab to display *Excel Options* dialog box. Select the *Add-Ins* tab on the left side of the dialog box. From the *Add-ins* window on the right of the dialog box, select *Analysis Toolpak*, and click *OK*.)

7.2.1 Descriptive Statistics

The *Descriptive Statistics* option provides a list of statistical information about our data set, including the mean, median, standard deviation, and variance. To use *Descriptive Statistics*, we select *Data > Analysis > Data Analysis* command on the *Ribbon* to display the *Data Analysis* dialog box. Choosing the *Descriptive Statistics* option from the *Data Analysis* dialog box (shown in Figure 7.5) displays a new window (shown in Figure 7.6).

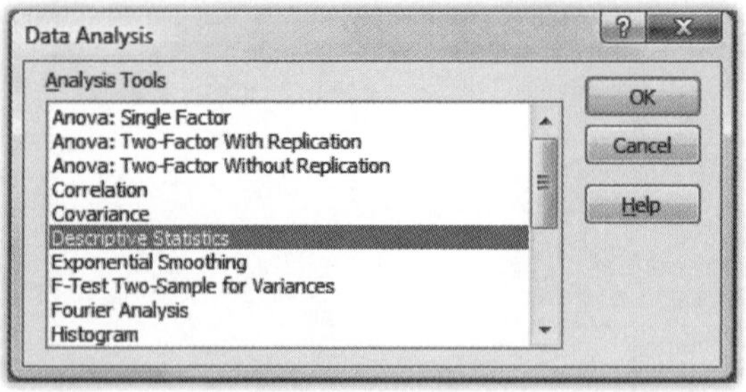

Figure 7.5 The Data Analysis dialog box provides a list of analytical tools.

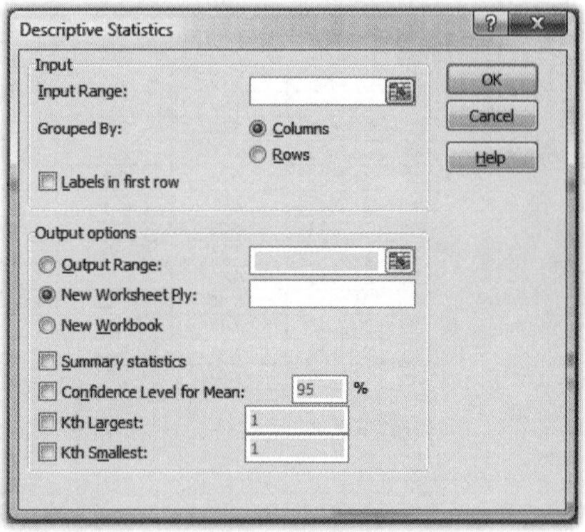

Figure 7.6 The Descriptive Statistics dialog box appears after it is chosen from the Data Analysis list.

The *Input Range* refers to the location of the data set. We check whether our data is *Grouped By Columns* or *Rows*. If there are labels in the first row of each column of data, then we check the *Labels in First Row* box. The *Output Range* refers to where we want the results of the analysis to be displayed in the current worksheet. We could also place the analysis output in a new worksheet or a new workbook. The *Summary Statistics* box calculates the most commonly used statistics from our data. We will discuss the last three options, *Confidence Level for Mean*, *Kth Largest*, and *Kth Smallest*, later in the chapter.

Let us now consider an example in order to appreciate the benefit of this tool. In Figure 7.7 below, there is a table containing quarterly stock returns for three different companies. We want to determine the average stock return, the variability of stock returns, and which quarters had the highest and lowest stock returns for each company. This information could be very useful for selecting a company in which to invest.

We use the Descriptive Statistics tool to answer these questions. In the Descriptive Statistics dialog box (see Figure 7.8), we enter the range *B3:D27* for the *Input Range*. (Notice that we do not select the first column, *Date*, since we are not interested in a statistical analysis of these values.) Next, we check that our data is *Grouped By Columns*; since we do have labels in the first row of each column of data, we check the *Labels in First Row* box. We now specify *G3* as the location of the output in the *Output Range* option. After checking *Summary Statistics*, we press *OK* (without checking any of the last three options) to observe the results shown below in Figure 7.9.

	A	B	C	D
1	Quarterly Stock Returns between 2005 and 2010			
2				
3	Date	MSFT	GE	INTEL
4	Q1 2005	0.04	-0.06	-0.11
5	Q2 2005	0.14	0.19	-0.06
6	Q3 2005	0.08	-0.02	0.12
7	Q4 2005	0.03	0.04	0.17
8	Q1 2006	-0.04	-0.03	-0.02
9	Q2 2006	-0.07	0.01	0.13
10	Q3 2006	0.10	0.00	-0.04
11	Q4 2006	-0.13	0.03	0.11
12	Q1 2007	0.04	-0.02	-0.05
13	Q2 2007	0.02	-0.03	-0.16
14	Q3 2007	0.08	0.07	-0.07
15	Q4 2007	0.10	-0.02	-0.04
16	Q1 2008	0.05	0.08	0.06
17	Q2 2008	-0.08	0.03	0.00
18	Q3 2008	0.01	0.01	0.17
19	Q4 2008	-0.04	-0.02	-0.01
20	Q1 2009	0.11	0.07	0.01
21	Q2 2009	-0.08	0.02	0.09
22	Q3 2009	0.08	0.02	-0.01
23	Q4 2009	-0.05	0.04	0.11
24	Q1 2010	-0.16	0.03	0.09
25	Q2 2010	0.02	0.00	-0.03
26	Q3 2010	0.10	-0.02	-0.11
27	Q4 2010	-0.03	0.01	0.14

Figure 7.7 Quarterly stock returns for three companies.

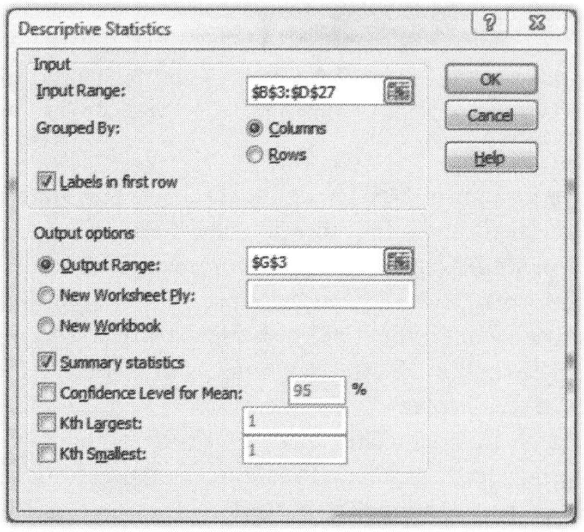

Figure 7.8 Filling the Descriptive Statistics dialog box for the above example data.

First, let us become familiar with the *Mean*, *Median*, and *Mode*. As already mentioned, the *Mean* is simply the average of all values in a data set, or all observations in a sample. We have already observed that without the Analysis Toolpak, the mean value can be found with the

AVERAGE function in Excel. The *Median* is the "middle" observation when the data is sorted in ascending order. If there is an odd number of values, then the median is truly the middle value. If there is an even number of values, then it is the average of the two middle values.

	G	H	I	J	K	L
1						
2						
3	*MSFT*		*GE*		*INTEL*	
4						
5	Mean	0.014	Mean	0.018	Mean	0.02
6	Standard Error	0.017	Standard Error	0.01	Standard Error	0.02
7	Median	0.026	Median	0.012	Median	-0
8	Mode	#N/A	Mode	#N/A	Mode	#N/A
9	Standard Deviation	0.081	Standard Deviation	0.051	Standard Deviation	0.096
10	Sample Variance	0.007	Sample Variance	0.003	Sample Variance	0.009
11	Kurtosis	-0.6	Kurtosis	4.824	Kurtosis	-1.1
12	Skewness	-0.45	Skewness	1.691	Skewness	0.039
13	Range	0.303	Range	0.252	Range	0.329
14	Minimum	-0.16	Minimum	-0.062	Minimum	-0.16
15	Maximum	0.144	Maximum	0.19	Maximum	0.171
16	Sum	0.325	Sum	0.428	Sum	0.476
17	Count	24	Count	24	Count	24

Figure 7.9 The results of the Descriptive Statistics analysis for the example data.

The *Mode* is the most frequently occurring value. If there is no repeated value in the data set, then there is no *Mode* value, as in this example (considering all decimal values). The *Mean* is usually considered the best measure of the central data value if the data is fairly symmetric; otherwise the *Median* is more appropriate. In this example, we can observe that the *Mean* and *Median* values for each company differ slightly; however, we use the *Mean* value to compare the average stock returns for this company. This analysis alone implies that GE and INTEL have higher stock returns, on average, than MSFT. But these values are still very close, so we need more information to make a better comparative analysis.

Now, let us consider the *Standard Error, Standard Deviation*, and *Sample Variance*. The standard deviation and sample variance measure the spread of the data from the mean. The *Sample Variance* is the average squared distance from the mean to each data point. The *Standard Deviation* is the square root of the *Sample Variance* and is more frequently used. Looking at these values for the example data, we can observe that INTEL has a highly varied stock return, while GE's is more stable. Therefore, even though they have the same *Mean* value, this difference in the *Standard Deviation* makes GE a more favorable stock in which to invest. We will discuss *Standard Error*, which is used in connection with trends and trendlines, in more detail later.

The *Standard Deviation*, usually referred to as **s**, is an important value in understanding variation in data. Most data, 68% of a Normal distribution, lies between $+s$ and $-s$ from the mean. Almost all of the data, 95% of a Normal distribution, lies between $+2s$ and $-2s$ from the mean. Any values in the data set that lie more than $\pm 2s$ or $\pm 3s$ from the mean should be noted as unusual. This unusual data can be further analyzed to look for ***outlier*** values. Outliers are data that are inconsistent with the main pattern of data. They can be measured by a multiplier of standard deviation or another set deviation from the mean value. Outliers can provide insightful information about a data set.

For example, if we create a chart of the GE data, we can observe that the second data value is an outlier since it is $\pm 2s = \pm 2{*}0.05 = \pm 0.1$ from the mean (0.02); in other words, any value above 0.12 or below -0.08 is an outlier. The second data value for GE is +0.19 (see Figure 7.10). This figure may imply that something significant happened to GE as a company during Q2 2005, that something affected the national economy, or that they faced any number of (un)predictable situations. However, since the second data value is the only outlier in the last five years of quarterly data for GE, it seems that the mean and standard deviation are accurate measures of the behavior of GE stock returns.

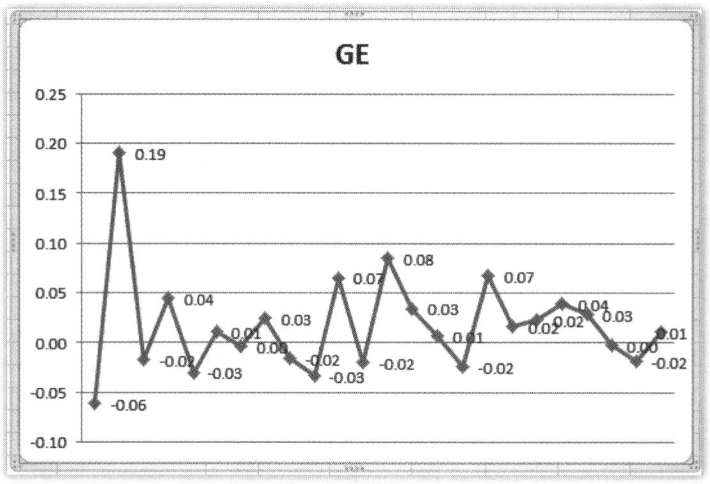

Figure 7.10 The second data point is an outlier since it is greater than *2s* from the mean.

We can identify outliers by looking at a chart of data, or we can actually locate values in the data set that are greater than *+2s* and smaller than *–2s*. To do so, we can place the following formula in an adjacent column to the data:

*=IF(ABS(data_value – mean_value)>2*s, "outlier",)*

This formula states that if the absolute value of the difference between the data value and the mean is greater than 2s, then the word "outlier" will appear in the cell. We reference the mean and standard deviation values from the results of the Descriptive Statistics analysis. We can now easily identify outliers by looking for the word "outlier" in the adjacent column. Using just the column of GE data and this formula, we can observe that we have identified the same outlier point for GE (see Figure 7.11). (Another formula could have been used with the IF and OR functions as well.)

Another way to discover outliers is by using *Conditional Formatting* with the *Use a formula to determine which cells to format* option. With the formula below, we can simply select the column of values in our data set and fill in the *Conditional Formatting* dialog box to highlight outlier points:

*=ABS(data_value – mean_value) > 2*s*

Again, concerning the GE data, we can apply *Conditional Formatting* to identify the outliers as cells highlighted in red. In Figure 7.12, we demonstrate how we applied the *Use a formula to determine which cells to format* option.

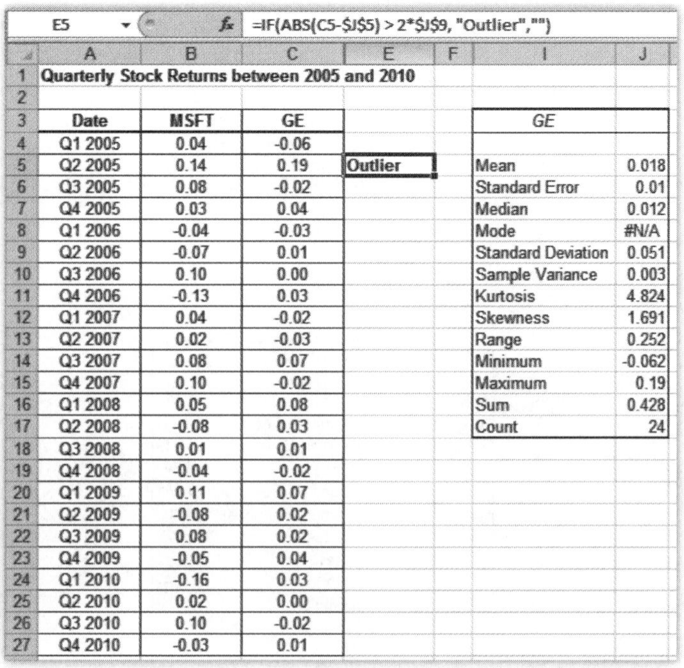

Date	MSFT	GE			GE	
Q1 2005	0.04	-0.06				
Q2 2005	0.14	0.19	Outlier		Mean	0.018
Q3 2005	0.08	-0.02			Standard Error	0.01
Q4 2005	0.03	0.04			Median	0.012
Q1 2006	-0.04	-0.03			Mode	#N/A
Q2 2006	-0.07	0.01			Standard Deviation	0.051
Q3 2006	0.10	0.00			Sample Variance	0.003
Q4 2006	-0.13	0.03			Kurtosis	4.824
Q1 2007	0.04	-0.02			Skewness	1.691
Q2 2007	0.02	-0.03			Range	0.252
Q3 2007	0.08	0.07			Minimum	-0.062
Q4 2007	0.10	-0.02			Maximum	0.19
Q1 2008	0.05	0.08			Sum	0.428
Q2 2008	-0.08	0.03			Count	24
Q3 2008	0.01	0.01				
Q4 2008	-0.04	-0.02				
Q1 2009	0.11	0.07				
Q2 2009	-0.08	0.02				
Q3 2009	0.08	0.02				
Q4 2009	-0.05	0.04				
Q1 2010	-0.16	0.03				
Q2 2010	0.02	0.00				
Q3 2010	0.10	-0.02				
Q4 2010	-0.03	0.01				

Figure 7.11 Identifying the outlier by using a formula with the IF and ABS functions.

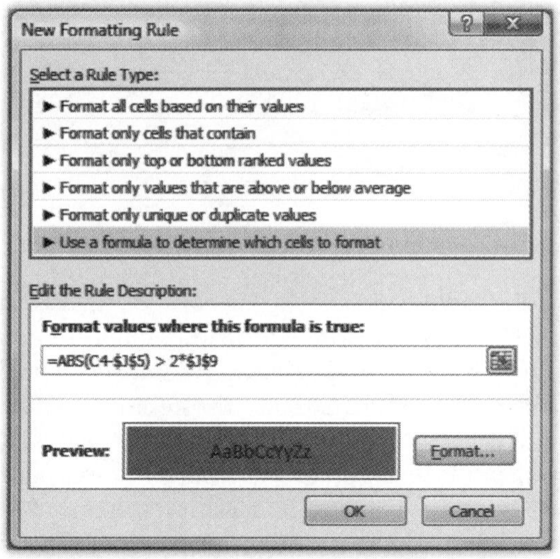

Figure 7.12 Applying the Use a formula ... option to the example data.

In Figure 7.13, we can observe that the same outlier point has been formatted.

Let us now return to the *Descriptive Statistics* results to understand the remaining analysis values. *Kurtosis* is a measure of the data's peaks. It compares the data peak to that of a Normal curve (which we will discuss in more detail in a later section). The *Skewness* is a measure of how symmetric or asymmetric data is. A *Skewness* value greater than +1 is the degree to which the data is skewed in the positive direction; likewise, a value less than –1 is the degree to which the data is skewed in the negative direction. A *Skewness* value between –1 and +1 implies symmetry.

The *Skewness* values for MSFT and INTEL imply that their data is fairly symmetric; however, the Skewness value for GE is 1.69, which implies that it is skewed positively. That is, there is a peak early on in the data and then the data is stable.

The *Range* is the difference between the minimum and maximum value in the data set. The smaller this value is, the less variable the data and therefore, the more desirable. The *Minimum*, *Maximum*, and *Sum* values are self-explanatory. *Count* reveals the number of values in the data set.

	A	B	C	E	F	I	J
1	Quarterly Stock Returns between 2005 and 2010						
2							
3	Date	MSFT	GE			*GE*	
4	Q1 2005	0.04	-0.06				
5	Q2 2005	0.14	0.19	Outlier		Mean	0.018
6	Q3 2005	0.08	-0.02			Standard Error	0.01
7	Q4 2005	0.03	0.04			Median	0.012
8	Q1 2006	-0.04	-0.03			Mode	#N/A
9	Q2 2006	-0.07	0.01			Standard Deviation	0.051
10	Q3 2006	0.10	0.00			Sample Variance	0.003
11	Q4 2006	-0.13	0.03			Kurtosis	4.824
12	Q1 2007	0.04	-0.02			Skewness	1.691
13	Q2 2007	0.02	-0.03			Range	0.252
14	Q3 2007	0.08	0.07			Minimum	-0.062
15	Q4 2007	0.10	-0.02			Maximum	0.19
16	Q1 2008	0.05	0.08			Sum	0.428
17	Q2 2008	-0.08	0.03			Count	24
18	Q3 2008	0.01	0.01				
19	Q4 2008	-0.04	-0.02				
20	Q1 2009	0.11	0.07				
21	Q2 2009	-0.08	0.02				
22	Q3 2009	0.08	0.02				
23	Q4 2009	-0.05	0.04				
24	Q1 2010	-0.16	0.03				
25	Q2 2010	0.02	0.00				
26	Q3 2010	0.10	-0.02				
27	Q4 2010	-0.03	0.01				

Figure 7.13 The outlier point is highlighted.

The last three options in the *Descriptive Statistics* dialog box, *Confidence Level for Mean*, *Kth Largest*, and *Kth Smallest*, can provide some extra information about our data. The *Confidence Level for Mean* calculates the mean value in the *Descriptive Statistics* report constrained to a specified confidence level. The mean is calculated using the specified confidence level (for example, 95% or 99%), the standard deviation, and the size of the sample data. The confidence level and the calculated mean are then added to the analysis report; we can compare the actual mean to this calculated mean based on the specified confidence level. (Remember that a confidence interval is only valid when the data is independently and identically distributed.)

The *Kth Largest* and *Kth Smallest* options provide the respectively ranked data value for a specified value of k. For example, for $k = 1$, the *Kth Largest* returns the maximum data value and the *Kth Smallest* returns the minimum data value. The value of *k* can range from 1 to the number of data points in the input.

Similar to the *Kth Largest* and *Kth Smallest* options with *Descriptive Statistics*, these Excel functions ***PERCENTILE.INC***, ***PERCENTILE.EXC***, ***PERCENTRANK.INC***, and ***PERCENTRANK.EXC*** are valuable when working with ranking numbers. The PERCENTILE.INC function returns a value for which a desired percentile *k* of the specified data_set falls below. The PERCENTILE.EXC function excludes the value of *k*-th percentile from the calculations. The formats of these functions are:

=PERCENTILE.INC(data_set, k) and *=PERCENTILE.EXC(data_set, k)*

For example, let us apply this formula to the MSFT data. If we want to determine what value 95 percent of the data falls below, we type the function:

=PERCENTILE.INC(B4:B27,0.95) and *=PERCENTILE.EXC(B4:B27,0.95)*

The result of PERCENTILE.INC is 0.108, which means that 95 percent of the MSFT data is less than or equal to 0.108. The result of PERCENTILE.EXC is 0.135, which means that 95 percent of the MSFT data is less than 0.135. The PERCENTRANK.INC and PERCENTRANK.EXC functions perform the complementary task. PERCENTRANK.INC returns the percentile of the *data_set* that falls below a given *value, inclusive.* PERCENTRANK.EXC calculates the same percentile, exclusive of the value of *k*. The format of this function is:

=PERCENTRANK.INC(data_set, k) and *= PERCENTRANK.EXC(data_set, k)*

For example, if we want to know what percent of the MSFT data falls below the value 0.108, inclusive of 0.108, we type:

=PERCENTRANK.INC(B4:B27, 0.108)

If we want to know what percent of the MSFT data falls below the value 0.135, exclusive of 0.135, we type:

=PERCENTRANK.EXC(B4:B27, 0.135)

The result in both cases is 0.95, or 95 percent. These functions prove beneficial when we want to discover what percent of the data falls below the mean. Using the MSFT data set again, we type:

=PERCENTRANK.EXC(B4:B27, 0.01)

The result is that 0.396, or about 40 percent of the data, is less than the mean. These Excel functions, along with the others mentioned above, when combined with the Descriptive Statistics analysis tool, can help determine much constructive information about data.

Summary

Descriptive Statistics:

Outliers	May be an unusual value among the values in the data set which lie more than ±2s or ±3s from the mean.
PERCENTILE.INC	A function that returns a value for which a desired percentile *k* of the specified data_set falls below, inclusive.
PERCENTILE.EXC	A function that returns a value for which a desired percentile *k* of the specified data_set falls below, exclusive.
PERCENTRANK.INC	A function that returns the percentile of the data_set that falls below a given value, inclusive.
PERCENTRANK.EXC	A function that returns the percentile of the data_set that falls below a given value, exclusive.

7.2.2 Histograms

Histograms calculate the number of occurrences, or frequency, with which values in a data set fall into various intervals. To create a histogram in Excel, we choose the *Histogram* option from the *Analysis Toolpak* list. A dialog box in which we will specify four main parameters then appears. These four parameters are: input, bins, output, and charts options (see Figure 7.14).

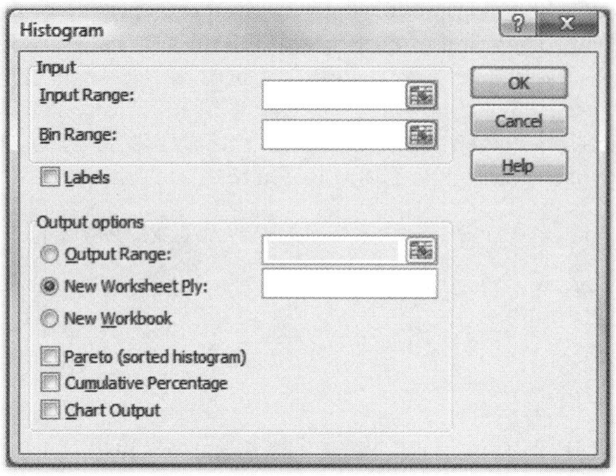

Figure 7.14 The Histogram dialog box.

The *Input Range* is the range of the data set. The *Bin Range* specifies the location of the bin values. ***Bins*** are the intervals into which values can fall; they can be defined by the user or can be evenly distributed among the data by Excel. If we specify our own bins, or intervals, then we must place them in a column on our worksheet. The bin values are specified by their upper bounds; for example, the intervals (0–10), (10–15), and (15–20) are written as 10, 15, and 20. The Output Range is the location of the output, or the frequency calculations, for each bin. This location can be in the current worksheet or in a new worksheet or a new workbook. The chart options include a simple *Chart Output* (the actual histogram), a *Cumulative Percentage* for each bin value, and a *Pareto* organization of the chart. (Pareto sorts the columns from largest to smallest.)

Let us look at the MSFT stock return data from the examples above. We may want to determine how often the stock returns are at various levels. To do so, we select *Data > Analysis > Data Analysis* from the *Ribbon* to display the *Data Analysis* dialog box. In the dialog box, select *Histogram* and click *OK*. In the Histogram dialog box that appears we specify the parameters of the *Histogram* as demonstrated in Figure 7.15. Our *Input Range* is the column of MSFT data, including the "MSFT" label in the first row. For now, we leave the *Bin Range* blank and let Excel create the bins, or intervals. We check *Labels* since we have included a label for our selected data. We pick a cell in the current worksheet as our *Output Range* and then select *Chart Output*. The resulting histogram and frequency values are shown in Figure 7.16.

First, let us discuss the *Bin* values. Remember that each bin value is an upper bound on an interval; that is, the intervals that Excel has created for this example are (below –0.16), (–0.16, –0.08), (–0.08, –0.01), (–0.01, 0.07), and (above 0.07). We can deduce that most of our data values fall in the last three intervals. It may have been more useful to use intervals relative to the mean and standard deviation of the MSFT data. In other words, we could create the intervals (below –2s), (–2s, –s), (–s, mean), (mean, s), (s, 2s), and (above 2s). To enforce these intervals, we create our own *Bin Range*. In a new column, we list the upper bounds of these intervals using the mean and standard deviation values from the *Descriptive Statistics* results for the MSFT data. We also create a title for this column to include in the *Bin Range* (see Figure 7.17).

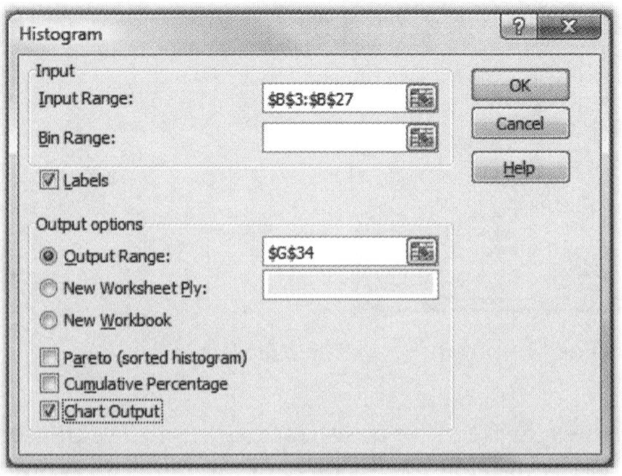

Figure 7.15 Entering data into the Histogram dialog box.

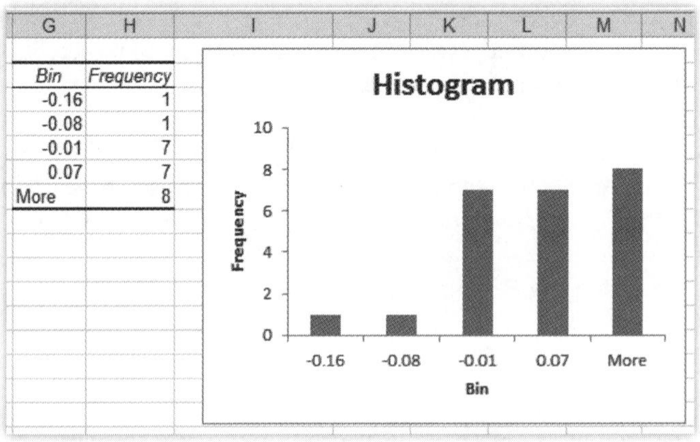

Figure 7.16 The resulting histogram and frequencies for the example data.

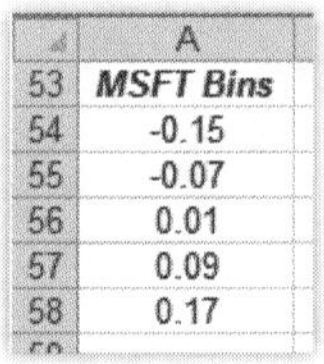

A
53 MSFT Bins
54 -0.15
55 -0.07
56 0.01
57 0.09
58 0.17

Figure 7.17 Creating the Bin Range for the example data.

We now select *Data > Analysis > Data Analysis* from the *Ribbon* to display the *Data Analysis* dialog box. In the dialog box, select *Histogram* and click *OK*. In the Histogram dialog box that appears we this time add the *Bin Range* (see Figure 7.18).

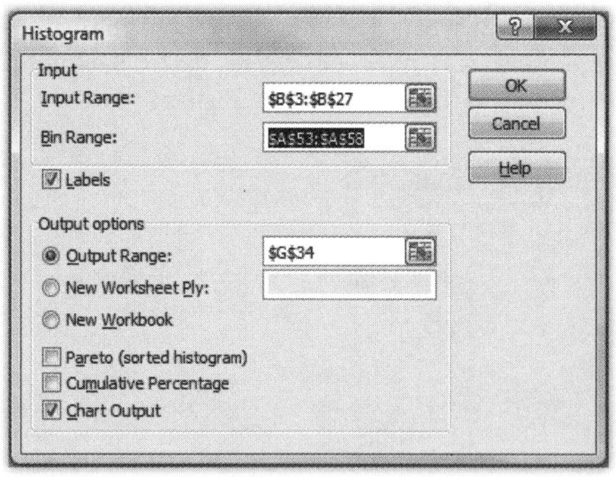

Figure 7.18 The *Histogram* dialog box now has a specified *Bin Range*.

Our Bin Range now calculates the frequencies and creates the histogram (see Figure 7.19). We can analyze this data to determine that the majority of our data lies above the mean (15 points above the mean versus 9 points below the mean). This conclusion validates the result of the PERCENTRANK function, as discussed in the previous section where we learned that 40 percent of the data values are below the mean; therefore 60 percent, or the majority, of our data is above the mean. We can also observe from this histogram result that there is one outlier; in other words, there is one data point that falls below –2s. We will perform some more analysis with these histogram results later in the chapter.

A histogram can also be formatted. As with any chart, we click on the histogram to activate the *Chart Tools* contextual tabs, and use the commands listed on these tabs to change the design, layout and format of the histogram. For example, we have removed the *Legend* from the histograms shown above. If desired, we can also modify the font of the axis labels by right-clicking on the axis and choosing *Format Axis* from the *short-cut menu*.

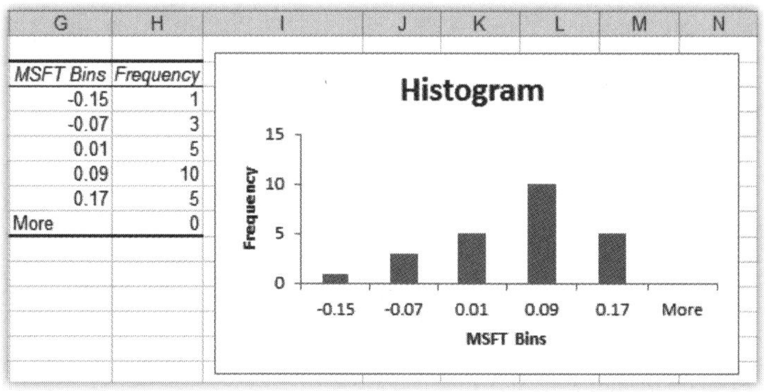

Figure 7.19 The resulting histogram uses the specified *Bin Range*.

We can also remove the gaps between the bars in the histogram to better recognize possible common distributions of the data. To remove these gaps, we double-click on a bar in the graph. The *Format Data Series* dialog box appears. On the *Series Options* window set the *Gap Width* to 0 (see Figure 7.20).

The histogram results can now be easily outlined to identify common distributions or other analyses (see Figure 7.21). We will discuss distributions later, but for now, let us next define some common histogram shapes.

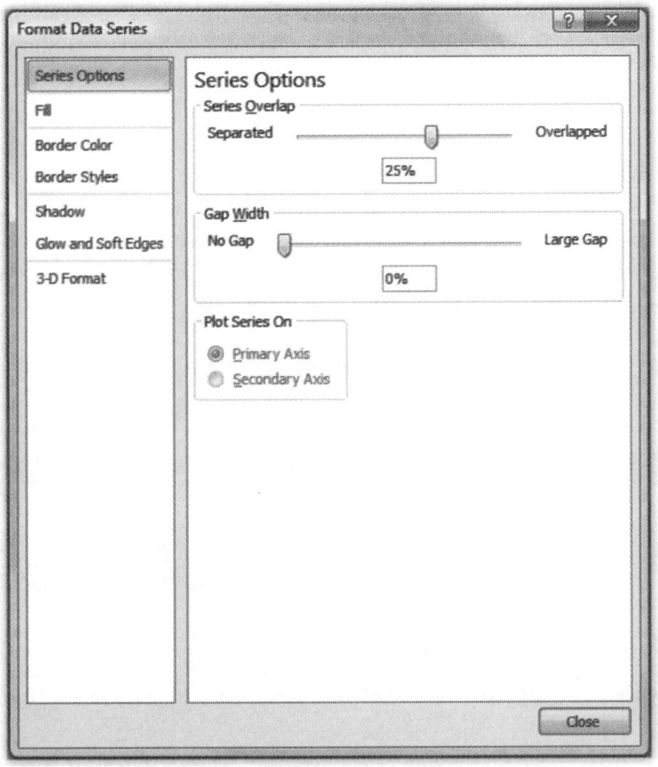

Figure 7.20 Removing the gaps by double-clicking on the bars, choosing *Format Data Series tab,* and setting the *Gap Width* to zero.

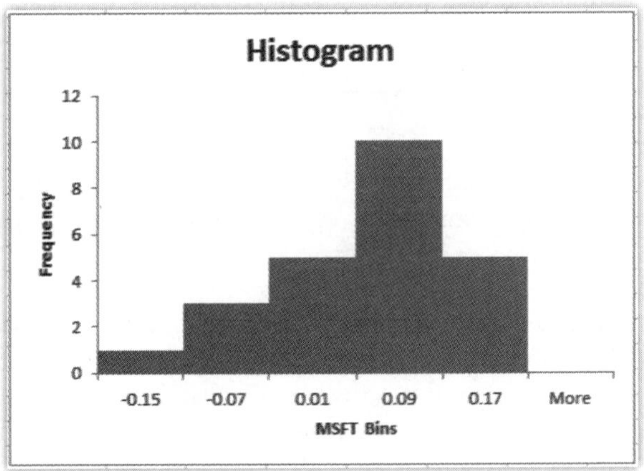

Figure 7.21 The histogram without gaps.

The histogram's four basic shapes are ***symmetric***, ***positively skewed***, ***negatively skewed***, and ***multiple peaks***. A histogram is symmetric if it has peaks and dips with equal amplitude. For example, a bimodal curve with two peaks and one dip may be symmetric if the peaks are of equal amplitude. A curve with only one peak is also symmetric; that is, if there is a central high part and almost equal lower parts to the left and right of the peak. For example, test scores are commonly symmetric; they are sometimes referred to as a bell curve because of their symmetric shape.

A skewed histogram only has one peak; however, the peak is not central, but far to the right with many lower points on the left, or far to the left with many lower points on the right. A positively skewed histogram has a peak on the left and many lower points (stretching) to the right. A negatively skewed histogram has a peak on the right and many lower points (stretching) to the left. Most economic data sets have skewed histograms. A skewed histogram may occur when the measured variable has a physical lower or upper limit. Multiple peaks imply that more than one source, or population, of data is being evaluated.

In our example, the MSFT stock returns seem to be fairly symmetric. Remember, the Skewness value from the Descriptive Statistics analysis was also between –1 and 1. However, we can also observe that there is some negative skewness.

Summary

Histograms:

Bins	The intervals of values for which frequencies are calculated.
Symmetric	A histogram with only one peak: a central high part with almost equal lower parts to the left and right of this peak.
Negatively Skewed	A histogram with a peak on the right and many lower points (stretching) to the left.
Multiple Peaks	A histogram with multiple peaks suggests that more than one source, or population, of data is being evaluated.

7.3 *Relationships in Data*

It is often helpful to determine if any relationship exists among data. This calculation is usually accomplished by comparing data relative to other data. Some examples include analyzing product sales in relation to particular months, production rates in relation to the number of employees working, and advertising costs in relation to sales.

Relationships in data are usually identified by comparing two variables: the ***dependent variable*** and the ***independent variable***. The dependent variable is the variable that we are most interested in. We may be trying to predict values for this variable by understanding its current behavior. The independent variable is the variable that we use as the comparison in order to make the prediction. There may be various independent variables with known values that we can use to analyze the relationship against the dependent variable. However, there should be one, or more, independent variables which provide the most accurate understanding of the dependent variable's behavior.

We can graph this data (with the *XY Scatter* chart type) by placing the independent variable on the x-axis and the dependent variable on the y-axis and then using a tool in Excel called a ***trend curve*** to determine if any relationship exists between these variables.

Summary

Dependent Variable The variable that a user is trying to predict or understand.

Independent Variable The variable used to make predictions.

Trend Curve The curve on a graph of data, with the independent variable on the x-axis and the dependent variable on the y-axis; it estimates the behavior of the dependent variable.

7.3.1 Trend Curves

To add a trend curve to our chart, we first click on our unstacked, 2-D, area, bar, column, line, stock, bubble or *xy scatter* chart to activate *Chart Tools* contextual tabs on the Ribbon. Next, we click on the *Chart Tools Layout > Analysis > Trendline* command to select a trend curves from the list that appears. Excel supports six types of trendlines: ***Exponential, Linear, Logarithmic, Polynomial, Power***, and ***Moving Average***. Some of these curves are illustrated in the *Trendline* drop-down list, which appears in Figure 7.22.

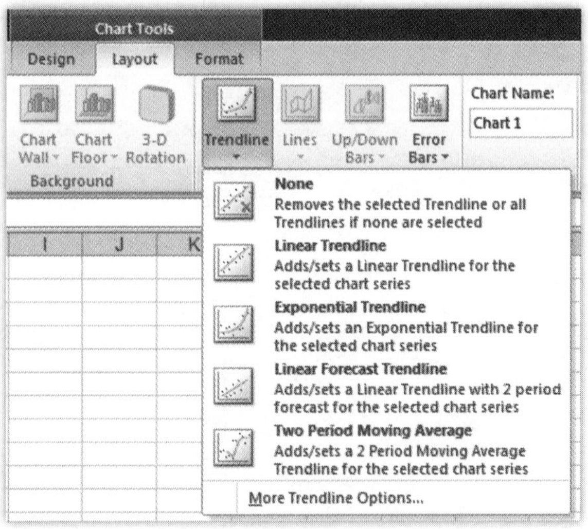

Figure 7.22 Trendline drop-down list displays different types of trendlines you can add to your chart.

Let us now discuss how to identify linear, exponential, and power trendlines in a chart. If a graph looks like a straight line would run closely through the data points, then a linear curve is best. If the dependent variable (on the y-axis) appears to increase at an increasing rate, then the exponential curve is more favorable. Similar to the exponential curve is the power curve; however, the power curve has a slower rate of increase in terms of the dependent variable.

Knowledge of the data which we are analyzing will also help in deciding which trend the data may follow.

Depending on which curve we select, Excel fits this type of trend curve to our data and creates a ***trendline*** in the chart. Excel test different equation to identify the trendline that best fits our data. We will discuss this in more detail later. For *Linear* trend curves, Excel produces the "best fitting" trendline of the selected trend curve by minimizing the sum of the squared vertical distances from each data point to the trendline. This vertical distance is called the error, or ***residual***. A positive error implies that a point lies above the line, and a negative error implies that a point lies below the line. This trendline is referred to as the ***least squares line***.

After we created the curve type that we feel best fits our data, we can change its format using the *Format Trendline* dialog box (see Figure 7.23) which appears when we double-click on the trendline. We can use this dialog box to change the type of the trendline by selecting one of the options listed. We can set trendline's name; we can either use the automatic name (default) or create a custom name. We can specify a period forward or backward for which we want to predict the behavior of our dependent variable. This period is in units of our independent variable. This is a very useful tool since it is one of the main motivations for using trend curves. The last set of options allows us to specify an intercept for the trendline and to display the trendline equation and the R-squared value on the chart. We will usually not check to Set Intercept; however, we always recommend checking to Display Equation and Display R-Squared Value. We will discuss the equation and the R-squared value for each trend curve in more detail later.

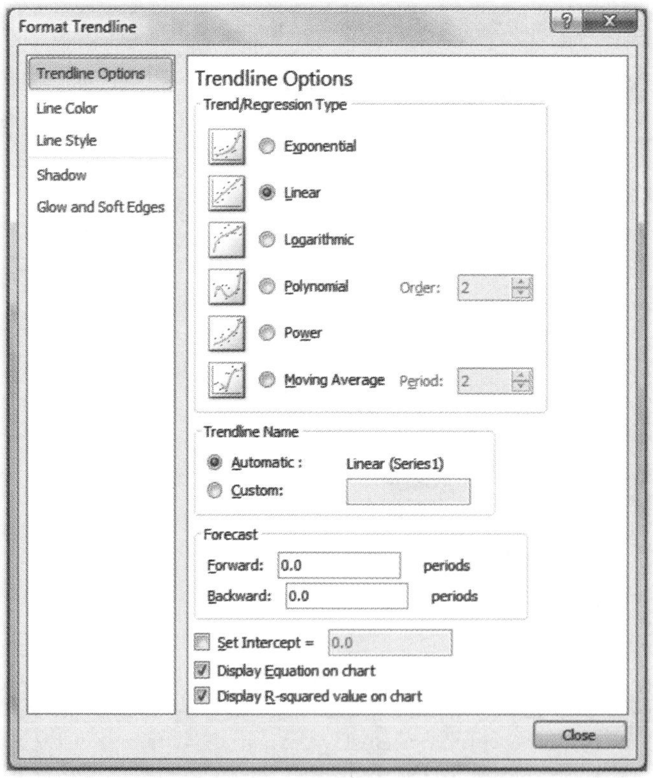

Figure 7.23 This dialog box allows you to modify the type, name, and other trendline options.

Let us compare some examples of these three different trend curves. We will begin with *Linear* curves. Suppose a company has recorded the number of "Units Produced" each month and the corresponding "Monthly Plant Cost" (see Figure 7.24). The company may be able to accurately determine how much they will produce each month; however, they want to be able to estimate their plant costs based on this production amount. They will therefore need to determine, first of all, if there is a relationship between "Units Produced" and "Monthly Plant Cost." If so, then they need to establish what type of relationship it is in order to accurately predict future monthly plant costs based on future unit production.

The dependent variable is therefore the "Monthly Plant Cost" and the independent variable is the "Units Produced." We begin this analysis by making an XY Scatter chart of the data (with the dependent variable on the y-axis and the independent variable on the x-axis). Figure 7.25 displays this chart of "Monthly Plant Cost per Units Produced."

	A	B	C
1	Production Cost		
2			
3	Month	Units Produced	Monthly Plant Cost
4	1	1260	$99,850
5	2	1007	$58,096
6	3	1096	$96,360
7	4	873	$65,675
8	5	532	$51,870
9	6	476	$27,462
10	7	482	$27,808
11	8	1173	$110,118
12	9	692	$67,470
13	10	690	$39,808
14	11	564	$32,538
15	12	470	$45,825

Figure 7.24 A record of the "Units Produced" and the "Monthly Plant Cost" for twelve months.

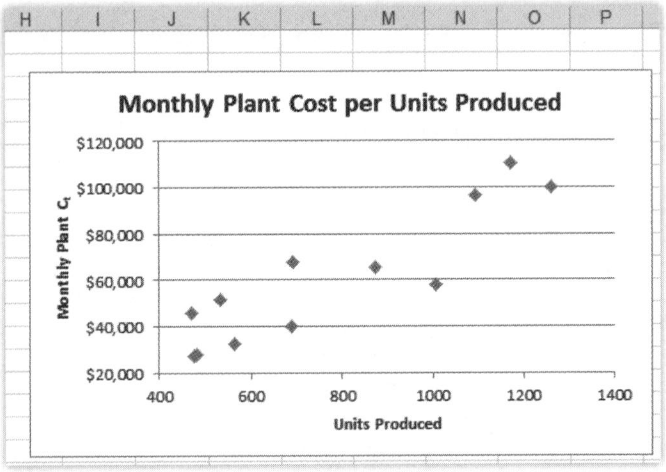

Figure 7.25 The XY Scatter Chart for the "Monthly Plant Cost per Units Produced."

We can now right-click on any of the data points and choose *Add Trendline* from the short-cut menu. The *Format Trendline* dialog box appears (see Figure 7.26). The *Linear* trend curve seems to fit this data best. (You might also think the *Power* trend curve fits well. It is okay to try different trend curves to evaluate which gives you the most accurate relationship for predictions.) We select *Linear* from the *Types* listed, and select *Display Equation on Chart* (see Figure 7.26).

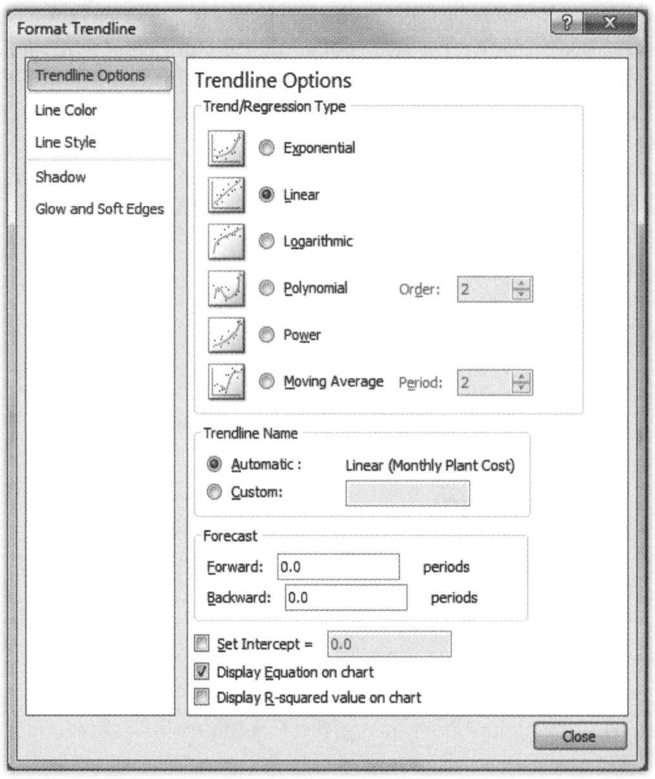

Figure 7.26 Selecting the Linear trend curve from the *Types* listed, and checking the Display Equation on the Chart option.

The trendline and the equation are then added to our chart, as illustrated in Figure 7.27.

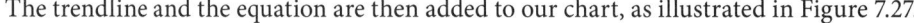

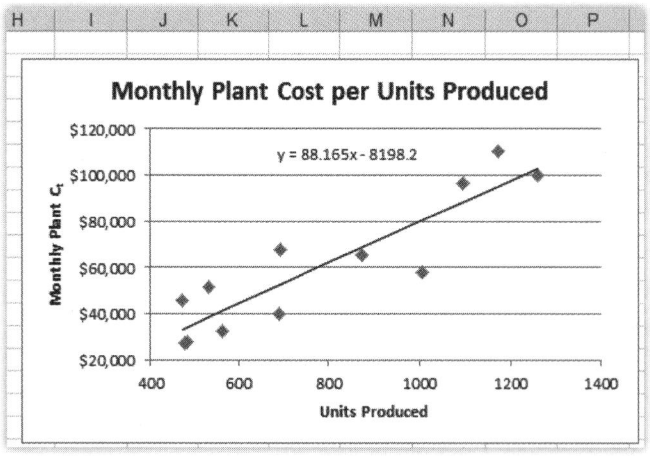

Figure 7.27 Adding the Linear trendline to the chart.

Let us now decipher what the trendline equation is. The *x* variable is the independent variable, in this example, the "Units Produced." The *y* variable is the dependent variable, in this example, the "Monthly Plant Cost." This equation suggests that for any given value of *x*, we can compute *y*. That is, for any given value of "Units Produced," we can calculate the expected "Monthly Plant Cost." We can therefore transfer this equation into a formula in our spreadsheet and create a column of "Predicted Cost" relative to the values from the "Units Produced" column. In Figure 7.28, the following formula operates in the "Predicted Cost" column:

*=88.165*B4 – 8198.2*

We copy this formula for the entire "Predicted Cost" column using relative referencing for each value in the "Units Produced" column. We then create an "Error" column, which simply subtracts the "Predicted Cost" values from the actual "Monthly Plant Cost" values. As the figure suggests, there is always some error since the actual data does not lie on a straight line. (Again, we could try calculating the "Predicted Costs" using a *Power* trend curve to compare the "Error" values.)

E4 fx =88.165*B4-8198.2

	A	B	C	D	E	F
1	Production Cost					
2						
3	Month	Units Produced	Monthly Plant Cost		Predicted Cost	Error
4	1	1260	$99,850		$102,890	$3,040
5	2	1007	$58,096		$80,584	$22,488
6	3	1096	$96,360		$88,431	-$7,929
7	4	873	$65,675		$68,770	$3,095
8	5	532	$51,870		$38,706	-$13,164
9	6	476	$27,462		$33,768	$6,307
10	7	482	$27,808		$34,297	$6,490
11	8	1173	$110,118		$95,219	-$14,898
12	9	692	$67,470		$52,812	-$14,658
13	10	690	$39,808		$52,636	$12,828
14	11	564	$32,538		$41,527	$8,988
15	12	470	$45,825		$33,239	-$12,586

Figure 7.28 Adding the "Predicted Cost" and "Error" columns to the table using the *Linear* trendline equation.

Now we have enough information to address the initial problem for this example: predicting future "Monthly Plant Costs" based on planned production amounts. In Figure 7.29, we have added "Units Produced" values for three more months. Copying the formula for "Predicted Cost" to these three new rows gives us the predicted monthly costs.

Note that since our prediction of the dependent variable relies on the independent variable, we cannot predict the independent variable itself. We may, however, predict future values of the dependent variable by extrapolation. That is, we can use new values of the independent variable, not originally given in the data, to predict future values of the dependent variable. This extrapolation can be done using the trendline equations.

Now, let us discuss *Exponential* trend curves. In Figure 7.30, we have "Sales" data for ten years. If we want to be able to predict sales for the next few years, we must determine what relationship exists between these two variables. So, our independent variable is "Years" and our dependent variable is "Sales."

	A	B	C	D	E
1	Production Cost				
2					
3	Month	Units Produced	Monthly Plant Cost		Predicted Cost
4	1	1260	$99,850		$102,890
5	2	1007	$58,096		$80,584
6	3	1096	$96,360		$88,431
7	4	873	$65,675		$68,770
8	5	532	$51,870		$38,706
9	6	476	$27,462		$33,768
10	7	482	$27,808		$34,297
11	8	1173	$110,118		$95,219
12	9	692	$67,470		$52,812
13	10	690	$39,808		$52,636
14	11	564	$32,538		$41,527
15	12	470	$45,825		$33,239
19	13	520			$37,648
20	14	670			$50,872
21	15	642			$48,404

Figure 7.29 Calculating the "Predicted Cost" for the next three months.

	A	B
1	Sales Data	
2		
3	Year	Sales
4	1	70
5	2	183
6	3	340
7	4	649
8	5	1243
9	6	1979
10	7	4096
11	8	6440
12	9	8459
13	10	12154

Figure 7.30 Sales per year.

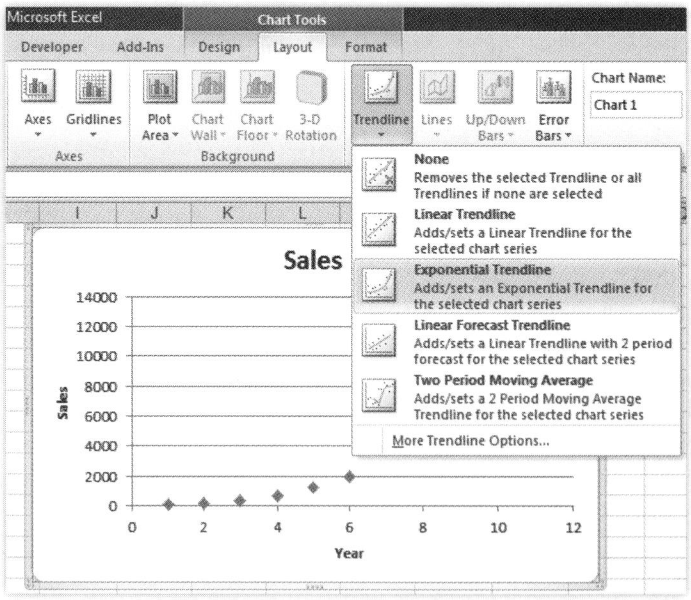

Figure 7.31 Choosing the Exponential trend curve.

After creating the *XY Scatter* chart of this data (x-axis as "Year," y-axis as "Sales"), we right-click on a data point to add the trendline (see Figure 7.31). This time, we choose an *Exponential* curve to fit our data. (Again the *Power* curve seems like another possible fit that we could test.) We also choose to display the trendline equation on the chart. Figure 7.32 displays the resulting chart with the trendline.

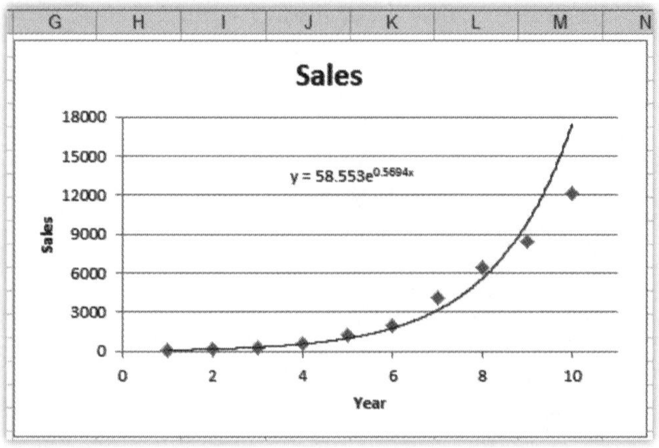

Figure 7.32 Adding the Exponential trendline to the charted data.

Let us analyze the equation provided on the chart. Again, the y variable represents the dependent variable, in this example, "Sales." The x variable represents the independent variable, in this example, "Year." We can therefore transform this equation into a formula in our spreadsheet and create a "Prediction" column in which we estimate sales based on the year. In Figure 7.33, we have done so using the following formula:

*=58.553*EXP(0.5694*A4)*

The EXP function raises e to the power in parentheses. We have copied this formula for all of the years provided in order to compare our estimated values to the actual values. Notice that there are some larger "Error" values as the years increase.

D4 | =58.553*EXP(0.5694*A4)

	A	B	C	D	E	F
1	Sales Data					
2						
3	Year	Sales		Prediction	Error	
4	1	70		103.48	33.48	
5	2	183		182.86	-0.14	
6	3	340		323.16	-16.84	
7	4	649		571.08	-77.92	
8	5	1243		1009.22	-233.78	
9	6	1979		1783.50	-195.50	
10	7	4096		3151.81	-944.19	
11	8	6440		5569.90	-870.10	
12	9	8459		9843.16	1384.16	
13	10	12154		17394.90	5240.90	

Figure 7.33 Calculating the "Prediction" values with the *Exponential* trendline equation.

We can now use this formula to predict sales values for future years. However, the *Exponential* trend curve has a sharply increasing slope that may not be accurate for many situations. For example, in six years from our current date, year 16, we have estimated about 530,000 sales using the *Exponential* trendline equation. This amount seems a highly unlikely number given previous historical data (see Figure 7.34). Even though the *Exponential* trend curve increases rapidly towards infinity, it is unlikely that sales will do the same. Therefore, for predicting values much further in the future, we may consider using a different trend curve (perhaps the *Power* curve).

D15 =58.553*EXP(0.5694*A15)

	A	B	C	D	E
1	Sales Data				
2					
3	Year	Sales		Prediction	Error
4	1	70		103.48	33.48
5	2	183		182.86	-0.14
6	3	340		323.16	-16.84
7	4	649		571.08	-77.92
8	5	1243		1009.22	-233.78
9	6	1979		1783.50	-195.50
10	7	4096		3151.81	-944.19
11	8	6440		5569.90	-870.10
12	9	8459		9843.16	1384.16
13	10	12154		17394.90	5240.90
14	...				
15	16			529841.05	

Figure 7.34 Using the Exponential trendline equation to predict sales for year 16.

Now, let us consider an example of a *Power* trend curve. In Figure 7.35, we are presented with yearly "Production" and the yearly "Unit Cost" of production. We want to determine the relationship between "Unit Cost" and "Production" in order to be able to predict future "Unit Costs."

	A	B	C
1	Production Data		
2			
3	Year	Production	Unit Cost
4	2002	64000	$ 3,700.00
5	2003	70000	$ 3,416.00
6	2004	100000	$ 3,125.00
7	2005	150000	$ 2,583.00
8	2006	175000	$ 2,166.00
9	2007	400000	$ 1,833.00
10	2008	785000	$ 1,788.00

Figure 7.35 Yearly Production and Unit Costs.

We begin by creating the XY Scatter chart and then right-clicking on a data point to add a trendline. This time we choose a *Power* curve to fit the data (see Figure 7.36). (*Exponential* may also be an appropriate fit for this data, but the slope of the recorded data points does not seem to be that steep.) Even though our data is decreasing, not increasing, it is the slope of the data points that we are observing in order to find a suitable fit. Again, we choose to display the trendline equation. Figure 7.37 demonstrates the resulting trendline with the charted data points.

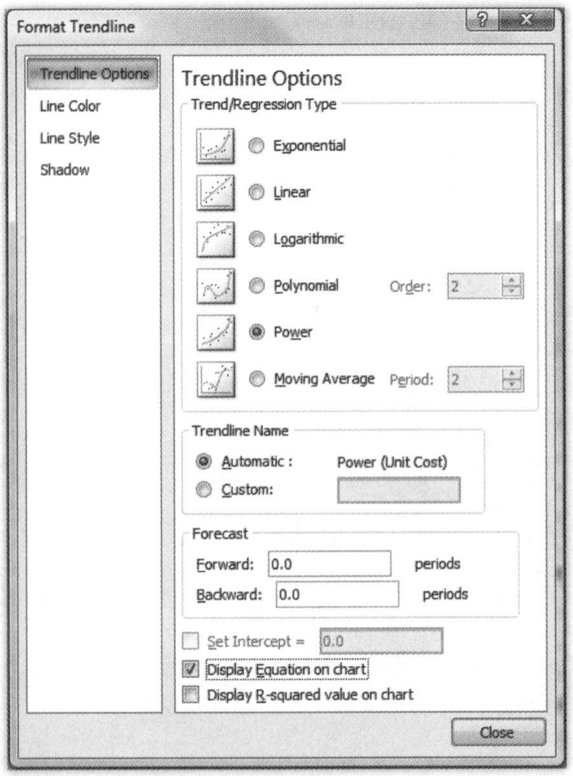

Figure 7.36 Choosing the *Power* curve.

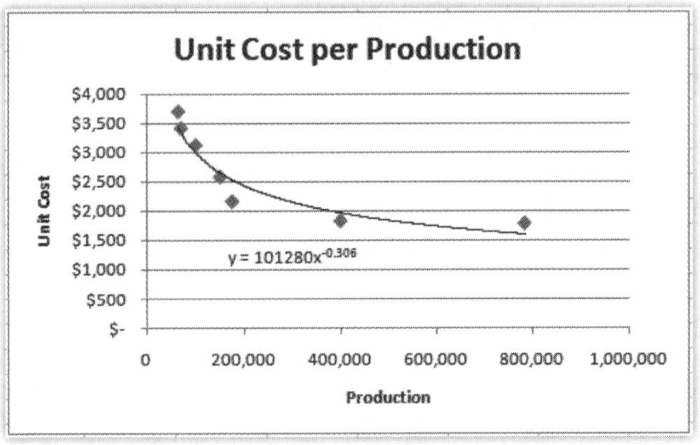

Figure 7.37 Fitting the *Power* curve to the "Unit Cost per Cumulative Production" chart.

Looking at the *Power* trendline equation, we again identify x to be the independent variable, in this case, "Production," and y to be the dependent variable, in this case, the "Unit Cost." We transform this equation into a formula on the spreadsheet in a "Forecast" column to compare our estimated values with the actual costs. We copy the following formula for all of the given years:

*=101280*B4^–0.306*

Figure 7.38 displays these forecasted cost values and the "Error" calculated between the forecasted and actual data. The error values, here shown as absolute error values, seem to be fairly stable, therefore implying a reliable fit.

E4 =101280*B4^(-0.306)

	A	B	C	D	E	F
1	Production Data					
2						
3	Year	Production	Unit Cost		Forecast	Error
4	2002	64000	$ 3,700.00		$3,426.36	$ 273.64
5	2003	70000	$ 3,416.00		$3,333.68	$ 82.32
6	2004	100000	$ 3,125.00		$2,988.98	$ 136.02
7	2005	150000	$ 2,583.00		$2,640.22	$ 57.22
8	2006	175000	$ 2,166.00		$2,518.57	$ 352.57
9	2007	400000	$ 1,833.00		$1,955.66	$ 122.66
10	2008	785000	$ 1,788.00		$1,591.09	$ 196.91

Figure 7.38 Creating the "Forecast" and "Error" columns with the *Power* trendline equation.

We would now like to make a note about using data with dates (for example the "Year" in the above example). If dates are employed as an independent variable, we must convert them into a simple numerical list. For example, if we had chosen to assign the "Year" column in the above example as an independent variable for predicting the "Unit Cost," we would have had to renumber the years from 1 to 7, 1 being the first year, 2 the second, etc., in which the data was collected. Using actual dates may yield inaccurate calculations.

Summary

Trend Curves:

Linear Curve	y = a*x – b
Exponential Curve	y = a*e^(b*x) or y = a*EXP(b*x)
Power Curve	y = a*x^b
Residual	The vertical distance, or error, between the trendline and the data points.
Least Squares Line	The trendline with the minimum squared residual error.

7.3.2 Regression

Another more accurate way to ensure that the relationships we have chosen for our data are reliable fits is by using regression analysis parameters. These parameters include the ***R-Squared value***, ***standard error***, ***slope*** and ***intercept***. We note here that Excel uses linear regression only. This means that the model we examine must be linear in its parameters.

The R-Squared value measures the amount of influence that the independent variable has on the dependent variable. The closer the R-Squared value is to 1, the stronger the linear relationship between the independent and dependent variables is. If the R-Squared value is closer to 0, then there may not be a relationship between them. We can then draw on multiple regression and other tools to determine a better independent variable to predict the dependent variable.

To determine the R-Squared value of a regression, or a trendline, we can use the *Format Trendline* dialog box on a chart of data and specify to *Display R-Squared Value on Chart* in the bottom of *Trendline Options* window (see Figures 7.23, 7.26 and 7.36). Let us review the previous three examples to discover their R-Squared values. We have gone back to our charts and added the R-Squared display option by right-clicking on the trendline previously created. We then *Format Trendline* to revisit the *Trendline Options* window and specify this new option.

For the first example, we fit a *Linear* trendline to the "Monthly Plant Cost per Units Produced" chart (see Figure 7.39). The R-Squared value is 0.8137, which is fairly close to 1. We could try other trend curves and compare the R-Squared values to determine which fit is the best.

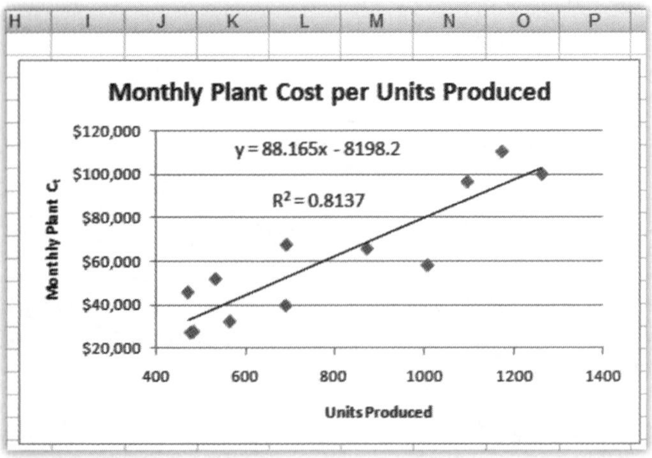

Figure 7.39 The R-Squared value on the Linear trendline.

In the following example, we fit an *Exponential* trendline to the "Sales per Year" chart (see Figure 7.40). The R-Squared value for this data is 0.9828. This value is very close to 1 and therefore a sound fit. Again, it is wise to compare the R-Squared values for *Exponential* and *Power* curves on a set of data with an increasing slope.

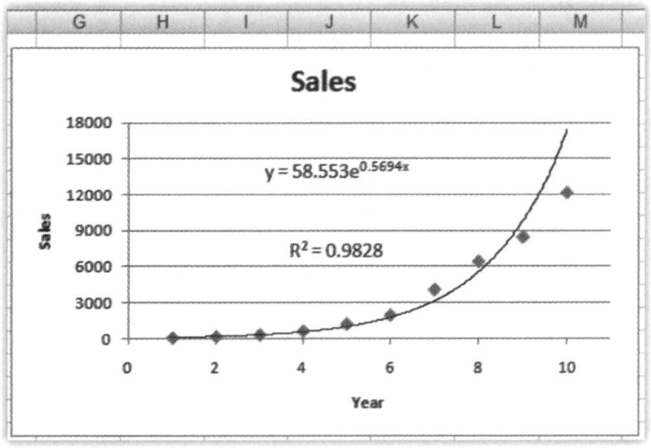

Figure 7.40 The R-Squared value for the Exponential trendline.

In the last example, we fit a *Power* trendline to the "Unit Cost per Cumulative Production" chart (see Figure 7.41). The R-Squared value is 0.9062, which is also very close to 1 and therefore an indication of a good fit.

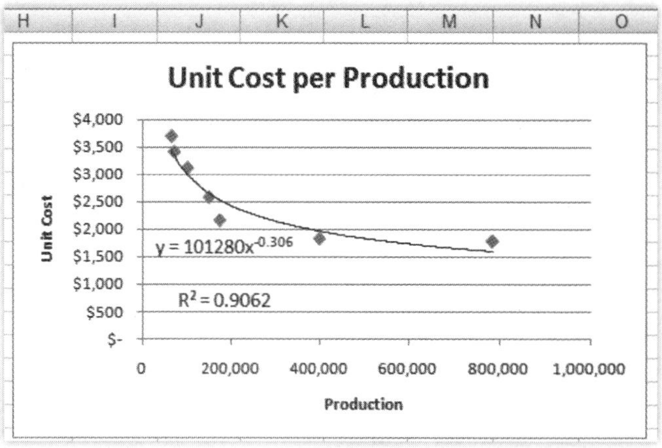

Figure 7.41 The R-Squared value with the Power trendline.

Excel's ***RSQ*** function can calculate an R-squared value from a set of data. Again, we note here that the model must be linear in its parameters in order to use Excel's regression tools and functions. The format of the RSQ function is:

=RSQ(y_range, x_range)

Note that this function only works with *Linear* trend curves. We must also make sure that we have entered the y_range, or the dependent variable data, before the x_range, or the independent variable data. In Figure 7.42, we have employed the RSQ function with the first example from above to measure the accuracy of a *Linear* trendline as applied to the "Monthly Plant Cost per Units Produced" data. We can verify that the result of this function is the same as the one attained with the R-Squared value.

The standard error measures the accuracy of any predictions made. In other words, it measures the "spread" around the least squares line, or the trendline. We have learned previously that this value can be found using *Descriptive Statistics*. It can also be calculated in Excel with the ***STEYX*** function. The format of this function is:

=STEYX(y_range, x_range)

Again, we note here that the model must be linear in its parameters in order to use Excel's regression tools and functions. In the example above, we have calculated the standard error using the STEYX function (see Figure 7.43). We can now use this value to check for outliers as we did using the standard deviation value in the previous sections. These outliers reveal how accurate our fit is with a *Linear* trendline.

Two other Excel functions that can be applied to a linear regression line of a collection of data are ***SLOPE*** and ***INTERCEPT***. The SLOPE function's format is:

=SLOPE(y_range, x_range)

Similarly, the intercept of the linear regression line of the data can be determined with the INTERCEPT function. The format of this function is:

=INTERCEPT(y_range, x_range)

C21 =RSQ(C4:C15,B4:B15)

	A	B	C
1	Production Cost		
2			
3	Month	Units Produced	Monthly Plant Cost
4	1	1260	$99,850
5	2	1007	$58,096
6	3	1096	$96,360
7	4	873	$65,675
8	5	532	$51,870
9	6	476	$27,462
10	7	482	$27,808
11	8	1173	$110,118
12	9	692	$67,470
13	10	690	$39,808
14	11	564	$32,538
15	12	470	$45,825
19			
20			
21		RSQ	0.8137

Figure 7.42 Using the RSQ function to calculate the R-Squared value of the *Linear* trendline.

C22 =STEYX(C4:C15,B4:B15)

	A	B	C
1	Production Cost		
2			
3	Month	Units Produced	Monthly Plant Cost
4	1	1260	$99,850
5	2	1007	$58,096
6	3	1096	$96,360
7	4	873	$65,675
8	5	532	$51,870
9	6	476	$27,462
10	7	482	$27,808
11	8	1173	$110,118
12	9	692	$67,470
13	10	690	$39,808
14	11	564	$32,538
15	12	470	$45,825
19			
20			
21		RSQ	0.8137
22		STEYX	$12,974

Figure 7.43 Using the STEYX function to calculate the standard error.

In Figure 7.44, we are finding the slope and intercept of the linear regression line of the "Monthly Plant Cost per Units Produced" data.

C25 =INTERCEPT(C4:C15,B4:B15)

	A	B	C	D
1	Production Cost			
2				
3	Month	Units Produced	Monthly Plant Cost	
4	1	1260	$99,850	
5	2	1007	$58,096	
6	3	1096	$96,360	
7	4	873	$65,675	
8	5	532	$51,870	
9	6	476	$27,462	
10	7	482	$27,808	
11	8	1173	$110,118	
12	9	692	$67,470	
13	10	690	$39,808	
14	11	564	$32,538	
15	12	470	$45,825	
19				
20				
21		RSQ	0.8137	
22		STEYX	$12,974	
23				
24		SLOPE	$88	
25		INTERCEPT	-$8,198	

Figure 7.44 Finding the slope and intercept with the SLOPE and INTERCEPT functions.

Summary

Regression:

R-Squared Value	Measures the amount of influence that the independent variable has on the dependent variable.
Standard Error	Measures the accuracy of any predictions made.

More Statistical Functions:

RSQ	Finds the R-squared value of a set of data.
STEYX	Finds the standard error of regression for a set of data.
SLOPE	Finds the slope of a set of data.
INTERCEPT	Finds the intercept of a set of data.

7.4 Distributions

We will now discuss some of the more common distributions that can be recognized when performing a statistical analysis of data. These are the ***Normal***, ***Exponential***, ***Uniform***, ***Binomial***, ***Poisson***, ***Beta***, and ***Weibull*** distributions. The Normal, Exponential and Uniform distributions are those most often used in practice. The Binomial and Poisson are also common distributions.

Most of these distributions have Excel functions associated with them. These functions are basically equivalent to using distribution tables. In other words, given certain parameters of a set of data for a particular distribution, we can look at a distribution table to find the corresponding area from the distribution curve. These Excel functions perform this task for us.

Let us begin with the Normal distribution. The parameters for this distribution are simply the value that we are interested in finding the probability for, and the mean and standard deviation of the set of data. The function that we apply with the Normal distribution is ***NORM.DIST***, and with these parameters, the format for this function is:

=NORM.DIST(x, mean, std_dev, cumulative)

We will use the *cumulative* parameter in many Excel distribution functions. This parameter takes the values *True* and *False* to determine if we want the value returned from the ***probability density function*** or the ***cumulative distribution function***, respectively. To distinguish between the cumulative distribution function and the probability density function, we must first define *discrete* and *continuous* distributions. With a discrete distribution, we can compute probabilities of a particular value. Therefore, with a discrete distribution, the *probability density function* (*pdf*) determines the probability that a value is exactly equal to x. With a continuous distribution, we can only compute probabilities over a range. Thus, the *cumulative distribution function* (*cdf*) determines the probability that a value in the data set is less than or equal to x. We will employ this general function definition to understand the *cumulative* parameter of other distribution functions as well.

For example, suppose annual drug sales at a local drugstore are distributed Normally with a mean of 40,000 and standard deviation of 10,000. What is the probability that the actual sales for the year are at most 42,000? To answer this, we use the NORM.DIST function:

=NORM.DIST(42000, 40000, 10000, True)

This function returns a 0.58 probability, or 58% chance, that given this mean and standard deviation for the Normal distribution, annual drug sales will be 42,000 (see Figure 7.45).

C8 | =NORM.DIST(A8,$B$4,$B$5,TRUE)

	A	B	C
1	Normal		
2			
3	Drug demand		
4	Mean	40000	
5	Std Dev	10000	
6			
7	Prob that demand is:		
8	42000		0.58

Figure 7.45 Using the NORM.DIST with the cumulative distribution function.

The cumulative distribution can also determine the probability that a value will lie in a given interval. Using the same example data, what is the probability that annual sales will be between 35,000 and 49,000? To find this value, we subtract the cdf values for these two bounds:

=NORM.DIST(49000, 40000, 10000, True) – NORM.DIST(35000, 40000, 10000, True)

This function returns a 0.51 probability, or 51% chance, that annual sales will be between 35,000 and 49,000 (see Figure 7.46).

C14 | =NORM.DIST(A12,$B$4,$B$5,TRUE)-NORM.DIST(A11,$B$4,$B$5,TRUE)

	A	B	C	D	E	F	G
1	Normal						
2							
3	Drug demand						
4	Mean	40000					
5	Std Dev	10000					
6							
7	Prob that demand is:						
8	42000		0.58				
9							
10	Prob that demand is between 35000 and 49000						
11	35000		0.31				
12	49000		0.82				
13	between		0.51				
14			0.51				

Figure 7.46 Using the NORM.DIST function with an interval of *x* values.

Related to the Normal distribution is the Standard Normal distribution. If the mean of our data is 0 and the standard deviation is 1, then placing these values in the NORM.DIST function with the *cumulative* parameter as *True* determines the resulting value from the Standard Normal distribution. There are also two other functions that determine the Standard Normal distribution value: ***STANDARDIZE*** and ***NORM.S.DIST***.

STANDARDIZE converts the *x* value from a data set of a mean not equal to 0 and a standard deviation not equal to 1 into a value that does assume a mean of 0 and a standard deviation of 1. That is, it computes a "z value." The format of this function is:

=STANDARDIZE(x, mean, std_dev)

The resulting standardized value is then used as the main parameter in the NORMSDIST function:

=NORM.S.DIST(standardized_x, cumulative)

This function then finds the corresponding probability from the Standard Normal distribution. These functions are valuable as they relieve much manual work in converting a Normal x value into a Standard Normal x value.

Let us now consider the same example as above to determine the probability that a drugstore's annual sales are 42,000 or less. We standardize this using the following function:

=STANDARDIZE(42000, 40000, 10000)

The result of this function is 0.2. We can then use this value in the NORM.S.DIST function to compute the probability:

=NORM.S.DIST(0.2, True)

This function again returns a probability of 0.58 that the sales will reach 42,000 or less (see Figure 7.47).

The Uniform distribution does not actually have a corresponding Excel function; however, there is a simple formula that models the Uniform distribution for the interval (a, b). This formula, or *pdf*, is:

= 1/(b−a)

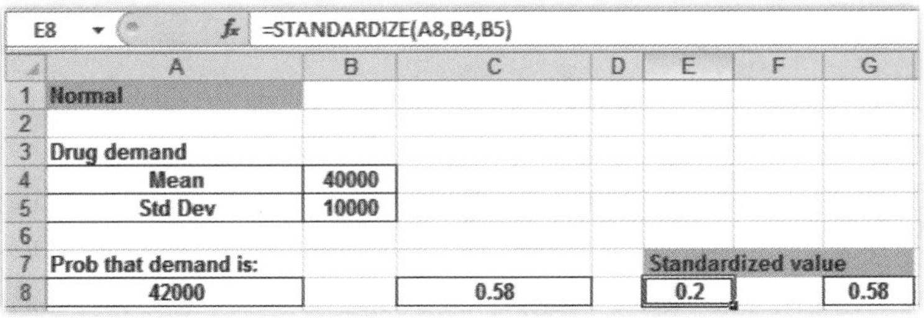

Figure 7.47 Using the STANDARDIZE and NORM.S.DIST functions.

To apply this formula in Excel, we recommend creating three columns: one for possible a values, one for possible b values, and one for the result of the Uniform *pdf* formula (see Figure 7.48).

The *cdf* formula for a value x which lies in the interval (a, b) is then:

*= (x − a)*PDF*

We can, therefore, complete our calculations in the example given (see Figure 7.48) by adding a cell for the x value and another for the cdf formula.

The Poisson distribution has only the mean as its parameter. The function we use for this distribution is ***POISSON.DIST*** and the format is:

=POISSON.DIST(x, mean, cumulative)

CDF_val | f_x =(x_val-a_val)*PDF_val

	A	B	C	D	E
1					
2	Uniform				
3					
4	a value	b value	PDF value		
5	2	5	0.3333		
6					
7		x value	CDF value		
8		4	0.6667		

Figure 7.48 Using the Uniform distribution formula for various values of *a* and *b*.

(Note that for the Poisson distribution, the mean may be in terms of *lambda*time*.) The Poisson distribution value is the probability that the number of events that occur is either between 0 and *x* (*cdf*) or equal to *x* (*pdf*).

For example, consider a bakery that serves an average of 20 customers per hour. Find the probability that, at the most, 35 customers will be served in the next two hours. To do so, we use the POISSON function with a mean value of lambda*time = 20*2.

*=POISSON.DIST(35, 20*2, True)*

This function returns a 0.24 probability value that no more than 35 customers will be served in the next two hours (see Figure 7.49).

A10 | f_x =POISSON.DIST(B8,A5*B7,TRUE)

	A	B	C	D	E
1					
2	Poisson				
3					
4	Customer Service Rate				
5	20	cust/hr			
6					
7	In Time:	2	hrs		
8	Numb of Cust	35			
9					
10	0.24				

Figure 7.49 Using the POISSON.DIST function with the service time.

The Exponential distribution has only one parameter: lambda. The function we use for this distribution is ***EXPON.DIST*** and its format is:

=EXPON.DIST(x, lambda, cumulative)

(Note that the *lambda* value is equivalent to *1/mean*.) The *cumulative* parameter is the same as described above. The *x* value is what we are interested in finding the distribution value for, and *lambda* is the distribution parameter.

A common application of the Exponential distribution is for modeling interarrival times. Let us use the bakery example from above. If we are told that, on average, 20 customers are served per hour and we assume that each customer is served as soon as he or she arrives, then the arrival rate is said to be 20 customers per hour. This arrival rate can be converted into the interarrival mean by inverting this value; the interarrival mean, or the Exponential mean, is therefore 1/20 hours per customer arrival. Therefore, if we want to determine the probability that a customer arrives in 10 minutes, we set $x = 10/60 = 0.17$ hour and lambda = 1/(1/20) = 20 hours in the EXPONDIST function:

=EXPON.DIST(0.17, 20, True)

This function returns a probability value of 0.96 that a customer will arrive within 10 minutes (see Figure 7.50).

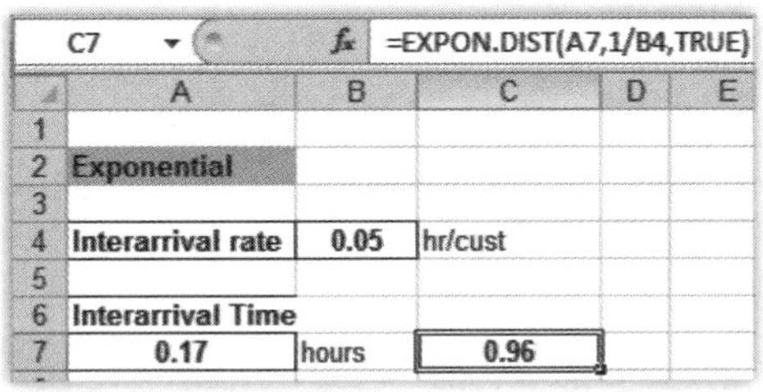
C7 fx =EXPON.DIST(A7,1/B4,TRUE)

	A	B	C	D	E
1					
2	Exponential				
3					
4	Interarrival rate	0.05	hr/cust		
5					
6	Interarrival Time				
7	0.17	hours	0.96		

Figure 7.50 Using the EXPON.DIST function with the interarrival time.

The Binomial distribution has the following parameters: the number of trials and the probability of success. We are trying to determine the probability that the number of successes is less than (using *cdf*) or equal to (*pdf*) some *x* value. The function for this distribution is ***BINOM.DIST*** and its format is:

=BINOM.DIST(x, trials, prob_success, cumulative)

(Note that the values of *x* and *trials* should be integers.) For example, suppose a marketing group is conducting a survey to find out if people are more influenced by newspaper or television ads. Assuming, from historical data, that 40 percent of people pay more attention to ads in the newspaper, and 60 percent pay more attention to ads on television, what is the probability that out of 100 people surveyed, 50 of them respond more to ads on television? To determine this, we use the BINOM.DIST function with the *prob_success* value equal to 0.60.

=BINOM.DIST(50, 100, 0.60, True)

This function returns a value of 0.03 that exactly 50 out of 100 people will report that they respond more to television ads than newspaper ads (see Figure 7.51).

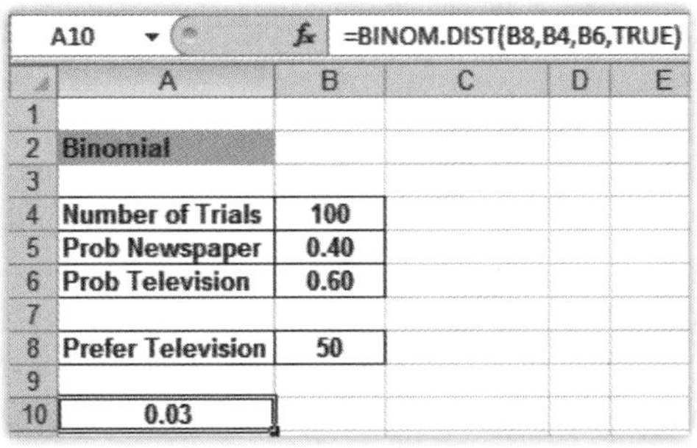
A10 fx =BINOM.DIST(B8,B4,B6,TRUE)

	A	B	C	D	E
1					
2	Binomial				
3					
4	Number of Trials	100			
5	Prob Newspaper	0.40			
6	Prob Television	0.60			
7					
8	Prefer Television	50			
9					
10	0.03				

Figure 7.51 Using the BINOM.DIST function with the survey data.

The Beta distribution has the following parameters: *alpha*, *beta*, *A*, and *B*. *Alpha* and *beta* are determined from the data set; *A* and *B* are optional bounds on the *x* value for which we want the Beta distribution value. The function for this distribution is ***BETA.DIST*** and its format is:

=BETA.DIST(x, alpha, beta, cumulative, A, B)

If *A* and *B* are omitted, then a standard cumulative distribution is assumed and they are assigned the values 0 and 1, respectively.

For example, suppose a management team is trying to complete a big project by an upcoming deadline. They want to determine the probability that they can complete the project in 10 days. They estimate the total time needed to be one to two weeks based on previous projects that they have worked on together; these estimates will be the bound values, or the *A* and *B* parameters. They can also determine a mean and standard deviation (or variance) from this past data to be 12 and 3 days, respectively. We can use this mean and standard deviation to compute the alpha and beta parameters; we do so using some complex transformation equations (shown in Figure 7.52), resulting in *alpha* = 0.08 and *beta* = 0.03. (Note that usually alpha and beta can be found in a resource table for the Beta distribution.) We can then use the BETA.DIST function as follows:

=BETA.DIST(10, 0.08, 0.03, True, 7, 14)

The result reveals that there is a 0.28 probability that they can finish the project in 10 or fewer days (see Figure 7.52).

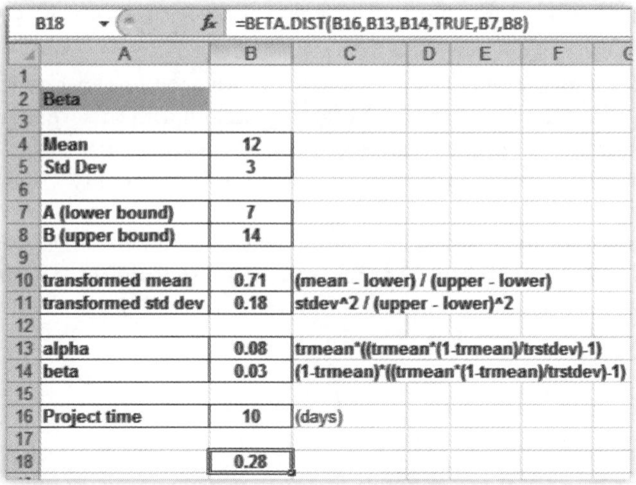

B18 =BETA.DIST(B16,B13,B14,TRUE,B7,B8)

	A	B	C
1			
2	Beta		
3			
4	Mean	12	
5	Std Dev	3	
6			
7	A (lower bound)	7	
8	B (upper bound)	14	
9			
10	transformed mean	0.71	(mean - lower) / (upper - lower)
11	transformed std dev	0.18	stdev^2 / (upper - lower)^2
12			
13	alpha	0.08	trmean*((trmean*(1-trmean)/trstdev)-1)
14	beta	0.03	(1-trmean)*((trmean*(1-trmean)/trstdev)-1)
15			
16	Project time	10	(days)
17			
18		0.28	

Figure 7.52 Using BETA.DIST and calculating the *alpha* and *beta* values.

The Weibull distribution has the parameters *alpha* and *beta*. The function we use for this distribution is ***WEIBULL.DIST*** and its format is:

=WEIBULL.DIST(x, alpha, beta, cumulative)

(Note that if *alpha* is equal to 1, then this distribution becomes equivalent to the Exponential distribution with *lambda* equal to 1/*beta*.) The Weibull distribution is most commonly employed to determine reliability functions. Consider the inspection of 50 light bulbs. Past data reveals that on average, a light bulb lasts 1200 hours, with a standard deviation of 100 hours (the variance could also be used here). We use these values and find alpha and beta to be 14.71 and 1243.44, respectively. (Note that usually alpha and beta can be located in a resource table for the Weibull distribution.) We can now use the WEIBULL.DIST distribution to determine the probability that a light bulb will be reliable for at least 55 days = 1320 hours.

=WEIBULL(1320, 14.71, 1243.44, True)

The result is a 0.91 probability that a light bulb will last up to 1320 hours, or 55 days (see Figure 7.53). This is also known as a reliability analysis; that is, finding the probability of survival.

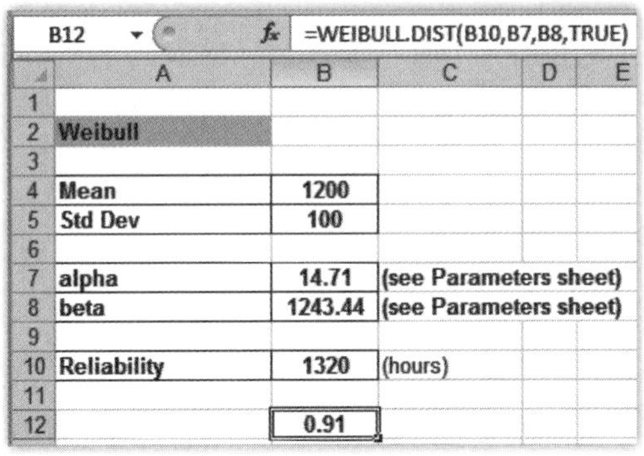

B12 =WEIBULL.DIST(B10,B7,B8,TRUE)

	A	B	C	D	E
1					
2	Weibull				
3					
4	Mean	1200			
5	Std Dev	100			
6					
7	alpha	14.71	(see Parameters sheet)		
8	beta	1243.44	(see Parameters sheet)		
9					
10	Reliability	1320	(hours)		
11					
12		0.91			

Figure 7.53 Using the WEIBULL.DIST function to determine the reliability of a light bulb.

When we build simulation models (see Chapter 9) we need to generate random numbers in Excel which are within a given distribution. To accomplish this we must use the inverse functions of the distribution functions we described above. An inverse function returns the inverse of the cumulative probability function. That is, if probability = DIST(x,...), then DISTINV(probability,...) = x.

Some of the inverse functions of the more common distributions are ***BETA.INV***, ***BINOM.INV***, ***LOGNORM.INV***, and ***NORM.INV***. We can find these functions listed under the *Formulas > Function Library > More Functions* drop-down menu on the *Ribbon*. The format of these inverse functions is:

=DIST.INV(probability, distribution_parameters)

The *probability* parameter is a number between 0 and 1. We will use the RAND function to generate a number between 0 and 1. For example, to generate random numbers from the *Normal* distribution, we would follow the next format:

=NORM.INV(RAND(), mean, std dev)

In Figure 7.54, we have entered this function in a column of cells for a *Normal* distribution with a mean of 50 and a standard deviation of 15. The function is entered as the following:

=NORM.INV(RAND(), 50, 15)

Note that most of the numbers generated are in the range between 35 (that is, 50 – 15) and 65 (that is, 50 + 15), with the majority being closer to 50.

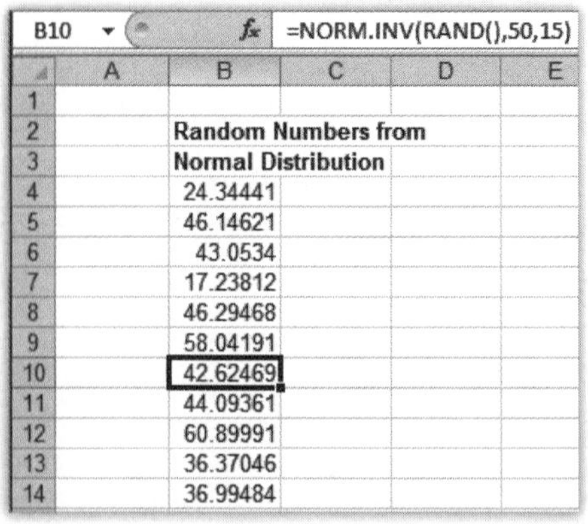

Figure 7.54 To generate a random number within a distribution, we use the RAND() function as the first parameter of the inverse distribution functions.

Summary

Distribution Functions:	**Parameters:**
NORM.DIST	*x, mean, std_dev, cumulative*
EXPON.DIST	*x, lamda, cumulative*
Uniform	*a, b*
BINOM.DIST	*x, trials, prob_success, cumulative*
POISSON.DIST	*x, mean, cumulative*
BETA.DIST	*x, alpha, beta, A, B*
WEIBULL.DIST	*x, alpha, beta, cumulative*
NORM.INV	*probability, mean, std_dev*
Other Distribution Functions:	F.DIST, GAMMA.DIST, HYPGEOM.DIST, LOGNORM.DIST, NEGBINOM.DIST, BETA.INV, BINOM.INV, LOGNORM.INV

7.5 Summary

- Some of Excel's basic statistical functions are: AVERAGE to find the mean, MEDIAN to find the median, and STDEV.P and STDEV.S to find the standard deviation of a set of data.
- The Analysis Toolpak is an Excel Add-In that includes statistical analysis techniques such as *Descriptive Statistics*, *Histograms*, *Exponential Smoothing*, *Correlation*, *Covariance*, *Moving Average*, and others.
- The *Descriptive Statistics* option provides a list of statistical information about a data set, including the mean, median, standard deviation, and variance.
- The *Mean* is the average of all values in a data set, or all observations in a sample. The *Median* is

the "middle" observation when data is sorted in ascending order. The *Mode* is the most frequently occurring value.

- The *Sample Variance* is the average squared distance from the mean to each data point. The *Standard Deviation, s,* is the square root of the *Sample Variance.* Any values in the data set that lie more than *+/–2s* from the mean are called *outliers.* Excel functions such as IF, ABS, and OR can identify outliers. Conditional Formatting can also be used.
- *Kurtosis* is a measure of a data's peaks. *Skewness* is a measure of how symmetric or asymmetric data is.
- The *Confidence Level for Mean* constrains the mean calculation to a specified confidence level. The *Kth Largest* and *Kth Smallest* options provide the respectively ranked data value for a specified value of k.
- Similar to the Kth Largest and Kth Smallest options with Descriptive Statistics are the two Excel functions PERCENTILE.INC, PERCENTILE.EXC, PERCENTRANK.INC and PERCENTRANK.EXC.
- Histograms calculate the number of occurrences, or frequency, which values in a data set fall into various intervals. Bins are the intervals into which values can fall; they can be defined by a user or can be evenly distributed among the data by Excel. The bin values are specified by their upper bounds.
- There are four basic shapes to a histogram: *symmetric, positively skewed, negatively skewed,* and *multiple peaks.*
- Relationships in data are usually identified by comparing the *dependent variable* and the *independent variable.* The dependent variable is a variable that the user tries to predict values for; the independent variable is the variable that the user employs as the comparison in order to make the prediction.
- We can graph this data (with the *XY Scatter* chart type) by placing the independent variable on the x-axis and the dependent variable on the y-axis and then using a *trend curve* to determine if any relationship exists between these variables. There are six basic trend curves that Excel can model: *Exponential, Linear, Logarithmic, Polynomial, Power,* and *Moving Average.*
- With Linear curves, there are two values that measure the accuracy of the relationship between the dependent and independent variables. The R-Squared value measures the amount of influence that the independent variable has on the dependent variable. It can be calculated from the trendline chart or with the RSQ function. The standard error also measures the accuracy of any predictions made from this relationship. This value can be determined using the STEYX function.
- The SLOPE and INTERCEPT functions also analyze a Linear trend curve.
- Some of the more common distributions that can be recognized when performing a statistical analysis of data are the *Normal, Exponential, Uniform, Binomial, Poisson, Beta,* and *Weibull* distributions. Most of these distributions have Excel functions associated directly with them and are basically equivalent to using distribution tables.
- Inverse distribution functions such as BETA.INV, BIONOM.INV, LOGNORM.INV and NORM.INV are used in simulation models to generate random numbers from a specific distribution.

7.6 *Exercises*

7.6.1 Review Questions

1. What function calculates the mean of a data set?
2. What is the difference between the mean, median, and mode of a set of data?
3. List some of the Analysis Toolpak's useful tools.
4. What statistical analysis values does the Descriptive Statistics tool provide?
5. From what value is the standard deviation derived?
6. How is an outlier identified?
7. Write an alternate formula for identifying an outlier using the IF and OR functions.
8. What is Skewness? What is an appropriate value of Skewness for a symmetric data set?
9. What is the difference between the result of the PERCENTILE.INC and PERCENTRANK.INC functions?

10. What are the bins of a histogram? How are they created?
11. What is a Pareto organization of a chart?
12. What are the four basic shapes of a histogram?
13. What is an example of a negatively skewed histogram?
14. Give an example of a dependent and independent variable relationship.
15. Can a trendline be fitted to any type of chart created in Excel?
16. What are the three most common trend curves?
17. What two values measure the accuracy of a Linear trendline?
18. What are the parameters of the Binomial distribution function?
19. Explain why we need to use inverse distribution functions.
20. How do you convert a Normal x value into a Standard Normal x value?

7.6.2 Hands-On Exercises

NOTE: Please refer to the file "Chapter_07_Exercises.xlsx" for the associated worksheets noted for the hands-on exercises. The file is available at: www.dssbooks.com.

1. A table provides a sample of the starting salaries of all geography graduates from a state university this year. What is your best estimate of a "typical" starting salary for a geography graduate? (Refer to worksheet "7.1".)
2. A quality expert at a soft drink bottling plant has been assigned to develop a plan to reduce the number of defective bottles that the plant produces. To find the cause of the defects, she plans to analyze factors associated with the bottling lines and the types of bottles being produced. The expert has randomly sampled sets of bottles from different bottling lines and counted the number of defective bottles in the sample. She records the bottling line, the size of the sample, and the number of nonconforming bottles. She then computes the fraction of nonconforming bottles. A table contains her results. Make the following modifications to this table. (Refer to worksheet "7.2".)
   - **a.** Fill in the values for the "Fraction Nonconforming" column by dividing the number of nonconforming bottles in the sample by the sample size. Display the results as a percentage.
   - **b.** Compute the mean and standard deviation of the fraction of nonconforming bottles found in the samples and record the results in the bottom right-hand corner of the spreadsheet.
3. In New York, Electro produces voltage that regulates equipment and then ships the equipment to Chicago. The voltage held is measured in NY before each unit is shipped to Chicago. The voltage held by each unit is also measured when the unit arrives in Chicago. A sample of voltage measurements at each city is provided. A voltage regulator is considered acceptable if it can hold a voltage of between 25 and 75 volts. (Refer to worksheet "7.3".)
   - **a.** Using Descriptive Statistics, comment on what you can observe about the voltages held by units before shipment and after shipment.
   - **b.** What percentage of units is acceptable before and after shipping?
   - **c.** Do you have any suggestions about how to improve the quality of Electro's regulators?
   - **d.** 10% of all NY regulators have a voltage exceeding what value?
   - **e.** 5% of all NY regulators have a voltage less than or equal to what value?
4. Given data regarding stocks, T. bills, and T. bonds over several years, create a histogram for each investment. (Refer to worksheet "7.4".) Create a bin range. Use this same bin range to create the histograms. Use the histograms to answer the following questions:
   - **a.** Which investment has the highest average return?
   - **b.** What is the probability of positive returns for each investment?
   - **c.** What is the probability of returns higher than 10% for each investment?
5. Using the above data, describe the type of histogram for each investment option: symmetric, positively skewed, negatively skewed, and multiple peaks.
6. A spreadsheet is used to record monthly returns on the S and P stock index and Dell stock. Find the following information. (Refer to worksheet "7.6".)

a. The slope of the least squares line of the Dell stock and S and P.

b. The R-Squared value of the Dell stock and S and P.

c. Which seems like a better investment, and why.

7. A given table lists the square footage and sales price for several houses. (Refer to worksheet "7.7".)

a. If you build a 400 square foot addition to your house, by how much do you feel you will increase its value?

b. What percentage of the variation in home values is explained by variation in house size?

c. A 2500 square foot house is selling for $470,000. Is this price out of line with typical home values? Explain.

8. Given additional information on the number of bedrooms and bathrooms for the above house data, which factor ("Square Footage," "Bedrooms," or "Bathrooms") has the strongest relationship with the sales price? (Refer to worksheet "7.8".)

9. Given the yearly revenues (in millions) of the companies, determine the following. (Refer to worksheet "7.9".)

a. Which company's revenues best fit an Exponential trend curve.

b. The annual percentage growth rate for revenues.

c. Predicted 2010 revenues.

10. A marketing manager estimates total sales as a function of price. (Refer to worksheet "7.10".)

a. Estimate the relationship between price and demand.

b. Predict the demand for the $69 price.

c. By how much will a 1 percent increase in price reduce the demand?

11. The manager of the sales department of a leading magazine publication has recorded the number of subscriptions sold for various numbers of sales calls. (Refer to worksheet "7.11".)

a. If he were to make 75,000 sales calls next month, how many subscriptions could he estimate selling?

b. If he wanted to sell 80,000 subscriptions, how many sales calls would he have to make?

12. A human resources manager wants to examine the relationship between annual salaries and the number of years that employees have worked at the company. A sample of collected data is given. (Refer to worksheet "7.12".)

a. Which should be the independent variable and which should be the dependent variable?

b. Estimate the relationship between these two variables. Identify the least squares line and interpret the results.

c. How well does this line fit the data?

13. Consider the relationship between the size of the population and the average household income level for several small towns. (Refer to worksheet "7.13".)

a. Which should be the independent variable and which should be the dependent variable?

b. Estimate the relationship between these two variables. Identify the least squares line and interpret the results.

c. How well does this line fit the data?

14. A bank is trying to prove that they do not practice gender discrimination. They have a record of the education level, age, gender, and salary of each employee. (Refer to worksheet "7.14".)

Determine which factor has the strongest relationship with the salary of the employees.

15. An electric company produces different quantities of electricity each month, depending on demand. A table lists the number of units of electricity produced and the total cost of producing each quantity. (Refer to worksheet "7.15".)

a. Which trend curve fits the data better, a Linear, Exponential, or Power curve?

b. What are the R-Squared values of each curve?

c. How much cost can they expect if they produce 800 units?

16. A new industrial production company wants to analyze their production time to determine if they have improved productivity after gaining a few months of experience. A table is used to record the times to produce each batch of products. (Refer to worksheet "7.16".)

a. Which curve best fits this data?

b. If this data follows a learning curve, then how much time can the company expect to spend producing the next batch?

17. Suppose that car sales follow a Normal distribution with a mean of 50,000 cars and a standard deviation of 14,000 cars.

a. There is a 1 percent chance that the car sales will be over how many cars next year?

b. What is the probability that they will sell less than or equal to 2.7 million cars during the next year?

18. Given that the weight of a typical American male follows a Normal distribution with a mean of 180 lb and standard deviation of 30 lbs, what fraction of American males weigh more than 225 lbs?

19. If a financial report shows an average income of $45,000 with a standard deviation of $12,000, what percentage of people on this report make more than $60,000, assuming this data follows a Normal distribution? Convert this into a Standard Normal distribution and answer the same question.

20. Assume that the monthly sales of a toys store follow an Exponential distribution with mean 560. What is the probability that sales will be over 600 in January?

21. The annual number of accidents occurring in a particular manufacturing plant follows a Poisson distribution with mean 15.

a. What is the probability of observing exactly 15 accidents at this plant?

b. What is the probability of observing less than 15 accidents?

c. You can be 99 percent sure that less than how many accidents will occur?

22. Using the Binomial distribution, assume that on average 95 percent of airline passengers show up for a flight. If a plane can seat 200 passengers, how many tickets should be sold to make the change of an overbooked flight less than or equal to 5 percent?

23. A professor gives his students a 20-question True or False exam. Each correct answer is worth 5 points. Consider a student who randomly guesses on each question.

a. If no points are deducted for incorrect answers, what is the probability that the student will score at least 60 points?

b. If 5 points are deducted for each incorrect answer what is the probability that the student will score at least 60 points?

24. Suppose that the interarrival time between customers at a bank are Exponentially distributed with a mean of 45 seconds. Generate twenty random customer interarrival times. Use these times to identify the arrival time of each customer at the bank.

25. A given table presents the weekly sales of floppy disk drives in a local computer dealer. (Refer to worksheet "7.25".)

a. Find the trendline that fits the data best (linear, exponential, etc).

b. Present the R-square for each trendline considered in part a.

c. What are the expected sales for weeks 13 and 14?

26. The length of an injection-molded plastic case that holds magnetic tape is normally distributed with mean 80.3 millimeters and standard deviation 0.2 millimeters.

a. What is the probability that a part is longer than 80.5 millimeters or shorter than 80 millimeters?

b. Assuming that the cases will continue to be produced using the current process, up to what length will a part be 99% of the time?

27. The weight of a Coca-Cola bottle is normally distributed with a mean of 12 ounces and a standard deviation of 0.5 ounces.

a. What is the probability that the bottle weights more than 13 ounces?

b. What is the probability that the bottle weights no more than 13 ounces and no less than 11 ounces?

c. What must the standard deviation of weight be in order for the company to state 99.9% of its bottles weight less than 13 ounces?

d. If the standard deviation remains 0.5 ounce, what must the mean be in order for the company to state that 99.9% of the bottles produced are less than 13 ounces?

28. The length of time (in seconds) that a user views a page on a Web site before moving to another page is lognormal random variable with parameters $\theta = 0.5$ and $\omega^2 = 1$.

a. What is the probability that a page is viewed for more than 10 seconds?

b. What is the length of time that 50% of users view the page?

c. Plot the density function of this distribution. Change the value of θ to 1 and plot the density function again.

29. The lifetime of a semiconductor laser follows a Weibull distribution with parameters α =2 and β = 700 hours.

a. Determine the probability that a semiconductor laser lasts at least 600 hours.

b. Determine the probability that a semiconductor laser fails before 400 hours.

c. Plot the density function of this distribution.

d. Use the inverse Wibull distribution to generate ten random numbers from this distribution.

CHAPTER eight

Solving Mathematical Programs

chapter OVERVIEW

8.1 Introduction

This chapter illustrates how to use the *Risk Solver Platform* as a tool to solve mathematical programs. We review the basic parts of formulating a mathematical program and present several examples of how the Solver interprets these parts of the program from the spreadsheet. We give examples of linear, integer, and nonlinear programming problems to show how the Solver can be used to solve a variety of mathematical programs. It is important for the reader to understand this chapter since many IE/OR and business spreadsheet-based DSS applications involve solving optimization problems, which are mathematical programs. The reader should be comfortable with preparing the spreadsheet for use with the Solver. In Chapter 19, we revisit the Solver using VBA commands. We provide several examples of DSS applications that use the Solver to solve optimization problems, such as Portfolio Management and Optimization. Please refer to Appendix A for information about the Standard Solver of Excel and the Premium Solver of Risk Solver Platform. This appendix also discusses Limitations and Manipulations of the Standard Solver.

In this chapter, the reader will learn how to:

- Formulate a mathematical program by determining its decision variables, constraints, and objective function.
- Understand the difference between linear, integer, and nonlinear programming problems.
- Use the Risk Solver Platform to solve a mathematical program.
- Prepare the spreadsheet with the model parts and then enter the corresponding cells into the Risk Solver Task Pane.
- Read the Solver reports.
- Solve an example of linear, integer, and nonlinear programming problem using the Risk Solver Platform.

8.2 Formulating Mathematical Programs

The Excel spreadsheet is unique because it is capable of working with complex mathematical models. Mathematical models transform a problem stated in words into a set of equations that clearly define the values that we are seeking, given the limitations of the problem. Mathematical models are employed in many fields, including all disciplines of engineering. In order to solve a mathematical model, we develop a mathematical program that can numerically be solved and retranslated into a qualitative solution to the mathematical model.

8.2.1 Parts of the Mathematical Program

A mathematical program consists of three main parts. The first is the ***decision variables***. *Decision variables* are the values that we must determine when we solve a mathematical program. For example, if a toy manufacturer wants to determine how many toy boats and toy cars to produce, we assign a variable to represent the quantity of toy boats produced, x_1, and the quantity of toy cars produced, x_2. Decision variables are defined as *negative*, *non-negative*, or *unrestricted*. An *unrestricted* variable can be either *negative* or *non-negative*. Decision variables may also be *integer* (take only integer values) or *binary* (take only 0 or 1 values).

The second part of the math program, called the ***objective function***, is an equation that represents the goal, or objective, of the model. In the same example of the toy manufacturer, we want to know the quantities of toy boats and toy cars to produce. However, the goal of the manufacturing plant's production may be to increase profit. If we know that we can profit $5 for every toy boat and $4 for every toy car, then our objective function is:

Maximize $5x_1 + 4x_2$

In other words, we want profit to drive us in determining the quantity of boats and cars to produce. Objective functions are either ***maximized*** or ***minimized***; most applications involve maximizing profit or minimizing cost.

The third part of the math program, the ***constraints***, are the limitations of the problem. That is, if we want to maximize our profit, as in the toy manufacturer example, we could produce as many toys as possible if we did not have any limits. However, in most realistic situations, there are certain limitations, or constraints, that we must consider. Constraints can be a limited amount of resources, labor, or requirements for a particular demand. These constraints are also written as equations, or inequalities in terms of the decision variables. That is, if we can use only 20 hours of labor in a week and we need 0.5 hour to produce each toy boat and 0.3 hour to produce each toy car, then we write our constraint as follows:

$0.5x_1 + 0.3x_2 \leq 20$

Summary

Decision Variables:	Variables assigned to quanities to be determined.
Objective Funtion:	An equation that states the objective of a model.
Constraints:	Equations or inequalities that state limits or requirements of a problem.

8.2.2 Linear, Integer, and Nonlinear Programming

There are three main categories of problems for which we can use the above mathematical program parts: ***linear programming (LP), integer programming (IP)***, and ***nonlinear programming (NLP)***.

Linear programming problems have a linear objective function and linear constraints. That is, there are no variables of multiple powers such as x^2 and x^3, and no terms involving two variables such as x_1x_2. In addition, LP problems consist of decision variables with any range or interval of values, $x \geq 0$ or $x \leq 0$. An example of an LP would be a production problem in which we want to maximize profit by determining how many of several different product types we want to produce. The objective function could therefore be expressed as:

$$z = \sum_{i=1}^{n} p_i x_i$$

where i = product number for n products, p_i = profit per product i, and x_i = amount produced of product i. This is therefore a linear objective function. If we assume that the constraints are also linear, then this is a linear programming problem. We will revisit this example in more detail in Section 8.3.1.

Integer programming is related to linear programming in that both the objective function and constraints are linear; however, some decision variables can have only integer values in a given range. Integer programming is also applied when *decision variables* are ***binary***, which means that they take only the values *true* or *false*, *yes* or *no*, *go* or *no go*—all of which are mathematically represented as 0 or 1, respectively. An example of an IP would be a capital budgeting problem in which we want to decide which projects to invest in and which not to invest in. This decision is a yes/no decision that can be represented by the following linear objective function:

$$z = \sum_{i=1}^{n} y_i x_i$$

where i = project number for n projects, y_i = NPV per project i, and x_i = decision whether or not to invest in project i. What makes it an integer programming problem is that we limit the values of x_i to 1 or 0 to reflect whether or not we have or have not invested in a project, respectively. We will revisit this example as well in more detail in Section 8.4.3.

Nonlinear programming problems do not have a linear objective function and/or constraints. NLP problems use more sophisticated methods to handle these complex equations. An example of a NLP would be a warehouse location problem in which we are trying to determine a warehouse location that minimizes the distance traveled in shipments to/from several facilities. The sum of the distances from multiple facilities to this warehouse would be calculated as follows:

$$z = \sum_{i=1}^{n} \sqrt{(x_i - x_w)^2 + (y_i - y_w)^2}$$

where i = facility number for n facilities, x_i and y_i = coordinates of each facility i, and x_w and y_w = coordinates of the warehouse. Even if the constraints are all linear, it is still a nonlinear programming problem since the objective function is nonlinear. We will also revisit this example in more detail in Section 8.4.4.

Several ***algorithms***, or methods of solving a mathematical program, are specific to linear, integer, and nonlinear programming problems. They must simultaneously consider each constraint in conjunction with the objective function. We will use the algorithms available in ***Risk Solver Platform*** to solve these problems. The Risk Solver Platform uses an algorithm called the *Simplex Method* to solve LP problems. The *SOCP Barrier Solver uses an interior point method* algorithm to solve LP and quadratic programming (QP) problems. The *nonlinear GRG Solver* handles smooth NLP programs. The *Evolutionary Solver* uses a hybrid of genetic, evolutionary algorithms and classical optimization methods to solve nonsmooth problems, such as IP problems. The *Interval Global Solver* uses interval methods to solve NLP problems, or find solutions to a system of nonlinear equations, or find an "inner solution" to a system of nonlinear inequalities. Details of obtaining the Risk Solver Platform for Education are available at the website: *www.dssbooks.com*. Note that the Risk Solver Platform and its subset products, such as the *Premium Solver*, and *Standard Solver* (which comes with Excel) are trademarks of *Frontline Systems, Inc.* The interface of Risk Solver Platform is different from the *Premium Solver* and *Excel's Solver*. The capabilities of the Premium Solver are identical to the Risk Solver Platform. However, the Standard Solver can use only LP Simplex, GRG Nonlinear, and Evolutionary algorithms. There also are limitations on the size of the problems that the Standard Solver can solve. Please refer to Appendix A for information about the Standard Solver.

Summary

Linear Programming:	Both the objective function and the constraints are linear. Decision variables can have any range or interval of values.
Integer Programming:	An LP in which decision variables can take only integer values in a given range or binary values.
Binary:	Decision variables that take only the values 0 or 1.
Nonlinear Programming:	Either the objective function or constraints or both are not linear.
Algorithm:	A method of solving a mathematical model.
Risk Solver Platform:	Solves LP, IP, and NLP models using a variety of algorithms.
Premium Solver:	Solves LP, IP, and NLP models using a variety of algorithms.
Standard Solver:	Uses LP Simplex, GRG Nonlinear, and Evolutionary algorithms.

8.3 *The Risk Solver Platform*

We will now discuss how to operate the *Risk Solver Platform*. In general, the Solver must understand the problem's mathematical program parts, which we take care of by preparing our spreadsheet to contain distinct cells for the decision variables, constraints, and objective function. We must then tell the Solver if we want to minimize or maximize the problem, or if we want to solve it for a particular value of the objective function. There are also several options that we can apply to give more specific instructions to the Solver for solving the problem.

(Note: Upon downloading Risk Solver Platform for Education from the text's website: www.dssbooks.com, you will see a new tab on the Ribbon. We recommend that you navigate the groups of commands listed in this tab in order to familiarize yourself with this package.)

8.3.1 The Risk Solver Steps

To operate the *Risk Solver Platform*, we must follow three steps: (1) read and interpret the problem, (2) prepare the spreadsheet, and (3) solve the model and review the results. We will now describe these steps in detail for the Risk Solver Platform using a Product Mix example problem. Please refer to Appendix A for a detailed description of these steps for the Standard Solver of Excel.

STEP 1: READ AND INTERPRET THE PROBLEM We must first determine the type of problem that we are dealing with (linear programming, integer programming, or nonlinear programming) and outline the model parts (decision variables, constraints, and objective function). This is the most important step. It is important to model the problem correctly; otherwise, solutions may be incorrect and misleading. Whether the problem is an LP, IP, or NLP model does not affect the model parts but does affect the *Engine* (algorithm) that is used by the Solver. The LP, IP, and NLP problems may also require some additional constraint specifications. In each case, we still need to determine the decision variables, the objective function, and the constraints. We need to write these mathematically, with the objective function and constraints in terms of the decision variables.

Product Mix Problem Description A company produces six different types of products. They want to schedule their production to determine how much of each product type should be produced in order to maximize their profits. This situation is known as the "Product Mix" problem.

Production of each product type requires labor and raw materials, but the company is limited by the amount of resources available. There is also a limited demand for each product, and no more than this demand per product type should be produced. Input tables for the necessary resources and the demand are provided.

This is a linear programming problem, as the constraints and objective function are linear with respect to the decision variables, as we will see below. Let's now outline the model parts.

Product Mix Decision Variables For the amount produced of each product type, we use the following variable representation:

$x_1, x_2, x_3, x_4, x_5, x_6$

In other words, x_1 is the amount produced of product 1, x_2 is the amount produced of product 2, etc. Note that all of these decision variables are non-negative; that is, we cannot produce a negative amount of any product type.

Product Mix Objective Function The objective is to maximize profit. Profit is calculated as the sum of the array multiplication of the unit profit, p, and the amount produced of each product type. We write this equation as follows:

$\text{Maximize } z = \Sigma_{j=1...,6}\, p_j x_j$

Here, p_1 is the amount of profit gained per unit of product 1. Therefore, $p_1{}^*x_1$ is the amount of profit per unit of product 1 times the number of units produced of product 1, thus yielding the total profit from product 1. The same follows for the other products, 2 through 6.

Product Mix Constraints There are two resource constraints: labor, l, and raw material, r. Available amounts are provided for each resource, and required amounts are provided for the production of each product type. We therefore say that the sum of the array multiplication of the resource requirements and the amount produced of each product type must be less than or equal to the amounts available of each resource. These equations are written:

Labor Constraint:

$\Sigma_{j=1...,6}\, l_j x_j \leq \text{available labor} = 4500$

Raw Material Constraint:

$\Sigma_{j=1,...6}\, r_j x_j \leq \text{available raw material} = 1600$

Here l_1 is the amount of labor required per unit produced of product 1. Similarly, r_1 is the amount of raw material required per unit produced of product 1. Therefore, the equations represent the total labor and raw material needed for all products.

There is also a constraint that we do not produce more than the specified demand D. Therefore, the amount produced of each product type must be less than or equal to the given demand quantities. This constraint can be written as follows:

Demand Constraint:

$x_j \leq D_j \quad \text{for} \quad j = 1 \text{ to } 6$

STEP 2: PREPARE THE SPREADSHEET Next, we transfer these parts of the model into our Excel spreadsheet, clearly defining each part of our model in the spreadsheet. The *Solver* interprets our model according to the location of these model parts on the spreadsheet.

In Figure 8.1, we show the overall spreadsheet layout for the Product Mix problem. We have organized our cells by input, decision variables, constraints, and objective function.

	A	B	C	D	E	F	G	H	I
1	**Product Mix**								
2									
3	Input		Product Type 1	Product Type 2	Product Type 3	Product Type 4	Product Type 5	Product Type 6	Available
4		Labor	6	5	4	3	2.5	1.5	4500
5		Raw Material	3.2	2.6	1.5	0.8	0.7	0.3	1600
6		Unit price	$12.50	$11.00	$9.00	$7.00	$6.00	$3.00	
7		Variable cost	$6.50	$5.70	$3.60	$2.80	$2.20	$1.20	
8									
9		Unit profit cont.	$6.00	$5.30	$5.40	$4.20	$3.80	$1.80	
10									
11									
12	Decision Variables		Product Type 1	Product Type 2	Product Type 3	Product Type 4	Product Type 5	Product Type 6	
13		Amount produced							
14			<=	<=	<=	<=	<=	<=	
15		Demand	960	928	1041	977	1084	1055	
16									
17	Constraints				Available				
18		Labor Used	0.00	<=	4500				
19		Raw Material Used	0.00	<=	1600				
20									
21	Objective Function								
22		Profit	$0.00						

Figure 8.1 The spreadsheet layout for the Product Mix.

Step 2.1: Place the Input Table If the input for the problem is provided for us, we just need to place it on the spreadsheet in the form of a table. We reference this input when forming our constraint and objective function formulas.

In our Product Mix problem, the input table is given. For each product type, we know the labor and raw materials needed to produce the product as well as the unit price and variable cost. We calculate the unit profit row by subtracting the variable cost from the unit price.

Step 2.2: Set the Decision Variables Cells Next, we create a column (or row) for the decision variables. These cells should be empty. The *Solver* places values in these cells for each decision variable as it solves the model. We recommend naming the range of decision variables for easier reference in constraint and objective function formulas.

In the Product Mix problem, the decision variable cells are in the row titled "Amount produced."

Step 2.3: Enter the Constraint Formulas Now we place the constraint equations in the spreadsheet; we enter those separately, using formulas, with an optional description next to each constraint. Because each constraint is in terms of the decision variables, these formulas should be in terms of the decision variable cells already defined.

Another important consideration when laying out the constraints in preparation for the *Solver* is that there must be individual cells for the right-hand side (RHS) values as well. We should also place all inequality signs in their own cells. This organization will become clear once we explain how the *Solver* interprets our model.

Another advantageous way to keep our constraints organized as we use the *Solver* is to name cells. We can also group constraints that have the same inequality signs. The benefit of this habit will become apparent once we input the model parts for the *Solver.*

In the Product Mix problem, we have labeled some ranges on the spreadsheet. We have named the Decision Variable range "PMDecVar," the Labor resource requirement row "PMLabor," the Raw Material resource requirement row "PMRawMat," and the Unit Profit row "PMUnitProfit." These names will be helpful for writing the constraint and objective function formulas as well as for inserting cell references in the Solver, although no range names are needed for the Solver to work correctly.

To prepare the constraint formulas, we use the SUMPRODUCT function. Remember from Chapter 4 that this function takes two arrays, or ranges, as parameters for which it will multiply and sum all values. Referring to the equations written earlier and the range names created, we write the constraint formulas as follows:

Labor Constraint:
=SUMPRODUCT(PMDecVar, PMLabor)

Raw Material Constraint:
=SUMPRODUCT(PMDecVar, PMRawMat)

The right-hand side values are equal to the "Available" amounts from the Input table (see Figure 8.2).

C18 =SUMPRODUCT(PMDecVar,PMLabor)

	A	B	C	D	E	F	G	H
12	Decision Variables		Product Type 1	Product Type 2	Product Type 3	Product Type 4	Product Type 5	Product Type 6
13		Amount produced						
14			<=	<=	<=	<=	<=	<=
15		Demand	960	928	1041	977	1084	1055
16								
17	Constraints				Available			
18		Labor Used	0.00	<=	4500			
19		Raw Material Used	0.00	<=	1600			

Figure 8.2 The Labor and Raw Material constraint formulas use the SUMPRODUCT function.

For the demand constraint, we simply need to ensure that the values in our decision variable range are less than each of the corresponding values in the "Demand" range. We do not require a formula for this constraint (see Figure 8.3).

	A	B	C	D	E	F	G	H
12	Decision Variables		Product Type 1	Product Type 2	Product Type 3	Product Type 4	Product Type 5	Product Type 6
13		Amount produced						
14			<=	<=	<=	<=	<=	<=
15		Demand	960	928	1041	977	1084	1055

Figure 8.3 The Demand Constraint does not require a formula.

Step 2.4: Enter the Objective Function Formula We can now place our objective function in a cell by transforming this equation into a formula in terms of the decision variables. The spreadsheet is now prepared for the *Solver* with all three parts of the model clearly displayed.

In the Product Mix problem, the objective function formula is also written with the SUMPRODUCT function (see Figure 8.4). Referring to the equation and range names above, we type the following formula:

=SUMPRODUCT(PMUnitProfit, PMDecVar)

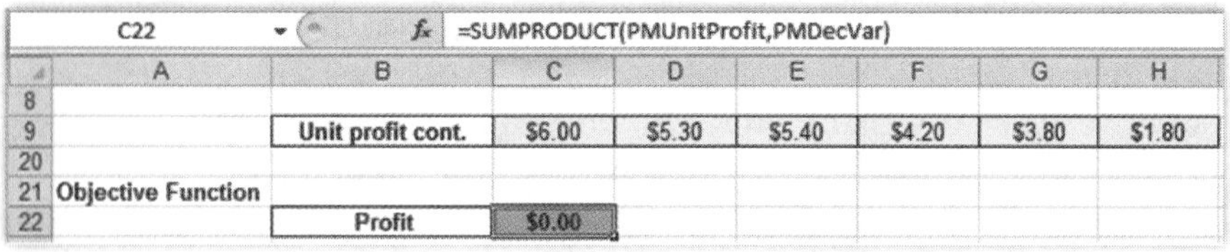
C22
=SUMPRODUCT(PMUnitProfit,PMDecVar)
A B C D E F G H
8
9 Unit profit cont. $6.00 $5.30 $5.40 $4.20 $3.80 $1.80
20
21 Objective Function
22 Profit $0.00

Figure 8.4 The objective function formula employs the SUMPRODUCT function.

STEP 3: SOLVE THE MODEL AND REVIEW THE RESULTS The *Risk Solver Platform* can now interpret this information and use algorithms to solve the model. The *Solver* receives the decision variables, constraint equations, and objective function equation as input into a hidden programming code that applies the algorithm to the data. We will explain in more detail how this programming works when we discuss VBA. To use the *Solver*, we click on the *Risk Solver Platform* > *Model* > *Model* command from the Ribbon. The *task pane* in Figure 8.5 then appears. The task pane lists a number of analytical tools available, such as *Sensitivity Analysis*, *Optimization*, *Simulation*, and *Decision Trees*. We will discuss simulation tools in Chapter 9. In this chapter we are interested in the optimization tools. The three important parts of the model that branch out of optimization tools are *Objective*, *Variables*, and *Constraints*. We will discuss how to use *Parameters* and *Results* to perform parametric optimization when solving the Capital Budgeting problem in Section 8.4.3.

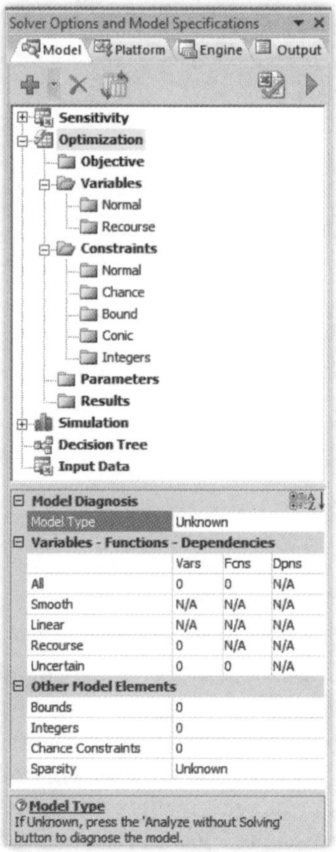

Figure 8.5 The Risk Solver task pane reads the decision variables, constraints, and objective function as parameters of the model.

Step 3.1: Set Objective The *objective*, which refers to the location of the formula for the objective function, can also be called the *set cell*. To set this cell, we select the cell where we typed the objective function formula (cell C22), and then click the *Risk Solver Platform > Optimization Model > Objective* button on the Ribbon. From the drop-down list that appears, we select *Max* and click on the *Normal* option from the flyout menu (see Figure 8.6). The *objective* drop-down menu lists other options, such as minimize the objective function or remove the current objective function of a problem. The Solver also provides options to optimize the value (*Normal*), the expected value (*Expected*), or the Value at Risk (*VaR*), etc., of the current selected cell. The selected objective cell will now appear in the task pane (see Figure 8.7). We can use the objective window of the task pane to change the address, sense, or value of the objective cell.

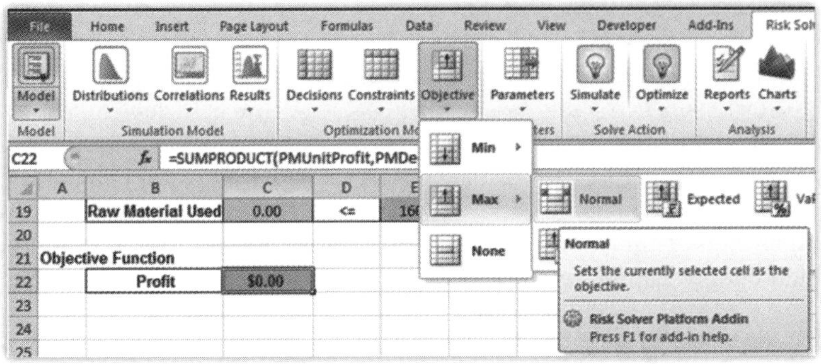

Figure 8.6 The Risk Solver Platform > Optimization Model > Objective button on the Ribbon is used to set the objective function cell and corresponding goal.

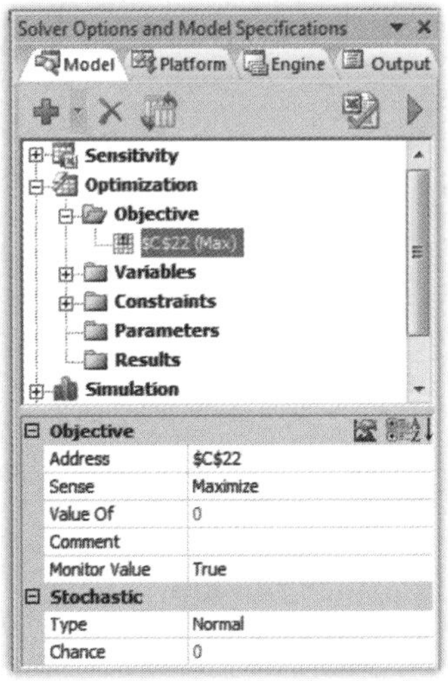

Figure 8.7 Use the objective window to change the address, sense, or value of the objective cell.

Step 3.2: Select Variables Next, we select the decision *variables*. We start by highlighting our decision variable cells, and then clicking on the *Risk Solver Platform > Optimization Model > Decisions* button on the *Ribbon*. From the drop-down menu that appears, select the *Normal* option. Note that if we have already named the range on our spreadsheet, that name appears automatically in the Solver task pane after the range is selected. The *Solver* places different values in these *changing cells* and checks the constraints and the objective function value against the formulas that we have provided until all are simultaneously satisfied. Other options listed under the *Decisions* drop-down list are *Recourse* and *Plot* (see Figure 8.8). Recourse decision variables are used to model stochastic programming problems. The plot option graphs the relationship that exists between the decision variables and the objective function or the constraints.

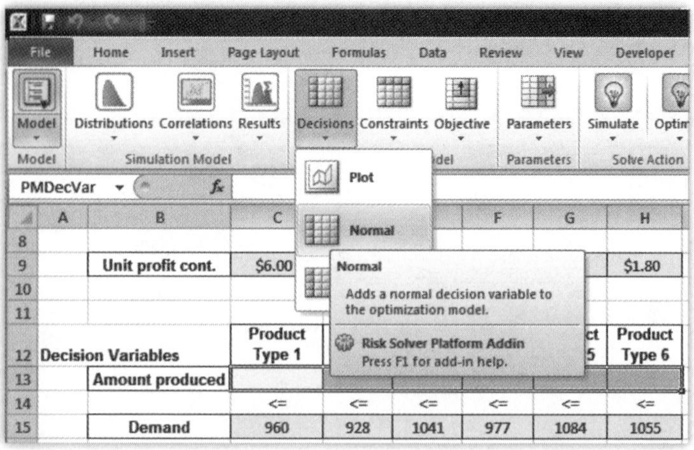

Figure 8.8 The Risk Solver Platform > Optimization Model > Decisions button on the Ribbon is used to set the decision variable cells.

For the Product Mix problem, the variable cells are set to the empty decision variable cells, which we named "PMDecVar." Select the objective cell C22 and click *Risk Solver Platform > Optimization Problem > Decisions* button on the *Ribbon*. Select *Plot* from the Decisions drop-down menu. The graph in Figure 8.9 confirms that the objective function of the Product Mix problem is linear.

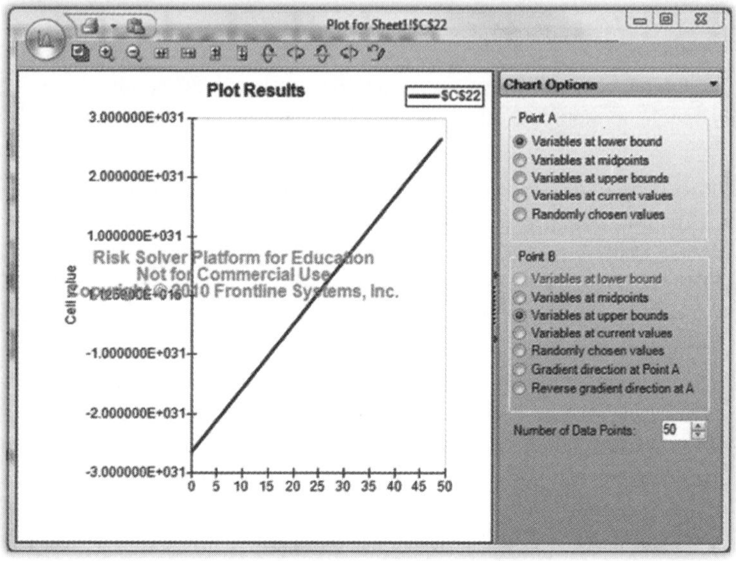

Figure 8.9 The Plot for the objective cell C22 indicates a linear relation between the decision variables and the objective function.

Step 3.3: Add Constraints Now, we need to specify our constraints. To do so, we click on the *Risk Solver Platform > Optimization Model > Constraints* button from the *Ribbon*. From the Constraints drop-down menu, select Normal and then click on the <= (inequality) sign from the flyout menu (see Figure 8.10). The dialog box shown in Figure 8.11 then appears. We must include the following two pieces of information in each added constraint: the cell with the constraint formula and the cell with the *RHS* value or a directly entered numerical value. We click *Add* to define the next constraints.

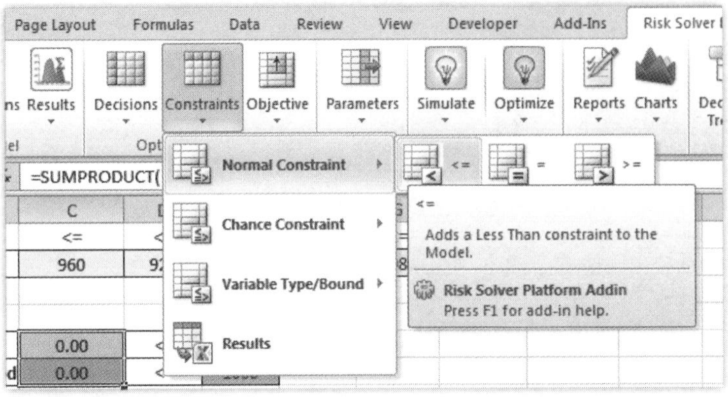

Figure 8.10 Click on Risk Solver Platform > Optimization Model > Constraints button from the Ribbon.

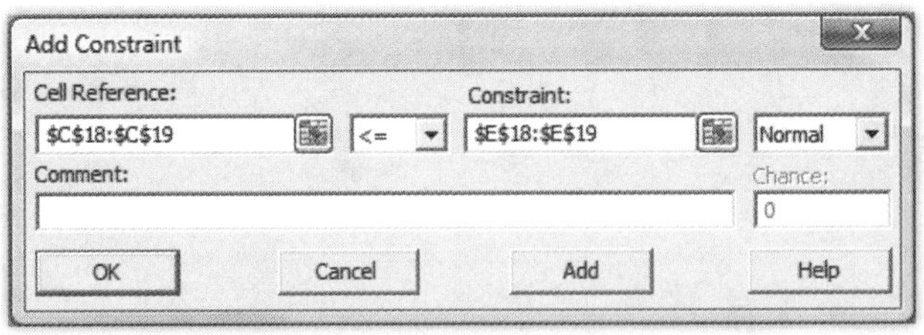

Figure 8.11 Adding constraints involves selecting the cell with the equation formula, choosing the inequality or equality sign, and selecting the cell with the RHS value. Comments are optional.

Excel allows us to define more than one constraint at a time. By grouping constraints that have the same inequality signs, we can select an entire range of constraint formulas and RHS values and choose the common inequality sign. Naming constraints with the same inequality can also clarify what we add to the *Solver* and prevent us from making any mistakes. If multiple ranges are not adjacent, we can select them by holding down the CTRL key or by separating them with commas in the Constraint window.

We have now added all of our constraints, so we press *OK*. We can observe all of the constraints we added. For the Product Mix problem, the labor and raw material constraints are listed using the column of constraint formulas (C18:C19) and the column of RHS values (E18:E19). Then the demand constraint is listed using the decision variable cells, named "PM-DecVar" (C13:H13) and the row of RHS values (C15:H15).

Note that demand constraints are listed as *bound* constraints; that means that the amount produced is limited (bound) by demand. To change the left-hand side, the right-hand side, and sense of a constraint, select the constraint from the Risk Solver task pane (as shown in Figure 8.12). Use the constraint window that appears in the bottom of the task pane to make the changes necessary. Figure 8.13 presents the completed task pane for the Product Mix problem.

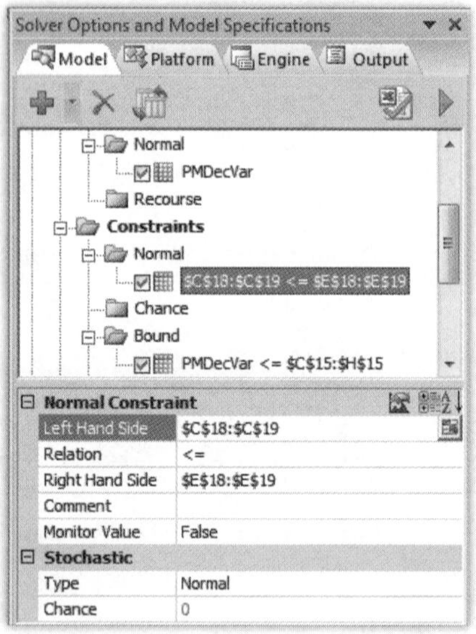

Figure 8.12 Upon selection of a normal constraint in the task pane, the normal constraint window appears. Use this window to change the address of the selected cell with the equation formula, the inequality or equality sign, and the cell with the RHS value.

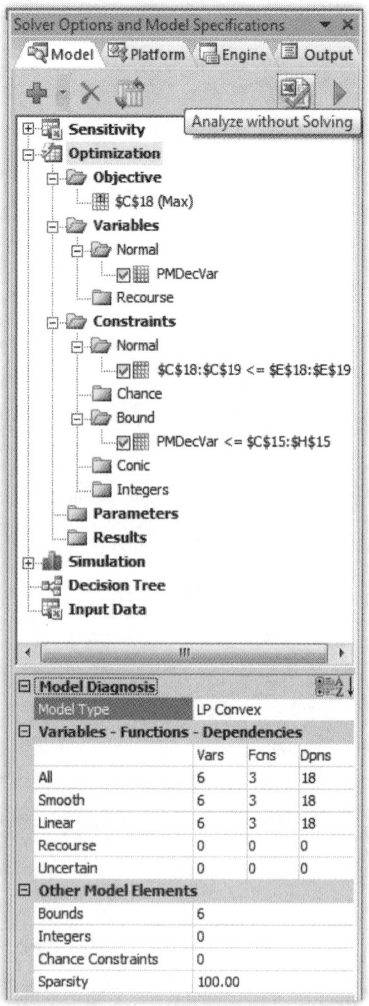

Figure 8.13 The final Risk Solver task pane lists decision variables, constraints, and the objective function of our model.

Step 3.4: Set Solver Options In *Step 1* we identified ours to be a linear programming problem. To ensure that this is the case prior to selecting a solution method, click on the *Analyze without Solving* button located in the upper-right corner of the task pane. The model diagnosis window in the bottom half of the task pane (see Figure 8.13) presents a summary of model characteristics. The model is diagnosed as *LP Convex.* All the variables, functions (objective and constraints), and dependencies are linear. We select *Standard LP/Quadratic Engine* to solve the problem.

Let's review and modify some of the *Risk Solver's* Platform and Engine related options before we do solve the model. Figure 8.14 presents the options selected in the *Platform* tab. We have changed the lower bound of the decision variables (*Decision Vars Lower*) to 0. We check that the *Solve Mode* is set to *Solve Complete Problem*, and the *Intended Model Type is Linear.* The rest of the options are kept at their default values.

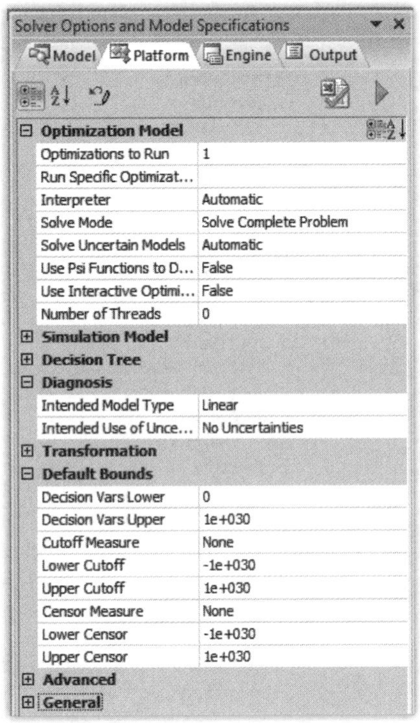

Figure 8.14 The Platform tab of task pane.

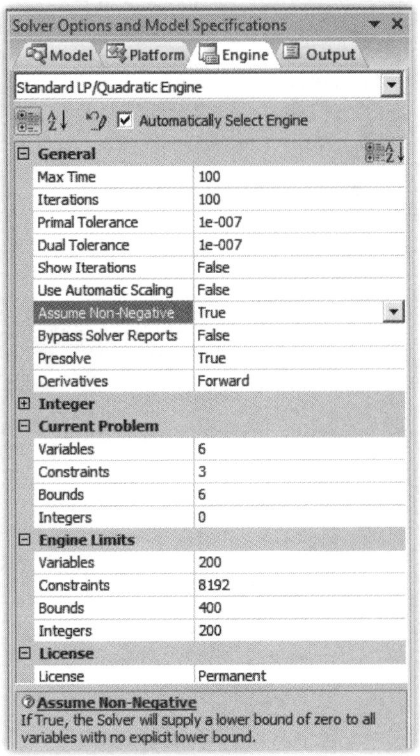

Figure 8.15 The Engine tab of the task pane.

Figure 8.15 presents the options we select in the *Engine* tab prior to solving the problem. We first discuss the options listed in the *General* window. *Max Time*, is the maximum time that the *Solver* should take to find a solution to the model. We can set a *maximum time* at a small value if we want a quick answer or at a large value if we allow the Solver to try to find a solution over a longer period of time. If we do not get a Solver solution using the default value for *Max Time*, we may consider resolving with a larger time value. The number of *iterations* is the next option; it affects the number of iterations (*pivots* for the *Simplex Solver*, or the major iterations for the *GRG* solver) for which the *Solver's* algorithm will run. We increase this value if the Solver is not able to find a solution initially. *Primal* (*dual*) *tolerance* is an upper bound on the amount by which the primal (dual) constraints can be violated and be considered feasible. Set the value of *Show Iterations* to *True* if you want the Solver to pause at every iteration. If you set the value of *Use Automatic Scaling* to *True*, then the Solver re-scales the values of the objective function and constraints internally. This is necessary when there is a mixture of large and small coefficient values in the constraints or the objective function and the possible values that the decision variable can take.

For example, if we are solving a binary IP problem whose decision variable values can only be 0 or 1 and whose constraint coefficients are in the hundreds of thousands, the Solver will not be able to recognize the problem as an LP model if we choose *Standard LP/Quadratic Engine*. In this case, we need to set *Use Automatic Scaling* to True in order to allow the Solver to internally scale the constraint coefficients and adjust the costs to maintain proportionality. Set the value of *Assume Non-Negative* property to *True* to ensure that the decision variables will not take negative values. Set the value of *Bypass Solver Reports* to *True* if you do not need the reports related to the current solution run. This helps reducing solution time when solving large problems. We suggest that you keep the value of this option to True when you are in the process of testing and validating your model. Set the value of *Presolve* to *True* to allow the Solver to perform a presolve step prior to applying the *primal* or *dual simplex* method. Select either option from the *Derivates* drop-down list to determine how the Solver computes derivates when solving *quadratic programming* (QP) problems.

Step 3.5: Solve the Model and Review the Results We now click on *Risk Solver Platform* > *Solve Action* > *Optimize* button on the *Ribbon*. From the Optimize drop-down menu, select *Solve Complete Problem*. During the time that the Solver seeks for a solution, the Output tab of the task pane (see Figure 8.16) becomes active and presents a description of the different events that occur while the problem is being solved. When the Solver finishes, a message is displayed at the bottom of the task pane indicating the status of the solution, which could be: "Solver found a solution. All constraints and optimality conditions are satisfied"; "Solver could not find a feasible solution"; or "The objective (Set Cell) values do not converge."

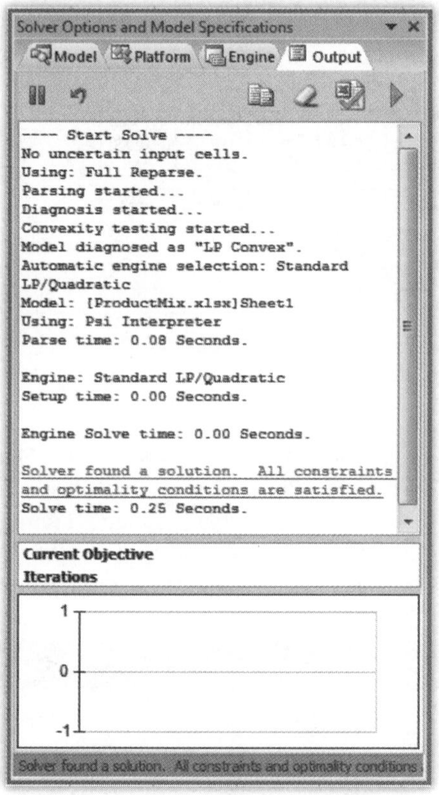

Figure 8.16 The Solver gives a description of the different events that occur while the problem is being solved. When it stops, the Solver also displays the status of the current solution.

If the Solver finds an optimal solution, then we are able to observe this solution in the background on our spreadsheet. The spreadsheet cells we set when formulating the model now have values for the decision variable cells. Therefore, they also have values in the constraint and objective function cells since they contain formulas referencing the decision variable cells. We can confirm that all constraints have been satisfied by noting that the values in the constraint cells with the *Solver* solution are all less than or equal to, or greater than or equal to, the *RHS* values, respectively. If a solution was not found, however, our problem may be infeasible or unbounded. We discuss these situations in the following section. There may also be an error in our model, so we may want to check our constraint and objective function formulas as well as the Solver Options we selected.

After reviewing this solution, we can opt to have some extra reports made from the *Solver* solution: the *Answer, Sensitivity, Limits, Structure* and *Parameter Analysis* reports. We will discuss these reports in more detail later. We now use the Solver to find the solution to the Product Mix problem. In Figure 8.17, the completed Solver solution is shown.

	A	B	C	D	E	F	G	H	I
1	**Product Mix**								
2									
3	Input		Product Type 1	Product Type 2	Product Type 3	Product Type 4	Product Type 5	Product Type 6	Available
4		Labor	6	5	4	3	2.5	1.5	4500
5		Raw Material	3.2	2.6	1.5	0.8	0.7	0.3	1600
6		Unit price	$12.50	$11.00	$9.00	$7.00	$6.00	$3.00	
7		Variable cost	$6.50	$5.70	$3.60	$2.80	$2.20	$1.20	
8									
9		Unit profit cont.	$6.00	$5.30	$5.40	$4.20	$3.80	$1.80	
10									
11									
12	Decision Variables		Product Type 1	Product Type 2	Product Type 3	Product Type 4	Product Type 5	Product Type 6	
13		Amount produced	0.00	0.00	0.00	596.67	1084.00	0.00	
14			<=	<=	<=	<=	<=	<=	
15		Demand	960	928	1041	977	1084	1055	
16									
17	Constraints				Available				
18		Labor Used	4500.00	<=	4500				
19		Raw Material Used	1236.13	<=	1600				
20									
21	Objective Function								
22		Profit	$6,625.20						

Figure 8.17 The final Solver solution.

The Solver Output tab reveals that a solution was successfully found (see Figure 8.16). We can view the final results in Figure 8.17. Notice that all constraints are met. The company now knows how much to produce for each product type and what their maximum profit will be. (There may be multiple solutions, but the Risk Solver Platform may not display all of them. You may try re-solving the problem with the previous optimal solution as the starting solution.)

Summary

Steps for using the Standard Solver

Step 1: Read and Interpret the Problem

1.1: Define Decision Variables

1.2: Define Objective Function

1.3: Define Constraint.

Step 2: Prepare the Spreadsheet

2.1: Place the Input Table

2.2: Set the Decision Variables Cells

2.3: Enter the Constraint Formulas

2.4: Enter the Objective Function Formula

Step 3: Solve the Model with Risk Solver Platform

3.1: Set the Objective

3.2: Select the Variables

3.3: Add the Constraints

3.4: Set the Solver Options

3.5: Solve the Model and Review the Results

Infeasibility An infeasible problem is one in which at least one of the constraints cannot be met. For this example, we consider infeasibility based on the Demand constraint. Note in the solution presented in Figure 8.17 that some of the product types did not meet their demand. Since the demand constraint inequalities were "<=", some of the demand is not satisfied in order to avoid the cost of production. Now let's assume that the company insists that the demand must always be met and some surplus quantities can be made too. We now need to change the Demand constraint inequality from "<=" to ">=". To do so, we select the *Demand* (*Bound*) *constraint* from the *Model* tab of the task pane, and change the *Relation* property to ">=" (see Figure 8.18).

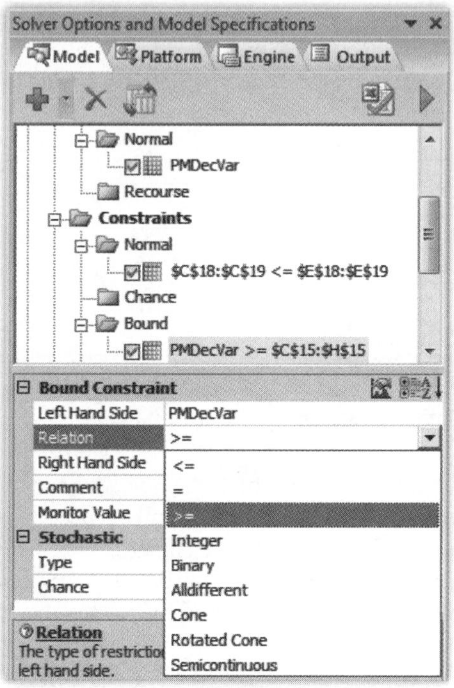

Figure 8.18 Changing the Demand Constraint inequality sign.

However, now when we *solve this problem*, the output window of the task pane conveys that the Solver could not find a feasible solution with this modified constraint (see Figure 8.19). If there are not enough resources available to meet the demand, then the solution is infeasible. The *Feasibility* Report, which is displayed as a new worksheet in the current workbook, identifies the exact constraints that are violated by the current solution. Such a report is very useful when solving large optimization problems. The Feasibility Report for this example (see Figure 8.20) indicates that constraint H13 >= H15 is violated. This is the demand constraint for product type 6. The result of this infeasible solution is shown in Figure 8.21.

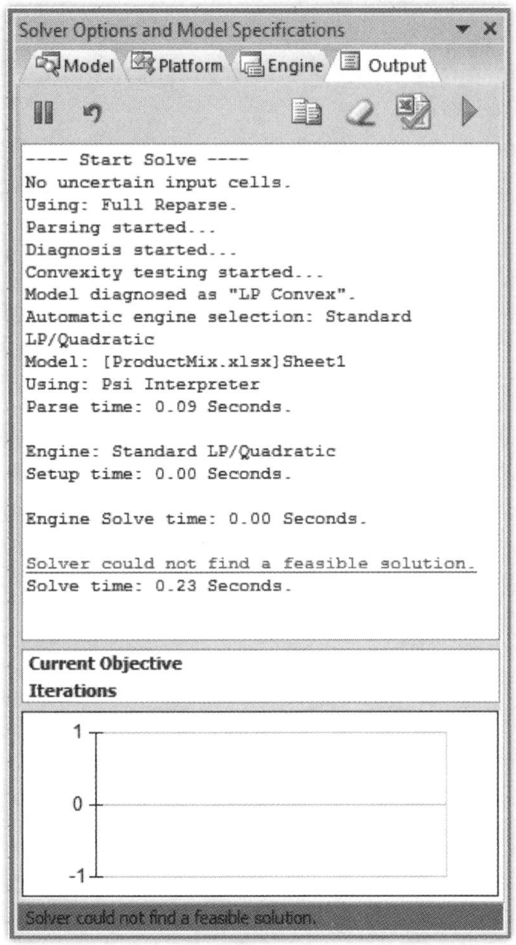

Figure 8.19 No feasible solution is found.

Unboundedness An unbounded problem is one in which the objective function can reach an unreasonably large number (if we are maximizing) or small number (if we are minimizing). Such a situation implies that the constraints are not inclusive enough. Consider, for example, that we want to minimize (rather than maximize) profits and the decision variables are allowed to take non-negative values. In this case the problem is unbounded since there are no lower bounds to limit the values of the decision variables, and as a result there is no bound on the objective function value. Therefore, the smaller (negative) the values assigned to the decision variables, the smaller the objective function becomes. To observe this, select *Objective* from the *Solver task pane* and change its sense to Minimize as shown in Figure 8.22. Set the value of *Assume Non-Negative* to *False* from the *General* properties window, in the *Engine* tab of the task pane. Now solve the problem. This time, the Solver indicates that objective values did not converge (see Figure 8.23). That means the minimum value of the objective function can be very small if the decision variables are allowed to take negative values.

F14 fx Violated

Microsoft Excel 14.0 Feasibility Report
Worksheet: [ProductMix.xlsx]Sheet1
Report Created: 2/21/2011 5:48:29 PM

Constraints that Make the Problem Infeasible

Cell	Name	Cell Value	Formula	Status	Slack
$C$19	Raw Material Used <=	1600.00	$C$19<=$E$19	Binding	0
$C$13	Amount produced Product Type 1	960.00	$C$13>=$C$15	Binding	0
$D$13	Amount produced Product Type 2	928.00	$D$13>=$D$15	Binding	0
$E$13	Amount produced Product Type 3	1041.00	$E$13>=$E$15	Binding	0
$F$13	Amount produced Product Type 4	977.00	$F$13>=$F$15	Binding	0
$G$13	Amount produced Product Type 5	1084.00	$G$13>=$G$15	Binding	0
$H$13	Amount produced Product Type 6	-23289.00	$H$13>=$H$15	Violated	-24344

Figure 8.20 The feasibility report identifies the constraint violated by the current solution.

	A	B	C	D	E	F	G	H	I
1	**Product Mix**								
2									
3	**Input**		**Product Type 1**	**Product Type 2**	**Product Type 3**	**Product Type 4**	**Product Type 5**	**Product Type 6**	**Available**
4		**Labor**	6	5	4	3	2.5	1.5	4500
5		**Raw Material**	3.2	2.6	1.5	0.8	0.7	0.3	1600
6		**Unit price**	$12.50	$11.00	$9.00	$7.00	$6.00	$3.00	
7		**Variable cost**	$6.50	$5.70	$3.60	$2.80	$2.20	$1.20	
8									
9		**Unit profit cont.**	$6.00	$5.30	$5.40	$4.20	$3.80	$1.80	
10									
11									
12	**Decision Variables**		**Product Type 1**	**Product Type 2**	**Product Type 3**	**Product Type 4**	**Product Type 5**	**Product Type 6**	
13		**Amount produced**	960.00	928.00	1041.00	977.00	1084.00	-23289.00	
14			<=	<=	<=	<=	<=	<=	
15		**Demand**	960	928	1041	977	1084	1055	
16									
17	**Constraints**				**Available**				
18		**Labor Used**	-14728.50	<=	4500				
19		**Raw Material Used**	1600.00	<=	1600				
20									
21	**Objective Function**								
22		**Profit**	($17,397.80)						

Figure 8.21 The infeasible result.

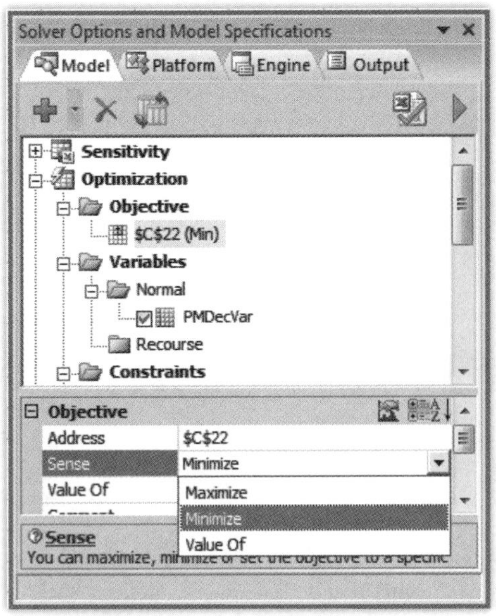

Figure 8.22 Change the sense of the objective cell to Minimize.

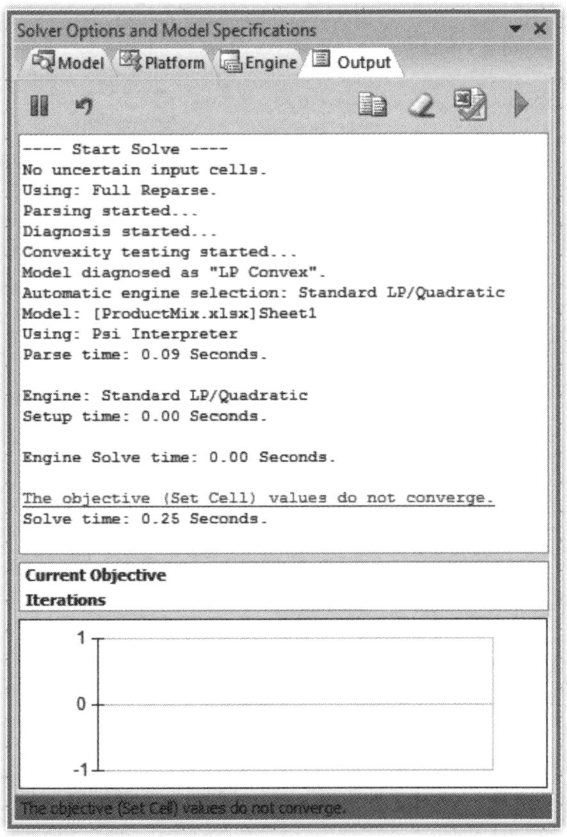

Figure 8.23 The Solver solution does not converge when we minimize profits and relax the non-negativity assumption.

8.3.2 Understanding Solver Reports

The three main reports available when using the Risk Solver Platform are the *Answer Report*, the *Sensitivity Report*, and the *Limits Report*. These reports are generated by Excel and displayed as new worksheets in the current workbook. To generate these reports, click on the *Risk Solver Platform > Analysis > Reports* button on the *Ribbon*. Select *Optimization* from the Reports drop-down menu. Next, select Answer, Sensitivity or Limits reports from the fly-out menu. We will now briefly review what information is contained in these reports.

Microsoft Excel 14.0 Answer Report
Worksheet: [ProductMix.xlsx]Sheet1
Report Created: 2/21/2011 6:08:47 PM
Result: Solver found a solution. All constraints and optimality conditions are satisfied.
Engine: Standard LP/Quadratic
Solution Time: 00 Seconds
Iterations: 0
Subproblems: 0
Incumbent Solutions: 0

Objective Cell (Max)

Cell	Name	Original Value	Final Value
$C$22	Profit <=	0	6625.2

Decision Variable Cells

Cell	Name	Original Value	Final Value	Type
$C$13	Amount produced Product Type	0.00	0	Normal
$D$13	Amount produced Product Type	0.00	0	Normal
$E$13	Amount produced Product Type	0.00	0	Normal
$F$13	Amount produced Product Type	0.00	597	Normal
$G$13	Amount produced Product Type	0.00	1084	Normal
$H$13	Amount produced Product Type	0.00	0	Normal

Constraints

Cell	Name	Cell Value	Formula	Status	Slack
$C$18	Labor Used <=	4500	$C$18<=$E$18	Binding	0
$C$19	Raw Material Used <=	1236	$C$19<=$E$19	Not Binding	364
$C$13	Amount produced Product Type	0	$C$13<=$C$15	Not Binding	960
$D$13	Amount produced Product Type	0	$D$13<=$D$15	Not Binding	928
$E$13	Amount produced Product Type	0	$E$13<=$E$15	Not Binding	1041
$F$13	Amount produced Product Type	597	$F$13<=$F$15	Not Binding	380
$G$13	Amount produced Product Type	1084	$G$13<=$G$15	Binding	0
$H$13	Amount produced Product Type	0	$H$13<=$H$15	Not Binding	1055

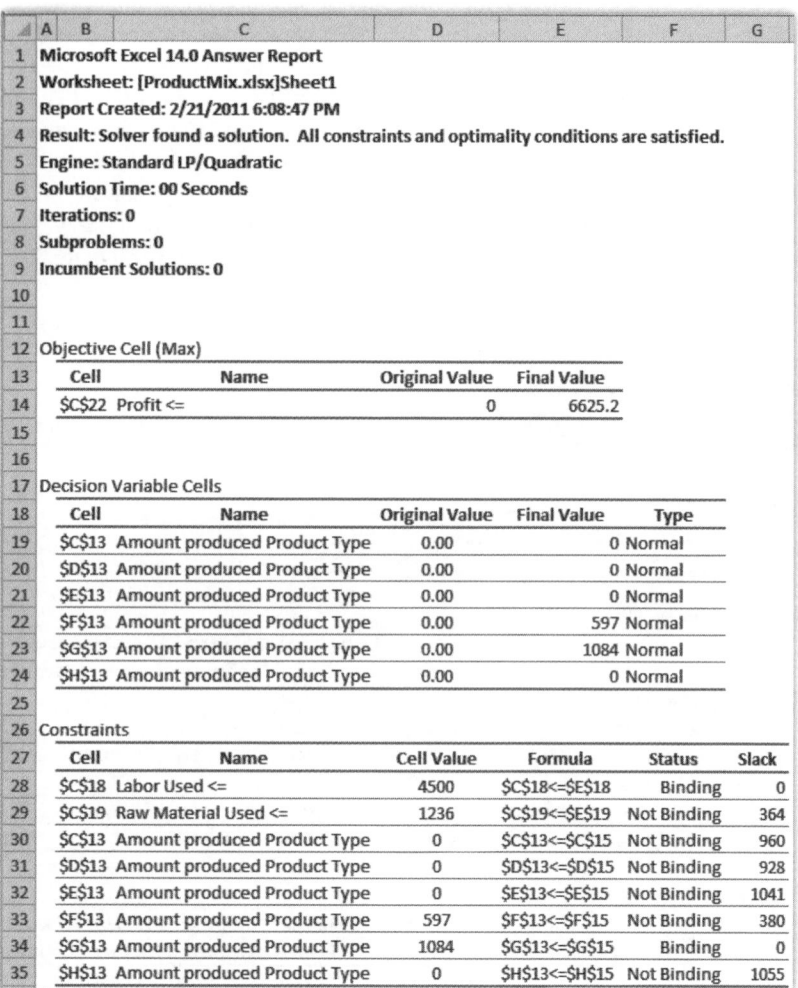

Figure 8.24 The Answer Report.

The Answer Report provides the original and final values of the objective cell, the decision variable cells, and the constraints (see Figure 8.24). It also gives the reference of all of these cells on the spreadsheet. The names for each cell are based on the row and column labels next to the tables on our spreadsheet. The formulas for the constraints are provided only as references for where the formulas are held; in other words, any functions used are not reported here. The status of the constraint part of the report conveys whether or not a constraint is binding. A constraint is binding when its slack value is zero. (The slack value is the limit on the change of the RHS value of a constraint that will not change the objective function value. For example, how important is it that the raw materials be less than or equal to 1,600? In the Answer Report, we see that the raw material constraint is not binding, since the value found by the Solver was 1,236 which still leaves a slack of 364. A binding constraint, on the other hand, shows that there can be no more improvement in the objective function. For example, the maximum allowed labor is used—and so that constraint is binding the objective function from further improvement by increasing labor.)

The Sensitivity Report provides information about the decision variable cells and the constraints (see Figure 8.25) as well as their final values. The reduced cost (or shadow price) and the allowable increase and decrease indicate how much flexibility can be allowed with any of these values in order to achieve the desired objective function value. (The reduced cost is the change that would occur in the objective function value for every unit change of a decision variable value. For example, in the current solution we produce 0 of product type 1; however, if we produced 1 unit of product type 1, the objective function value would change by –2.4. The shadow price is the change that would occur in the objective function value for every unit change of a constraint RHS value. For instance, if we use one more unit of total labor, the objective function value would change by 1.4.)

Microsoft Excel 14.0 Sensitivity Report
Worksheet: [ProductMix.xlsx]Sheet1
Report Created: 2/21/2011 6:11:41 PM

Objective Cell (Max)

Cell	Name	inal Value
$C$22	Profit <=	6625.2

Decision Variable Cells

Cell	Name	Final Value	Reduced Cost	Objective Coefficient	Allowable Increase	Allowable Decrease
$C$13	Amount produced Product Type 1	0	-2.40	6	2.4	1E+30
$D$13	Amount produced Product Type 2	0	-1.70	5.3	1.7	1E+30
$E$13	Amount produced Product Type 3	0	-0.20	5.4	0.2	1E+30
$F$13	Amount produced Product Type 4	597	0.00	4.2	0.36	0.15
$G$13	Amount produced Product Type 5	1084	0.30	3.8	1E+30	0.3
$H$13	Amount produced Product Type 6	0	-0.30	1.8	0.3	1E+30

Constraints

Cell	Name	Final Value	Shadow Price	Constraint R.H. Side	Allowable Increase	Allowable Decrease
$C$18	Labor Used <=	4500	1.40	4500	1141	1790
$C$19	Raw Material Used <=	1236	0.00	1600	1E+30	364

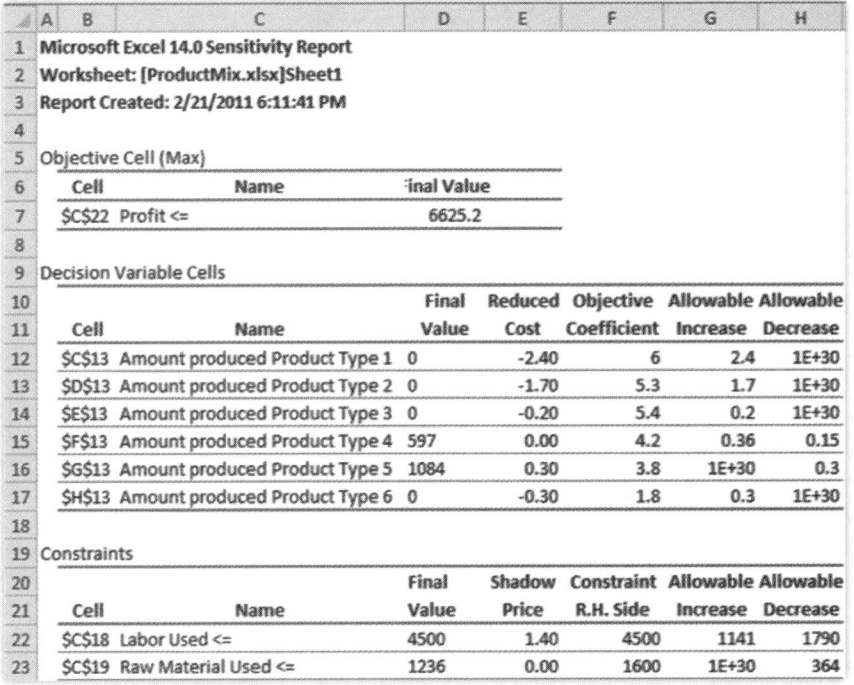

Figure 8.25 The Sensitivity Report.

The Limits Report provides information about the Objective Cell and the Decision Variable Cells (see Figure 8.26); it also includes the value of each cell. The lower and upper limits of the Decision Variable Cells are listed next to the corresponding Objective Cell value that would result if the Decision Variable Cell had the limit value.

Microsoft Excel 14.0 Limits Report
Worksheet: [ProductMix.xlsx]Sheet1
Report Created: 2/21/2011 6:14:29 PM

Cell	Objective Name	Value
$C$22	Profit <=	$6,625

Cell	Decision Variable Name	Value	Lower Limit	Objective Result	Upper Limit	Objective Result
$C$13	Amount produced Product Type 1	$0	0.00	$6,625	0.0	$6,625
$D$13	Amount produced Product Type 2	$0	0.00	$6,625	0.0	$6,625
$E$13	Amount produced Product Type 3	$0	0.00	$6,625	0.0	$6,625
$F$13	Amount produced Product Type 4	$597	0.00	$4,119	596.7	$6,625
$G$13	Amount produced Product Type 5	$1,084	0.00	$2,506	1084.0	$6,625
$H$13	Amount produced Product Type 6	$0	0.00	$6,625	0.0	$6,625

Figure 8.26 The Limits Report.

8.4 *Applications*

Mathematical models are utilized in many fields to formulate a problem into equations that can be solved using algorithms. The *Solver* allows managers and investors to solve these problems without knowing how the algorithms work. However, each problem must still be interpreted so that the *Solver* can read the correct *objective cells*, *decision variable cells*, and *constraints*. Below are a few examples of applications with the correct interpretation of these three model parts. These examples are grouped by linear, integer, and nonlinear programming problems. It is important to ensure that constraints and options are specified to reflect what type of problem is being solved.

8.4.1 Transportation Problem

An example of a linear programming problem is a transportation problem. A company ships their products from three different plants (one in Los Angeles, one in Atlanta, and one in New York City) to four regions of the United States (East, Midwest, South, West). Each plant has a limited capacity on how many products can be sent out, and each region has a demand of products that they must receive. There is a different transportation cost between each plant, or each city, and each region. The company wants to determine how many products each plant should ship to each region in order to minimize the total transportation cost.

The input for this problem is in the first table in Figure 8.27. It contains the unit transportation cost between each city and each region. It also displays the capacity per plant and the demand per region.

The decision variables are the amount to ship from each plant to each region. We have created a table with empty cells for these decision variables. We may represent them mathematically as follows:

x_{ij} = *amount shipped from plant in city i to region j*

	A	B	C	D	E	F	G	H	I	J
1	**Transportation**									
2	Where products should be produced and how they should be shipped to customers.									
3										
4	**Inputs**									
5			EAST	MIDWEST	SOUTH	WEST		CAPACITY		
6		LA	$5.00	$3.50	$4.20	$2.20		10000		
7		ATLANTA	$3.20	$2.60	$1.80	$4.80		12000		
8		NEW YORK CITY	$2.50	$3.10	$3.30	$5.40		14000		
9										
10		DEMAND	9000	6000	6000	13000				
11										
12	**Decision Variables**									
13	**and Constraints**									
14			EAST	MIDWEST	SOUTH	WEST		Sent		Capacity
15		LA						0.00	<=	10000
16		ATLANTA						0.00	<=	12000
17		NEW YORK CITY						0.00	<=	14000
18										
19		Received								
20			>=	>=	>=	>=				
21		Demand	9000	6000	6000	13000				
22										
23	**Objective Function**									
24		Total Cost	$0.00							

Figure 8.27 The spreadsheet preparation for the Transportation problem.

There are two constraints for this problem: demand and capacity. We need to ensure that the total number of products shipped from a plant (to each region) is less than or equal to its capacity, and we also need to ensure that the total number of products received by a region (from each plant) is greater than or equal to its demand. We have used the SUM function to create a column and row for these respective constraints. We have then copied the capacity and demand from the input table as the RHS value. We may represent these two constraints mathematically as follows:

$\Sigma_{j=1,\ldots,4} x_{ij} \leq u_i$ *for each i* *(here, u_i = capacity per plant at city i)*

$\Sigma_{i=1,\ldots,3} x_{ij} \leq d_j$ *for each j* *(here, d_j = demand per region j)*

We create these constraint formulas in Excel by using the SUM function. For the capacity constraint, we create a column titled "Sent" to the right of the decision variable table. In this column, we sum the total shipment amounts from each city to all plants. Each city has a separate formula in this column. For example, for "LA," there is a cell in the "Sent" column with the formula to sum all shipment amounts from "LA" shipped to each region. For the demand constraint, we create a row titled "Received" below the decision variable table. In this row, we sum the total shipment amounts from all cities to a particular plant. Each region has a separate formula in this row. For example, for the "East" region, there is a cell in the "Received" row with the formula to sum all shipment amounts from each city shipped to the "East" region.

The objective function is to minimize the total transportation costs. We need to sum the array multiplication between the given costs between each plant and region with the amount shipped between each plant and region. We can represent this mathematically as follows:

Minimize $z = \Sigma_{i=1,\ldots,3} \Sigma_{j=1,\ldots,4} c_{ij} x_{ij}$ *(here, c_{ij} = cost of shipping from plant in city i to region j)*

To create this formula in Excel, we use the SUMPRODUCT function. We have also named the range of decision variables as "TransShipped" and the range of input costs as "TransCosts," so the formula for the objective function is simply:

=SUMPRODUCT(TransShipped, TransCosts)

We are now ready to use the Solver (see Figure 8.27). We set the objective cell and choose Min for our objective function. We then set the variables (notice that the name of this range appears in the Solver task pane). We add both the capacity and demand constraints to the constraint list. Figure 8.28 displays the completed Risk Solver task pane. It is also very important that we specify two options for this linear programming problem as well: *select Standard LP/Quadratic Engine* as the solution method; and set the value of *Assume Non-Negative* property to *True* since negative values for the decision variables would not make sense in the context of this problem.

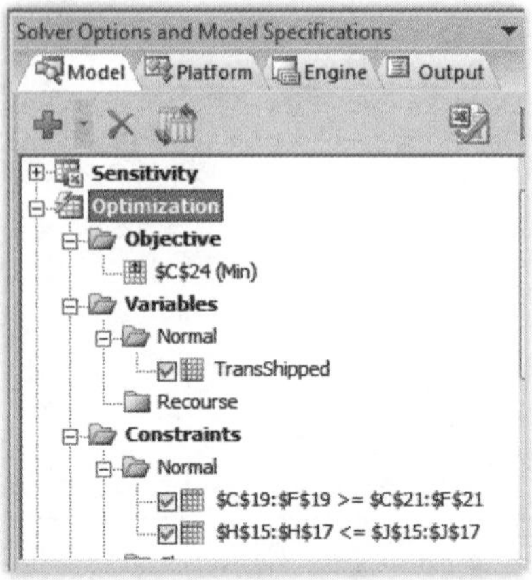

Figure 8.28 Completing the Risk Solver task pane.

The Solver solution appears in Figure 8.29. We have found the number of products to be shipped from each plant to each region and the value of the resulting minimal transportation cost. We can also check that all constraints have been met.

	A	B	C	D	E	F	G	H	I	J
1	**Transportation**									
2	Where products should be produced and how they should be shipped to customers.									
3										
4	**Inputs**									
5			EAST	MIDWEST	SOUTH	WEST		CAPACITY		
6		LA	$5.00	$3.50	$4.20	$2.20		10000		
7		ATLANTA	$3.20	$2.60	$1.80	$4.80		12000		
8		NEW YORK CITY	$2.50	$3.10	$3.30	$5.40		14000		
9										
10		DEMAND	9000	6000	6000	13000				
11										
12	**Decision Variables**									
13	**and Constraints**									
14			EAST	MIDWEST	SOUTH	WEST		Sent		Capacity
15		LA	0.00	0.00	0.00	10000.00		10000.00	<=	10000
16		ATLANTA	0.00	3000.00	6000.00	3000.00		12000.00	<=	12000
17		NEW YORK CITY	9000.00	3000.00	0.00	0.00		12000.00	<=	14000
18										
19		Received	9000.00	6000.00	6000.00	13000.00				
20			>=	>=	>=	>=				
21		Demand	9000	6000	6000	13000				
22										
23	**Objective Function**									
24		Total Cost	$86,800.00							

Figure 8.29 The Solver solution to the Transportation problem.

8.4.2 Workforce Scheduling

Another example of a linear programming problem is a Workforce Scheduling problem. A company wants to schedule its employees for every day of the week. Employees work 5 consecutive days, so the company wants to schedule on which day each employee starts working, or, in other words, how many employees start their five-day work week each day. There is a certain minimum number of employees needed each day of the week. The objective function is to find the schedule that minimizes the total number of employees working for the week.

As shown in the first table of Figure 8.30, the main input for this problem is the number of workers needed for each day of the week. We also know that each employee works 5 consecutive days. We have represented this schedule in the second table by recording a sequence of 1's beginning on the day listed in each row. So, the Monday row has a 1 in the Monday, Tuesday, Wednesday, Thursday, and Friday columns. The Tuesday row has a 1 in the Tuesday, Wednesday, Thursday, Friday, and Saturday columns, and so on. This table of consecutive 1's will be used for the constraint formula to calculate the number of people working each day.

D17 | =SUMPRODUCT(SchedDecVar,D9:D15)

	A	B	C	D	E	F	G	H	I	J
1	**Scheduling**									
2										
3	Inputs									
4			Monday	Tuesday	Wednesday	Thursday	Friday	Saturday	Sunday	
5		Number needed	17	13	15	17	9	9	12	
6										
7	Decision Variables			Employees work 5 consecutive days						
8	and Constraints	Number starting	Day worker starts	Monday	Tuesday	Wednesday	Thursday	Friday	Saturday	Sunday
9			Monday	1	1	1	1	1		
10			Tuesday		1	1	1	1	1	
11			Wednesday			1	1	1	1	1
12			Thursday	1			1	1	1	1
13			Friday	1	1			1	1	1
14			Saturday	1	1	1			1	1
15			Sunday	1	1	1	1			1
16										
17			Number working	0	0	0	0	0	0	0
18				>=	>=	>=	>=	>=	>=	>=
19			Number needed	17	13	15	17	9	9	12
20										
21	Objective Function									
22		Total	0							

Figure 8.30 The spreadsheet preparation for the Workforce Scheduling problem.

The decision variables for this problem are the number of employees who will begin working (for 5 consecutive days) on each day of the week. We can represent this mathematically as follows:

x_i = *number of employees that start work on day i*

The column next to the second table with empty cells (B9:B15) is for the decision variables. We have also named this range "SchedDecVar."

There is only one constraint for this problem, which is to ensure that the total number of employees working on a given day (regardless of which day they started working) is greater than or equal to the number of employees needed on that particular day. We can represent this mathematically as follows:

$\Sigma_{j=1,\ldots,7} x_i s_{ij} \geq d_i$ *for each i = 1,…,7* *(here,* s_{ij} *= five-day shift values for each day j*
d_i *= number employees needed on day i)*

To create these formulas in Excel, we again use the SUMPRODUCT function. We sum the array multiplication of the decision variable column with the column of 1's for each day. Since we have named our decision variable range, this formula is:

=SUMPRODUCT(SchedDecVar, D9:D15)

This formula appears in Figure 8.30. The *DayColumn* letter value would change from D to J for Monday through Sunday, respectively.

The objective function is to minimize the total number of employees needed. Mathematically, this can be written as follows:

$$\textit{Minimize } z = \Sigma_{i=1\ldots,7} x_i$$

To determine this value, we simply need to sum the total number of employees starting on each day of the week. The formula we use is:

=SUM(SchedDecVar)

We are now ready to use the Solver (see Figure 8.31), so we specify the objective and choose Min for the objective function. We then set the variables. Notice that the name of this range appears in the Solver task pane. We next add one constraint to the constraint list. It is also very important that we specify Standard LP/Quadratic Engine for solving the problem, and set the Assume Non-Negative property to True.

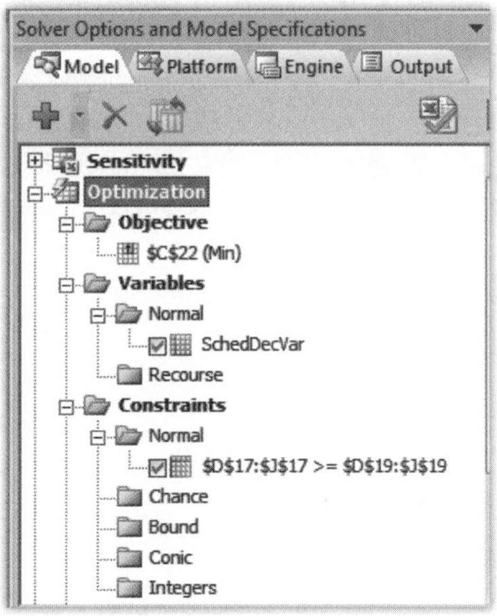

Figure 8.31 The completed Solver task pane for the Workforce Scheduling problem.

The Solver solution, shown in Figure 8.32 reveals the number of employees who will start work on each day of the week. We can also check that all the constraints are met. However, we notice that some of the results of the decision variables and objective function are non-integer.

Technically, this solution is correct for the way we communicated with the Solver, but it is not realistic to hire a total of 19.33 employees.

	A	B	C	D	E	F	G	H	I	J
1	**Scheduling**									
2										
3	**Inputs**									
4			Monday	Tuesday	Wednesday	Thursday	Friday	Saturday	Sunday	
5		Number needed	17	13	15	17	9	9	12	
6										
7	**Decision Variables**			Employees work 5 consecutive days						
8	**and Constraints**	Number starting	Day worker starts	Monday	Tuesday	Wednesday	Thursday	Friday	Saturday	Sunday
9		5.00	Monday	1	1	1	1	1		
10		2.33	Tuesday		1	1	1	1	1	
11		0.00	Wednesday			1	1	1	1	1
12		4.33	Thursday	1			1	1	1	1
13		0.00	Friday	1	1			1	1	1
14		2.33	Saturday	1	1	1			1	1
15		5.33	Sunday	1	1	1	1			1
16										
17			Number working	17.00	15.00	15.00	17.00	11.67	9.00	12.00
18				>=	>=	>=	>=	>=	>=	>=
19			Number needed	17	13	15	17	9	9	12
20										
21	**Objective Function**									
22		Total	19.33							

Figure 8.32 The Solver solution for the Workforce Scheduling problem.

Therefore, we need to enforce integer decision variables, thus making this an integer programming problem. To accomplish this, we first highlight the range of decision variables and then click on the *Risk Solver Platform > Optimization Model > Constraints* button on the *Ribbon*. From the *Constraints* drop-down menu, select *Variable Type/Bound*. Select *Integer* from the options in the fly-out menu as shown in Figure 8.33.

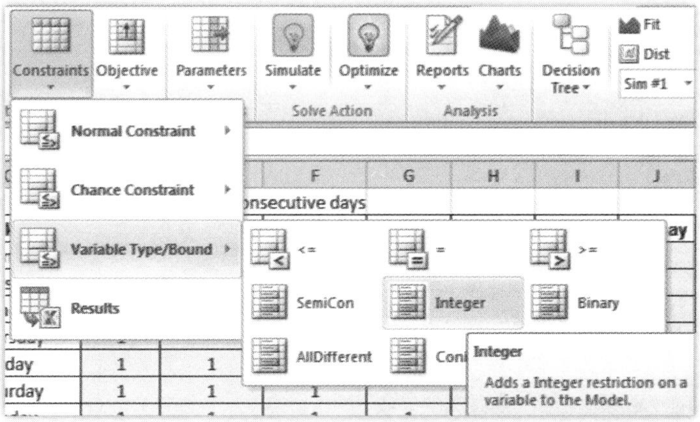

Figure 8.33 The additional constraint enforces the decision variables to be integers.

Note that an extra constraint has been added to the constraint list in the Solver task pane (see Figure 8.34). Since we named our decision variable range, this new constraint is displayed in the constraint list simply as:

SchedDecVar = integer

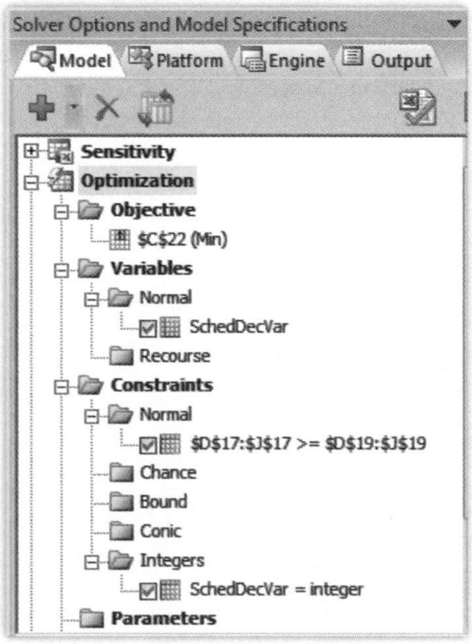

Figure 8.34 The modified Solver task pane.

The updated solution now has integer values for the decision variables and an objective function value that is more realistic (see Figure 8.35).

	A	B	C	D	E	F	G	H	I	J
1	Scheduling									
2										
3	Inputs									
4			Monday	Tuesday	Wednesday	Thursday	Friday	Saturday	Sunday	
5		Number needed	17	13	15	17	9	9	12	
6										
7	Decision Variables			Employees work 5 consecutive days						
8	and Constraints	Number starting	Day worker starts	Monday	Tuesday	Wednesday	Thursday	Friday	Saturday	Sunday
9		8	Monday	1	1	1	1	1		
10		0	Tuesday		1	1	1	1	1	
11		2	Wednesday			1	1	1	1	1
12		5	Thursday	1			1	1	1	1
13		0	Friday	1	1			1	1	1
14		3	Saturday	1	1	1			1	1
15		2	Sunday	1	1	1	1			1
16										
17			Number working	18	13	15	17	15	10	12
18				>=	>=	>=	>=	>=	>=	>=
19			Number needed	17	13	15	17	9	9	12
20										
21	Objective Function									
22		Total	20							

Figure 8.35 The updated Solver solution for the Scheduling problem.

Let's consider that the management is expecting an increase of business on Saturdays. We may wonder what will happen to the total number of employees required if the number needed on a Saturday increased from 9 to 16. We could increase manually the value of Number Required by adding one unit at a time and reoptimizing the corresponding problem. However, as the number of problems we test increases, this procedure will become cumbersome. The Risk Solver Platform provides an easier way to automate this process by performing multiple parameterized optimizations.

We first need to make some modifications to our spreadsheet (see Figure 8.36) before performing multiple optimizations. We have 8 different scenarios to optimize. For each scenario we identify the number of employees needed on a Saturday (cells M10:M17).

The first modification we make to our model is writing this formula in cell I19 (which represents Saturday requirements.):

=PsiOptParam(M10:M17)

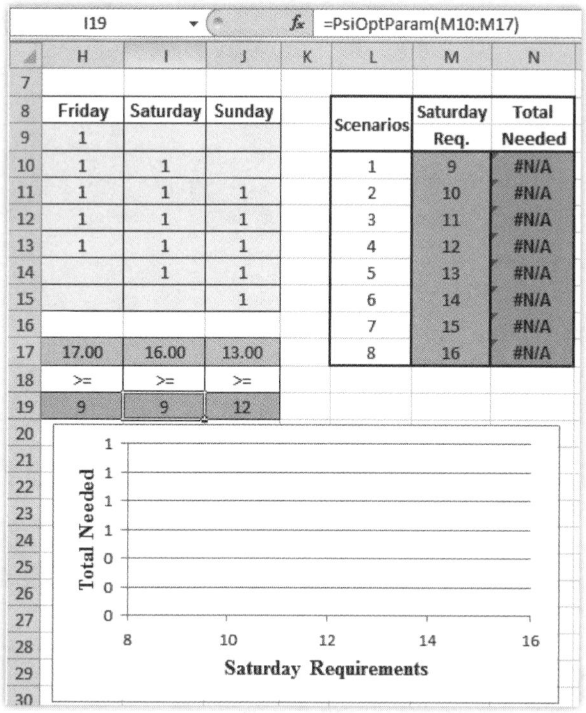

Figure 8.36 Problem modifications to handle parameterized optimization.

The *PsiOptParam()* is a function available in Risk Solver Platform, and supports multiple parameterized optimizations. This function changes the value of a parameter in the problem (cell I19) as each optimization run is performed.

The second modification we make is writing this formula in cell N10:

=PsiOptValue($C22$,L10)

We copy this formula to cells N10:N17. The *PsiOptValue()* function allows us to gain access to the optimal solution value (cell C22) of each optimization run. Initially, the values of *PsiOptValue()* function in cells N10:N17 is N/A since we have not executed the multiple optimization runs yet. Finally, we set the value of *Optimizations to Run* property to 8 in the Platform tab of Solver task pane, and solve the problem. Figure 8.37 presents the total number of employees needed as Saturday requirements increase. The solution presented in cells B9:B15 corresponds to the fourth optimization run. To observe solutions of other runs, select the corresponding *Opt #* from *Tools* group of *Risk Solver Platform* tab on the *Ribbon*.

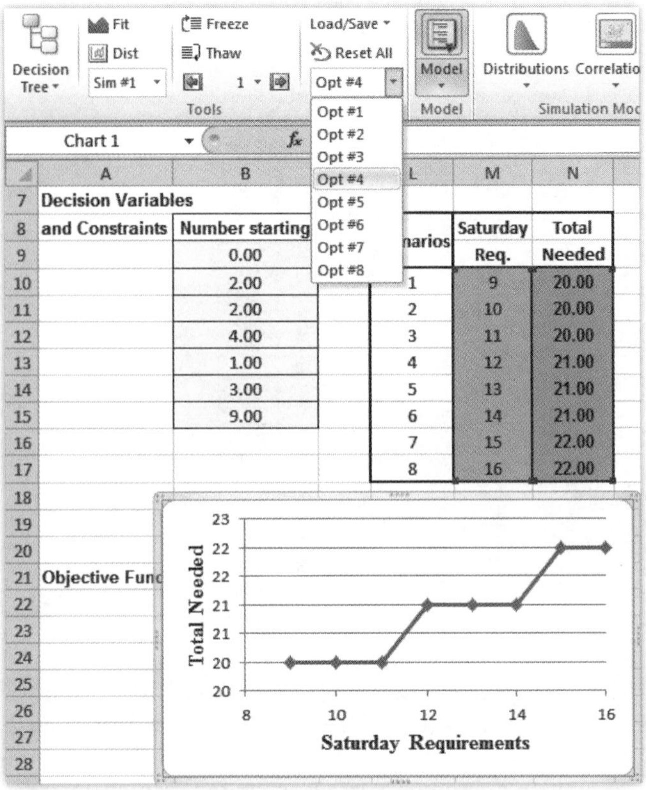

Figure 8.37 Total number of employees needed as Saturday requirements increase.

8.4.3 Capital Budgeting

An example of an integer programming problem is the Capital Budgeting problem; it has an additional integer constraint which allows the decision variables to take only binary values (0 or 1). In this problem, there are 20 projects in which a company, or individual, can invest. Each project's net present value (NPV) and cost per year are provided. The company, or investor, wants to determine how much to invest in each project, given a limited amount of yearly funds available, in order to maximize the total NPV of the investment.

The input table lists the NPV and yearly costs for each project (see Figure 8.38).

The decision variables for this problem are the projects that we do and do not invest in. These will have *yes/no* or *go/no go* values. We represent these binary options using 1's and 0's. Mathematically, the decision variables can be written as follows:

$y_i = \{0,1\}$ = *no/yes for investing in project i*

We have to ensure that the decision variables are given only binary values when we add constraints to the Solver. We name this range "CBDecVar."

There is only one constraint for this problem, which is that no more than the yearly available funds can be spent annually. Since each project has associated yearly costs, we must sum the costs of all of the projects that we have invested in each year to determine if this constraint is met. This constraint is written mathematically as:

$\Sigma_{i=1,\ldots,20} y_i c_{ij} \le u_j$ *for each* $j = 1,\ldots,6$ *(here,* c_{ij} *= cost of investing in project i in year j)*

	A	B	C	D	E	F	G	H	I
1	**Capital Budgeting**								
2									
3	**Inputs**		**NPV**	**Cost Year 1**	**Cost Year 2**	**Cost Year 3**	**Cost Year 4**	**Cost Year 5**	**Cost Year 6**
4		**Project 1**	$928	$398	$180	$368	$111	$108	$123
5		**Project 2**	$908	$151	$269	$248	$139	$86	$83
6		**Project 3**	$801	$129	$189	$308	$56	$61	$23
7		**Project 4**	$543	$275	$218	$220	$54	$70	$59
8		**Project 5**	$944	$291	$252	$228	$123	$141	$70
9		**Project 6**	$848	$80	$283	$285	$119	$84	$37
10		**Project 7**	$545	$203	$220	$77	$54	$44	$42
11		**Project 8**	$808	$150	$113	$143	$67	$101	$43
12		**Project 9**	$638	$282	$141	$160	$37	$55	$64
13		**Project 10**	$841	$214	$254	$355	$130	$72	$62
14		**Project 11**	$664	$224	$271	$130	$51	$79	$58
15		**Project 12**	$546	$225	$150	$33	$35	$107	$63
16		**Project 13**	$699	$101	$218	$272	$43	$90	$71
17		**Project 14**	$599	$255	$202	$70	$3	$75	$83
18		**Project 15**	$903	$228	$351	$240	$60	$93	$80
19		**Project 16**	$859	$303	$173	$431	$60	$90	$41
20		**Project 17**	$748	$133	$427	$220	$59	$40	$39
21		**Project 18**	$668	$197	$98	$214	$95	$96	$74
22		**Project 19**	$888	$313	$278	$291	$66	$75	$74
23		**Project 20**	$655	$152	$211	$134	$85	$59	$70

Figure 8.38 The input table for the Capital Budgeting problem.

To create these formulas in Excel, we again use the SUMPRODUCT function. The arrays for this function are the decision variables and the column of yearly costs from the input table. Since the decision variable values are binary, only the costs for the projects in which we will invest will be summed. Applying the range name given to the decision variables, the formula for the cost incurred in year 1 is:

SUMPRODUCT(CBDecVar,D4:D23)

Similar expressions can be formed for other years. The objective function is to maximize the total NPV. Mathematically, it is written as follows:

$Maximize\ z = \Sigma_{i=1,\ldots,20}\, y_i p_i$ (here, p_i = NPV for project i)

To determine this, we sum the array multiplication of the decision variables and the column of NPV values for each project. We have named this NPV column "CB_NPV." Using this range name and the name of the decision variable range, this formula is:

=SUMPRODUCT(CBDecVar, CB_NPV)

See Figure 8.39 for the location and formulation of these model parts.

Now we are ready to use the Solver. After specifying the objective cell and Max for the objective function, the Variables, and the one constraint, we must also include the additional binary variable constraint. To do so, we highlight the decision variables and use the constraints drop-down menu on the Ribbon to set the variable type to binary as is Figure 8.40. Now, when we return to the Solver task pane (see Figure 8.41), we can see that this additional constraint has been added as:

CBDecVar = binary

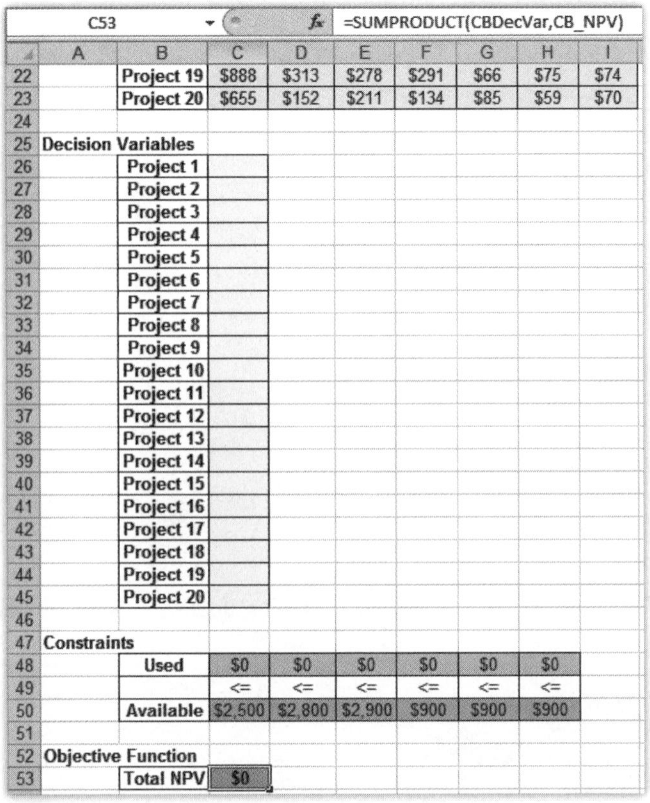
C53
=SUMPRODUCT(CBDecVar,CB_NPV)
A B C D E F G H I
22 Project 19 $888 $313 $278 $291 $66 $75 $74
23 Project 20 $655 $152 $211 $134 $85 $59 $70
24
25 Decision Variables
26 Project 1
27 Project 2
28 Project 3
29 Project 4
30 Project 5
31 Project 6
32 Project 7
33 Project 8
34 Project 9
35 Project 10
36 Project 11
37 Project 12
38 Project 13
39 Project 14
40 Project 15
41 Project 16
42 Project 17
43 Project 18
44 Project 19
45 Project 20
46
47 Constraints
48 Used $0 $0 $0 $0 $0 $0
49 <= <= <= <= <= <=
50 Available $2,500 $2,800 $2,900 $900 $900 $900
51
52 Objective Function
53 Total NPV $0

Figure 8.39 Spreadsheet preparation for the Capital Budgeting problem.

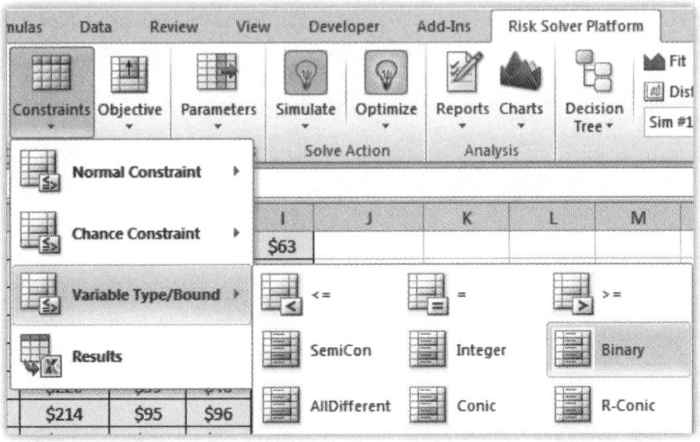

Figure 8.40 Adding an additional constraint to enforce binary decision variable values.

We select the *Standard Evolutionary Engine* as the solution method for this problem, and set the value of *Assume Non-Negative* property to True. The Engine tab of the task pane displays the options of this *Engine* as shown in Figure 8.42. We set the values of *convergence*, and *maximum time without improvement* as shown, and keep the rest of the parameters at their default values.

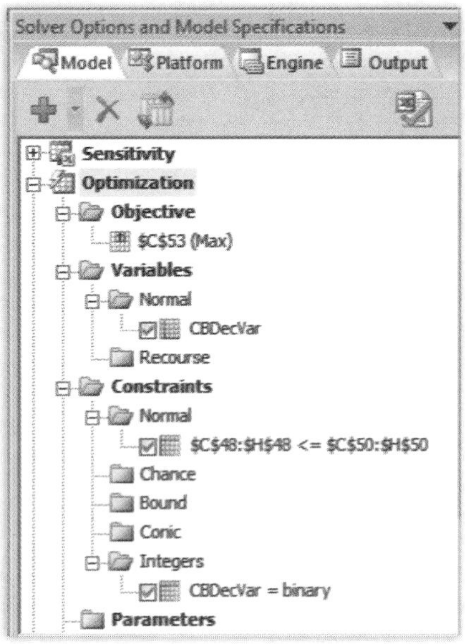

Figure 8.41 The completed Solver task pane for the Capital Budgeting problem with binary decision variables.

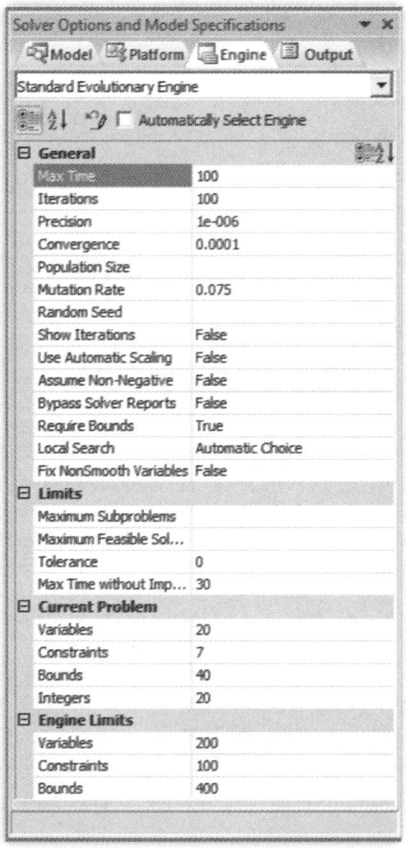

Figure 8.42 The Standard Evolutionary Engine window options.

Now, when we apply the Solver, we find that several iterations of the Genetic Algorithm are being run. The objective function value for each iteration is plotted in the task pane. As you see from Figure 8.43, the integer gap for the solution found is zero, which implies that the solution found is optimal.

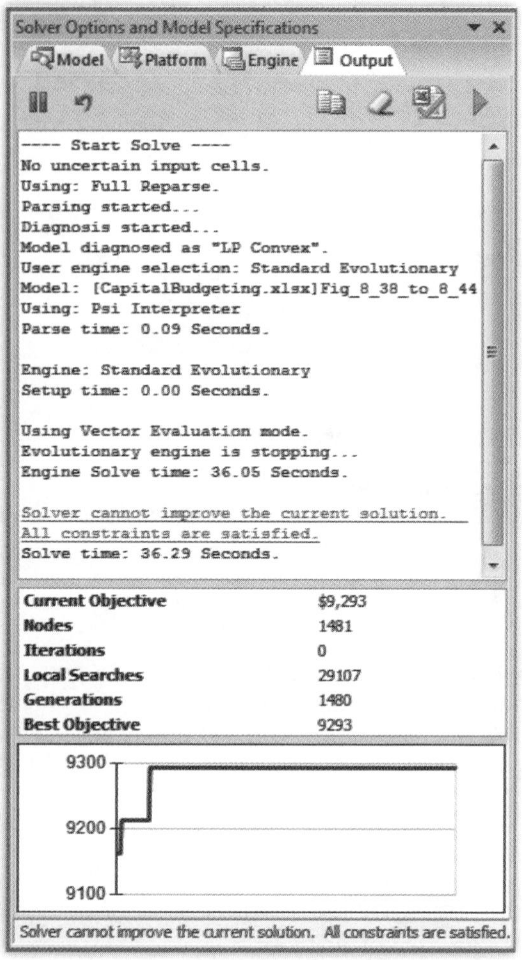

Figure 8.43 The Solver Results window explains why the Solver stopped.

Note that the solution found is provided as 1's and 0's in the column of decision variables (see Figure 8.44). This result can be interpreted as invest in the projects with 1's; do not invest in the projects with 0's. Therefore, in order to maximize NPV, we should invest in only 12 of the projects.

8.4.4 Warehouse Location

The Warehouse Location problem is an example of a nonlinear programming problem. A company stores all of its products in one warehouse. Its customers are in cities around the United States and the management is trying to determine the best location for their warehouse in order to minimize total transportations costs. Each city's location is identified by its latitude and longitude. The number of shipments made to each city is also provided. We are to determine the warehouse location based on its latitude and longitude values.

	A	B	C	D	E	F	G	H	I
22		Project 19	$888	$313	$278	$291	$66	$75	$74
23		Project 20	$655	$152	$211	$134	$85	$59	$70
24									
25	Decision Variables								
26		Project 1	0						
27		Project 2	1						
28		Project 3	1						
29		Project 4	0						
30		Project 5	0						
31		Project 6	1						
32		Project 7	1						
33		Project 8	1						
34		Project 9	1						
35		Project 10	1						
36		Project 11	0						
37		Project 12	0						
38		Project 13	0						
39		Project 14	1						
40		Project 15	1						
41		Project 16	1						
42		Project 17	0						
43		Project 18	0						
44		Project 19	1						
45		Project 20	1						
46									
47	Constraints								
48		Used	$2,460	$2,684	$2,742	$876	$895	$702	
49			<=	<=	<=	<=	<=	<=	
50		Available	$2,500	$2,800	$2,900	$900	$900	$900	
51									
52	Objective Function								
53		Total NPV	$9,293						

Figure 8.44 The Solver solution for the Capital Budgeting problem.

The input for this problem is the location of each city identified by its latitude and longitude. We are also provided with the number of shipments made to each city. This input is illustrated in the first table of Figure 8.45. We have named the column of shipments "WHShipments."

	A	B	C	D	E
1	Warehouse Location				
2					
3					
4	Inputs		Latitude	Longitude	Shipments
5		Atlanta	33.8	84.4	18
6		Boston	42.3	71.0	6
7		Chicago	41.8	87.7	16
8		Denver	39.8	104.9	15
9		Houston	29.8	95.4	12
10		LA	34.1	118.4	19
11		Miami	25.8	802.0	5
12		New Orleans	30.0	89.9	9
13		New York	40.7	73.9	14
14		Philadelphia	40.0	75.1	7
15		Phoenix	33.5	112.1	8
16		Salt Lake City	40.8	111.9	12
17		San Fransisco	37.8	122.6	16
18		Seattle	41.6	122.4	7
19					
20	Decision Variables		Latitude	Longitude	
21		Warehouse			
22					
23	Constraints				
24		Both Lat and Long must be <= 120 and >= 0			

Figure 8.45 Spreadsheet preparation for the *Warehouse Location* problem.

The two decision variables are the latitude and longitude values of the warehouse location. We will represent them mathematically as follows:

a = warehouse latitude, b = warehouse longitude

We have created two empty cells for these and named each one "WHLat" and "WHLong," respectively.

There is only one constraint for this problem, which is that the latitude and longitude for the warehouse location must be between the values of 0 and 120. Mathematically, this can be written as follows:

$$0 \leq a \leq 120$$
$$0 \leq b \leq 120$$

We only need to add the constraint that they be less than or equal to 120 since non-negativity is a Solver option.

We now need to keep track of the distances between each city and the possible warehouse location. These distances are calculated using the following nonlinear equation:

$d_j = 69\sqrt{((a - a_j)^2 + (b - b_j)^2)}$ *(here, d_j = distance per city j and a_j and b_j are the latitude and longitude for each city j, respectively)*

In Excel, this equation can be created using the SQRT function as follows:

*=69*SQRT((WHLat-CityLatitude)^2 + (WHLong-CityLongitude)^2)*

The *CityLatitude* and *CityLongitude* are calculated from the columns of the input table for each city row. The SQRT function calculates the square root, which is a nonlinear manipulation of the decision variables. This column of distances appears in Figure 8.46. We have named this column "WHDist." (*Note*: The value 69 is based on the earth's curvature and is only used when computing latitude and longitude distances for U.S. cities.)

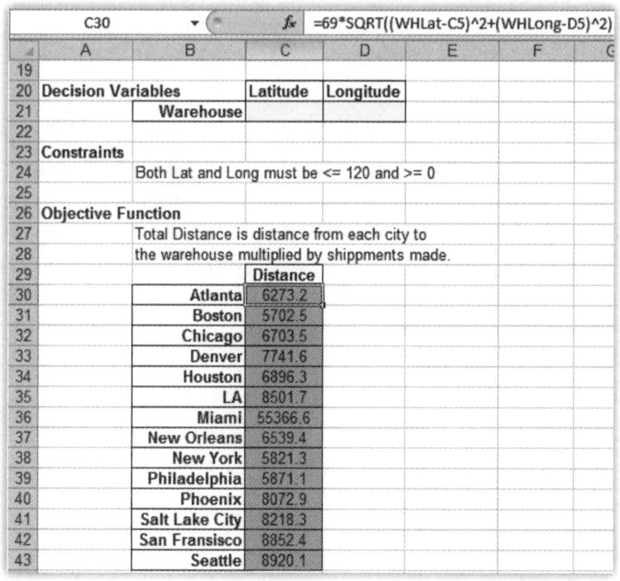
C30
=69*SQRT((WHLat-C5)^2+(WHLong-D5)^2)
Decision Variables
Latitude
Longitude
Warehouse
Constraints
Both Lat and Long must be <= 120 and >= 0
Objective Function
Total Distance is distance from each city to
the warehouse multiplied by shippments made.
Distance
Atlanta 6273.2
Boston 5702.5
Chicago 6703.5
Denver 7741.6
Houston 6896.3
LA 8501.7
Miami 55366.6
New Orleans 6539.4
New York 5821.3
Philadelphia 5871.1
Phoenix 8072.9
Salt Lake City 8218.3
San Fransisco 8852.4
Seattle 8920.1

Figure 8.46 Calculating the distance between each city and the possible warehouse location.

The objective function is to minimize the total distance traveled from the warehouse to each city. It can be written mathematically as follows:

Minimize $z = \Sigma_{=1 \text{ to } 14} d_j s_j$ *(here,* s_j *= shipments sent to city j)*

In Excel, we use the SUMPRODUCT function to find the sum of the array multiplication between this column of distances and the column of shipments made to each city from the input table. Since we have named both of these ranges, the formula for the objective function is:

=SUMPRODUCT(WHDist, WHShipments)

See Figure 8.47. The completed optimization model is presented in Figure 8.48.

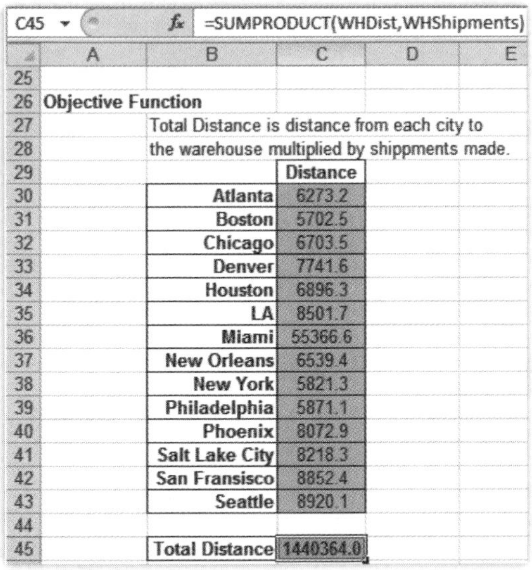
C45
=SUMPRODUCT(WHDist,WHShipments)
Objective Function
Total Distance is distance from each city to
the warehouse multiplied by shippments made.
Distance
Atlanta 6273.2
Boston 5702.5
Chicago 6703.5
Denver 7741.6
Houston 6896.3
LA 8501.7
Miami 55366.6
New Orleans 6539.4
New York 5821.3
Philadelphia 5871.1
Phoenix 8072.9
Salt Lake City 8218.3
San Fransisco 8852.4
Seattle 8920.1
Total Distance 1440364.0

Figure 8.47 The objective function formula for the Warehouse Location problem.

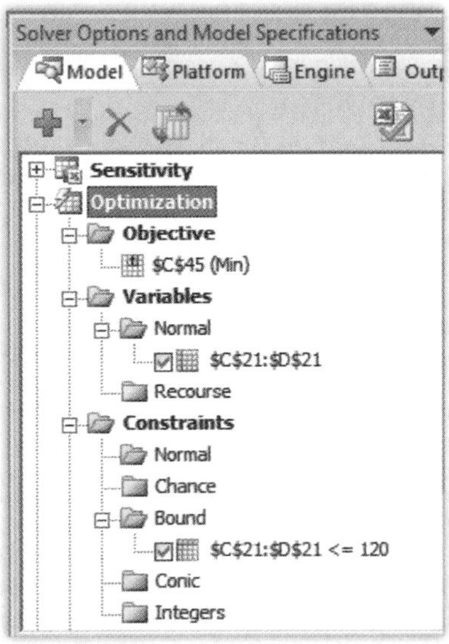

Figure 8.48 The completed optimization model for the Warehouse Location problem.

Let us now use the Standard GRG Nonlinear Engine to solve this nonlinear programming problem. We begin by setting the objective cell and choosing Min for the objective function. Then we set the variables and the constraints, and set the value of Assume *Non-Negative* to True. Next, we choose Standard GRG Nonlinear Engine from the list presented in the Engine tab of the task pane (see Figure 8.49). We set the value of Max Time and iterations to 100, and keep the rest of the parameters at their default values as shown. Now we are ready to solve the problem. The *output* of Solver's task pane indicates that the Solver has converged to the current solution (see Figure 8.50).

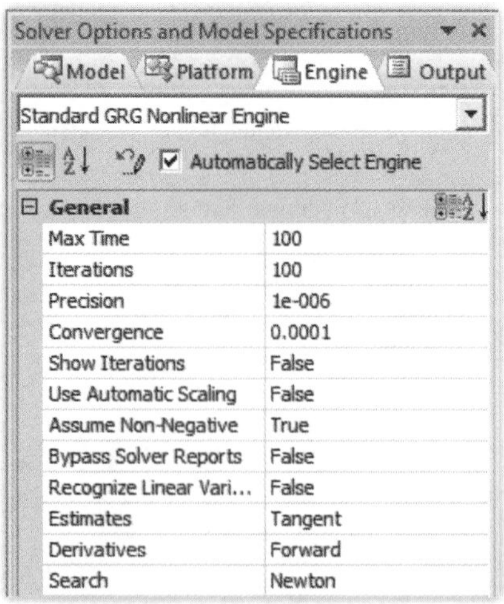

Figure 8.49 The GRG Engine general properties.

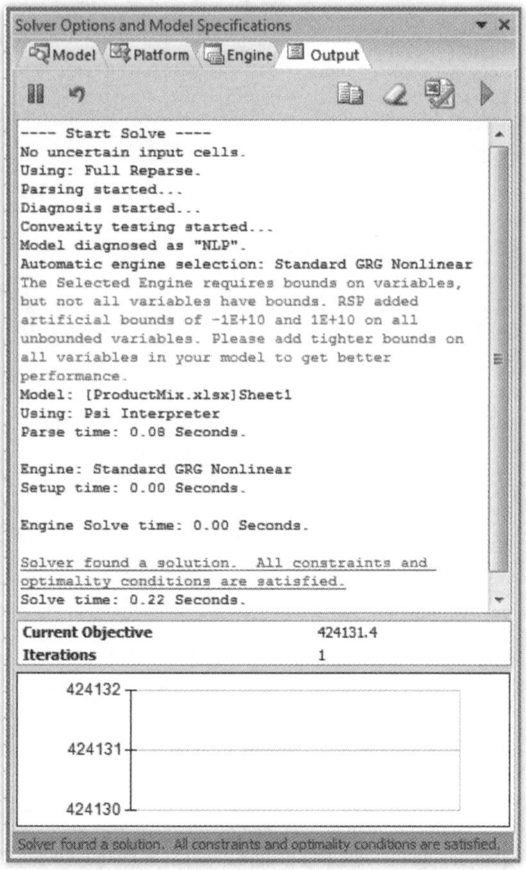

Figure 8.50 The *output tab* of Solver's task pane indicates that the Solver has converged to the current solution.

The solution appears in Figure 8.51. The latitude and longitude for the warehouse location are displayed with the corresponding total minimal distance to be traveled to each city for all shipments.

	A	B	C	D
19				
20	Decision Variables		Latitude	Longitude
21		Warehouse	37.45	102.54
22				
23	Constraints			
24		Both Lat and Long must be <= 120 and >= 0		
25				
26	Objective Function			
27		Total Distance is distance from each city to		
28		the warehouse multiplied by shippments made.		
29			Distance	
30		Atlanta	1277.1	
31		Boston	2202.1	
32		Chicago	1067.3	
33		Denver	229.4	
34		Houston	722.4	
35		LA	1118.2	
36		Miami	48269.1	
37		New Orleans	1012.8	
38		New York	1989.1	
39		Philadelphia	1901.8	
40		Phoenix	713.5	
41		Salt Lake City	685.6	
42		San Fransisco	1384.0	
43		Seattle	1399.6	
44				
45		Total Distance	424131.4	

Figure 8.51 The Solver solution for the Warehouse Location problem.

To summarize, we have taken in this chapter five examples of linear programming, integer programming, nonlinear programming, and parameterized optimization models, and demonstrated how to formulate and solve them in Excel. We have included several practice additional formulations in the Excel worksheets for this chapter and we encourage the reader to work them out.

8.5 *Summary*

- The three parts of a mathematical model are decision variables, objective function, and constraints.
- The three primary types of mathematical models are linear, integer, and nonlinear programming problems.
- Using Risk Solver Platform involves three main steps: reading and interpreting the problem to determine the three parts of the model, preparing the spreadsheet so that the Solver can read the data, and running the Solver.
- Several applications of mathematical modeling exist for which Solver can be a useful tool. Some LP examples are transportation and workforce scheduling. An IP example is capital budgeting, and an NLP example is a warehouse location problem.
- We use the multiple parameterized optimization capabilities of Risk Solver Platform to solve a multiscenario workforce scheduling problem.

8.6 Exercises

8.6.1 Review Questions

1. What are the three components of a mathematical model?
2. How does integer programming differ from linear programming?
3. How do we identify an NLP problem?
4. What are the three main steps involved in using Risk Solver Platform?
5. How should constraint equations be entered into a spreadsheet when using the Solver?
6. How is the objective cell used in the Solver?
7. How can you ensure that negative quantities are not produced in a Solver solution?
8. What additional constraint is necessary to change a linear programming Solver model into an integer programming model?
9. What additional constraint is needed to enforce binary decision variables?
10. Give an example of an instance when the Solver could be applied to solve a problem. State what the objective function, decision variables, and constraints would be for your example.
11. What is a parameterized optimization problem?
12. Discuss how you would use two Risk Solver Platform functions dedicated to multiple parameterized optimizations.
13. What are the main solution engines used by the Solver?
14. What does this message imply: "Solver could not find a feasible solution"?
15. What are the two parameters for the Standard GRG Nonlinear Engine that are set in Solver task pane?

8.6.2 Hands-On Exercises

Note: *Please refer to the file "Chapter_08_Exercises.xlsx" for the associated worksheets noted for the hands-on exercises. The file is available at www.dss-books.com.*

1. Use the Risk Solver Platform to determine the solution to the following LP model:

   Maximize $Q = 3X + 4Y - 5Z$

   Subject to: $5X + Z \leq 1502$

   $X + 4Y \leq 100$

   $10Z - 2X - 3Y \geq 20$

   $X, Y, Z \geq 0$

2. A distribution center for a department store has four trucks available to deliver products to retail stores. The company accrues shipping costs for all boxes that it ships and losses for all boxes that cannot fit on one of the four trucks and must be shipped later. Construct a model formulation that minimizes the total cost by determining the optimal number of boxes of each product to be delivered by each truck. Each truck has a trailer volume of 1000 ft^3 and a weight limit of 50,000 lbs. (Refer to worksheet 8.2.)
3. Referring to the model formulated in the previous exercise, use the Solver to find the optimal number of boxes of each product to ship in each truck. Adjust the values for amount, size, weight, cost of shipping, and loss if shipped late, and use the Risk Solver Platform to find the optimal solution.
4. A toy company is expanding its toy vehicle product line. The company formerly produced only toy trains but now is expanding the line to include toy cars, trucks, and airplanes. The amount of each type of vehicle to produce must now be determined. A given table displays the expected production cost, sales price, required machine hours, and required labor hours to produce a single unit of each type of toy vehicle. It costs $200 an hour to run the machine that produces cars, trucks, and trains and $250 an hour to run the machine that produces airplanes. All toy assembly workers are paid a wage of $7.25 an hour. Based on historical data, the product line manager forecasts that the demand for trains, cars, and trucks will be at least 500 units, and the demand for airplanes will be at least 250 units. The production cost of all toy vehicles cannot exceed $10,000, and no more than 1,000 labor hours can be spent on production. Formulate this problem as an integer programming model that will maximize the profit earned by the company's toy vehicle product line. Use the Risk Solver Platform to find the optimal number of each type of toy vehicle to produce. (Refer to worksheet 8.4.)

5. Consider the problem presented in the previous exercise. Use multiple parameterized optimization capabilities of the Risk Solver Platform to see the impact of increasing production costs from $10,000 to $20,000 (in increments of $1,000) on profits. Graph the relationship between production costs and optimal profits. Comment on the results.
6. An agricultural supply company is developing a livestock feed mix that will consist of three ingredients: A, B, and C. An input table displays nutrition and cost information per ounce of each of these ingredients. The company wants to create a mix that contains no more than 750 calories per ounce and no more than 10 grams of fat. The desired mix should also meet at least 25% of the Recommended Daily Allowance (RDA) of each of the following nutrients: Vitamin A, Vitamin D, and Protein. The company wants to develop the feed mix as cheaply as possible. Formulate this problem as a linear programming model, and use the Solver to find the optimal percentages of each ingredient to include in the feed mix. (Refer to worksheet 8.6.)
7. Using the Solver model that you developed in the previous exercise to perform the following.
   a. Trace the dependents of each decision variable.
   b. Trace the precedents of the target cell and the constraint cells.
   c. Use the multiple parameterized optimization capabilities of Risk Solver Platform to see the impact of increasing the amount of calories per ounce from 750 to 1,000 (in increments of 10) on costs.
8. A hardware manufacturer uses four workstations to produce nuts and bolts. An input table provides the number of minutes required to create a batch of nuts or bolts at each workstation. Another input table lists the cost of machining a batch of nuts or bolts. The machines at each workstation run for 16 hours a day, 5 days a week. A minimum of 700 batches of nuts and 1,000 batches of bolts must be produced each week. Use the Solver to determine the optimal number of batches of nuts and bolts to produce at each workstation in order to minimize the cost of machining. (Refer to worksheet 8.8.)
9. Suppose that you have $0.97 worth of coins in your pocket. You know that you have three times as many nickels as there are dimes. You also know that you have at least five pennies and no more than two quarters. Use the Solver to determine what number of each coin type you have in your pocket.
10. A venture capitalist is trying to determine which of three projects to finance: project A, project B, and/or project C. She plans to finance as many projects as necessary to maximize her total return. She has a total of $400,000 to invest in the first year and $200,000 to invest in each subsequent year. An input table displays the implementation cost per year (in thousands of dollars) of each project. Projects A, B, C will yield an estimated return of $550,000, $750,000, and $675,000, respectively, at the end of three years. Formulate this problem as a binary programming model, and use the Solver to find the optimal combination of projects for the capitalist to finance. Use the multiple parameterized optimization capabilities of Risk Solver Platform to see the impact of increasing the total budget from $800 to $1,000 (in increments of $100) on maximum return. Assume that a $100 increase in the total budget is distributed as follows: $50 for year 1, $25 for year 2, and $25 for year 3. (Refer to worksheet 8.10.)
11. An engineering student is trying to determine how many hours of studying to devote to each of his subjects in order to maximize his overall grade-point average this semester. To do so, he predicts the grade average he will receive for studying different amounts of time in each of his classes. An input table displays his predictions. He wants to study no more than a total of 40 hours per week. He estimates that the amount of time he should study physics is double the amount of time he should study economics, and the amount of time he should study calculus is in between those two values. He also estimates that he will devote equal amounts of time to calculus and chemistry. Formulate this problem as a linear programming model, and use the solver to find the optimal solution. (Refer to worksheet 8.11.)
12. During each 4-hour period, a small town's police force requires the following number of on-duty

police officers: 8 from midnight to 4 AM, 7 from 4 AM to 8 AM, 6 from 8 AM to noon, 6 from noon to 4 PM, 5 from 4 PM to 8 PM, and 4 from 8 PM to midnight. Each police officer works two consecutive 4-hour shifts. Formulate and solve an LP that can be used to minimize the number of police officers needed to meet the daily requirements.

13. A retailer store accepts orders made by telephone 7 days a week, from 8 AM to 5 PM. The management has estimated the number of people needed daily in the call center to cover incoming orders. The employees work 5 consecutive days per week. The salary is $100/day to work on Monday through Friday and $150/day to work on the weekend. Formulate the problem as an integer programming problem that minimizes the cost of staffing the call center. Use Risk Solver Platform to optimize this problem. (Refer to worksheet 8.13.)

14. Refer to Hands-On Exercise 12. Suppose part-time staff working 3 consecutive days during Monday to Friday can be hired at a cost of $110/day. The increased cost reflects the higher training and turnover costs associated with part-time employees. The number of such staff cannot exceed 5. Extend the integer programming model to incorporate this option. Use the Risk Solver Platform to optimize the problem.

15. A production company blends silicon and nitrogen to produce two types of fertilizers. Fertilizer 1 contains 40% nitrogen and 60% silicon. Fertilizer 2 contains 30% nitrogen and 70% silicon. The selling price for fertilizer 1 is $70/lb and for fertilizer 2 is $40/lb. The company can purchase up to 80 lbs of nitrogen at $15/lb and up to 100 lbs of silicon at $10/lb. The company should produce at least 80 lbs of fertilizer 1 and at least 30 lbs of fertilizer 2. Determine the amounts of fertilizers 1 and 2 that maximize the profit. Formulate this problem as a linear programming problem and use the Risk Solver Platform to find the solution.

16. A local bakery sells blueberry and chocolate muffins in packs of four. In a week, the bakery bakes, at most, 65 packs of muffins. The cost and demands per pack are presented in an input table. It costs $.50 to hold a pack of blueberry muffins and $.40 to hold a pack of chocolate muffins in inventory for a week. Formulate and solve an LP to minimize total cost of meeting next three weeks' demands. (Refer to worksheet 8.16.)

17. A company supplies goods to three customers, each of whom requires 30 units. The company has two warehouses. Warehouse 1 has 40 units available and warehouse 2 has 30 units available. The costs of shipping 1 unit from the warehouse to a customer are shown in worksheet 8.17. There is a penalty for each unmet customer unit of demand. With customer 1, a penalty cost of $90 is incurred, with customer 2, $80, and with customer 3, $110. Formulate and solve a transportation problem to minimize the sum of shortage and shipping costs. (Refer to worksheet 8.17.)

18. Referring to the above problem, suppose that extra units could be purchased and shipped to either warehouse for a total cost of $100 per unit and that all customer demand must be met. Formulate and solve this transportation problem to minimize the sum of purchasing and shipping costs.

19. A currency trader faces the following 1-day currency exchange problem that involves U.S. dollars, English pounds, and Japanese yen. In the beginning of the day, he has an inventory of 40,000 dollars, 90,000 pounds, and 100,000 yen. By the end of the day, he must have an inventory of at least 50,000 dollars, 75,000 pounds and 60,000 yen. The exchange rates are given in an input table (for example, one can exchange 1 U.S. dollar for 0.61 English pound). (Refer to worksheet 8.19.)

During the day, the currency trader exchanges the starting inventory for different currencies to create the required ending inventory while maximizing the surplus inventory of U.S. dollars. Formulate this problem as a linear program and use the Risk Solver Platform to find the solution.

20. A computer company must purchase 700 customized hard drives for the new model that is planning to launch next year. An input table presents the quotes received from three different vendors. For example, Company C will require a fixed cost of $9,000 to set up the machines to produce the hard drives. In addition, it will charge \$270 per unit sold. Formulate the vendor selection problem as an integer programming model. Use the Risk Solver Platform to solve the problem. (Refer to worksheet 8.20.)

21. Refer to Hands-On Exercise 20. Reformulate the problem and reoptimize using the Risk Solver Platform under the additional constraint that no vendor is allowed to supply more than 65% of the total number of units required.

22. A manufacturing company uses trucks to ship products from the production plant to the warehouse. The following network represents the available routes between the plant and the warehouse. The numbers in brackets (d, t) present the length of the route d and the time t it takes to cross the road segment.

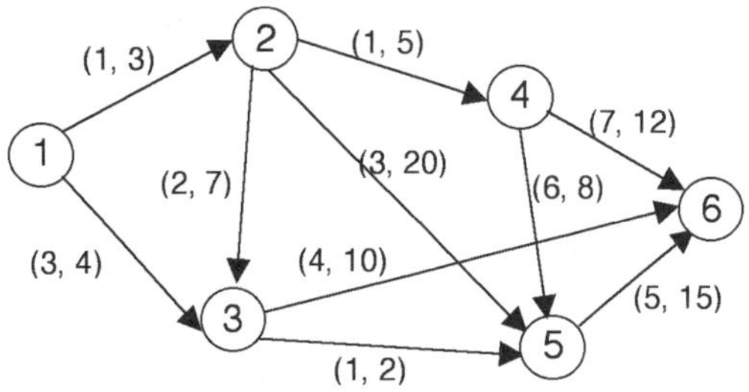

Find the shortest path (in terms of distance) from the plant (node 1) to the warehouse (node 6). Formulate the problem as an integer program and use Risk Solver Platform to find the solution.

23. Refer to Hands-On Exercise 22. Find the longest path (in terms of time) that connects the plant (node 1) with the warehouse (node 6). Formulate the problem as an integer programming problem and use Risk Solver Platform to find the solution.

24. The Markowitz problem provides the foundations for single-period investment theory. The problem is stated as follow: "Given that an investor has n assets. The corresponding mean rates of return are: $\bar{r}_1, \bar{r}_2, \ldots \bar{r}_n$ and the co-variances are σ_{ij} for $i, j = 1, \ldots, n$. The problem is to find a minimum-variance portfolio for a given fixed mean value returns ($\bar{r}$)." A portfolio is defined by a set of weights w_i, $i = 1, \ldots, n$, that sum to 1 (Luenberger 1998). The following is a NLP formulation of the problem:

$$Min: \frac{1}{2}\sum_{i,j=1}^{n} w_i w_j \sigma_{ij}$$

Subject to:

$$\sum_{i=1}^{n} w_i \bar{r}_i = \bar{r}$$

$$\sum_{i=1}^{n} w_i = 1$$

Given the covariance matrix and the rates of return for three assets, find the minimum variance portfolio that gives an expected return equal to 0.5.

$$v = \begin{bmatrix} 2 & 1 & 0 \\ 1 & 2 & 1 \\ 0 & 1 & 2 \end{bmatrix}$$

25. Refer to the Markowitz problem stated in Hands-On Exercise 24. Use the multiple parameterized optimization capabilities of Risk Solver Platform to see the impact of increasing the expected return from 0.5 to 0.9 (in increments of 0.02) on portfolio variance. Graph the relationship between expected return and portfolio variance (the efficient frontier).

CHAPTER

nine Simulation

chapter OVERVIEW

9.1 Introduction

This chapter defines simulation and describes how simulation can be performed in Excel. We present two simple what-if analysis tools of Excel: Scenario Manager and Data Tables. We also discuss how to build advanced simulation models in Excel using Risk Solver Platform. Input data analysis, random number generating, and output analysis are three important steps when building a simulation model. We discuss tools available in Risk Solver Platform in support of these analyses. In the last section of this chapter we illustrate through three different applications how to use Risk Solver Platform to build simulation models. We revisit the simulation topic in Chapter 20 with VBA. In that chapter, we will illustrate how to automate many runs of a simulation using user-provided parameter values. We have developed several decision support system case studies that use simulation, such as Birthday Simulation, Queuing Simulation, Reliability Analysis, and Retirement Planning.

In this chapter, the reader will learn how to:

- Use simulation as a modeling tool.
- Perform simple spreadsheet simulation using Data Tables and the Scenario Manager.
- Use input analysis, output analysis, and random number generating tools of Risk Solver Platform to build advanced simulation models.
- Solve three examples of simulation models.

9.2 Defining Simulation

Simulation is a modeling tool that is used to imitate a real-world process to better understand system behavior. Authentic system behavior can be estimated through the use of distributions. For example, if we were simulating customers being served at a bank, we may not know exactly how often customers will arrive, but based on historical data (or system observation) we may be able to estimate that customer interarrival time has an exponential distribution with a mean of 5 minutes. From these distributions, a user can generate random numbers to evaluate multiple strategies and predict future performance.

Simulation is a useful tool in that it can make observations through trial and error without the cost of materials, labor, and time that would be necessary to observe the same results of the original process. For example, if the supervisor of a paper mill wants to determine how production will be affected by a change in the rate of raw material input, it would be very costly to observe the actual effects in the mill. He/she would have to instruct employees to change the rate of placing raw materials in the first machine, possibly change the processing times of some following machines, react to any malfunctions caused by this change, and possibly get an undesirable result, thus having to change everything back to how it originally was. By using simulation, he/she could see what would happen numerically without modifying the actual process. If the simulation model showed an increase in production by changing the rate of incoming raw materials, the supervisor could implement the change; otherwise, he/she would not need to waste time if production did not increase.

Simulation is different from optimization in that instead of seeking to optimize an objective function value, it simulates the behavior of a system to assess its performance under several scenarios. There are many applications in which simulation becomes useful; we will discuss these applications in the following sections.

The focus of this chapter is simulation; however, in the next section we discuss two simple *what-if* analysis tools that Excel offers. These tools are *Scenario Manager* and *Data Tables.* Simulation is a more powerful than what-if analysis tools. However, what-if analysis is used more often than simulation by managers in the business world. This is mainly because many managers are unaware of Excel's ability to perform simulation, and the benefits of using simulation tools. The discussion about what-if analysis tools of Excel will help you understand the advantages of using simulation.

9.3 *What-If Analysis Tools in Excel*

In what-if analysis we change the value of an uncertain problem input in order to observe its impact on some problem outputs. By making a series of such changes we gain insights about how sensitive problem output values are to changes in the problem input values. We next discuss two what-if analysis tools available in Excel: Scenario Manager and DataTables.

9.3.1 Scenario Manager

The Scenario Manager tool allows us to vary up to 32 input cells for various values, or scenarios, and observe the results of several output cells. A scenario can be thought of as a set of input values that represent our tentative decision alternatives. The Scenario Manager will create a Scenario Report, which shows the resulting output values for each scenario of input values.

Let's consider an example to illustrate the benefits of using the *Scenario Manager.* In the table shown in Figure 9.1, there is a list of inputs for a company's sales. These inputs are tax rate, year 1 sales, sales growth, year 1 price, year 1 cost, interest rate, cost growth, and price growth. Then there is a table of outputs for five years. The outputs are unit sales, unit price, unit cost, revenue, costs, before-tax profits, tax, after-tax profits, and total net present value (NPV). The unit sales, unit price, and unit cost are actually inputs calculated using the growth rates from the input table.

NPV | fx =NPV(intrate,C21:G21)

	A	B	C	D	E	F	G
1							
2	**Company Sales**						
3							
4	*Inputs*	Tax Rate	0.4				
5		Year 1 Sales	10000				
6		Sales Growth	0.1				
7		Year 1 Price	$9.00				
8		Year 1 Cost	$6.00				
9		Interest Rate	0.15				
10		Cost Growth Rate	0.05				
11		Price Growth Rate	0.03				
12							
13	*Outputs*	Year	1	2	3	4	5
14		Unit Sales	10000	11000	12100	13310	14641
15		Unit Price	$9.00	$9.27	$9.55	$9.83	$10.13
16		Unit Cost	$6.00	$6.30	$6.62	$6.95	$7.29
17		Revenues	$90,000.00	$101,970.00	$115,532.01	$130,897.77	$148,307.17
18		Costs	$60,000.00	$69,300.00	$80,041.50	$92,447.93	$106,777.36
19		Before Tax Profits	$30,000.00	$32,670.00	$35,490.51	$38,449.83	$41,529.81
20		Tax	$12,000.00	$13,068.00	$14,196.20	$15,379.93	$16,611.92
21		After Tax Profits	$18,000.00	$19,602.00	$21,294.31	$23,069.90	$24,917.89
22							
23		NPV	$70,054.34				

Figure 9.1 The initial input and output cells.

For this example, let's focus on the company's after-tax profits for each of the five years as well as their total NPV. We want to consider three different scenarios for year 1 sales, sales growth, and year 1 price, and choose various values of these inputs for best, worst, and most likely scenarios.

We begin by selecting the input cells, or changing cells, for year 1 sales, sales growth, and year 1 price: *C5:C7.* Click on *Data > Data Tools > What-If Analysis* command on the Ribbon. From the drop-down list that appears, select *Scenario Manager.* Click on the *Add* command in the *Scenario Manager* dialog box that appears in order to add a new scenario. We name this scenario the Best Case scenario (Figure 9.2) and click *OK.* On the *Scenario Values* dialog box, give the values 20,000, 0.4, and 10 for these inputs, respectively (see Figure 9.3). We repeat this process to create the next scenario.

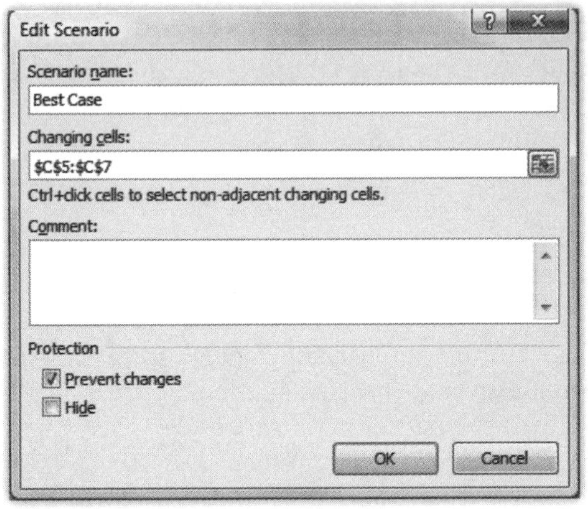

Figure 9.2 Naming the Best Case Scenario and selecting the changing input cells.

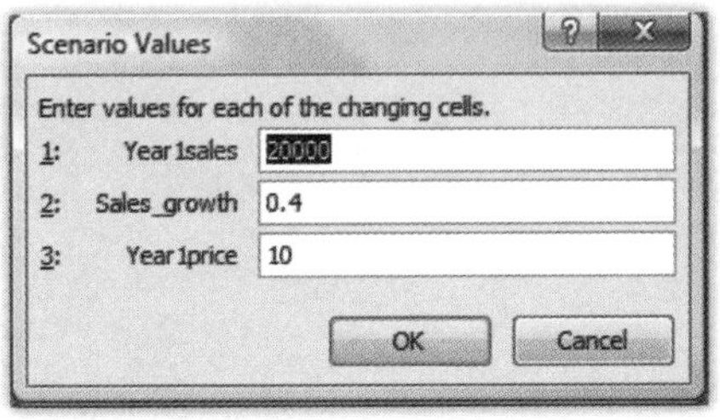

Figure 9.3 Specifying the values for the Best Case inputs.

Let's name this the Worst Case scenario and select the same input cells. We give them the values 5,000, 0.2, and 5, respectively.

Finally, we create the Most Likely scenario using the same input cells with the values 10,000, 0.5, and 7.5. Figure 9.4 illustrates the list of scenarios that we have created in the Scenario Manager dialog box.

We now choose *Summary* and select the "after-tax profit row" (for all five years), which is in cells *C21* and *G21,* and the NPV cell, which is cell *C23,* as the outputs (see Figure 9.5). We then press *OK* to create the *Scenario Report.*

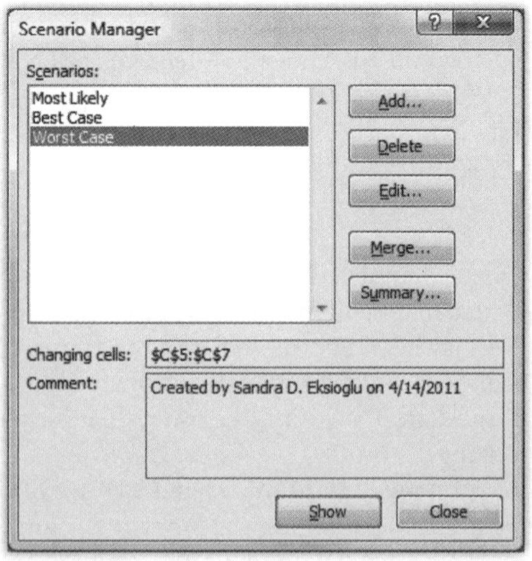

Figure 9.4 Creating the three scenarios.

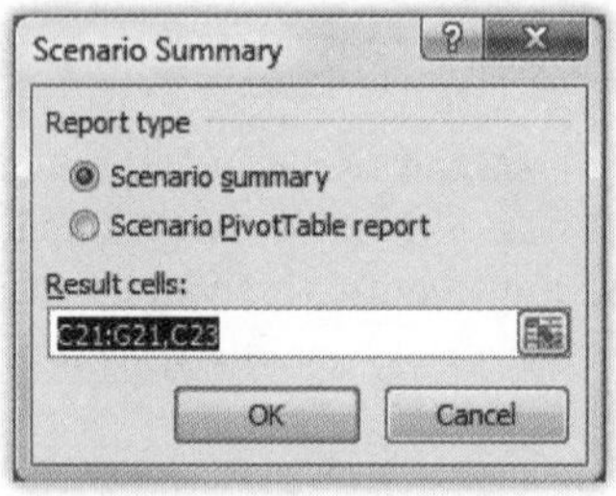

Figure 9.5 Selecting the output cells to create the Scenario Report.

The *Scenario Report* (see Figure 9.6) exhibits the output cells, or result cells, for each scenario as well as the current values from the initial tables. Now, we can easily observe the NPV of the Best Case, Worst Case, and Most Likely scenarios by looking at the last row of the *Scenario Report*. This is especially helpful if output and input cells are spread out on the spreadsheet, since results are grouped together in the report.

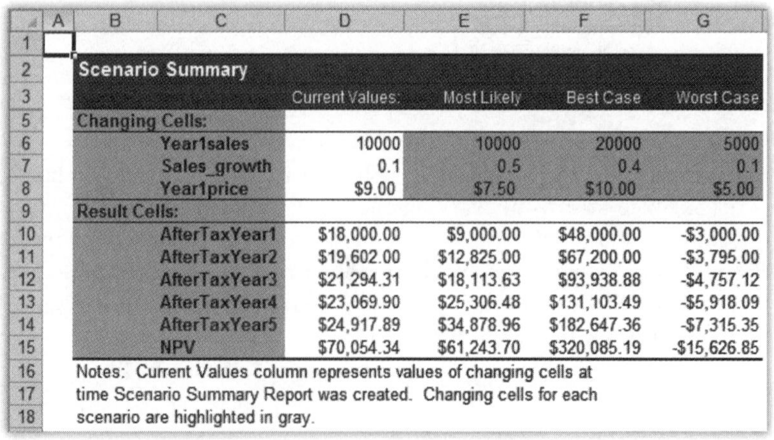

	A	B	C	D	E	F	G
1							
2		Scenario Summary					
3				Current Values:	Most Likely	Best Case	Worst Case
5		Changing Cells:					
6			Year1sales	10000	10000	20000	5000
7			Sales_growth	0.1	0.5	0.4	0.1
8			Year1price	$9.00	$7.50	$10.00	$5.00
9		Result Cells:					
10			AfterTaxYear1	$18,000.00	$9,000.00	$48,000.00	-$3,000.00
11			AfterTaxYear2	$19,602.00	$12,825.00	$67,200.00	-$3,795.00
12			AfterTaxYear3	$21,294.31	$18,113.63	$93,938.88	-$4,757.12
13			AfterTaxYear4	$23,069.90	$25,306.48	$131,103.49	-$5,918.09
14			AfterTaxYear5	$24,917.89	$34,878.96	$182,647.36	-$7,315.35
15			NPV	$70,054.34	$61,243.70	$320,085.19	-$15,626.85
16		Notes: Current Values column represents values of changing cells at					
17		time Scenario Summary Report was created. Changing cells for each					
18		scenario are highlighted in gray.					

Figure 9.6 The Scenario Report shows the outputs for the various input values in each scenario.

Note that we have named our input and output cells in order to see the names shown in the first column of the *Scenario Report*. If we do not name these cells, the cell reference will be shown instead (i.e., *C23* instead of "NPV"). Also note that some icons are provided next to the row numbers and column letters to hide some parts of the report and to show others.

9.3.2 Data Tables

We use Data Tables to determine how some outputs vary in response to changes in input. Data Tables use a spreadsheet to refer to cells that may contain formulas or functions for some output and input of a problem. For example, we may have input as sales price and output as profit. The input cell would just contain a numerical value, but the output cell would contain a formula that calculates profit based on quantity sold and profit per unit. We could then use a Data Table to vary the price values and observe the change in profit.

There are two types of *Data Tables*: ***one-way Data Tables*** and ***two-way Data Tables***. A *one-way Data Table* enables us to determine how changing one input will change any number of outputs. In the above example of unit profit and total profit, unit profit is the only input value that needs changing, so we would create a *one-way Data Table*. *Two-way Data Tables* allow us to determine how changing two inputs affects a single output. For example, if we varied unit profit and quantity sold as input, we could observe changes in total profits. Since two inputs are changing, we would use a *two-way data table.*

Let's consider an example to illustrate both *one-way* and *two-way Data Tables*. In Figure 9.7, we provide a list of inputs and outputs for ticket sales. The *total profit* is calculated by finding the unit profit (price minus cost per ticket) and multiplying this value by the number of salespersons and the average number of tickets sold per person. Using the input cells shown, the formula for the total profit would be:

*=(B6–B7)*B4*B5*

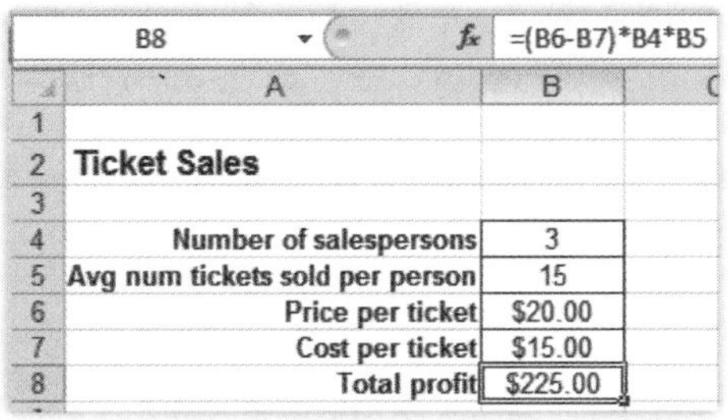
B8 | =(B6-B7)*B4*B5

	A	B
1		
2	Ticket Sales	
3		
4	Number of salespersons	3
5	Avg num tickets sold per person	15
6	Price per ticket	$20.00
7	Cost per ticket	$15.00
8	Total profit	$225.00

Figure 9.7 The initial list of inputs and outputs contains values and formulas.

The first Data Table we want to create will show the different profit values as we vary the price per ticket. Since we are only varying one input, this will be a *one-way Data Table*. Let's begin by creating a column of various prices per ticket. We will vary these prices from $16.00 to $24.00 per ticket. Then we copy (or move) the formula used in cell B8 to a cell in the first row of the Data Table (above the first price value in the input columns). Figure 9.8 shows the preparation for this Data Table.

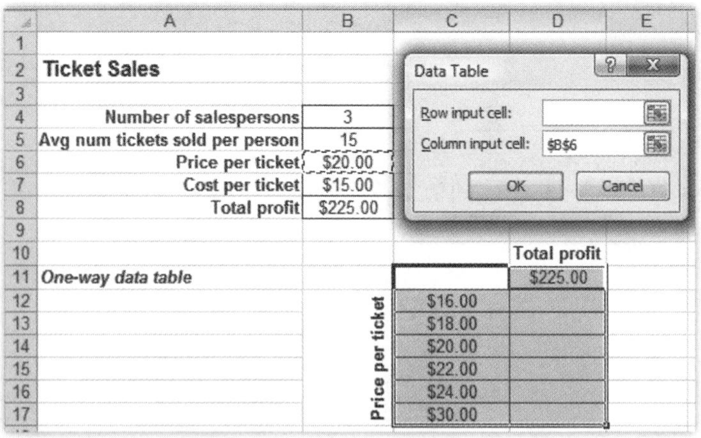

Figure 9.8 Using the price per ticket initial cell reference as the *column input*.

We now click on *Data > Data Tools > What-if Analysis* command on the Ribbon. From the drop-down menu that appears, we select *Data Table.* Since we are varying price as the input, and we have these varying values in the first column of the Data Table, we should specify the location of the price value in our initial list of inputs and outputs as the *Column Input Cell* in the *Data Table* dialog box; this is cell B6 (see Figure 9.8). Once we press *OK*, Excel completes the Data Table. In Figure 9.9, we find that various profit values have been calculated for each possible price per ticket listed.

		Total profit
		$225.00
Price per ticket	$16.00	$45.00
	$18.00	$135.00
	$20.00	$225.00
	$22.00	$315.00
	$24.00	$405.00
	$30.00	$675.00

Figure 9.9 The final Data Table shows various profit values as the price per ticket changes.

Now suppose that we are curious to see how the combination of price per ticket and number of salespersons affects the total profit. Since we are varying two inputs, we should now create a *two-way Data Table.* We again begin by creating a column of varying prices per ticket. Then, we create a row for varying numbers of salespersons (above the first price value in the input column). Now, in the cell above the input column of prices and next to the input row of number of salespersons, we again copy the formula for total profit. Figure 9.10 illustrates the preparation for this Data Table.

First, select the Data Table (C21:H27). Next, we click on *Data > Data Tools > What-if Analysis* command on the Ribbon. From the drop-down menu that appears we select *Data Table.* This time, we will reference both the *Row Input Cell* and *Column Input Cell.* The *Row Input Cell* will be the number of salespersons, which is cell B4, in the initial list of inputs and outputs. The *Column Input Cell* will again be cell B6 for price per ticket (see Figure 9.7). We press *OK* to see the completed data table. For any combination of price per ticket and number of salespersons (among the varying values specified), we can find the calculated total profit (see Figure 9.11).

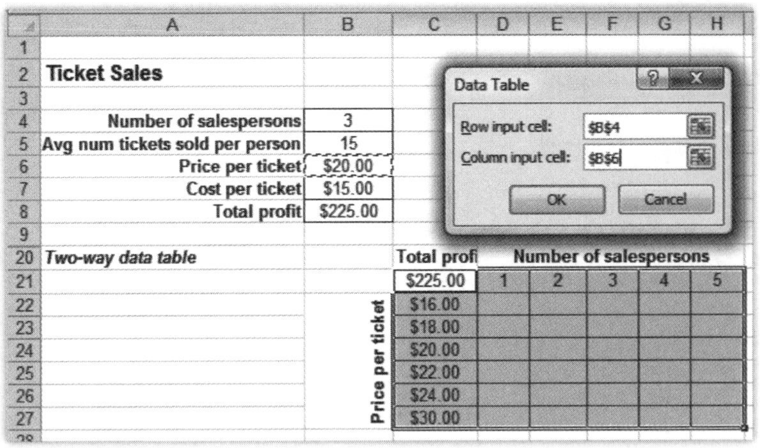

Figure 9.10 The preparation for the two-way Data Table that varies both price per ticket and number of salespersons. The number of salespersons is the *Row Input Cell* and the price per ticket is the *Column Input Cell*.

	Total profit	Number of salespersons				
	$225.00	1	2	3	4	5
Price per ticket	$16.00	$15.00	$30.00	$45.00	$60.00	$75.00
	$18.00	$45.00	$90.00	$135.00	$180.00	$225.00
	$20.00	$75.00	$150.00	$225.00	$300.00	$375.00
	$22.00	$105.00	$210.00	$315.00	$420.00	$525.00
	$24.00	$135.00	$270.00	$405.00	$540.00	$675.00
	$30.00	$225.00	$450.00	$675.00	$900.00	$1,125.00

Figure 9.11 The final Data Table shows various profit values for combinations of number of salespersons and prices per ticket.

Summary

What-If Analysis in Excel: Excel uses Scenario Manager and Data Tables as what-if analysis tools.

Scenario Analysis: Performs all possible alternative actions and notes the varying results from these different situations.

Data Tables: Used to determine how outputs vary in response to changes in input.

9.4 *Simulation Using the Risk Solver Platform*

Simulation can be thought of as a higher level what-if scenario analysis. In a simulation, the values that problem inputs take are not selected by the user; instead these values are automatically generated using Excel functions. As a result, the values assigned to input parameters and the results from the simulation are unbiased. The Risk Solver Platform provides a full-featured Monte Carlo simulation tool. The Risk Solver Platform makes it very easy to perform a large number of simulation trials. The results from these trials are summarized using graphs and tables.

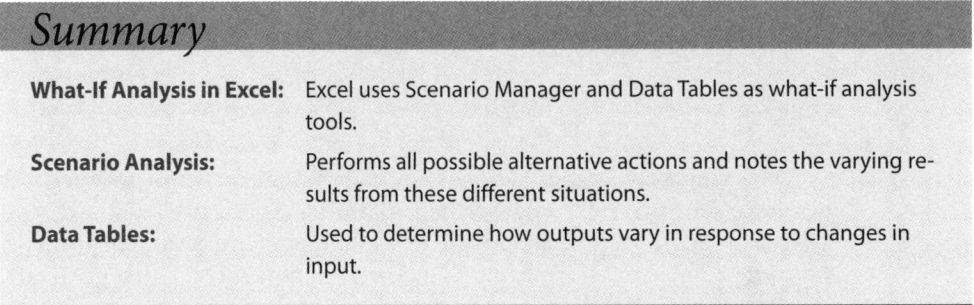

In this section we will discuss tools available in the Risk Solver Platform for generating random numbers, fitting a distribution to a set of data, and analyzing the results of a simulation. Through the applications presented in Section 9.5 we discuss how to set up your spreadsheet and use the tools described here to build a simulation model and analyze the results.

Note: In this and the following sections we use the terms *simulation run* and *simulation trial*. Two simulation runs refer to two different simulation scenarios of a problem. In each scenario, the functions we use to generate problem parameters or some other problem settings are different. Two simulation trials of the same simulation run refer to the same simulation scenario. In each trial, the value of random parameters is different due to using different streams of random numbers. The total number of trials defines the sample size of the simulation results.

9.4.1 Generating Random Numbers within Distributions

An important part of building a simulation model is creating many trials of possible input values. We will therefore explain how to use some important Risk Solver Platform functions to generate various input data values for several trials of a simulation run.

Simulation is useful because it can handle the variability of parameters in a model. That is, we may not know many settings in a process with full certainty; or we may be aware of a range of numbers into which values fall, but not know the exact figures. For example, assume that there is a shipment company that is dependent on a variety of suppliers before its workers can organize and ship their products. The company's staff knows which suppliers will be delivering goods within a few days, but they do not know the exact day or time when each delivery will arrive. This variability affects their business, since they cannot satisfy their customers' demands until they receive products from their suppliers. To put this situation into a model, we would not be able to assign a constant rate to the arrival of goods from suppliers. Therefore, we would want to study the arrival rates over a time and fit a distribution to the arrival rate that closely matches the suppliers' patterns. Once we know the distribution of a certain parameter, we can generate random numbers within this distribution to observe the effect on satisfying customer demand. Therefore, it is now appropriate to introduce the concepts of *distributions* and *random numbers*.

In Chapter 4, we mentioned that Excel offers *Math & Trig* functions that we can use to generate random numbers. For example, the RAND function is used to generate random numbers between 0 and 1. The ***RAND*** function does not have any parameters. The RAND formula is:

RAND()

RAND is useful for generating test data or any data with random patterns. We can manipulate this RAND value if we want to generate values outside the interval between 0 and 1. If we want to generate numbers between a lower bound (*LB*) and an upper bound (*UB*), multiply this RAND value by (*UB* – *LB*) and add *LB*.

=RAND()(UB – LB) + LB*

We demonstrate this particular use of RAND in Figure 9.12. Here we want to generate heights, widths, and depths to calculate some probable packaging volumes. We type the following function to create random numbers between 1 and 10:

*=RAND()*9 + 1*

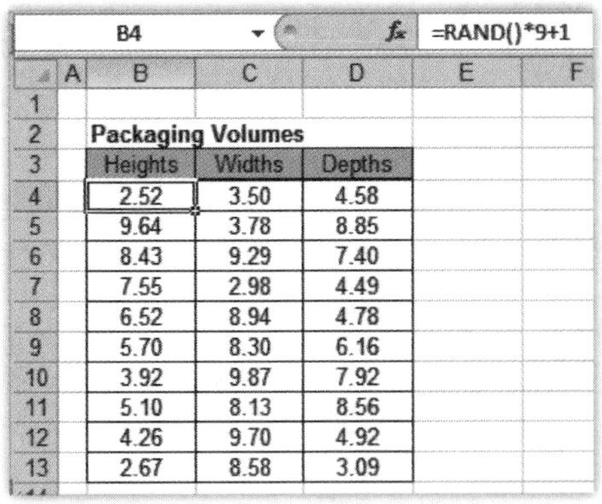

Figure 9.12 The RAND function can be manipulated to change the range of the random numbers produced. Here the range is changed from the default of 0 to 1, to 1 to 10.

We can convert these random numbers into random integers by changing the format of the cells in which we entered this function. Simply use the *number* group of the *home* tab to set the number of decimal places to 0.

Excel offers other tools one can use to generate random numbers. In Chapter 7 we discuss one of the inverse distribution functions of Excel, NORM.INV. This function is used to generate random numbers that follow a Normal distribution.

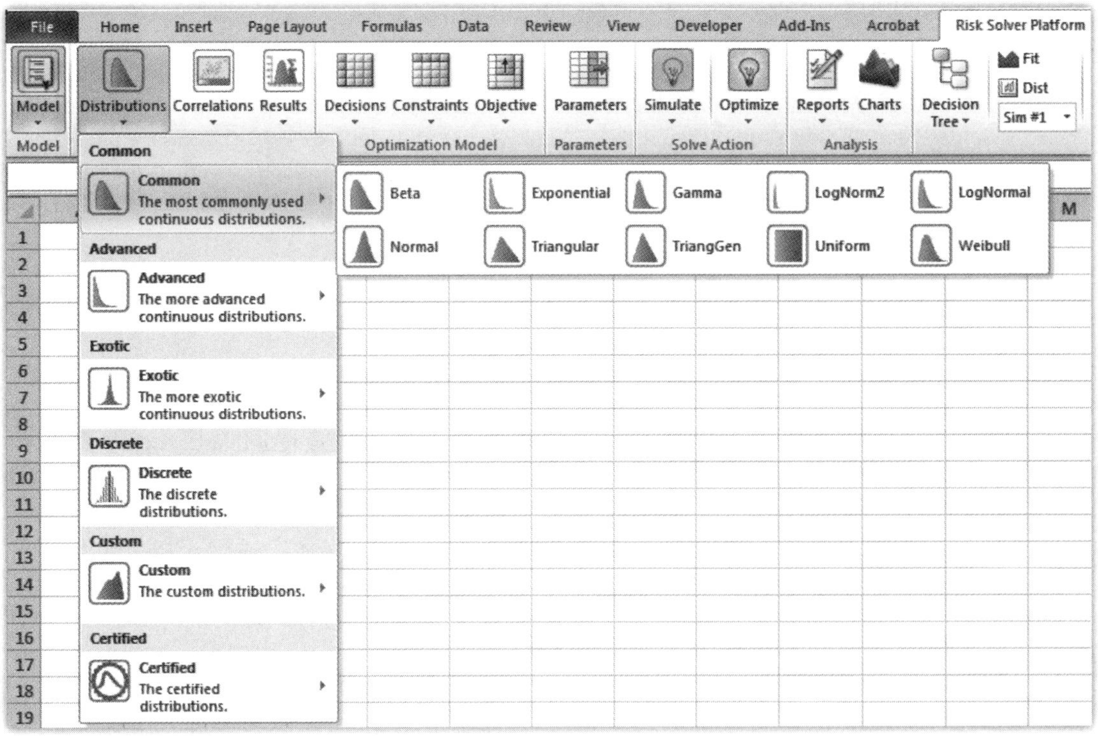

Figure 9.13 The galleria of common distribution functions in the Risk Solver Platform.

The Risk Solver Platform offers galleries of *Psi* functions that can be used to generate random numbers from distributions. We click on the *Risk Solver Platform* > *Simulation Model* > *Distributions* command on the *Ribbon* to see a list of function galleries available (Figure 9.13). From the *Common* distributions fly-out menu, we select *Normal*. In the dialog box that appears (see Figure 9.14) we can change the default values of mean and standard deviation of this distribution. This dialog box also gives graphical representations of the corresponding density function and cumulative distribution function, as well as distribution percentiles and other statistics.

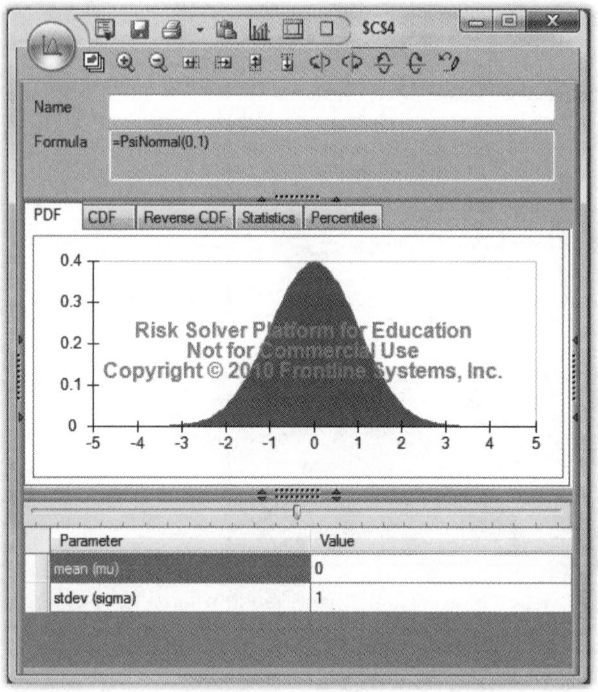

Figure 9.14 The density function for a standard normal random variable.

The custom galleria of distribution functions is very useful to randomly generate numbers from a distribution that does not fit with the ones listed by the Risk Solver Platform. In one of the examples discussed earlier we had estimated that year 1 sales will most likely be 10,000 units. In the best case, 20,000 units, and in the worst case, 5,000 units. We also estimated the probabilities of having a good first-year sales (0.5), or having a bad year (0.2). We can now use this information to randomly generate first-year sales. From the *Custom* distributions fly-out menu we select *Discrete*. This function takes two arguments: *Values* and *Weights*. *Values* is an array of the possible values that year 1 sales can take, and *Weights* is an array of the corresponding probabilities. The dialog box presented in Figure 9.15 appears upon the selection of this function. We update the values and weights of the parameters in the corresponding boxes as shown in this figure. A graph of the corresponding distribution function appears in the main window of the dialog box.

Note: When using random functions in a worksheet, the numbers generated will change with every operation performed in the worksheet. That is, after creating the table in Figure 9.12, if we were to then type new text or data into another cell on the same worksheet, the initial random numbers shown would automatically recalculate new random numbers in our range. To prevent this automatic recalculation from occurring, go to the *File* tab on the Ribbon and select *Options*. In the *Excel Options* dialog box select the *Formulas* tab on the left. On the *Calculation* section, check *Manual*. We can now use *F9* to recalculate the random numbers if necessary. But note that some other functions may not recalculate automatically when copied after changing the *Calculation* option to *Manual*.

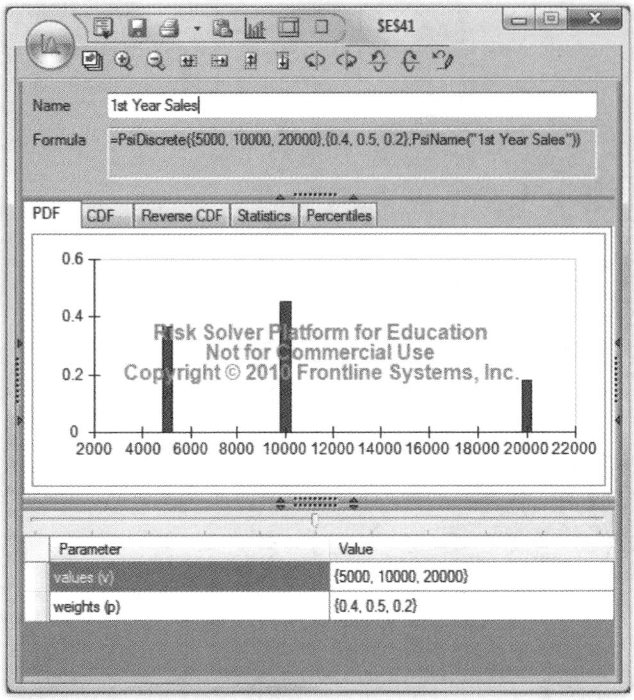

Figure 9.15 The density function for a custom discrete random variable.

9.4.2 Fitting a Distribution to a Set of Data

The functions we use in a simulation model to generate random data are not chosen arbitrarily. To identify a function that best describes the behavior of a problem input, we need to follow two steps. First, we gather historical data about the problem input. Second, we analyze the data to identify its distribution. The Risk Solver Platform provides tools that make the process of fitting a distribution to a data set very easy.

For example, in the Single Server Queuing application discussed later in this chapter, the interarrival time of customers at the ATM machine is exponentially distributed with a mean of 2.89 minutes. We use historical data (Figure 9.16) to identify the distribution of customer interarrival time at the ATM. We click the *Risk Solver Platform > Tools > Fit* command on the *Ribbon*. On the *Fit Options* dialog box that appears, we type the location of the sample data, range B2:B51; check the *Continuous* option button; check *Chi-Square* statistics *Goodness of Fit Test*; and click on *Fit* command. The goodness of fit is a statistical test that evaluates how well a known distribution fits the data sample. The Risk Solver Platform fits a number of distributions to the sample data, ranks them based on goodness of fit criteria and displays the best fitting distributions. Based on the results displayed in Figure 9.17, exponential is the distribution that best fits our data.

It often happens that we do not have historical data about a problem input. This is the case in the example above when we estimate the first-year sales in order to calculate after-tax profits. In this example, the sales manager estimates potential first-year sales (Best, Most Likely, and

Worst Case Scenarios), and corresponding likelihood. The Risk Solver Platform can use this information to randomly generate first-year sales as shown in section 9.4.1.

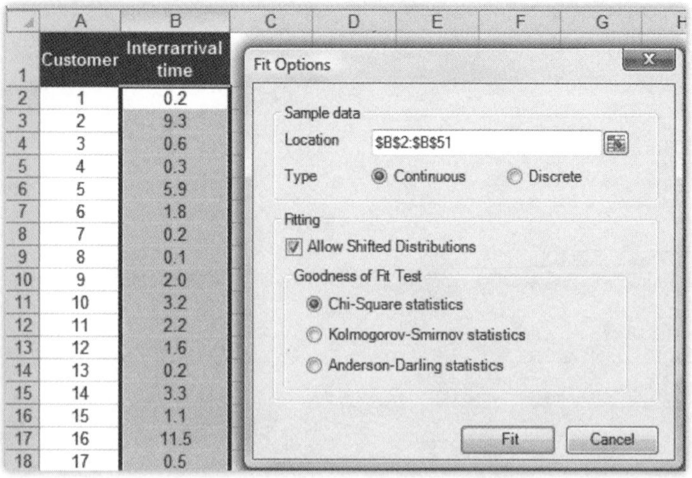

Figure 9.16 Customer interarrival time at the ATM.

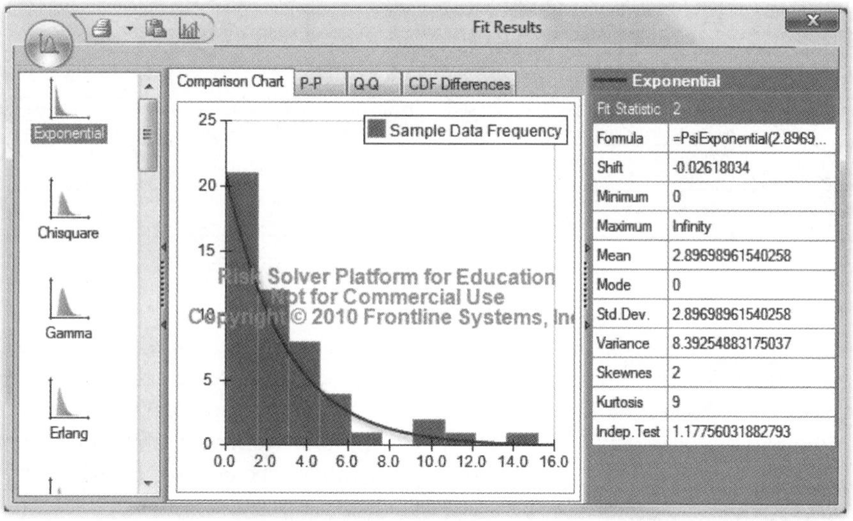

Figure 9.17 The results of Goodness of Fit Test.

9.4.3 Analyzing Simulation Results

The Risk Solver Platform offers a number of tools to analyze the results of a simulation model. Most of these tools are located on the *Analysis* group on the *Ribbon*. We show how to use most of these tools in the applications section, later in this chapter.

A Simulation Report is automatically generated when we run a simulation model. To see this report, we select Simulation from *Risk Solver Platform* > *Analysis* > *Reports* drop-down menu on the *Ribbon*. We next select *Simulation* from the fly-out menu that appears.

Figure 9.18 presents the Simulation Report for the News Vendor problem application (see section 9.5.1). The report gives general simulation information, such as the number of simulation runs, trials per simulation, random number generator used, sampling method, etc. The

Simulation Report also provides summary information about the uncertain variables and functions used in the model.

Report Created: 4/17/2011 9:03:13 AM
Simulation time: 0.094 seconds.

General Simulation Information

Simulation Options		Value
Simulations Run		1
Trials per Simulation		1000
Number of Error Trials		0
Current Simulation		1
Random Number Generator	CMRG	
Sampling Method	Latin Hypercube	
Random Number Stream	Independent Stream	
Simulation Seed		0
Interpreter Used	Automatic	
Correlations Used	Yes	

Model Information	Quantity
Uncertain Variables	1
Uncertain Functions	1
Correlated Variables	0

Global Bounds	Measure	Value
Lower Cutoff	None	-1E+30
Upper Cutoff	None	1E+30
Lower Censor	None	-1E+30
Upper Censor	None	1E+30

Uncertain Variable Summary Information

Cell	Name	Distribution	Mean	Std Dev	Minimum	Maximum	25th Percentile	50th Percentile	75th Percentile
$C$10	Demand	PsiDiscrete(E4:E6,F4:F6)	205	41.53311931	150	250	150	200	250

Uncertain Function Summary Information

Cell	Name	Formula	Mean	Std Dev	Minimum	Maximum	25th Percentile	50th Percentile	75th Percentile
$I$10	Total Profit	G10+H10-F10+PsiOutput()	422.25	164.1379108	205	600	205	402.5	600

Figure 9.18 The Simulation Report for the News Vendor problem application.

The Risk Solver Platform also generates *Parameters* and *Sensitivity Analysis* Reports. The goal of sensitivity analysis is to identify input parameters that greatly impact the outputs of a model. The Solver can identify automatically for you an input parameter of interest. For example, in the News Vendor problem application worksheet, select cell I10 (Total Profit) and then click on *Risk Solver Platform* > *Parameters* > *Parameters* command from the *Ribbon*. From the drop-down menu select *Identify*. The *Tornado Sensitivity Chart* shown in Figure 9.19 appears.

Based on the chart, sales price greatly impacts profits. We may be interested now to see what happens to the total profit if the sales price of the comic calendars varies from $2 to $10. We substitute the sales price of $4.7 in cell C4 with the formula "*=PsiSimParam(2,10,4.7)*" function which defines a lower, upper, and base case value for this parameter. We set the value of *Simulations to Run* property to 10 in the *Platform* tab of the *task pane*, and then run the simulations. The value of this parameter will change during each simulation run. Now, we select *Simulation* > *Parameter Analysis Report* from the *Risk Solver Platform* > *Analysis* > *Reports* drop-down menu on the *Ribbon*. Figure 9.20 presents the summary results from running multiple simulations. In the next session we show how to generate other simulation reports.

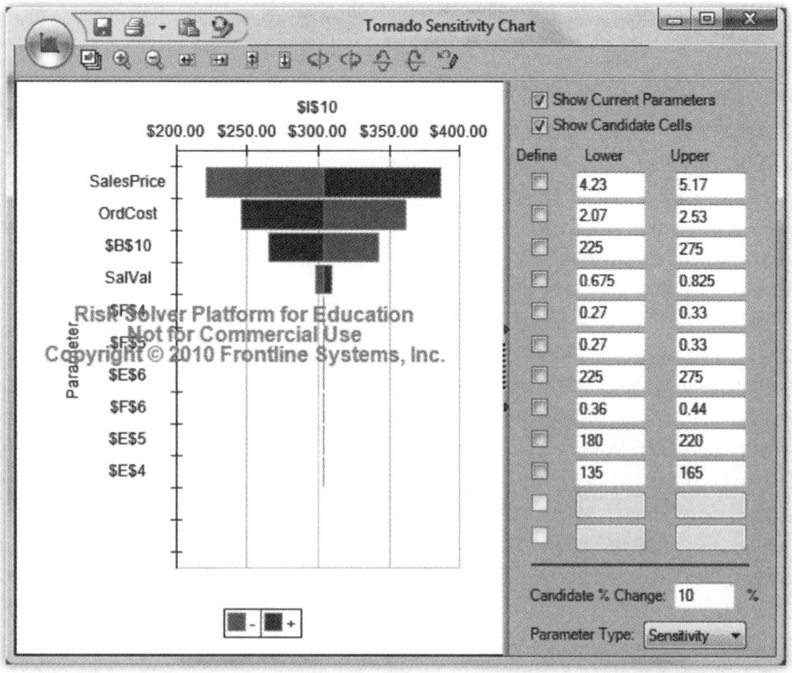

Figure 9.19 Tornado Sensitivity Chart for total profit of the News Vendor problem.

	A	B	C	D	E	F	G	H	I	J	K	L	M	N
1	SalesPrice	Minimum	Maximum	Mean	StdDev	Variance	Skewness	Kurtosis	Mode	MeanAbsDev	ValueAtRisk	CondValueAtRisk	ExpLoss	Percentile
2	$2.00	-200	-75	-131.25	51.94	2698	-0.19	-1.53	-75	45	-75	-131.25	-131.25	-75
3	$2.80	-80	125	32.75	85.19	7257	-0.19	-1.53	125	73.8	125	32.75	-24	125
4	$3.60	40	325	196.75	118.43	14025	-0.19	-1.53	325	102.6	325	196.75	0	325
5	$4.40	160	525	360.75	151.67	23004	-0.19	-1.53	525	131.4	525	360.75	0	525
6	$5.20	280	725	524.75	184.91	34194	-0.19	-1.53	725	160.2	725	524.75	0	725
7	$6.00	400	925	688.75	218.16	47593	-0.19	-1.53	925	189	925	688.75	0	925
8	$6.80	520	1125	852.75	251.40	63203	-0.19	-1.53	1125	217.8	1125	852.75	0	1125
9	$7.60	640	1325	1016.75	284.64	81022	-0.19	-1.53	1325	246.6	1325	1016.75	0	1325
10	$8.40	760	1525	1180.75	317.89	101052	-0.19	-1.53	1525	275.4	1525	1180.75	0	1525
11	$9.20	880	1725	1344.75	351.13	123293	-0.19	-1.53	1725	304.2	1725	1344.75	0	1725
12	$10.00	1000	1925	1508.75	384.37	147743	-0.19	-1.53	1925	333	1925	1508.75	0	1925

Figure 9.20 The Parameter Analysis Report indicates that the higher the price, the higher the profits from selling the comic calendar.

Summary

Random Number Generator: An algorithm that generates random numbers between 0 and 1.

Psi Functions: **PsiNormal, PsiDiscrete, PsiBeta, PsiLogNormal, PsiGamma, PsiBinomial, PsiChiSquare**

Goodness of Fit Test: A statistical test to evaluate how well a distribution fits a set of data.

Sensitivity Analysis: The goal of this analysis is to estimate how changes in input parameters impact problem outputs.

9.5 *Applications*

The first step in building a simulation model using the Risk Solver Platform is to set up our Excel worksheet to identifying model inputs and corresponding outputs.

In a simulation model there is at least one problem input that is stochastic in nature. We model stochasticity by generating random numbers from a particular distribution function. The ***Model*** tab of the of the Risk Solver's task pane lists all problem inputs, which are referred to as ***Uncertain Variables***.

The values that problem outputs take depend on the value of the stochastic problem inputs. Problem outputs are functions that use problem inputs to perform certain calculations. Usually, we are interested only in some problem outputs. To make this choice clear to the Risk Solver Platform, we add ***+PsiOutput()*** to the existing formula of an output cell. The Risk Solver Platform lists problem outputs in the Model tab of the task pane. Problem outputs are referred to as ***Uncertain Functions***.

During simulation, a number of simulation trials are performed. We are interested in calculating summary statistics about problem outputs. To accomplish this, we use functions such as ***PsiMean(), PsiStdDev(), PsiMax(),*** etc. These functions are listed as ***Statistic Functions*** in the Model tab of the task pane. The single argument of these functions is the address of the problem output cell. Finally, we set the value of ***Trials per Simulation*** property at the Platform tab of the task pane and run the simulation.

We will now explain through three well-known applications how to use the Risk Solver Platform in Excel in order to build advanced simulation models. Please note that there are many other areas and models for which simulation is a beneficial tool in addition to the models described here.

9.5.1 News Vendor Problem

A bookstore must determine how many 2012 comic calendars to order in September of 2011. It costs $2.30 to order each calendar, and the store sells each one for $4.70. After January 1, 2012, any unsold calendars can be returned to the supplier for a salvage value of $0.75 each. Our best guess is that the number of calendars demanded is governed by the probabilities shown in the following table:

Demand	Probability
150	0.3
200	0.3
250	0.4

So, how many calendars should the company order? Let's set up our spreadsheet by listing the inputs and outputs. For inputs, we know the ordering cost, sales price, and salvage value. We are also provided with a table of possible demands with their corresponding probabilities (see Figure 9.21).

I10 | =G10+H10-F10+PsiOutput()

	A	B	C	D	E	F	G	H	I
1	**News Vendor Problem**								
2									
3	*Inputs*	Ordering Cost	$2.30		Demand	Prob.			
4		Sales Price	$4.70		150	0.30			
5		Salvage Value	$0.75		200	0.30			
6					250	0.40			
7									
8									
9		Number Ordered	Demand	Number Sold	Number Returned	Costs	Sales Revenue	Salvage Revenue	Total Profit
10		150	250	150	0	$345.00	$705.00	$0.00	$360.00
11									
12		Expected Profit	#N/A						
13		Std. Dev. Profit	#N/A						

Figure 9.21 Input data for the News Vendor Problem.

The expected number of calendars sold will be based on these demands and probabilities. We will use the ***PsiDiscrete()*** function to randomly generate demand. This function takes two arguments: *Values* and *Weights*. *Values* is an array of the possible values that demand can take, and *Weights* is an array of the corresponding probabilities. We type the following formula in cell C10 to randomly generate demand.

=PsiDiscrete(E4:E6,F4:F6)

To determine the expected number of calendars sold, we use the *IF* function. This function compares demand and number of calendars ordered. If demand is smaller, then the number sold will be equal to demand. Otherwise, the number of calendars sold will be equal to the number ordered. We type the following formula in cell D10 to calculate the number of calendars sold.

=IF(C10<B10,C10,B10)

Next, we list problem outputs; these are costs, sales revenue, salvage revenue, and profit. Costs are equal to the number ordered times the ordering cost. The sales revenue is equal to number sold times the sales price. The salvage revenue is the number returned times the salvage value. The number returned is considered to be the difference between the number ordered and the number sold; however, if the number sold is greater than the number ordered, this value is 0. The profit is then the sales revenue plus the salvage revenue minus the costs.

Although all the outputs listed above are important, recall that the main objective of this simulation model is to estimate profits. We make the Risk Solver Platform aware of this fact by adding the ***PsiOutput()*** function to the Total Profit formula in Cell I10 (see Figure 9.21). The Risk Solver Platform automatically collects statistics about this *output cell.* Note that, in order to use the *PsiOutput()* function, the rest of the formula on cell I10 should either contain, or be referencing a cell that contains a ***Psi*** function. For example, cell G10 references cell C10, which uses the *PsiDiscrete(E4:E6,F4:F6)* function *to randomly generate demand.*

Let's initially consider that the store plans to order 150 calendars. We set the total number of simulation runs to 1,000 by assigning this value to the *Trials per Simulation* property in the *Platform* tab of the *Risk Solver task pane.* We want to know the expected profit and corresponding standard deviation over these 1,000 simulation runs. We type the function ***PsiMean(I10)*** in cell C12 and ***PsiStdDev(I10)*** in C13 to calculate these values. You can click on *Risk Solver Platform > Simulation Model > Results* command on the *Ribbon* to access galleries of other *Psi* functions that are used in a similar way to calculate and report simulation results of output cells (only) on the spreadsheet.

Finally, we click on the *Risk Solver Platform > Solve Action > Simulate* command on the *Ribbon*. The results of the simulation are presented in Figure 9.22. The expected profit is $360 and the standard deviation is $0.

	A	B	C	D	E	F	G	H	I
1	News Vendor Problem								
2									
3	*Inputs*	Ordering Cost	$2.30		Demand	Prob.			
4		Sales Price	$4.70		150	0.30			
5		Salvage Value	$0.75		200	0.30			
6					250	0.40			
7									
8									
9		Number Ordered	Demand	Number Sold	Number Returned	Costs	Sales Revenue	Salvage Revenue	Total Profit
10		150	150	150	0	$345.00	$705.00	$0.00	$360.00
11									
12		Expected Profit	$360.00						
13		Std. Dev. Profit	$0.00						

Figure 9.22 Results from simulating the News Vendor problem when number ordered is 150.

Figure 9.23 presents the *Model* tab of the *Risk Solver task pane*. The task pane lists the uncertain variables, uncertain functions, and the statistical functions in this model. The statistical functions listed are the *PsiMean()* and *PsiStdDev()* function. You can click on the output cell (I10) to see a graphical representation of the distribution of the total profit values calculated during the simulation (Figure 9.24). Recall that the number ordered was initially set to 150. The probability that demand is greater than or equal to 150 is equal to 1. Therefore, all calendars orders are sold, and the corresponding expected profit is $360.

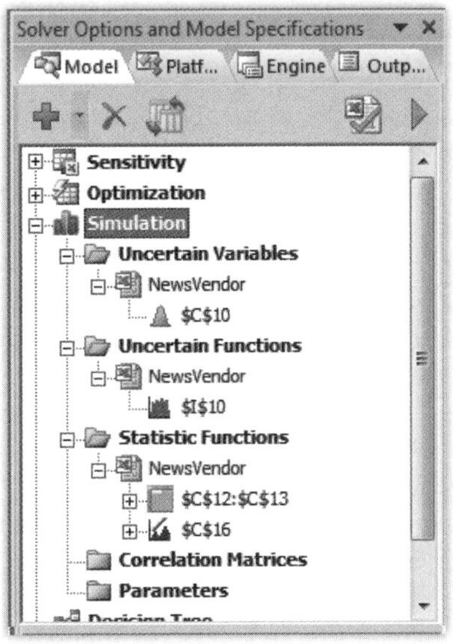

Figure 9.23 *Model* tab of the *Risk Solver task pane for the simulation model.*

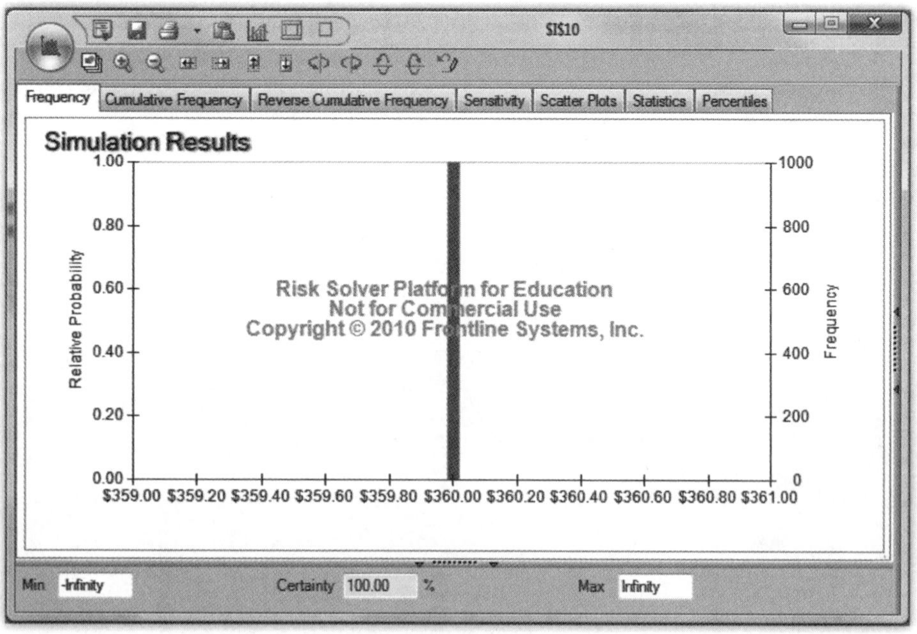

Figure 9.24 *Simulation results when number ordered is 150.*

Let now see how expected profits change if the number of calendars ordered increases to 250. Figure 9.25 presents the results of simulation. The expected profits have now increased to $422.

C16 fx =1-PsiTarget(I10,C15)

	A	B	C	D	E	F	G	H	I
1	**News Vendor Problem**								
2									
3	*Inputs*	Ordering Cost	$2.30		Demand	Prob.			
4		Sales Price	$4.70		150	0.30			
5		Salvage Value	$0.75		200	0.30			
6					250	0.40			
7									
8									
9		Number Ordered	Demand	Number Sold	Number Returned	Costs	Sales Revenue	Salvage Revenue	Total Profit
10		250	250	250	0	$575.00	$1,175.00	$0.00	$600.00
11									
12		Expected Profit	$422.25						
13		Std. Dev. Profit	$164.14						
14									
15		Target Value:	$500.00						
16		P(Profit > Target):	40.00%						

Figure 9.25 The expected profits increase to $422 when order quantity is 250. There is a 40% chance that profits will be greater than $500.

In this application we also use the ***PsiTarget()*** function to calculate the probability that profits will be greater than a target value of $500. This function takes two arguments, the cell we are investigating and the target value. The function itself returns the probability that the investigated value is less than the target value. Therefore, we type the following in cell C16.

=1-PsiTarget(I10,C15)

We double click on the output cell I10 to display the Simulation Results dialog box shown in Figure 9.26. The graph in the center of the dialog box presents the distribution of profits. The maximum profit is $600, and the minimum profit is $205.

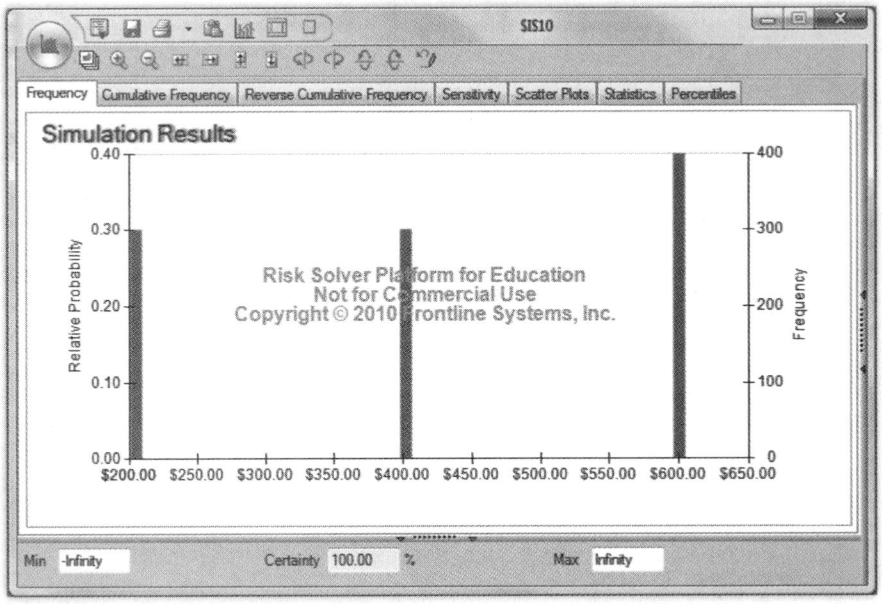

Figure 9.26 The Simulation Results dialog box gives detailed information about the distribution of profits.

9.5.2 A Single Server Queuing Problem

This application is adapted from Case Study 10. We refer the user to this case study to learn more about assumptions and definitions of a single server queuing model.

Let consider an automatic teller machine (ATM) where customers arrive at a mean interarrival time of 3 minutes. Interarrival times are exponentially distributed. The service time at this ATM has a triangular distribution with parameters 2, 4 and 9 minutes. We want to know the average and maximum customer waiting time in the queue to be served, and the utilization of the ATM machine.

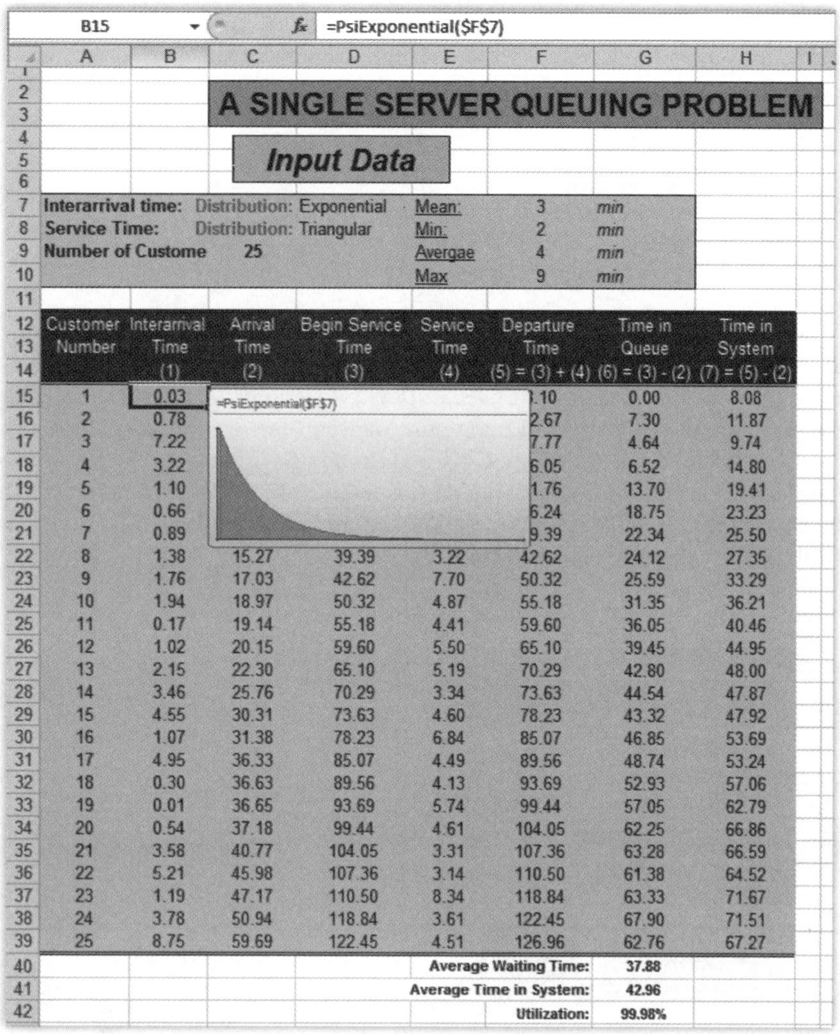

B15 =PsiExponential($F$7)

A SINGLE SERVER QUEUING PROBLEM

Input Data

Interarrival time:	Distribution: Exponential	Mean:	3	min
Service Time:	Distribution: Triangular	Min:	2	min
Number of Custome	25	Avergae	4	min
		Max	9	min

Customer Number	Interarrival Time (1)	Arrival Time (2)	Begin Service Time (3)	Service Time (4)	Departure Time (5) = (3) + (4)	Time in Queue (6) = (3) - (2)	Time in System (7) = (5) - (2)
1	0.03				.10	0.00	8.08
2	0.78				2.67	7.30	11.87
3	7.22				7.77	4.64	9.74
4	3.22				6.05	6.52	14.80
5	1.10				1.76	13.70	19.41
6	0.66				6.24	18.75	23.23
7	0.89				9.39	22.34	25.50
8	1.38	15.27	39.39	3.22	42.62	24.12	27.35
9	1.76	17.03	42.62	7.70	50.32	25.59	33.29
10	1.94	18.97	50.32	4.87	55.18	31.35	36.21
11	0.17	19.14	55.18	4.41	59.60	36.05	40.46
12	1.02	20.15	59.60	5.50	65.10	39.45	44.95
13	2.15	22.30	65.10	5.19	70.29	42.80	48.00
14	3.46	25.76	70.29	3.34	73.63	44.54	47.87
15	4.55	30.31	73.63	4.60	78.23	43.32	47.92
16	1.07	31.38	78.23	6.84	85.07	46.85	53.69
17	4.95	36.33	85.07	4.49	89.56	48.74	53.24
18	0.30	36.63	89.56	4.13	93.69	52.93	57.06
19	0.01	36.65	93.69	5.74	99.44	57.05	62.79
20	0.54	37.18	99.44	4.61	104.05	62.25	66.86
21	3.58	40.77	104.05	3.31	107.36	63.28	66.59
22	5.21	45.98	107.36	3.14	110.50	61.38	64.52
23	1.19	47.17	110.50	8.34	118.84	63.33	71.67
24	3.78	50.94	118.84	3.61	122.45	67.90	71.51
25	8.75	59.69	122.45	4.51	126.96	62.76	67.27
					Average Waiting Time:	37.88	
					Average Time in System:	42.96	
					Utilization:	99.98%	

Figure 9.27 Model setup for a single server queuing problem.

Figure 19.27 presents the problem setup. We have created a table in order to calculate the waiting time and time in the system for each customer. Column (1) of this table presents the interarrival time for each customer. We use the ***PsiExponential($F$7)*** function in cells B15:B39 to randomly generate the intearrival time. Column (2) calculates the arrival time. The arrival time for a customer is the sum of the arrival time of the previous customer and his or her interarrival time. If the queue is empty, a customer begins service upon arrival. Otherwise, if the queue is not empty, the customer will have to wait until the customer who entered the system right before her leaves the system. For example, the first customer begins service as soon as she arrives in the system. The beginning service time (column (3)) for the second customer is the maximum of her arrival time and the departure time of the first customer ***(=MAX(C16, F15))***. Service time (column (4)) is randomly generated using the ***PsiTriangular($F$8,$F$9,$F$10)*** function in cells E15:E39. Column (5) presents the departure time ((5) = (3) + (4)), column (6) presents the time in the queue ((6) = (3) – (2)), and column (7) presents the total time in the system ((7) = (5) – (2)) for each customer. We are also calculating the average waiting time in the queue and the average time in the system for the first 25 customers. We plan to run a number of simulations and collect statistics about the mean waiting time, mean time in the system, and utilization; therefore, we use the ***PsiOutput()*** function in cells G40, G41, and G42 as shown below. Using this function is an indication that we want the Risk Solver Platform to track the values in cells G40:G42 during the simulation.

Cell G40: *=AVERAGE(G15:G39) + PsiOutput()*
Cell G41: *=AVERAGE(H15:H39) + PsiOutput()*
Cell G42: *=SUM(E15:E39)/F39 + PsiOutput()*

We set the value of *Trials per Simulation* property equal to 5,000 using the *Platform* tab at the *Risk Solver Task Pane*. Figure 9.28 presents the summary of results table we have prepared. We use the ***PsiMean(G40)***, ***PsiStdDev(G40)***, and ***PsiMax(G40)*** to calculate the sample mean, standard deviation, and maximum waiting time over all simulation trials. Similarly, we use ***PsiMean(G41)***, ***PsiStdDev(G41)***, and ***PsiMax(G41)*** to calculate the sample mean, standard deviation, and maximum time in the system; and ***PsiMean(G42)***, ***PsiStdDev(G42)***, and ***PsiMax(G42)*** to calculate the sample mean, standard deviation, and maximum utilization. Initially, the value of these cells is N/A.

N7 fx =PsiMean(G40)

	J	K	L	M	N	O	P
4							
5		Summary of Results					
6							
7		Mean Waiting time			#N/A	Min	
8		Std. Dev. Of Waiting Time			#N/A	Min	
9		Max. Waiting Time			#N/A	Min	
10							
11		Mean Time in System			#N/A	Min	
12		Std. Dev. Of Time in System			#N/A	Min	
13		Max Time in System			#N/A	Min	
14							
15		Mean Utilization			#N/A		
16		Std. Dev. Of Utilization			#N/A		
17		Max. Utilization			#N/A		

Figure 9.28 Summary of results table for the single server queuing model.

Figure 9.29 presents the *Model* tab of the *task pane*. We now run this simulation model by clicking on the green arrow at the top right corner of the task pane. Figure 9.30 presents the results of the simulation. Double click on cell G40 to open the Risk Solver Platform Summary of Statistics dialog box (Figures 9.30 (b), 9.30 (c), 9.30 (d)). The average waiting time in the queue is 25.45 minutes (Figure 9.30 (a)). The waiting time varies, however, anywhere between 5 and 52 minutes (Figure 9.30 (b)). The Sensitivity chart (Figure 9.30(c)) indicates that waiting time is highly sensitive to customer arrival in the system (column B) and service time (column E). Figure 9.30 (d) indicates that only 25% of the customers wait up to 20minutes.

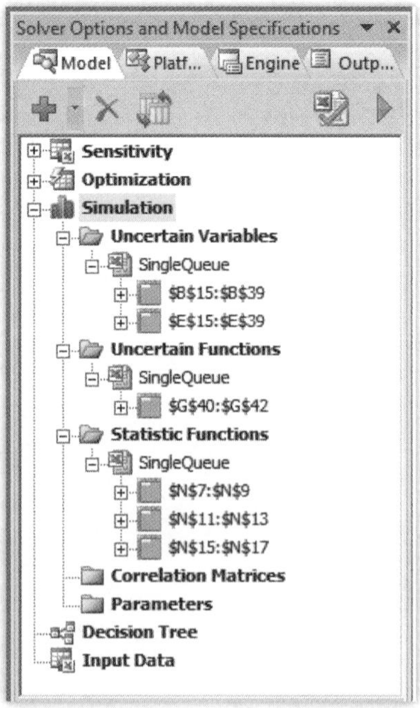

Figure 9.29 Model tab of the task pane.

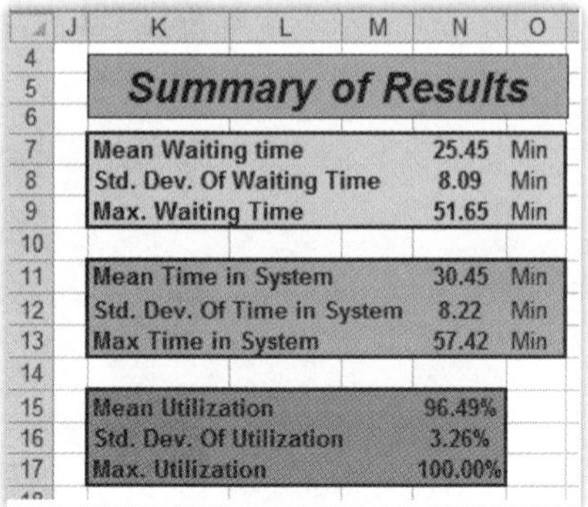

Summary of Results		
Mean Waiting time	25.45	Min
Std. Dev. Of Waiting Time	8.09	Min
Max. Waiting Time	51.65	Min
Mean Time in System	30.45	Min
Std. Dev. Of Time in System	8.22	Min
Max Time in System	57.42	Min
Mean Utilization	96.49%	
Std. Dev. Of Utilization	3.26%	
Max. Utilization	100.00%	

(a) Summary of results tables.

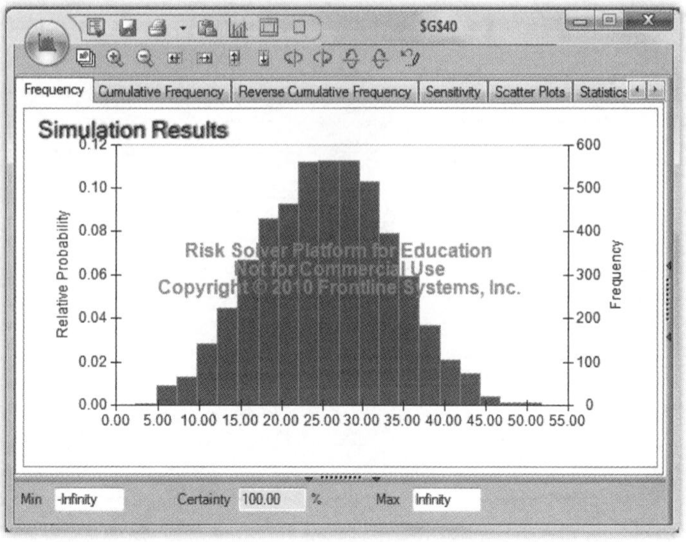

(b) The distribution of average waiting time in the queue.

Figure 9.30 Simulation models.

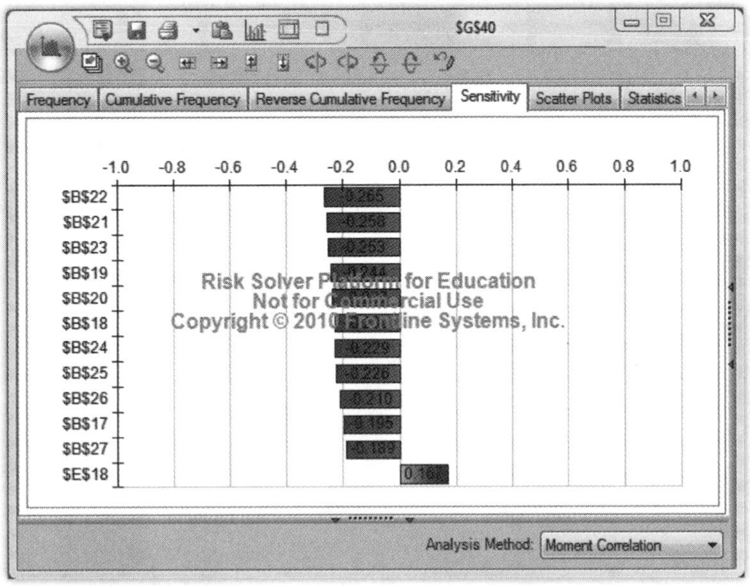

(c) Sensitivity chart of average waiting time in the queue.

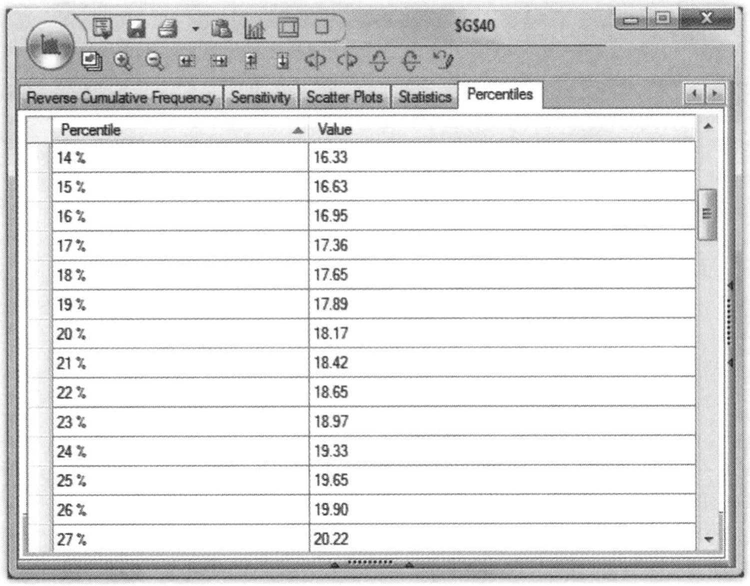

Percentile	Value
14 %	16.33
15 %	16.63
16 %	16.95
17 %	17.36
18 %	17.65
19 %	17.89
20 %	18.17
21 %	18.42
22 %	18.65
23 %	18.97
24 %	19.33
25 %	19.65
26 %	19.90
27 %	20.22

(d) Percentiles of the distribution of waiting time in the queue.

Figure 9.30 Simulation models. *(Cont.)*

Let's consider that we can reduce the maximum service time at the ATM by replacing the existing machine with a faster one. The different machines that are available in the market can decrease the maximum service time from 9 minutes to 5, 6, 7, and 8 minutes. Before deciding which machine to purchase, we need to analyze their impact on customer waiting time. We will perform 5 simulation runs. In each run we change to 5, 6, 7, 8, and 9 the third parameter of the triangular distribution we use to randomly generate the service time. We will display in a table (see Figure 9.31) the sample minimum, maximum, and mean waiting for each simulation run. In cell F10 we type "***=PsiSimParam(K21:K25)***" to ensure that in each simulation run the value of this parameter will change according to the values in cells K21:K25. We set the value of Simulations to Run property to 5, and Trials per Simulation at 5,000. Figure 9.32 presents the results of the simulation. It is obvious that faster ATM machines reduce the waiting time in the queue (Figure 9.32(a)). We reach to a similar conclusion by looking at the trend chart in Figure 9.32(b). To create this chart, we click on *Risk Solver Platform > Analysis > Charts* command. From the drop-down menu that appears, select *Multiple Simulations.* In the *Multiple Simulation* fly-out menu we select *Trend.*

	J	K	L	M	N
18					
19		Maximum		Waiting Time	
20		Service Tim	Min	Mean	Max
21		5	=PsiMin($G$40,1)	=PsiMean($G$40,1)	=PsiMax($G$40,1)
22		6	=PsiMin($G$40,2)	=PsiMean($G$40,2)	=PsiMax($G$40,2)
23		7	=PsiMin($G$40,3)	=PsiMean($G$40,3)	=PsiMax($G$40,3)
24		8	=PsiMin($G$40,4)	=PsiMean($G$40,4)	=PsiMax($G$40,4)
25		9	=PsiMin($G$40,5)	=PsiMean($G$40,5)	=PsiMax($G$40,5)

Figure 9.31 Formulas used to present the min, mean, and max sample waiting time for all five simulation runs.

	J	K	L	M	N
18					
19		Maximum		Waiting Time	
20		Service Time	Min	Mean	Max
21		5	0.99	11.47	30.58
22		6	1.29	14.70	35.77
23		7	1.83	18.15	41.01
24		8	2.51	21.75	46.27
25		9	3.32	25.47	51.54

(a) Sample minimum, mean and maximum waiting times for different service times.

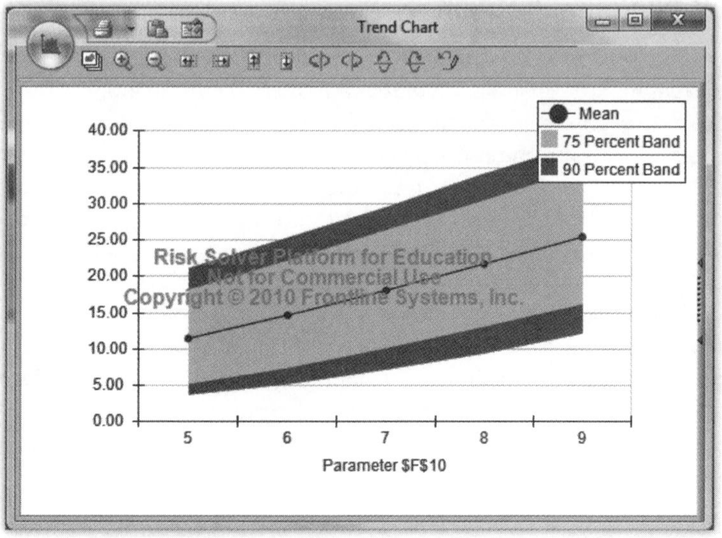

(b) Trend chart of waiting times.

Figure 9.32 Simulation results.

Finally, we want to know how sensitive the simulation results are to changes in customer interarrival time in the system. We type "**=*PsiSenParam(3,10)***" in cell F7, and set the value of *Simulations to Run* property to 5. During each simulation run, the Risk Solver Platform will change the value of the problem parameter in cell F7 (mean intearrival time) automatically from 3 to 10. To view the Sensitivity Report in Figure 9.33, we select cell G40, and then click on *Risk Solver Platform* > *Analysis* > *Charts* command. From the drop-down menu that appears, select *Sensitivity Analysis.* In the *Sensitivity Analysis* fly-out menu we select *Parameter Analysis.*

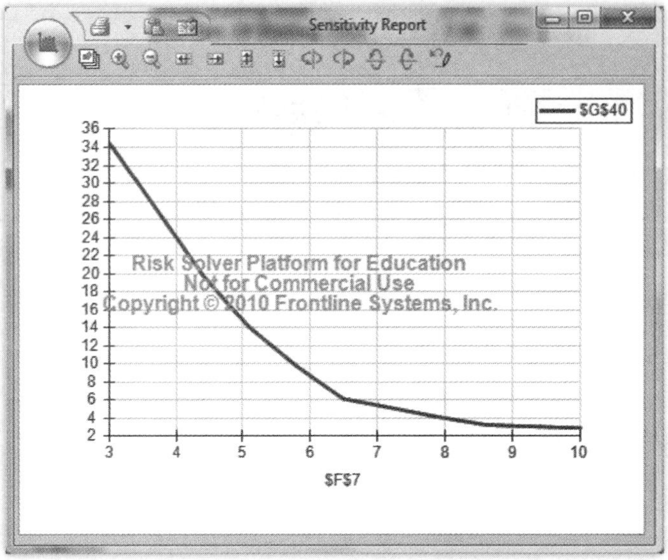

Figure 9.33 Waiting time in queue is sensitive to customer interarrival time. Small interarrival times (customers arriving frequently) cause long waiting time in the queue to be served at the ATM.

9.5.3 Retirement Planning Problem

This problem is adapted from Case Study 8. We refer the user to this case study to learn more about assumptions and the formulation of the retirement planning model.

Jane is building a retirement plan for herself. She wants to ensure that she has enough funds when she retires, 25 years from now. Jane is considering investing her current savings and a percentage of her salary increase to this retirement plan (Figure 9.34). Her plan is to invest in T-bills, bonds, and stocks. The question in her mind is whether she will be able to achieve her desired return due to market return uncertainties on T-bills, bonds, stocks, and salary increase uncertainties.

Jane has collected historical data (1993 to 2011) about the annual rate of return of the three investment options (Figure 9.35). She uses this historical data to set up her problem. The market annual return for each investment option is randomly generated using the ***PsiResample()*** function. This function generates new data point by considering past historical data. For example, to generate a market return from T-bills in the current year, we use this function in cell B14 (Figure 9.36).

Retirement Planning				
Current Savings	$30,000		Desired Total Return	$1,000,000
Current Salary	$70,000		Expected Total Return	
Salary Increase	5.28%		Std.Dev of Expected Return	
Percent Salary to Invest	2.64%		P(Total Return > Desired Return)	

Asset Allocation			Initial Investment		
T. Bills	Bonds	Stocks	T. Bills	Bonds	Stocks
0.50	0.23	0.27	$15,923.85	$7,324.97	$8,598.88

Figure 9.34 Input data for the Retirement Planning problem.

=PsiResample(P$14:P$32)

Hist Data for Bootstrapping			
Year	Bills	Bonds	Stocks
1990	0.0508	0.1675	0.2384
1991	0.0512	-0.0067	-0.0718
1992	0.0718	-0.0116	0.0656
1993	0.1038	-0.0122	0.1844
1994	0.1124	-0.0395	0.3242
1995	0.1471	0.0185	-0.0491
1996	0.1054	0.4035	0.2141
1997	0.088	0.0068	0.2251
1998	0.0985	0.1543	0.0627
1999	0.0772	0.3097	0.3216
2000	0.0616	0.2444	0.1847
2001	0.0547	-0.0269	0.0523
2002	0.0635	0.0967	0.1681
2003	0.0837	0.1811	0.3149
2004	0.0781	0.0618	-0.0317
2005	0.056	0.193	0.3055
2006	0.0351	0.0805	0.0767
2007	0.029	0.1824	0.0999
2008	0.039	-0.0777	0.0131

Figure 9.35 Historical data on investment returns.

B14 =PsiResample(P$14:P$32)

T. Bills	Bonds	Stocks	T. Bills	Bonds	Stocks
0.40	0.30	0.30	$12,000.00	$9,000.00	$9,000.00

	Market Returns (from Bootstrapping)			Ending Investment Returns						Yearly Investment		
Year	T. Bills	Bonds	Stocks	T. Bills	Bonds	Stocks	Total Returns	Yearly Salary	Addition to Savings	T. Bills	Bonds	Stocks
0	0.0985	-0.0116	0.0767	$13,182	$8,896	$9,690	**$31,768**	$76,614	$3,619	$14,155	$10,616	$10,616
1	0.0781	0.0805	0.3149	$15,260	$11,471	$13,959	**$40,690**	$83,853	$3,961	$17,861	$13,396	$13,396
2	0.0772	-0.0395	0.2384	$19,240	$12,866	$16,589	**$48,695**	$91,776	$4,336	$21,212	$15,909	$15,909
23	0.056	0.1543	0.0999	$345,618	$283,343	$269,990	**$898,951**	$611,130	$28,871	$371,129	$278,347	$278,347
24	0.0351	-0.0777	0.1844	$384,155	$256,719	$329,674	**$970,548**	$668,873	$31,599	$400,859	$300,644	$300,644
25	0.0718	0.193	0.0131	$429,641	$358,669	$304,583	**$1,092,892**	$732,071	$34,585	$450,991	$338,243	$338,243

Figure 9.36 Retirement Planning simulation model setup.

Jane calculates the ending investment returns for each investment option by considering the amount invested and the corresponding annual return. For example, the investment return from bonds in the current year (cell F14) is calculated as follows.

=G$10(1+C14)*

Jane believes that her expected salary increase rate will be between 5% and 10%. We use the "***=PsiUniform(0.05, 0.1)***" in cell D5 to randomly generate this increase. Jane's yearly salary for the next 25 years is then adjusted based on this rate. She plans to invest only half of the salary increase for retirement (cell D6) and calculates these additional savings in range J14:J39. The total of current and additional savings is reinvested based on her asset allocation schema (range C10:E10). Cell H39 gives the total amount Jane would have saved in 25 years. Since we are interested to monitor the values of H39 during the simulation, we type the "***+PsiOutput()***" function in H39.

=SUM(E39:G39)+PsiOutput()

To calculate the expected total return and corresponding standard deviation we use the "***=PsiMean(H39)***" and "***=PsiStdDev(H39)***" functions. Finally, we calculate the probability that the total returns are greater than the desired return from this retirement plan by using the ***PsiTarget()*** function in cell I6 as follows. The value in cell I3 is $1,000,000. This is the amount that Jane is targeting to have by the time she retires.

=1-PsiTarget(H39,I3)

We set the *Trials per Simulation* property to 10,000 in the *task pane*, and run this simulation. Double click on cell H39 to display the Summary of Statistics dialog box shown in Figure 9.37. The results from the simulation indicate that the expected returns from this retirement plan are $952,279. There is a 39.2% probability that Jane will achieve her desired total return before retirement.

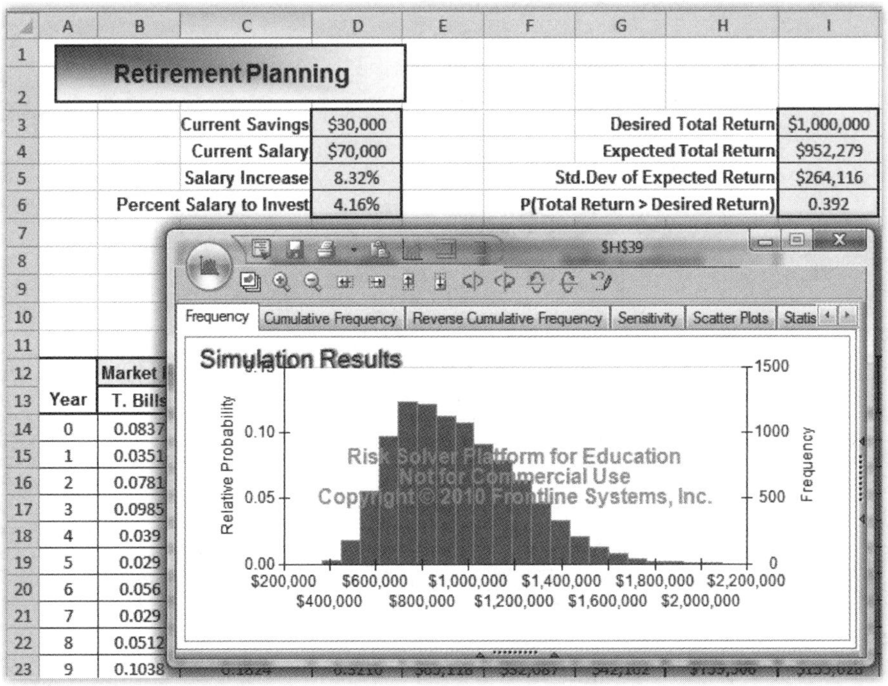

Figure 9.37 Results from simulating the problem.

Jane is wondering whether the asset allocation scheme that she is currently using (0.5 in T-bills, 0.23 in bonds, and 0.27 in stocks) is optimal. Therefore, she builds the following optimization model to identify an allocation of her assets that maximize the expected profits.

The decision variables in the optimization model are in cells C10:E10. There are only two constraints in this model. First, the total allocation should be equal to one ***(SUM(C10:E10) = 1)***. We set the formula in cell B10 equal to "***=SUM(C10:E10)***". Second, each allocation variable should be a number between 0 and 1. Figure 9.38 presents the optimization *Model* tab of the *task pane*. We execute this optimization-simulation model by clicking on the green arrow on the top-right corner of the task pane.

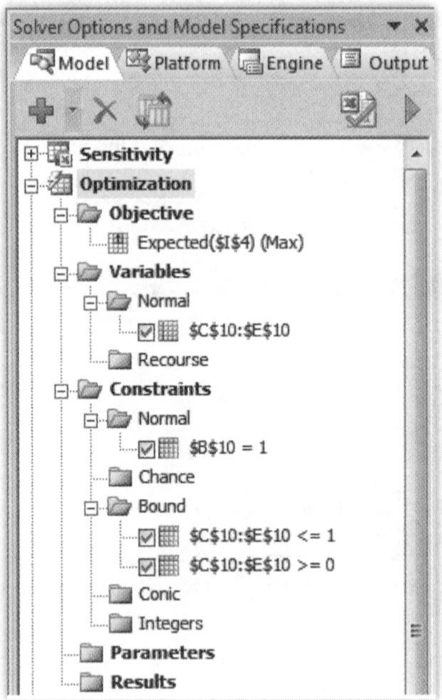

Figure 9.38 Optimization Model tab of the task pane.

Based on the results of this optimization-simulation model, Jane should invest solely in stocks (Figure 9.39). Although this is a very profitable reallocation of her investments, Jane wants a diverse portfolio to minimize her risk.

Jane plans to perform 10 simulations, each with a different investment allocation scheme. Figure 9.40 presents the asset allocation scheme for each scenario. She types "***=PsiSimParam(T14:T23)***" in cell C10, "***=PsiSimParam(U14:U23)***" in cell D10, and "***=PsiSimParam(V14:V23)***" in cell E10 to indicate that the values on cells C10:E10 will change during each simulation run based on the values in cells T14:V23. Next, she types "***=PsiMean(H39,1)***" in cell W14, "***=PsiStdDev(H39,1)***" in X14, and "***=1- PsiTarget(H39,I3,1)***" in cell Y14 in order to collect statistics, such as, mean standard deviation, and probability of returns over the target value, during the simulation. The new parameter, 1, listed in these formulas indicates that the results from the first simulation will be presented in these cells. As we copy these formulas to the range W14:Y23, the value of this parameter changes from 1 to 2,…,10, indicating the corresponding simulation run. Finally, we set the number of *Simulations to Run* to 10 in the *Platform* tab of the *Task Pane*, and run the simulations.

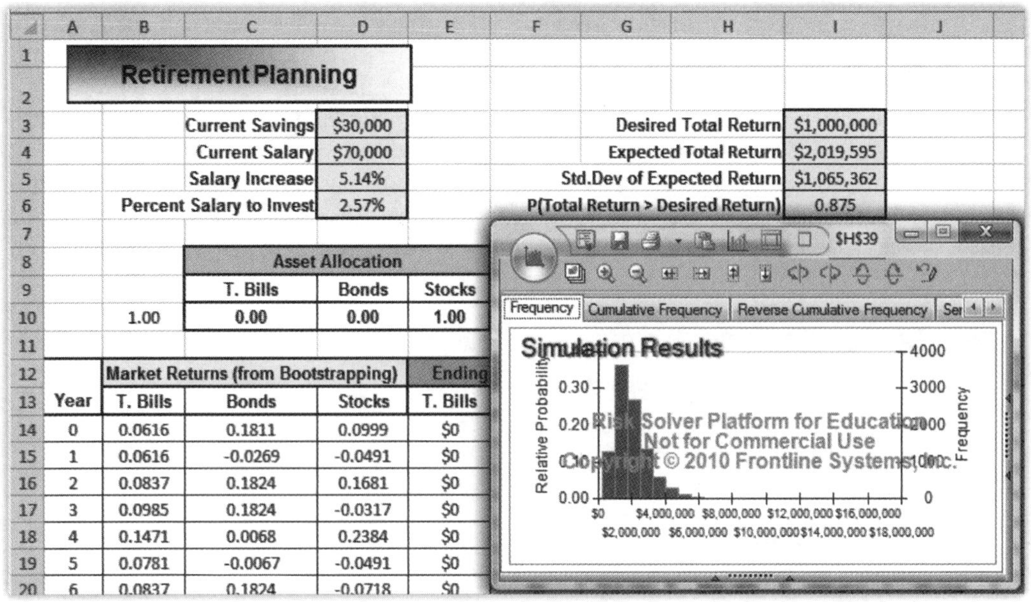

Figure 9.39 Jane should invest soley in stocks to maximize her expected profits.

W14 =PsiMean($H$39,1)

Model Number	Asset Allocation T. Bills	Bonds	Stocks	Expected Return	Standard Deviation	Return > Desired
1	0.4	0.3	0.3	#N/A	#N/A	#N/A
2	0.3	0.3	0.4	#N/A	#N/A	#N/A
3	0.2	0.3	0.5	#N/A	#N/A	#N/A
4	0.1	0.3	0.6	#N/A	#N/A	#N/A
5	0.0	0.3	0.7	#N/A	#N/A	#N/A
6	0.3	0.4	0.3	#N/A	#N/A	#N/A
7	0.3	0.3	0.4	#N/A	#N/A	#N/A
8	0.3	0.2	0.5	#N/A	#N/A	#N/A
9	0.3	0.1	0.6	#N/A	#N/A	#N/A
10	0.3	0.0	0.7	#N/A	#N/A	#N/A

Figure 9.40 Asset allocation schemes identified by Jane.

The results from these simulations are presented in Figure 9.41(a). The *Box-Whisker* chart in Figure 9.41(b) presents the mean, median, 25th percentile, 75th percentile, minimum, and maximum values of expected return for each simulation run. To create this chart we select the range W13:W23, and then click on the *Risk Solver Platform > Analysis > Charts* drop-down menu on the *Ribbon*. From the list of options that appears we select *Multiple Simulations*, and from the corresponding fly-out menu we choose *Box-Whisker*. These results help Jane understand the fluctuations on her retirement funds as she moves from one investment scenario to the next.

Model Number	Asset Allocation			Expected Return	Standard Deviation	Return > Desired
	T. Bills	Bonds	Stocks			
1	0.4	0.3	0.3	$1,009,931	$296,495	47.10%
2	0.3	0.3	0.4	$1,143,920	$351,264	62.20%
3	0.2	0.3	0.5	$1,286,567	$436,829	70.60%
4	0.1	0.3	0.6	$1,448,346	$509,910	79.80%
5	0.0	0.3	0.7	$1,630,141	$660,212	84.00%
6	0.3	0.4	0.3	$1,064,758	$327,469	51.70%
7	0.3	0.3	0.4	$1,138,282	$341,755	62.70%
8	0.3	0.2	0.5	$1,232,345	$395,706	67.80%
9	0.3	0.1	0.6	$1,318,077	$452,911	73.00%
10	0.3	0.0	0.7	$1,404,362	$507,725	77.50%

(a) Results from each simulation run.

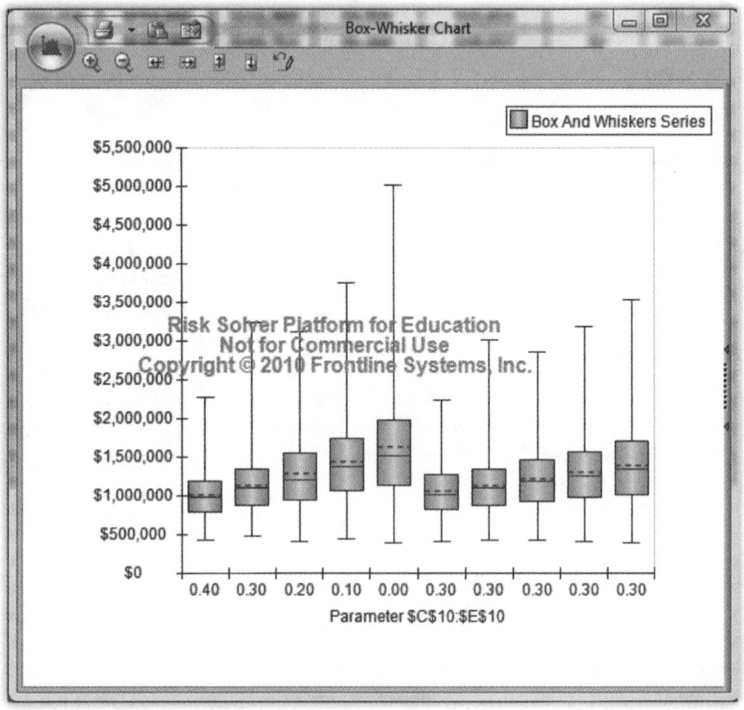

(b) Box-Whisker chart for expected returns.

Figure 9.41 Multiple simulations results.

9.6 *Summary*

- Simulation is a tool used to model and analyze the behavior of complex systems.
- Simulation is used not to find the best result given certain inputs, but rather to find the best inputs given a desired result.

- In what-if analyses, we change the value of a certain problem input to observe its impact on problem outputs. Excel provides two what-if analysis tools: Scenario Manager and Data Tables.
- A random number generator is an algorithm used to generate identical and uniformly distributed numbers between 0 and 1. The RAND() function of Excel generates random numbers.
- The Risk Solver Platform uses galleries of Psi functions to generate numbers from a particular distribution. The most frequently used functions are PsiNormal, PsiDiscrete, PsiBeta, and PsiBinomial.
- The Goodness of Fit Test is a statistical test to evaluate how well a distribution fits a set of data.
- The goal of Sensitivity Analysis is to estimate the impact of changes on problem inputs to problem outputs.
- Applications of simulation include the News Vendor problem, the Single Server Queuing problem, and the Retirement Planning problem.

9.7 *Exercises*

9.7.1 Review Questions

1. What is a simulation?
2. How do simulation models differ from optimization models?
3. What are the two what-if analysis tools of Excel?
4. What function of Excel will you use to generate a random number between 0 and 1?
5. Name four functions of the Risk Solver Platform that are used to generate numbers from a particular distribution.
6. What statistical test do we use to verify whether a theoretical distribution fits our data set?
7. The first-year sales of a new product are estimated to be 1,000, 2,000, 3,000, 4,000, or 5,000 units. The chances that sales will take any of these values are equal. What function of the Risk Solver Platform will you use to randomly generate first-year sales?
8. Which Risk Solver Platform function will you use for generating a random number from an exponential distribution? What parameters are required by this function?
9. If given a gamma distribution with an alpha value of 5 and a beta value of 8, what is the appropriate functional expression to generate a random number using the Risk Solver Platform?
10. Give an example of an application of simulation.

9.7.2 Hands-On Exercises

Note: *Please refer to the file "Chapter_09_Exercises.xlsx" for the associated worksheets noted for the hands-on exercises. The file is available at: www.dssbooks.com.*

1. A student needs a grade average of at least 93.0 points to receive an A in one of his classes. The student's grade average is computed by averaging the student's score on five different tests given in the class. Each test is scored out of 100 points, and the highest grade the student can receive is 100 points since no extra credit is offered. The student received the following grades on the first three tests: 86, 94, and 88. He is trying to determine if it is possible for him to earn an A in the class and if so, what grades he must earn on the final two tests in order to earn an A. Use the Scenario Manager tool of Excel to determine if the student can possibly receive an A in the class, and, if he can, determine what combinations of grades on the final two tests will enable him to do so.
2. Generate five random numbers for each of the following distributions:
   a. Exponential distribution with a mean of 12.
   b. Beta distribution with an alpha of 4 and a beta of 3.
   c. Chi-squared distribution with 6 degrees of freedom.
   d. Standard normal cumulative distribution.
3. In Chapter 3, Hands-On Exercise 4, you completed a table that determines the height of a cylinder given its volume and radius. Use Scenario Manager to complete the table again for each of the following cylinder volumes: 10, 15, 20, 25, and 30 ft^3. Recall that the height of a cylinder can be computed with the following formula:

Height = Volume/(Radius^2). (Refer to worksheet 9.3.)

4. A bakery receives its ingredients from one of three vendors. Each vendor under consideration charges different prices for each different ingredient. The tax rates vary by the state in which the vendors are located, and the shipping costs vary by the distances the supply must travel. A given table displays the prices, tax rates, and shipping costs per pound for each vendor. The management has to choose a vendor for each ingredient. It has been estimated that 200 lbs of ingredients will be needed per month. Use Scenario Manager to help the management to choose a vendor for each ingredient. (Refer to worksheet 9.4.)

5. A materials engineer is conducting a test on the fracture toughness of an expensive ceramic material. The engineer wants to report on the results of 50 trials but can only afford to actually conduct 10 trials since testing the material renders it unusable. Her results so far have followed a chi-squared distribution with 3.5 degrees of freedom. Using random number generation, predict 40 more possible trial results for the engineer to use.

6. A company is opening up a new distribution center in Gainesville, Florida. Five different banks have offered the company loan plans; each plan's cash flow is provided. Initially, assume that the interest rate is 5%. (Refer to worksheet 9.6.)

a. Create a spreadsheet that finds the net present value and the internal rate of return of each loan.

b. Run several scenarios that change the interest rate to 3%, 3.5%, 4%, and 4.5%.

c. View the scenario summary. Which interest rate would the company prefer? Which bank can provide the most economical loan plan for the company?

7. Suppose that you have just been hired by Sturdy Boxes, Inc., to manage the production floor. On your first day, you realize that the garbage compactor is full of cardboard boxes. After questioning the workers, you find out that those boxes were not cut and shaped correctly in the Flex-O machine. The problem is that the Flex-O machine's blades are not replaced quickly enough after it has been discovered that misshapen boxes are being produced. After studying daily production reports, you determine that the time for the first failure to occur follows a normal distribution with an average of 4 hours and a standard deviation of 15 minutes. If the time to process each box has a normal distribution with an average of 30 seconds and a standard deviation of 3 seconds, how many boxes should be processed before the blades on the Flex-O machine should be replaced? Use Risk Solver to simulate 10 scenarios with 1,000 runs each and find the minimum value to approximate the number of boxes to produce before replacing the blade. Your objective is to use each blade as long as possible but change it before failures start to occur.

8. A PVC pipe manufacturer has recently approximated the effect of certain factors on the amount of time it takes to produce a certain length of PVC pipe. These factors include the pressure and temperature of the liquid PVC and the radius and thickness of the pipe. The time that it takes to produce PVC pipe is shortest when the liquid PVC pressure is at 20 psi, the liquid PVC temperature is 240 degrees Fahrenheit, the radius is at its minimum setting of one-half inch, and the thickness of the pipe is at its minimum setting of one-eighth inch. The time to produce a 12-foot pipe at these settings follows a normal distribution with a mean of 85 seconds and a standard deviation of 6 seconds. Below are the approximated effects of each factor on the mean time necessary to produce a 12-foot PVC pipe. Note that P is the liquid PVC pressure setting, T is the liquid PVC temperature setting, R is the radius of the pipe, and TH is the thickness of the pipe.

*Liquid PVC pressure factor = 1 + (20 – P)/(20 * 10)*

*Liquid PVC temperature factor = 1 + (240 – T)/(240 * 10)*

*Radius factor = 1 + (R – 0.5)/(0.5 * 10)*

*Thickness factor = 1 + (TH – 0.125)/(0.125 * 10)*

Use Scenario Manager to find the approximate time to produce a 12-foot PVC pipe for each of the following settings:

a. P = 21 psi, T = 230°F, R = 1", TH = 0.25

b. P = 18 psi, T = 250°F, R = 2", TH = 0.35

c. P = 24 psi, T = 235°F, R = 5", TH = 0.5

d. P = 17 psi, T = 245°F, R = 3", TH = 0.25

9. A wholesaler receives hundreds of products from several manufacturers and distributes the products among the company's retail stores. Most of the products have a fairly constant supply and demand, but the distribution manager has realized that the demand rate and supply time of several of the products fluctuate significantly. At times, the demand is so high that the wholesaler cannot provide the supply in time to meet the demand. At other times, the supply arrives well before the demand and sits in inventory until it is distributed. The distribution manager would like to order all the products at an appropriate time so that they will arrive in time to meet demand without accumulating too much. After studying past trends, the distribution manager approximated the distributions of the demand rate and supply time for one of the products. Assume that the product is perishable and only good for the month in which it is ordered. Also assume that the product is ordered in batches of 100. The supply time follows a normal distribution with the following parameters (where D is the amount of demand). (Refer to worksheet 9.9.)

*Mean = ceiling[20 * (1 + (D – 200) / 200)],Standard deviation = 3*

a. The wholesaler should identify the approximate number of batches to order to meet the demand and the approximate number of days to allow for delivery so that the delivery will arrive in time for the next month. Build a simulation model and use the Risk Solver Platform to perform 5,000 runs of this simulation to identify the timing and the number of batches to order.

b. Use the Risk Solver Platform to find the number of batches to order if the time of supply arrival has a normal distribution with the following parameters:

*Mean = ceiling[A * (1 + (D – B) / B)], where A is the value of the mean for an order size of B batches, Standard deviation = S*

i. A = 15, B = 160, S = 5

ii. A = 25, B = 220, S = 2

iii. A = 12, B = 210, S = 4

10. A local company currently sells 40,000 units of a product for $45 each. The unit variable cost of production for the product is $5. The company is thinking about cutting the product price by 30%. It is sure that this will increase sales by an amount between 10% and 50%. Perform a sensitivity analysis to show how profit will change as a function of the percentage increase in sales (ignore fixed costs).

a. Using Data Tables

b. Using the Scenario Manager

c. Using Simulation in the Risk Solver Platform

11. A GMC dealer believes that demand for next year's trucks will be normally distributed with a mean of 200 and a standard deviation of 30. His cost of receiving a truck is $30,000, and he sells each truck for $45,000. The leftover trucks can be sold for $40,000. He is considering ordering 200, 220, 240, 260, 280, or 300 trucks. How many should he order?

12. The game of Keno is played as follows: 80 balls (numbered 1 to 80) are mixed up and 20 balls are randomly drawn. Before the 20 balls are drawn, the player chooses 10 different numbers. If at least 5 of the numbers are drawn, the player wins. Build a simulation model to determine the probability that the player will win.

13. Suppose you are bidding for an oil well that you believe will yield $40 million (including the cost of developing and mining the oil) in profits. Three competitors are bidding against you and each competitor's bid is assumed to follow a normal random variable with a mean of $30 million and a standard deviation of $4 million. Build a simulation model to help you decide on the amount that you should bid. Your goal is to bid less than $40 million but yet have at least a 90% chance of winning the bid.

14. Two basketball teams are ready for the best-of-seven NBA finals. The two teams are evenly matched, but the home team wins 60% of the games played between the two teams. The sequence of home and away games is to be chosen by Team A. Team A has the home edge and will be the home team for four of the seven games. They have the following sequence choices for the home games.

a. Sequence 1: Team A, A, B, B, A, B, A

b. Sequence 2: Team A, A, B, B, B, A, A

Use simulation to prove that each sequence gives Team A the same chance of winning.

15. The game of Chuck-a-Luck is played as follows: You select a number between 1 and 6 and toss three dice. If your number does not appear on any of the dice, you lose $1. If your number appears x times you win $x. On the average, how much money will you win or lose on each play of the game?

16. In August 2011, a car dealer is trying to determine how many 2012 cars should be ordered. Each car ordered in August 2011 costs $20,000. The demand for the dealer's 2012 models has the probability distribution shown in a given table. Each car sells for $25,000. If the demand for 2012 cars exceeds the number of cars ordered in August 2011, the dealer must reorder at a cost of $22,000 per car. Excess cars may be disposed of at $18,000 per car. Use simulation to determine how many cars should be ordered in August 2011. Use the Risk Solver Platform to build an optimization-simulation model that identifies the optimal order quantity. For your optimal order quantity, find the distribution of the expected profit. (Refer to worksheet 9.16.)

17. In the above exercise, suppose now that the demand for cars is normally distributed with a mean of 40 and a standard deviation of 7. Build a simulation model to determine the order quantity. For this optimal order quantity, determine the distribution of the expected profit.

18. A ticket from Miami to Orlando sells for $150. The plane can hold 100 people. It costs $8,000 to fly an empty plane. The airline incurs variable costs of $30 per person on the plane. If the flight is overbooked, anyone who cannot get a seat receives $300 in compensation. On average, 95% of all people who have a reservation show up for the flight. To maximize the expected profit, how many reservations for the flight should be taken? Build a simulation model to determine this number.

19. An emergency room at a nearby hospital has an average of 2 patients arriving every hour (exponentially distributed). Upon entering, each patient fills out a form; this always takes 5 minutes. Then each patient is processed by one of two registration clerks. This takes an average of 7 minutes (exponentially distributed). Then each patient walks 2 minutes to a waiting room and waits to meet the doctor. The time it takes the doctor to see a patient averages 20 minutes with a standard deviation of 10 minutes (normally distributed). Create a spreadsheet simulation model and use the Risk Solver Platform to answer these questions:

a. On average, how long does a patient spend in the emergency room?

b. On average, how much of this time is spent waiting for a doctor?

c. What percentage of the time is the doctor busy?

d. Calculate the percentage reduction of customer waiting time if the hospital hired one additional doctor.

20. A person plays a game in which 2 dice are thrown. If the total outcome is 7 or 11, the person wins the game. Use simulation to find the probability of a win.

21. Jane is buying a house that costs $210,000. A financial institution is willing to lend her the money. The bank provides different rates depending on the amount of down payment and the duration of the loan. A given table presents the interest rate for different loan durations and amount of down payment. Use two-way Data Tables to calculate the monthly payments that Jane will be making to pay off the loan under each scenario. (Refer to worksheet 9.21.)

22. A fast-food, drive-through-only restaurant is considering hiring new employees. It has been estimated that each additional employee will reduce the service time by 10%. Some data have been collected (the times are in minutes). The manager of the restaurant would like to perform a simulation analysis to see if hiring new employees would be beneficial. (Refer to worksheet 9.22.)

a. Use the Risk Solver Platform to simulate the arrival and service time of 100 customers using the information provided above.

b. Estimate the expected waiting time per customer, expected total time in the system, the longest waiting time, and the percentage of time the server (drive through window) is idle.

c. Assume that one additional employee was hired. Recalculate the expected waiting time per customer, expected total time in the system, the longest waiting time, and the percentage of time a server is idle.

Hint: Build a spreadsheet model similar to the one presented in the Single Server Queuing application.

23. The coffee shop in a university town faces the problem of determining how many bagels to order per day from a nearby bakery. For planning purposes, the bakery requires that a fixed amount of bagels be ordered every day in a given month. At the end of the month, the order size may be changed. Based on past observations, the coffee shop manager has identified a distribution of daily demand for bagels for the current month. (Refer to worksheet 9.23.)

It costs $0.1 to buy a bagel from the bakery, regardless of the quantity ordered. The bagels are sold for $1.05. Leftover bagels are disposed at the end of the day. The manager is interested in identifying an order size for the current month that would maximize the profits.

a. Randomly generate the demand for the 30 days of the current month using the distribution given above. Consider an order size of 25. Use the Risk Solver Platform to run a simulation with 5,000 trials. Calculate expected profits and corresponding standard deviation. Based on the results of the simulation is 25 an optimal order quantity?

b. Use the Risk Solver Platform tools to perform a sensitivity analysis of expected profits with respect to order size.

c. Create an optimization-simulation model to identify the optimal order quantity for the given distribution of demand.

24. Given tables present the distribution of the interarrival time and service time of the jobs in a service center. Build a spreadsheet model similar to the one presented in the Single Server Queuing application. Use this model to estimate the expected waiting time per job, expected total time in the service center, and the longest waiting time for 100 jobs under the following two different service rules. (Refer to worksheet 9.24.)

a. First In First Out (FIFO)—jobs are served in the order they arrive.

b. Last In First Out (LIFO)—the last job to arrive.

CHAPTER

ten Working with Large Data

chapter OVERVIEW

10.1 *Introduction*

This chapter explains how to work with external data or large data in Excel. For the database discussion, we assume the reader has some previous knowledge of database software, such as Microsoft Access. This chapter is not intended to cover all basic database concepts such as database design. For more information on databases, we refer the reader to the book by Pol and Ahuja, "*Developing Web-Enabled Decision Support Systems.*" In this chapter, we also illustrate how to import data from text files, webpages, and databases. Knowing how to import data to the spreadsheet environment is an important attribute for developing a DSS. In many real-life applications, large amounts of data will be stored in a separate database; some or all of this data may need to be imported or referenced as input for the model in the DSS. We revisit this topic in Chapter 21 to illustrate how this can be done using VBA. We have developed several DSS applications which use these features, such as the University Information System application.

In this chapter, the reader will learn how to:

- Import data from a text file, webpage, or database.
- Create pivot tables using data from an external database.
- Sort and filter a database table in Excel.
- Create "official" Excel Tables to store and analyze data.
- Work with database functions in Excel.
- Apply database validation and consolidation in Excel.

10.2 *Importing Data*

Excel offers many tools for working with and analyzing large amounts of data. In many cases, an Excel user may not be given data in a worksheet to manipulate. If this is the case, we can use the *Get External Data* group of commands on the *Data* tab of *Excel Ribbon* to transfer this data to a worksheet where Excel analysis tools can be applied. In this chapter we discuss three sources from which we can import data into Excel: a text file, a webpage, and a database.

10.2.1 Text Files

In order to import data from a text file, we use the *Text Import Wizard.* If we click the *Data > Get External Data > From Text* command on the Ribbon, and then we try to open a text file in Excel, this Wizard will appear. There are three simple steps to follow to use the Wizard. The first step is to specify how we want to organize our data into columns for Excel. There are two main options: *Fixed Width* and *Delimited.* If we choose *Fixed Width*, Excel will guess how to separate our data into columns. The second step of the Wizard will then give us a chance to modify this guess. If we choose the *Delimited* option, we specify what character will be used as a separator, for example: commas, spaces, tabs, etc. This character choice would be done in the second step of the Wizard with the *Delimited* option. The third step of the Wizard in both cases is to specify any particular numerical formatting to be applied to the data as it is imported into Excel. Let's take a closer look at the *Text Import Wizard* through an example:

Figure 10.1 presents a text file that records the number of hours ten employees worked for three consecutive weeks. The file records each employee's start date and hours worked for three weeks. This file has been saved as a ".txt" file.

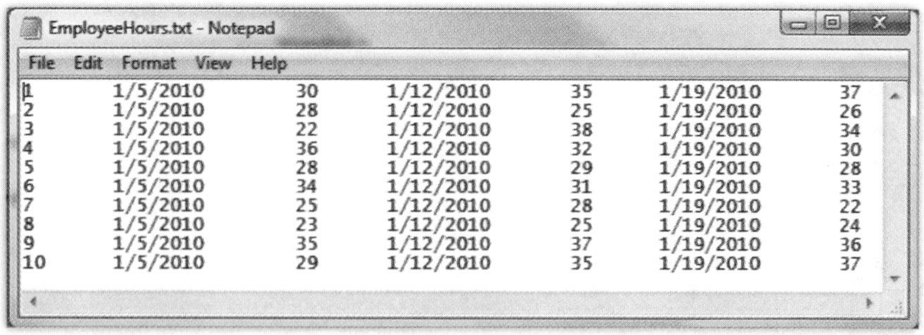

Figure 10.1 Text file of employee hours.

The supervisor of these employees may be interested in calculating the average hours worked per employee and the average hours worked every Monday. To take advantage of Excel tools and functions that will help her accomplish this, she must import this text file into Excel. After ensuring the above data is saved as a text file, we open Excel and choose *Data > Get External Data > From Text* from the Ribbon; then select the above text file. The *Text Import Wizard* will appear (see Figure 10.2).

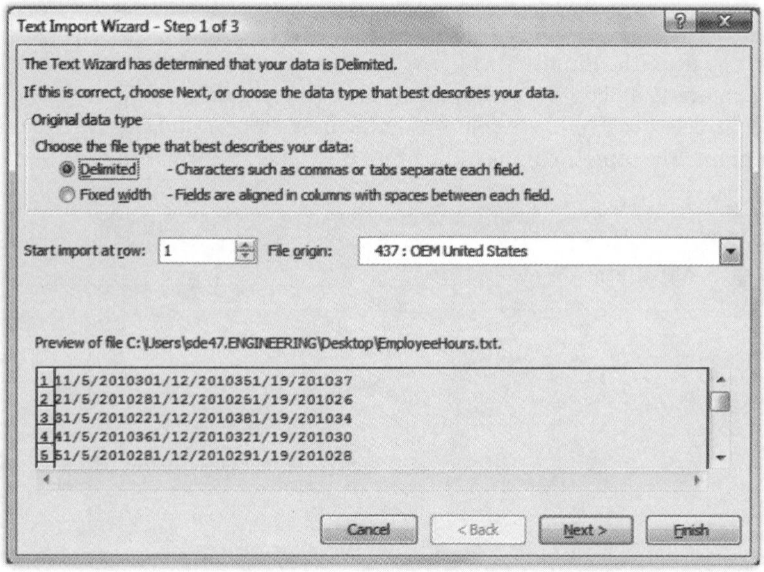

Figure 10.2 Step 1 of the Text Import Wizard.

For the first step of the Wizard, we will choose the *Delimited* option. We notice that tabs separate the text file data. Excel may have guessed this if we had selected the Fixed Width option, but it is still important to ensure that tabs are used (notice that "/" marks are also used in the dates which might be considered as a separator in Excel's guess). In the second step of the Wizard, we select "Tab" as the delimiter (see Figure 10.3). We could try other options to preview the columns that would appear. For example, we could check "Other" and enter the "/" mark in the adjacent space to preview an incorrect separator for the data.

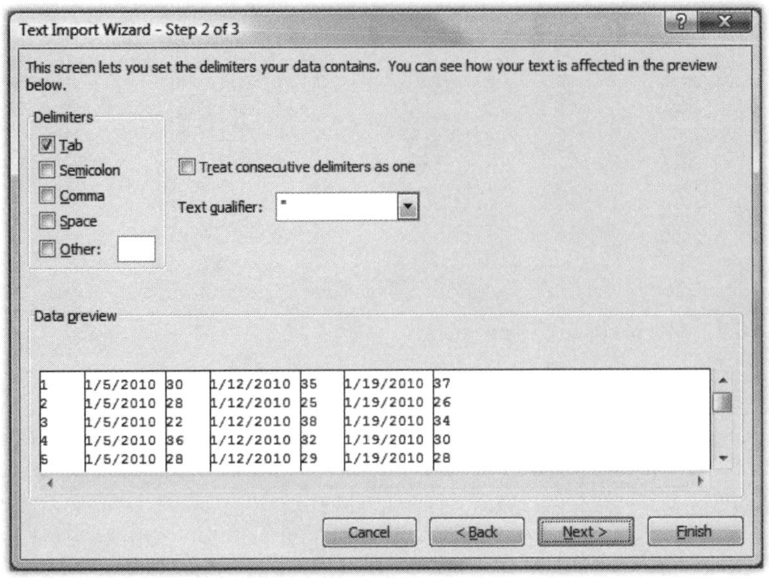

Figure 10.3 Step 2 of the Text Import Wizard.

Next, we go to the third step of the Wizard and specify any numerical formatting for the data (see Figure 10.4). For this text, the second, forth, and sixth columns should be entered as dates. So, we select each of these columns in the preview area and choose "Date: MDY" as the format option. The other columns can be kept in "General" formatting.

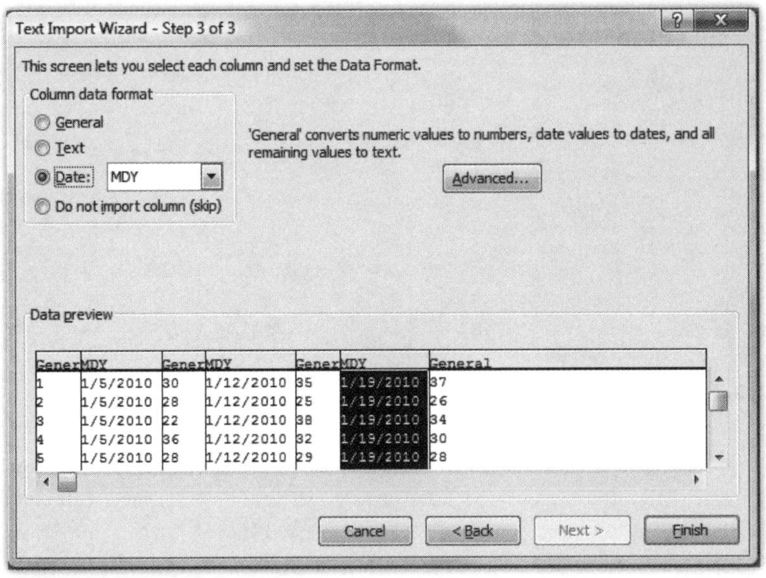

Figure 10.4 Step 3 of the Text Import Wizard.

We are now done with the *Text Import Wizard*; the text data should now be imported into Excel columns, as shown in Figure 10.5.

	A	B	C	D	E	F	G
1	1	1/5/2010	30	1/12/2010	35	1/19/2010	37
2	2	1/5/2010	28	1/12/2010	25	1/19/2010	26
3	3	1/5/2010	22	1/12/2010	38	1/19/2010	34
4	4	1/5/2010	36	1/12/2010	32	1/19/2010	30
5	5	1/5/2010	28	1/12/2010	29	1/19/2010	28
6	6	1/5/2010	34	1/12/2010	31	1/19/2010	33
7	7	1/5/2010	25	1/12/2010	28	1/19/2010	22
8	8	1/5/2010	23	1/12/2010	25	1/19/2010	24
9	9	1/5/2010	35	1/12/2010	37	1/19/2010	36
10	10	1/5/2010	29	1/12/2010	35	1/19/2010	37

Figure 10.5 The text file data imported into Excel columns.

The employer can now use the Excel AVERAGE function to compute the averages that she was looking for (per employee and per date). She can also organize her data by adding column headings and other formatting (see Figure 10.6).

	A	B	C	D	E	F	G	H	I
1	EmployeeID	Date 1	Hours 1	Date 2	Hours 2	Date 3	Hours 3		Average Hours
2	1	1/5/2010	30	1/12/2010	35	1/19/2010	37		34.00
3	2	1/5/2010	28	1/12/2010	25	1/19/2010	26		26.33
4	3	1/5/2010	22	1/12/2010	38	1/19/2010	34		31.33
5	4	1/5/2010	36	1/12/2010	32	1/19/2010	30		32.67
6	5	1/5/2010	28	1/12/2010	29	1/19/2010	28		28.33
7	6	1/5/2010	34	1/12/2010	31	1/19/2010	33		32.67
8	7	1/5/2010	25	1/12/2010	28	1/19/2010	22		25.00
9	8	1/5/2010	23	1/12/2010	25	1/19/2010	24		24.00
10	9	1/5/2010	35	1/12/2010	37	1/19/2010	36		36.00
11	10	1/5/2010	29	1/12/2010	35	1/19/2010	37		33.67
12									
13		Average Hours	29		31.5		30.7		

Figure 10.6 The final organized data with average calculations.

10.2.2 Web Addresses

In order to import data from a webpage, we use the *Data > Get External Data > From Web* command on the Ribbon. In the *New Web Query* dialog box that appears, we can enter the web address that contains the data we want to import. There will then be a preview of this website in the window. We can select what sections of data we want to import; that is, we may not want to import everything being displayed on the webpage. The possible data sections will be marked by small arrows. Select the arrows for all the data we are interested in and then click *Import.* Excel will prompt us to select a cell in the worksheet for where we want to place this imported data. Excel will import the data and separate it into columns, as done on the webpage. There is no prompt for how to separate this data, but Excel usually makes a good guess. We can always reorganize our data in the spreadsheet, if desired.

Let's consider an example. The following web address contains current stock quotes (see Figure 10.7) reported by CNN:

http://money.cnn.com/

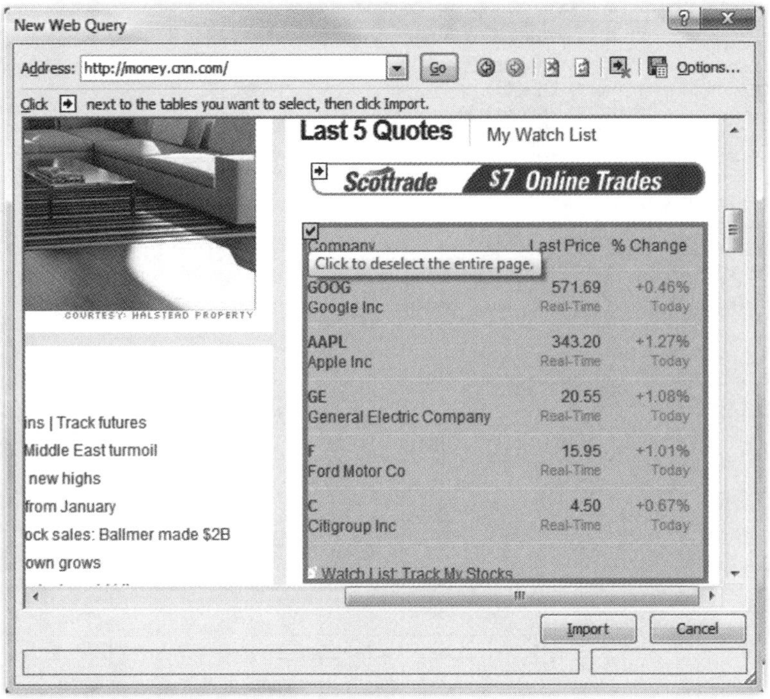

Figure 10.7 Web query for the CNN Money information.

Suppose we are interested in maintaining a worksheet with this data in order to compare the values of different stocks, or to analyze how a possible portfolio of this stock is doing. To import this data, we first copy the web address of this page. Then, we click on the *Data > Get External Data > From Web* command on the Ribbon and simply paste the web address into the "Address" window of the *New Web Query* dialog box (see Figure 10.7).

In the above webpage preview, we can see the small arrows in yellow boxes that Excel has placed on different sections of data. Since we are only interested in the actual stock data for a group of companies, we select the arrow next to "Company." Notice as we place our cursor on this arrow that a square appears around the entire section of data associated with that arrow. After we click the arrow, it will become a check mark, indicating that we wish to import this data. Now that we are done selecting data, we click *Import*. Finally, we must specify where in the worksheet we would like to paste the data (see Figure 10.8).

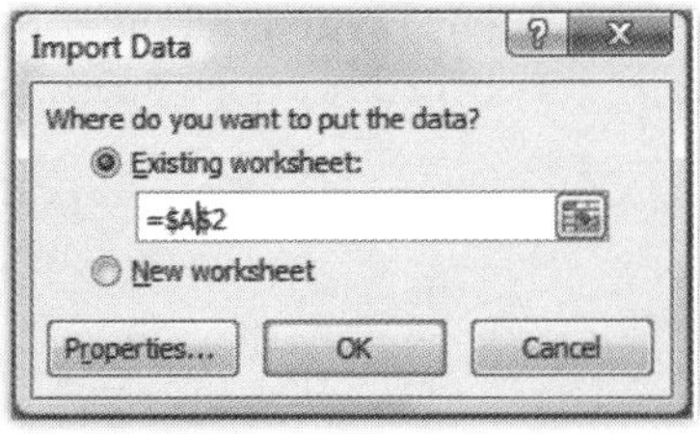

Figure 10.8 Location of the imported data.

The data has now been transferred to the worksheet, as seen in Figure 10.9. Excel has also formed appropriate columns.

	A	B	C
1			
2	Company	Last Price	% Change
3	GOOG	569.09	-3.16%
4	Google Inc	Close	Today
5	AAPL	338.89	-0.67%
6	Apple Inc	Close	Today
7	GE	20.33	-0.97%
8	General Electric	Close	Today
9	F	15.79	1.54%
10	Ford Motor Co	Close	Today
11	C	4.47	0.90%
12	Citigroup Inc	Close	Today

Figure 10.9 Imported data is separated into columns.

We can now further format this data for future analysis. We have added a title to the table and left a place to enter the date and time when this query was made (see Figure 10.10). We may then keep a record of "Last Price" values, or others, as we continue to repeat this query in the future. To repeat a query, we use the *Refresh All* command from the *Data > Connection* group of the Ribbon. Simply select the range of queried data in the worksheet and select *Refresh All > Refresh* from the drop-down menu. Any changes on the webpage will be reflected on the worksheet.

	A	B	C
1	**CNN Reporting**		
2	**Date:**	**Time:**	
3	Company	**Last Price**	**% Change**
4	GOOG	$571.63	0.45%
5	**Google Inc**	Real-Time	Today
6	AAPL	$342.07	0.94%
7	**Apple Inc**	Real-Time	Today
8	GE	$20.52	0.93%
9	**General Electric Company**	Real-Time	Today
10	F	$15.89	0.63%
11	**Ford Motor Co**	Real-Time	Today
12	C	$4.49	0.45%
13	**Citigroup Inc**	Real-Time	Today

Figure 10.10 The web data is organized for analysis.

10.2.3 Databases

You can import data that is stored in an external database into Excel. For example, to import data from an Access database, we click on the *Data > Get External Data > From Access* command on the Ribbon. From here we can browse to find a database file with which we want to work. Excel can also import data from databases in formats such as dBase, FoxPro, SQL Server, etc. To import data from these databases we click on the *Data > Get External Data > From Other Sources* command on the Ribbon.

To illustrate how we import a Microsoft Access database in Excel, we will use a previously created database. This database is titled *Books* and has a short record of a number of books. The fields are: *ISBN, Title, Author,* and *Copyright Year.* To work with this data in Excel, we prepare a new worksheet. First, we click on the *Data > Get External Data > From Access* command on the Ribbon; the Select Data dialog box appears. You use this dialog box to locate the Access file, and click *Ok*. Next, the *Import Data* window in Figure 10.11 will appear.

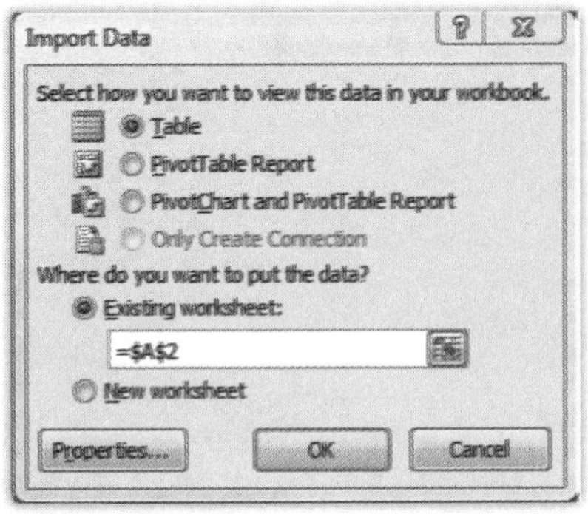

Figure 10.11 To import data, choose *Data > Get External Data > From Access* command on the Ribbon and specify where to place the data.

The *Import Data* window gives you options to display the data in the workbook. We select the *Table* option. We next specify where we want the imported data to be located. In this case, we choose a cell in the worksheet, say *A2*, and press *OK*. The imported data will then be copied to the worksheet, as illustrated in Figure 10.12. Notice that the changes you make to this data in Excel cannot be sent back to the original Access database. However, you can update the Excel table to reflect changes made in the Access database by selecting the table and clicking on *Data > Connections > Refresh All* command of the Ribbon.

As you should have realized, Excel provides powerful data analysis and presentation tools. Excel also supports storing more than one million rows of data. However, storing a large database in Excel will slow your application. A good practice is to maintain your data on external databases, and import into Excel only a subset of this data which you need to analyze. You can simply accomplish this by performing a query to load a subset of the data into your Excel worksheet. A ***query*** is a search for a particular set of data from the database; it is similar to filtering.

	A	B	C	D
1				
2	ISBN	Title	Author	Copyright Year
3	1238765645	Programming in VBA	JB White	2010
4	1238765841	Working with Excel	LK Grey	2005
5	1238781253	Engineering Applications	RS Johnson	2010
6	1245765645	Algorithm Design	OB Myers	2007
7	1267765645	Modeling with C++	JB White	2007
8	1458765645	Advances in Optimization	PM Willson	2010
9	1258765646	Programming with C	JB White	2009
10				

Figure 10.12 The data has now been imported into the worksheet in Excel.

For example, we want to create a report that lists the copyright year and title of all books written by JB White. To do this, on the Ribbon, we click on *Data > Get External Data > From Other Sources*. In the drop-down menu that appears we select *From Microsoft Query*. We will then see the dialog box in Figure 10.13, which configures the data source for the query. Since we are using a database in Microsoft Access, the only change we need to make here is to select *MS Access Database* from the list of *Databases*; then we press *OK*.

The next window will provide a list of files that match this data source type (see Figure 10.14). In the list, we should find the file, *Books.accdb*; we select it and press *OK*. Now, we begin to define our query.

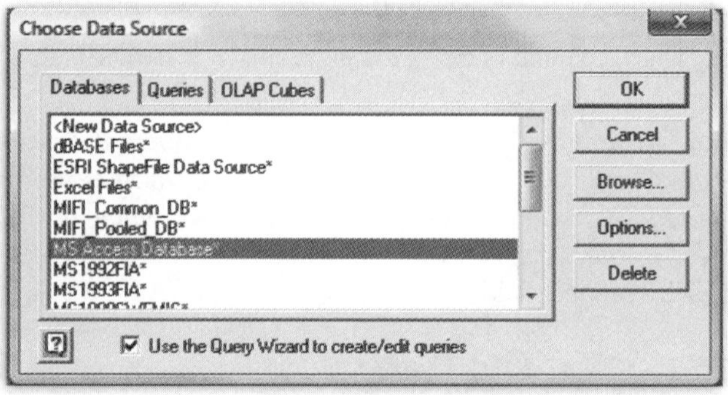

Figure 10.13 To choose a data source, we need to specify the type of database we are using.

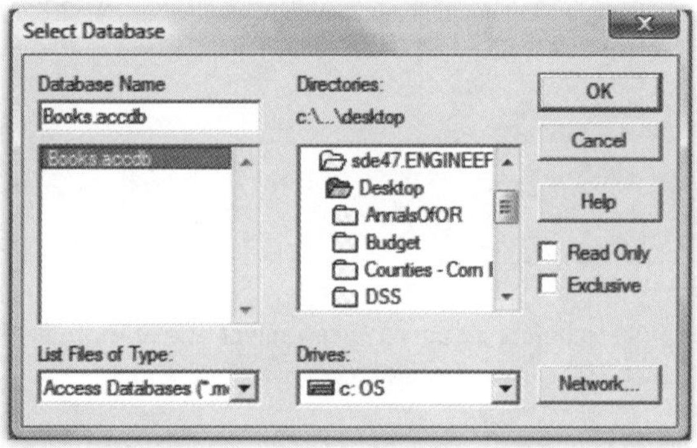

Figure 10.14 Selecting *Books.accdb* from the list of files that match our data source.

The first step in defining our query is to specify which columns of data that we want to appear in our final table. We click the + sign next to the table name, *tblBooks*, to see a list of all the column titles. In Figure 10.15, we selected the *Title*, *Author*, and *Copyright Year* columns. We click *Next* to arrive at the next step.

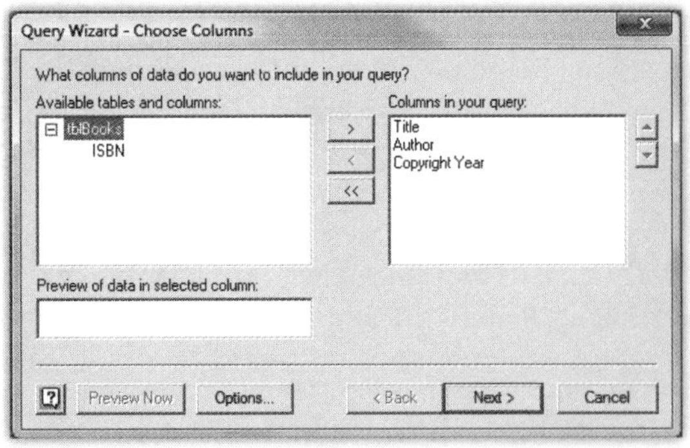

Figure 10.15 Selecting which columns of data we want to appear in our final table.

Now, we specify how we want to filter this data. This is the query definition (see Figure 10.16). First, we select the column title, or field, by which we want to filter our data. Then, we select an equality type and a value from that field. In this case, we decide to filter the data by selecting all entries whose *Author* is *equal to JB White* and click *Next*. Note that we can have multiple filters among each available field.

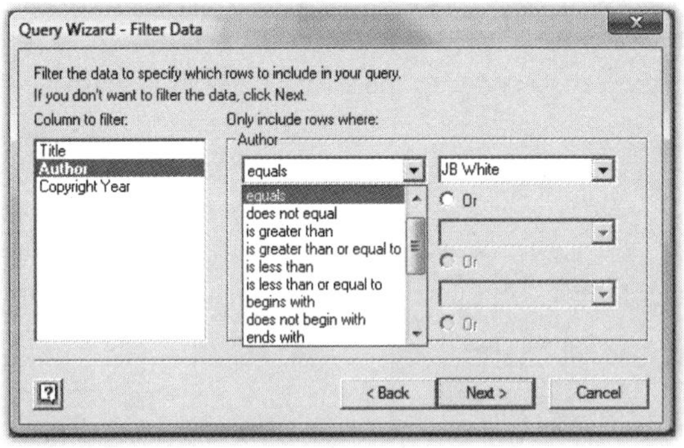

Figure 10.16 Filtering data is how to define a query. We can select one or more fields, equality and a value from the field(s) by which we want to filter the data.

Then, it is necessary that we choose how to sort the data in the final table (see Figure 10.17). We have decided to sort by the *Copyright Year* in *Ascending Order*. Again, note that we can have multiple sorts; Section 10.4.1 presents an example of multiple sorting.

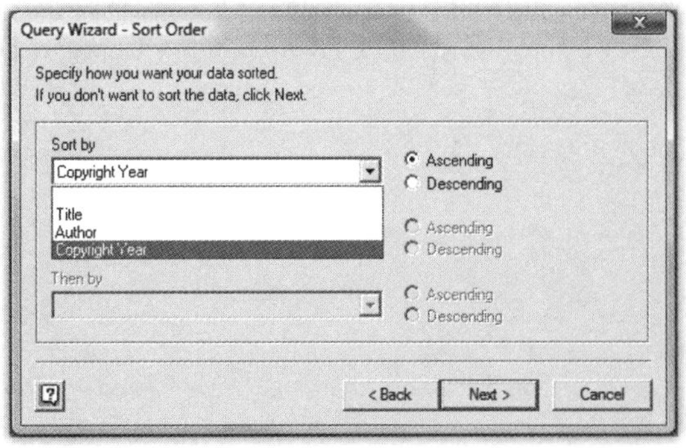

Figure 10.17 Specifying how to sort the data in the final table.

After pressing *Next*, we arrive at the last step in creating our query. This step requires us to decide whether we want to place the data from this query in Excel, or view it in its original data source. We will view our data in Excel (see Figure 10.18). To view the final table, we click *Finish*.

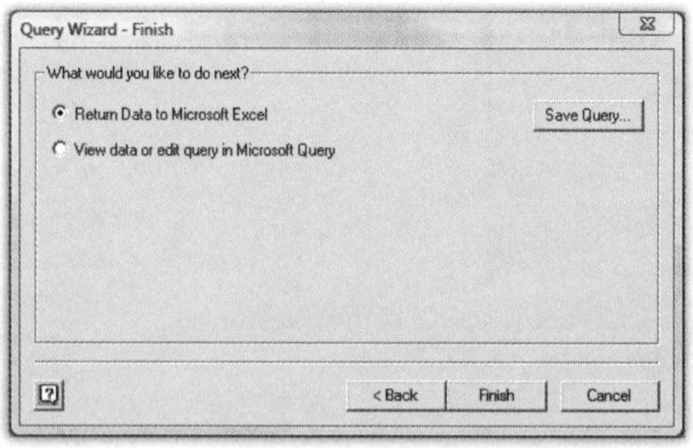

Figure 10.18 Selecting to view the results of the query in Excel.

After we pick a place in our worksheet to situate the table, the result of the query is transferred to Excel (refer to Figure 10.19). Notice here that only the books written by JB White are shown in the table and that all of the books are sorted in an ascending order by *Copyright Year.*

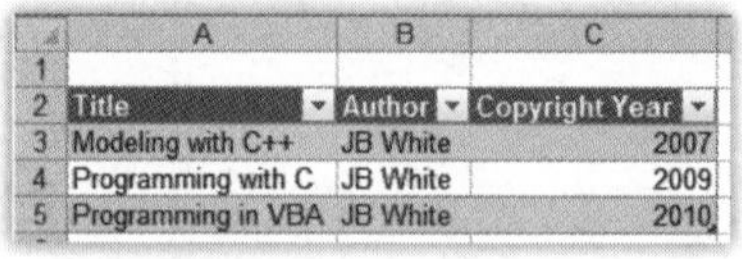

	A	B	C
1			
2	Title	Author	Copyright Year
3	Modeling with C++	JB White	2007
4	Programming with C	JB White	2009
5	Programming in VBA	JB White	2010

Figure 10.19 Formatting data in a table to use in our worksheet.

Databases constitute an important part of Excel applications. Involving VBA code in database applications extends our options in organizing our data.

10.3 *Creating Pivot Tables from External Data*

When we discussed Pivot Tables in Chapter 6, we mentioned that we can use data not only in our spreadsheet, but also from an external data source to create a pivot table. In the first step of the Pivot Table dialog box, we select the type of data that we want to use (see Figure 10.20). To use external data, select *Use an external data source* from the list of options. In this window we also select a location for the pivot table in the existing worksheet, and click *Choose Connection to specify where the actual data is saved.*

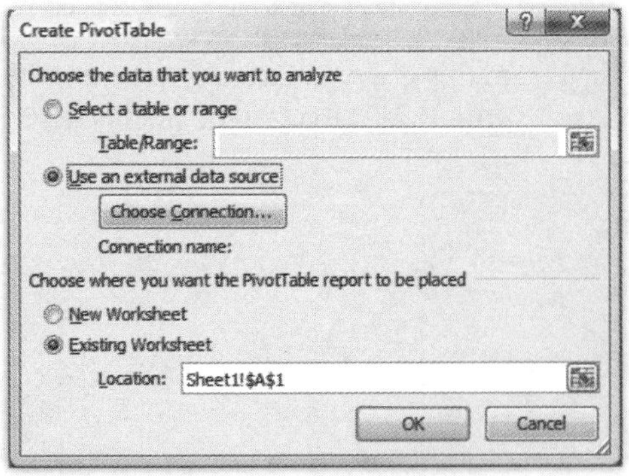

Figure 10.20 Choosing external data as the source of the pivot table.

We will then be prompted to select the actual data (see Figure 10.21). If our data file is not listed on the existing connections window, we click on the *Browse for More* to specify the location of our data, and then click *Open*.

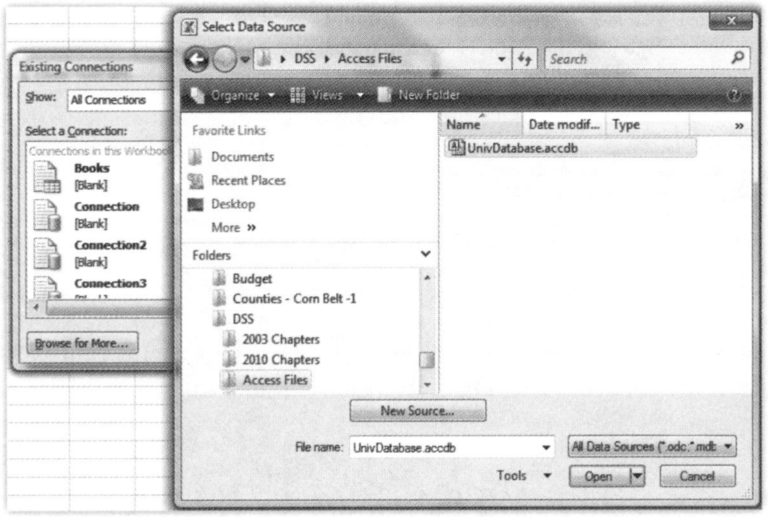

Figure 10.21 Select the data source for the pivot table.

We will use some example data from a Microsoft Access database file. We are now prompted to select one of the existing tables and queries of the selected database (see Figure 10.22).

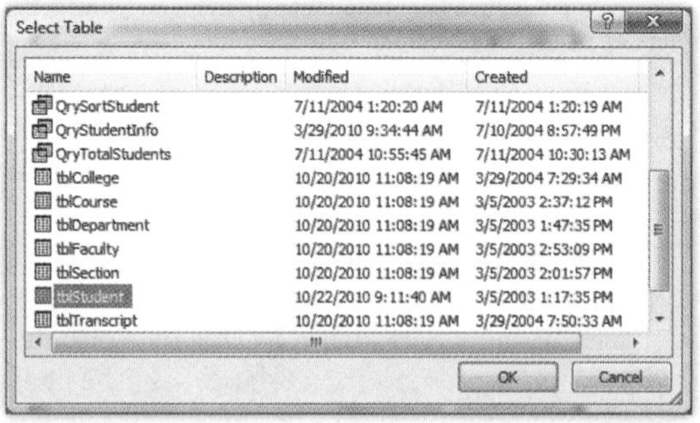

Figure 10.22 Selecting the MS Access Database data type.

In this example database, we have several tables and queries of data for a University System Database. Let's look at the data in the Student Table to make an analysis of the number of students by gender and seniority in each department by using a pivot table. We select the Student Table from the *Select Table* dialog box and click *OK*. An empty pivot table is created (see Figure 10.23). We now can use the *PivotTable Field List* to build our table.

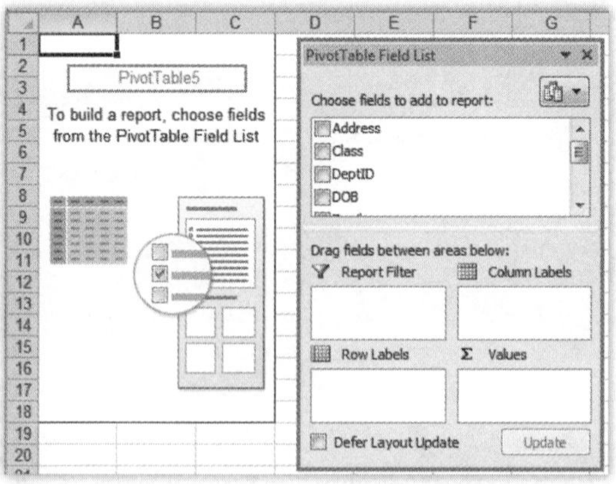

Figure 10.23 Use the PivotTable Field List to build the pivot table.

Just as we did in Chapter 6, we specify the layout and location of the pivot table and other options. Figure 10.24 presents the final pivot table. We can see the number of students by seniority and by gender for each department. We use the *Refresh All* command to update changes that may been made to the external database.

	A	B	C	D	E	F	G	H
1	Count of StudentID	Column Labels						
2	Row Labels	CAHER	CAPP	CISE	ECE	ISE	PHY	Grand Total
3	F	44	47	42	33	32		198
4	Freshman	3	3	2	5	2		15
5	Graduate	20	12	20	12	11		75
6	Junior	9	12	9	7	7		44
7	Senior	7	15	7	3	9		41
8	Sophomore	5	5	4	6	3		23
9	M	48	68	73	54	58	1	302
10	Freshman	2	9	9	4	4		28
11	Graduate	18	18	18	21	17	1	93
12	Junior	14	22	16	6	16		74
13	Senior	8	13	17	12	9		59
14	Sophomore	6	6	13	11	12		48
15	(blank)		1	1				2
16	(blank)		1	1				2
17	Grand Total	92	116	116	87	90	1	502

Figure 10.24 The final pivot table with the external data.

10.4 *Using Excel as a Database*

Excel defines any well-defined table of items grouped by similar categories as a *database*. A database can be defined more generally as a storage area of multiple entities, their attributes, and their relationships. Technically, what Excel defines as a database is really a database table; we will however use the term *database* for the remainder of this chapter. Let us consider an example of a database in Excel. A teaching assistant for a course may develop a detailed table of student records; he could consider this table a database. In this database, he can store the students' names, homework grades, exam scores, and attendance, and he can also calculate their class average in the same table (see Figure 10.25). The commands listed in the *Data* tab of Ribbon provide several simple functions that can be performed on Excel databases.

10.4.1 Sorting

The first database function we will discuss is ***sorting***. To sort means to order all entries in a database by a particular ***field***; a field is a category name. (In Figure 10.25, each column heading of the table is a database field name.) In the example shown in Figure 10.25, we see that the names of the students are in no particular order. To place the names in alphabetical order, we can sort the entire database by the field of *Student Name*.

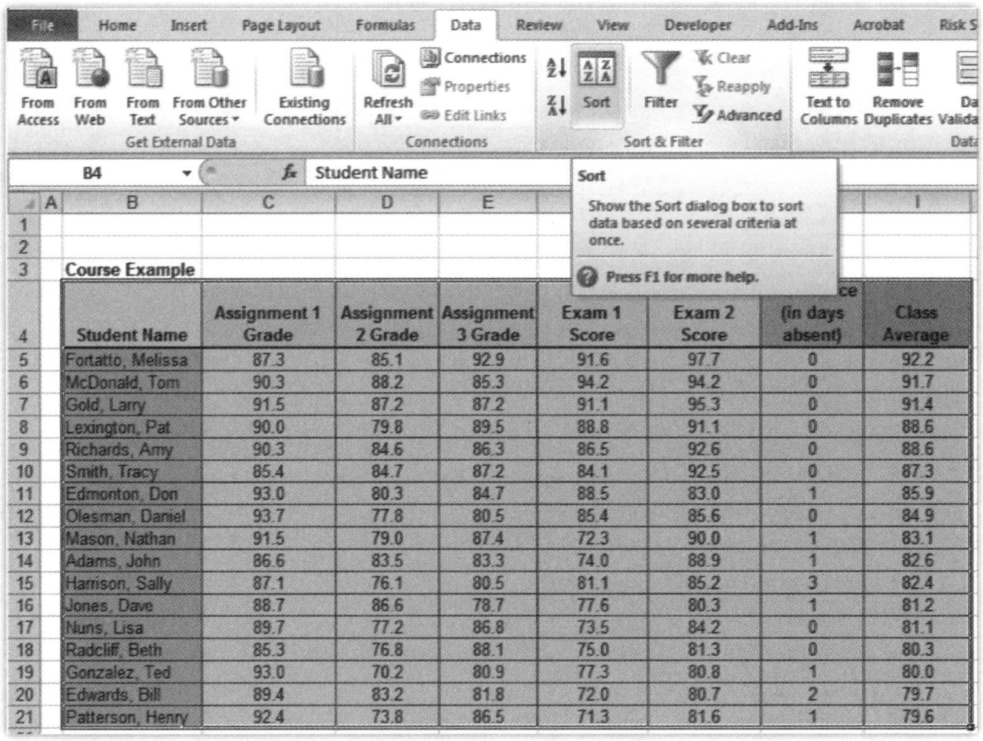

Figure 10.25 This database of student records for a course contains eight fields.

To do so, we highlight the entire database, including the field names; this is the range *B4:I21*. Next, we click on the *Data > Sort & Filter > Sort* command on the Ribbon. We will then see the Sort dialog box shown in Figure 10.26.

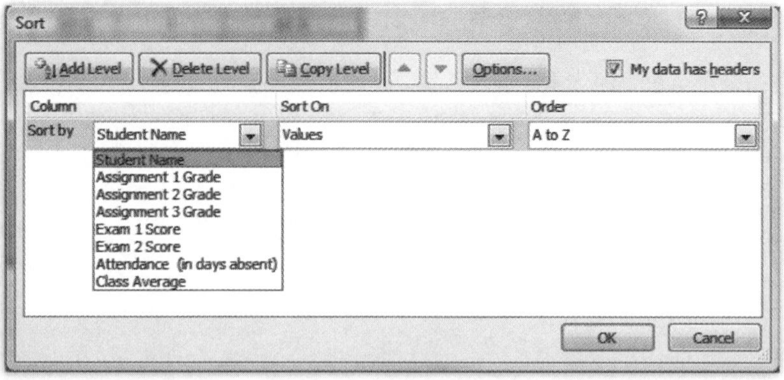

Figure 10.26 The Sort dialog box allows us to choose a column name by which to sort, an attribute to sort on, and a sorting order.

We can select any field name to sort by; we have chosen *Student Name* in the *A to Z* (Ascending) *Order*. We can see the results of this sort in Figure 10.27.

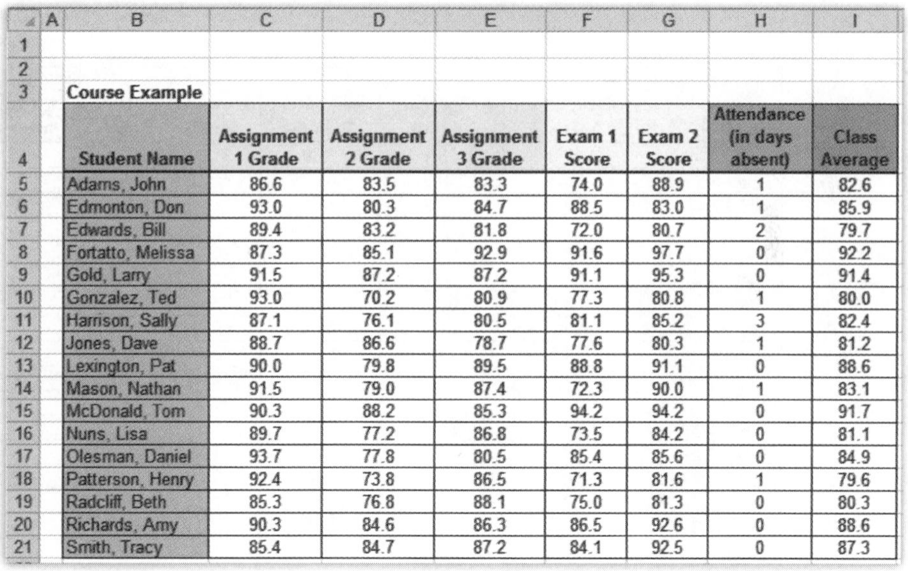

	A	B	C	D	E	F	G	H	I
1									
2									
3		Course Example							
4		Student Name	Assignment 1 Grade	Assignment 2 Grade	Assignment 3 Grade	Exam 1 Score	Exam 2 Score	Attendance (in days absent)	Class Average
5		Adams, John	86.6	83.5	83.3	74.0	88.9	1	82.6
6		Edmonton, Don	93.0	80.3	84.7	88.5	83.0	1	85.9
7		Edwards, Bill	89.4	83.2	81.8	72.0	80.7	2	79.7
8		Fortatto, Melissa	87.3	85.1	92.9	91.6	97.7	0	92.2
9		Gold, Larry	91.5	87.2	87.2	91.1	95.3	0	91.4
10		Gonzalez, Ted	93.0	70.2	80.9	77.3	80.8	1	80.0
11		Harrison, Sally	87.1	76.1	80.5	81.1	85.2	3	82.4
12		Jones, Dave	88.7	86.6	78.7	77.6	80.3	1	81.2
13		Lexington, Pat	90.0	79.8	89.5	88.8	91.1	0	88.6
14		Mason, Nathan	91.5	79.0	87.4	72.3	90.0	1	83.1
15		McDonald, Tom	90.3	88.2	85.3	94.2	94.2	0	91.7
16		Nuns, Lisa	89.7	77.2	86.8	73.5	84.2	0	81.1
17		Olesman, Daniel	93.7	77.8	80.5	85.4	85.6	0	84.9
18		Patterson, Henry	92.4	73.8	86.5	71.3	81.6	1	79.6
19		Radcliff, Beth	85.3	76.8	88.1	75.0	81.3	0	80.3
20		Richards, Amy	90.3	84.6	86.3	86.5	92.6	0	88.6
21		Smith, Tracy	85.4	84.7	87.2	84.1	92.5	0	87.3

Figure 10.27 The database is now sorted in alphabetical order by *Student Names*.

Note also that in the *Sort* dialog box, we can sort by more than one field at a time. Click on *Add Level* button to insert another set of search controls. For example, in Figure 10.28, we have sorted by *Class Average* in *Descending Order* and then by *Student Name* in *Ascending Order*. Observe that the values for *Class Average* in cells *I8* and *I9* are the same (*88.6*) and the student names are listed alphabetically by last name (*Lexington* and *Richards*).

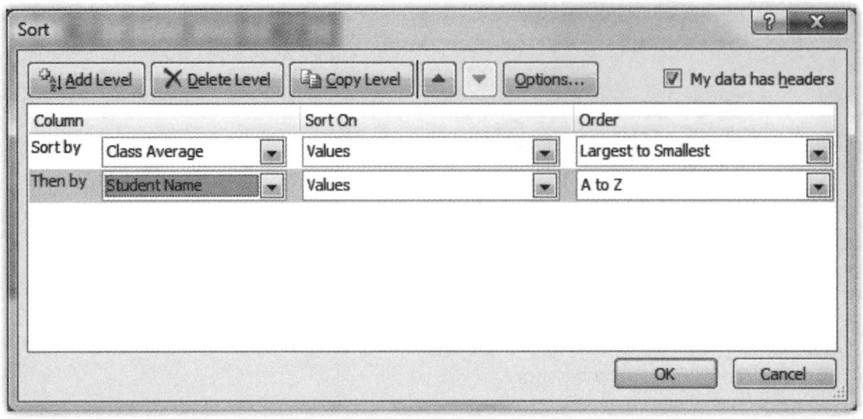

(a)

Course Example

	Student Name	Assignment 1 Grade	Assignment 2 Grade	Assignment 3 Grade	Exam 1 Score	Exam 2 Score	Attendance (in days absent)	Class Average
5	Fortatto, Melissa	87.3	85.1	92.9	91.6	97.7	0	92.2
6	McDonald, Tom	90.3	88.2	85.3	94.2	94.2	0	91.7
7	Gold, Larry	91.5	87.2	87.2	91.1	95.3	0	91.4
8	Lexington, Pat	90.0	79.8	89.5	88.8	91.1	0	88.6
9	Richards, Amy	90.3	84.6	86.3	86.5	92.6	0	88.6
10	Smith, Tracy	85.4	84.7	87.2	84.1	92.5	0	87.3
11	Edmonton, Don	93.0	80.3	84.7	88.5	83.0	1	85.9
12	Olesman, Daniel	93.7	77.8	80.5	85.4	85.6	0	84.9
13	Mason, Nathan	91.5	79.0	87.4	72.3	90.0	1	83.1
14	Adams, John	86.6	83.5	83.3	74.0	88.9	1	82.6
15	Harrison, Sally	87.1	76.1	80.5	81.1	85.2	3	82.4
16	Jones, Dave	88.7	86.6	78.7	77.6	80.3	1	81.2
17	Nuns, Lisa	89.7	77.2	86.8	73.5	84.2	0	81.1
18	Radcliff, Beth	85.3	76.8	88.1	75.0	81.3	0	80.3
19	Gonzalez, Ted	93.0	70.2	80.9	77.3	80.8	1	80.0
20	Edwards, Bill	89.4	83.2	81.8	72.0	80.7	2	79.7
21	Patterson, Henry	92.4	73.8	86.5	71.3	81.6	1	79.6

(b)

Figure 10.28 (a) First sort by *Class Average* from Largest to Smallest and then by *Student Name* using the *A to Z Order*. (b) The database is now sorted.

There is one more option to specify in the *Sort* window; this is the *My data has headers* option. It simply informs Excel whether or not the field names are already specified by column names in a *header row*. If there is a *header row*, which we have marked in the above example, then the field names appear in a list as column titles. If, however, we uncheck the *My data has headers* checkbox, there would only be column names in the field list (see Figure 10.29).

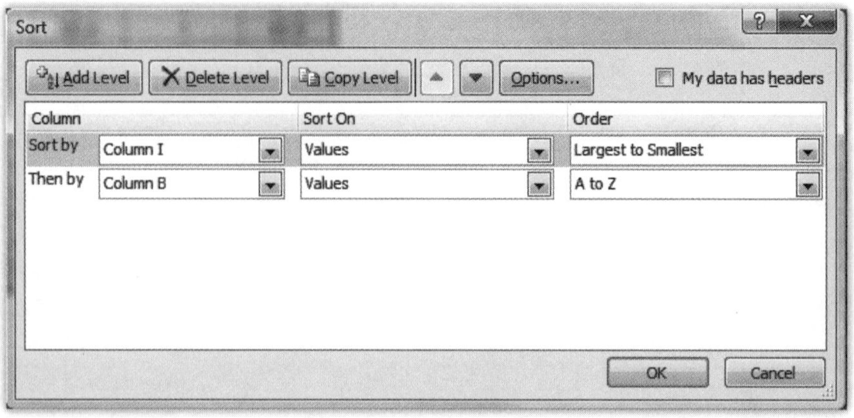

Figure 10.29 If we uncheck *My data has headers* checkbox, the Excel column names are used as field names instead of as column titles in the database.

We can also sort within a row. To do this, we click the *Options* button on the Sort dialog box. The window shown in Figure 10.30 appears. We can also select whether our data is *Case Sensitive* or not. To sort within a row, we will need to change the *Orientation* option from "top to bottom" to "left to right."

Figure 10.30 Sort Options include sorting from top to bottom or left to right.

Once we press *OK* and return to the main Sort dialog box, we notice that the field lists show row numbers instead of column numbers (see Figure 10.31). These numbers refer to the row numbering on the spreadsheet; they are not relevant to our table.

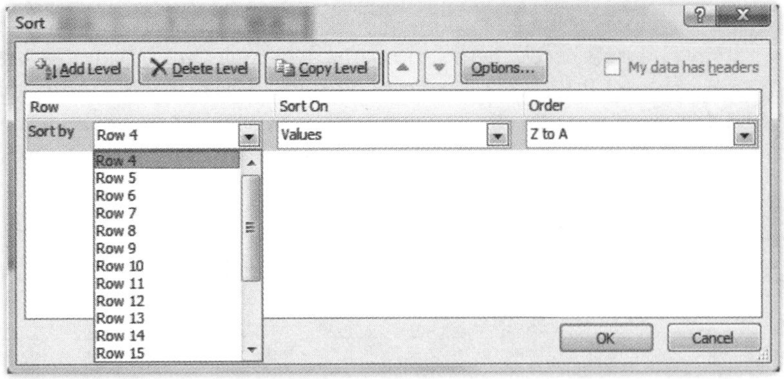

Figure 10.31 The fields are now listed by row number.

Using the student data, let's choose row 4 to sort by since it has the titles of the different grades. If we sort by *Row 4* in *Z to A* order, we will see the table shown in Figure 10.32.

	A	B	C	D	E	F	G	H	I
1									
2									
3		**Course Example**							
4		**Student Name**	**Exam 2 Score**	**Exam 1 Score**	**Class Average**	**Attendance (in days absent)**	**Assignment 3 Grade**	**Assignment 2 Grade**	**Assignment 1 Grade**
5		Fortatto, Melissa	97.7	91.6	92.2	0	92.9	85.1	87.3
6		McDonald, Tom	94.2	94.2	91.7	0	85.3	88.2	90.3
7		Gold, Larry	95.3	91.1	91.4	0	87.2	87.2	91.5
8		Lexington, Pat	91.1	88.8	88.6	0	89.5	79.8	90.0
9		Richards, Amy	92.6	86.5	88.6	0	86.3	84.6	90.3
10		Smith, Tracy	92.5	84.1	87.3	0	87.2	84.7	85.4
11		Edmonton, Don	83.0	88.5	85.9	1	84.7	80.3	93.0
12		Olesman, Daniel	85.6	85.4	84.9	0	80.5	77.8	93.7
13		Mason, Nathan	90.0	72.3	83.1	1	87.4	79.0	91.5
14		Adams, John	88.9	74.0	82.6	1	83.3	83.5	86.6
15		Harrison, Sally	85.2	81.1	82.4	3	80.5	76.1	87.1
16		Jones, Dave	80.3	77.6	81.2	1	78.7	86.6	88.7
17		Nuns, Lisa	84.2	73.5	81.1	0	86.8	77.2	89.7
18		Radcliff, Beth	81.3	75.0	80.3	0	88.1	76.8	85.3
19		Gonzalez, Ted	80.8	77.3	80.0	1	80.9	70.2	93.0
20		Edwards, Bill	80.7	72.0	79.7	2	81.8	83.2	89.4
21		Patterson, Henry	81.6	71.3	79.6	1	86.5	73.8	92.4

Figure 10.32 The table is now sorted by row 4.

Sorting is a useful database function as it allows us to organize our data in multiple ways. It becomes even more valuable as the size of our database grows. It can also function as a search tool. For example, it can help us find an item name in an alphabetical listing.

Summary

Sorting: Ordering all entries in a database by a particular field or fields.

Field: Attributes which describe an entity

10.4.2 Filtering

The next database function we will discuss is ***filtering***. Filtering differs from sorting in that it selects a specified set of data from the database instead of ordering the entire database. Filtering allows us to select rows in a database by specifying a specific value for one or more fields. For example, referring to Figure 10.25, instead of ordering all of the data by sorting by *Class Average*, we could select to view only the row items that have a *Class Average* equal to *88.6*. To do so, we begin by highlighting the entire database, including column titles, cells *B4:I21*. Then, we click on the *Data > Sort & Filter > Filter* command on the Ribbon. This selection will transform the database by adding drop-down arrows to each field (see Figure 10.33).

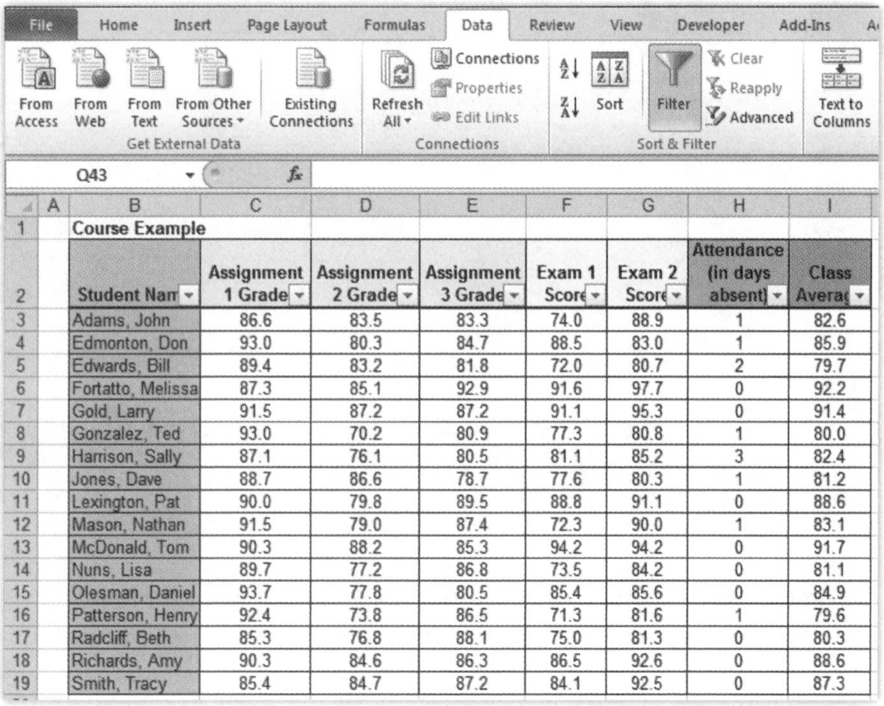

Student Name	Assignment 1 Grade	Assignment 2 Grade	Assignment 3 Grade	Exam 1 Score	Exam 2 Score	Attendance (in days absent)	Class Average
Adams, John	86.6	83.5	83.3	74.0	88.9	1	82.6
Edmonton, Don	93.0	80.3	84.7	88.5	83.0	1	85.9
Edwards, Bill	89.4	83.2	81.8	72.0	80.7	2	79.7
Fortatto, Melissa	87.3	85.1	92.9	91.6	97.7	0	92.2
Gold, Larry	91.5	87.2	87.2	91.1	95.3	0	91.4
Gonzalez, Ted	93.0	70.2	80.9	77.3	80.8	1	80.0
Harrison, Sally	87.1	76.1	80.5	81.1	85.2	3	82.4
Jones, Dave	88.7	86.6	78.7	77.6	80.3	1	81.2
Lexington, Pat	90.0	79.8	89.5	88.8	91.1	0	88.6
Mason, Nathan	91.5	79.0	87.4	72.3	90.0	1	83.1
McDonald, Tom	90.3	88.2	85.3	94.2	94.2	0	91.7
Nuns, Lisa	89.7	77.2	86.8	73.5	84.2	0	81.1
Olesman, Daniel	93.7	77.8	80.5	85.4	85.6	0	84.9
Patterson, Henry	92.4	73.8	86.5	71.3	81.6	1	79.6
Radcliff, Beth	85.3	76.8	88.1	75.0	81.3	0	80.3
Richards, Amy	90.3	84.6	86.3	86.5	92.6	0	88.6
Smith, Tracy	85.4	84.7	87.2	84.1	92.5	0	87.3

Figure 10.33 The database is filtered with selection options for each field.

We then select the arrow attached to the *Class Average* field. Here, we select a particular data value, say *88.6*, that will reconstruct the database so that it only displays the rows whose *Class Average* entries match the value chosen (see Figure 10.34). We can again display the entire database by clicking on the option arrow of *Class Average* and selecting the *Select All* checkbox.

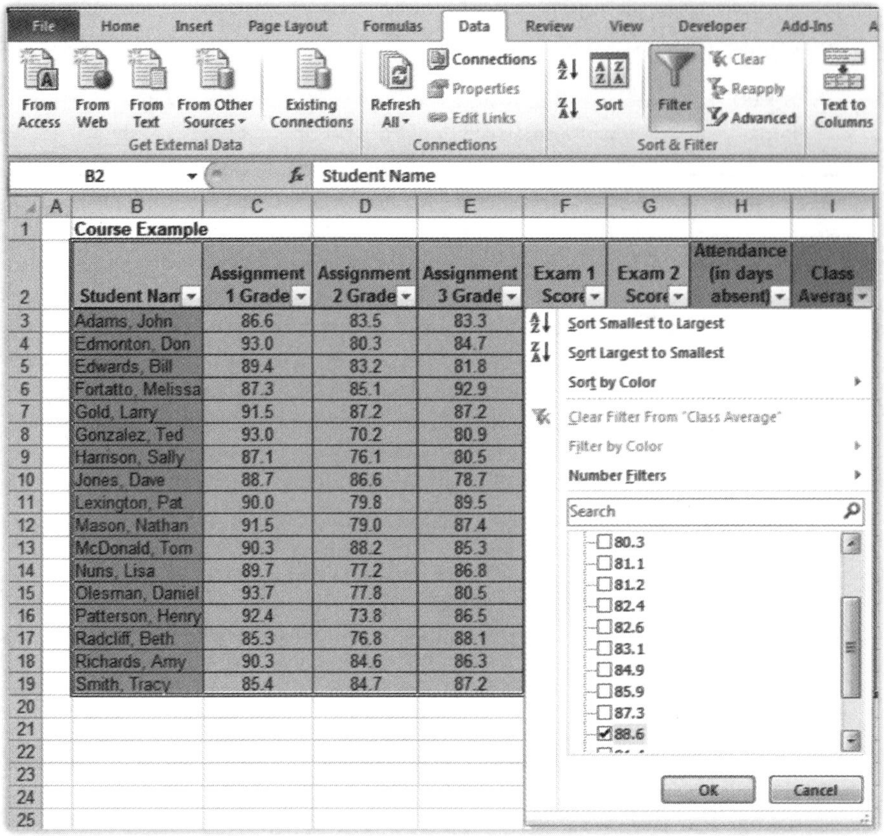

(a)

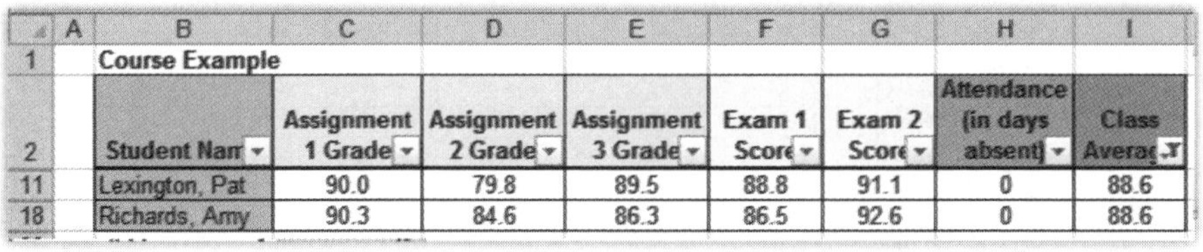

(b)

Figure 10.34 (a) Selecting the drop-down list of values in the *Class Average* field. (b) The database is filtered to only show data entries with a *Class Average* equal to *88.6*.

On the filtered field drop-down menu, upon the selection of the *Number Filters* option, a flyout menu appears that presents a number of options we can use when filtering a database (see Figure 10.35). One of these options is *Top 10*. Selecting *Top 10* allows us to display 10 entries (or another specified amount) or 10 percent (or another specified percent) of the entries on the top or bottom of the database. In Figure 10.36, we chose to show the top 10 entries.

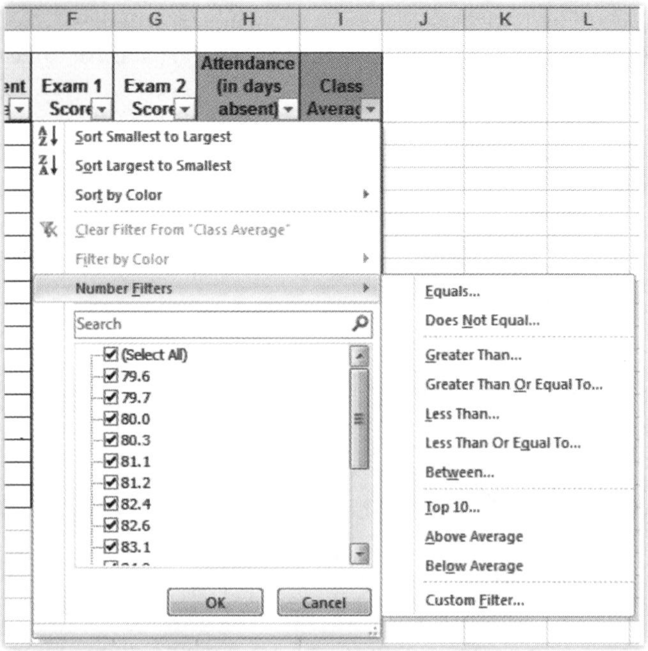

Figure 10.35 The *Number Filters* flyout menu lists a number of options to filter the data by.

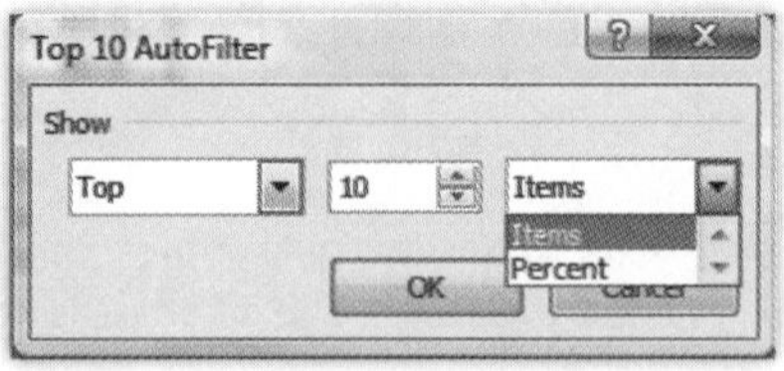

(a)

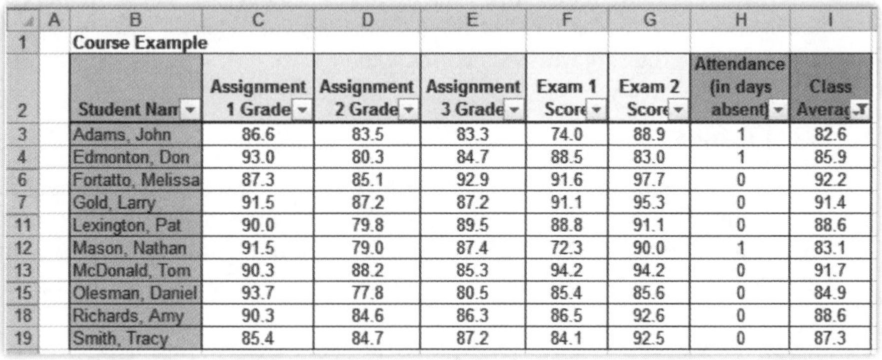

	A	B	C	D	E	F	G	H	I
1		Course Example							
2		Student Nam	Assignment 1 Grade	Assignment 2 Grade	Assignment 3 Grade	Exam 1 Score	Exam 2 Score	Attendance (in days absent)	Class Averag
3		Adams, John	86.6	83.5	83.3	74.0	88.9	1	82.6
4		Edmonton, Don	93.0	80.3	84.7	88.5	83.0	1	85.9
6		Fortatto, Melissa	87.3	85.1	92.9	91.6	97.7	0	92.2
7		Gold, Larry	91.5	87.2	87.2	91.1	95.3	0	91.4
11		Lexington, Pat	90.0	79.8	89.5	88.8	91.1	0	88.6
12		Mason, Nathan	91.5	79.0	87.4	72.3	90.0	1	83.1
13		McDonald, Tom	90.3	88.2	85.3	94.2	94.2	0	91.7
15		Olesman, Daniel	93.7	77.8	80.5	85.4	85.6	0	84.9
18		Richards, Amy	90.3	84.6	86.3	86.5	92.6	0	88.6
19		Smith, Tracy	85.4	84.7	87.2	84.1	92.5	0	87.3

(b)

Figure 10.36 Choosing the *Top 10* option from the flyout menu. (a) Specifying *Top* or *Bottom*, a certain number, and *items* or *percent*. (b) The database is updated to show only the number of entries specified.

Another option listed in the *Number Filters* flyout menu is the *Custom Filter* option which gives us a set of inequality specifications to use for filtering the data. We can choose to view entries whose field value is less than, greater than, or equal to a certain value. There is also an *And/Or* option which allows us to narrow our search to a particular range of values. For example, in Figure 10.37, we have specified to list only the entries whose *Class Average* is between the values *81.1* and *82.4*.

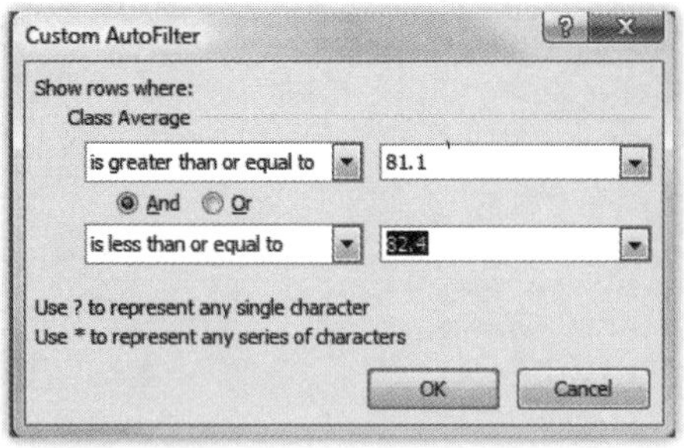

(a)

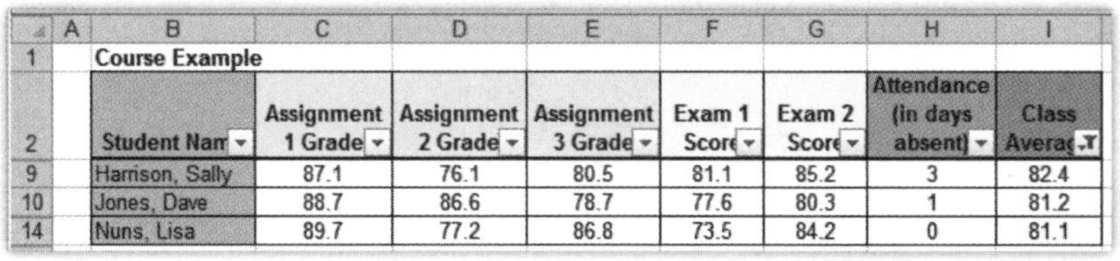

	A	B	C	D	E	F	G	H	I
1		Course Example							
2		Student Nam	Assignment 1 Grade	Assignment 2 Grade	Assignment 3 Grade	Exam 1 Score	Exam 2 Score	Attendance (in days absent)	Class Average
9		Harrison, Sally	87.1	76.1	80.5	81.1	85.2	3	82.4
10		Jones, Dave	88.7	86.6	78.7	77.6	80.3	1	81.2
14		Nuns, Lisa	89.7	77.2	86.8	73.5	84.2	0	81.1

(b)

Figure 10.37 Selecting the *Custom* option. (a) Specifying to show only entries with *Class Average* values greater than or equal to 81.1 and less than or equal to 82.4. (b) The database is updated to show only these entries.

Filtering is useful for locating specific data in a database. We can define a select group of data by choosing a field entry that they have in common. There are many applications of databases for which filtering will be a necessary tool.

10.4.3 Excel Tables

Excel is designed to store data in a table. A table is a range which contains data organized in rows and columns. Each row and column has a heading to describe the content of the table. The *Table* feature of Excel however makes the task of organizing and manipulating data in tables much easier. We will use the data presented in Figure 10.25 to discuss some features of *Tables*.

To create a table we select range B3:J20 and then click on the *Insert > Tables > Table* command on the Ribbon. The "official" Excel Table presented in Figure 10.38 is created. Upon selecting any cells of this table, the *Table Tools* contextual tab on the Ribbon is activated. Note that in this table, each column has a drop-down list which we use to sort and filter the data. At the lower-right corner of the table there is a small control that we can click and drug to extend the table horizontally or vertically.

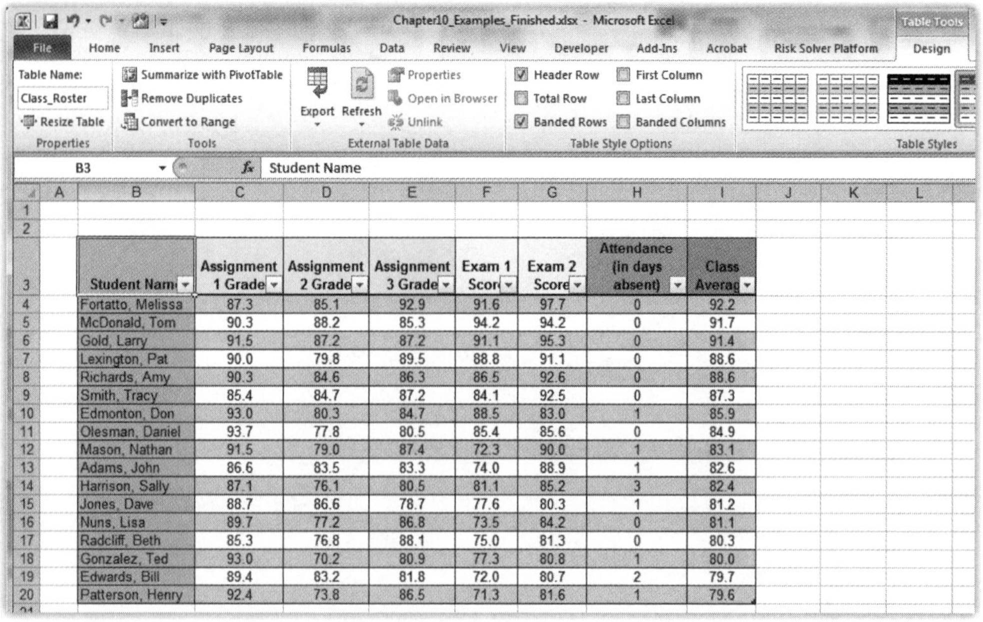

Student Nam	Assignment 1 Grade	Assignment 2 Grade	Assignment 3 Grade	Exam 1 Scor	Exam 2 Score	Attendance (in days absent)	Class Averag
Fortatto, Melissa	87.3	85.1	92.9	91.6	97.7	0	92.2
McDonald, Tom	90.3	88.2	85.3	94.2	94.2	0	91.7
Gold, Larry	91.5	87.2	87.2	91.1	95.3	0	91.4
Lexington, Pat	90.0	79.8	89.5	88.8	91.1	0	88.6
Richards, Amy	90.3	84.6	86.3	86.5	92.6	0	88.6
Smith, Tracy	85.4	84.7	87.2	84.1	92.5	0	87.3
Edmonton, Don	93.0	80.3	84.7	88.5	83.0	1	85.9
Olesman, Daniel	93.7	77.8	80.5	85.4	85.6	0	84.9
Mason, Nathan	91.5	79.0	87.4	72.3	90.0	1	83.1
Adams, John	86.6	83.5	83.3	74.0	88.9	1	82.6
Harrison, Sally	87.1	76.1	80.5	81.1	85.2	3	82.4
Jones, Dave	88.7	86.6	78.7	77.6	80.3	1	81.2
Nuns, Lisa	89.7	77.2	86.8	73.5	84.2	0	81.1
Radcliff, Beth	85.3	76.8	88.1	75.0	81.3	0	80.3
Gonzalez, Ted	93.0	70.2	80.9	77.3	80.8	1	80.0
Edwards, Bill	89.4	83.2	81.8	72.0	80.7	2	79.7
Patterson, Henry	92.4	73.8	86.5	71.3	81.6	1	79.6

Figure 10.38 An Excel Table.

Excel Tables make it easy adding columns and building calculated columns. For example, we want to calculate the average of the grades students made on their assignments. We start by typing the heading of this new column. Excel automatically creates and formats the new column using the same style we have chosen for the table itself. Next, we type the formula "***=AVERAGE (C4:E4)***" in cell J4. The formula is automatically propagated to all cells in this column (see Figure 10.39). Tables also support structured references. Rather than using cell references, formulas use table names and column headings. For example, the formula in cell J12 (see Figure 10.39) uses the table name "Class_Roster" and column names "Assignment 1 Grade" rather than cell names.

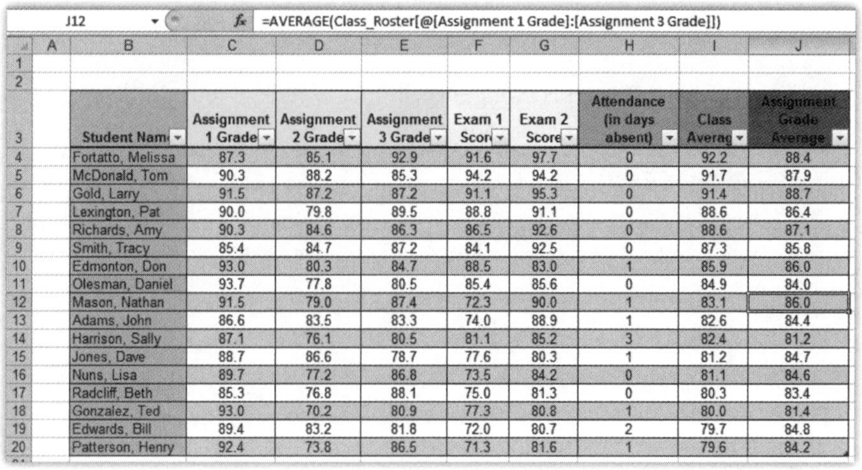

Student Nam	Assignment 1 Grade	Assignment 2 Grade	Assignment 3 Grade	Exam 1 Scor	Exam 2 Score	Attendance (in days absent)	Class Averag	Assignment Grade Average
Fortatto, Melissa	87.3	85.1	92.9	91.6	97.7	0	92.2	88.4
McDonald, Tom	90.3	88.2	85.3	94.2	94.2	0	91.7	87.9
Gold, Larry	91.5	87.2	87.2	91.1	95.3	0	91.4	88.7
Lexington, Pat	90.0	79.8	89.5	88.8	91.1	0	88.6	86.4
Richards, Amy	90.3	84.6	86.3	86.5	92.6	0	88.6	87.1
Smith, Tracy	85.4	84.7	87.2	84.1	92.5	0	87.3	85.8
Edmonton, Don	93.0	80.3	84.7	88.5	83.0	1	85.9	86.0
Olesman, Daniel	93.7	77.8	80.5	85.4	85.6	0	84.9	84.0
Mason, Nathan	91.5	79.0	87.4	72.3	90.0	1	83.1	86.0
Adams, John	86.6	83.5	83.3	74.0	88.9	1	82.6	84.4
Harrison, Sally	87.1	76.1	80.5	81.1	85.2	3	82.4	81.2
Jones, Dave	88.7	86.6	78.7	77.6	80.3	1	81.2	84.7
Nuns, Lisa	89.7	77.2	86.8	73.5	84.2	0	81.1	84.6
Radcliff, Beth	85.3	76.8	88.1	75.0	81.3	0	80.3	83.4
Gonzalez, Ted	93.0	70.2	80.9	77.3	80.8	1	80.0	81.4
Edwards, Bill	89.4	83.2	81.8	72.0	80.7	2	79.7	84.8
Patterson, Henry	92.4	73.8	86.5	71.3	81.6	1	79.6	84.2

Figure 10.39 An Excel Table makes it easy to add calculated fields, such as "Assignment Grade Average" column in this example.

When a table is created using data from multiple sources, duplicated rows or columns of data may be created. Tables make it easy to remove duplicates. You click on the *Table Tools Design > Tools > Remove Duplicates* command on the Ribbon. The Remove Duplicates dialog box shown in Figure 10.40 appears. For example, to remove any duplicates of student names and corresponding records, we select the *Student Name* from the list of columns presented in this dialog box, and click *OK*.

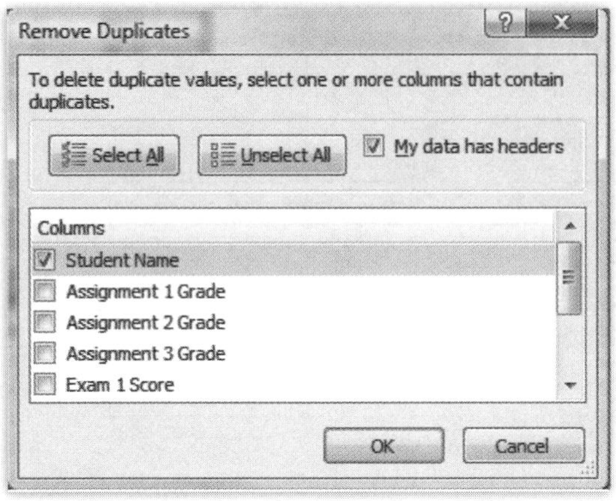

Figure 10.40 Remove Duplicates dialog box.

10.4.4 DFunctions

There is a group of Excel functions that are meant specifically for working with Excel as a database; we call these functions ***Dfunctions***. They include ***DSUM***, ***DAVERAGE***, ***DMIN***, and ***DMAX***, which are essentially database versions of the functions SUM, AVERAGE, MIN and MAX, which we discussed in Chapter 4. Dfunctions differ from the previously described functions because they specify certain criteria before performing the function. That is, the syntax of these functions has extra parameters (we use DSUM to illustrate the general format):

=DSUM(database, field, criteria)

The *criteria* parameter is a range of cells that includes a cell or cells with a field name and a cell or cells below the field name with a specified criterion. In preparation for using *Dfunctions*, we must add a few rows to our database (see Figure 10.41). These rows contain our criteria and must repeat our field names. We will define the *Dfunction* for this example in a new cell below these criteria. Using the example from Figure 10.25 one more time, let's find the minimum *Exam 2* score for students with a *Class Average* above *85.0*.

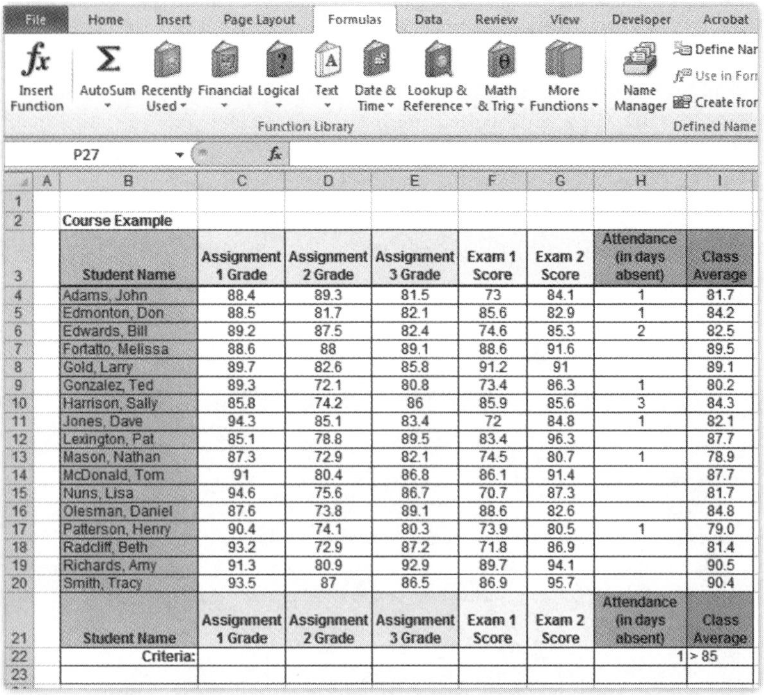

	B	C	D	E	F	G	H	I
1								
2	**Course Example**							
3	**Student Name**	**Assignment 1 Grade**	**Assignment 2 Grade**	**Assignment 3 Grade**	**Exam 1 Score**	**Exam 2 Score**	**Attendance (in days absent)**	**Class Average**
4	Adams, John	88.4	89.3	81.5	73	84.1	1	81.7
5	Edmonton, Don	88.5	81.7	82.1	85.6	82.9	1	84.2
6	Edwards, Bill	89.2	87.5	82.4	74.6	85.3	2	82.5
7	Fortatto, Melissa	88.6	88	89.1	88.6	91.6		89.5
8	Gold, Larry	89.7	82.6	85.8	91.2	91		89.1
9	Gonzalez, Ted	89.3	72.1	80.8	73.4	86.3	1	80.2
10	Harrison, Sally	85.8	74.2	86	85.9	85.6	3	84.3
11	Jones, Dave	94.3	85.1	83.4	72	84.8	1	82.1
12	Lexington, Pat	85.1	78.8	89.5	83.4	96.3		87.7
13	Mason, Nathan	87.3	72.9	82.1	74.5	80.7	1	78.9
14	McDonald, Tom	91	80.4	86.8	86.1	91.4		87.7
15	Nuns, Lisa	94.6	75.6	86.7	70.7	87.3		81.7
16	Olesman, Daniel	87.6	73.8	89.1	88.6	82.6		84.8
17	Patterson, Henry	90.4	74.1	80.3	73.9	80.5	1	79.0
18	Radcliff, Beth	93.2	72.9	87.2	71.8	86.9		81.4
19	Richards, Amy	91.3	80.9	92.9	89.7	94.1		90.5
20	Smith, Tracy	93.5	87	86.5	86.9	95.7		90.4
21	**Student Name**	**Assignment 1 Grade**	**Assignment 2 Grade**	**Assignment 3 Grade**	**Exam 1 Score**	**Exam 2 Score**	**Attendance (in days absent)**	**Class Average**
22	Criteria:						1	> 85
23								

Figure 10.41 Adding criteria rows to the bottom of the database with the repeated field names. The criterion specified in I22 is associated with the DMIN function that finds the minimum Exam 2 score of students with a Class Average above 85.

To do this, we click on the *Formulas* > *Function Library* > $\mathbf{f_x}$ *Insert Function* command from the Ribbon and find the function category labeled Database. We can now view all of the Dfunctions and choose ***DMIN*** from the list (see Figure 10.42). After selecting DMIN, a new dialog box will appear that guides us through defining the function.

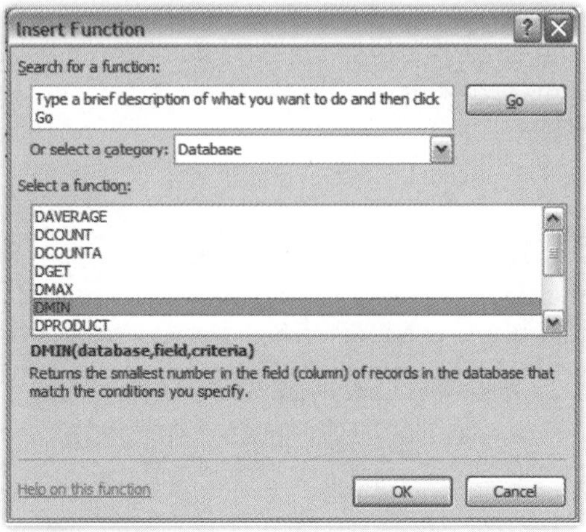

Figure 10.42 In the insert function dialog box, selecting the *Database* category to view all *Dfunctions*.

Here we begin by defining the *database* parameter, which is the entire database excluding the new criteria rows, cells *B3:I20*. The *field* parameter is the name of the field in which we are searching for a minimum value, in this case, the *Exam 2 Score*. We specify the minimum value by entering the cell with this field name, which is *G3*. (We could also just enter the title of the field here.) Lastly, the *criteria* parameter includes the field name and criteria value cells. In this scenario, we want to find the minimum *Exam 2* score for only the students with a *Class Average* above *85*. Therefore, in the criteria cells, ">*85*" is the criterion in the *Class Average* field. So for this parameter, we enter the cells *I21:I22*. The final DMIN function is then as follows (also see Figure 10.43):

=DMIN(B3:I20, G3, I21:I22)

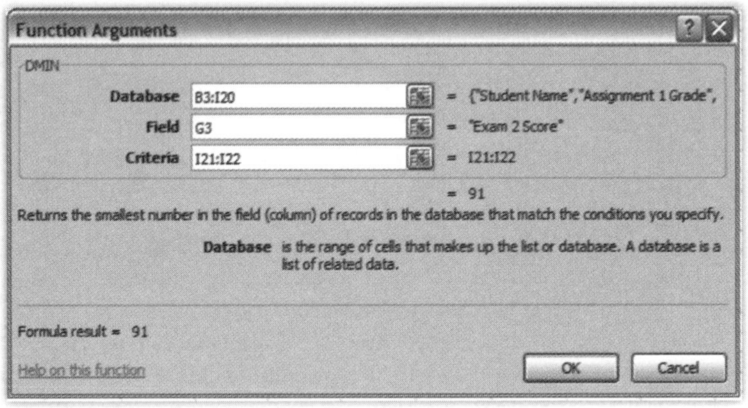

Figure 10.43 Each argument is defined here for the DMIN function. Explanations of each argument are provided below the entry fields.

After entering this *Dfunction*, we will find the minimum *Exam 2 Score* to be *91* (see Figure 10.44).

We have illustrated another scenario that searches for the minimum *Exam 2 Score* for the students with exactly *1* absence. In this case, the number *1* is the criterion for the *Attendance* field. Notice that the DMIN function in this case has the same *database* and *field* parameters but different *criteria* since we are now reviewing a condition in the *Attendance* field instead of the *Class Average* field (see Figure 10.44).

=DMIN(B3:I20, G3, H21:H22)

The other *Dfunctions* can be used in a similar fashion. After clicking the f_x command and choosing a *Dfunction* from the *Database* category, the *Function Arguments* window will guide us through defining our database and criteria for which we want to perform the selected function. *Dfunctions* are useful for databases as they allow us to consider many options in our search, or query, for a particular value.

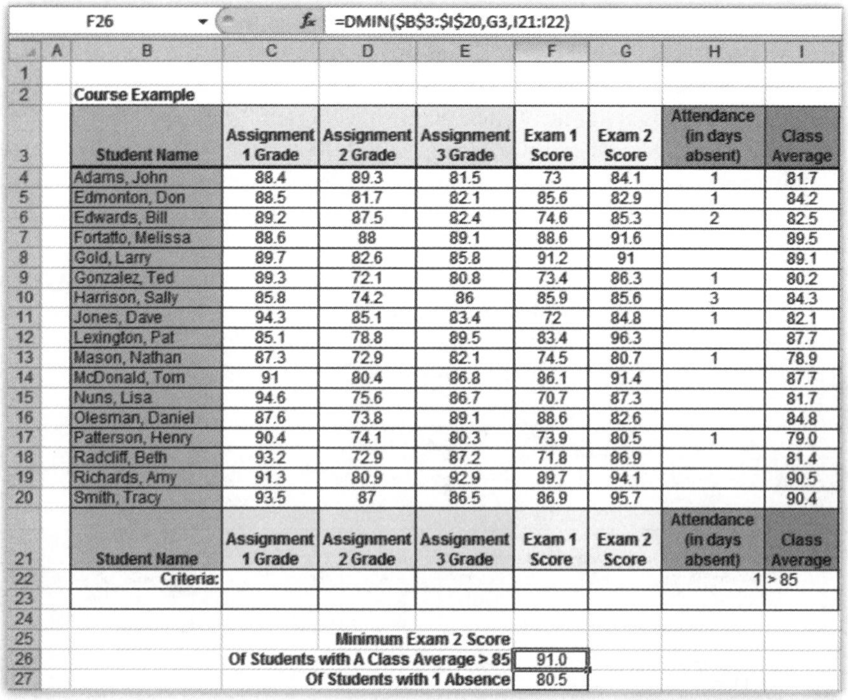

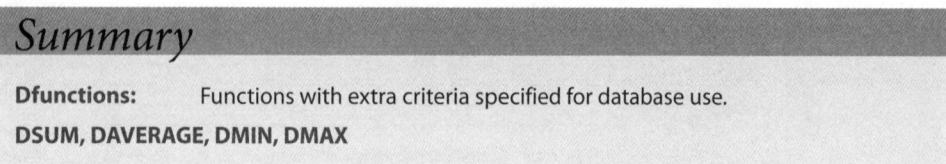

F26 =DMIN($B$3:$I$20,G3,I21:I22)

	A	B	C	D	E	F	G	H	I
1									
2		Course Example							
3		Student Name	Assignment 1 Grade	Assignment 2 Grade	Assignment 3 Grade	Exam 1 Score	Exam 2 Score	Attendance (in days absent)	Class Average
4		Adams, John	88.4	89.3	81.5	73	84.1	1	81.7
5		Edmonton, Don	88.5	81.7	82.1	85.6	82.9	1	84.2
6		Edwards, Bill	89.2	87.5	82.4	74.6	85.3	2	82.5
7		Fortatto, Melissa	88.6	88	89.1	88.6	91.6		89.5
8		Gold, Larry	89.7	82.6	85.8	91.2	91		89.1
9		Gonzalez, Ted	89.3	72.1	80.8	73.4	86.3	1	80.2
10		Harrison, Sally	85.8	74.2	86	85.9	85.6	3	84.3
11		Jones, Dave	94.3	85.1	83.4	72	84.8	1	82.1
12		Lexington, Pat	85.1	78.8	89.5	83.4	96.3		87.7
13		Mason, Nathan	87.3	72.9	82.1	74.5	80.7	1	78.9
14		McDonald, Tom	91	80.4	86.8	86.1	91.4		87.7
15		Nuns, Lisa	94.6	75.6	86.7	70.7	87.3		81.7
16		Olesman, Daniel	87.6	73.8	89.1	88.6	82.6		84.8
17		Patterson, Henry	90.4	74.1	80.3	73.9	80.5	1	79.0
18		Radcliff, Beth	93.2	72.9	87.2	71.8	86.9		81.4
19		Richards, Amy	91.3	80.9	92.9	89.7	94.1		90.5
20		Smith, Tracy	93.5	87	86.5	86.9	95.7		90.4
21		Student Name	Assignment 1 Grade	Assignment 2 Grade	Assignment 3 Grade	Exam 1 Score	Exam 2 Score	Attendance (in days absent)	Class Average
22		Criteria:						1	> 85
23									
24									
25				Minimum Exam 2 Score					
26				Of Students with A Class Average > 85		91.0			
27				Of Students with 1 Absence		80.5			

Figure 10.44 The DMIN function uses the criteria in the *Class Average* field and the criteria in the *Attendance* field.

Summary

Dfunctions: Functions with extra criteria specified for database use.

DSUM, DAVERAGE, DMIN, DMAX

Some other functions that are not *Dfunctions* are also useful to manage database data in Excel. One group of these functions, ***COUNT*** functions, has four main sub-functions: ***COUNT***, ***COUNTA***, ***COUNTBLANK***, and ***COUNTIF***. The ***COUNT*** function simply counts the number of cells with numerical values in a given range. The format of the function is as follows:

=COUNT(range)

The ***COUNTA*** function counts all of the cells with data of any kind in a given range of cells. That is, it will count the number of cells with numbers or text, or any other non-blank cell. The format for this function is:

=COUNTA(range)

The ***COUNTBLANK*** function counts the number of blank cells in a given range. It can be helpful for finding empty entries in a data table. The format for this function is:

=COUNTBLANK(range)

Let's use these three functions on the student data in the previous example. Suppose we want to determine the number of assignments and exams in the record. To use the COUNT function, we must highlight a row of grades, excluding the row of assignment titles. We must exclude the row of assignment and exam titles because the COUNT function only counts cells with numerical values. If we use the COUNT function with the cells *C4:G4*, we find that 5 total assignments and exams have been recorded. To count the number of students in the class, we can use the COUNTA function with the first column of data (*B4:B20*); the result is 17 students.

Now suppose that we want to determine the number of students who never had an absence. We can remove the "0"s from the column of absences so that there are blanks instead. Now we can use the COUNTBLANK function with the attendance column (H4:H20); the result is that 9 students have perfect attendance records. See Figure 10.45 for these results.

F31 =COUNTBLANK(H4:H20)

	A	B	C	D	E	F	G	H	I
1									
2		Course Example							
3		Student Name	Assignment 1 Grade	Assignment 2 Grade	Assignment 3 Grade	Exam 1 Score	Exam 2 Score	Attendance (in days absent)	Class Average
4		Adams, John	88.4	89.3	81.5	73	84.1	1	81.7
5		Edmonton, Don	88.5	81.7	82.1	85.6	82.9	1	84.2
6		Edwards, Bill	89.2	87.5	82.4	74.6	85.3	2	82.5
7		Fortatto, Melissa	88.6	88	89.1	88.6	91.6		89.5
8		Gold, Larry	89.7	82.6	85.8	91.2	91		89.1
9		Gonzalez, Ted	89.3	72.1	80.8	73.4	86.3	1	80.2
10		Harrison, Sally	85.8	74.2	86	85.9	85.6	3	84.3
11		Jones, Dave	94.3	85.1	83.4	72	84.8	1	82.1
12		Lexington, Pat	85.1	78.8	89.5	83.4	96.3		87.7
13		Mason, Nathan	87.3	72.9	82.1	74.5	80.7	1	78.9
14		McDonald, Tom	91	80.4	86.8	86.1	91.4		87.7
15		Nuns, Lisa	94.6	75.6	86.7	70.7	87.3		81.7
16		Olesman, Daniel	87.6	73.8	89.1	88.6	82.6		84.8
17		Patterson, Henry	90.4	74.1	80.3	73.9	80.5	1	79.0
18		Radcliff, Beth	93.2	72.9	87.2	71.8	86.9		81.4
19		Richards, Amy	91.3	80.9	92.9	89.7	94.1		90.5
20		Smith, Tracy	93.5	87	86.5	86.9	95.7		90.4
21		Student Name	Assignment 1 Grade	Assignment 2 Grade	Assignment 3 Grade	Exam 1 Score	Exam 2 Score	Attendance (in days absent)	Class Average
22		Criteria:						1	> 85
23									
24									
29					Number of assignments	5			
30					Number of students	17			
31					Number of students with perfect attendance	9			

Figure 10.45 Using the COUNT, COUNTA, and COUNTBLANK functions.

The ***COUNTIF*** function is probably the most useful COUNT function. It counts the number of cells in a given range that meet a specified criterion. The format for this function is:

=COUNTIF(range, criterion)

The criterion can contain some helpful characters such as * for a sequence of unknown values or ? as a single wild card value.

Let's use the COUNTIF function to determine the number of students who have an A (≥ 90), a B+ (≥ 85), or a B (≥ 80) as their final grades. First, we need to find the number of students with an A by using the COUNTIF function as follows:

=COUNTIF(I4:I20, ">=90")

Now, to determine the number of students with a B+, we want to count the grades that are < 90 and ≥ 85. However, since we cannot have multiple criteria with this function, we will first just count the number of students with final averages ≥ 85. This will result in the number of students with an A or a B+. Then, we subtract the previous result from this result to find the number of students with B+'s only. We repeat this process to find students with a B. See Figure 10.46 for the results.

F34 =COUNTIF(I4:I20,">=85")

	A	B	C	D	E	F	G	H	I
1									
2		Course Example							
3		Student Name	Assignment 1 Grade	Assignment 2 Grade	Assignment 3 Grade	Exam 1 Score	Exam 2 Score	Attendance (in days absent)	Class Average
4		Adams, John	88.4	89.3	81.5	73	84.1	1	81.7
5		Edmonton, Don	88.5	81.7	82.1	85.6	82.9	1	84.2
6		Edwards, Bill	89.2	87.5	82.4	74.6	85.3	2	82.5
7		Fortatto, Melissa	88.6	88	89.1	88.6	91.6		89.5
8		Gold, Larry	89.7	82.6	85.8	91.2	91		89.1
9		Gonzalez, Ted	89.3	72.1	80.8	73.4	86.3	1	80.2
10		Harrison, Sally	85.8	74.2	86	85.9	85.6	3	84.3
11		Jones, Dave	94.3	85.1	83.4	72	84.8	1	82.1
12		Lexington, Pat	85.1	78.8	89.5	83.4	96.3		87.7
13		Mason, Nathan	87.3	72.9	82.1	74.5	80.7	1	78.9
14		McDonald, Tom	91	80.4	86.8	86.1	91.4		87.7
15		Nuns, Lisa	94.6	75.6	86.7	70.7	87.3		81.7
16		Olesman, Daniel	87.6	73.8	89.1	88.6	82.6		84.8
17		Patterson, Henry	90.4	74.1	80.3	73.9	80.5	1	79.0
18		Radcliff, Beth	93.2	72.9	87.2	71.8	86.9		81.4
19		Richards, Amy	91.3	80.9	92.9	89.7	94.1		90.5
20		Smith, Tracy	93.5	87	86.5	86.9	95.7		90.4
21		Student Name	Assignment 1 Grade	Assignment 2 Grade	Assignment 3 Grade	Exam 1 Score	Exam 2 Score	Attendance (in days absent)	Class Average
22		Criteria:						1	> 85
23									
24									
33				Number of students with A		2			
34				Number of students with B+		6	4		
35				Number of students with B		15	9		

Figure 10.46 Using The COUNTIF function with the student data.

Similar to the COUNTIF function is the ***SUMIF*** function. The SUMIF function will calculate the values in a given range that meet a specified criterion. This function is also similar to the DSUM function that we discussed earlier in this section. The format of the SUMIF function is:

=SUMIF(range, criteria, sum_range)

Even though we use the SUMIF function in the same manner as the DSUM function, it only allows for a single criterion. That is, DSUM requires a criteria range whereas SUMIF has the criteria as a parameter. Therefore, when using Excel as a database, we recommend using the DSUM function instead of the SUMIF function to handle multiple criteria.

10.4.5 Data Validation

Most database applications have data validation capabilities. It enforces a certain format or type of data to be entered by the user for particular input. To use data validation, select the cell(s) we want to validate and then click on *Data > Data Tools > Data Validation* command on the Ribbon. The dialog box shown below will appear (see Figure 10.47).

There are three main tabs in this window: Settings, Input Message, and Error Alert. In the Settings tab, we specify the criteria for the data that will be entered into the selected cell. As shown in Figure 10.48, there is a list of criteria including Whole Numbers, Dates, Text Lengths, and others.

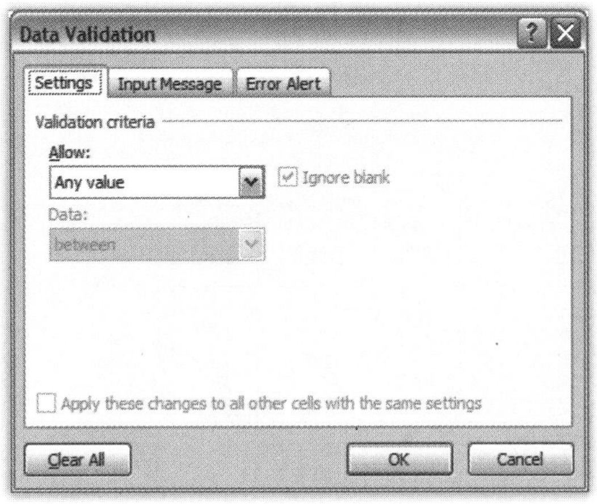

Figure 10.47 The Data Validation dialog box.

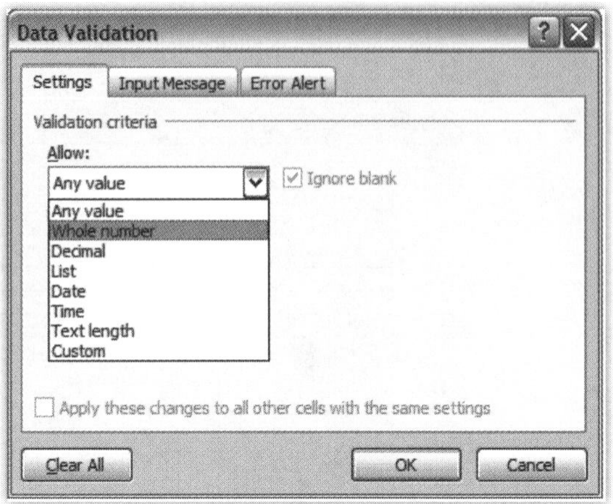

Figure 10.48 The criteria options for the data entry.

Depending on which criteria are selected from the list, we will have a few more options to further specify these criteria. For example, if we choose *Whole Number* from the list, we then choose from a list of inequalities (greater than, less than or equal to, between, etc.) and provide some numerical bounds (either as single numbers or as ranges as shown in Figure 10.49).

The Input Message tab allows us to create a comment that will appear next to the cell after it is selected. This message is intended to guide the user to enter the correct data. For example, in Figure 10.50, we have created the message "Please enter a whole number between 0 and 5 only." This message matches the criterion we specified.

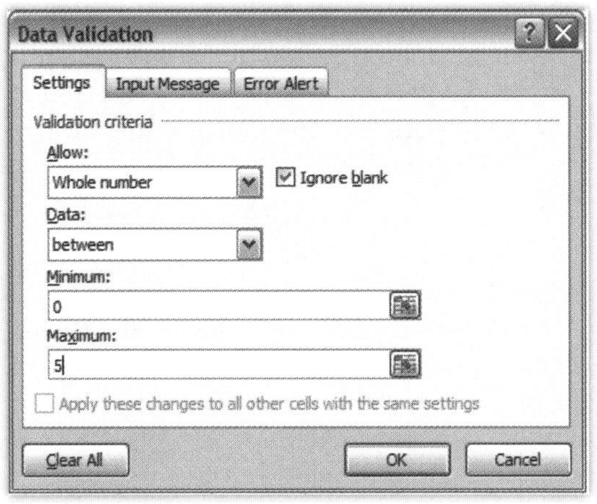

Figure 10.49 Specifying inequality and bounds for the Whole Number criterion.

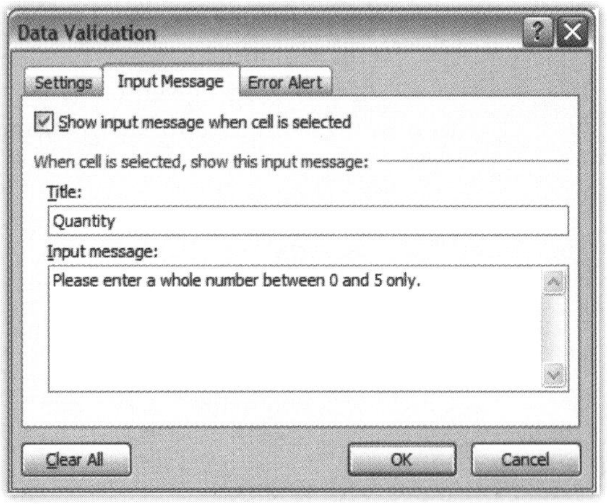

Figure 10.50 Input Message to guide user to follow the criterion.

The Error Alert allows us to display a message to the user after he or she has entered any data incorrectly. We can choose to have an Error, Warning, or Information symbol on this message box also; each symbol has a different set of options for the user in the message box. In Figure 10.51, we have chosen the Warning symbol and have entered the message, "You must enter a whole number between 0 and 5!"

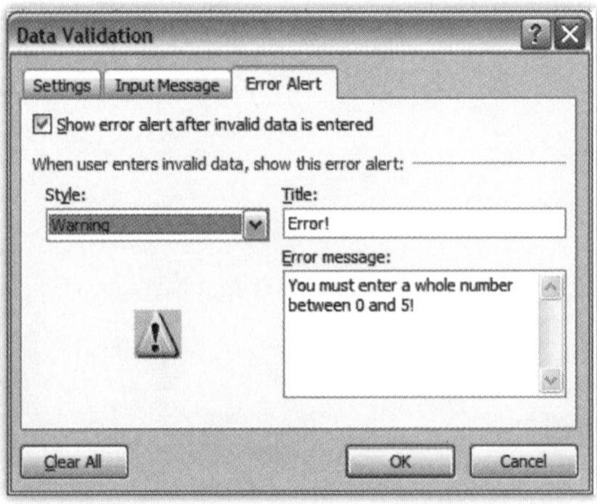

Figure 10.51 Creating an Error message to warn users if they enter any incorrect data.

Let's consider an example. Suppose we have a record of customer orders. For each order, the date, quantity, and price of the order are noted. If a maximum of 5 products can be sold in any one order, we can apply the above Whole Number validation to the Quantity column. The Input Message for this validation appears when a cell in the Quantity column is selected (see Figure 10.52). If we enter a number greater than 5 (or less than 0), then the Warning message created in the Error Alert tab will appear (see Figure 10.53).

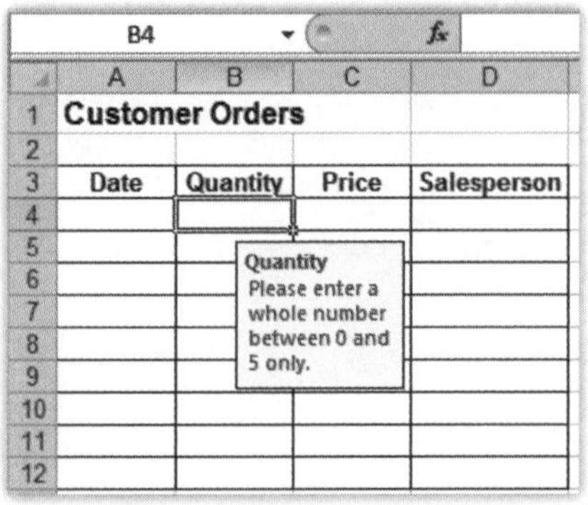

Figure 10.52 When selecting the validated cell, the Input Message appears.

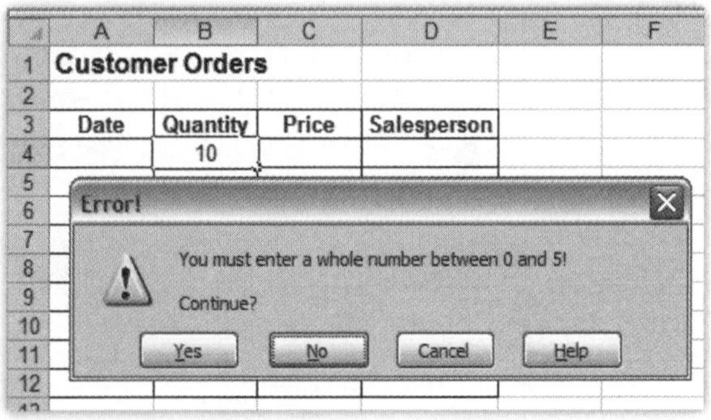

Figure 10.53 If a user enters incorrect data, the Warning message appears.

We could also validate the Date column in this example by choosing the Date criterion. We may, for example, specify that this record is for dates before February 1st only (see Figure 10.54).

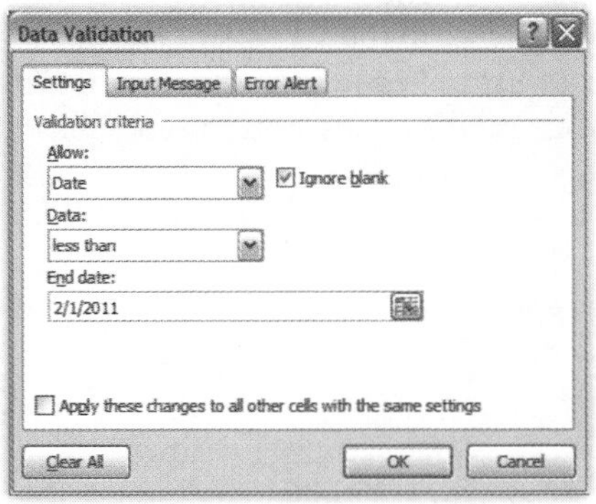

Figure 10.54 Specifying the Date criterion.

This time, let's choose the Information alert type. The Input Message and alert are shown in Figure 10.55 for a selected cell in the Date column.

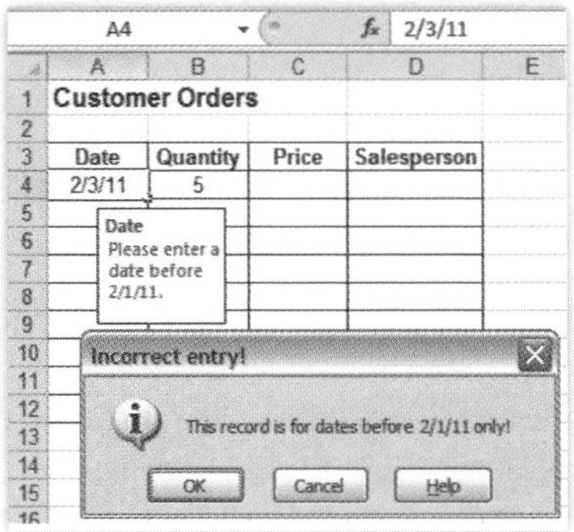

Figure 10.55 The Input message and Information alert.

Another interesting criterion, Custom, is similar to the Formula Is option used in Conditional Formatting (see Chapter 4). With the Custom criterion, the user applies a formula to the first cell in the selected range that is being validated. For example, in Figure 10.56, we are checking if the value entered is a number or not by using the Informational function ISNUMBER. If the result of this formula is false, then the Error Alert message will appear.

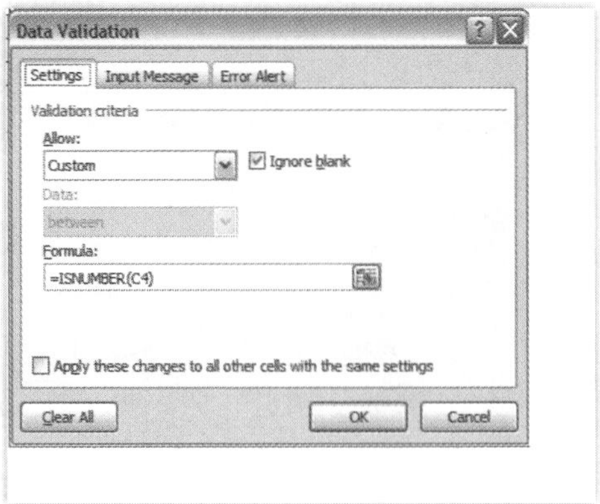

Figure 10.56 The Custom criterion uses a formula to check for errors.

One last unique criterion is List. It allows us to create a list box, or drop-down box, of options for users to choose from as their entry value. We must create a source for this list somewhere in the spreadsheet. For example, if we have an additional column in the Customer Order table for the Salesperson who took the order, we may want to limit this entry to the list of valid salespersons working for the company. In the spreadsheet below, there is a list of salesperson names. We can then select List from the criteria options and highlight this range of names as the source (see Figure 10.57).

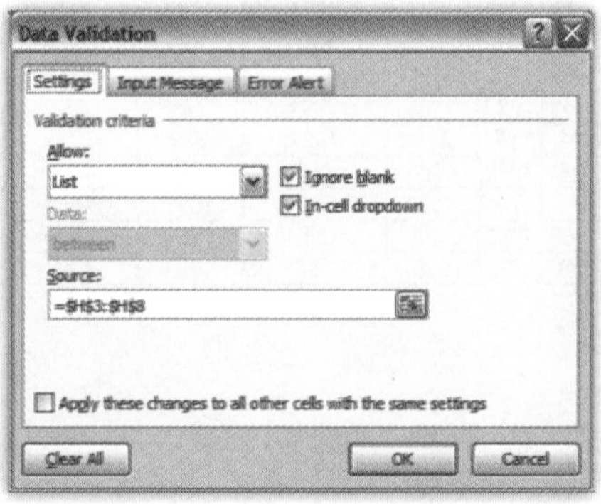

Figure 10.57 The list of names becomes the source for the List criterion.

Then, we can set the Input Message and Error Alert so that the users know they can only enter a salesperson name from the provided list. When they select a cell from the Salesperson column, a drop-down arrow will appear providing them with this list of valid names (see Figure 10.58).

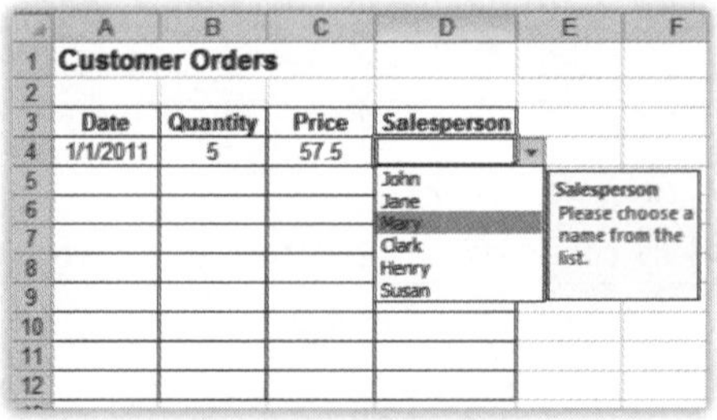

Figure 10.58 The List criterion provides a list of valid entry values.

10.4.6 Data Consolidation

Another database tool available in Excel, data consolidation, allows us to compare and combine multiple sources of data into a new spreadsheet. Let's consider an example.

Suppose that we have monthly sales recorded for various products in two different marketing regions (see Figure 10.59). If we want to know the total sales per month (among all regions) for each product, we would want to use data consolidation.

Region 1 Sales

Product	January	February	March	April	May	June	July	August	September	October	November	December
A	1060	1187	722	1258	1760	377	470	1201	1584	1685	376	1926
B	1201	1898	925	1885	1056	1802	984	757	1262	226	444	571
C	500	1014	1889	782	688	210	868	1124	1660	501	1163	1297
D	1840	1299	820	643	864	888	263	1045	1032	1129	1088	1350
E	1009	216	866	593	549	689	1418	1693	1294	622	1032	374
F	889	434	413	549	1773	438	647	1673	1083	960	1583	1239
G	1452	648	627	755	517	1841	1472	1859	370	1675	537	832
H	1989	1602	302	1627	1817	1399	1592	1712	1834	1892	740	477
I	450	807	201	1445	1427	1632	526	1075	522	966	746	1183
J	1337	1663	802	1186	1272	1797	283	695	1042	1635	859	1452
K	900	989	1490	1962	1553	1699	1022	1168	1991	1520	573	1350
L	1223	1976	1973	1927	1718	411	1187	279	1828	620	1783	1046
M	1751	1655	1359	1893	1766	678	1279	1806	890	1762	403	1899
N	1845	1697	1585	445	1292	883	1706	1877	698	1099	1842	538
O	753	1020	932	570	1648	1489	1953	562	1863	1255	1745	856
P	587	1473	1024	1726	1445	919	218	939	497	1633	891	1441

(a)

Region 2 Sales

Product	January	February	March	April	May	June	July	August	September	October	November	December
A	266	1281	269	1223	544	1559	1238	585	797	708	837	1196
B	796	1909	1121	897	1906	1891	1705	1635	240	934	1283	480
C	1743	670	293	738	1858	1400	730	1360	1514	1821	1931	538
D	1045	387	1402	567	1331	803	545	1714	375	1703	1160	1010
E	1548	513	1564	1652	1007	579	656	1905	264	1161	1876	1376
F	207	444	500	1322	303	1411	485	1700	1422	1690	1916	1358
G	1099	554	1647	365	1199	1988	306	1815	1329	1397	425	247
H	1592	1198	617	1334	1750	1563	1041	480	537	1890	422	383
I	562	796	494	452	998	1053	1608	1844	493	1673	1368	1255
J	821	1802	815	540	286	1373	1948	984	352	339	398	1029
K	299	723	1038	882	1051	838	1478	1281	1252	487	1231	1017
L	1565	436	297	968	566	574	1470	1106	1206	893	1093	1357
M	946	1004	1100	1728	818	1425	1506	1016	1734	1681	1841	594
N	366	1270	1902	526	1395	1660	1759	1045	1846	1262	473	1495
O	1599	1299	490	1830	1181	690	1539	508	1101	1194	1375	1850
P	1550	320	1995	396	1674	1223	1219	655	863	729	1278	1717

(b)

Figure 10.59 A record of monthly sales per product for two different regions.

We begin by creating a new spreadsheet (right-click on a sheet name and choose *Insert* from the list of options, then in the dialog box that appears select *Worksheet* and click on the *OK* button). In this new sheet, we select *Data > Data Tools > Consolidate* command on the Ribbon. The dialog box shown below will appear (see Figure 10.60).

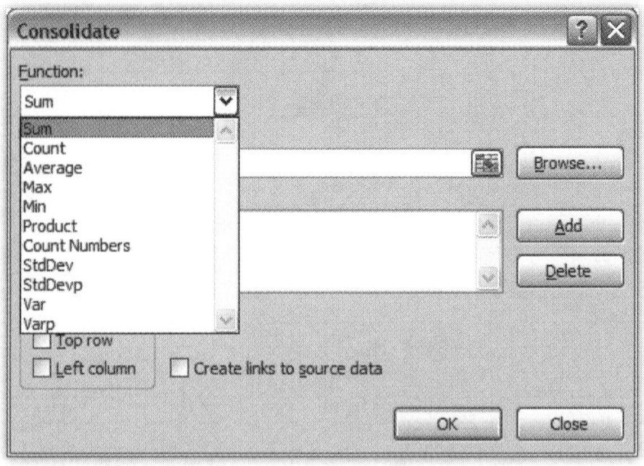

Figure 10.60 In the Data Consolidate dialog box multiple functions are available in the data consolidation tool.

The data consolidation tool provides a list of functions that can be applied to the data as it is consolidated. These functions include Sum, Count, Max, Min, etc. For this example, let's use the Sum function since we want to find the total number of sales in both regions. After selecting the function, we must choose the references of the data that we want to consolidate. In this case, we select the entire table from both the Region 1 Sales and Region 2 sales spreadsheets. Next, we select the Top row and Left column check boxes for the location of data labels (since we have selected these labels in the reference as well). We also make sure to check the box "Create Links to source data." This option ensures that any change made to the source data (that is, the original tables) will be reflected automatically in the consolidated table. The completed data consolidation dialog box appears in Figure 10.61.

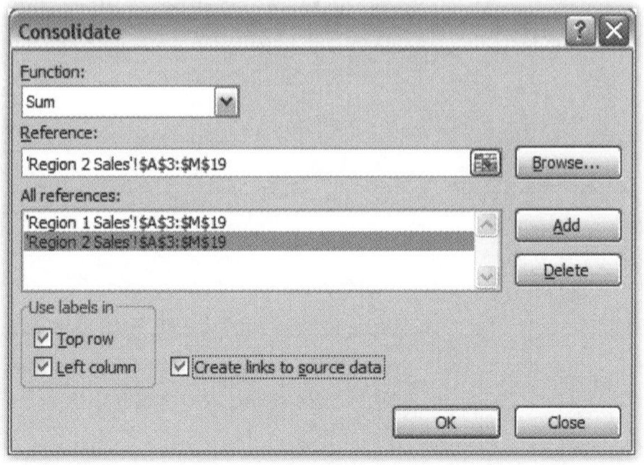

Figure 10.61 The completed data consolidation dialog box.

Figure 10.62 displays the resulting consolidated table. Excel has calculated the sum of the sales of each product per month. Notice that some small + icons appear on the left side of the table. We can click these to expand the hidden rows that show the sources (or the references) of the consolidated data.

Total Sales

	January	February	March	April	May	June	July	August	September	October	November	December
A	1326	2468	991	2481	2304	1936	1708	1786	2381	2393	1213	3122
B	1997	3807	2046	2782	2962	3693	2689	2392	1502	1160	1727	1051
C	2243	1684	2182	1520	2546	1610	1598	2484	3174	2322	3094	1835
D	2885	1686	2222	1210	2195	1691	808	2759	1407	2832	2248	2360
E	2557	729	2430	2245	1556	1268	2074	3598	1558	1783	2908	1750
F	1096	878	913	1871	2076	1849	1132	3373	2505	2650	3499	2597
G	2551	1202	2274	1120	1716	3829	1778	3674	1699	3072	962	1079
H	3581	2800	919	2961	3567	2962	2633	2192	2371	3782	1162	860
I	1012	1603	695	1897	2425	2685	2134	2919	1015	2639	2114	2438
J	2158	3465	1617	1726	1558	3170	2231	1679	1394	1974	1257	2481
K	1199	1712	2528	2844	2604	2537	2500	2449	3243	2007	1804	2367
L	2788	2412	2270	2895	2284	985	2657	1385	3034	1513	2876	2403
M	2697	2659	2459	3621	2584	2103	2785	2822	2624	3443	2244	2493
N	2211	2967	3487	971	2687	2543	3465	2922	2544	2361	2315	2033
O	2352	2319	1422	2400	2829	2179	3492	1070	2964	2449	3120	2706
P	2137	1793	3019	2122	3119	2142	1437	1594	1360	2362	2169	3158

Figure 10.62 The consolidated data table.

10.5 *Summary*

- We can import text files, webpage information, and database tables into Excel using the commands listed in the *Data > Get External Data* tab on the *Ribbon.*
- Queries can be made to data being imported from a database.
- Pivot Tables can use external data, such as from databases, as their source.
- Sorting and Filtering are helpful tools for organizing large data.
- The "official" Excel Table makes the process of organizing and manipulating data easier.
- There are several functions, called *Dfunctions,* that can be used on large data in Excel. There are also some other functions, such as COUNT functions and SUMIF, that can be used with large data.
- *Data Validation* and *Data Consolidation* are database tools available in Excel which allow us to enforce a certain format or type of data to be entered by the user for particular input and compare and combine multiple sources of data into a new spreadsheet, respectively.

10.6 *Exercises*

10.6.1 Review Questions

1. Define the terms *sorting* and *field* and discuss how they are related.
2. What are the two ways to *sort* a set of data?
3. How does *filtering* differ from *sorting*?
4. How does selecting to filter the data affect the display of the spreadsheet?
5. What does the *Top 10* option from a filtered drop-down list allow you to do?
6. What does the *Custom* option from a filtered drop-down list allow you to do?
7. Give an example of an instance when *filtering* data in an Excel database may be necessary.
8. What are some of the benefits of using an "official" Excel Table?
9. How do *Dfunctions* differ from ordinary functions?
10. List five *Dfunctions* available in Excel.
11. What must be included in the criteria parameter of a *Dfunction* expression?
12. How are *Dfunctions* useful?
13. How can you refer to an external database when using *Dfunctions*?

14. What is a query?
15. How can you run a query before data has been imported from an external database?

10.6.2 Hands-On Exercises

NOTE: Please refer to the file "Chapter_10_Exercises.xlsx" and "UniversityInformationSystem.mdb" for the associated worksheets or databases noted for the hands-on exercises. The file is available at: www.dssbooks.com.

1. The management in a manufacturing company has decided to promote the most efficient of the assembly line workers. To qualify for this promotion a worker should have attended the assembly of at least 330 units of output per week, during the last five weeks; should have attended on average the assembly of at least 400 units of output per week; and finally should have attended the assembly of no more than 6 defective units of output per week in the last five weeks. (Refer to worksheet "10.1".)
   a. Filter the content of the database presented below to determine which workers should have earned the promotion.
   b. The most efficient of the workers will further be promoted to team leader. Filter the database of workers being promoted to identify the team leader. Hint: To identify the team leader, find the maximum average output during the five weeks period.
2. Consider the database presented in Hands-On Exercise 1.
   a. Create an Excel Table using this data.
   b. Sort the information by employee name in ascending order.
   c. Count the number of employees that attended the assembly of more than 400 units of output during week 1.
   d. Count the number of employees that attended on average the assembly of at most 5 defective products per week.
   e. Add a new column to this table called "Max Defects" that finds the maximum number of defects per employee. Observe how the formula you type in cell N3 is propagated to the rest of the rows.
3. A quality inspector at a manufacturing plant must periodically take a sample of the products being produced and perform measurements to ensure that the products' dimensions are within certain tolerances. The product passes the inspection if the measurement is within 0.25 cm of the 20.00 cm target value. The inspector obtains the following set of measurements (in centimeters) for one of the samples: {20.18, 19.87, 19.93, 19.99, 20.23, 20.01, 20.17, 19.88, 19.02, 19.96, 20.53}.
   a. Create an Excel Table to input the inspector's measurements. Using logical functions, add a column to the database that indicates whether each measurement passes or fails the inspection.
   b. Use Dfunctions to compute each of the following values for your database:
      - The number of products that pass the inspection
      - The standard deviation of all products undergoing inspection
      - The standard deviation of all products that pass the inspection
      - The variance of all products undergoing inspection
      - The variance of all products that pass the inspection
4. Another quality inspector in the manufacturing plant mentioned in the previous problem must measure the length, width, and weight of a variety of products. The measurements the inspector obtains are provided in the table below. To meet inspection requirements, each product must be between 1.5 ft and 2.0 ft long, between 1.0 ft and 1.5 ft wide, and weigh between 1.0 lbs and 2.0 lbs. Use Dfunctions to compute the following values for this database. (Refer to worksheet "10.4".)
   a. Use the data to create an Excel Table. Use the commands in the Table Tool Design tab to identify and remove duplicates of data (samples with exactly the same length, width and weight).
   b. The number of products that pass the inspection
   c. The standard deviation and variance of the product lengths
   d. The standard deviation and variance of the product widths
   e. The standard deviation and variance of the product weights

5. Consider the student record database presented in Figure 10.25. (Refer to worksheet "10.5".)
   a. Use filtering to display the name, grade and attendance of all the students that never missed a class.
   b. Use filtering to display the name, grade, and attendance of all the students that missed three classes.
   c. Calculate the class average for the students that never missed a class.
   d. Calculate the class average for the students that missed three classes. Is there a relationship between the number of classes missed and the class average?
6. Consider the student record database presented in Figure 10.25. (Refer to worksheet "10.6".)
   a. Use filtering to display the name, grade, and attendance of all the students that performed better than average in the 1st Exam.
   b. Use filtering to display the name, grade and attendance of all the students that performed better than average in the 2nd Exam. Is there a relation, in terms of grade, between the students that performed better than average in the 1st and 2nd exam?
7. A credit card company maintains a database to store information about its cardholders. Cardholders that meet certain requirements are eligible to receive the platinum-level membership that includes a higher credit limit and additional benefits. These requirements are: the cardholder should currently have a minimum credit line of $3,000; the cardholder should have made at most one late payment; the cardholder began using the card prior to year 2000. Use Dfunctions to determine how many of the cardholders listed are eligible for this membership. (Refer to worksheet "10.7".)
8. Read Hands-On Exercise 7. Present the name, enrollment date, credit limit and the number of late payments for the cardholders that are eligible for the platinum-level membership.
9. Using the given table, create an "official" Excel Table and find the following. (Refer to worksheet "10.9".)
   a. The number of songs not sung by Spears.
   b. The number of songs sung between June 1, 2004 and July 4, 2006.
   c. The number of songs sung by singers with an "e" in their name.
10. A table presents sales information of a company that sells beauty products in different regions of the US. Answer the following questions. (Refer to worksheet "10.10".)
    a. What are the total sales in the Midwest?
    b. What is the total amount of money Ashley made?321
    c. What is the number of transactions with a greater than average sales amount?
11. The Text option in Data Validation enables you to generate an error message when the number of characters in a cell is not of a desired length. Use the Text option to ensure that each cell in the range A1:A10 will contain at most 5 characters (including blanks).
12. You are entering employee names in the cell range B1:B10. Use Data Validation to ensure that no employee's name is entered more than twice in this column. (Hint: Use the COUNTIF function.)
13. Suppose you have asked an assistant to enter values in a debt database. There is a column each for names, phone numbers, and price owed. Use Data Validation to ensure that only text is entered as a name, phone numbers have 10 digits, and price owed is never negative.
14. The URL *http://www.baseball-reference.com/b/bondsba01.shtml* contains Barry Bonds' major league baseball statistics. Import this data into Excel and perform some analysis of these values.
15. Find a website on foreign exchange rates. Import this data to Excel and save the query. Then run this query again to find the updated exchange rates.
16. Use the following information to create a text file. Import the file to Excel using the appropriate delimiter.

Untitled - Notepad

File Edit Format View Help

```
11,039.28      1,536.38      1,920.67
7,760.48       3,859.04      12,844.16
10,659.48      4,916.39      2,041.66
14,345.66      11,897.50     13,500.15
```

17. Place the following data in a text file and import it into Excel. Do not import the address or zip code columns.

Untitled - Notepad

File Edit Format View Help

```
Name           Address          Zip     Phone
John Smith     123 L.Lane       34285   342-6754
Susan Henry    453 J. Street    34245   546-2435
Tom Golfer     298 34th Ave     23445   345-6547
Joe Samual     290 B. Blvd.     34245   637-4235
Tina Tosser    582 23th St.     32456   654-6754
Mac Night      349 Main St.     34256   453-6577
```

18. Using information recorded for the project teams of a class, perform the following actions. (Refer to worksheet "10.18".)

a. Sort the list by presentation grades in ascending order

b. Sort the list by report grades in descending order

c. Sort the team member names alphabetically

19. Consider the database in Hands-On Exercise 10. Answer the following questions.

a. Which transactions made the top 5 percent of sales (in dollars)?

b. For which transactions was the amount sold during 2004 more than 50 units?

c. Present the lip gloss transactions during the first 6 months of 2004.

d. Identify the eye liner transactions that brought more than the average (dollars) made on eye liners.

20. The given database presents the sales transactions for different products in two different regions. Perform the following data consolidations. (Refer to worksheet "10.20".)

a. Identify the Max sales (over both regions) for each product in each month.

b. Count the number of sales made (over both regions) for each product during the three months period.

21. Consider the data presented in Hands-On Exercise 20. Use *Dfunctions* to find the following. (Refer to worksheet "10.20".)

a. The average amount sold during the first half of March in region 1.

b. The average amount of product A sold during the second half of January in region 1.

c. The minimum amount of product B sold during the month of February in region 1.

d. Total amount sold in January 1st in region 1.

22. A professor saved the results from three different exams he gave in his class, in three tables. Use the Data Consolidation tools in Excel to create the following. (Refer to worksheet "10.22".)

a. A table that presents for each student the identification number, as well as the grades of the three exams.

b. A table that presents the average exam grade for each student.

c. A table that presents the maximum grade received in an exam for each student.

d. A table that presents the minimum grade received in an exam for each student.

23. A retail store keeps the information about the products carried in the inventory in an excel spreadsheet. Use Data Validations tools to insure the following. (Refer to worksheet "10.23".)

a. The identification number for each item is a number that has exactly five digits.

b. Inventory level for each item cannot be negative.

c. The unit price for each item is at least $150.

d. A product condition should be either fair, or good, or very good.

e. The purchase date for the items in the inventory should not be less that 1/1/2000.

24. A University carries the information about the current students in an MS Access database. (Refer to tblStudents in the database file.)

a. Import table tblStudents in Excel.

b. Display detailed information (Student Id, Last Name, First Name, etc) about the graduate students that have been enrolled no earlier than 1/1/2000.

c. Display detailed information (Student Id, Last Name, First Name, etc) about the undergraduate students that have earned at least 6 credits.

d. Display detailed information (Student Id, Last Name, First Name, etc) about the undergraduate students from Florida.

25. A University carries the information about the instructors in an MS Access database. (Refer to tblInstructors in the database file.)

a. Import this table in Excel.

b. The minimum wage for instructors in this University is $40,000. Insure that no instructor is hired for less than $40,000.

c. Display detailed information (Instructor Id, Last Name, First Name, etc) about the instructors that have earned the title Professor.

d. The office of Human resources needs detailed information about the instructors that are not USA citizens. Display detailed information about those instructors.

e. Display detailed information about the instructors that make top 10% of the annual salary.

CHAPTER

eleven Introduction to the Visual Basic Environment

chapter OVERVIEW

11.1 Introduction

This chapter introduces the Visual Basic environment. We expect the reader to have read the chapters in Part I of the book or to have an equivalent knowledge of Excel. It is important for the reader to be comfortable in the spreadsheet environment, as Visual Basic for Applications (VBA) will be used to perform the same spreadsheet functions that are done in Excel along with some other advanced Excel object manipulations. VBA brings a dynamic element to spreadsheet DSS applications. With VBA, we will modify the spreadsheet, create a user interface, perform simulation models and solve optimization problems. In this chapter, we begin by understanding the environment in which we will be using VBA and the basics of this programming language.

In this chapter, the reader will learn how to:

- Work in the Visual Basic Editor environment.
- Use the Project Explorer, Properties, and Code Windows.
- Understand the difference between a property, method, and event.
- Use the Object Browser.

11.2 The Visual Basic Editor

The Visual Basic Editor (VBE) is the environment in which you work with VBA programming code. To open the VBE from Excel, go to *Developer* tab on the *Ribbon*. Click on the *Visual Basic* command under the *Code* group. Note that, the Developer tab is not one of the default tabs of Excel Ribbon. To activate this tab, right-click on the Ribbon; then, select *Customize the Ribbon* from the list of options presented. Excel displays the Customize Ribbon tab of the Excel Options dialog box. Select the Developer tab from the list box on the right of the dialog box and then click on OK. You can also press *Alt-F11* to activate VBE.

Once you have entered the VBE, you will see the window shown in Figure 11.1. Excel and VBE have separate windows that you can toggle between. Customize the *Quick Access Toolbar* by adding the Visual Basic command, so you can quickly access VBE from Excel. You can use Excel icon from VBE. You can also toggle between the windows just by pressing *Alt+F11* in either window. To view the execution of the code, write VBA code in the VBE first and then go to Excel. Or, you can record a macro in Excel and then check the code automatically created in the VBE. We will discuss this more in Chapter 12, "Recording Macros."

11.2.1 Project Explorer

There are three main windows in VBE: the Project Explorer, the Properties Window, and the Code Window. The Project Explorer lists all projects in any open workbook. Each workbook has a project, and each project can have several parts, namely its ***objects***, modules, and ***forms***. Each of these project parts can have VBA code associated with it. Excel automatically lists the *objects*; they are the worksheets and the workbook itself. In Figure 11.1, you will notice that there are no *modules* or *forms* in this project, only the worksheet and workbook *objects*.

The *modules* contain the VBA code for any macro, which does not have to be associated with a particular worksheet; that is, the *modules* have macros that can be executed in any worksheet at any time. There are two types of *modules*: standard and class. Standard *modules* are used for writing general procedures, or sections of code, to perform different tasks with

Excel *objects*. We will perform these tasks by using *properties* and *methods* to manipulate Excel *objects*. There are sets, or libraries, of properties and methods available in VBA for all Excel *objects*. Class modules are used to create new properties and methods for more advanced coding. For now, we will focus on standard modules; please refer to Appendix C for more information on class modules.

Forms are the user interface tools in Excel. *Forms* have two design areas: the user display and any VBA code associated with user display items. We will discuss these user *forms* in more detail in Chapter 18.

To add a user *form* or *module* to your project, simply click *Insert > User Form* or *Insert > Module*, respectively. You can also use the icon to see a drop down list of insert options. [Note: You also have the option to insert a Procedure, which is either a macro (subroutine) or a function, or a Class Module, which defines the properties and methods of an object.] You can insert *objects*, *modules*, or *forms* from other projects by using *Insert > File* or *File > Import File*. Every time a new part of a project is inserted, including when a new worksheet is added from the Excel workbook, you will see it bookmarked in the Project Explorer for easy reference.

Summary

Objects:	Elements in a workbook, including the workbook and worksheets.
Modules:	Contain VBA code for any macro.
User Forms:	User interface that has both user display design and VBA code.

11.2.2 Properties Window

The Properties window contains detailed information about any selected project part from the Project Explorer. For example, in Figure 11.1, you can see the properties for the workbook *object* since it has been selected in the Project Explorer.

This window displays basic properties and more advanced ones that are adjustable, such as the font size of all the text in a worksheet or user *form* items. The user *form* properties tend to be the most commonly used. Each object in a user *form* has its own list of properties; that is, a text box can have a different font type than a label on a user *form*. Again, we will discuss user *forms* in more detail in Chapter 18. We will not discuss the various properties here, but recommend that you go ahead and experiment with changing some of them.

11.2.3 Code Window

The main window is the Code window, which is in the central section of the VBE. This window displays the VBA code for the highlighted project in the Project Explorer. Macros are recorded as *procedures* in VBA. When you record macros, you simultaneously create VBA code in the Visual Basic Editor.

There are two main types of procedures: sub and function. We will discuss both in more detail in Chapter 15. Sub procedures are always created when a user records a macro in Excel. The statement *Sub* and the macro name introduce the code. The code ends with the command *End Sub*. The VBE automatically generates these two statements when a new sub procedure is inserted.

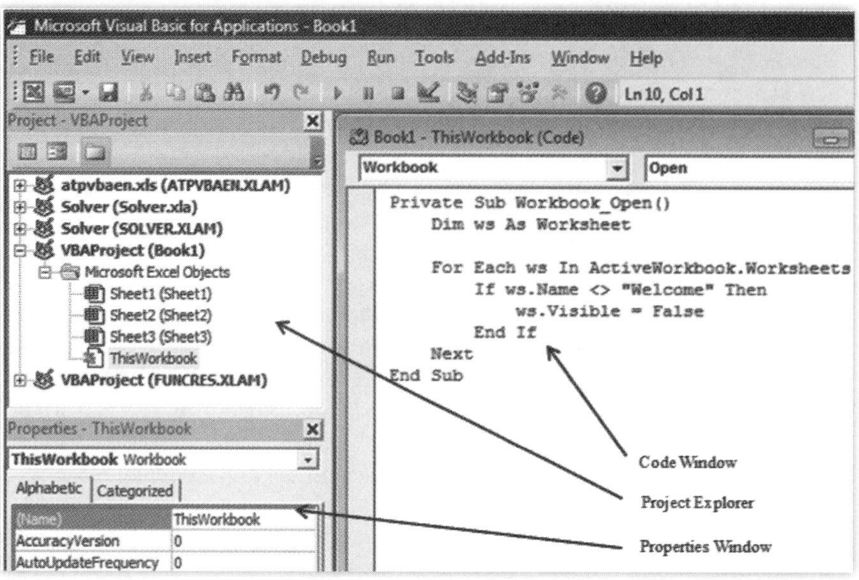

Figure 11.1 VBE windows: the Project Explorer, Properties Window and Code Window.

11.2.4 Immediate and Watch Windows

Two other VBE windows are the Immediate window and the Watch window. These windows are useful for debugging purposes. Whatever you type into the Immediate window is executed as soon as you enter it. In the Watch window, variable names, when typed, are "watched" by VBE and displayed whenever their values change. We will use these windows when discussing debugging in Appendix B.

Summary

Project Explorer: Lists all projects in any open workbook.

Properties Window: Contains detailed information about any selected project part from the Project Explorer.

Code Window: Displays the VBA code for the highlighted project in the Project Explorer.

Immediate Window: Whatever you type is executed as soon as you enter it.

Watch Window: Variable names are displayed whenever their values change.

11.2.5 VBE Toolbars

There are four toolbars in VBE: *Standard, Edit, Debug,* and *UserForm*. We will primarily use the Standard toolbar for now and we will discuss the Debug toolbar in Appendix B. The Standard toolbar allows you to switch to the Excel window, insert a user *form*, *module*, or procedure, and save our current code modifications (see Figure 11.2). It also includes several standard editing options, such as cut, copy, paste, search, undo, and redo. The Standard toolbar allows you to run, pause, or stop your code. You can also view the design mode of our *form* design (which we will discuss in more detail in Chapter 18) and view or hide the Project Explorer, Properties Window, Object Browser, and User Form Toolbox. The final icon is for help options.

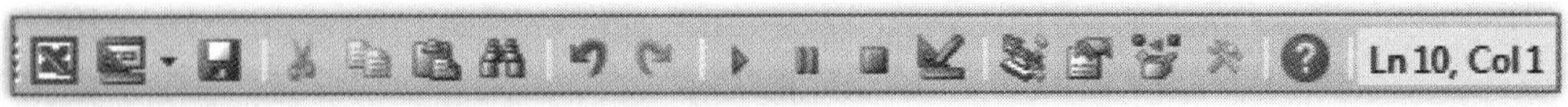

Figure 11.2 The Standard VBE toolbar.

11.3 *The Object Browser*

Another important part of the Visual Basic Editor is the Object Browser. To view the Object Browser, either go to *View > Object Browser* or press the icon in the Standard toolbar.

Before understanding the purpose of the Object Browser, let's review from Chapter 2 the idea of an *object* and the *object model*. A few examples of Excel *objects* are the workbook, the worksheet, a range of cells, and a cell itself. Excel *objects* are grouped according to their order in what is known as the object hierarchy. That is, the workbook object includes the worksheet object, which includes the range object, which includes the cell object. This entire system of objects is known as the *object model*.

The Object Browser provides a list of ***properties***, ***methods***, and ***events*** of all Excel objects that may be manipulated in VBA (see Figure 11.3). *Properties* are the physical descriptions of all Excel objects. For example, a range object can have a length property and a cell object may have a font size property. The description of the particular property is called the ***value*** of the property. To continue the example, a length property could have a value of two and a font size property could have a value equal to 12. Properties are designated by the icon in the Object Browser.

Methods are the actions that can be performed on an *object*. For example, a user may *select* a chart, and then *copy* and paste elsewhere. The elements of a *method* statement are called the ***arguments*** of the method. For example, a chart can be pasted to a certain destination; the specification of that paste type would be an argument of the paste method for the chart object. Methods may also include functions or sub procedures. Methods are designated by the icon in the Object Browser.

Events are actions that are performed on controls. A control is a user interface object, such as a button or check box. We discuss controls and events in more detail in Chapters 12 and 18. Events are designated by the icon in the Object Browser.

Summary

Properties:	Descriptions of an object.
Values:	Descriptions of a particular property.
Methods:	Action performed on an object.
Arguments:	Elements of a method statement.
Events:	Actions performed by a control.

There are a few more terms to be familiar with when using the Object Browser. Groups of related objects are called ***classes***; collections of VBA and Excel object *classes* are called ***libraries***; and the properties, methods, and constants of a selected *class* of *objects* are known as the ***members*** of the *class* of *objects*. Use the Object Browser to search different *libraries* of *objects* for a list of all *classes* of a specified *object*. This allows you to research the *class* members to find out which methods and properties can be applied. Please refer to Appendix C for more information on VBA classes and object-oriented programming.

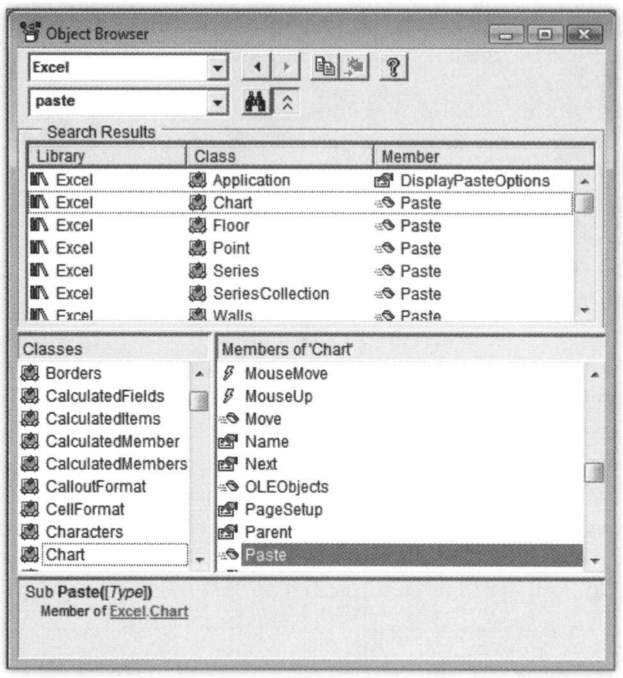

Figure 11.3 The Object Browser lists all libraries of properties, methods and events in VBA and Excel.

To find all of the properties and methods associated with a particular object, first select a library from the library drop-down list at the top of the window; then type the *object* name in the search field. For example, if we select the Excel library and type "worksheet" in the search field, we see the results shown in Figure 11.4. Two windows appear; the first is the Search Results window, which displays a list of *classes* to which the *object* belongs to, and the second shows all *classes* and members related to the selected search result.

For example, in Figure 11.4, we have selected the first worksheet result from the Search Results window; we can see that the worksheet *object* has been located under *class* in the window below. We can now view all of the members of this *class* and view a more detailed description of the property, method, or constant selected in the bottom window. Here, we have selected the *Activate* method from the member list, which is described as an *Event* and a *Member of Excel worksheet*.

The Object Browser is a very useful tool for determining the best way to manipulate an *object* of interest.

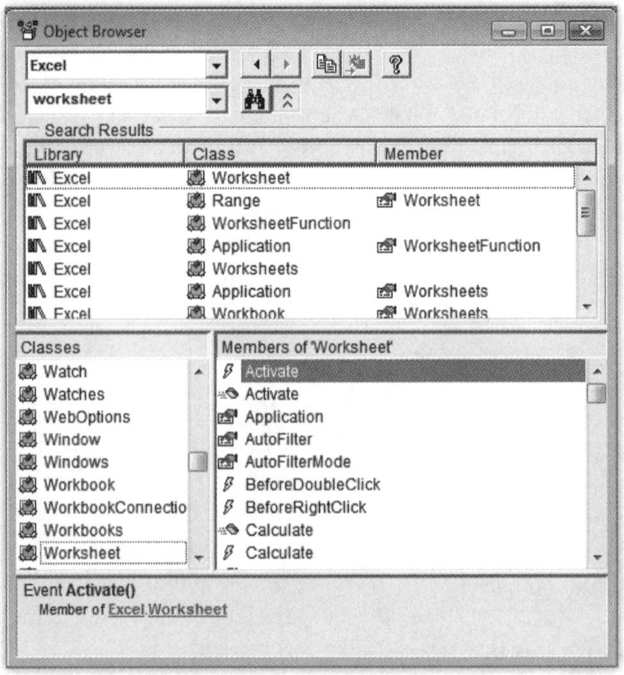

Figure 11.4 Search results for a worksheet as an Excel *object* in the Object Browser.

Summary

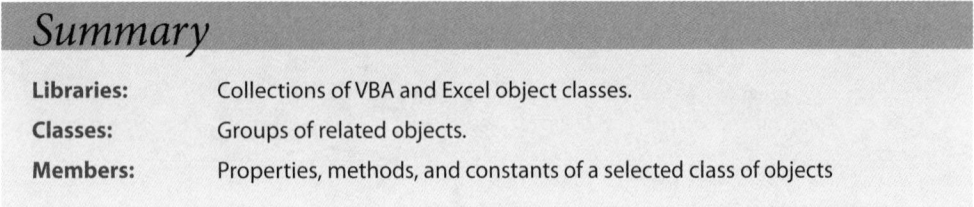

Libraries:	Collections of VBA and Excel object classes.
Classes:	Groups of related objects.
Members:	Properties, methods, and constants of a selected class of objects

11.4 *Summary*

- The Visual Basic Editor (VBE) is the environment in which we work with VBA programming code.
- There are three main windows in VBE: the Code Window, the Project Explorer, and the Properties Window.
- The Project Explorer lists all projects in any open workbook. Each workbook has a project, and each project can have several parts: its *objects*, *modules*, and *forms*. Each of these project parts can have VBA code associated with it.
- The Properties window contains detailed information about any selected project part from the Project Explorer. We can adjust the basic properties and more advanced ones in this window. These properties include font size of all the text in a worksheet and user form items. The user form properties tend to be the most commonly used.
- The main window is the Code Window, which is in the central section of the VBE. This window displays the VBA code for the highlighted project in the Project Explorer. When we record macros, we simultaneously create VBA code in the Visual Basic Editor.
- The Immediate Window and the Watch Window are more useful for debugging purposes. Whatever we type in the Immediate Window is executed as soon as we enter it. In the Watch Window, variable names, when typed, are "watched" by VBE and displayed whenever their values change.

- There are three main toolbars in VBE: Standard, Edit, and Debug.
- The Object Browser provides a list of *properties* and *methods* of all Excel objects that may be manipulated in VBA. *Properties* are the physical descriptions of all Excel *objects*, and the description of the particular *property* is called the *value* of the *property*.
- Methods are the actions that can be performed on the object. The elements of a method statement are called the *arguments* of the method.
- Groups of related objects are called *classes*; collections of VBA and Excel *object classes* are called *libraries*; and the *properties*, methods, and constants of a selected class of objects are known as the *members* of the *class* of *objects*.

11.5 *Exercises*

11.5.1 Review Questions

1. List and define the three parts of an Excel project.
2. What is the difference between a property and a method?
3. Using the Object Browser, give three examples of properties within the Chart class.
4. Using the *Object Browser*, identify whether the items listed below are a function, a property, or an event. Next, list a class for which the selected item is a member of.
   - **a.** WindowActivate
   - **b.** Cells
   - **c.** SumIf
   - **d.** Protect
   - **e.** ColorIndex
5. What is a procedure?
6. What are the two main procedure types?
7. What are the options listed on the Edit toolbar?
8. Using the Object Browser, find the arguments of the Sort method.
9. Do the Project Explorer and Properties windows have to be open at all times?
10. How do you insert a module into a project?

CHAPTER

twelve

Recording Macros

chapter OVERVIEW

12.1 Introduction

This chapter gives an introduction to working with the Visual Basic for Applications (VBA) programming language through the discussion of macros. Recording macros will automatically create VBA code which we can review in order to understand how VBA performs basic Excel functions. It is very important that the user understands the material in this chapter as this is the basics for reading, understanding, and writing VBA code. We also introduce some basic user interface in this chapter. This user interface creates a connection between the VBA code and the Excel spreadsheet so that the user can easily perform the actions written in VBA. We discuss user interface development in more detail in Chapter 18. In developing a spreadsheet-based DSS, we will use VBA to enhance the basic spreadsheet functionality. It is important to understand how to select and manipulate Excel objects using various properties and methods. We discuss the most commonly used properties and methods in detail in Chapter 13; however, this chapter will introduce the reader to basic VBA coding and Excel object manipulation.

In this chapter, the reader will learn how to:

- Record a macro.
- Write simple VBA procedures.
- Create event procedures.
- Assign macros to Form Control objects in Excel.
- Customize the Ribbon and Quick Access Toolbar by assigning macros.

12.2 Macros

Macros are technically defined as units of VBA code. In Excel, macros can be considered a way to automate a series of actions in a spreadsheet application. Macros can either be created directly with VBA code in the Visual Basic Editor, or they can be recorded in Excel. To record a macro, you must know exactly the actions that we wish to perform and then use the ***Record Macro*** command under the Code group of Developer tab. You can then translate standard Excel functionality into the VBA code.

Summary

Macro:	A way to automate a series of actions in a spreadsheet application.
Record Macro:	Creates a *macro* and builds the associated VBA code.

12.2.1 Recording Macros

Let's consider the simple example of combining the actions of copying and pasting data. Figure 12.1 presents a table of used car information that a dealer has in his database. He wants to place the data highlighted in yellow in a newspaper advertisement. To prepare for recording the macro, you should rehearse the steps needed to copy these four columns and paste them into the cells below. You begin by selecting the first three columns (Make, Model, and Year) of the Used Cars table and then, while pressing the CTRL key, select the last column (Price). You then either *right-click* and choose *Copy* from the shortcut menu, or use the shortcut key CTRL-C to copy the selected data. Then, you place the cursor in the first cell of the Newspaper Information table (cell C19) and paste the data either by *right-clicking* and choosing *Paste* from the shortcut menu, or by using the shortcut key CTRL-*V*.

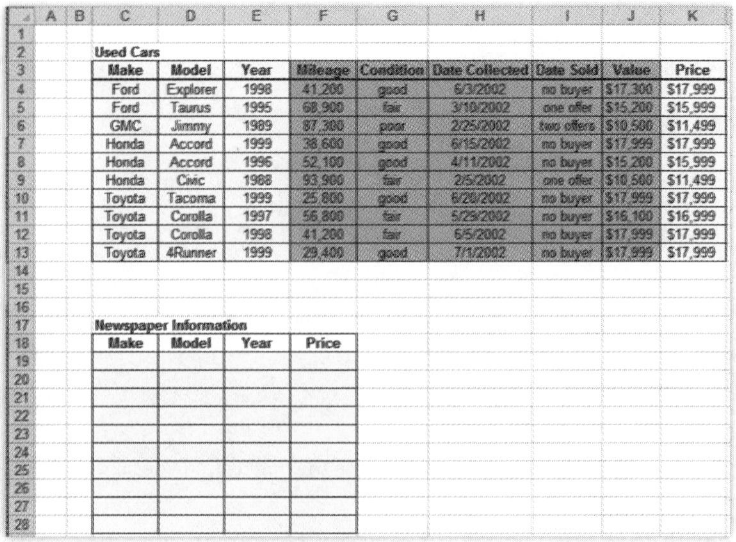

Used Cars

Make	Model	Year	Mileage	Condition	Date Collected	Date Sold	Value	Price
Ford	Explorer	1998	41,200	good	6/3/2002	no buyer	$17,300	$17,999
Ford	Taurus	1995	68,900	fair	3/10/2002	one offer	$15,200	$15,999
GMC	Jimmy	1989	87,300	poor	2/25/2002	two offers	$10,500	$11,499
Honda	Accord	1999	38,600	good	6/15/2002	no buyer	$17,999	$17,999
Honda	Accord	1996	52,100	good	4/11/2002	no buyer	$15,200	$15,999
Honda	Civic	1988	93,900	fair	2/5/2002	one offer	$10,500	$11,499
Toyota	Tacoma	1999	25,800	good	6/28/2002	no buyer	$17,999	$17,999
Toyota	Corolla	1997	56,800	fair	5/29/2002	no buyer	$16,100	$16,999
Toyota	Corolla	1998	41,200	fair	6/5/2002	no buyer	$17,999	$17,999
Toyota	4Runner	1999	29,400	good	7/1/2002	no buyer	$17,999	$17,999

Newspaper Information

Make	Model	Year	Price

Figure 12.1 Copying information from Used Cars to Newspaper Information.

Now that you know the exact steps you need to perform when recording the macro, you are ready to initiate the *recording*. To do so, you click on Developer > Code > *Record Macro* command on the Ribbon.

After pressing the *Record Macro* button, the window in Figure 12.2 appears. Here, you name the macro and define its location as well any shortcut keys that we wish to associate with it. For this example, you can simply name this macro "CarCopyPaste" and apply it to this workbook without any associated shortcut key. After pressing *OK*, the *Record Macro* command at the Code group is transformed into the *Stop Recording* button.

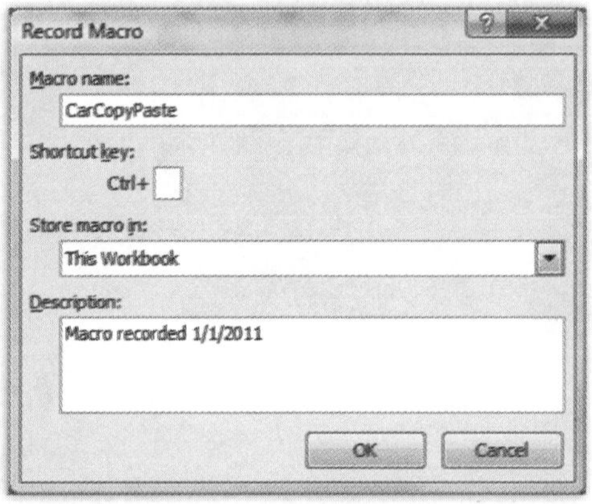

Figure 12.2 The Record Macro window prompts us to create a name for the *macro* we are about to record. We can also define the location of the macro and associate a shortcut key with it.

Once you start recording, *every* action you perform on the spreadsheet will be written into the macro code. Since you are prepared for the copy and paste task, you can just repeat the steps mentioned above and copy and paste the yellow columns from the Used Cars table into the Newspaper Information table. Once you have finished pasting the cells, you press the *Stop Recording* button. You are now finished recording the macro.

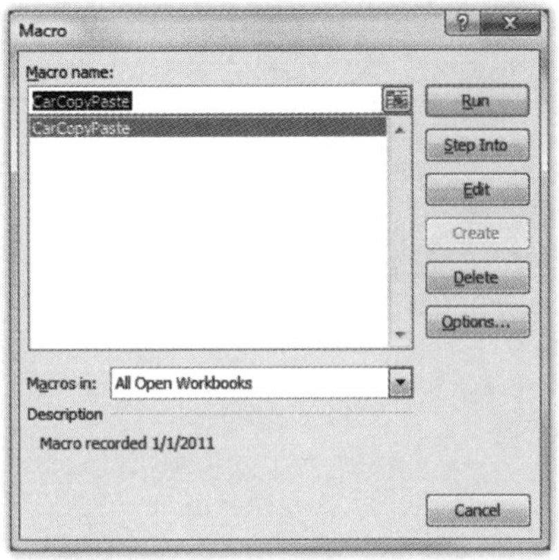

Figure 12.3 To play a recorded *macro*, we choose the *macro* name desired and press *Run*.

To ensure that the macro was correctly recorded, you can erase the data just pasted into the Newspaper Information table and run the macro. Click on the ***Macros*** command button under the Code group. The Macro window will appear (see Figure 12.3). You can then select the "CarCopyPaste" macro from the list and click *Run*. All of the copy and paste actions we recorded should then be performed; this results in the complete tables in Figure 12.4. The final step is saving the workbook where the macro is written as an *Excel Macro-Enabled Workbook (*.xlsm)*. The extension of the workbook changes from *xlsx* to *xlsm*. Notice that, Excel will not save the macros you build unless the workbook is saved as an xlsm file.

Macros can be very useful when repetitive and tedious tasks need to be performed. We can create a macro for each task using the *Record Macro* button and then play the macro for the associated task you need to perform.

Used Cars

Make	Model	Year	Mileage	Condition	Date Collected	Date Sold	Value	Price
Ford	Explorer	1998	41,200	good	6/3/2002	no buyer	$17,300	$17,999
Ford	Taurus	1995	68,900	fair	3/10/2002	one offer	$15,200	$15,999
GMC	Jimmy	1989	87,300	poor	2/25/2002	two offers	$10,500	$11,499
Honda	Accord	1999	38,600	good	6/15/2002	no buyer	$17,999	$17,999
Honda	Accord	1996	52,100	good	4/11/2002	no buyer	$15,200	$15,999
Honda	Civic	1988	93,900	fair	2/5/2002	one offer	$10,500	$11,499
Toyota	Tacoma	1999	25,800	good	6/20/2002	no buyer	$17,999	$17,999
Toyota	Corolla	1997	56,800	fair	5/29/2002	no buyer	$16,100	$16,999
Toyota	Corolla	1998	41,200	fair	6/5/2002	no buyer	$17,999	$17,999
Toyota	4Runner	1999	29,400	good	7/1/2002	no buyer	$17,999	$17,999

Newspaper Information

Make	Model	Year	Price
Ford	Explorer	1998	$17,999
Ford	Taurus	1995	$15,999
GMC	Jimmy	1989	$11,499
Honda	Accord	1999	$17,999
Honda	Accord	1996	$15,999
Honda	Civic	1988	$11,499
Toyota	Tacoma	1999	$17,999
Toyota	Corolla	1997	$16,999
Toyota	Corolla	1998	$17,999
Toyota	4Runner	1999	$17,999

Figure 12.4 After running the copy and paste *macro*, both tables are complete.

Summary

Steps in Recording a Macro:

1. Choose *Developer tab > Code group > Record Macro button.*
2. Perform sequence of actions in Excel.
3. Choose *Developer tab > Code group > Stop Recording button.*

12.2.2 The VBA Code

Let us now determine how the *Macro Recorder* actually creates VBA code while we are performing standard Excel functionality. In Chapter 10, we learned how to *sort* and *filter.* In this example, suppose there is a database for the Miami Airport that lists Flight Destinations, Number of Stops, Class (Economy or Business), and Price (see Figure 12.5). We want to be able to *filter* this information so that we can do the following: view flights to Beijing, view flights to Hong Kong, and view all flights. We also want to be able to *sort* the data by Number of Stops and by Price.

First, let us review what needs to be done to filter a list. We need to highlight the entire table (cells *B3:E15*), then select *Data* tab > *Sort & Filter group* > *Filter command* from the Ribbon. Next, to filter for specific flight destinations, we simply select Beijing, Hong Kong, or All from the filter drop-down list near Destination. Now we just need to record these steps as three separate macros.

	A	B	C	D	E	F
1						
2		*Flight Availabilities from Miami, FL*				
3		Destination	Stops	Class	Price	
4		Beijing	5	Economy	*$700*	
5		Beijing	4	Economy	*$900*	
6		Hong Kong	5	Economy	*$1,100*	
7		Beijing	3	Economy	*$1,300*	
8		Hong Kong	4	Economy	*$1,400*	
9		Hong Kong	4	Business	*$1,750*	
10		Hong Kong	3	Economy	*$1,800*	
11		Beijing	3	Business	*$1,900*	
12		Beijing	2	Business	*$2,000*	
13		Hong Kong	3	Business	*$2,100*	
14		Hong Kong	3	Business	*$2,200*	
15		Hong Kong	2	Business	*$2,500*	
16						

Figure 12.5 Database of flight information for the Miami Airport.

For the first macro, we press the *Developer* > *Code* > *Record Macro* button, and name the macro "ViewBeijingFlights." Then, we highlight the data and click on the *Data* > Sort & *Filter* > *Filter* command. Select Beijing from the Destination filter options, select cell *A1*, and finally press the *Stop* button.

For the second macro, we press the *Developer* > *Code* > *Record Macro* command under, and name the macro "ViewHongKongFlights." Then, we highlight the data and click on the *Data* > Sort & *Filter* > *Filter* command. Select cell *A1*, and finally press the *Stop* command.

For the third macro, we press the *Developer* > *Code* > *Record Macro* command, and name the macro "ViewAllFlights." Then, we highlight the data and click on the *Data* > Sort & *Filter* > *Filter* button. Select cell *A1*, and finally press the *Stop* command.

After testing the macros to make sure that they perform the correct actions, you can now view the created VBA code. To do this, you simply go to VBE (by pressing *Alt+F11*) and click on Module1 in the Project Explorer. Then, you find the three macros recorded as separate sub procedures with the names that you assigned (see Figure 12.6). Note: There will usually be some comments created with our macro (such as "Macro created by"); comment lines begin with a single quotation mark. These comments are not part of the code and can be deleted. In Figure 12.6, we have already deleted these comments.

```
Sub ViewHongKongFlights()
    Range("B3:E15").Select
    Selection.AutoFilter
    Selection.AutoFilter Field:=1, Criteria1:="Hong Kong"
    Range("A1").Select
End Sub
Sub ViewBeijingFlights()
    Range("B3:E15").Select
    Selection.AutoFilter
    Selection.AutoFilter Field:=1, Criteria1:="Beijing"
    Range("A1").Select
End Sub
Sub ViewAllFlights()
    Range("B3:E15").Select
    Selection.AutoFilter
    Selection.AutoFilter Field:=1
    Range("A1").Select
End Sub
```

Figure 12.6 The VBA code created from recording the three filtering macros.

The first line of code for all three macros, *Range("B3:E15"). Select* is an example of the Select Method for the Range Object. To code this directly, you simply type the word *Range* and specify its range (there are other ways to identify a range, which we will discuss in Chapter 13). Then, you type a period and an automatic drop-down list of corresponding methods and properties will appear. You can either choose *Select* from the list or just type it directly (notice that as soon as we type an *S*, the VBE will automatically try to guess which method or property we want to use and type it for us).

The next line of code, *Selection.AutoFilter*, uses the Selection as the object and AutoFilter as the method. Again, you can view a list of methods and properties associated with the Selection object by typing *Selection* and a period.

The third line of code, *Selection.AutoFilter Field:=1, Criteria1:=...*, is an example of an argument of a method. Here, the method is AutoFilter and the arguments are Field and Criteria. The Field is the column of data in the selected range that we want to filter from, and the Criteria is the value of the filter drop-down arrow next to this field. For this example, Field 1 is the "Destination" column and we use the Criteria of "Hong Kong" and "Beijing." When you want to view all of the data, you can either specify the Criteria as "All" or leave it blank, as shown above.

Notice that we are actually typing the AutoFilter method twice in our code. You will often find that some coding redundancies will happen with the *Macro Recorder*. You can actually modify these macros directly in the VBA code by deleting the first *Selection.AutoFilter* statement from each sub procedure (see Figure 12.7). To test the macros again, we return to Excel (press *Alt+F11*).

The last line of code, *Range("A1").Select*, selects a cell so that the filtered data is not still highlighted after performing the macro.

```
Sub ViewHongKongFlights()
    Range("B3:E15").Select
    Selection.AutoFilter Field:=1, Criteria1:="Hong Kong"
    Range("A1").Select
End Sub
Sub ViewBeijingFlights()
    Range("B3:E15").Select
    Selection.AutoFilter Field:=1, Criteria1:="Beijing"
    Range("A1").Select
End Sub
Sub ViewAllFlights()
    Range("B3:E15").Select
    Selection.AutoFilter Field:=1
    Range("A1").Select
End Sub
```

Figure 12.7 Modifying the VBA code to reduce redundancies.

Now we want to create the sorting macros. Again, we should first review the steps needed to sort the data. We highlight the same range of data and click on *Data > Sort & Filter > Sort* command. Next, we specify our sorting criteria and order in the Sort dialog box.

To record the first sorting macro, we press the Developer > Code > *Record Macro* command, and name the macro "SortByStops," then we highlight the data, and click on *Data > Sort & Filter > Sort* command. Select "Stops" from the "Sort by" list, select "Values" from the "Sort on" list, and select "Largest to Smallest" from the "Order" list, then press OK to close the Sort dialog box. Select cell *A1*, and then press the Stop Recording command.

To record the second sorting macro, we press the Developer > Code > *Record Macro* command, and name the macro "SortByPrice." We then highlight the data and click on *Data > Sort & Filter > Sort* command. Select "Price" from the "Sort by" list, select "Values" from the "Sort on" list, and select "Largest to Smallest" from the "Order" list, then press OK to close the Sort dialog box. Select cell *A1*, and then press the Stop Recording button.

We can now test these macros and return to VBE to view the code (see Figure 12.8). This code will also appear in Module1. The first line of code for these macros is the same as the filtering macros; it just selects the range we are interested in sorting. The last line of code is also the same; it just selects a cell to de-highlight the data.

The second line of code clears all the *SortFields* objects in the active worksheet. The third line of code creates a new sort field and returns a *SortFields* object. (Notice the line-continuation code "_" in this long line of code.) Recall that Excel objects are organized in a hierarchical fashion. In this case, *ActiveWorkbook* is an Excel object, and *Worksheets* is a collection of object in the *ActiveWorkbook*. Similarly, *SortFields* is a collection of objects within the *Sort* object. The *Add* method of *SortFields* object has a number of arguments. The arguments we specified when recording the macro were: Key1, which was the column selected from the "Sort by" list; SortOn, which was the sort by values option; and Order1, which was the Ascending or Descending option. The forth line of code uses the With construct (which we will discuss in Chapter 13) to set several properties of object *Sort*. The source of these properties is other options available from the Sort dialog box. These may be useful for future applications, but for this example we can delete most of these properties, other than the *SetRange* and *Apply* which identify the range and apply the sort properties. It is always a good idea to retest our macros after modifying the code.

```
(General)                                    ViewBusinessFlights

Sub SortByStops()
    Range("B3:E15").Select
    ActiveWorkbook.Worksheets("Fig_12.5_to_12.20").Sort.SortFields.Clear
    ActiveWorkbook.Worksheets("Fig_12.5_to_12.20").Sort.SortFields.Add Key:=Range _
        ("C3:C15"), SortOn:=xlSortOnValues, Order:=xlDescending, DataOption:= _
        xlSortNormal
    With ActiveWorkbook.Worksheets("Fig_12.5_to_12.20").Sort
        .SetRange Range("B3:E15")
        .Header = xlGuess
        .MatchCase = False
        .Orientation = xlTopToBottom
        .SortMethod = xlPinYin
        .Apply
    End With
    Range("A1").Select
End Sub
Sub SortByPrice()
    Range("B3:E15").Select
    ActiveWorkbook.Worksheets("Fig_12.5_to_12.20").Sort.SortFields.Clear
    ActiveWorkbook.Worksheets("Fig_12.5_to_12.20").Sort.SortFields.Add Key:=Range _
        ("C3:C15"), SortOn:=xlSortOnValues, Order:=xlDescending, DataOption:= _
        xlSortNormal
    With ActiveWorkbook.Worksheets("Fig_12.5_to_12.20").Sort
        .SetRange Range("B3:E15")
        .Header = xlGuess
        .MatchCase = False
        .Orientation = xlTopToBottom
        .SortMethod = xlPinYin
        .Apply
    End With
    Range("A1").Select
End Sub
```

Figure 12.8 Adding the code for the two sorting macros to the module.

In our updated code (see Figure 12.9), we see that the Key is specified by the range name of the column that we are sorting by. For the first macro, Range("C4:C15") corresponds to the Stops column. Similarly, for the second macro, Range("E4:E15") corresponds to the Price column. The Order is specified by "xlAscending" or "xlDescending." This "xl" notation appears several times and denotes an Excel-specific option or constant.

Again, VBE is helpful while typing this code. If we type *SortFields* and a period and then select *Add* from the list of methods and properties, a small dialog box comes into view; it lists the possible arguments that we can use with the *Add* method.

Now, let us try creating the macro originally from the VBA code and then we can view its performance in Excel. Suppose that we also want to filter the Business or Economy Class flights. We know from recording the above filtering macros what code is required; however, some of the arguments will be different.

```
(General)

Sub SortByStops()
    ActiveWorkbook.Worksheets("Fig_12.5_to_12.20").Sort.SortFields.Clear
    ActiveWorkbook.Worksheets("Fig_12.5_to_12.20").Sort.SortFields.Add Key:=Range _
        ("C4:C15"), SortOn:=xlSortOnValues, Order:=xlDescending
    With ActiveWorkbook.Worksheets("Fig_12.5_to_12.20").Sort
        .SetRange Range("B3:E15")
        .Apply
    End With
    Range("A1").Select
End Sub
Sub SortByPrice()
    ActiveWorkbook.Worksheets("Fig_12.5_to_12.20").Sort.SortFields.Clear
    ActiveWorkbook.Worksheets("Fig_12.5_to_12.20").Sort.SortFields.Add Key:=Range _
        ("E4:E15"), SortOn:=xlSortOnValues, Order:=xlAscending
    With ActiveWorkbook.Worksheets("Fig_12.5_to_12.20").Sort
        .SetRange Range("B3:E15")
        .Apply
    End With
    Range("A1").Select
End Sub
```

Figure 12.9 Updated code with only the necessary arguments listed.

First, we need to make sure that we are in the VBE Code Window. So, we move down to a new line under our last sorting macro and type the beginning of this new filtering macro as a sub procedure:

Sub ViewEconomyFlights()

After typing this line and pressing enter, the line *End Sub* automatically appears. These statements are the first and last line of any sub procedure:

Sub SubName()
End Sub

Now, referring to the filtering code from before, we need to select the range we want to filter. In this case, we will be using the same range as in the previous filtering macros, so we can type the same line of code:

Range("B3: E15").Select

We can now use the AutoFilter method for this selection. We can either type AutoFilter directly or choose it from the list of methods and properties that appear after typing the period after Selection.

Selection.AutoFilter

When we are typing the arguments for the AutoFilter method, we will encounter some differences from our previous recorded macros. Previously, the Field argument was equal to "1," which is the first column of the range. However, this time instead of filtering by Destination, we are filtering by Class, which is the third column. Therefore, the Field argument should be "3." For the first of these two new macros, the Criteria argument needs to be "Economy," since that is the Class value we will be filtering. So, the complete AutoFilter statement should be:

Selection.AutoFilter Field:=3, Criteria1:= "Economy"

Note that we have typed *Criteria1* and not just *Criteria*, because there can be more than one criterion when filtering. All we have left is the last line of code, which will select a cell in order to de-highlight the filtered range.

Range("A1").Select

For the next macro, which will filter Business Class flights, the code will be the same, except the Criteria argument will be "Business" instead of "Economy." Therefore, we can just copy and paste what we have already typed a few lines of below. We must also remember to change the name of the sub procedure to "ViewBusinessFlights."

The final code for these two macros is displayed in Figure 12.10. We can now save our work and return to the Excel window in order to test our macros.

```
(General)
        .SetRange Range("B3:E15")
        .Apply
    End With
    Range("A1").Select
End Sub

Sub ViewEconomyFlights()
    Range("B3:E15").Select
    Selection.AutoFilter Field:=3, Criteria1:="Economy"
    Range("A1").Select
End Sub
Sub ViewBusinessFlights()
    Range("B3:E15").Select
    Selection.AutoFilter Field:=3, Criteria1:="Business"
    Range("A1").Select
End Sub
```

Figure 12.10 The two new filter macros typed directly as VBA code below the previously recorded macros.

We recommend that you experiment with typing other macros directly with VBA code. If you are unsure of how to perform a function, just record the macro first from Excel. Then, you can simply view the code created in VBE and use it to create a new macro.

Summary

Main Sub Procedure Code:

Sub SubName() ... (code here) ...

End Sub

Some Objects, Methods, and Arguments used:

Object = Range, Method = Select

Object = Selection, Method = AutoFilter, Arguments = Field, Criteria

Object = SortFields, Method = Add, Arguments = Key, SortOn, Order

12.2.3 Event Procedures

Events are actions that take place in the Excel window and are linked directly to a set of actions in VBA code. We connect events to code by using ***Event Procedures***. Examples of event procedures include *Click*, *Change*, and *Activate*. For each Excel object selected in the Project Explorer, there is a list of associated objects in a drop-down menu in the upper-left hand corner of the Code Window. After selecting an object from this list, you can view corresponding events in the drop-down menu in the upper-right hand corner of the Code Window. Each object in Excel has its own corresponding list of event procedures. In Figure 12.11, we see a list of event procedures for the workbook object that we selected from the Project Explorer. We will see many objects and events when we discuss user forms in Chapter 18.

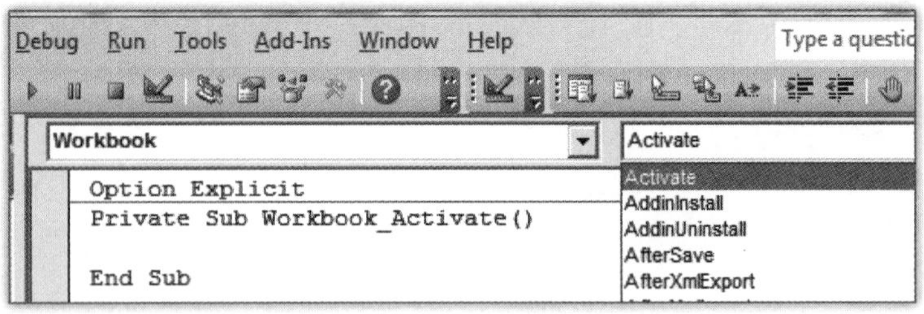

Figure 12.11 Event procedures for the workbook object listed in the drop-down menu.

An event procedure is just like a sub procedure, except that it is associated with a particular action of an Excel object. The name structure of event procedures is also different from that of sub procedures; that is, sub procedures can have almost any name (as we saw when giving names to macros we recorded) while event procedures have the name structure *object_event*. Event procedures are necessary when building user interfaces. For example, instead of asking the user to run a macro to perform the filtering discussed above, we may want to have some buttons on the screen that will perform corresponding *macros* when clicked. To do this, we first create a button and then use a *Click* event procedure.

To create a button in Excel, we can use the *Developer > Controls* group on the Ribbon. Click on the *Insert* drop-down command. The *Form Controls* and *ActiveX Controls* dialog box shown in Figure 12.12 then appears. Form Controls work different from ActiveX controls. ActiveX controls, a subset of those available on UserForms (to be discussed in Chapter 18), are more difficult to work with but give you flexibility when working with controls. There are several objects that can be placed on the spreadsheet: command buttons, scroll bars, list boxes, etc. For now, let's choose the *Command Button* object by clicking on its icon at the ActiveX Controls dialog box. Then, click on the spreadsheet where you want the button to appear.

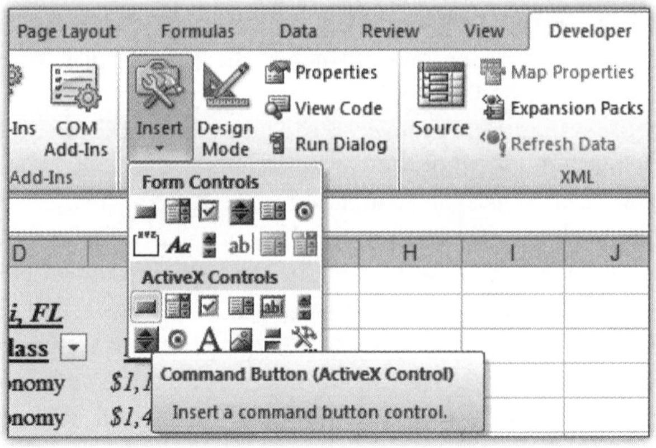

Figure 12.12 Form Controls and ActiveX Controls dialog box appears when clicking on the Insert drop-down command.

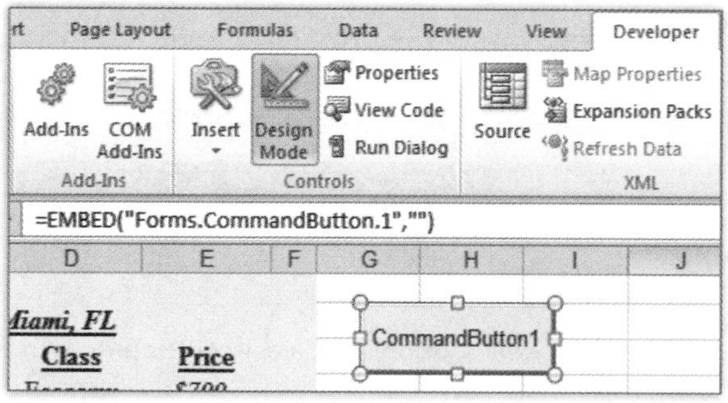

Figure 12.13 Selecting Command Button icon from ActiveX Controls dialog box and placing the button on the spreadsheet.

We must now view the Properties window of the Command Button to specify its name and caption values. When we work with ActiveX Controls, the *Design Mode* command under the Developer > Controls group is activated. To view the Properties window, you can simply click on the *Properties* command in the Controls group (see Figure 12.14). These properties are important for manipulating any object in the ActiveX Controls dialog box. For example, aside from the name and caption of an object, we can change its font, size, and color from the list of properties. There are also some other specific properties associated with different objects. For example, a scroll bar object has a minimum value, maximum value, and change amount properties that can be set.

For the command button we just created, we enter the name *cmdHongKong* and give the caption "View Hong Kong Flights" for the Name and Caption properties, respectively. Let us clarify that the name property of an object becomes the name of the actual object which we may refer to in our code (such as *cmdHongKong*) whereas the caption property of an object is the text that is displayed on the object ("View Hong Kong Flights"). (We start the button name with the letters "cmd" since it is a command button. This is not required by Excel or VBA, but it is a good programming practice in order to keep track of the type of objects created. We list other abbreviations for controls in Chapter 18.) We see that our button is updated as we enter the caption information in the Properties window. We can also modify the font or button colors at this time; however, we will not detail all of these options here.

Now that the Command Button has been created, we are ready to write the event procedure that associates a set of actions with the *Click* event for this button. To create event procedures for a Control Toolbox object, we must write the code in the appropriate worksheet object in VBE, not in a module. That is, this control becomes an object associated with the worksheet object in which it is placed. For this example, we will create the event procedure in the Sheet1 object module from the Project Explorer. We can use exactly the same code as we recorded above to filter the Hong Kong flights. However, we must re-title that sub procedure as a new event procedure by typing instead:

Sub cmdHongKong_Click()

Here, we have entered the name of the Command Button (as we specified in the Properties window in Excel) and then an underscore followed by the type of event with which we want to associate the code. We could also have selected the Command Button *cmdHongKong* from the drop-down list at the top of the Code window and then selected *Click* in the list of events (see Figure 12.15). The Command Button now appears in the list of objects for the selected worksheet, since it has been placed in this worksheet.

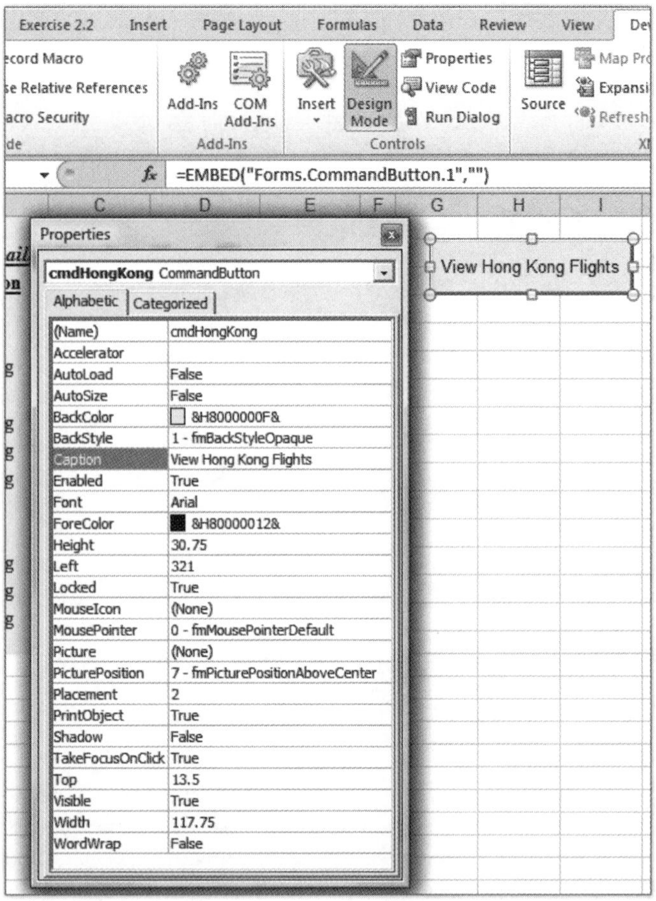

Figure 12.14 The Properties window for the command button. Modifying the Name and Caption properties.

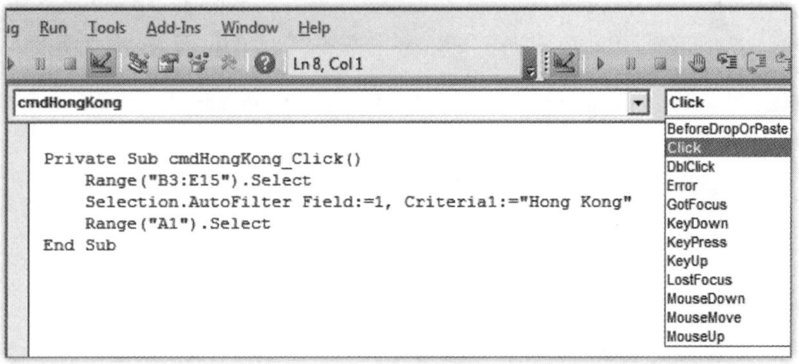

Figure 12.15 The event procedure code for the *Click* event of the *cmdHongKong* Command Button.

Notice that in front of the procedure's name, VBE automatically inserted the word *Private*. This implies that the procedure can only be called from the sheet module in which the code was written. However, we may not always want to limit our coding in this way. Private and public procedures will be discussed in more detail in Chapter 15.

Now, we should return to Excel to test the functionality of our button. We must first make sure that we are no longer in *Design View*. Design View is active when we are creating or modifying any ActiveX Controls object on the sheet. To activate or deactivate the Design View, just click the *Design View* command in Developer tab > Controls group. Now we can click "View Hong Kong Flights" and see that the filtering works correctly (see Figure 12.16).

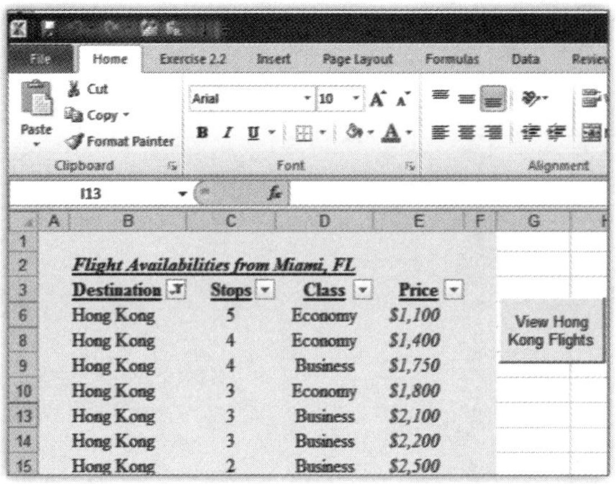

Figure 12.16 Clicking the Command Button runs the associated event procedure to *filter* the data.

We could now create similar Command Buttons for the other macros that we previously recorded. This time we will use Form Controls listed on the Insert drop-down dialog box (see Figure 12.12). To choose the *Button* object you should click on it, and then click somewhere on the spreadsheet. The *Assign Macro* dialog box appears (see Figure 12.17). From here, we see a list of all macros created in this workbook. For our first button, we select the "ViewHongKong-Flights" and click OK. We now edit the caption and change the format of the Button. You can simply right-click on the Button and then select *Edit Text* option from the shortcut menu (see Figure 12.18). We replace its default caption "Button 1" by typing "View Hong Kong Flights." To change the format of the *Button* you can select the *Format Control...* option from the shortcut menu. The *Format Control* dialog box (see Figure 12.19) allows you to change the font type, style and size of the caption, or change its alignment, etc. Now that the Button is created and the macro has been assigned, we are ready to execute the macro by clicking on it.

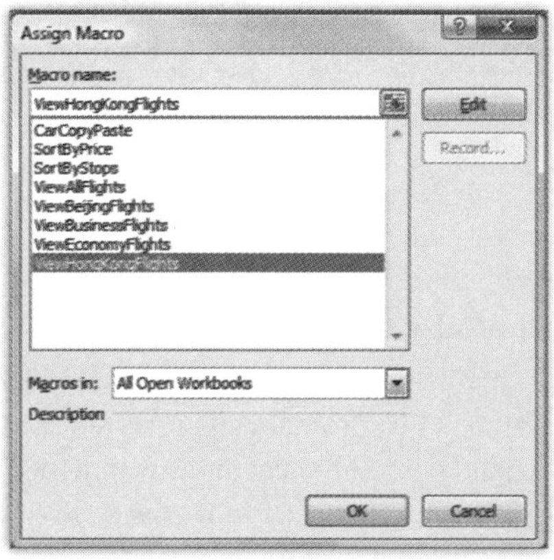

Figure 12.17 Selection the macro to be assigned to the Button created on the spreadsheet.

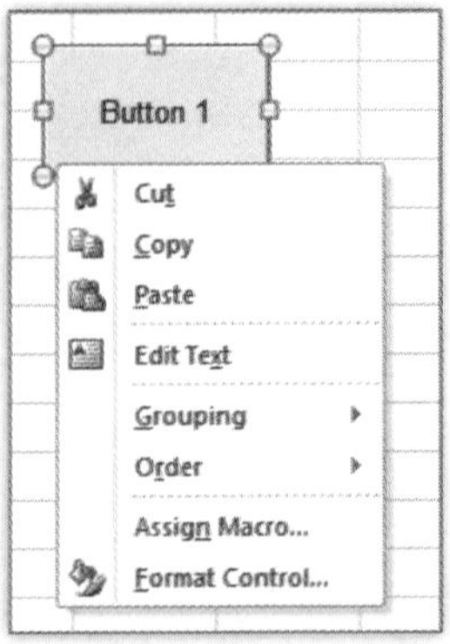

Figure 12.18 The shortcut menu appears when you right-click on the Button object.

This procedure demonstrates another advantage of creating buttons since any public macro from any module can be assigned to any object on any sheet. This way we are not limited to a private event procedure. We can repeat this method until we have created a button for each of our macros for this example (see Figure 12.18).

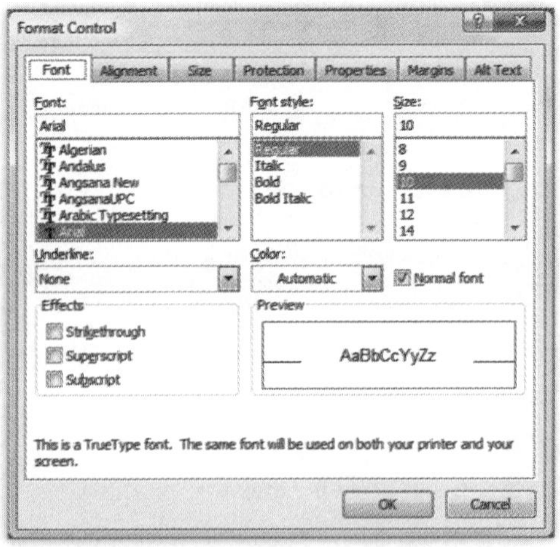

Figure 12.19 The Format Control dialog box.

To review, there are two options for creating buttons with which to associate macros. These are: selecting an ActiveX Controls or Form Controls listed in the Insert drop-down dialog box listed in the Developer tab > Controls group. Using an ActiveX control requires us to set various properties to manipulate formatting. We must also create a name for the control which we use when writing an event procedure. This event procedure code must be located in the worksheet object (selected from the Project Explorer) in which the control is placed. When using Form Controls, we can change their default caption and format them easily. We can also assign any macro or any public procedure from any module to this button. Some ActiveX controls are very unique and can be used often with user forms (as described in Chapter 18); however, for creating buttons, using Form Controls is probably the simpler choice.

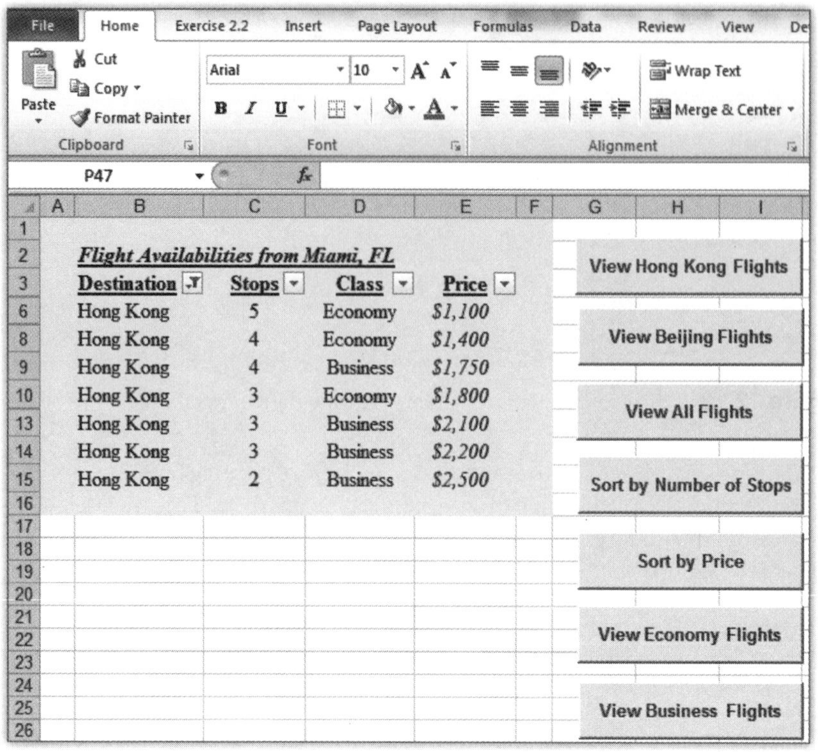

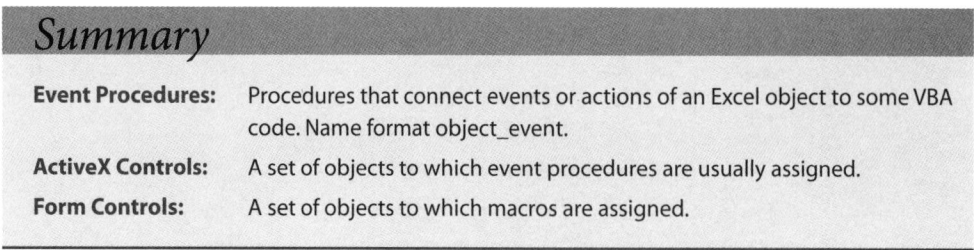

Figure 12.20 Creating a button to assign to each macro using the Form Controls.

Summary

Event Procedures: Procedures that connect events or actions of an Excel object to some VBA code. Name format object_event.

ActiveX Controls: A set of objects to which event procedures are usually assigned.

Form Controls: A set of objects to which macros are assigned.

12.3 *Customizing the Ribbon and Quick Access Toolbar*

Creating buttons as a user interface can greatly aid a user unfamiliar with macros in performing desired functions. Another useful way to help a user with macros is to create new tabs and groups in the Ribbon with icons designated for each macro. You can also add macros to the Quick Access Toolbar to reach faster to macros that you frequently use. We will show how to create a new tab in the Ribbon, called "MyMacros." Within this tab we will create two groups of commands, one titled "Filter" and the other "Sort." Within each group we will add the corresponding macros created earlier.

To customize the Ribbon, right-click on the Ribbon, and then select Customize the Ribbon from the list of options presented. Excel displays the Customize Ribbon tab of the Excel Options dialog box (Figure 12.21). Excel gives you the options to either add groups of command buttons to an existing tab of the Ribbon associated with our macros, or create a new tab. To create a new tab, press the *New Tab* button in the bottom right side of Excel Options dialog box. Next, select the New Tab (Custom) from the Main Tabs list, and then click-on the *Rename* button. Title the tab "MyMacros" (see Figure 12.22). The new tab will appear on the list of main tabs in the right side of the Excel Options dialog box.

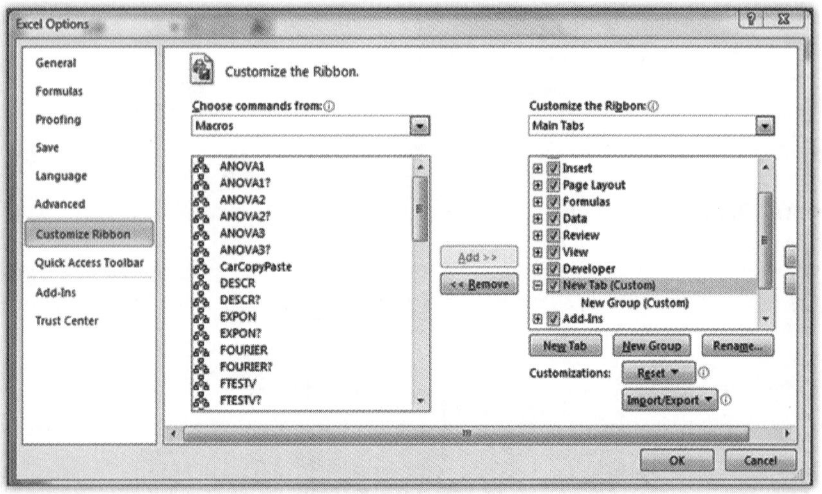

Figure 12.21 Creating a new tab on the Ribbon.

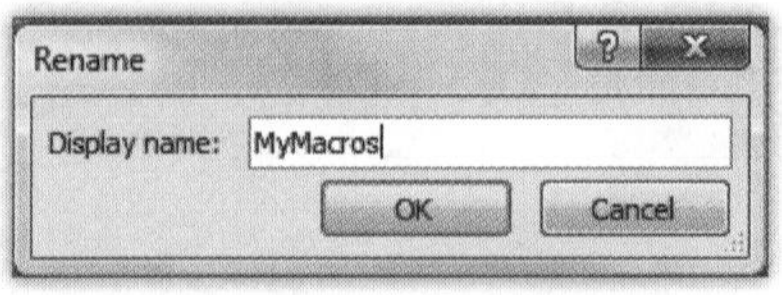

Figure 12.22 Title the new tab.

We now add two new Groups under this tab by clicking on the *New Group* button. Select the *New Group (Custom)* listed under MyMacros, and click on the Rename button to title these groups as shown in Figure 12.22. Now, you are ready to add the corresponding macros under the Filter or Sort groups.

We initially add macros to the Filter group. To display a list of all the macros contained in the current workbook you should select *Macros* from the *Choose commands from:* drop-down menu on the left side of Excel Options dialog box. From this list, select "ViewAllFlights" and then click on the *Add* button. The macro is now listed under the Filter tab. Similarly, add "ViewBusinessFlights" and "ViewEconomyFlights" to the Filter group (see Figure 12.23). You can rename the commands (macros) within each group by clicking on the *Rename* button. We change the name of each command to "All," "Business," and "Economy." We also assigned an icon to each command using the selection provided by Excel (Figure 12.24).

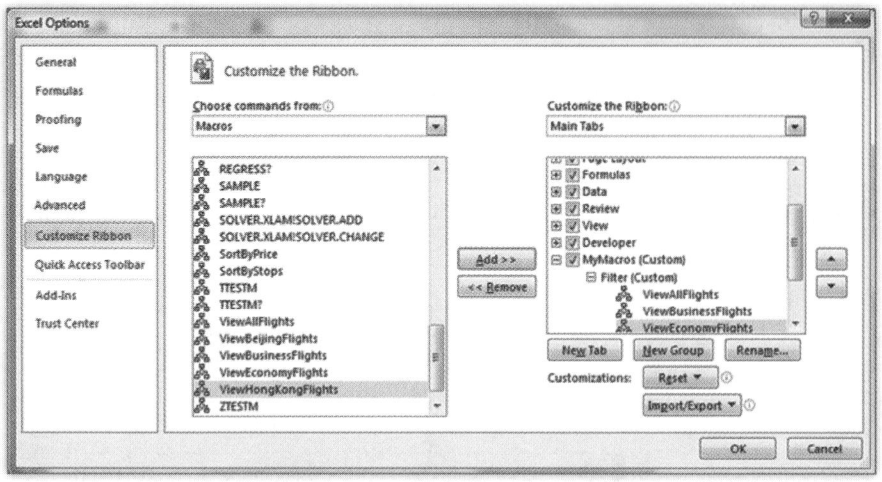

Figure 12.23 Add macros to the Filter group of MyMacros tab.

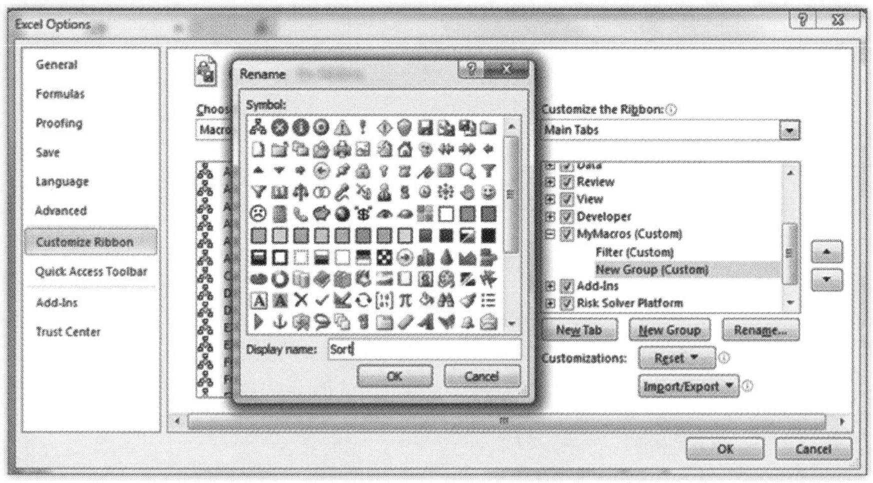

Figure 12.24 Assign icons to a command on the MyMacros tab.

We follow similar steps to add the "SortByPrice" and "SortByStops" macros to the Sort group. We use the Rename button to change the icon assigned to these macros and change the name to "Price" and "Stops" correspondingly. We finally use the *Move up* arrow of Excel Options dialog box to relocate the new tab right after the Home tab in the Ribbon as shown in Figure 12.25.

Figure 12.25 MyMacros tab on the Ribbon.

You can also customize the Quick Access Toolbar. In this toolbar you can easily add your macros following these easy steps. For example, to add the "ViewAllFFlights" macro, right click on the "All" command under the Filter group of MyMacros tab. Select the *Add to Quick Access Toolbar* from the list of options presented. Follow similar steps in order to add the "SortByStops" macro. The corresponding icons will appear in the Quick Access Toolbar as shown in Figure 12.25. These examples show how easy it is to assign macros to existing or new tabs. Again, customizing the Ribbon and Quick Access Toolbar can be an excellent tool in building a solid user interface.

12.4 Summary

- Macros are technically defined as units of VBA code. In Excel, a macro can be thought of as a means to automate a series of actions in a spreadsheet application. Macros can either be created directly with VBA code in the Visual Basic Editor, or recorded in Excel.
- To record a macro, we must know exactly the actions that we wish to perform and then use the *Macro Recorder*. Then, we can translate standard Excel functionality into VBA code.
- Steps to *Record* a *Macro*: 1. *Developer tab > Code group > Record Macro button*; 2. Perform a sequence of actions in Excel; 3. Choose *Developer tab > Code group > Stop Recording button.*
- Main Sub Procedure Code:
  Sub SubName()
  … (code here) …
  End Sub
- Some Objects, Methods, and Arguments used: Object = Range, Method = Select, Object = Selection, Method = AutoFilter, Arguments = Field, Criteria, Object = SortFields, Method = Add, Arguments = Key, SortOn, Order.
- Events are actions that can take place in the Excel window that cause an action to occur in the VBA code. We connect events to code by using *Event Procedures*. Examples of event procedures include *Click*, *Change*, and *Activate.*
- An event procedure is just like a sub procedure, except that it is associated with a particular action of an Excel object. Instead of asking a user to run a macro to perform the filtering discussed above, we may want to have some buttons on the screen that will perform corresponding macros when clicked. To do this, we would first create the button, then use a *Click* event procedure. To create a button in Excel, we need to use the Form *Controls and ActiveX Controls listed in the Developer tab > Controls group > Insert drop-down menu.*
- Creating buttons as a user interface can greatly aid a user unfamiliar with macros to perform desired functions. Another useful way to help a user with macros is to add icons of designated macros to existing or new groups and tabs of the Ribbon. This technique is called customizing the Ribbon. One can as well customize the Quick Access Toolbar by adding icons of macros that are frequently used.

12.5 Exercises

12.5.1 Review Questions

1. What is the definition of a macro?
2. What are the steps involved in recording a macro?
3. How can you initiate the *Macro Recorder*?
4. What are some methods that can be used with the Selection object?
5. How could the filter code in the example in section 12.2.2 be further simplified?
6. How do you find event procedures for an object?
7. What is the difference between using a command button from the ActiveX Controls and Form Controls?
8. How do you assign a macro to a new group within an existing tab of the Ribbon?

9. How do you add a macro to the Quick Access Toolbar?
10. What are some of the properties associated with the scroll bar control?

12.5.2 Hands-On Exercises

***NOTE:** Please refer to the file "Chapter_12_Exercises.xlsx" for the associated worksheets noted for the hands-on exercises. The file is available at: www.dssbooks.com.*

1. Several cells contain row headings that will be used to create a table in Excel. Create a macro that does the following: copies the cells from their current location and pastes them in the range C1:C5. Assign this macro to a button. (Refer to worksheet "12.1".)
2. Consider the cells given in Hands-On Exercise 1. Create a macro to format the cells as follows: left-align the text, resize the column width, and set the font size to 12pt, font style to bold and font color to read. (Refer to worksheet "12.2".)
3. Create a macro that takes the row headings presented in Hands-On Exercise 1 and transposes them to column headings. (Refer to worksheet "12.3".)
4. A quality engineer has prepared a control chart to monitor the thickness of circuit boards being produced at the plant. Data is collected through the random measuring of 3 circuit boards where each lot is sampled over the course of one month.
   - The upper and lower control limits for the X-bar chart are calculated as follows:

     $$\bar{\bar{X}} \pm 1.023 * \bar{R}$$

   - The upper and lower control limits for the R-bar chart are calculated as follows: $UCL = 2.575 * \bar{\text{R}}$ and $LCR = 0 * \bar{\text{R}}$

   Create a macro to conditionally format the data in the table presented above. Set the formatting condition for cells B2:D11 so that if the value in one of the cells is not between the control limits for X-bar chart, the text font of the cell will be bolded and the cell will fill yellow. Set the formatting condition for cells F2:F11 so that if the value in one of the cells is not between the control limits for R-bar chart, the text font of will be bolded and the cell will fill red. (Refer to worksheet "12.4".)
5. A professor has an excel file with a sheet for each of the classes he is teaching this semester. Each sheet contains the following information on all of his students: last name, first name, absences, test scores, quiz scores, and total grade. The professor would like to create the following macros with shortcut keys. (Refer to worksheet "12.5".)
   a. AutoFilter the selected data (shortcut key "f")
   b. Sort the data by last names (shortcut key "l")
   c. Sort the data by final grade (shortcut key "g")
   d. Conditionally format the selected data so that students with more than 3 absences will be highlighted in yellow (shortcut key "a")
6. Often when class work is done in Excel, the professor requests that the final answer of a problem be boxed in. Create a macro that will box in a selected cell and assign this macro to a button using Form Controls so that the program can be easily accessible.
7. The exchange rates on currencies of various countries change constantly. Based on the current exchange rates with respect to US dollar, create a macro that sorts the following countries in a descending order of their exchange rates: United States, Great Britain, Canada, European Union, South Africa, Australia, Brazil, New Zealand, China, and Mexico. (Refer to worksheet "12.7".)
8. Create a macro for finding the sum, mean, and standard deviation for any set of numbers placed in Column A. What values result when this macro is run for the following sets of numbers?
   a. {1, 2, 3, 4, 5, 6, 7, 8, 9, 10}
   b. {8, 6, 7, 5, 3, 0, 9}
   c. {1776, 1234, 378, 2521, 2020, 1492, 1453, 1126}
9. Write a procedure that selects the data cells in range A1:A6, and creates a copy in cells B1:B6. The data in cells B1:B6 should be such that: the first letter of phrases/names is capitalized, the data is arranged numerically and then alphabetically, and finally the data type is displayed next to each cell (C1:C6). (Refer to worksheet "12.9".)
10. The workers on an assembly line in a computer manufacturing facility have been complaining about the temperature of the facility. The facility's industrial engineer has recorded the productivity of workers at various temperatures

to find the optimal temperature for production. Record a macro that will make a line graph of a table of these recorded values, give it a title, label the axis, and remove the legend. (Refer to worksheet "12.10".)

11. A consumer agency ran a test on different brands of concrete to determine which brand of concrete is the strongest and most dependable. The different brands of concrete were used to make 10 solid cylinders each. A concrete compression machine determined the amount of force in pounds that the cylinders could hold. Record a macro that gives the average, minimum, and maximum values for each brand of concrete, then makes a bar graph that includes the average, min, and max for each brand of concrete, and labels the legend appropriately. (Refer to worksheet "12.11".)

12. Consider the data given in Chapter 10, Hands-On Exercise 9. Create a macro to perform the tasks below. Create four command buttons. Assign each macro to one of the buttons created. (Refer to worksheet "12.12".)
   - **a.** Sort the data by singer's name.
   - **b.** Sort the data by performance date.
   - **c.** Highlight the songs that last at least 4minutes.
   - **d.** Count the number of songs sung by Eminem.

13. Using the provided data, perform the following. (Refer to worksheet "12.13".)
   - **a.** Record a macro called "Scramble" that scrambles all of the rows of the table above, so that after running the macro, no row is in the same position that it was just in. Create a button on the sheet and assign the macro to it.
   - **b.** Record a macro called "QuarterAverages" that lists the average profits for each quarter. Consider that after running the macro created in part a, the current position of the rows will change. Therefore, the macro should give the average profits for each quarter independent of the location of this information. Create a button on the sheet and assign the macro to it.
   - **c.** Record a macro called "BranchAverages" that list the average profit for each branch. Consider that after running the macro created in part a, the current position of the rows will change. Create a button on the sheet and assign the macro to it.

   You should now be able to scramble the rows by any amount, and still use your recorded macros to find the correct average for each quarter and for each branch.

14. John owns an ethnic food restaurant. The waiters and hosts have mentioned few customer complaints about the quality of food and service. John has decided to find out the most common customer complaints. He left comment cards in each table asking the customers to write down any complaints that they have. Consider a given collection of complaints obtained from the comment cards. (Refer to worksheet "12.14".)
   - **a.** Record a macro that will create a Pareto chart with the given information.
   - **b.** Create a button and assign the macro to it.
   - **c.** Comment on the results from Pareto Chart.

15. Place a scroll bar in the spreadsheet. Assign it to cell B3. Modify the properties so that any movement, or change, in the scroll bar will change the value in B3 to be any even number between 2 and 20.

16. Create three circles on the spreadsheet and format them to be black. Label them "Go," "Caution," and "Stop," respectively. Assign a macro to each, such that the following is done.
   - **a.** When the "Go" button is pressed, it turns green and the others turn black;
   - **b.** When the "Caution" button is pressed, it turns yellow and the others turn black; and
   - **c.** When the "Stop" button is pressed, it turns red and the others turn black.

17. Create a new Group of commands under the Home tab called "Zoom." Add the *Zoom In* command button to this group. This button is listed under All Commands list in the Excel Options dialog box. This buttons zoom in the spreadsheet every time you click on. Also add the *Zoom Out* command button to the Zoom group in order to zoom out the spreadsheet every time the button is clicked on.

18. Record a macro that takes data from a given table, creates a graph, and adds a Linear trendline. (Refer to worksheet "12.18".)

19. Create your own procedure that will graph given data and add a trendline. (*Hint*: Use the recorded macro from the above problem and reduce the code to only that which is needed.) (Refer to worksheet "12.19".)

a. Make the trendline in your procedure an exponential trend curve.
b. Create another procedure for graphing data and creating a Power trend curve.

20. Create three buttons on the spreadsheet: Linear Curve, Exponential Curve, and Power Curve. Also display the R-squared value. Use these buttons to quickly analyze which curve best fits any given set of data. (Refer to worksheet "12.20".)

21. Consider the database given in hands-on exercise 10.10. Record macros to do the following. Create four buttons and assign the recorded macros. (Refer to worksheet "12.21".)
    a. Sort the data by date, and within each date sort the data by product name.
    b. Calculate the total, average and standard deviation of the number of units sold.
    c. Calculate the total, average and standard deviation of the dollar amount made.
    d. Calculate the total, average and standard deviation of the dollar amount made per region.

22. Record macros that randomly generate data from the following distributions.
    a. Uniform between 0 and 1.
    b. Uniform between 10 and 20.
    c. Standard normal.
    d. Normal with mean 10 and standard deviation 3.
    e. Exponential with lambda 2.

    Create buttons and assign the macros recorded. Create a Group under the Home tab called "Rand. Generator." Add the macros to this Group.

23. A manufacturing company is considering replacing some of its older equipment. The new equipment costs $500,000. The management is considering getting a loan from one of the three major local banks. A given table presents the payment schedule for each loan. To make a decision it is important to know the following.
    a. The present value for each investment at 10% interest rate.
    b. The internal rate of return for each investment.
    c. The payment amount if the loan were to be paid in 5 equal yearly payments at a 5% interest rate.
    d. The number of years it would take to pay off the loan given that the interest rate is 10% and the company makes equal yearly payments of $100,000.

    Record macros to perform each of the tasks described above. Create buttons and assign the macros recorded. Add the macro to the Quick Access Toolbar (Refer to worksheet "12.23".)

24. Record macros that find the following.
    a. The sine of a given angle.
    b. The cosine of a given angle.
    c. The tangent of a given angle.

    Create buttons and assign the macros recorded. Create a new Tab called "My Functions." Add a New Group called "Trig Functions." Set the macros created in this Group.

25. Given a set of data located in column A of a spreadsheet, record macros to find the following. (Refer to worksheet "12.25".)
    a. The maximum value.
    b. The minimum value.
    c. The average value.
    d. The sum of all data.
    e. The standard deviation of the data.
    f. A bar chart of the data.
    g. Create command buttons and assign the macros recorded.

CHAPTER

thirteen More on Objects

chapter OVERVIEW

13.1 *Introduction*

This chapter gives an overview of how to perform basic Excel tasks in VBA. We describe several common properties and methods of various objects in Excel. We also illustrate how to reference, create names, and use Excel functions in VBA. This is a very important chapter for the reader to review since these tasks will be performed often in the DSS development process. For example, since we are developing spreadsheet-based DSS applications, the reader should know how VBA is used to dynamically invoke any of the spreadsheet functions available in Excel. The objects, properties, and methods in this chapter are used often in many of the DSS applications we develop in Part III of the book. We should be able to display values on the spreadsheet, set cell formatting, insert or execute functions, and manipulate other Excel objects dynamically in VBA.

In this chapter, the reader will learn how to:

- Use various properties and methods for commonly manipulated objects.
- Program using the *With* construct.
- Perform cell referencing and naming in VBA.
- Use Excel formulas and functions in VBA.

13.2 *More on Properties and Methods*

Using VBA code allows us to manipulate objects in Excel to a more advanced degree than does simple Excel functionality. It is important to understand how to find object methods and properties with the *Object Browser* and VBE tools. We will now discuss in more detail some of the most commonly used objects as well as their methods and properties.

13.2.1 Workbooks and Worksheets

Workbooks may not be manipulated often if we are only working with one; however, if we are working with multiple workbooks, we may need to know certain methods and properties.

For example, we want to take some values from a workbook called "CH13 Workbook1" and transfer them into a chart or another form of analysis in a different workbook, "CH13 Workbook2." In "CH13 Workbook1," suppose we have recorded the Revenue and Cost of a particular company's production over 12 months (see Figure 13.1). In "CH13 Workbook2," we want to create two charts: Revenue vs. Cost for months 6 to 12, and Profit for months 1 to 5 (see Figure 13.2). For the second chart, we will also need to calculate the profit values.

	A	B	C	D
1	**Data**			
2				
3	**Month**	**Revenue**	**Cost**	
4	1	$ 200.00	$ 150.00	
5	2	$ 100.00	$ 150.00	
6	3	$ 500.00	$ 150.00	
7	4	$ 600.00	$ 150.00	
8	5	$ 400.00	$ 150.00	
9	6	$ 200.00	$ 150.00	
10	7	$ 100.00	$ 150.00	
11	8	$ 200.00	$ 150.00	
12	9	$ 200.00	$ 150.00	
13	10	$ 500.00	$ 150.00	
14	11	$ 600.00	$ 150.00	
15	12	$ 700.00	$ 150.00	
16				

Figure 13.1 "CH13 Workbook1" presents Revenue and Cost values for months 1 to 12.

For the first chart in "CH13 Workbook2," we will need to copy the data in cells *A9:C15* of "CH13 Workbook1" and paste it into cells *A5:C11* of "CH13 Workbook2." Let's do this using VBA code. We will type our code in a module in "CH13 Workbook2," since this is our final workbook in which the charts will be created. First, we save the workbook where the macro is written as an *Excel Macro-Enabled Workbook (*.xlsm)*. Excel will not save your macros unless the workbook is saved as an xlsm file. Next, we insert a new module by clicking *Insert > Module* or by using the *Insert Module* icon in the VBE Standard toolbar. Be sure that we have selected the correct workbook object in the Project Explorer before inserting the module so that the module is inserted into the correct workbook. Now, we create the sub procedure and give it a name:

```
Sub WorkbookDemo()
End Sub
```

Before copying the data, we need to specify which workbook is ***active***. An active workbook is the workbook on which every following line of code will be performed. To make a workbook active, we use the ***Activate*** method. We want to *activate* "CH13 Workbook1.xlsx" first so that we can copy the data. So, we type:

```
Workbooks("CH13 Workbook1.xlsx").Activate
```

Notice that we have written the object in the plural, as "workbooks", since it is technically a *collection* of objects. Also note that we could have typed the full extension of the workbook name if it was not in the same directory as our other workbook: *Workbooks("..\CH13 Workbook1.xlsx").Activate*. Figure 13.3 illustrates the drop-down list of methods and properties for the workbook object where we can find *Activate*.

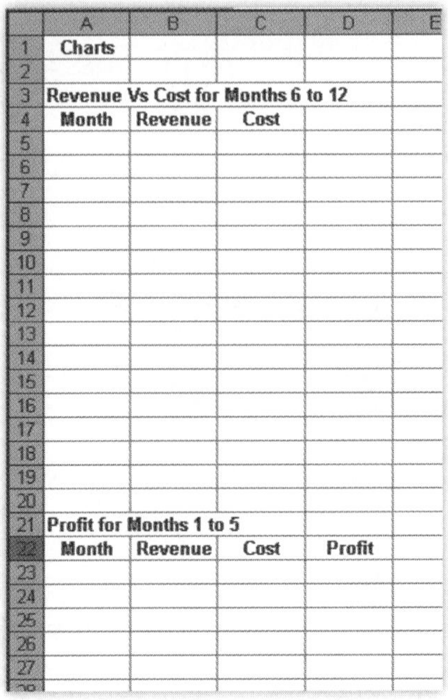

Figure 13.2 "CH13 Workbook2" with two charts, one for Revenue vs. Cost and another for Profit.

Now that we have activated the appropriate workbook, we need to copy the required cells of data for the first chart. We use the Range object to refer to the cells we want to copy, and then we use the ***Copy*** method to copy them. We will discuss more methods and properties of the Range object in the next section.

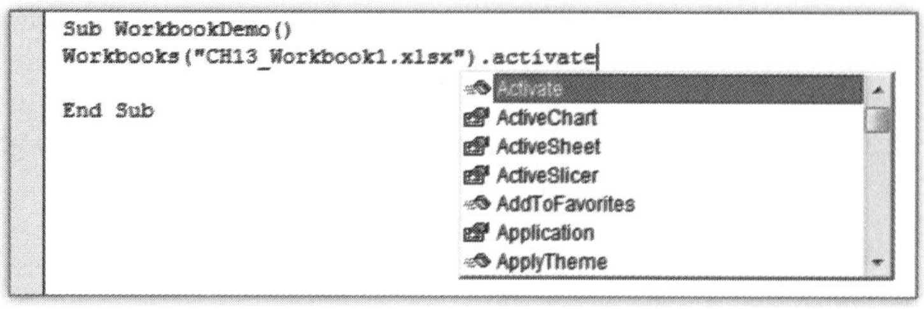

Figure 13.3 Selecting the *Activate* method of Workbooks from the drop-down list of methods and properties.

Range("A9:C15").Copy

Now we need to paste this data into "CH13 Workbook2"; however, we must first activate this workbook before referring to any cells in it. So, we again use the *Activate* method:

Workbooks("CH13 Workbook2.xlsx").Activate

Now that it is active, we can use the Range object again and the ***PasteSpecial*** method. This method takes an argument that specifies how the data should be pasted (see the drop-down list in Figure 13.4). We will use the argument *xlPasteAll* to paste the data as is. Note that there is another way to copy and paste data in VBA using the Application object. We will discuss it in detail in the next few sections.

Range("A5:C11").PasteSpecial xlPasteAll or
Range("A5:C11").PasteSpecial Paste = xlPasteAll

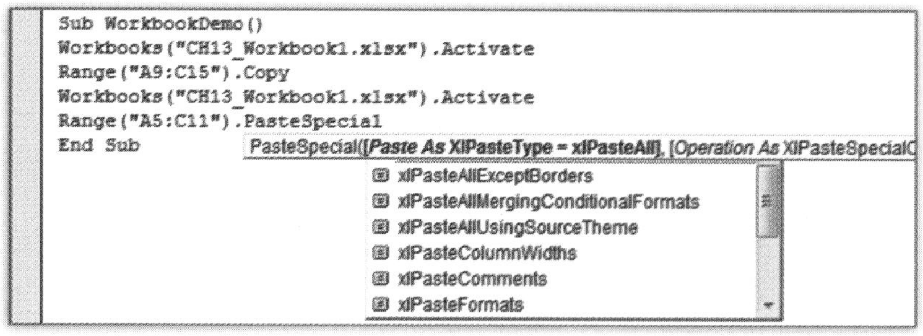

Figure 13.4 The dialog box and drop-down list that appear to find an argument for the *PasteSpecial* method.

Using the same methods, we can now type the VBA code to copy and paste the data for the second chart. See Figure 13.5 for the final code. Let's now go to Excel in "CH13 Workbook2. xlxs," to test our macro. After playing the *WorkbookDemo macro*, "CH13 Workbook2.xlsx" should have all the necessary data, as seen in Figure 13.6.

```
Sub WorkbookDemo()
Workbooks("CH13_Workbook1.xlsx").Activate
Range("A9:C15").Copy
Workbooks("CH13_Workbook1.xlsx").Activate
Range("A5:C11").PasteSpecial xlPasteAll

Workbooks("CH13_Workbook1.xlsx").Activate
Range("A4:C8").Copy
Workbooks("CH13_Workbook1.xlsx").Activate
Range("A23:C27").PasteSpecial xlPasteAll
End Sub
```

Figure 13.5 Code that copies two different sets of data from one workbook to another.

The workbook "CH13_Workbook2.xlsx" can now be used to create charts or perform further analysis. Note that the *Profit* column in the second table of this workbook still has to be calculated. For now, we can simply type the formula "*=B23 – C23*" into cell *D23* and copy the formula to the cells below. At the end of this chapter, we will discuss how to enter formulas using VBA.

	A	B	C	D	E
1	**Charts**				
2					
3	**Revenue Vs Cost for Months 6 to 12**				
4	**Month**	**Revenue**	**Cost**		
5	6	$ 200.00	$ 150.00		
6	7	$ 100.00	$ 150.00		
7	8	$ 200.00	$ 150.00		
8	9	$ 200.00	$ 150.00		
9	10	$ 500.00	$ 150.00		
10	11	$ 600.00	$ 150.00		
11	12	$ 700.00	$ 150.00		
12					
13					
14					
15					
16					
17					
18					
19					
20					
21	**Profit for Months 1 to 5**				
22	**Month**	**Revenue**	**Cost**	**Profit**	
23	1	$ 200.00	$ 150.00		
24	2	$ 100.00	$ 150.00		
25	3	$ 500.00	$ 150.00		
26	4	$ 600.00	$ 150.00		
27	5	$ 400.00	$ 150.00		
28					

Figure 13.6 "CH13 Workbook2" after the macro *WorkbookDemo* has run.

Like workbooks, the most commonly used method of worksheets is *Activate*. As we work with different worksheets, we need to activate whichever one we are currently referencing or operating. For example, say we have three worksheets: "Welcome" with just text; "Input" with a table of input data; and "Analysis" with charts or other forms of analysis. If we want to copy some data from the "Input" worksheet, we need to activate it before referencing any of its ranges or using the copy method. Then, to create a chart or show the value of some function of that data on the "Analysis" worksheet, we would need to activate the "Analysis" worksheet first.

Aside from the *Activate* method, a very common property of worksheets is ***Visible***. The *Visible* property takes the value *True* or *False* to indicate whether or not the worksheet (along with the worksheet tab at the bottom of the screen) can be seen by the user. This property can be useful when preparing a decision support system, as it is part of good navigation in GUI design. Using the same worksheets in the above example, we may, for instance, want users only to view the "Welcome" worksheet first. We could then allow them to view the "Input" and "Analysis" worksheets after clicking a command button.

In the case studies in Part III of this book, we use a subroutine associated with the ***Open*** event procedure of the workbook that hides all worksheets except "Welcome." While there are several ways to accomplish this, we will now discuss the simplest. (In our code, we actually define a variable of the data type *object* and use the *For, Next* and *If, Then* structures, which we will discuss in the next few chapters.)

We first go to the VBE and double click on *Workbook* from the *Project Explorer* window. Then, we click on the drop-down list of event procedures and choose *Open* (see Figure 13.7). The event procedure *Workbook_Open()* immediately appears. (We will discuss the difference between *private* and *public* sub procedures in Chapter 15.)

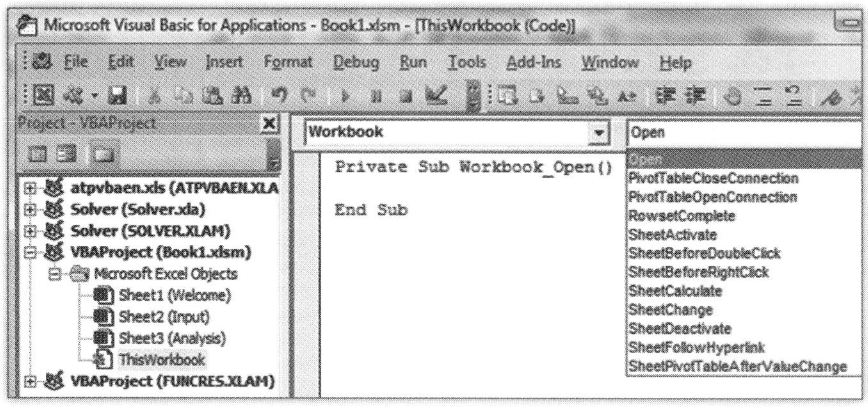

Figure 13.7 *Open*, an event of the workbook object.

Now we want to enter our code. We first need to make sure that the "Welcome" worksheet is visible. To do this, we type the following:

Worksheets("Welcome").Visible = True

Notice that we can refer to the Project Explorer for the names of all worksheets in the workbook. Next, we want to make sure that both the "Input" and "Analysis" worksheets are hidden. So, we set their *Visible* properties to *False.*

Worksheets("Input").Visible = False
Worksheets("Analysis").Visible = False

Since worksheets are objects defined in VBA, once we type the period after the statement *Worksheets("..name..")*, we see a drop-down list of properties and methods. From here, we can also find the *Visible* property. Figure 13.8 presents the complete code. We can go to the Excel window to test the *macro.*

```
Option Explicit

Private Sub Workbook_Open()
    Worksheets("Welcome").Visible = True
    Worksheets("Input").Visible = False
    Worksheets("Analysis").Visible = False
End Sub
```

Figure 13.8 The *Workbook_Open* procedure makes the "Welcome" worksheet *visible* and hides the "Input" and "Analysis" worksheets.

We can use the *Visible* property to hide and show worksheets as we navigate the user through the program. We will discuss this process in more detail in Chapter 19.

Both the workbook and worksheet objects also have the ***Name*** property. It can be used to assign a name to a workbook or worksheet. For example, if we wanted to change the name of the "Welcome" worksheet to "Introduction," we would type the following in VBA:

Worksheets("Welcome").Name = "Introduction"

This property can also be used for the Range object, but we will discuss this in more detail in a later section.

If desired, we can use the ***Sheets*** object instead of Worksheets. It allows us to refer to a Chart sheet as well as a worksheet. Both have the same set of properties and methods.

There are additional properties and methods available for the workbook and worksheet objects; however, we will most often use those that we have discussed.

Summary

Objects	Properties	Values	Methods	Arguments
Workbook	Name	"name"	Activate	–
Worksheet	Name	"name"	Activate	–
	Visible	True or False	Copy	–
Range	Name	"name"	PasteSpecial	xlPasteAll xlPasteFormats xlPasteValues

13.2.2 Ranges

The Range object is probably the most commonly used in Excel. We have already seen the *Name* property and the *Copy* and *PasteSpecial* methods used earlier with the Range object. We also learned about the *Sort* and *AutoFilter* methods used in Chapter 12. We now want to review a few more important properties and methods.

One more common method is ***Cut***. After cutting a cell or range of cells, we can use the *PasteSpecial* method to paste the values in any worksheet or any workbook. However, the *Cut* method also has its own paste feature: the ***Destination*** argument. We can cut and paste in one statement as follows:

Range("A1:F12").Cut Destination:=Range("A13")

The *Destination* argument can take any range from any worksheet or workbook as its value. Many of the properties for the Range object can be used to adjust formatting. For example, to change the color of any range of cells, we use the ***Interior*** property. When we enter a range in VBA and then choose the *Interior* property, we type another period after *Interior* to see a list of sub properties (see Figure 13.9). From this list of sub properties, we chose ***ColorIndex*** and enter a number signifying a specific color, or ***Color*** and enter either a ***VB Constant*** (*vbRed*, *vbYellow*, etc) or a specific color using the ***RGB function***. (For a list of color indices, search for *PatternColor Index* in VBA Help; for a list of common *VB Constants* for colors, search for *Color Constants* in VBA Help; for a list of common RGB values, search for *RGB Function* in VBA Help.)

We could enter either of the following lines of code to format our range to have red cells:

```
Range("A1:F12").Interior.ColorIndex = 3
Range("A1:F12").Interior.Color = vbRed
```

When we type either line in the VBE and then run the macro in Excel, the worksheet appears as we have shown in Figure 13.10 with the "Welcome" worksheet from the earlier examples.

Another useful sub property of *Interior* is ***Pattern***. We can choose *xlSolid*, *xlChecker*, and others as values to this sub property. We encourage you to experiment with them.

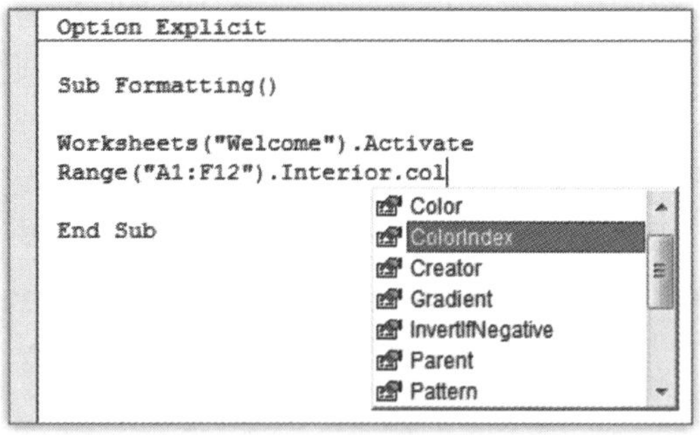

Figure 13.9 The *Interior* property has a set of sub properties that can be used to format ranges.

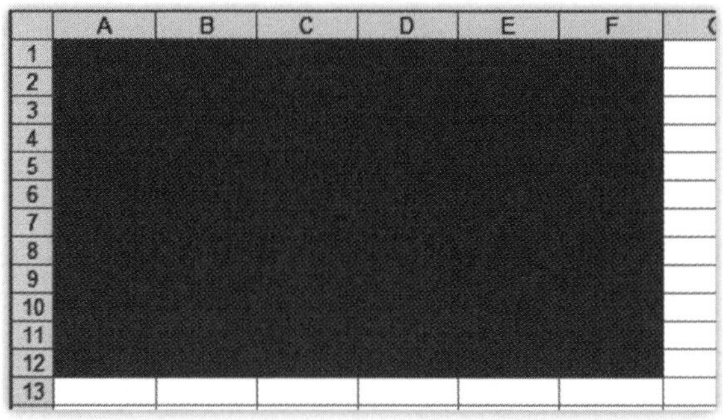

Figure 13.10 Both the *ColorIndex* and *Color* sub properties can be used to format the interior of ranges.

A common formatting modification in Excel involves the borders of a range. This format setting is often used when creating tables and organizing data in the Excel spreadsheet. There are a few ways to change range borders. One way is to use the ***Borders*** property.

Let us create a small table on the "Input" worksheet in the above example. We begin by creating our sub procedure in VBA; we will name it *Borders()*. First, we activate the "Input" worksheet using the method discussed in Section 13.2.1. Then, we specify the range where we want our table to be located, followed by the *Borders* property (see Figure 13.11). If we type another period after the *Borders* property, we see a list of sub properties. These are specific formatting options for the border of the range, such as ***LineStyle***, ***Color***, and ***Weight***. Let's begin by setting the border weight of our range to *xlThick*, a predefined ***XL Constant***:

Range("B3:D10").Borders.Weight = xlThick

If we now run our macro in Excel, we should see the table shown in Figure 13.12. Note: We can get more help on any object, property, or method by placing the cursor on the word in the code and then pressing the F1 key.

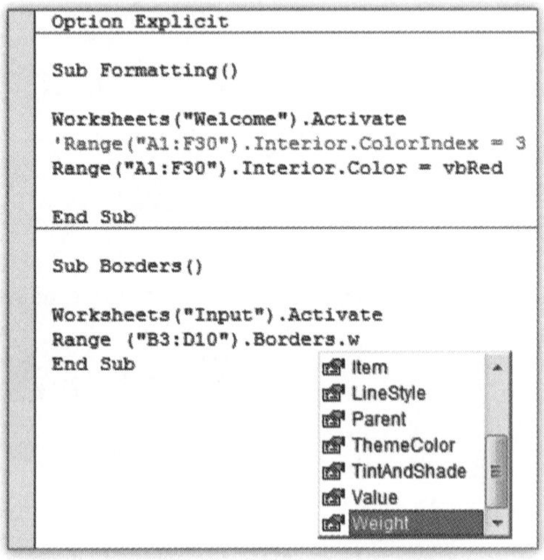
Option Explicit
Sub Formatting()
Worksheets("Welcome").Activate
'Range("A1:F30").Interior.ColorIndex = 3
Range("A1:F30").Interior.Color = vbRed
End Sub
Sub Borders()
Worksheets("Input").Activate
Range ("B3:D10").Borders.w
End Sub
Item
LineStyle
Parent
ThemeColor
TintAndShade
Value
Weight

Figure 13.11 The *Borders* property has a list of sub properties available.

Quick Programming Note: To ignore a line of code while experimenting with programming or debugging, we can type an apostrophe, '. This will make the font of the following code green in the VBE, denoting that it should not be read when the code is run (see Figure 13.11). We can also use this method to enter comments in our code. Placing comments in our code is a very important practice in programming. For example, we may want to explain what a certain sub procedure's function is to another user using our code. We could simply type an apostrophe, followed by a brief text description of our code. This is beneficial to reminding us of what is being done for future reference or debugging and also for communicating what we have done to other programmers who may read our code. We discuss commenting and other programming principles in more detail in Chapter 24.

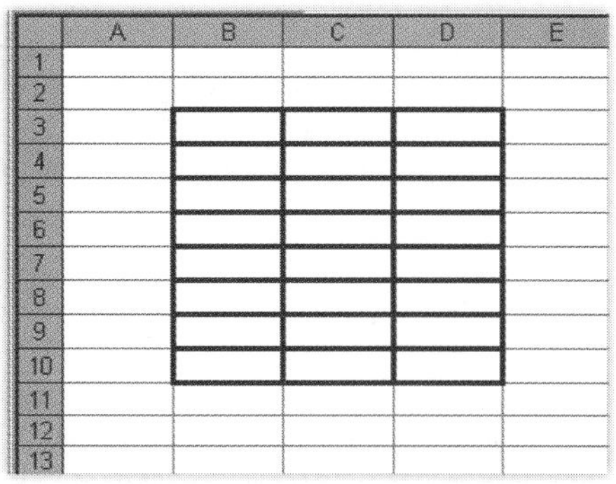

Figure 13.12 This range has the *Borders* property with the *Weight* sub property value equal to *xlThick.*

Now we can try setting some other sub property values. For example, let's make the *Line Style* of the first row of our range dashed instead of solid by typing:

Range("B3:D3").Borders.LineStyle = xlDash

We have again used an *XL Constant*, *xlDash*, to specify the desired line style. Let's also modify the color of the second and third row's borders by using the *Color* sub property. We make this section of border yellow by typing:

Range("B4:D5").Borders.Color = vbYellow

See Figure 13.13 for the final code and Figure 13.14 for the result of the macro in Excel.

```
Sub Borders()

Worksheets("Input").Activate
Range("B3:D10").Borders.Weight = xlThick
Range("B3:D3").Borders.LineStyle = xlDash
Range("B4:D5").Borders.Color = vbYellow

End Sub
```

Figure 13.13 Specifying the *Weight, LineStyle,* and *Color* sub properties.

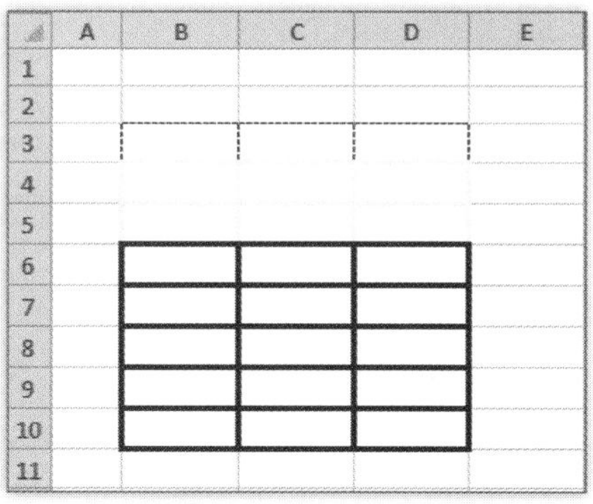

Figure 13.14 The result of the *Borders()* macro.

Instead of typing a period after the *Borders* property of the Range object, we can type an open parenthesis and receive a new list of *XL Constants* (see Figure 13.15). These constants allow us to specify what section of the border we want for our range. For example, if we chose *xlEdgeBottom*, we will only have a border on the bottom of the entire range.

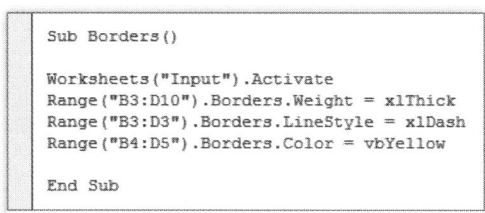

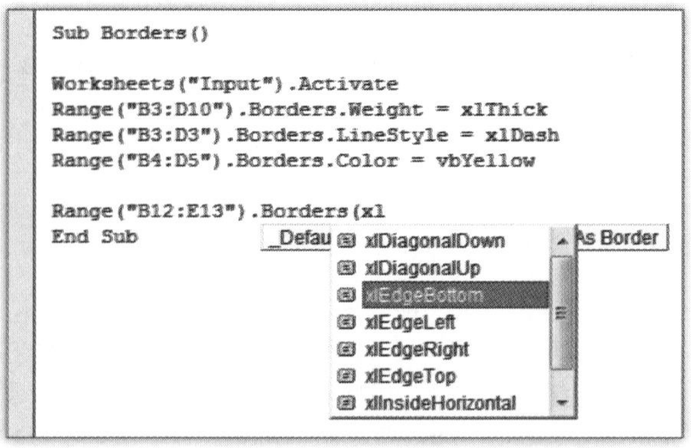
Sub Borders()
Worksheets("Input").Activate
Range("B3:D10").Borders.Weight = xlThick
Range("B3:D3").Borders.LineStyle = xlDash
Range("B4:D5").Borders.Color = vbYellow
Range("B12:E13").Borders(xl
End Sub
_Defau
As Border
xlDiagonalDown
xlDiagonalUp
xlEdgeBottom
xlEdgeLeft
xlEdgeRight
xlEdgeTop
xlInsideHorizontal

Figure 13.15 *Borders* can also take predefined *xl* values to convey which set of borders should be modified.

Let's specify a new range and set the *Borders* property to *xlInsideHorizontal* so that each row of our range has a line above and below it. Now that we have selected *xlInsideHorizontal* from the drop-down list, we can further specify the same sub properties we used above by typing another period. Let's set the weight of this border to *xlThick*.

Range("B12:E14").Borders(xlInsideHorizontal).Weight = xlThick

See Figure 13.16 for the modified sub procedure and Figure 13.17 for the result of the modified macro in Excel.

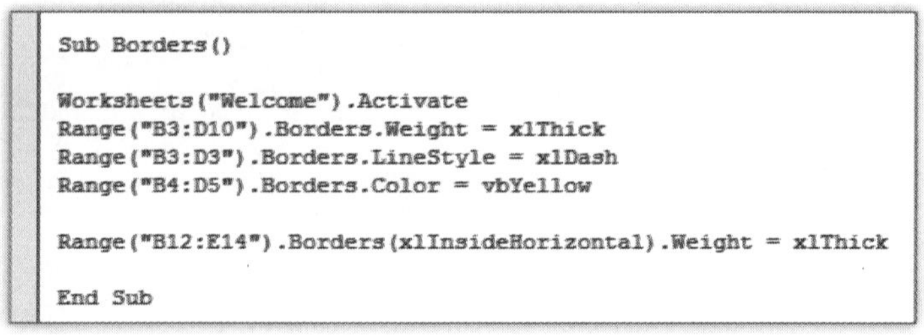
Sub Borders()
Worksheets("Welcome").Activate
Range("B3:D10").Borders.Weight = xlThick
Range("B3:D3").Borders.LineStyle = xlDash
Range("B4:D5").Borders.Color = vbYellow
Range("B12:E14").Borders(xlInsideHorizontal).Weight = xlThick
End Sub

Figure 13.16 The last line of code in the *Borders()* sub procedure specifies the *Weight* value for the horizontal border line.

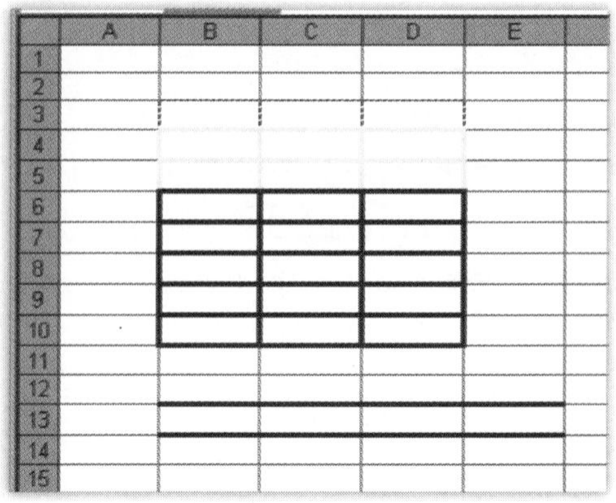

Figure 13.17 The result of the modified *Borders()* macro.

The other way to specify the desired border formatting is by using a method instead of a property, specifically the ***BorderAround*** method. *BorderAround* has arguments similar to the sub properties of the *Borders* property; these are ***LineStyle***, ***Weight***, and ***Color***. As with other methods, the structure for entering arguments uses **:=**. Take, for example, the following line of code:

Range("B15:C17").BorderAround LineStyle:=xlSolid, Weight:=xlThick

Notice that in Figure 13.18, that the VBE provides us with a list of *XL Constants* for this argument's values. In Figure 13.19, we have also added the argument *Color:=RGB(0,0,255)*. This argument uses either the *RGB Function* or a *VB Constant* to specify the color. Here, we have given the RGB values for the color blue. See Figure 13.20 for the final *Borders()* macro result.

Note that the limitation of the *BorderAround* method is that it only affects the outlining border of the range and can not add borders inside the range [as with the property *Borders(xlInsideHorizontal)* for example].

```
Sub Borders()

Worksheets("Welcome").Activate
Range("B3:D10").Borders.Weight = xlThick
Range("B3:D3").Borders.LineStyle = xlDash
Range("B4:D5").Borders.Color = vbYellow

Range("B12:E14").Borders(xlInsideHorizontal).Weight = xlThick

Range("B15:C17").BorderAround LineStyle := xlSolid, Weight:=
End Sub          BorderAround([LineStyle], [Weight As XlBorderWeight = x   xlHairline   As Xl
                                                                           xlMedium
                                                                           xlThick
                                                                           xlThin
```

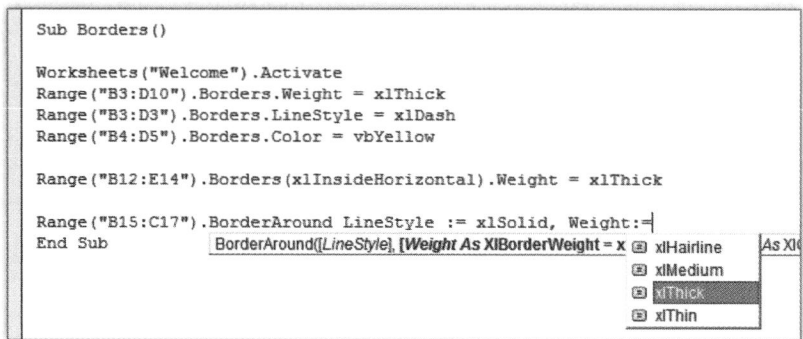

Figure 13.18 The *BorderAround* method has arguments for *LineStyle*, *Weight*, and *Color*.

```
Option Explicit

Sub Formatting()

Worksheets("Welcome").Activate
'Range("A1:F30").Interior.ColorIndex = 3
Range("A1:F30").Interior.Color = vbRed

End Sub

Sub Borders()

Worksheets("Welcome").Activate
Range("B3:D10").Borders.Weight = xlThick
Range("B3:D3").Borders.LineStyle = xlDash
Range("B4:D5").Borders.Color = vbYellow

Range("B12:E14").Borders(xlInsideHorizontal).Weight = xlThick

Range("B15:C17").BorderAround LineStyle:=xlSolid, Weight:=xlThick, Color:=RGB(0, 0, 255)

End Sub
```

Figure 13.19 The *Borders()* sub procedure now includes the *BorderAround* method for a given range.

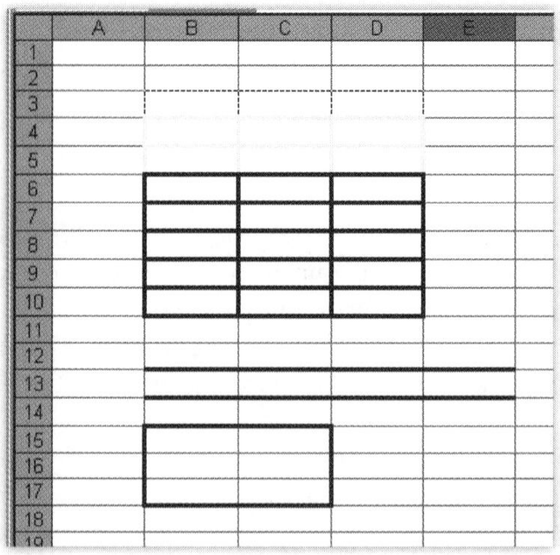

Figure 13.20 The result of the final *Borders()* macro.

There are two more basic properties of the Range object that we would like to discuss. The first, ***Value***, is a very important property, as it allows us to assign the value of what will actually be stored in the range. This value can be a string of text, a numerical value, a formula, or a variable value. We will discuss formulas later on in this chapter and variables in the following chapter, but for now let's consider an example of setting the range value to a string of text or a numerical value.

Suppose we want to list some numerical results in a table on an "Analysis" sheet from the above examples. We first want a title for the table: "Analysis Sheet." To enter this text into a cell using VBA, we simply specify the range we want and use the *Value* property as follows:

Range("A2").Value = "Analysis Sheet"

Notice that since the value of this cell is text, we include it in quotation marks. However, for numerical values, or variable names, no quotation marks are necessary. Let's now enter two values, a sum and an average, in the table. The first value can be entered as follows:

Range("B3").Value = 350

In Figure 13.21, we have entered row titles for these two values and the values themselves in a sub procedure called *ValueFont()*. See Figure 13.22 for the macro result in Excel.

```
Sub ValueFont()

Worksheets("Analysis").Activate
Range("A2").Value = "Analysis Sheet"
Range("A3").Value = "Value Sum"
Range("B3").Value = 350
Range("A4").Value = "Value Average"
Range("B4").Value = 80

End Sub
```

Figure 13.21 Assigning text values and some numerical values to different ranges.

	A	B	C
1			
2	Analysis Sheet		
3	Value Sum	350	
4	Value Average	80	
5			

Figure 13.22 The result of the *ValueFont()* macro.

We can insert additional numerical formatting to a range value by using the ***Format*** function. This function performs the same actions as formatting a cell in Excel. The structure for this function is:

Format(Expression, Format)

The expression is the value to which we want to apply the formatting. For example, the notation *"(###) ###-####"* specifies a numerical custom format. We can also use the range property ***NumberFormat*** to accomplish the same formatting. Please note that we may need to reference an Object Library in order to use the Format function. This library can be referenced by choosing *Tools > References > Microsoft Office Object Library*, for the latest edition found in our list.

The last Range property we will discuss is the ***Font*** property. The *Font* property also has a list of sub properties (see Figure 13.23). Some of the more commonly used sub properties are ***Bold***, ***Size***, and ***Color***.

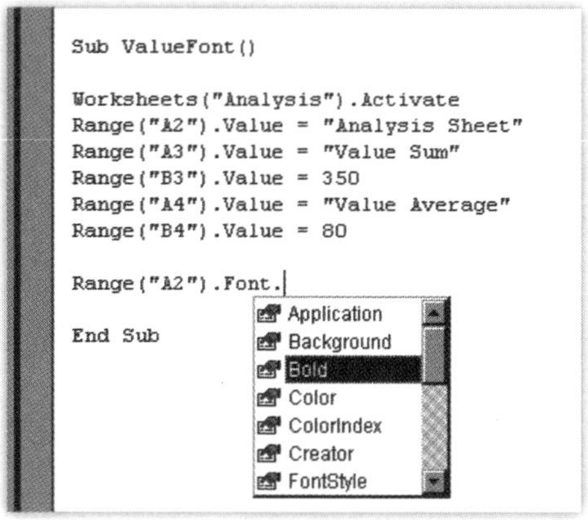
Sub ValueFont()
Worksheets("Analysis").Activate
Range("A2").Value = "Analysis Sheet"
Range("A3").Value = "Value Sum"
Range("B3").Value = 350
Range("A4").Value = "Value Average"
Range("B4").Value = 80
Range("A2").Font.
End Sub
Application
Background
Bold
Color
ColorIndex
Creator
FontStyle

Figure 13.23 The *Font* property has a set of sub properties.

Suppose we want to make the title of the table we just created in the *ValueFont()* sub procedure bold. The *Bold* sub property takes the values *True* and *False*. We therefore name the range where the title is, use the *Font* property, and set the *Bold* sub property equal to *True*.

Range("A2").Font.Bold = True

We may also want to make the title have a larger font. To do this, we simply increase the value of the *Size* sub property.

Range("A2").Font.Size = 14

We can also make the numerical values in our table red. We could use either the *ColorIndex* or *Color* sub properties to do this. If we are using the *Color* sub property, we set the value equal to an *RGB function* or a *VB Constant*. Let's use the *VB Constant vbRed* for this example:

Range("B3:B4").Font.Color = vbRed

See Figure 13.24 for the modified *ValueFont()* sub procedure. The modified macro result is shown in Figure 13.25.

```
Sub ValueFont()

Worksheets("Analysis").Activate
Range("A2").Value = "Analysis Sheet"
Range("A3").Value = "Value Sum"
Range("B3").Value = 350
Range("A4").Value = "Value Average"
Range("B4").Value = 80

Range("A2").Font.Bold = True
Range("A2").Font.Size = 14
Range("B3:B4").Font.Color = vbRed

End Sub
```

Figure 13.24 The *Font* sub properties of *Bold, Size,* and *Color.*

	A	B	C
1			
2	**Analysis Sheet**		
3	Value Sum	350	
4	Value Average	80	
5			

Figure 13.25 The result of the modified *ValueFont()* macro.

Aside from these common properties, the Range object additionally offers a set of methods that are very useful. We have already discussed *Copy* and *PasteSpecial*, which we will use quite often, as well as *Sort* and *AutoFilter*, which are also quite useful. Additionally, there are three common methods that can be used to clear cells. These are the ***Clear***, ***ClearContents***, and ***ClearFormats*** methods. (There are others, but these are the three most common.)

Let's use the table we created in the "Analysis" worksheet to experiment with these methods. To do so, we create a sub procedure *ClearCells()* and again activate the "Analysis" worksheet. (Remember that this step is important because even if this macro is run from another worksheet, it will only clear cells from the "Analysis" worksheet.) Let's begin by clearing the formatting we did to the numerical values (see Figure 13.26). To do this, we use the *ClearFormats* method.

Range("B3:B4").ClearFormats

Running this macro will demonstrate that the numerical values are no longer red, but rather the default color of black.

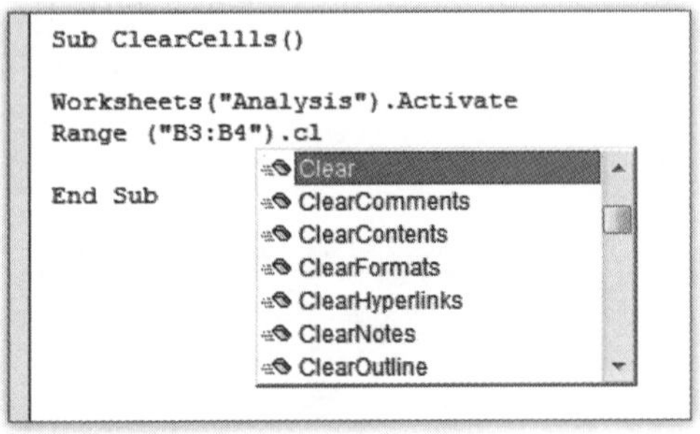

Figure 13.26 The drop-down list of properties and methods for the Range object displays all of the clear methods.

There is an important difference between the next two methods: *ClearContents* and *Clear*. *ClearContents* removes all values from the specified range. However, that is all it removes; all of the formatting will stay as it is. This method is useful if we want to retain the formatting for a particular range. For example, if we want to change the title of our analysis table, we can use the *ClearContents* method, since we still want the new title to be bold and a larger font.

In Figure 13.27, we have cleared our current table's title using the *ClearContents* method and given the title range a new value.

Range("A2").ClearContents
Range("A2").Value = "Results"

The result of this macro is now shown in Figure 13.28.

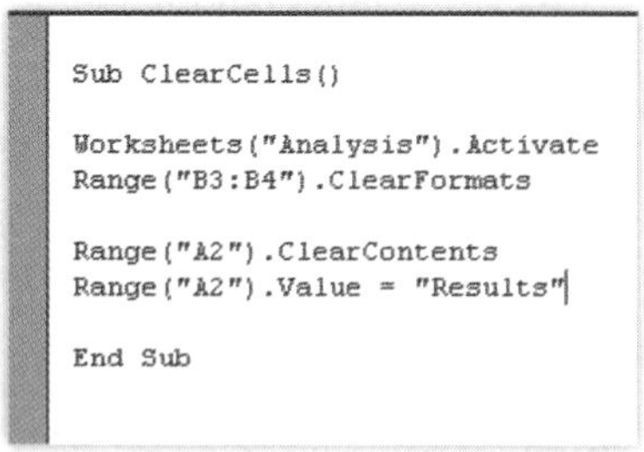

Figure 13.27 Using the *ClearFormats* method to change the range font formatting. The *ClearContents* method only clears the range value.

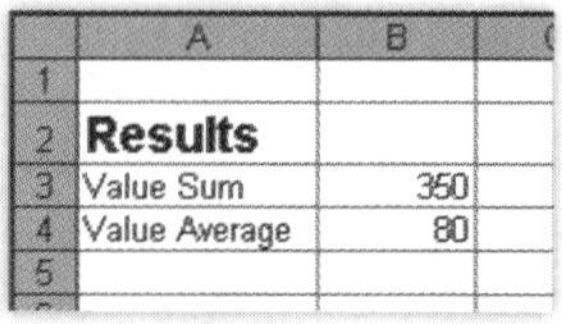

Figure 13.28 The result of the *ClearCells()* macro. The numbers are no longer red and the table heading has been changed; however, the formatting of the table heading is the same.

The *Clear* method, on the other hand, clears everything in the specified range, including values, formatting, formulas, and comments. We have reentered the new title code using the *Clear* method instead of the *ClearContents* method to show the difference (see Figure 13.29).

Range("A2").Clear
Range("A2").Value = "Results"

Note that when this macro is run, the new title is no longer bold or a large font (see Figure 13.30).

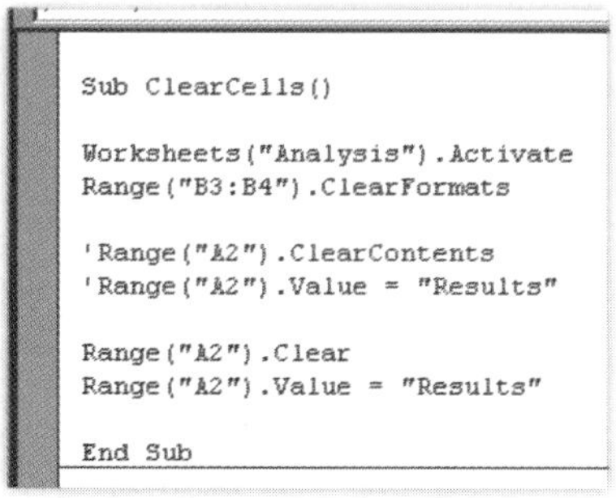

Figure 13.29 The *Clear* method clears all formatting and values from the range.

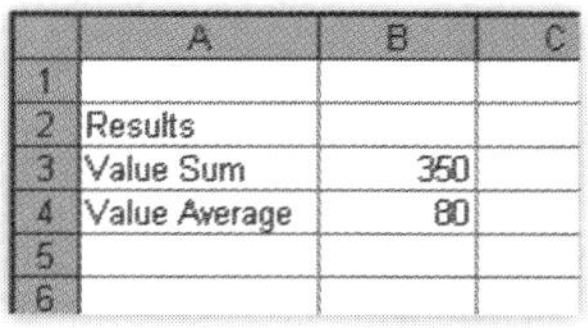

Figure 13.30 The result of the modified *ClearCells()* macro. Note that the formatting of the table heading has been cleared.

Summary

The Range Object

Properties	Values	Methods	Arguments
Interior	ColorIndex, Color, Pattern	Cut	Destination
Borders	Weight, LineStyle (XL Constants), Color (RGB, VB Constant), XL Border Constants	BorderAround	Weight, LineStyle, Color
Font	Bold (True,False), Size (number), Color (RGB, VB Constant)	Clear ClearContents ClearFormats	–
Value	Text, numerical, formula, variable	Sort AutoFilter	Key, Order Field, Criteria

Also associated with formatting the Range object is the ***FormatConditions*** object, which places conditional formatting on a specified range of cells. Therefore, hierarchically, it is related to a specific Range object. There are three main methods and several properties for this object. To apply conditional formatting to a range, use the ***Add*** method. Its format is as follows:

Range(cells or name).FormatConditions.Add(Type, Operator, Formula)

The *Type* argument takes values such as: *xlBlanksCondition, xlCellValue, xlDatabar, xlExpression, xlTop10, etc.* These argument values refer to the different conditional formatting rules. For example, if we want to format blank cells to be red in the range *C1:C10*, then *the* ***Add*** method is used as follows:

Range("C1:C10").FormatConditions.Add Type:=xlBlanksCondition

We can also use the ***Add*** method to ass Data Bars in the range *C1:C10* as follows:

Range("C1:C10").FormatConditions.Add Type:=xlDatabar

The *Operator* and *Formula* arguments are required when the *Type* argument of the *Add* method is *xlCellValue*. The *Operator* argument determines the inequality for the conditional formatting comparison, and has several values: *xlLess*, *xlLessEqual*, *xlGreaterEqual*, and *xlBetween*, among others. The *Formula* argument is the right hand side of the inequality of this comparison. For example, if we want to format a range of cells to be red if their values are less than 10, the *Formula* argument value would be 10 (and the *Operator* argument value would be *xlLess*). There can be up to two *Formula* arguments. (For example, we would need two when we have the *xlBetween Operator.*) Note that we can only add three conditional formats to one range of cells; therefore, if we use the *Add* method more than three times, it will not work.

The second method is ***Modify***. Use this method to modify a conditional format that has already been added. In case there is more than one format on a range of cells, we must first index the FormatConditions object to specify which format to modify. The arguments for the *Modify* method are the same as the *Add* method. The values we allot to the arguments using the *Modify* method overwrite all initial or previous values. The format is below:

Range(cell or name).FormatConditions(Index).Modify(Type, Operator, Formula)

We can also delete a conditional format by indexing a particular *FormatConditions* object and using the ***Delete*** method; there are no arguments for this method.

Once we have added a conditional format, we must then use the properties of this object in order to determine what we want the formatting to be after the condition has been met. These properties are actually the same formatting properties we have discussed already for the Range object: Interior, Font, and Borders. These properties, along with their sub properties, can be used with a particular *FormatConditions* object, as follows:

Let's look at a quick example to understand how these methods and properties are put together. In Figure 13.31(a), in the range *C1:C10*, there is a list of numbers between 1 and 20. If we want to place a conditional format on this range so that any cell with a value greater than 10 becomes red, we type the following code:

```
Range("C1:C10").-FormatConditions.Add Type:=xlCellValue, Operator:=xlGreater, Formula1:=10
Range("C1:C10").FormatConditions(1).Interior.Color = vbRed
```

If we want to place a conditional format on this range so that any blank cell becomes yellow, we type the following code:

```
Range("C1:C10").-FormatConditions.Add Type:= xlBlanksCondition Range("C1:C10").
FormatConditions(2).Interior.Color = vbYellow
```

The result of running a procedure containing this code is portrayed in Figure 13.31(b).

(a) (b)

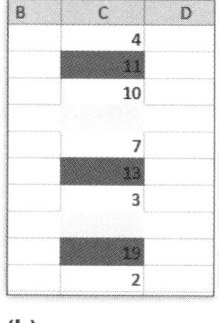

Figure 13.31 (a) A list of ten numbers between 1 and 20. (b) Applying the conditional formatting to color cells with values less than 10 as red.

Summary

The FormatConditions Object

Properties	**Methods**	**Arguments**
Interior, Color, ColorIndex	Add	Type, Operator, Formula
Font, Bold, Style	Modify	Type, Operator, Formula
Borders, Weight, Style	Delete	–

There are other basic properties and methods for the Range object. We recommend that you search through the *Object Browser* in the *Range* class for a full list of options. Remember, another easy way to learn how to find a particular VBA code is to record a macro first and then simply view the generated code (as we demonstrated in Chapter 12). You can then *modify* this code according to your specific formatting preferences.

13.2.3 Charts

There are many aspects of the chart object that can be modified. In Chapter 5, we created charts by deciding the chart type, data source, possible data series, and several chart options. All of these parts of the chart object can be modified directly in the VBA code.

Let's consider an example. Suppose we have some financial data in a "Charts" worksheet for which we want to create a bar graph. In order to initialize the chart creation, we need to use the *Add* method of the Chart object. Note that we can also specify ***Before***, ***After***, or ***Count*** as arguments for this method, but they are not required. We simply type:

```
Charts.Add
```

To set other options for the chart, we actually use the ***ActiveChart*** object rather than the Chart object. With the Chart object, we are limited to methods such as ***Copy***, ***Delete***, and ***Select***. Therefore, we use the ActiveChart object to specify the chart type, source data, and other chart options because we need to specify a specific chart before modifying it. So, we either *Add*, or, more commonly, *Select* a chart to activate it before we use any methods or properties.

Let's now set some of the chart options that we would select using the Chart Wizard. First, we need to determine what type of chart we want: bar graph, pie chart, or scattered chart, etc. To do this, we use the ***ChartType*** property, which takes *XL Constants* as values. In this example, we want a bar graph, which is designated by *xlColumnClustered.*

```
ActiveChart.ChartType = xlColumnClustered
```

Now we need to select the source data for this chart. To do so, we use the ***SetSourceData*** method. This method has several arguments, but we only need to use two for now: ***Source*** and ***PlotBy***. We use the *Source* argument to specify the location of our data, giving both the worksheet and range names. The *PlotBy* argument, as we may remember from the Chart Wizard, allows us to choose whether we want to plot our data by its columns or rows. In this case, as in most, we want to plot by columns. For our example let's use the *SetSourceData* method as follows:

```
ActiveChart.SetSourceData Source:=Sheets("Charts").Range("A3:B6"), PlotBy:=xlColumns
```

Notice that we have used the Sheets object instead of the Worksheets object here to locate our data (refer to Section 13.1.1). The third main option we should now decide upon is our chart location. As we may remember from Chapter 5, we can either have our chart appear in a new Chart sheet or as an object in any specified worksheet. To specify the chart location, we use the ***Location*** method. This method takes two arguments: ***Where*** and ***Name***. The *Where* argument can take one of three *XL Constant* values: *xlLocationAsObject*, *xlLocationAsNewSheet*, or *xlLocationAutomatic*. The third option is simply our current default. The *Name* argument is the text name of the worksheet or the chart sheet where the chart will be displayed. For our example, we keep our chart as an object in the "Charts" worksheet.

ActiveChart.Location Where:=xlLocationAsObject, Name:="Charts"

We have now completed specifying the necessary options of a basic chart. These three options – chart type, source data, and location – are needed to create any chart. We can now modify some of the additional chart options. Most of these options are controlled by properties of the *ActiveChart* object. There are several of these properties, but we will demonstrate just a few.

Let's begin by opting to hide the chart legend. To do this, we use the ***HasLegend*** property, which takes the value *True* or *False*. To hide the legend, we type:

ActiveChart.HasLegend = False

Another option is whether or not to title the chart, and if so, what that title is. We can set this option in VBA using the ***HasTitle*** and ***ChartTitle*** properties of the ActiveChart object. The *HasTitle* property also takes *True* and *False* values; however, the *ChartTitle* property has a set of sub properties that can be given specific values. Before assigning a title to the chart, we should first set the *HasTitle* property to *True.*

ActiveChart.HasTitle = True

The ChartTitle property has several sub properties, including *Font, Border, Interior,* and other formatting options. For this example, we are interested in the ***Text*** sub property. This sub property allows us to enter the text that will become the title of our chart; in this case, we name the chart "Annual Report."

ActiveChart.ChartTitle.Text = "Annual Report"

See Figure 13.32 for the completed *Graph()* sub procedure; the resulting chart is shown in Figure 13.33. Notice that the chart type is a bar graph and that the highlighted data range is our source data for the chart. Also take note of its location as an object in the "Charts" worksheet, the title, and the hidden legend.

```
Sub Graph()

    Worksheets("Charts").Activate
    Charts.Add
    ActiveChart.ChartType = xlColumnClustered

    ActiveChart.SetSourceData Source:=Sheets("Charts").Range("A3:B6"), PlotBy:=xlColumns
    ActiveChart.Location Where:=xlLocationAsObject, Name:="Charts"

    ActiveChart.HasLegend = False
    ActiveChart.HasTitle = True
    ActiveChart.ChartTitle.Text = "Annual Report"

End Sub
```

Figure 13.32 The *Graph()* sub procedure creates a chart and sets some properties.

There are some other useful methods and properties of charts that allow further modification of formatting and data analysis. For example, to use a chart type that is not from the standard list, we can use the method ***ApplyCustomType***. Let's convert our graph from the above example into a 3D bar graph. To do this, we set the ***ChartType*** argument of the *ApplyCustomType* method to "xl3DcolumnClustered."

ActiveChart.ApplyCustomType ChartType:=xl3DColumnClustered

There are some other argument values for this method that we can experiment with. Another important method of the ActiveChart object is ***SeriesCollection***. The *SeriesCollection* method first requires a numerical indication of which series should be manipulated. In our example, we only have one series of data, so we specify it by typing:

ActiveChart.SeriesCollection(1)

Even though *SeriesCollection* is listed as a method in the *Object Browser*, we more commonly treat it as a property. We can view a list of sub properties by typing another period after this enumeration. Some of these sub properties include ***Add***, ***Extend***, ***HasDataLabels***, and other formatting options. For example, we can change the color of our series by using the ***Interior*** and ***ColorIndex*** sub properties:

ActiveChart.SeriesCollection(1).Interior.ColorIndex = 37

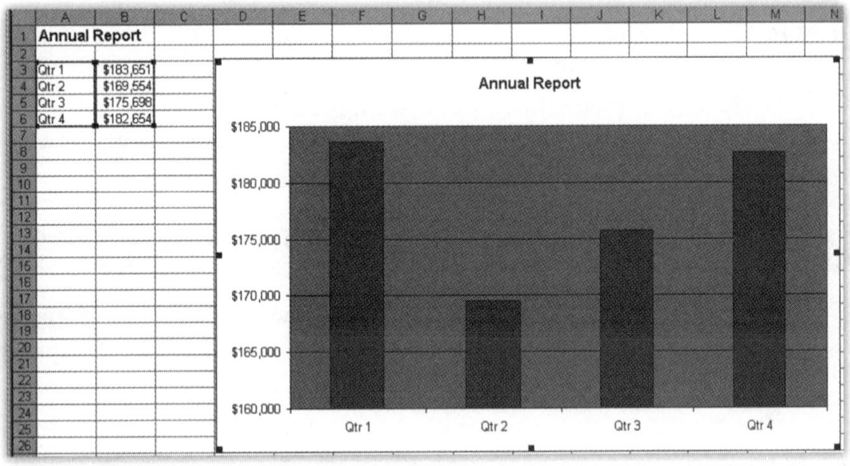

Figure 13.33 The resulting chart created by the *Graph()* macro has the chart type, source data, location, and chart options set by the VBA code.

See Figure 13.34 for the final *Graph()* sub procedure and Figure 13.35 for the results of the modified macro.

```
Sub Graph()

    Worksheets("Charts").Activate
    Charts.Add
    'ActiveChart.ChartType = xlColumnClustered
    ActiveChart.ApplyCustomType ChartType:=xl3DColumnClustered
    ActiveChart.SetSourceData Source:=Sheets("Charts").Range("A3:B6"), PlotBy:=xlColumns
    ActiveChart.Location Where:=xlLocationAsObject, Name:="Charts"

    ActiveChart.HasLegend = False
    ActiveChart.HasTitle = True
    ActiveChart.ChartTitle.Text = "Annual Report"

    ActiveChart.SeriesCollection(1).Interior.ColorIndex = 37

End Sub
```

Figure 13.34 Adding the *ApplyCustomType* and *SeriesCollection* methods of the ActiveChart object to the sub procedure.

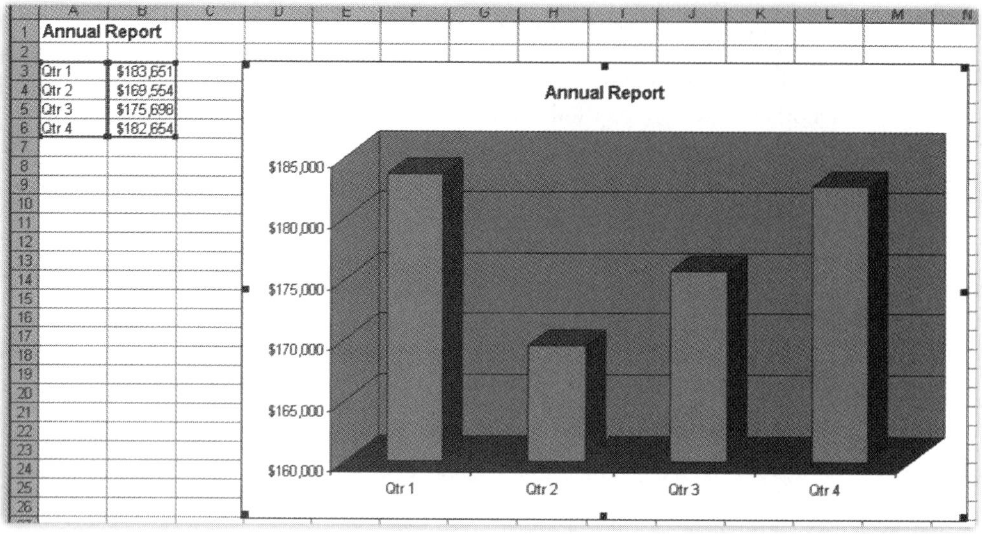

Figure 13.35 The result of the modified *Graph()* procedure.

There are other properties and methods of the Chart object, or ActiveChart object, that can be useful. We recommend that you experiment on your own by using the example in Figure 13.35 as a reference.

Summary

Objects	**Properties**	**Values**	**Methods**	**Arguments**
Charts			Add	Before, After, Count
			Copy, Delete, Select	
ActiveChart	ChartType	XL Constants	SetSourceData	Source, PlotBy
	HasLegend	True, False	Location	Where, Name
	HasTitle	True, False		
	ChartTitle	Text ("name")	ApplyCustomType	ChartType
	SeriesCollection	Add, Extend, HasDataLabels Interior, ColorIndex		

Quick Programming Note: If we are creating an application in which a user generates a chart based on his or her data, we will need to ensure that our chart is dynamic; that is, it does not have a fixed Data Range for its Source Data. To make such a dynamic application, we do not recommend adding a new chart in the code. If we do this, we will have multiple charts in the spreadsheet cumulating each time a user runs our application. Even if we select and delete any previous charts before creating a new one, this approach would also require several lines of code to set the chart details upon each creation. The idea in building a dynamic application is to try to minimize coding as much as possible by doing some preparation in the spreadsheet.

We recommend creating a chart in Excel first and then just selecting and modifying the source data in the code. This way, we can set all the formatting of the chart in the spreadsheet without several lines of code. Once we have created and formatted the chart (set to any temporary range of source data), note its name or shape index on the spreadsheet. (Find the shape index by noting how many shapes, buttons, or other drawing objects were already in the spreadsheet when we added the chart. The indexing begins at 1.) Once we have found the name or shape index, the only code we need in order to make the chart dynamic is to select the chart and modify its source data:

```
ActiveSheet.Shapes("Chart 1").Select or ActiveSheet.Shapes(1).Select
ActiveChart.SetSourceData(Source, PlotBy)
```

By using this approach, the user can input any number of values to be charted. Then, using the *End* property or another method to select this input range, we can set this range as the *Source* argument value in the *SetSourceData* method.

13.2.4 Drawing Objects

Drawing objects, or shapes, can be useful to help the user visualize a problem scenario or a suggested solution. We can use the commands in the *Illustration* group of the *Insert* tab in the *Ribbon* to draw a variety of shapes on the spreadsheet. These objects can be formatted using VBA code.

Before formatting specific drawing objects though, it is a good idea to name them. Naming drawing objects can be important when we want to search through several different shapes and modify a particular one, or a few. Drawing objects, or shapes, can be named either in Excel by using the *Formulas* tab > *Defined Names* group > Define Name command in the Ribbon as discussed in Chapter 3, or in VBA.

For example, let's consider a small graph, or network, consisting of five nodes and five arcs. To draw this network, we first choose a circular object from the ***Basic Shapes*** object from ***Shapes*** drop-down menu of the *Illustration* group, place it on the spreadsheet and copy and paste it four times. These are our five nodes (see Figure 13.36). Now, to draw the arcs, we use a ***Lines*** object from the ***Shapes*** drop-down menu, place it on the spreadsheet, copy and paste it four times, and then situate each between a pair of nodes (see Figure 13.36).

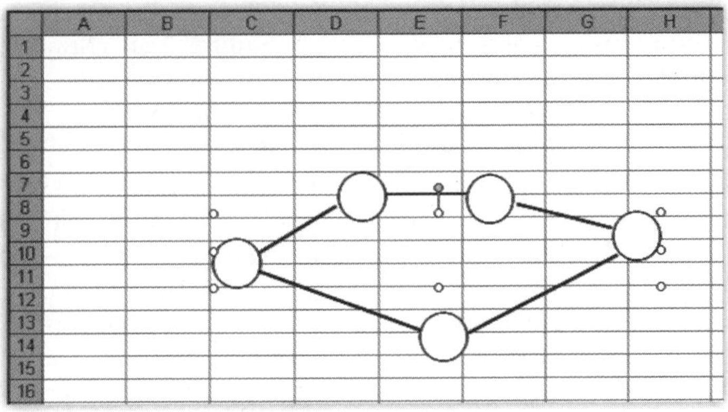

Figure 13.36 Creating a network consisting of five nodes and five arcs by drawing circular objects and line objects from the *Drawing Toolbar*.

Let's first name our objects using Excel. To do so, we select the first and the last node in the network by holding down the *Shift* key. Then, we group them by *right-clicking* and choosing *Group* > *Group* from the short-cut menu. Next, with this new group selected, we click *Formulas* tab > *Defined Names* group > Define Name command from the Ribbon. Let's name this set of objects "Tnodes." Repeating this method, we now select the remaining three nodes, group them, and name them "Inodes." Now, we select all of the arcs, group them, and name them "Arcs." If we select any of these sets of objects, we see the appropriate name appear in the *name window*. (For example, the "TNodes" are selected in Figure 13.36.)

We can also name drawing objects in VBA using the ***Shapes*** object and its properties and methods. As a quick example, let's draw a simple circle from the *Basic Shapes*. We click on the circle to view the name that appears in the *name window*; in our case, the Excel-generated name is "Oval 21." Let's now go to the VBE and create a new sub procedure called *Network()*. First, we activate the relative worksheet, "DrwgObj," that we are working on. Now, to access our shapes, we refer to the ***ActiveSheet*** that we are working with and then type the following:

ActiveSheet.Shapes("Oval 21").Select

The ***Select*** method is necessary for shapes before applying further properties or methods. We have now selected the circle that we drew in our spreadsheet. To name this drawing object, we simply use the ***Name*** property on our ***Selection***. Let's call this object "Test."

Selection.Name = "Test"

See Figure 13.37 for the code in the Network() sub procedure. To view the result of running this *macro* in Excel, see Figure 13.38. Notice that after running the *macro*, the name "Test" appears in the *name window* when the circle is selected.

```
Sub Network()

    Worksheets("DrwgObj").Activate
    ActiveSheet.Shapes("Oval 21").Select
    Selection.Name = "Test"

End Sub
```

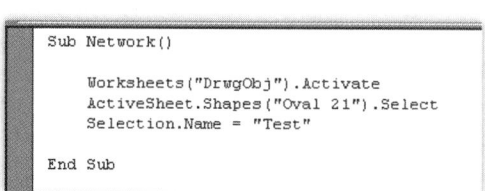

Figure 13.37 Using *ActiveSheet*, *Shapes*, and *Selection* to apply the *Name* property to the drawing object.

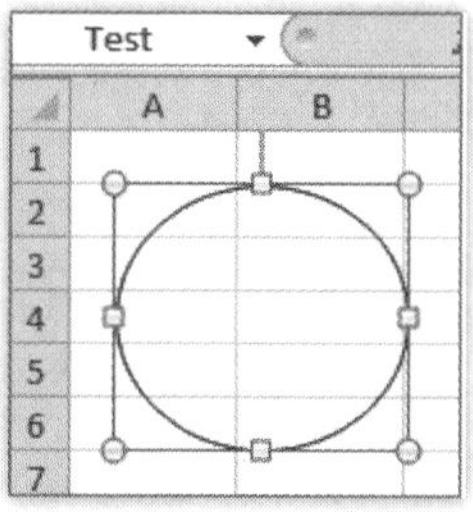

Figure 13.38 Naming the circle "Test" by running the *Network() macro*.

Quick Programming Note: Naming a drawing object can be done both in Excel and in VBA; however, we should consider whether or not it is necessary to use VBA code to name our objects. If we are writing a dynamic program, one in which our shapes have not yet been drawn or require some user input, then we will have to use VBA to identify and name the objects. However, if we are designing a program that allows the user to manipulate previously created shapes, it is better to create the names in Excel to save coding space and time.

To move shapes in the worksheet, we should cut and paste them to a range. However, the *Cut* method used with shapes does not allow the *Destination* argument. To paste a shape after cutting it, we must use the ***Paste*** method of the ActiveSheet object. This method also uses the *Destination* argument. The upper left hand corner of the shape will be pasted in the specified range. For example, in the following code, we have cut the "Test" circle and pasted it in cell *C1* to illustrate moving a shape:

ActiveSheet.Shapes("Test").Cut
ActiveSheet.Paste Destination:=Range("C1")

Now, let's return to our previously drawn network. Since we have grouped and named our shapes already in Excel, we do not need to create the names again with VBA. We can go ahead and format our sets of shapes in the *Network()* sub procedure. First, let's change the color of the "TNodes" to red. To do this, we use the ***ShapeRange*** and ***Fill*** properties. These properties include the sub properties of ***ForeColor*** and ***SchemeColor***. We set the *SchemeColor* to the color index of 10 to make the shapes' fill setting red.

ActiveSheet.Shapes("TNodes").Select
Selection.ShapeRange.Fill.ForeColor.SchemeColor = 10

We can similarly color the "INodes" grey by using the same properties; the color index for grey is 22 (see Figure 13.39).

```
Sub Network()

    ActiveSheet.Shapes("TNodes").Select
    Selection.ShapeRange.Fill.ForeColor.SchemeColor = 10

    ActiveSheet.Shapes("INodes").Select
    Selection.ShapeRange.Fill.ForeColor.SchemeColor = 22

    ActiveSheet.Shapes("Arcs").Select
    Selection.ShapeRange.Line.Weight = 3#
    Selection.ShapeRange.Line.EndArrowheadStyle = msoArrowheadOpen

End Sub
```

Figure 13.39 The *Network()* sub procedure modifies the formatting of the network shape objects.

Now let's format the arcs. We can modify the color, thickness, and ends of the line drawing object. For this example, we first increase the line weight from the default of 0.75 to 3.0. To do this, we use the *ShapeRange* and ***Line*** properties. With the *Line* property, we set the ***Weight*** sub property by giving the numerical value followed by a number sign (#). We again begin the code by selecting the appropriate Shape object.

ActiveSheet.Shapes("Arcs").Select
Selection.ShapeRange.Line.Weight = 3#

There are other sub properties of *Line* that we can experiment with. To modify the ends of the line drawing object, we can use six main sub properties: ***EndArrowheadStyle***, ***EndArrowheadLength***, ***EndArrowheadWidth*** and ***BeginArrowheadStyle***, ***BeginArrowheadLength***, ***BeginArrowheadWidth***. The values of these sub properties are ***MSO Values*** that are pre-defined by Excel. For this example, we change our lines to have an arrow at the end. (That is, they all have arrows that point to the right of the screen). To do this, we use the *EndArrowheadStyle* property and the "msoArrowheadOpen" value.

Selection.ShapeRange.Line.EndArrowheadStyle = msoArrowheadOpen

See Figure 13.39 for the final *Network()* sub procedure. Figure 13.40 depicts the result of running this macro on our network in Excel.

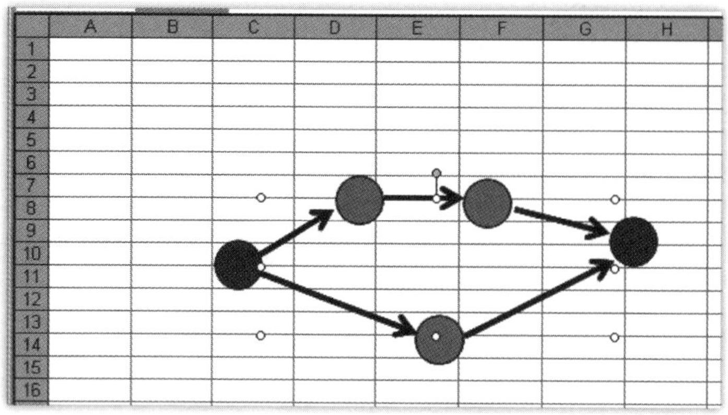

Figure 13.40 The result of the *Network()* macro.

Again, there are other useful properties and methods that can be applied to drawing objects; however, these will probably be the most common ones we use.

Summary

Objects	Properties	Values	Methods	Arguments
ActiveSheet	Shapes	("name"), (#)	Select,	–
Shape Selection			Cut,	–
ShapeRange			Paste	Destination
	Name	"name"	Add	–
	Line	Weight (#)		
	Fill	ForeColor, SchemeColor		
	End and Begin ArrowheadStyleLength, Width	MSO Values		

13.2.5 Application

The Application object is useful for some common functions as well as some other features for running VBA code. We will discuss the Application functions in a later section. For now, we will illustrate three very useful Application properties and methods.

The first is the ***ScreenUpdating*** property (see Figure 13.41). This property, which takes the values *True* or *False*, help our code run more efficiently. When the *ScreenUpdating* property is set to *False*, none of the following actions in the VBA code will be reflected on the Excel screen while the macro is being run. This property is a good programming idea since it keeps users from seeing the screen flicker while each code item is processed and therefore helps the code run faster. When we have reached the end of a long sequence of code, we should remember to set the *ScreenUpdating* property back to *True* so that the user can see the results of the macro on the screen.

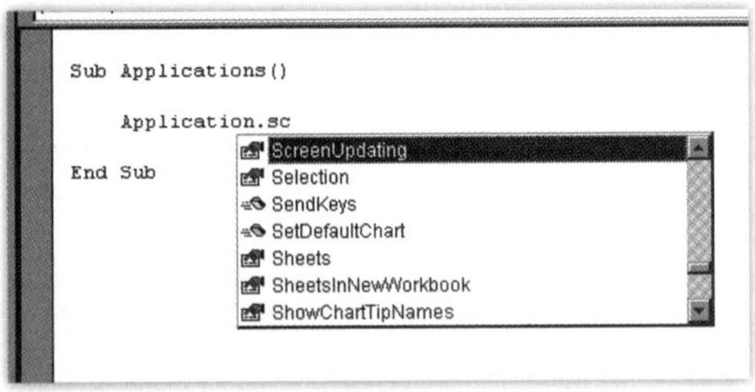

Figure 13.41 The Application object has several properties and methods, including the *ScreenUpdating* property.

Let's consider an example. Suppose we are creating a meal plan for each day of the week. We have three possible daily meal plans, and we want to assign each one to the days in the week (see Figure 13.42). Suppose we have randomly decided to copy and paste the first meal plan to Days 1, 4, and 7, the second meal plan to Days 2 and 4, and the third meal plan to Days 3 and 6.

	A	B	C	D	E	F	G
1	**Possible Daily Meal Plans**						
2	bagel		cereal		eggs		
3	tuna salad		turkey		bean salad		
4	pasta		rice		pizza		
5	apple		yogurt		ice cream		
6							
7							
8	**Day 1**	**Day 2**	**Day 3**	**Day 4**	**Day 5**	**Day 6**	**Day 7**
9							
10							
11							
12							

Figure 13.42 The possible daily meal plans on the spreadsheet.

We have a simple sequence of VBA code that will copy and paste each range appropriately (see Figure 13.43). If we first run this *macro* without using the *ScreenUpdating* property in the code, we can see the screen flicker as the copying and pasting actions take place. We will go ahead and add the following lines of code to the beginning and end of the macro:

Application.ScreenUpdating = False
Application.ScreenUpdating = True

If we run the macro again, we notice an increase in speed and an elimination of screen flickering. See Figure 13.43 for the completed *Applications()* sub procedure and Figure 13.44 for the result of the macro.

```
Sub Applications()

    Application.ScreenUpdating = False

    Range("A2:A5").Copy
    Range("A9").PasteSpecial
    Range("D9").PasteSpecial
    Range("G9").PasteSpecial
    Range("C2:C5").Copy
    Range("B9").PasteSpecial
    Range("E9").PasteSpecial
    Range("E2:E5").Copy
    Range("C9").PasteSpecial
    Range("F9").PasteSpecial

    Application.ScreenUpdating = True

End Sub
```

Figure 13.43 The *Applications()* sub procedure uses the *ScreenUpdating* property at the beginning and end of the code.

We may also notice that when the macro has completed running in Excel, we can see that the last range that was copied is still highlighted with a flashing dashed-outline. This leads us to another useful property of the Application object: the ***CutCopyMode*** property. When the *CutCopyMode* is set to *True*, which is the default, Excel keeps the last range which was copied highlighted until another action takes place. However, if the last action in our code is to copy and paste a range, we do not want the user to see this flashing range. To avoid this, we can simply set the *CutCopyMode* property to *False* at the end of our code (before setting the *Screen Updating* property back to *True*).

	A	B	C	D	E	F	G
1	Possible Daily Meal Plans						
2	bagel		cereal		eggs		
3	tuna salad		turkey		bean salad		
4	pasta		rice		pizza		
5	apple		yogurt		ice cream		
6							
7							
8	Day 1	Day 2	Day 3	Day 4	Day 5	Day 6	Day 7
9	bagel	cereal	eggs	bagel	cereal	eggs	bagel
10	tuna salad	turkey	bean salad	tuna salad	turkey	bean salad	tuna salad
11	pasta	rice	pizza	pasta	rice	pizza	pasta
12	apple	yogurt	ice cream	apple	yogurt	ice cream	apple
13							

Figure 13.44 The result of running the *Applications()* macro.

In Figure 13.45, we have added the following line of code to the *Applications()* sub procedure:

Application.CutCopyMode = False

We have also added a line that selects the range *A1* so that the last range where we pasted values is not highlighted. We can see the difference in the resulting macro in Figure 13.46.

We would now like to discuss the Application object method, ***Wait***. The *Wait* method takes a time value as its argument; that is, it will pause the program until the specified time value has been reached. Recalling from Chapter 4, we know the ***Now*** function calculates the current time.

In VBA, *Now* is a constant for the current time value. We can also use the function ***TimeValue*** in VBA to assign an integer-valued time amount.

```
Sub Applications()

    Application.ScreenUpdating = False

    Range("A2:A5").Copy
    Range("A9").PasteSpecial
    Range("D9").PasteSpecial
    Range("G9").PasteSpecial
    Range("C2:C5").Copy
    Range("B9").PasteSpecial
    Range("E9").PasteSpecial
    Range("E2:E5").Copy
    Range("C9").PasteSpecial
    Range("F9").PasteSpecial
    Range("A1").Select

    Application.CutCopyMode = False
    Application.ScreenUpdating = True

End Sub
```

Figure 13.45 Adding two lines of code to the *Applications()* sub procedure, including the *Cut-CopyMode* property.

	A	B	C	D	E	F	G
1	**Possible Daily Meal Plans**						
2	bagel		cereal		eggs		
3	tuna salad		turkey		bean salad		
4	pasta		rice		pizza		
5	apple		yogurt		ice cream		
6							
7							
8	**Day 1**	**Day 2**	**Day 3**	**Day 4**	**Day 5**	**Day 6**	**Day 7**
9	bagel	cereal	eggs	bagel	cereal	eggs	bagel
10	tuna salad	turkey	bean salad	tuna salad	turkey	bean salad	tuna salad
11	pasta	rice	pizza	pasta	rice	pizza	pasta
12	apple	yogurt	ice cream	apple	yogurt	ice cream	apple
13							

Figure 13.46 The result of the modified *macro* does not show any highlighted ranges.

Let's consider another example. With the data in the *Applications()* sub procedure, we can change the color of the possible meal plans to yellow, and the actual daily meal plans to blue by using the *Interior* and *Color* properties of the Range object. However, between changing the first range to yellow and the second to blue, we want to ask the program to wait three seconds. To do this, between these two lines of code, we type the following:

Application.Wait (Now + TimeValue("0:00:03"))

Now the program will wait until the time value reaches the current time plus three seconds of time. See the modified sub procedure in Figure 13.47. Go ahead and experiment with running the macro in Excel to note the delay in coloring the ranges. The result of the macro can be seen in Figure 13.48.

The *Wait* method will become useful when creating simulation programs, as we will see in Chapter 20. There are some other Application properties and methods we can experiment with, but these three are the most commonly used.

```
Sub Applications()

    Application.ScreenUpdating = False

    Range("A2:A5").Copy
    Range("A9").PasteSpecial
    Range("D9").PasteSpecial
    Range("G9").PasteSpecial
    Range("C2:C5").Copy
    Range("B9").PasteSpecial
    Range("E9").PasteSpecial
    Range("E2:E5").Copy
    Range("C9").PasteSpecial
    Range("F9").PasteSpecial
    Range("A1").Select

    Application.CutCopyMode = False
    Application.ScreenUpdating = True

    Range("A2:E5").Interior.Color = vbYellow
    Application.Wait (Now + TimeValue("0:00:03"))
    Range("A9:G12").Interior.Color = vbBlue

End Sub
```

Figure 13.47 The *modified Applications()* sub procedure uses the *Wait* method between two formatting commands for ranges in the spreadsheet.

	A	B	C	D	E	F	G
1	**Possible Daily Meal Plans**						
2	bagel		cereal		eggs		
3	tuna salad		turkey		bean salad		
4	pasta		rice		pizza		
5	apple		yogurt		ice cream		
6							
7							
8	**Day 1**	**Day 2**	**Day 3**	**Day 4**	**Day 5**	**Day 6**	**Day 7**
9	bagel	cereal	eggs	bagel	cereal	eggs	bagel
10	tuna salad	turkey	bean salad	tuna salad	turkey	bean salad	tuna salad
11	pasta	rice	pizza	pasta	rice	pizza	pasta
12	apple	yogurt	ice cream	apple	yogurt	ice cream	apple
13							

Figure 13.48 The result of the modified macro. There was a three-second delay between the yellow and blue color changes.

Summary

Objects	**Properties**	**Values**	**Methods**	**Arguments**
Application	ScreenUpdating	True, False	Wait	Now, TimeValue ("0:00:00")
	CutCopyMode	False, xlCut, xlCopy		

13.3 *The With Construct*

We will be discussing programming structures in detail in Chapter 16; however, there is a simple construct we would like to describe at this point. The ***With*** construct is basically used to set several properties of one object in an enclosed statement.

For example, if we want to modify several formatting aspects of a certain range, we need several different lines of code:

Range("A1:C8").Interior.Color = vbRed
Range("A1:C8").Font.Bold = True
Range("A1:C8").Font.Name = "Arial"
Range("A1:C8").Borders(xlEdgeBottom).LineStyle = xlDash

Using the *With* statement, we can reduce the coding by naming the range object first and then simply listing all the properties:

```
With Range("A1:C8")
    .Interior.Color = vbRed
    .Font.Bold = True
    .Font.Name = "Arial"
    .Borders(xlEdgeBottom).LineStyle = xlDash
End With
```

See Figures 13.49 and 13.50 for the VBA code in the Borders2() sub procedure and the result of running the macro in Excel.

Notice that there is still a period before each property within the construct. Also notice that the code ends with the statement ***End With***. As with most programming structures, which we will see in Chapter 16, there will be a beginning and ending statement specific to each structure. When using the *With* construct, we must always start using *With* followed by the object name and always end using *End With.*

```
Sub Borders2()
    Worksheets("Analysis").Activate

    With Range("A1:C8")
        .Interior.Color = vbRed
        .Font.Bold = True
        .Font.Name = "Arial"
        .Borders(xlEdgeBottom).LineStyle = xlDash
    End With

End Sub
```

Figure 13.49 The *Borders2()* sub procedure uses the *With* construct to format a specified range.

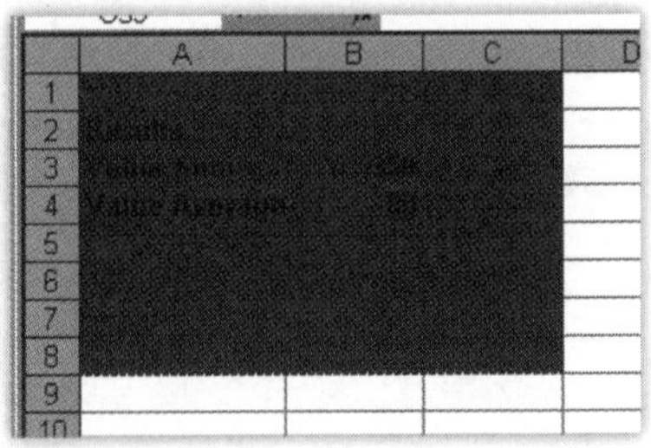

Figure 13.50 The result of the *Borders2() macro.*

Let's look at one more illustration of the *With* construct by referring to a previous example. When discussing the charts, we wrote a sub procedure, *Graph()*, which used many properties and methods of the ActiveChart object, as shown in Figure 13.51. We can simplify this code by using the *With* construct with the ActiveChart object. In Figure 13.52, we can see a modified code in the *Graph2()* sub procedure that performs the same actions as the original *Graph()* sub procedure, but this time, the *With* construct is used.

```
Sub Graph()

    Worksheets("Charts").Activate
    Charts.Add
    'ActiveChart.ChartType = xlColumnClustered
    ActiveChart.ApplyCustomType ChartType:=xl3DColumnClustered
    ActiveChart.SetSourceData Source:=Sheets("Charts").Range("A3:B6"), PlotBy:=xlColumns
    ActiveChart.Location Where:=xlLocationAsObject, Name:="Charts"

    ActiveChart.HasLegend = False
    ActiveChart.HasTitle = True
    ActiveChart.ChartTitle.Text = "Annual Report"

    ActiveChart.SeriesCollection(1).Interior.ColorIndex = 37

End Sub
```

Figure 13.51 The original *Graph()* sub procedure uses many properties and methods of the ActiveChart object.

```
Option Explicit

'With Construct

Sub Graph2()
    Worksheets("Charts").Activate
    Charts.Add
    ActiveChart.ApplyCustomType ChartType:=xl3DColumnClustered

    With ActiveChart
        .ApplyCustomType ChartType:=xl3DColumnClustered
        .SetSourceData Source:=Sheets("Charts").Range("A3:B6"), PlotBy:=xlColumns
        .Location Where:=xlLocationAsObject, Name:="Charts"
        .HasLegend = False
        .HasTitle = True
        .ChartTitle.Characters.Text = "Annual Report"
    End With

    ActiveChart.SeriesCollection(1).Interior.ColorIndex = 37
End Sub
```

Figure 13.52 The new *Graph2()* sub procedure uses the *With* construct with the ActiveChart object.

Summary

The With Construct

With ObjectName

    .property or

    .method

End With

13.4 *Referencing and Names in VBA*

We discussed referencing and naming in Excel in detail in Chapter 3. We will now explain how to do so in VBA. Referencing will apply mostly to ranges and cells; we can also use the names of other Excel objects to reference these ranges. As we have already learned in this chapter, naming an object is as simple as assigning a value to its *Name* property; however, some extra notes should be made regarding naming ranges.

13.4.1 Referencing Ranges and Cells

There are several ways to reference ranges and cells using VBA. The first one we will describe uses the ***Offset*** property, which considers the named range to be in the 0th row and 0th column. It then offsets the range selection by a certain row count below and column count to the right of this named range. That is, if we type the following statement

Range("A1").Offset(1, 0)

we would be referring to cell *A2*, whereas if we typed

Range("A1").Offset(0, 1)

we would be referring to cell *B1*.

	A	B	C	D	E	F	G	H	I	J	K
1	**Airline Survey**										
2											
3	**Passenger**	**1**	**2**	**3**	**4**	**5**	**6**	**7**	**8**	**9**	**10**
4	Age	24	35	52	43	67	28	32	34	47	45
5	Gender	M	M	F	M	F	F	M	M	F	F
6	# Flights per year	3	10	8	12	2	4	6	10	4	4
7	# Times in ATL	3	7	4	9	0	3	3	6	1	2
8	# Times in JFK	1	2	7	6	1	2	1	5	2	2
9	# International Trips	0	2	0	2	0	1	1	2	1	0
10											
11											

Figure 13.53 A table of data for an airline survey.

Let's consider an example. Suppose we have a table of data collected from an airline survey (see Figure 13.53). We will use cell *A3* as our range name since it is at the corner of the table. If we want to highlight the 10th passenger, we can use the *Offset* property in the following way:

Range("A3").Offset(0, 10).Interior.ColorIndex = 15

This command looks at cell *A3* and moves 0 rows down and 10 columns to the right (see Figure 13.54). The result of this code is shown in Figure 13.55.

```
Sub Referencing()

    Worksheets("Referencing").Activate
    Range("A3").Offset(0, 10).Interior.ColorIndex = 15

End Sub
```

Figure 13.54 Using the *Offset* property to count 0 rows and 10 columns from the named range.

	A	B	C	D	E	F	G	H	I	J	K
1	**Airline Survey**										
2											
3	**Passenger**	**1**	**2**	**3**	**4**	**5**	**6**	**7**	**8**	**9**	**10**
4	Age	24	35	52	43	67	28	32	34	47	45
5	Gender	M	M	F	M	F	F	M	M	F	F
6	# Flights per year	3	10	8	12	2	4	6	10	4	4
7	# Times in ATL	3	7	4	9	0	3	3	6	1	2
8	# Times in JFK	1	2	7	6	1	2	1	5	2	2
9	# International Trips	0	2	0	2	0	1	1	2	1	0
10											

Figure 13.55 The result of the *Referencing()* macro. The 10th passenger is highlighted.

We can also highlight the entire column of data for the 10th passenger using the *Offset* property. To do this, we refer to a larger range by typing the following:

Range(Range("A3").Offset(1, 10), Range("A3").Offset(6, 10)).Interior.ColorIndex = 6

This command finds the first and last cell of the range by using the *Offset* property (see Figure 13.56). The result of this macro is shown in Figure 13.57.

```
Sub Referencing()

    Worksheets("Referencing").Activate
    Range("A3").Offset(0, 10).Interior.ColorIndex = 15
    Range(Range("A3").Offset(1, 10), Range("A3").Offset(6, 10)).Interior.ColorIndex = 6

End Sub
```

Figure 13.56 The large range uses the *Offset* property to highlight all of the data for the 10th passenger.

	A	B	C	D	E	F	G	H	I	J	K
1	**Airline Survey**										
2											
3	**Passenger**	**1**	**2**	**3**	**4**	**5**	**6**	**7**	**8**	**9**	**10**
4	Age	24	35	52	43	67	28	32	34	47	45
5	Gender	M	M	F	M	F	F	M	M	F	F
6	# Flights per year	3	10	8	12	2	4	6	10	4	4
7	# Times in ATL	3	7	4	9	0	3	3	6	1	2
8	# Times in JFK	1	2	7	6	1	2	1	5	2	2
9	# International Trips	0	2	0	2	0	1	1	2	1	0
10											

Figure 13.57 The result of the modified *Referencing()* macro.

The *Offset* property can also be used to refer to cells above and to the left of the named range. To do this, simply use negative values as the row and column counts, respectively.

Another way to reference cells using VBA is with the ***Cells*** property. Unlike the *Offset* property, which considers the named range to be in the (0, 0) position, the *Cells* property considers the named range to be in the (1, 1) position. That is, using the *Offset* property to reference cell *A2* from cell *A1*, we would type:

Range("A1").Offset(1, 0)

However, to use the *Cells* property, we would reference in the following way:

Range("A1").Cells(2, 1)

Therefore, returning to our previous example with the airline survey data, if this time we want to highlight the 4th passenger using the *Cells* property from cell *A3*, we would type:

Range("A3").Cells(1, 5).Interior.ColorIndex = 15

Notice that it may be confusing to shift our counting scheme; that is, since the named range is included as the first row and first column, we have to reference 5 columns even though we are looking for the fourth entry. It is therefore usually better when using the *Cells* property to make a named range the first cell in the table rather than the first cell on the corner of the table. That is, if we want to use the *Cells* property to highlight the 7th passenger, we can use cell *B3* as our named range and thus count the 7th column to the right. We would now type:

Range("B3").Cells(1, 7).Interior.ColorIndex = 15

See Figure 13.58 for the modified macro and Figure 13.59 for the result.

```
Sub Referencing()

    Worksheets("Referencing").Activate
    Range("A3").Offset(0, 10).Interior.ColorIndex = 15
    Range(Range("A3").Offset(1, 10), Range("A3").Offset(6, 10)).Interior.ColorIndex = 6

    Range("A3").Cells(1, 5).Interior.ColorIndex = 15
    Range("B3").Cells(1, 7).Interior.ColorIndex = 15

End Sub
```

Figure 13.58 Using the *Cells* property to highlight the 4th and 7th passengers. Notice the named range changes.

	A	B	C	D	E	F	G	H	I	J	K
1	**Airline Survey**										
2											
3	**Passenger**	**1**	**2**	**3**	**4**	**5**	**6**	**7**	**8**	**9**	**10**
4	Age	24	35	52	43	67	28	32	34	47	45
5	Gender	M	M	F	M	F	F	M	M	F	F
6	# Flights per year	3	10	8	12	2	4	6	10	4	4
7	# Times in ATL	3	7	4	9	0	3	3	6	1	2
8	# Times in JFK	1	2	7	6	1	2	1	5	2	2
9	# International Trips	0	2	0	2	0	1	1	2	1	0
10											
11											

Figure 13.59 The result of the modified *Referencing() macro.*

The next two properties, ***Columns*** and ***Rows***, reference columns and rows in the named range, respectively. When we wanted to highlight all of the 10th passenger's information in a previous example using *Offset*, we referenced this column of data using a long range expression. We can shorten this code by using the *Columns* property.

The *Columns* property takes a numerical index value to find the numbered column within the named range. Suppose that this time we want to highlight all of the third passenger's information. We would type:

Range("B3:K9").Columns(3).Interior.ColorIndex = 5

```
Sub Referencing()

    Worksheets("Referencing").Activate
    Range("A3").Offset(0, 10).Interior.ColorIndex = 15
    Range(Range("A3").Offset(1, 10), Range("A3").Offset(6, 10)).Interior.ColorIndex = 6

    Range("A3").Cells(1, 5).Interior.ColorIndex = 15
    Range("B3").Cells(1, 7).Interior.ColorIndex = 15

    Range("B3:K9").Columns(3).Interior.ColorIndex = 5

End Sub
```

Figure 13.60 Using the Columns property to find the third column of data.

This command looks at the third column of the range of data; it considers *Columns(1)* to be the first column of data (in this case *B3:B9*). This additional code is added to the Referencing() sub procedure shown in Figure 13.60. The result of the macro is presented in Figure 13.61.

	A	B	C	D	E	F	G	H	I	J	K
1	**Airline Survey**										
2											
3	**Passenger**	**1**	**2**	**3**	**4**	**5**	**6**	**7**	**8**	**9**	**10**
4	Age	24	35	52	43	67	28	32	34	47	45
5	Gender	M	M	F	M	F	F	M	M	F	F
6	# Flights per year	3	10	8	12	2	4	6	10	4	4
7	# Times in ATL	3	7	4	9	0	3	3	6	1	2
8	# Times in JFK	1	2	7	6	1	2	1	5	2	2
9	# International Trips	0	2	0	2	0	1	1	2	1	0
10											
11											

Figure 13.61 The result of the Columns property in the modified *macro*.

The *Rows* property works in a similar way; a numerical index value of the desired row should be given. With respect to the named range, the *Rows* property considers the first row of data to be *Rows(1)* . For example, if we want to make all of the Age data in our table have red font, we can use the *Rows* property in the following way:

Range("B3:K9").Rows(2).Font.Color = vbRed

```
Sub Referencing()

    Worksheets("Referencing").Activate
    Range("A3").Offset(0, 10).Interior.ColorIndex = 15
    Range(Range("A3").Offset(1, 10), Range("A3").Offset(6, 10)).Interior.ColorIndex = 6

    Range("A3").Cells(1, 5).Interior.ColorIndex = 15
    Range("B3").Cells(1, 7).Interior.ColorIndex = 15

    Range("B3:K9").Columns(3).Interior.ColorIndex = 5
    Range("B3:K9").Rows(2).Font.Color = vbRed

End Sub
```

Figure 13.62 Using the *Rows* property to change the font of the second row of data.

See Figure 13.62 for the modified code and Figure 13.63 for the result of the macro.

	A	B	C	D	E	F	G	H	I	J	K
1	**Airline Survey**										
2											
3	**Passenger**	**1**	**2**	**3**	**4**	**5**	**6**	**7**	**8**	**9**	**10**
4	Age	24	35	52	43	67	28	32	34	47	45
5	Gender	M	M	F	M	F	F	M	M	F	F
6	# Flights per year	3	10	8	12	2	4	6	10	4	4
7	# Times in ATL	3	7	4	9	0	3	3	6	1	2
8	# Times in JFK	1	2	7	6	1	2	1	5	2	2
9	# International Trips	0	2	0	2	0	1	1	2	1	0
10											

Figure 13.63 The result of the modified *Referencing()* macro.

The ***Hidden*** property is another useful property of Rows and Columns. It takes the values *True* and *False* and is equivalent to *right-clicking* on a row(s) or column(s) heading and choosing *Hide* or *Unhide* from the list of drop-down options. The format is as follows:

Range(cells or name).Rows.Hidden = True or False or

Range(cells or name).Columns.Hidden = True or False

This property can be useful in keeping necessary values or formulas in cells hidden from the user. It can also be useful in designing dynamic programs for which we may need to create several tables but do not know how many until the user informs we. In this case, instead of generating several tables in the code, we can generate the largest amount of tables we would need and keep them hidden. Then, we can simply unhide the rows or columns for the number of tables needed by the user.

There is also a specific formatting method that can be used with the Rows or Columns reference; this is the ***AutoFit*** method. This method is equivalent to selecting *Home* tab > *Cells* group > *Format* command from the Excel Ribbon, and selecting *AutoFit Row Height* and *AutoFit Column Width* options from the drop-down menu. *It* causes the row height or column width to increase or decrease in order to fit the size of the value in the range. This method has no arguments, and its format is:

Range(cells or name).Rows.AutoFit or

Range(cells or name).Columns.AutoFit

As in the spreadsheet, this type of formatting can also be applied to an entire column or row. That is, instead of selecting a particular range, we can select the column or row heading and format it to AutoFit.

The next two properties, ***EntireColumn*** and ***EntireRow***, are used to modify every column or row in the named range, including the column or row settings for the entire worksheet. For example, if we use the *EntireColumn* property on the table range *B3:K9*, it will affect every column in this range (columns *B, C, D, E, F, G, H, I, J,* and *K*) for its entire length on the worksheet. If we want to shift the alignment of our numerical values from the center to the left of each cell, we type the following:

Range("B3:K9").EntireColumn.HorizontalAlignment = xlLeft

Now, the text in every column in this range for its entire length will be left-aligned. That is, even if we type a new value in row 10 or below, or rows 1 and 2, in the columns *B* through *K*, it will automatically be left-aligned.

The *EntireRow* property works in the same way. Suppose we want a thicker border between the Age and Gender rows of the table. Also suppose that we plan to expand this table by adding more passengers. We would therefore like to use the *EntireRow* property so that the new entries will still have a thicker border between the Age and Gender values. So, we use *B4:K5* as the named range and format an *Inside-Horizontal* border.

Range("B4:K5").EntireRow.Borders(xlInsideHorizontal).Weight = 3

Now, there is a thick border between rows 4 and 5 for the entire worksheet. See Figure 13.64 for these additional lines of code and Figure 13.65 for the result of the modified macro.

```
Sub Referencing()

    Worksheets("Referencing").Activate
    Range("A3").Offset(0, 10).Interior.ColorIndex = 15
    Range(Range("A3").Offset(1, 10), Range("A3").Offset(6, 10)).Interior.ColorIndex = 6

    Range("A3").Cells(1, 5).Interior.ColorIndex = 15
    Range("B3").Cells(1, 7).Interior.ColorIndex = 15

    Range("B3:K9").Columns(3).Interior.ColorIndex = 5
    Range("B3:K9").Rows(2).Font.Color = vbRed

    Range("B3:K9").EntireColumn.HorizontalAlignment = xlLeft
    Range("B4:K5").EntireRow.Borders(xlInsideHorizontal).Weight = 3

End Sub
```

Figure 13.64 Using the *EntireColumn* and *EntireRow* properties to format the table and worksheet.

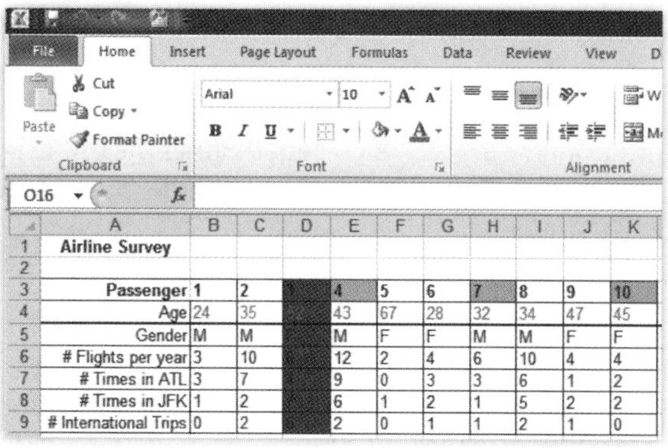

	A	B	C	D	E	F	G	H	I	J	K
1	Airline Survey										
2											
3	Passenger	1	2		4	5	6	7	8	9	10
4	Age	24	35		43	67	28	32	34	47	45
5	Gender	M	M		M	F	F	M	M	F	F
6	# Flights per year	3	10		12	2	4	6	10	4	4
7	# Times in ATL	3	7		9	0	3	3	6	1	2
8	# Times in JFK	1	2		6	1	2	1	5	2	2
9	# International Trips	0	2		2	0	1	1	2	1	0

Figure 13.65 The result of the modified macro shows the left-alignment and thick border.

The last property for referencing that we will describe is the ***End*** property. It is very useful as it can help us find the end of a row or column of any range of data. The *End* property can take four values: xlDown and xlUp for columns, and xlToRight and xlToLeft for rows. We do not need to name an entire data range to use this property; just one cell in the data range works.

For example, using the above data, the code *Range("A3").End(xlToRight)* would reference cell *K3* since that is the last cell in the row with data in it. This property can be useful in referencing a large row or column of data for which we do not know the last cell of data.

Suppose we want to copy and paste the titles of the table to create another table below it. We would type the following to reference the range of table titles:

Range("A3", Range("A3").End(xlDown)).Copy

This code will copy the range *A3:A9* since *A9* contains the last cell of data looking down from *A3*. See Figure 13.66 for the final *Referencing()* sub procedure and Figure 13.67 for the final macro result.

```
Sub Referencing()

    Worksheets("Referencing").Activate
    Range("A3").Offset(0, 10).Interior.ColorIndex = 15
    Range(Range("A3").Offset(1, 10), Range("A3").Offset(6, 10)).Interior.ColorIndex = 6

    Range("A3").Cells(1, 5).Interior.ColorIndex = 15
    Range("B3").Cells(1, 7).Interior.ColorIndex = 15

    Range("B3:K9").Columns(3).Interior.ColorIndex = 5
    Range("B3:K9").Rows(2).Font.Color = vbRed

    Range("B3:K9").EntireColumn.HorizontalAlignment = xlLeft
    Range("B4:K5").EntireRow.Borders(xlInsideHorizontal).Weight = 3

    Range("A3", Range("A3").End(xlDown)).Copy
    Range("A12").PasteSpecial

End Sub
```

Figure 13.66 Using the *End* property to copy and paste the table titles.

Remember that we can also use the *End* property to search up and left from a cell in the middle or end of a data range.

Note: The *End* property only works for one data type at a time. That is, if we have a list of data with both numbers and text, the *End* property will search until it finds the last entry of the first data type. For example, in a table with the values "1, 2, three, 4" in four consecutive cells, the *End* property would select the cell containing the value "2" not "4." The *End* property also only works if there is at least one value in the cell adjacent to the specified range from which we are searching. That is, if we have one value "Input" in the range from which we are searching, and there are currently no values in the "Input" column or row, the *End* property will not select a cell. We discuss some tricks for avoiding these problems in Chapter 16.

These properties are the most useful ways to reference our data. We suggest practicing with them as they will be helpful in managing and manipulating large data.

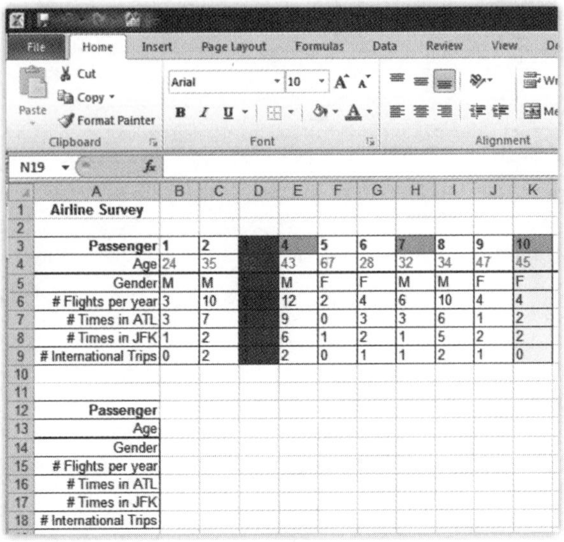

Figure 13.67 The result of the final *Referencing()* macro.

Summary

Referencing Ranges and Cells in VBA

Offset:	Initial = (0,0); Count = (rows down, columns right)
Cells:	Initial = (1, 1); Count = (rows down, columns right)
Rows:	Initial row count = 0; give row number in data
Columns:	Initial column count = 0; give column number in data
EntireRow:	Affects entire row in a worksheet of range rows
EntireColumn:	Affects entire column in a worksheet of range columns
End:	Finds the last cell of data in a row or column

13.4.2 Naming Ranges

As we have already discussed, the most common way to assign object names is by using the *Name* property. The names that we will assign most often will probably be for the Range object. When we name a range in Excel using *Formulas > Defined Names > Define Name* command on the Ribbon, the name appears in the *name window* whenever the corresponding range is selected. The same occurs after naming a range in VBA.

Let's return to the above example. Suppose we want to name a range of passenger numbers "Passengers." We will use the *Name* property. We will also need to use the *End* property (to the right, or to the end of the first row), if we suppose that we do not know how many passengers are in the table.

Range("A3", Range("A3").End(xlToRight)).Name = "Passengers"

If we now highlight the entire range of data in the row beginning with *A3*, we see the range name appear in the *name window* in the upper left hand corner of the window (see Figures 13.68 and 13.69).

```
Sub Naming()

    Range("A3", Range("A3").End(xlToRight)).Name = "Passengers"

End Sub
```

Figure 13.68 The *Naming()* sub procedure uses the *Name* property to give a name to the range.

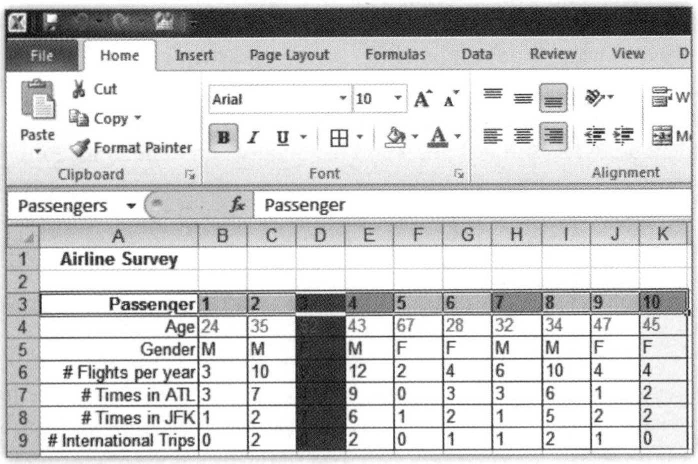

Figure 13.69 The "Passengers" range is highlighted and the name appears in the *name window*.

Now that we have named the range, we can refer to it by its name for future use. If we want to add a thick border around this range, we simply type:

Range("Passengers").BorderAround Weight:=xlThick

See Figures 13.70 and 13.71 for the code and the result of the modified macro.

```
Sub Naming()

    Range(Range("A3"), Range("A3").End(xlToRight)).Name = "Passengers"
    Range("Passengers").BorderAround Weight:=xlThick

End Sub
```

Figure 13.70 The range name can now be used to directly reference the range.

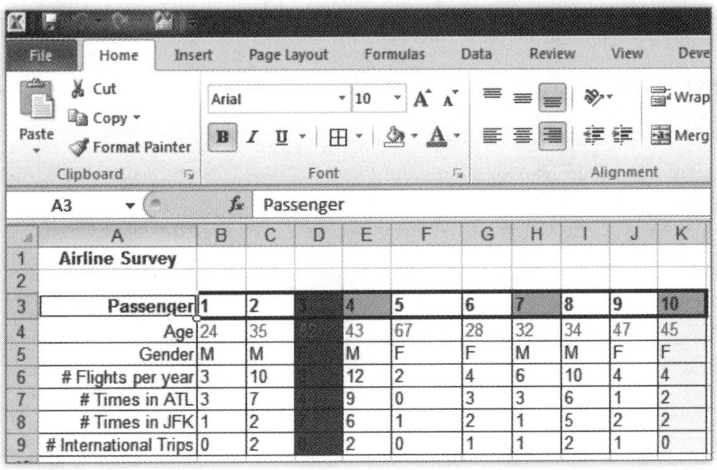

Figure 13.71 The result of the modified *Naming() macro.*

Quick Programming Note: As we have mentioned before, it is always a good idea to see what code is necessary and what code can be eliminated by preparation in Excel. Once a range is named, it is much easier to refer to it throughout the code; however, we can name the range in Excel first and then just use the already-defined range name in the VBA code. Only if the range is dependent on user input is it necessary to actually name the range in the code instead of in Excel.

13.5 *Formulas in VBA*

Much of Excel requires the use of formulas. As we develop spreadsheet-based decision support systems, much of our programs may use formulas as well. As we will see in Chapters 14 and 16, we can make many simple calculations using variables and programming structures. However, it is still important to know how to use all of the functions and formulas available in Excel with VBA code.

There are two main ways to use Excel-defined formulas in VBA: using the Range object and using the Application object.

13.5.1 Using the Range object

There are two main properties to use with the Range object that allow us to use the Excel spreadsheet functions in our VBA code. The first is the ***Formula*** property. It allows us to enter any Excel formula as we would in a spreadsheet by entering the formula, including the equals sign, as the property value. Reference the cells using column letters and row numbers.

For example, using the Airline Survey data, if we want to find the total number of international trips taken by all passengers, we can put it in the cell *L9* by typing:

Range("L9").Formula = "=SUM(A9:K9)"

We can also apply a formula to a range of cells. Suppose that we want to not only calculate the total number of international flights, but also the total number of flights per year, times in ATL and times in JFK for each passenger. Since each sum references its respective row of values of equal length, we can enter the entire array of formulas using one line of code:

Range("L6:L9").Formula = "=SUM(A6:K6)"

Remember from Chapter 3 that since relative referencing is used, the formula will automatically modify for each relative row of data. See Figures 13.72 and 13.73 for the code and result of this macro.

```
Sub Formulas()

    Range("L6:L9").Formula = "=SUM(A6:K6)"

End Sub
```

Figure 13.72 Using the *Formula* property to assign a formula to a range of cells.

The other property that can be used to enter any Excel formula in VBA code is the ***FormulaR1C1*** property. It enters formulas using the *R1C1 Notation* that we discussed in Chapter 3. If we were to calculate the same sum of international flights that we did using the *Formula* property, we would type:

Range("L9").FormulaR1C1 = "=SUM(RC[–10]:RC[–1])"

This calculates the sum of values beginning in *L9* referenced to the same row and 10 columns previous to *L9* referenced to the same row and 1 column previous, which is *B9:K9*.

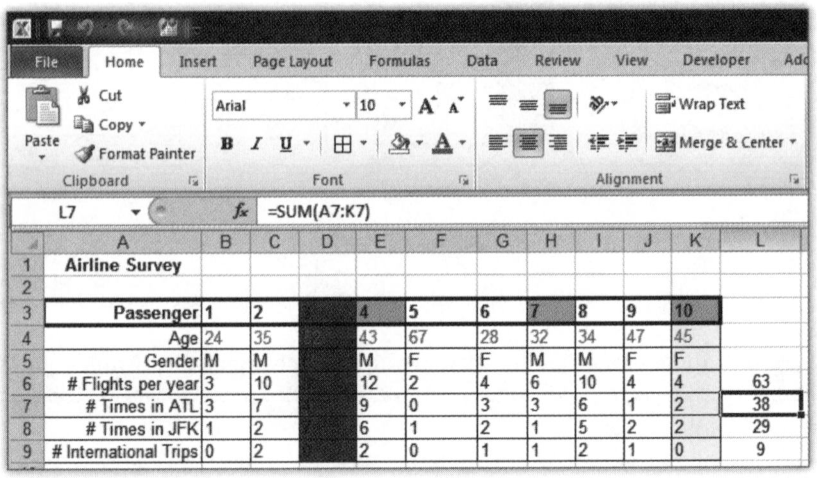

Figure 13.73 The formulas assigned the array use relative referencing.

Let's use this property to calculate the average age of passengers in the table. We can place the result of this calculation in cell *L4* by typing:

Range("L4").FormulaR1C1 = "=AVERAGE(RC[–10]:RC[–1])"

If we were to place the result of this same calculation in cell *A11* instead, the code would change to:

Range("A11").FormulaR1C1 = "=AVERAGE(R[–7]C[1]:R[–7]C[10])"

See Figure 13.74 for these two modifications of the *Formulas()* macro and verify that both codes return the same value when the macro is run in Figure 13.75.

```
Sub Formulas()

    Range("L6:L9").Formula = "=SUM(A6:K6)"

    Range("L4").FormulaR1C1 = "=AVERAGE(RC[-10]:RC[-1])"
    Range("A11").FormulaR1C1 = "=AVERAGE(R[-7]C[1]:R[-7]C[10])"


End Sub
```

Figure 13.74 The *FormulaR1C1* property enters an Excel formula using *R1C1 Notation*.

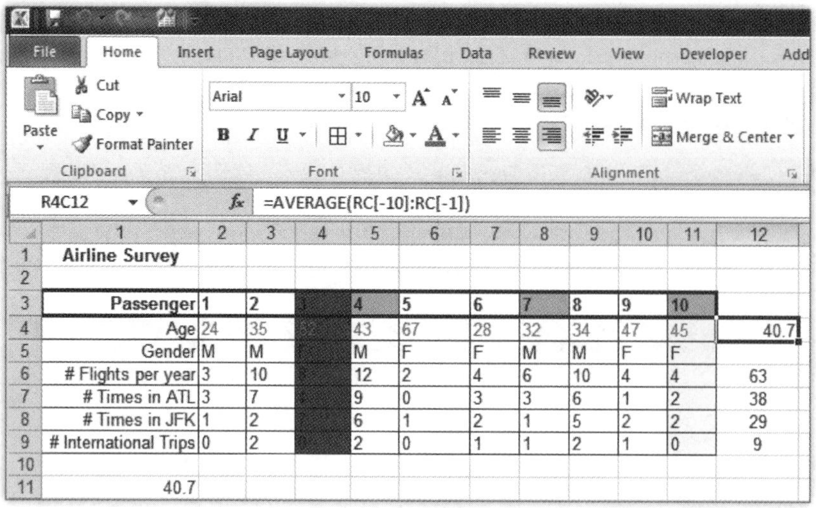

Figure 13.75 Both cells *A11* and *L4* calculate the same sum using different *R1C1 Notation*.

Note that the *FormulaR1C1* property can also be applied to a range of cells as we did with the *Formula* property.

Both of these properties are very useful for applying all Excel functions to a program. Whether we referencing with column letters and row numbers, or *R1C1 Notation* will depend on the particular usage.

We would like to quickly mention one other method that can be useful when working with formulas in VBA: the ***AutoFill*** method. As we learned in Chapters 3 and 4, if we enter a formula or value in a cell and want to copy it to an adjacent row or column, we can just place the cursor on the edge of the range until we see a small cross, then copy-and-drag to paste the values in the highlighted range. This operation is performed in VBA using the *AutoFill* method.

The *AutoFill* method takes two arguments: ***Destination*** and ***Type***. The named range for the *AutoFill* method will contain the formula or value that we want to copy; the *Destination* range gives the location of the range we want to paste these values to, and the *Type* argument allows us to specify exactly what we want to copy and paste (as in the *PasteSpecial* method).

For example, say we want to calculate the average number of flights and airport visits in the Airline Survey table in the column next to the calculated sums. We could first calculate the average number of flights per year in cell *M6* and then use the *AutoFill* method to copy and paste this formula into the three cells below. We would type the following two lines of code:

```
Range("M6").FormulaR1C1 = "=AVERAGE(RC[-11]:RC[-2])"
Range("M6").AutoFill Destination:=Range("M6:M9"), Type:=xlFillDefault
```

See Figures 13.76 and 13.77 for the code and result of the modified macro.

```
Sub Formulas()

    Range("L6:L9").Formula = "=SUM(A6:K6)"

    Range("L4").FormulaR1C1 = "=AVERAGE(RC[-10]:RC[-1])"
    Range("A11").FormulaR1C1 = "=AVERAGE(R[-7]C[1]:R[-7]C[10])"

    Range("M6").FormulaR1C1 = "=AVERAGE(RC[-11]:RC[-2])"
    Range("M6").AutoFill Destination:=Range("M6:M9"), Type:=

End Sub
```

- xlFillCopy
- xlFillDays
- xlFillDefault
- xlFillFormats
- xlFillMonths
- xlFillSeries
- xlFillValues

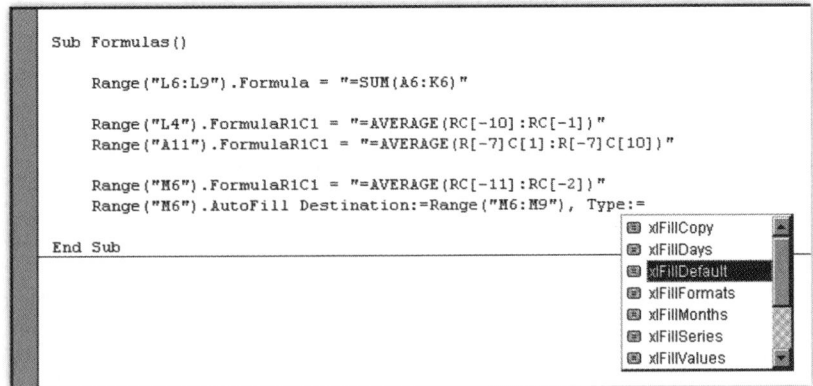

Figure 13.76 The *AutoFill* method copies a formula or value in the named range to a specified destination range.

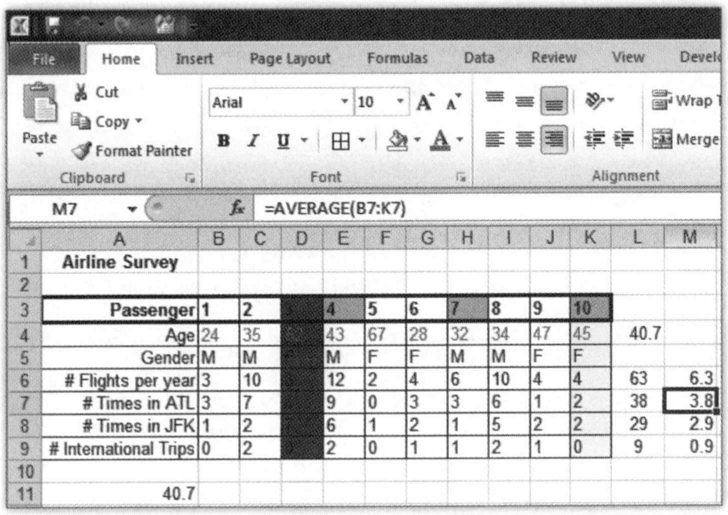

Figure 13.77 Calculating the average values for each row.

Summary

Formulas with Ranges and Cells in VBA

Formula:	Reference by column letter and row number
ForumlaR1C1:	R1C1 Notation
AutoFill:	Destination and Type as arguments

13.5.2 Using the Application Object

The Application object has several Excel-defined functions as sub properties of the ***WorksheetFunction*** property. There are many functions to choose from (see Figure 13.78), including most of the functions available from the Excel function list. For now, we will just demonstrate three of the main ones: ***Max***, ***Min***, and ***Average***.

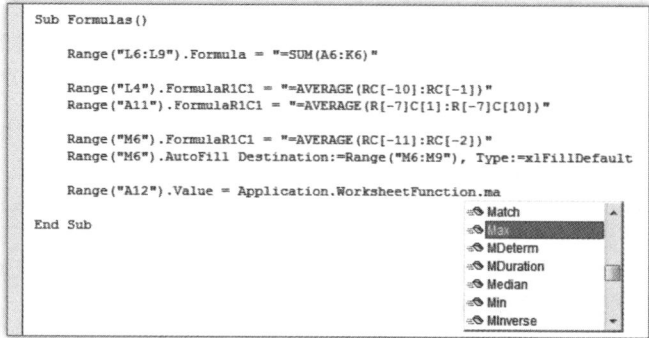

```
Sub Formulas()

    Range("L6:L9").Formula = "=SUM(A6:K6)"

    Range("L4").FormulaR1C1 = "=AVERAGE(RC[-10]:RC[-1])"
    Range("A11").FormulaR1C1 = "=AVERAGE(R[-7]C[1]:R[-7]C[10])"

    Range("M6").FormulaR1C1 = "=AVERAGE(RC[-11]:RC[-2])"
    Range("M6").AutoFill Destination:=Range("M6:M9"), Type:=xlFillDefault

    Range("A12").Value = Application.WorksheetFunction.ma

End Sub
                                                       Match
                                                       Max
                                                       MDeterm
                                                       MDuration
                                                       Median
                                                       Min
                                                       MInverse
```

Figure 13.78 The *WorksheetFunction* property of the Application object has several Excel functions as sub properties.

Let's continue modifying the *Formulas()* sub procedure to perform calculations on the Airline Survey data. We can first calculate the maximum number of flights per year taken by any passenger using the *Max* sub property of the *WorksheetFunction* property. We place the value of this calculation below the table in cell *A12* by typing the following:

Range("A12").Value = Application.WorksheetFunction.Max(Range("B6:K6"))

The sub properties, such as *Max*, require the range of values for which they are performing the calculation; in this case, we have entered *Range("B6:K6")*, which is the row with the number of flights per year. We can similarly calculate the minimum number of times to ATL and place this result in the next cell, *A13*:

Range("A13").Value = Application.WorksheetFunction.Min(Range("B7:K7"))

See Figure 13.79 for the addition of these two lines of code as well as an additional line that calculates the average number of times to JFK. Figure 13.80 displays the result of the modified macro.

```
Sub Formulas()

    Range("L6:L9").Formula = "=SUM(A6:K6)"

    Range("L4").FormulaR1C1 = "=AVERAGE(RC[-10]:RC[-1])"
    Range("A11").FormulaR1C1 = "=AVERAGE(R[-7]C[1]:R[-7]C[10])"

    Range("M6").FormulaR1C1 = "=AVERAGE(RC[-11]:RC[-2])"
    Range("M6").AutoFill Destination:=Range("M6:M9"), Type:=xlFillDefault

    Range("A12").Value = Application.WorksheetFunction.Max(Range("B6:K6"))
    Range("A13").Value = Application.WorksheetFunction.Min(Range("B7:K7"))
    Range("A14").Value = Application.WorksheetFunction.Average(Range("B8:K8"))

End Sub
```

Figure 13.79 Adding three calculations to the *Formulas()* sub procedure using the *Worksheet Function* property.

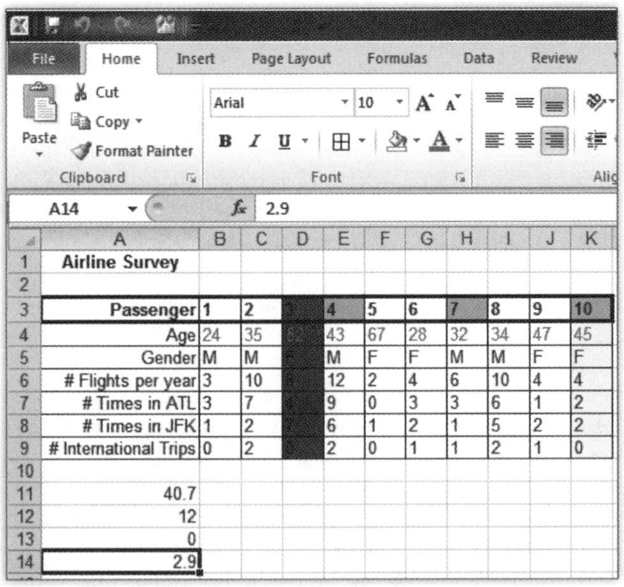

Figure 13.80 The result of the last three calculations in cells *A12, A13,* and *A14.*

One last useful WorksheetFunction sub property is **Round**. The *Round* sub property takes an initial value and the number of decimal places to round to as input. The format is as follows:

Range(cells or name).Value = Application.WorksheetFunction.
Round(Range(cells or name).Value, number_decimal_places)

Summary

Formulas with the Application object in VBA

Property:	**Sales Property:**
WorksheetFunction	Max(…range…)
	Min(…range…)
	Average(…range…)
	Round(value or range, number of decimal places)

We again recommend that you experiment with some of the other sub properties of the *WorksheetFunction* property of the Application object. This particular method of using formulas may be useful when you do not want to record the results as a formula in a cell, for example, when setting variable values.

13.6 Summary

- The workbook and worksheet objects use the *Activate* method to select a workbook or worksheet on which to perform associated code. The worksheet object also uses the *Visible* property to hide or unhide a worksheet.
- Almost all Excel objects have the *Name* property, which can be used to assign a text value to the name of any of these objects.
- The Range object uses the following properties: *Interior* (with sub properties *ColorIndex*, *Color*, and *Pattern*); *Borders* (with sub properties *Weight*, *LineStyle*, *Color*, and *XL Border Constants*); *Font* (with sub properties *Bold*, *Size*, and *Color*); and *Value*. The Range object also uses the following methods: *BorderAround*, *Clear*, *ClearContents*, *ClearFormats*, *Sort*, *AutoFilter*, *Copy*, and *PasteSpecial*.
- The Chart object uses the methods *Add*, *Copy*, *Delete*, and *Select*. The ActiveChart object uses the methods *SetSourceData*, *Location*, *Apply CustomType*, *ChartType*, *HasLegend*, *HasTitle*, *ChartTItle*, and *SeriesCollection*. Remember that it is necessary to set the chart type, source data, and location for any new chart before modifying any options.
- Drawing objects, or shapes, are associated with four different objects: ActiveSheet, Shape, Selection, and ShapeRange. These objects use the following properties: *Shapes*, *Name*, *Fill*, *Line*, *EndArrowheadStyle*, *EndArrowheadLength*, *End ArrowheadWidth*, *BeginArrowheadStyle*, *Begin ArrowheadLength*, and *BeginArrowheadWidth*. They also use the *Select* and *Add* methods.
- The Application object uses the *Screen Updating* and *CutCopyMode* properties. It also uses the *Wait* method with the *Now* and *Time Value* arguments.
- The *With* construct can help reduce code when modifying several properties of one object.
- There are several properties of the Range object to reference ranges and cells. These are *Offset*, *Cells*, *Rows*, *Columns*, *EntireRow*, *EntireColumn* and *End*.
- Formulas can be used in VBA with the Range object and the Application object. The Range object uses the *Formula*, *FormulaR1C1* properties. We can also use the *AutoFill* property to copy formulas with the Range object. The Application object uses the *WorksheetFunction* property with several sub properties, including *Min*, *Max*, and *Average*.
- Make sure to review the *Quick Programming Notes* provided in the chapter to improve the efficiency of the code.

13.7 Exercises

13.7.1 Review Questions

1. What is the purpose of activating a workbook? A worksheet?
2. What argument do you use with the *PasteSpecial* method in order to paste only the values of a copied range?
3. Explain the purpose of the *Visible* property of worksheets. What does each possible value of the *Visible* property change in a worksheet?
4. List the different ways to change the color of ranges and provide an example of each that is different from the examples in the chapter.
5. How do you format the borders of a range? List three properties used in formatting borders.
6. What property of a range allows you to modify the font of the contents? Name three of the most common sub properties. Provide an example using one of the sub properties that is different from the examples in the chapter.
7. Describe the functions of three common methods used to clear cells.
8. What object do you use to specify the chart type and source data?
9. Name four methods of chart objects.
10. What do you need in order to apply properties and methods to a shape?
11. How do the *ScreenUpdating* and the *CutCopyMode* properties improve a program?
12. What is the purpose of the *With* construct? Provide an example that is different from the examples in the chapter.

13. What is the difference between referencing cells using the Offset property and the Cells property? What are the arguments for each?
14. What are the *Columns* and *Rows* properties used for?
15. What is the purpose of the *End* property? Name the possible arguments.
16. What property do you use to enter a formula into a range? To enter a formula using *R1C1 Notation* into a range?
17. What method in VBA can you use to give the same result as copy-and-drag in Excel?
18. What property allows the use of Excel functions in VBA?

13.7.2 Hands-On Exercises

NOTE: Please refer to the file "Chapter_13_Exercises .xlsx" for the associated worksheets noted for the hands-on exercises. The file is available at: www .dssbooks.com.

1. Open a new workbook and save it as "Exercise.xls." Then, write a sub that performs the following.
   a. Rename "Sheet1" to "Exercise Sheet."
   b. Create a rectangle on the sheet large enough to display a sentence.
   c. Give the rectangle a background color.
   d. Center the text vertically and horizontally.
   e. Modify the rectangle to NOT move or size with cells.
2. Write a sub called "CreateOval" that performs the following.
   a. Creates an oval on the active worksheet
   b. Centers the text "This is an oval." horizontally and vertically in the oval.
   c. Adds a fill color to the oval.
   d. Write a sub called "EnlargeOval" that enlarges the oval a small but noticeable amount. Create a button labeled "Enlarge Oval" and assign the macro to it.
   e. Create the following subs that perform the appropriate actions and assign each one to its own button: "ShrinkOval," "MoveDown," "MoveLeft," "MoveRight," and "MoveUp."
3. Write a sub called "FormatRanges" that formats three ranges as shown below (red background with blue border and white dashes, green background with blue dashed border and black diagonals, blue background with green border and black diagonal dashes). In your code, use the following at least one time:
   a. ColorIndex property
   b. Color property
   c. RGB function
   d. BorderAround method

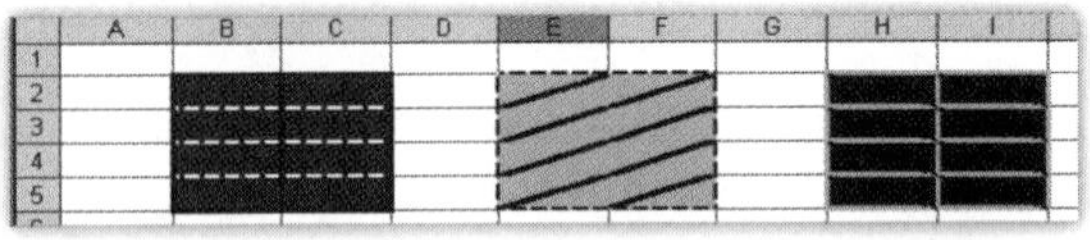

4. Given a grade sheet table, use VBA to perform the following actions. (Refer to worksheet "13.4".)
   a. Change the font of the headings to Times New Roman size 12 and bold the letters.
   b. Give each column of the table its own background color.
   c. Add a border under the headings. The border's color should be read and its thickness medium.
   d. Create student ID numbers from 1 to 5 using the AutoFill method.
5. With the table from the previous exercise, use VBA to fill in the grades for the quizzes and exams and calculate their final grades. (Refer to worksheet "13.5".)
   a. Create random grades for the quizzes and exams according to Normal(75, 7) using the AutoFill method. Grades should be integer values.
   b. Insert an "Average" column and use the Fill method to enter a formula into the column that calculates each student's average.
   c. Insert a "Letter Grade" column and use the Fill method to enter a formula that will calculate each student's letter grade (A = 90:100, B = 80:90, C = 70:80, D = 60:70, F = 0:60).
   d. Sort the table according to the "Average" column in ascending order.
   e. Filter the table such that only the students with a passing grade (>= C) are shown. Prior to executing your code, if all of the students have passing grades, manipulate the grades so that at least one of the students has a failing grade. (*Hint*: First record a *macro* that uses a Custom Filter.)

6. A given table contains information about a company's electrical use and costs. Create a column chart to plot the Demand vs. Month data values, then perform the following tasks. (Refer to worksheet "13.6".)
   a. Create a sub called "ViewCosts" that modifies the chart to display Costs vs. Month with the appropriate axis labels and formats. Create a button labeled "View Costs Chart" and assign the sub to it.
   b. Repeat part (a) with an appropriately named sub and button for the Energy Consumed.
   c. Repeat part (a) with an appropriately named sub and button for the Demand.
   d. Create a sub called "ChangeToLineChart" that will change the chart type to Line Chart. Create a button labeled "Change to Line Chart" and assign the sub to it.
   e. Repeat part (d) for changing the chart type to Column Chart.
7. An automobile manufacturer began selling energy-efficient Hybrids in 1997. To test the market, the manufacturer only produced 20,000 units for the first year. As the model became more popular and in more demand, the manufacturer continued to expand production. Information about the sales of the Hybrids is given in a table. (Refer to worksheet "13.7".)
   a. Enter the information into a worksheet.
   b. Create a line chart with no source data and place it on the worksheet.
   c. Create a sub called "ViewNumOfUnits" that performs the following:
      i. Removes any borders from the table and places a border around the "# of Units" column.
      ii. Modifies the chart to appropriately display the information.
      iii. Gives a title to the series "# of Units."
      iv. Changes the color of the chart's line as follows: black for # of Units, red for Revenue, blue for Cost, and green for Profit.
      v. Create a button labeled "View # of Units" and assign the sub to it.
8. Three column headings for the following distributions are given: exponential(5), normal(5,1), uniform(2,10). (Refer to worksheet "13.8".)
   a. Name the three cells under the distribution headings "CurrentRow." Write a sub called "RandomValues" that performs the following:
      i. Enters an appropriate formula into each cell of the range "CurrentRow" that calculates a random number from the corresponding distribution.
      ii. Names the three cells under the distribution headings in the next row down "CurrentRow."
   b. Create a button on the worksheet called "Random Values" and assign it the sub "RandomValues." Click the button several times. Realize that after each press of the button, an additional row of random variables is calculated. Create a table with 20 rows of random variables.
   c. Write a sub called "RandomValuesGraph" that creates a Line Chart with markers that plot the 20 values under the distribution headings. Label each series in the legend according to the distribution.
9. Write a sub called "InitialChart" that performs the following.
   a. Enters a formula into cell "A1" that calculates an exponential value using the row number as lambda. From this cell, create a column of thirty exponential values. (Hint: Use the Fill method.)
   b. Using the column of numbers created in part (a), create a scatter chart with a y-axis in logarithmic scale. The chart title is "Exponential Line," the x-axis title is "Non-Logarithmic," and the y-axis title is "Logarithmic." Add an exponential trendline and display the equation on the chart. Is your trendline perfectly straight?
   c. Then, write a sub called "ModifiedChart" that performs the following:
      i. Enters a formula into cell "B1" that calculates the square of the row value. From this cell, create a column of thirty similar values.
      ii. Modifies the source data of the chart created by "InitialChart." Modify the titles and trendline accordingly.
10. Write a sub procedure that performs the following.
    a. Generates a list of random numbers between 10 and 50. (*Hint:* Insert the RAND-

BETWEEN function into a column on the spreadsheet.)

b. Copies and pastes these values on top of itself so that the values do not change. (Make sure to paste the values only and keep the copied cells from flashing.)

c. Using the Application object, outputs the *Max* and *Min* of these values to the spreadsheet.

11. A marketing manager is trying to determine which marketing method has the greatest influence on product sales. Using the collected spending data given, create different charts for each marketing method (ex: TV vs. Sales, Radio vs. Sales, etc.). Make all of these charts separate sheets (full size charts). Create a button for each chart on the data sheet. When you press a button, the data sheet should be hidden and the corresponding chart sheet should be shown.

12. ***Race Animation:*** "The Turtle and The Hare". Create a simple animation to represent the race between the turtle and the hare. Prepare your spreadsheet by creating some shapes and buttons as shown in the figure below. Name the shapes appropriately. Also name a starting cell for each (Example: B4 = "TStart" and B7 = "HStart").

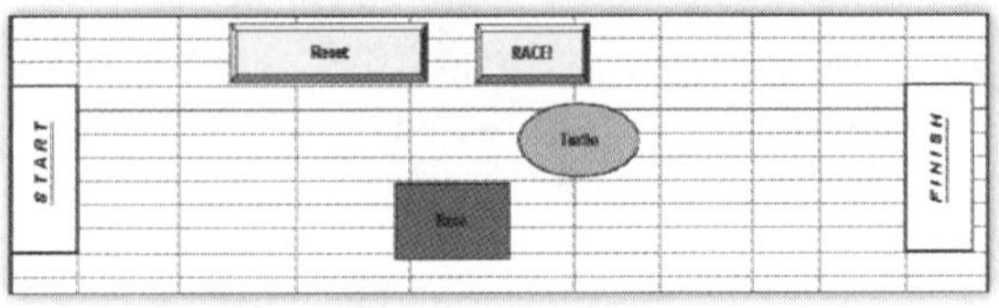

Now work on the following procedures:

a. The racing procedure should cut and paste the shapes using the Offset property to space their movements. Try to vary these statements such that the turtle's movements are relatively constant, and the hare's movements are large at first and then stop.

b. Add animation by using the Application.Wait method.

c. The reset procedure should bring both shapes back to the starting line.

13. ***Quality Control:*** Create an X-bar chart by manipulating and graphing data provided. (Refer to worksheet "13.13".)

a. Using a Scatter graph, graph the data values for each sample given.

b. Calculate the mean and standard deviation of this data.

c. Add a line to the chart for the mean value, 3-sigma (3*standard deviation) above the mean, and 3-sigma below the mean as shown below.

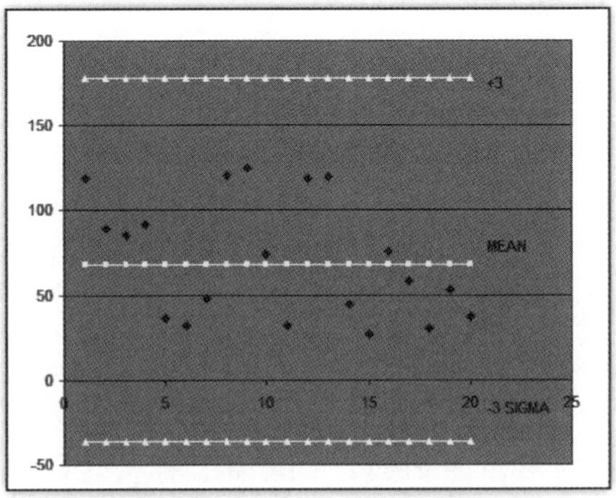

d. After a user has entered 20 data values, your procedure should calculate the mean and standard deviation and then update the source data of the chart.

14. Create a simple shopping and billing program as shown below. (Refer to worksheet "13.14".)

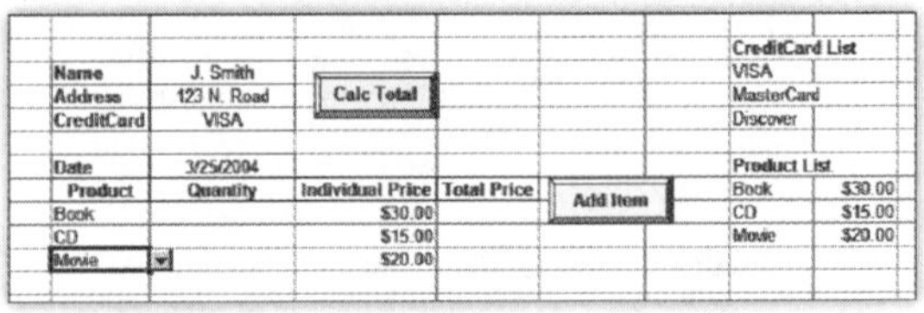
CreditCard List
VISA
MasterCard
Discover
Name
J. Smith
Address
123 N. Road
CreditCard
VISA
Calc Total
Date
3/25/2004
Product
Quantity
Individual Price
Total Price
Add Item
Book
$30.00
CD
$15.00
Movie
$20.00
Product List
Book $30.00
CD $15.00
Movie $20.00

The program should work as follows:

a. A user should fill in his or her name and address and, using data validation, select his or her credit card type from a list. (Refer to Chapter 10 for using data validation.)

b. Update the value in the "Date" cell to today's date (using an Excel function).

c. Then the shopper should select from a list of products, again using data validation, and enter the quantity he or she wants.

d. After the shopper selects a product, he or she should click the "Add Item" button. This button should find the "Individual Price" for the product using a lookup function.

e. When the user is done selecting products, he or she should click the "Calc Total" button.

This button should find the total price for each product and the total price overall. You should then add some formatting to the final product list and tell the user how much will be charged to his or her credit card (enter this statement into a cell below the product list).

15. **Map Search:** Help a salesperson in a rural area find the best route from any origin to visit all the cities based on either shortest distance or shortest time. Use the given tables for the time and distance between cities. (Refer to worksheet "13.15".)
    a. Create two separate procedures that take the value in the origin cell and find it in the table (by matching a value either in the first column or first row of the corresponding table).
    b. Then find the minimum distance or time in that city's row or column. Use lookup functions to find the city name with the minimum distance or time and then repeat the previous action. Do this until all of the cities have been traversed.
    c. Bonus: Add animation by coloring the cities in a map as they are selected to be traversed.
16. A given table provides flight information of an airline company. Use VBA to perform the following. (Refer to worksheet "13.16".)
    a. Create a sub called FlightsToAtlanta that highlights the flights that have Atlanta as the destination city.
    b. Create a sub called FlightsFromMiami that highlights the flights that have Miami as the start city.
    c. Create a sub that highlights the flights that run daily.
    d. Create a sub that highlights the flights that last at least 5 hours.

    Create buttons on this worksheet and assign the subs created to the buttons.
17. A given table provides flight information of an airline company. Use VBA to perform the following. (Refer to worksheet "13.17".)
    a. Create a sub that presents the number of customers that have a reservation for flight with FlightNr 1 to flight with FlightNr 6.
    b. Create a sub that calculates the average amount of payments made.
    c. Create a sub that finds the maximum and minimum payment amount.
    d. Create a sub that calculates the total amount made from Economy class flights, Club and Business class.
18. The following table presents information about the faculty at a university. Use VBA to perform the following. (Refer to worksheet "13.18".)
    a. Sort the information by hire date.
    b. Calculate the average, min and max salary.
    c. Filter the data so that only the information about the Professors is displayed.
    d. Filter the data so that only the information about the Operations Research Professors is presented.
19. Create a subroutine that fills the squares of a 6 by 6 table in a checkered pattern, as shown below. In your code, use the Wait method and Offset property.

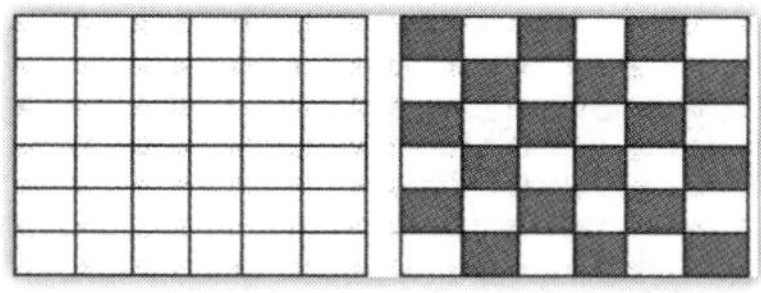

20. A given table is part of the database of a small town hotel. Use VBA to find the following. (Refer to worksheet "13.20".)
    a. The In Date and Out Date of customer Regina Murphy using the VLOOKUP function.
    b. Name the table as Reservations.
    c. Highlight the third row of the table using the Rows property.
    d. Highlight the information about the fines paid using the Columns property.
    e. Hide the TotalAmt paid column.
    f. Centrally align the BookingId column. Centrally align the RoomType column using the EntireColumn property.
    g. Find the name of the customer that made the last reservation using the End property.

CHAPTER fourteen

Variables

chapter OVERVIEW

14.1 Introduction

This chapter and the next three chapters illustrate the main topics of programming in VBA: variables, sub procedures, function procedures, programming structures, and arrays. These chapters will be especially important to the reader with little or no programming experience.

This chapter discusses the use of variables in the VBA programming language. We show the reader how to create variables of various data types, assign values to them from the programmer and from the user, and how to use them in functions and formulas. At this point, we are advancing the level of which we will use VBA from simple Excel object manipulation to other programming functionality. By understanding variables, the reader will be able to use more advanced programming structures and even implement algorithms when developing a DSS.

In this chapter, the reader will learn how to:

- Declare variables of different data types in VBA.
- Declare both private and public variables.
- Use variables in the Message Box and Input Box user interfaces.
- Use variables in mathematical, trigonometric, and derived math functions.
- Use variables in conversion and string functions.
- Work through two detailed examples of a simple DSS application which uses basic Excel object manipulation, variables, and a simple user interface.

14.2 Variable Declarations and Data Types

To declare a variable in VBA, we use the command ***Dim***, which is followed by the name of the variable and the data type for this variable. For example, to declare the variable *i* as an integer, we type the following:

Dim i As Integer

(There are other possible declarations that we mention later in this section.) We recommend that all variables used in a code are declared first. To force variable declarations to be made, we may write the phrase ***Option Explicit*** at the top of the module. Each variable declared in VBA must have a specified data type. If one is not specified, it will be assumed as a ***Variant*** data type. A *Variant* variable assumes the data type of the last value assigned to the variable. (We do not recommend using *Variant* data types; it is better programming practice to have a specific variable name and corresponding memory allocated to the data type for which a variable will be used.) Below are examples of correct and incorrect formats for defining two integer variables (in the incorrect example, *i* is defined as a *Variant*):

Correct: *Dim i As Integer, j As Integer*
Incorrect: *Dim i, j As Integer*

Names given to variables should not conflict with pre-set names used by VBA in common functions or programming structures. We should also avoid repeating names we may have already given to sub procedures or function procedures. We recommend for variable names of more than one word, we capitalize each new word, for example: *SizeOne* or *SizeTwo*.

It is important to keep a naming convention for all variables in our program. That is, if we want to keep track of variable data types, we may use the convention *intSize* to show that this variable is an integer data type and similarly prefix other variable names to reflect their data type. We may want to name variables as they pertain to a particular category of variables such as *CarsProfit*, *CarsCost*, *TrucksProfit*, *TrucksCost*, etc. We should pick a naming convention and be consistent in using this convention throughout the code. We discuss variable naming as a programming principle in Chapter 25.

A ***data type*** categorizes the values that can be assigned to a variable. There are several different data types available in VBA; for now, we will focus on the following seven most common data types: *integer, double, string, Boolean, range, worksheets, object.*

14.2.1 Integer and Double

Integers and ***doubles*** are both numerical values (there are many other numerical data types such as *long* and *single* which we will not review in detail here; more information can be found using the Microsoft Help tool). *Integers* are non-decimal numbers ranging in value from –32,768 to 32,767. *Doubles* have values from –1.79769E308 to –4.94065E–324 for negative values and from 4.94065E–324 to 1.79769E308 for positive values.

We will use *integers* very often for simple numerical values, for counting in loops, and for enumerating arrays. *Integers* are also important data types when solving integer programming problems with VBA (see Chapter 19). To declare a variable to be an *integer*, we use the following format (in this example, the variable name is *number*):

```
Dim number As Integer
```

The *double* data type is necessary when working with data that is non-integer and/or very large. *Double* data types may be used as values in tables or arrays. To declare a variable as a *double* we use the following format (in this example the variable name is *data*):

```
Dim data As Double
```

In future examples, we will often use both *integer* and *double* variables in our code.

14.2.2 String

A ***string*** is a segment of text. This text can include upper- and lower-case letters, punctuation marks, and numbers; however, these numbers cannot be used in calculations, as they will be viewed as text.

To declare a variable as a *string*, we use the following format (in this example the variable name is *label*):

```
Dim label As string
```

We will use *strings* to name objects, label objects, and label data in spreadsheets.

14.2.3 Boolean

A ***Boolean*** is a variable whose value is either *True* or *False*. To declare a variable as a *Boolean*, we use the following format (in this example the variable name is *found*):

```
Dim found As Boolean
```

We will use *Boolean* variables often in logic statements, *If, Then* statements, and loops (see Chapter 16). We will discuss *Boolean* variables in more detail later.

14.2.4 Constant

A ***constant*** is a variable whose value is permanently set in its declaration statement. For example, we may define a constant *PI* to always have the value 3.14159. To declare a variable as a constant, we use the following format:

```
Const INFINITY = 10000000000
```

Notice that to define constants, we do not use the *Dim* statement; instead we use a new declaration statement ***Const***. The value we assign to the constant is set in this declaration statement using the "=" sign. Notice also that we capitalize all constant variables as a naming convention.

14.2.5 Range

A ***range*** is an object variable that can be used with all of the properties and methods of the Range object. To declare a variable as a *range* variable, we use the following format (in this example the variable name is *MyRange*):

```
Dim MyRange As Range
```

We must also use the ***Set*** declaration to initialize the value of a *range* variable. For example, to set *MyRange* equal to cell *A1*, we would type the following:

```
Set MyRange = Range("A1")
```

We will use *ranges* often to increase the efficiency of our code. For example, we may frequently reference a particular cell while creating a table; therefore, the range name for this cell may appear often in our code. However, if we ever want to shift the position of the table we are creating, we would have to modify our entire code at every point where the referenced cell appears. To avoid this tedious task, we could instead define a *StartCell* as a *range* variable. We can set the value of this *range* variable at the beginning of our code and reference this *StartCell* variable name throughout the remainder of the code. Therefore, if we want to shift the table we are creating, the only change we have to make to the code is in the initialization of the *StartCell* *range* variable.

We may also use *ranges* to make our code more dynamic. For example, if we are creating a table and want to place it where our user wants to place it, we may take from an *Input Box* the name of a cell and then set our *range* variable equal to this range value. That is, users may want to start their table in cell *C4*. If they entered this cell name as *text* in an *Input Box*, we might use the following code to initialize our *StartCell*.

```
Dim text As String, StartCell As Range
text = InputBox("Enter starting cell for table:")
Set StartCell = Range(text)
```

We will use *ranges* often and see more examples of how to best utilize a *range* variable soon.

14.2.6 Worksheets

The ***worksheet*** data type defines a Worksheets object. This variable can be assigned any of the properties or methods used with the Worksheets object. To declare a variable as a single *worksheet*, we type the following format (in this example *ws* is the variable name):

Dim ws As Worksheet

We may use this variable when creating an event procedure, such as *Workbook_Open()*, which may refer to many worksheets in the workbook. For example, we may want to create a loop that hides all worksheets except the "Welcome" worksheet by checking the *Name* property of a *worksheet* variable assigned to each worksheet in the loop. We will see a detailed example of this technique in Chapter 16.

We may also want to use this variable when creating a function procedure that performs a method on a worksheet. For example, we may want to create a function that closes the active worksheet. In this case, we would want to use a *worksheet* variable in the procedure. We will see a detailed example of this technique in Chapter 15.

14.2.7 Object

The ***object*** variable can be used to define any object in Excel. This can be considered a drawing object, a range, a worksheet, or any other object. Any of the properties or methods associated with any object in Excel can be used with the *object* variable. To declare an *object* variable, we type the following format (here *MyObject* is the name of the variable):

Dim MyObject As Object

Even though this is a variable with a wide range of properties and methods, its running time is slower than when a specific class of objects is defined. Therefore, if we know we want to create an *object* variable that will only be used with properties or methods associated with the Range object, it is better to declare a *range* variable instead.

Summary

Data Type	Possible Values	Properties and Methods
Variant	(any)	(corresponding to the data type of the last value assigned to the variable)
Integer	non-decimal; –32,768 to 32,767	–
Double	negative: –1.79769E308 to –4.94065E–324 positive: 4.94065E–324 to 1.79769E308	–
String	text or number	–
Boolean	true or false	–
Constant	(any)	–
Range	–	as with Range object
Worksheets	–	as with Worksheet object
Object	–	as with any Excel object

14.3 *Variable Scope*

It is important to understand the scope of each variable we declare. We must check the code to see if a variable will be used in only one sub procedure or function procedure, or if it will be used in several different procedures.

14.3.1 Private and Public Variable Declarations

There are two types of variable declarations: ***Private*** and ***Public***. A private variable is declared using the *Dim* statement. This variable can be private on a procedure level or on a module level.

If we declare a variable as private on a procedure level, then it can only be used in the sub procedure in which we defined it. That is, if we declare the integer variable *i* in a sub procedure called *Sub1*, we cannot use the variable *i* in another sub procedure called *Sub2* unless we again declare the variable in the second sub procedure. These variables will therefore be unique and may hold different values. To do so, we would need to type the following:

```
Sub Sub1()
        Dim i As Integer
        . . .
End Sub
------------
Sub Sub2()
        Dim i As Integer
        . . .
End Sub
```

Alternately, if we declare a variable with the *Dim* statement on a module level, then it can be used in any sub procedure in that module; however, it cannot be used in other modules. For example, we could declare the variable *i* at the top of our module and refer to it in both *Sub1* and *Sub2* without having to declare it again.

```
Dim i As Integer
------------
Sub Sub1()
        . . . . . .
End Sub
------------
Sub Sub2()
        . . . . . .
End Sub
```

If we consider both *Sub1* and *Sub2* to be in *Module1*, we could not use the variable *i* in any procedure in another module, *Module2*, without declaring it again.

A public variable, on the other hand, can be used in any sub procedure in any module. To declare a public variable, we use the *Public* statement. For example, if we declare the variable *i* using the *Public* statement at the top of any module, say *Module1*, we can use it in *Sub1*, *Sub2*, and in any procedure in *Module2* without having to declare it again. To do this, we would type the following at the top of any module:

Public i As Integer

It is common programming practice to use private variables often and public variables only when needed. That is, to avoid errors while running the code, we should try to create variables with as small a scope as possible. However, in some cases we may need to use public variables in order to keep the variable value as several different procedures are performed. We will give examples of this scenario when we discuss user interface procedures in Chapter 18. We also review variable scope as a programming principle in Chapter 24.

14.3.2 Keeping Track of Variable Values

To keep track of variable values as our code is running, we can use the *Watch* window in the VBE. To do this, click on *View > Watch Window* from the menu. Then, just highlight any variable from the *Code Window* and drag it to the *Watch Window*. As we run the program (for example, using the *Step-Into* debugging function, as explained in Appendix B), we will be able to observe the values of variables changing in the *Watch Window*. We can also hold the cursor over a variable name in the *Code Window* to see a small display of its value.

Summary

Private:	Declared using the *Dim* statement.
	Procedure level = only used in a particular sub procedure.
	Module level = used in any procedure only in a particular module.
Public:	Declared using the *Public* statement.
	Can be used in any procedure of any module.

14.4 *Variables in User Interface*

Message Boxes and ***Input Boxes*** allow us to communicate with the user using VBA code. A Message Box prints information to a small dialog box, and an Input Box prompts the user to enter information into a small dialog box.

14.4.1 Message Boxes

A Message Box can print a string of text or a variable value. The VBA code to generate a Message Box is *MsgBox*. To print a string of text, we could, for example, type the following (the resulting Message Box is also provided):

MsgBox "This is a string of text."

To print a variable, we type the following, where *size* is a variable name:

MsgBox size

We can print both text and variables in one Message Box by concatenating them with an & sign. For example, given that *h* and *w* are variable names:

MsgBox "The height is " & h & " and the width is " & w & "."

We can use the statement ***vbCrLf*** to enter a new line of text in the Message Box by concatenating it with the string or variable values. For example, we can retype the above statement on two separate lines as follows (see the resulting Message Box below):

MsgBox "The height is " & h & vbCrLf & " and the width is " & w & "."

MsgBox can also be used as a function in VBA. If used as a function, then more settings for the dialog box can be defined as arguments for the function; recall that arguments in brackets, "[ ]", are optional. The function format is:

MsgBox (prompt, [buttons], [title], [helpfile, context])

The ***prompt*** is either the string or variable (or concatenation of both) that is displayed in the dialog box; this function is required, all other arguments are optional. The ***buttons*** argument takes a *VB Constant* value to determine the number and style of buttons available to the user. The table below lists some of the more common button types and the image below is an example of the *vbYesNo* button type.

vbOKOnly	Displays an **OK** button only.
vbOKCancel	Displays **OK** and **Cancel** buttons.
vbYesNoCancel	Displays **Yes**, **No**, and **Cancel** buttons.
vbYesNo	Displays **Yes** and **No** buttons.

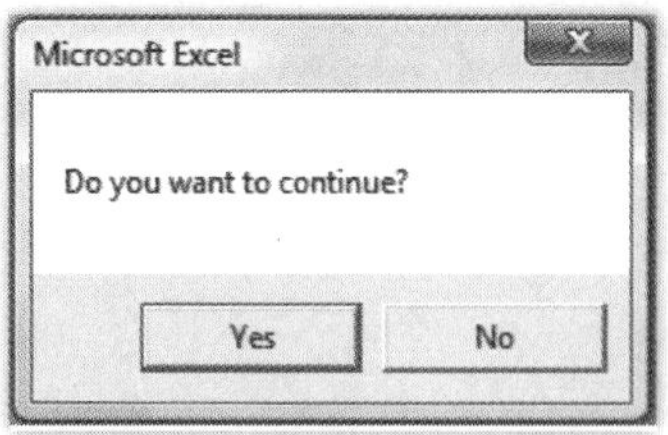

The ***title*** argument allows us to enter text that we want to appear as the title of the dialog box. We will usually ignore the ***helpfile*** and ***context*** arguments, which allow us to give help options to the user.

We can also capture the user's response to the Message Box. For example, we may want to take different actions in the code if the user presses *YES* or *NO* (we will give an example of this when we discuss programming structures in Chapter 16). To do this, we can declare a variable called ***response*** as an integer data type. Then, set this variable equal to the *MsgBox* function, and we can check the value of this response using the *VB Constants* shown below:

vbOK	If response was **OK**
vbCancel	If response was **Cancel**
vbAbort	If response was **Abort**
vbRetry	If response was **Retry**
vbIgnore	If response was **Ignore**
vbYes	If response was **Yes**
vbNo	If response was **No**

To determine the user's response, we will use some programming structures that we will discuss in Chapter 16.

14.4.2 Input Boxes

Input Boxes allow the user to enter a value for any variable type. The user has a prompt, an *OK* and *Cancel* button, and an empty text box as shown in the image below:

An Input Box is created using the ***InputBox*** VBA function. Since Input Boxes receive some input from the user, the *InputBox* function is always assigned to a variable. This function takes the following general form:

variable = InputBox (prompt, [title], [default], [xpos], [ypos], [helpfile, context])

The *prompt* and *title* arguments of the *InputBox* function are the same as those of the *MsgBox* function; likewise, *prompt* is the only required argument. Notice that unlike the *MsgBox* function, there is no *buttons* argument for the *InputBox* function; the only button on an Input Box is *OK*. The ***default*** argument allows us to enter a default value to display in the Input Box; this default value is entered if no change is made in the dialog box. The ***xpos*** and ***ypos*** arguments allow us to position the Input Box relative to the left and top edges of the screen. The *helpfile* and *context* arguments are the same as those of the *MsgBox* function.

The *InputBox* function is always assigned to a variable (as with the *response* variable for the *MsgBox* function). We may want the user to enter a parameter before drawing an object (size, height, etc) or a value to be used in a calculation. As we will see shortly, there are several different variable data types that can be defined in VBA; therefore, the *InputBox* function can be used to capture a value for any of these data types in their possible respective situations.

Note that Input Boxes always have an *OK* and *Cancel* button. To determine if the user has pressed *Cancel* rather than *OK*, we can simply check the value of variable we assigned to the *InputBox* function. If the variable value is "", then the user has pressed *Cancel* (or never entered a value). It is useful to have some error checking statements after receiving data from an Input Box; we will discuss this in more detail in Chapter 16.

Summary

Message Box:	Prints information to a small dialog box.
	MsgBox "text"
	MsgBox (prompt, [buttons], [title], [helpfile, context])
Input Box:	Prompts user to enter information into a small dialog box.
	variable = InputBox (prompt, [title], [default], [xpos], [ypos], [helpfile, context])

14.5 VBA Math Functions

Now that we are familiar with some variable types, we can use typical math functions in VBA without needing to create a formula in the spreadsheet (as demonstrated at the end of Chapter 13). There are several math and trigonometric functions available in VBA. We can also use these functions to derive other functions (such as using a sine function to create an arcsine function). We will explain some of the most common math and trigonometric functions here and also provide a few examples of derived functions.

14.5.1 Typical Math Functions

We will describe seven basic math functions: *Abs, Sqr, Mod, Int, Rnd, Exp,* and *Log.* There are other math functions available in VBA; however, these seven are the most commonly used.

The ***Abs*** function calculates the absolute value of a variable or expression. This function can be used with both integer and double data types (as well as with other numerical variables). It will return the same data type that is used in the function. For example:

Abs(–10) = 10

The ***Sqr*** function calculates the square root of a number. It can also be used with any numerical data type (greater than 0); however, it will always return a double data type. For example:

Sqr(100) = 10

The ***Mod*** function calculates the modular value of a number, given its divisor (that is, it gives the remainder when a number is divided by the divisor). The format of this function is *divisor Mod number.* Consider the example below.

```
Sub ModularFunction()
    Dim x As Integer, y As Integer

    x = 2
    y = 4
    MsgBox x Mod y          'answer is 2

    x = 4
    y = 2
    MsgBox x Mod y          'answer is 0
End Sub
```

The ***Int*** function truncates a double variable and returns the integer part; therefore, the result is always an integer data type. For positive numbers, the *Int* function always rounds down; for negative numbers, the *Int* function returns the first negative integer less than or equal to the original variable value. For example:

Int(5.6) = 5
Int(–4.3) = –5

The ***Rnd*** function generates a random number as we saw with the RAND function in Excel. This random number is uniformly distributed between the values of 0 and 1. We can either enter a seed as a parameter for the function, or leave the seed value blank. To create random integers in a specific range, use the formula:

*Int((upperbound – lowerbound + 1) * Rnd + lowerbound)*

The ***Exp*** function raises the constant *e* to a power given in the function statement. The value returned is always a double data type. For example:

Exp(2) = e^2 = *7.389056099*

The ***Log*** function calculates the natural log (the logarithm with base *e*, of a given number). The result is a double data type. We can calculate logarithms with base *n* for any number by dividing the natural logarithm of that number by the natural logarithm of *n*. For example, to calculate the log of 15 with base 10 ($Log_{10}15$), type:

Log(15) / Log(10) = 1.176091259

This is actually a derived function that we will talk about later in this section. We will offer examples of these functions toward the end of the chapter.

The *Log* function can also be used with the *Rand* function to generate random values from the Exponential distribution. As we learned in Chapter 8, there is a set of inverse functions in Excel that can be used with the RAND function to generate random numbers from distributions. For example, the Excel functions needed to generate a random number from the Exponential distribution are:

= –mean LN (RAND())*

To accomplish this in VBA using the *Log* and *Rand* functions, set a variable equal to the following:

*–mean * Log(Rnd())*

We will discuss more functions for working with distributions in VBA in Chapter 20.

14.5.2 Trigonometric Functions

We will describe four basic trigonometric functions: *Sin, Cos, Tan*, and *Atn*. These functions all take an angle as a parameter, and this angle value should be entered in radians. (To convert degrees to radians, multiply degrees by *PI*/180. Here, *PI* is a previously defined constant for the value 3.14159 or, more precisely, the value of the Excel function found in *Application.WorksheetFunction.PI()*.)

The ***Sin***, ***Cos***, and ***Tan*** functions take an angle and return the ratio of two sides of a right triangle. The value returned is a double data type. The result of the *Sin* and *Cos* functions are always between –1 and 1. For example:

Sin(PI/4) = 0.7071067812
Cos(PI/3) = 0.5
Tan(PI/6) = 0.5773502692

The ***Atn*** function calculates the arctangent of a given ratio. The result is an angle in radians, which is a double data type between –*PI*/2 to *PI*/2 radians. (To convert radians to degrees, multiply radians by 180/*PI*.) For example:

Atn(0.5773502692) = PI/6

VBA does not have many more pre-defined trigonometric functions; however, we can derive several other trigonometric functions using these four functions.

14.5.3 Derived Math Functions

Using the above functions, we can derive other functions. There is a long list of examples of derived functions in *Microsoft Visual Basic Help*; we will demonstrate just a few here.

We can derive the arcsine or inverse sine function using the *Atn* and *Sqr* functions and name it the ***Arcsin*** function. This function is defined as follows:

*Arcsin(X) = Atn(X / Sqr(–X * X + 1))*

We can derive the secant function using the *Cos* functionand name it ***Sec***. It is defined as follows:

Sec(X) = 1 / Cos(X)

We will use function procedures to create these and other derived math functions. We see an example of this technique in Chapter 15.

Summary

Math Function	Input Data Type	Resulting Data Type	Resulting Value
Abs	numerical	numerical > 0	absolute value
Sqr	numerical > 0	double	square root
Mod	numerical	numerical	modular
Int	double	integer	integer value
Rnd	numerical	double; (0,1)	random number
Exp	numerical	double	e^x
Log	numerical	double	$\log_e x$
Trigonometric Function	**Input Data Type**	**Resulting Data Type**	**Resulting Value**
Sin	numerical (radians)	double	sine of an angle
Cos	numerical (radians)	double	cosine of an angle
Tan	numerical (radians)	double	tangent of an angle
Atn	numerical	double	arctangent of a ratio
Derived Functions	**Uses**	**Equation**	
Arcsin	*Atn, Sqr*	*Atn(X / Sqr(–X * X + 1))*	
Sec	*Cos*	*1 / Cos(X)*	
Log$_n$x	*Log*	*Log(x) / Log(n)*	

14.5.4 Conversion Functions

There are several functions in VBA that can be used to convert one data type to another. These functions can be useful for many reasons. For example, it may be necessary to convert input which was initially given as a Variant data type to another specific data type before performing calculations. Even though a Variant is usually treated as the initial data type value it is assigned, converting a Variant variable will ensure the data type used for subsequent actions. This conversion may be more relevant when the variable is intended to have a numerical value. Two main conversion functions used with numerical values are ***CInt*** and ***CDbl***. *CInt* converts a variable to an integer data type and *CDbl* converts a variable to a double data type. The input for these functions can be any variable or expression.

CInt(variable or expression)

CDbl(variable or expression)

If we are converting a variable to an integer or double data type using these functions, the variable value must meet the range requirements of the data type to which we are converting. That is, we cannot convert a number that is larger than 32,767 to an integer data type. However, if a variable value is decimal (or fractional), it can still be converted to an integer, but will be rounded down in the process. The variable or expression we are converting can also be a string.

If this is the case, these functions will extract the numerical values from the string. For example, the following string expression would be converted as shown:

CInt("4321 Main St") = 4321

The ***Val*** function also extracts a numerical value from a string. The input for this function is an expression. However, note that using the *Val* function will not enforce any data type on the extracted number. Therefore, we recommend using one of the numerical conversion functions directly:

Val(expression)

Any numeric expression can also be converted to a string using the ***CStr*** function. The input for this function is again any variable or expression:

CStr(variable or expression)

For example, if a numerical expression is used with this function, the result is:

CStr(25.1278) = "25.1278"

This function can also be used to convert *Boolean* data types to *True* or *False* strings, depending on the *Boolean* variable's value.

Conversions can also be useful when working with dates. There are several formats in which a user can enter a date. For example: January 1, 2011 or Jan 1, 2011 or 1/1/11, etc. However, to work with dates in our code for comparisons or calculations, we will need to ensure that the input is converted to a *Date* data type. This can be done using the ***CDate*** function. The input for this function should be a variable or expression containing a valid date in some format:

CDate(variable or expression)

Two other useful conversion functions are ***Asc*** and ***Chr***. These functions, which use the ASCII list of numbers and characters, can be used to convert letters to numbers and numbers to letters, respectively:

Asc(character)

Chr(number)

This function may be useful, for example, if we have an array of letter values (A through Z) that we need to convert to numerical values in order to perform comparisons or calculations. We could use the following functions:

Asc("A") = 65

Chr(65) = "A"

For a complete list of conversion functions, search for *Type Conversion Functions* in the VBA Help window.

14.5.5 String Functions

Similar to the text functions in Excel that we discussed in Chapter 4, there are several string functions available in VBA. Two useful string functions are ***UCase*** and ***LCase***, which can be used to convert a string into all upper case or all lower case, respectively. The input for these functions is string variables or string expressions:

UCase(string variable or string expression)

LCase(string variable or string expression)

To extract a segment from a string value, we can use the ***Mid*** function. To use this function, we enter the string value or string variable name, the number indicating the position from which we want to begin the extraction, and the number of characters we want to extract. The format of this function is as follows:

Mid(string variable or string expression, starting_position, length)

For example, to extract the middle name from a person's full name, we may use the *Mid* function. Say the person's name is JohnHenrySmith; to extract the middle name Henry and store it to a string variable, we would use the *Mid* function as follows:

MidName = Mid("JohnHenrySmith", 5, 5)

Another useful string function is ***Len***. This function determines the length of a string variable value or string expression:

Len(string variable or string expression)

Summary

Conversion Function	**Input**	**Resulting Data Type**
CInt	variable or expression	integer
CDbl	variable or expression	double
Val	expression	numerical value
CStr	variable or expression	string
CDate	variable or expression	date
Asc	character	number
Chr	number	character
String Function	**Input**	**Resulting Value**
UCase	string variable or string expression	string in all UPPERCASE
LCase	string variable or string expression	string in all lowercase
Mid	string variable or string expression, starting position, and length of extraction	segment of a string
Len	string variable or string expression	length of the string

14.6 Applications

Let's consider two applications, or extended examples, in which we implement some of the new techniques learned in this chapter. First, we will work with Message Boxes, Input Boxes, and some various data types. Then, we will work with several different functions.

14.6.1 Creating and Modifying Shapes

Let's create a program in which a user can create either a square or a circle, label its shape, and position its shape on the spreadsheet. We also want to keep track of how many squares and circles the user has created and allow his or her to delete a square or circle as well.

We begin by preparing the following spreadsheet. We provide a brief description of the program and several buttons (which we create using drawing objects), as in Figure 14.1. Preparing the spreadsheet before writing any code is a skillful way to outline what code needs to be written. It also allows us to think about what can be done in Excel to save time and space in the coding.

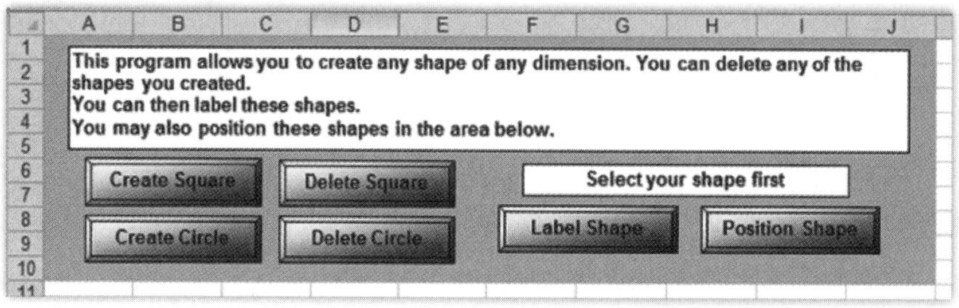

Figure 14.1 Preparing the spreadsheet before any code is written.

The first sub procedure we want to write creates a square. To do this, we will first declare variables that can be assigned to an Input Box to find the desired width and height of the square. We will call these variables *width* and *height*. Both of these variables should be define as double data types, so we write the following code:

```
Sub CreateSquare()
        Dim width As Double, height As Double

        width = InputBox("Please enter the width of your square:", "Width", 50)
        height = InputBox("Please enter the height of your square:", "Height", 50)
End Sub
```

The *InputBox* parameters have the respective prompts needed: a title for each Input Box and a default value = 50. Now we will use the *AddShape* method associated with the ActiveSheet and Shapes objects to create the square. The shape type parameter should be *msoShapeRectangle*. The position parameters can be anything for now, and we will set the width and height parameters as our variable values. Therefore, we add the following line of code:

```
ActiveSheet.Shapes.AddShape(msoShapeRectangle, 146.25, 289.5, width, height).Select
```

Here, 146.25 and 289.5 are the coordinates of the upper left-hand corner of the Excel window. Now, we can type the code that displays a Message Box telling the user that the macro has run successfully and the square has been created:

MsgBox "Your square has been created."

The final code appears in Figure 14.2. We can now assign this macro to the "Create Square" button and test it to make sure a square is drawn (see Figure 14.3).

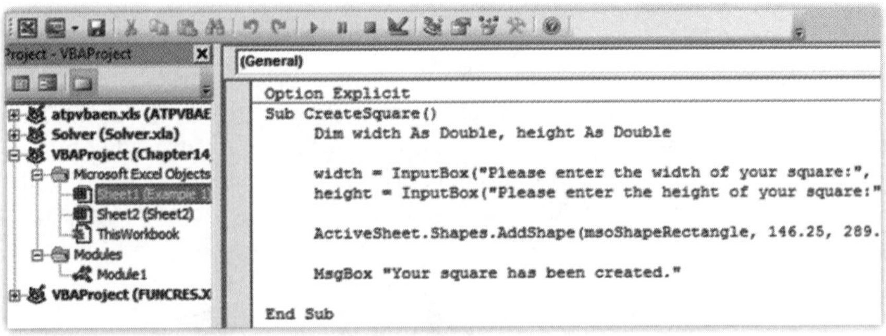

Figure 14.2 The final *CreateSquare()* sub procedure.

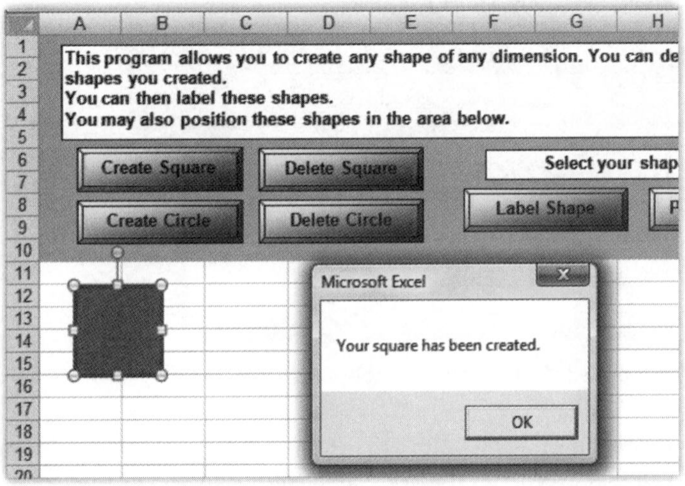

Figure 14.3 The Message Box from the macro with the created square.

We can now create a similar sub procedure to create a circle. Here, however, we declare a *radius* variable instead of *width* and *height*. We can then insert this *radius* variable as both the width and height parameters of the *AddShape* method. We do this to guarantee that a circle, not an oval, is created. The *msoAutoShapeType* for a circle is *msoShapeOval*. The code for this sub procedure appears in Figure 14.4. We assign this macro to the "Create Circle" button; the Input Box for this sub procedure is in Figure 14.5.

```
Sub CreateCircle()
    Dim radius As Double

    radius = InputBox("Please enter the radius of your circle:", "Radius", 50)

    ActiveSheet.Shapes.AddShape(msoShapeOval, 75#, 289.5, radius, radius).Select

    MsgBox "Your circle has been created."

End Sub
```

Figure 14.4 The *CreateCircle()* procedure is similar to the *CreateSquare()* procedure, except that a *radius* variable is used.

Note that we have declared *width* and *height* as private variables on the procedure level for the *CreateSquare()* sub procedure, and *radius* as a private variable in the *CreateCircle()* sub procedure. If we had decided to use a width and height value, instead of radius, to create the circle it would have been more efficient to declare *width* and *height* as either private variables on the module level or as public variables. In doing so, we could have used *width* and *height* in both sub procedures and only declared them once.

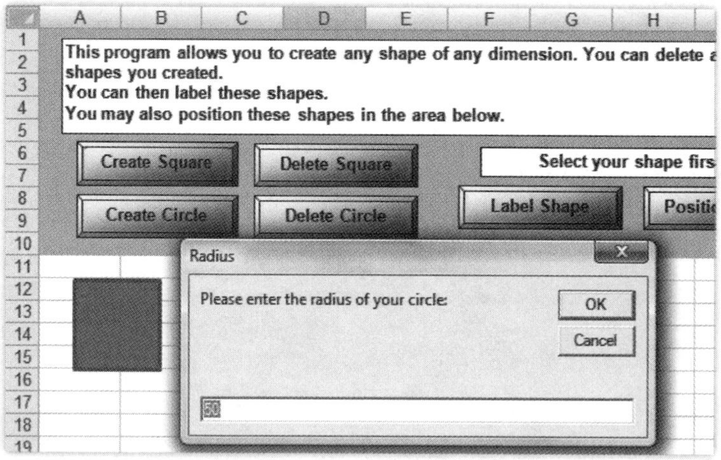

Figure 14.5 The Input Box for the *radius* variable value.

Let's now consider how we will be able to tell the user how many squares and circles s/he has created. We will first need two variables: *NumSquares* and *NumCircles*, which both can be integer data types. We first need to initialize these variables to start with value 0. We cannot perform this initialization in either the *CreateSquare()* or *CreateCircle()* sub procedures since we want to increase these values each time the *macros* are called. Therefore, we can either create a new sub procedure called *Main()* or *Initialize()* and assign it to a new "Start" button, or we can use the *Workbook_Open()* event procedure. In future case studies, we will usually have a "Welcome" sheet with a "Start" button assigned to some *Main()* sub procedure; however, for now let's use the *Workbook_Open()* event procedure.

We create a *Workbook_Open()* event procedure in the Workbook object module of our current VBA project. In this procedure, we want to initialize the *NumSquares* and *NumCircles* variables at 0. Since we want to use these variables in the Workbook object and in our main module, we must declare them as public variables by using the *Public* statement. We do this at the top of our macro as shown in Figure 14.6.

```
Option Explicit

Public NumSquares As Integer, NumCircles As Integer

Sub CreateSquare()
    Dim width As Double, height As Double

    width = InputBox("Please enter the width of your square:",
    height = InputBox("Please enter the height of your square:
```

Figure 14.6 Declaring the *NumSquares* and *NumCircles* variables publicly.

In the *Workbook_Open()* event procedure, we can also clear the range of cells where the shapes will most likely be created and/or positioned. We assume this range is *A12:K50* and specify that it is in our first worksheet using the *Delete* method. The complete code for the *Workbook_Open()* procedure appears in Figure 14.7.

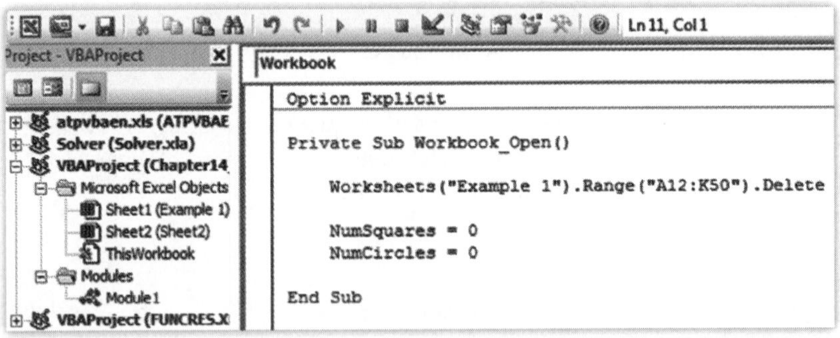

Figure 14.7 This *event procedure* initializes the variable values and clears previously created shapes.

Now we can return to the *CreateSquare()* and *CreateCircle()* sub procedures and insert code that will increase the corresponding variable values and display this value (instead of the original Message Box) to the user. These additional lines of code are:

NumSquares = NumSquares + 1
MsgBox "You now have " & NumSquares & " squares in your worksheet."

NumCircles = NumCircles + 1
MsgBox "You now have " & NumCircles & " circles in your worksheet."

To increment variable values in VBA, we use the statement: *variable* = *variable* + 1. Similarly, to decrement variable values in VBA, we use: *variable* = *variable* – 1.

The new Message Box appears in Figure 14.8 after creating two squares.

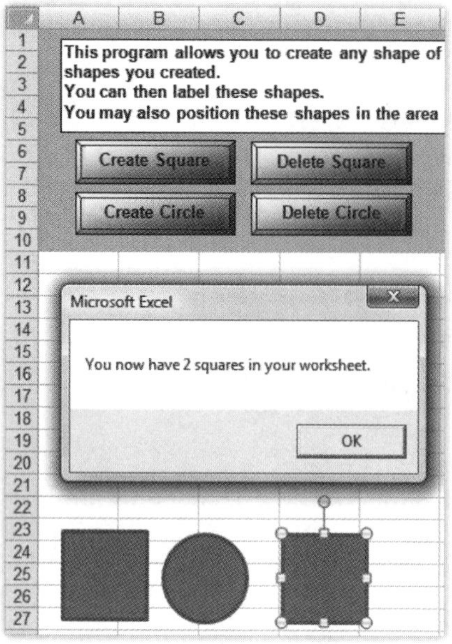

Figure 14.8 Creating and counting two squares.

Let's now create sub procedures to delete a square and a circle. Our code will ask the user to select the shape he or she wishes to delete before pressing one of the "Delete" buttons on the spreadsheet. The code for both macros is then simply:

Selection.Delete

We also need to decrease the *NumSquares* or *NumCircles* variable values for each corresponding shape that is deleted; this way, the count is correct the next time we create one of these shapes. The final code for both the *DeleteSquare()* and *DeleteCircle()* procedures appears in Figure 14.9. These macros are assigned to the two delete buttons.

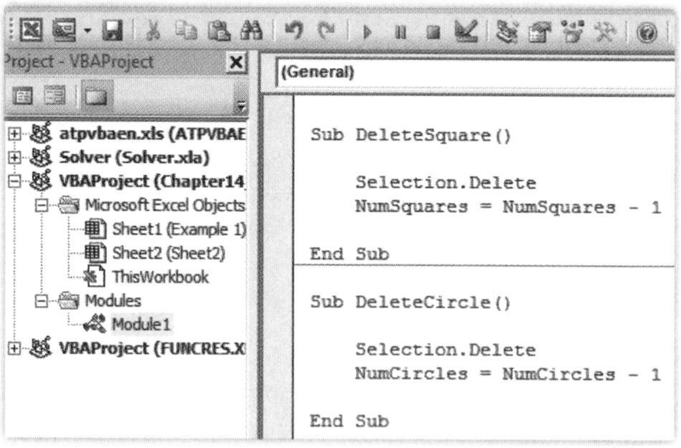

Figure 14.9 These procedures delete the selected shape and decrease the corresponding count variable.

We have two more sub procedures to construct: *LabelShape()* and *PositionShape()*. For both macros, we will ask the user to first select a shape; this way we can use the Selection object in the same way as the *Delete* sub procedures.

To label our shape, we first prompt the user to see what text will be used as the label. We declare a private variable called *text* and assign it to an Input Box as follows:

text = InputBox("Please enter label for your shape:", "Shape Label", "Square 1")

We assign a title and default value to this Input Box. Now, we can use the Selection object with the *Characters* property and *Text* sub property and assign the value equal to our *text* variable.

Selection.Characters.Text = text

The *LabelShape()* procedure appears in Figure 14.10. We assign this macro to the "Label Shape" button; the result of running this macro in Excel appears in Figure 14.11.

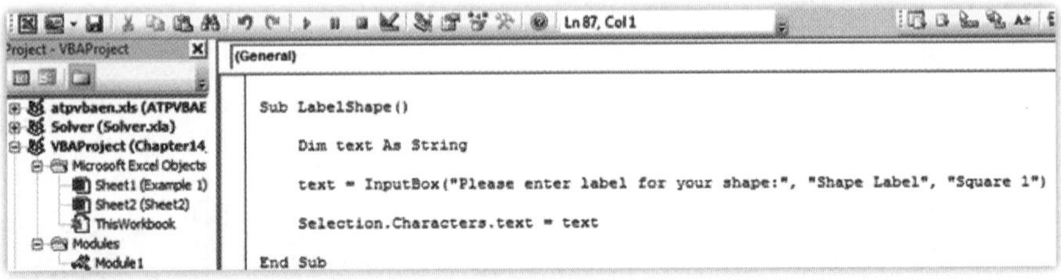

Figure 14.10 The *LabelShape()* sub procedure.

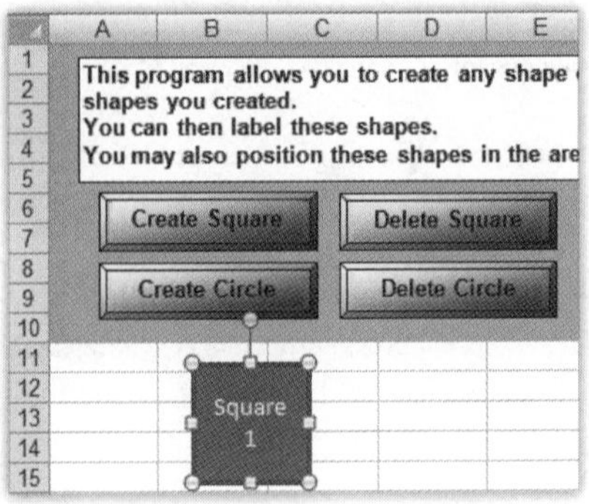

Figure 14.11 The created square has been labeled "Square 1."

Instead of asking the user to provide two numerical values for the *left* and *top* arguments of the *AddShape* method in order to position a shape, we will cut and paste the selected object to a specified range. We will first declare a private variable called *position* to capture the range name where the user wants to move the selected object. We will then use a *range* variable called *place* to use this range value in our *Paste* method. The variable declarations, *InputBox* function, and *range* assignment are coded as follows:

```
Dim position As String, place As Range

position = InputBox("Please enter cell name where you would like to position
        your shape (below A12):", "Position", "A12")
Set place = Range(position)
```

We now use the *Cut* method on the Selection object and then use the ActiveSheet object and *Paste* method to paste the object to the desired range. We specify this range with the *Destination* argument as demonstrated below:

Selection.Cut
ActiveSheet.Paste Destination:=place

The final code is displayed in Figure 14.12. This macro is assigned to the "Position Shape" button. The result of positioning the selected square in cell *A12* appears in Figure 14.13.

```
Sub LabelPosition()
    Dim position As String, place As Range

    position = InputBox("Please enter cell name where you would " & _
        "like to position your shape (below A12):", "Position", "A12")
    Set place = Range(position)

    Selection.Cut
    ActiveSheet.Paste Destination:=place

End Sub
```

Figure 14.12 The *PositionShape()* sub procedure.

[**Note:** To continue a line of code onto the next line in the Code Window, use the *underscore* (_). If we are continuing a line of code in the middle of a text string, we must concatenate it (with the & sign) and use quotation marks, as shown in Figure 14.12.]

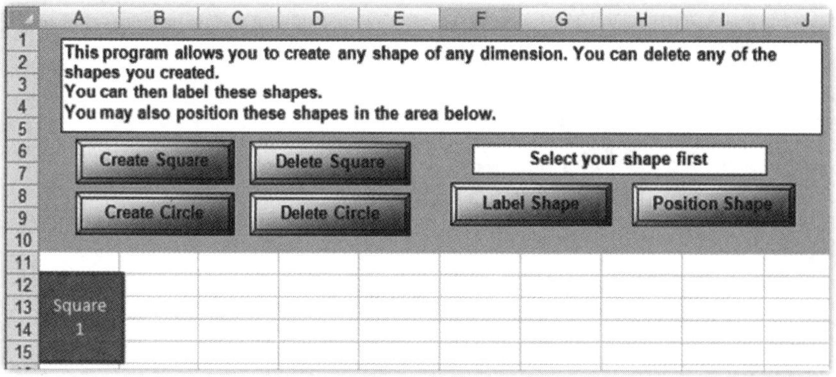

Figure 14.13 The result of the positioning *macro.*

We have created six simple sub procedures along with one event procedure to complete the functionality of this program.

14.6.2 Making Calculations and Creating a Report

We will now create a program that can make various calculations and create reports. The user will be able to generate random numbers in a specified interval that will then be converted to their absolute value and made into integers. The program will also calculate each of the numbers' square root, exponential power, and natural logarithm. The user can also provide an angle to calculate the number's sine, cosine, and tangent. Finally, we will provide a "Clear All" button to clear current reports.

We first prepare our spreadsheet with the appropriate buttons (drawing objects) and table headings (see Figure 14.14). Let's only calculate one random number and one angle at a time for now. (We will learn loop structures in Chapter 16 to expand this ability.) We only need three sub procedures for this program: *CalcRandNum()*, *CalcAngles()*, and *ClearAll()*.

We'll begin with the random number generation and calculations. First, we want to ask the user to specify an interval in which he or she wants the random number to be generated. We will use the *InputBox* function to acquire this interval from the user with two variables. We declare these as private variables in the *CalcRandNum()* sub procedure and name them *low* and *upp*. We define the prompt, title, and default values of the *InputBox* function as follows:

```
low = InputBox("Please enter the lower bound of the interval in which you" & _
   "would like to generate a random number: ", "Lower Bound", -10)
upp = InputBox("Please enter the upper bound of the interval in which you" & _
   "would like to generate a random number: ", "Upper Bound", 10)
```

We now use the following function to generate a random number in this interval:

```
x = (upp - low + 1) * Rnd() + low
```

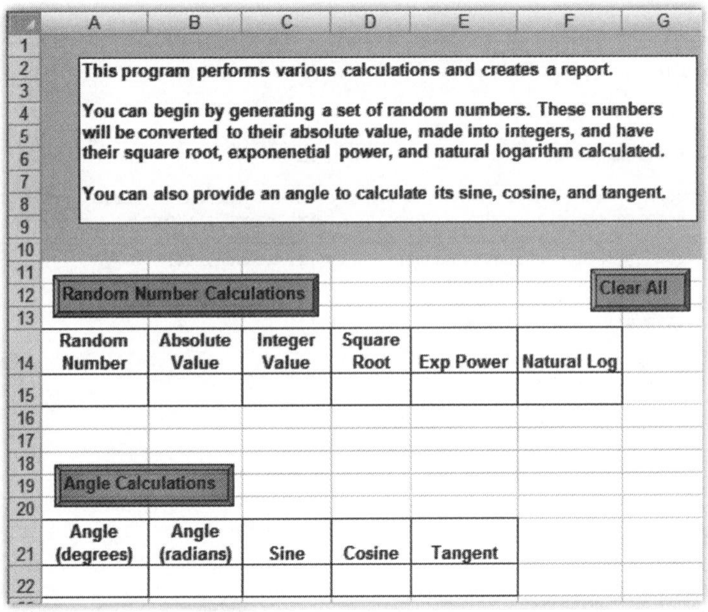

Figure 14.14 Preparing the spreadsheet before writing the sub procedures.

Next, we define *x* as a public variable, as we will use it to perform calculations in the *CalcAngles()* sub procedure as well. We can insert this random number into the first column of the random number calculation table. Since we will be inserting all other random number calculations into the same table, we will use a range variable for this table (as in the *StartCell* example) and use it to reference all report values. We define this range variable as a public variable since we will use it in the *ClearAll()* procedure as well. We name this variable *RandStart* and declare it as follows:

Public RandStart As Range

Now we should set this variable to a particular range in the worksheet. We do this in the *CalcRandNum()* sub procedure by typing:

Set RandStart = Worksheets("Example 2").Range("A14")

We can use this variable as a Range object and apply the *Offset* method to insert calculation results into our table. So, we insert the first value, the random number generated in the specified interval, into the first column:

RandStart.Offset(1, 0).Value = x

We can now use the *Value* property of our range variable to insert all other calculations directly; that is, we do not need to make the calculation first and then insert the value. Instead, we can do both in one step. The final code appears in Figure 14.15. (Notice that the *Sqr* and *Log* functions are used with the *Abs* function to ensure that no errors are created.) This macro is assigned to the "Random Number Calculations" button. The result of this macro is shown in Figure 14.16.

```
Sub CalcRandNum()

    Dim low As Integer, upp As Integer

    Set RandStart = Worksheets("Example 2").Range("A14")

    low = InputBox("Please enter the lower bound of the interval in which you" & _
    "would like to generate a random number: ", "Lower Bound", -10)
    upp = InputBox("Please enter the upper bound of the interval in which you" & _
    "would like to generate a random number: ", "Upper Bound", 10)

    x = (upp - low + 1) * Rnd() + low
    RandStart.Offset(1, 0).Value = x

    RandStart.Offset(1, 1).Value = Abs(x)
    RandStart.Offset(1, 2).Value = Int(x)
    RandStart.Offset(1, 3).Value = Sqr(Abs(x))
    RandStart.Offset(1, 4).Value = Exp(x)
    RandStart.Offset(1, 5).Value = Log(Abs(x))

End Sub
```

Figure 14.15 The *CalcRandNum()* sub procedure.

11						
12	Random Number Calculations				Clear All	
13						
14	Random Number	Absolute Value	Integer Value	Square Root	Exp Power	Natural Log
15	4.816498	4.816498	4.000000	2.194652	123.531700	1.572047

Figure 14.16 The result of the *CalcRandNum()* procedures.

For the *CalcAngles()* sub procedure, let's begin by asking the user to enter an angle in degrees (since most users will be more familiar with degrees than radians). We do this using the *InputBox* function, with the prompt, title, and default value defined:

x = InputBox("Enter an angle value in degrees:", "Angle value", 45)

Notice we used the same x value as before, which we declared as a public variable. We now need to convert this value into radians before using any trigonometric calculations. To do so, we will first need to declare the constant *PI*. We declare it in the same area in which we declare public variables, by typing:

Const PI = 3.14

We can now use the following formula to make the angle conversion:

*x = x * PI / 180*

Now we use another range variable in this procedure to insert calculation values into the angle calculation table. We also declare it as a public variable so that we can use it again in the *ClearAll()* procedure. We name this variable *AngleStart* and declare it as follows:

Public AngleStart As Range

We can now use the *Offset* method again to insert into the report: the original degree value of the angle; the converted radian value of the angle; and the *Sin*, *Cos*, and *Tan* calculation results. The final code for this sub procedure is provided in Figure 14.17. This macro is assigned to the "Angle Calculations" button; the result of this macro appears in Figure 14.18.

```
Option Explicit

Const pi = 3.14
Public AngleStart As Range, RandStart As Range, x As Double

Sub CalcAngles()

    Set AngleStart = Worksheets("Example 2").Range("A21")

    x = InputBox("Enter an angle value in degrees:", "Angle value", 45)
    AngleStart.Offset(1, 0).Value = x

    x = x * pi / 180
    AngleStart.Offset(1, 1).Value = x

    AngleStart.Offset(1, 2).Value = Sin(x)
    AngleStart.Offset(1, 3).Value = Cos(x)
    AngleStart.Offset(1, 4).Value = Tan(x)

End Sub
```

Figure 14.17 The *CalcAngles()* sub procedure and all public declarations.

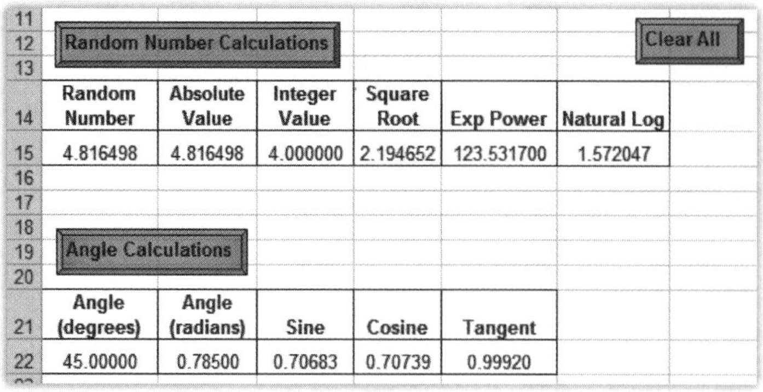

Random Number Calculations

Clear All

Random Number	Absolute Value	Integer Value	Square Root	Exp Power	Natural Log
4.816498	4.816498	4.000000	2.194652	123.531700	1.572047

Angle Calculations

Angle (degrees)	Angle (radians)	Sine	Cosine	Tangent
45.00000	0.78500	0.70683	0.70739	0.99920

Figure 14.18 The result of the macro.

The last procedure to write is the *ClearAll()* sub procedure. This procedure will simply clear the values in both tables. We will use the *ClearContents* method so as to keep the borders and the table's other formatting features. We will only clear the second row of both tables. (That is, we will not clear and retype table headings.) To do this, we use the *RandStart* and *AngleStart* variables to define the ranges that we want to clear. To clear the second row of the random number calculation table, we type:

Range(RandStart.Offset(1, 0), RandStart.Offset(1, 5)).ClearContents

To clear the second row of the angle calculation table, we type:

Range(AngleStart.Offset(1, 0), AngleStart.Offset(1, 4)).ClearContents

These are the only two lines of code in this procedure. We can now assign this macro to the "Clear All" button and perform a test to make sure that it works.

14.7 Summary

- Message Boxes and Input Boxes allow us to communicate with the user using VBA code. A Message Box prints information to a small dialog box, and an Input Box prompts the user to enter information into a small dialog box.
- The *MsgBox* function format is: *MsgBox (prompt, [buttons], [title], [helpfile, context]).* The *prompt* argument is required; all others are optional. We can capture the user's response to our Message Box by setting the *response* variable equal to the *MsgBox* function. We can check the value of this response using *VB Constants.*
- The *InputBox* function has the following format: *InputBox (prompt, [title], [default], [xpos], [ypos], [helpfile, context]).* The *prompt* argument is required; all others are optional. The *InputBox* function is always assigned to a variable.
- A data type categorizes the values that can be assigned to a variable.
- To declare a variable in VBA, use the command *Dim*. It is important to remember that VBA for Excel is *case-sensitive.*
- Integers and doubles are both numerical values. Integers are non-decimal numbers ranging in value from –32,768 to 32,767. Doubles have values from –1.79769E308 to –4.94065E–324 for negative values and from 4.94065E–324 to 1.79769E308 for positive values.
- A string is a segment of text. This text can include both upper- and lower-case letters, punctuation marks, and numbers.
- A *Boolean* is a variable whose value is either *True* or *False.*

- A range is a variable that can be used with all of the properties and methods of the Range object. We can use this data type to define a *StartCell*. We can set the value of this *range* variable at the beginning of our code and reference this *StartCell* variable name throughout the remainder of the code.
- The worksheets data type defines a Worksheets object. This variable can be assigned any of the properties or methods used with the Worksheets object.
- The object variable can be used to define any object in Excel, whether it is a drawing object, a range, a worksheet, or any other object. Any of the properties or methods associated with any object in Excel can be used with the *object* variable.
- There are several math functions in VBA that can be used with variables or values; some are:
  - The *Abs* function calculates the absolute value of a variable.
  - The *Sqr* function calculates the square root of a number.
  - The *Mod* function calculates the modular of a number given its divisor.
  - The *Int* function removes the decimal part of a double variable and returns the integer part; therefore the result will be an integer data type.
  - The *Rnd* function generates a random number.
  - The *Exp* function raises the constant *e* to some power given in the function statement.
  - The *Log* function calculates the natural log (the logarithm with base *e*, of a given number).
- There are a few trigonometric functions in VBA that we can use with variables or values:
  - The *Sin*, *Cos*, and *Tan* functions take an angle and return the ratio of two sides of a right triangle.
  - The *Atn* function calculates the arctangent of a given ratio. The result is an angle in radians, which is always a double data type.
- We can also derive other functions using the predefined VBA functions:
  - The *Arcsin* function calculates the arcsine or inverse sine as follows:

    *Arcsin(X) = Atn(X / Sqr(–X * X + 1))*
  - The *Sec* function finds the secant and is defined as follows:

    Sec(X) = 1 / Cos(X)
- There are several conversion functions in VBA:
  - *CInt* converts to integer data type
  - *CDbl* converts to double data type
  - *Val* finds numerical value in an expression
  - *CStr* converts to string data type
  - *CDate* converts to date data type
  - *Asc* converts characters to numbers
  - *Chr* converts numbers to characters
- There are several string functions in VBA:
  - *UCase* converts the string to all uppercase
  - *LCase* converts the string to all lowercase
  - *Len* finds the length of the string
- There are two types of variable declarations: *Public* and *Private*.
- We declare a private variable using the *Dim* statement. If it is declared on the procedure level, it can only be used in the particular sub procedure in which it is defined. If it is declared on the module level, it can be used in any procedure in that module, but only in the particular module in which it is defined.
- We declare a public variable using the *Public* statement. It can be used in any procedure in any module.
- To keep track of variable values while running our code, we can use the *Watch Window* in order to observe several variable values at once, or we can place the cursor over a particular variable in the *Code Window*.

14.8 Exercises

14.8.1 Review Questions

1. What is the difference between Message Boxes and Input Boxes? List the arguments and give an example of each type of box.
2. List seven variable types and give an example of each.
3. Can a string variable be set to the value of any number variable, such as integer or double, and vice versa? If so, how does the number change?
4. Can worksheet and object variables both be used to reference worksheets? Can a worksheet variable be set to an object variable, and vice versa?

5. What is the result of the following code:

```
Sub PIN()
        Dim x As Integer, y as integer
        x = InputBox("Enter last two digits of SSN:")
        y = InputBox("Enter birthday month:")
        MsgBox "Your new PIN number is: "& y & x &
int(10 *Rnd + 1)
End Sub
```

6. With what data types can the *Len* function be used?
7. Which function is a better option in order to find a numerical value of an expression: *CInt* or *Val*? Why?
8. Can *CDate* be used with any data type?
9. Where are the variables declared if to be used only in a private procedure? Where are the variables declared if to be used in a particular module? Where are the variables declared if to be used in a public procedure?
10. Does a variant data type become automatically converted after it is assigned a value?
11. Provide an example of a Derived Math Function.
12. How would you write the LN(RAND()) function of Excel, in VBA?
13. What is the ASCII numerical value of "M"? What is the letter for the ASCII number 100?
14. Create the following Message Box. (*Bonus*: How can you make the text right-aligned instead of left-aligned? *Hint*: Look at the button options.)

15. Create a Message Box similar to the one previous problem. Prompt the user for an initial value first and then display the countdown.

14.8.2 Hands-On Exercises

NOTE: *Please refer to the file "Chapter_14_Exercises.xlsx" for the associated worksheets noted for the hands-on exercises. The file is available at: www.dssbooks.com.*

1. Write a procedure that can do the following:
   a. Prompt the user for his or her name.
   b. Convert the name to all uppercase letters.
   c. Prompt the user for his or her address.
   d. Extract the numerical part of the address.
   e. Place on the spreadsheet the converted name and the numerical part of the address.
2. Write a procedure to do the following:
   a. Declare a variable as a string.
   b. Set this variable to an Input Box for the user to enter a value.
   c. Display a Message Box that presents the length of the string.
   d. Repeat this process for a variant data type and a double data type.
   e. Why is the length of the double data type always the same?
3. Create a sub called "NameAndAge" that performs the following. (Give an appropriate title for each Message Box and Input Box.)
   a. Asks for the user's name and stores it in a string variable.
   b. Asks for the user's age and stores it in an integer variable.
   c. Displays a message similar to: "*User's Name* is *User's Age* years old."
4. Create a sub called "Average" that asks the user to input two integers and then presents the average of the two numbers. Provide an appropriate title for each Message Box and Input Box.
   a. Use an Input Box for each integer and direct the user to enter an integer value.
   b. Store the two integers in integer variables: *Integer1* and *Integer2*.
   c. Store the result of the average calculation in single variable: *Result*.
   d. Display the result rounded to two decimals in a message similar to: "The average of *Integer1* and *Integer2* is *Result*."

5. Create a template for a "For Sale" sign as shown below.

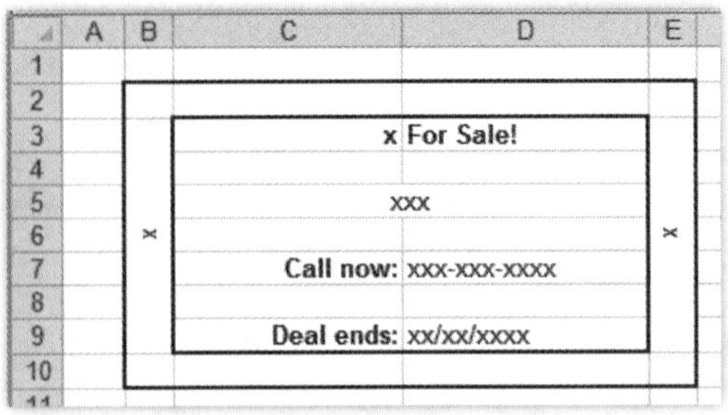

Perform the following tasks. (you may want to use several range names). (Refer to worksheet "14.5".)

- **a.** Ask the user to enter the item name in an Input Box. Place this value in the template everywhere the word "Item" appears.
- **b.** Ask the user to enter a description of the item. Place this text in the template accordingly.
- **c.** Ask the user to enter his or her phone number and place it in the template.
- **d.** Ask the user to enter the date on which his or her sale ends and place it in the template.

6. Create a sub called "StringManipulation" that performs the following actions. Assign an appropriate title for each Message Box and Input Box.

- **a.** Ask the user to input four characters of a word in string variable *FirstWord* and display the variable in a message.
- **b.** Ask the user to input four characters of a word in string variable *MiddleWord* and display the variable in a message.
- **c.** Ask the user to input four characters of a word in string variable *LastWord* and display the variable in a message.
- **d.** Concatenate the *FirstWord*, *MiddleWord*, and *LastWord* into one word, store it in *Word*, and then display the contents of *Word*.

7. Write a subroutine that executes the following. (Refer to worksheet "14.7".)

- **a.** Ask the user for his or her name.
- **b.** Ask the user for his or her student ID in the form 1234–5678.
- **c.** Create a pin number for each user with the last, forth, first, and second numbers in his or her student number.
- **d.** Print out the data in the following format: Name, ID Number, Pin.

8. Create different sub procedures that generate the following sequences of numbers so that the sequences are generated one number at a time each time a corresponding button is pushed:

- **a.** Even numbers
- **b.** Odd numbers
- **c.** Fibonacci
- **d.** Geometric

9. Perform the following tasks for creating a user-defined chart of user-provided data:

- **a.** Ask the user to input the title of two columns of data.
- **b.** Ask him or her to also provide you with five points for each column.
- **c.** Output all of this information to the spreadsheet.
- **d.** Ask the user what kind of chart he or she wants. Only provide three options and make sure the user supplies you with the exact chart type name that Excel uses (for example: *xlColumnClustered*).
- **e.** Create a chart of the data that you enter into the spreadsheet of the chart type the user provided.

10. Create a highlighting program. Allow a user to select a range of text and then highlight it by specifying a color.

- **a.** After the user selects the range of cells they want to highlight, prompt them for the color they want to use. Only give them a few choices. Hint: use ColorIndex property (Example: ColorIndex = 3 for red).
- **b.** Then, apply this color formatting to their selection.

11. Create labels.

- **a.** Begin by prompting the user for his or her name and address. Output these values onto the spreadsheet as a mailing label. Assign this *macro* to a button.
- **b.** Create another button that will allow the user to copy and paste this label as many times as desired. (*Hint*: Use the *End* property.)

12. Combine VBA with Excel functions. Using the given table of product sales per month, prompt the user for a product name and a month number. Use these values along with a *LOOKUP*

function to search for the amount sold for the specified product during the specified month. (Refer to worksheet "14.12".)

13. Create a dynamic chart.

- **a.** Let the user press a button that prompts him or her to enter a value. The user can press this button multiple times and each new value will be added to a column of data.
- **b.** When the user is done adding data, he or she can press another button that will create a chart of this data. The source data of this chart will change each time; use range names and the *End* property to accomplish this. A new chart should not be created each time; the source data should just be updated.
- **c.** Create a button that clears all previous data.

14. Create a histogram from scratch (without using the Data Analysis toolpak). Create a procedure that performs the following (refer to Chapter 7 for more on histograms):

- **a.** Randomly generates 30 data points from uniform distribution between 5 and 30.
- **b.** Uses the intervals (5 – 10), (10 – 15), (15 – 20), (20 – 25), and 25+ to calculate frequencies.
- **c.** Uses the Application object and a counting function to find the frequency of the randomly generated data for each of the intervals in part (b).
- **d.** Creates a table with the intervals and the corresponding frequency values.
- **e.** Graphs this data as a bar chart.

15. Perform the following extensions to the *Creating and Modifying Shapes* application:

- **a.** Add the ability to create a triangle, delete a triangle, and count the number of triangles currently displayed.
- **b.** Add an option to format the selected shape.
  - **i.** Prompt the user to specify what color he or she wants the shape to be.
  - **ii.** Prompt the user to specify what line thickness he or she wants the shape to have.

16. Perform the following extensions to the *Making Calculations and Creating Reports* application:

- **a.** Add a table below the angle calculation table that reports the results of an arctangent calculation.
- **b.** Create a button called "Arc Tangent" to which you will assign a macro called *CalcArcTan()*.
- **c.** This macro should prompt the user for a ratio, calculate the arctangent, and convert the answer to degrees. (All three values should be displayed in the table.)

17. Create a sub called "RandomColors" that assigns colors in a random way to each cell of the range D4:H8. (*Hint:* set the *ColorIndex* property of each cell in the range to a random integer between 1 and 10.)

18. Create a sub called "ConvertInputs." Give an appropriate title for each Message Box and Input Box. This sub should perform the following:

- **a.** Declare a double variable called *InputValue*;
- **b.** Set *InputValue* equal to the result from an Input Box requesting the user to enter a number; and
- **c.** Return the square of *InputValue* rounded to three decimal numbers.

19. Create a sub called "ActivateWorksheet." Give an appropriate title for each Message Box and Input Box. This sub should do the following:

- **a.** Ask the user for the name of a worksheet to activate;
- **b.** Activate the worksheet if it exists in the active workbook; and
- **c.** Otherwise, display an appropriate message.

20. On a spreadsheet, create three triangle shapes. Name these shapes "Tri1," "Tri2," and "Tri3" respectively. Create a sub called "FindObject." This sub should:

- **a.** Ask the user for the name which triangle to select;
- **b.** Ask the user what color they want to make this triangle; and
- **c.** Change the color of the specified triangle appropriately.

21. Write a subroutine that will performs the following using a given data table. (Refer to worksheet "14.21".)

- **a.** Calculates the mean, standard deviation, minimum, maximum and mean squares error (MSE) for the data in the range A2:A21.
- **b.** Prints the results in a report format on the worksheet.

22. Create a small program that can calculate the distance between cities. Given the X-Coord (latitude) and Y-Coord (longitude) of several US cities, create four buttons corresponding to the following options: find vertical distance; find horizontal distance; find Euclidean distance; and compare three cities to see which pair is closest. (Refer to worksheet "14.22".)

- The Euclidean distance is calculated using the following equation:

$$\sqrt{(Lat1 - Lat2)^2 + (Long1 - Long2)^2}$$

- Perform these options by prompting the user for the city names with an Input Box. Then use a lookup function to find the necessary latitude or longitude values. Use VBA functions to find the values that you are looking for and display them to the user in a Message Box.
- For the comparative option, prompt the user to enter three cities and then assign three variables to the distance between each pair of cities. Use *Application.WorksheetFunction* to find the minimum of these variable values. Then display a Message Box to the user with the pair of city names that are the closest.

23. Create an address book. Given a list of people and addresses, create a procedure that allows a user to search for a particular name and returns the address from the table. (Refer to worksheet "14.23".)

a. Search for the name using the *match* function and the Application object. Name the range that contains the names in the address table.

b. Then use the *Offset* property (or *Cells* property) to gather the corresponding information. You may need to name another range to make this easier.

c. Present this information to the user in a Message Box as shown below:

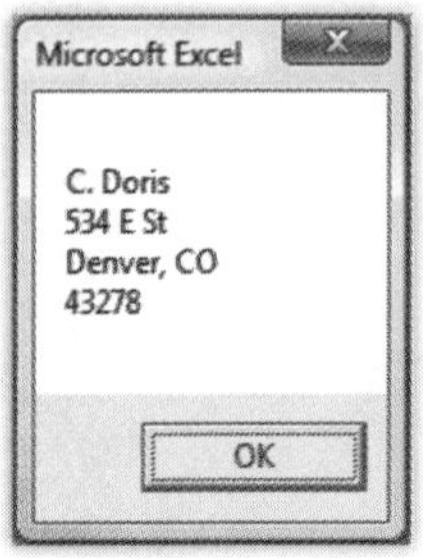

24. Create a personal budget organizer that keeps track of the companies to which you pay bills each month. (Refer to worksheet "14.24".)

a. Record the name and account number for each company and the amount and date of the last payment.

b. The user should be able to add a new company to the list. He or she should provide the name and account number using Input Boxes.

c. The user should also be able to enter a new payment. To do so, he or she should first provide the company name through an *Input Box*. Then, the user can enter the amount and date of the payment via Input Boxes as well. Use a *match* function to enter the payment information into the right row in the table.

d. The user should also be able to see how much he or she spent in bills for the month. Calculate this total and display it to the user in a Message Box.

25. Use visual basic to perform the following tasks:

a. Create a procedure which does the following:

i. Clears the content of the current worksheet.

ii. Randomly generate 10 numbers between 1 and 10.

iii. Finds the mean and standard deviation of the numbers generated and stores them as variables.

b. Create a procedure which does the following:

i. Generates 10 random numbers from the Normal distribution using the mean and standard deviation found in part (a). Use the Application object and the *Rnd()* VBA function to generate the random numbers.

ii. Graph the data generated in part (a) and the Normal random variables using a Line chart.

c. Create a procedure which does the following:

i. Generates 10 random numbers from the Exponential distribution using the mean found in part (a). Use the Application object and the *Log()* and *Rnd()* functions to generate the random numbers.

ii. Graph the data generated in part (a) and the Exponential random variables using a Line chart.

d. Assign each procedure to a button. To the first button called "Reset" assign the procedure of part (a). To the second and third buttons, called "Compare to Normal" and "Compare to Exponential," assign the procedure created in parts (b) and (c).

26. Create a procedure called "CurrencyConverter" that converts a certain amount of money to another currency type. We provide a table with the exchange rates of 5 different currency types. The procedure should do the following. (Refer to worksheet "14.26".)
    a. Ask the user to choose a currency type to convert the money from and a currency type to convert the money to.
    b. Ask the user to input the amount of money to be converted.
    c. Find the exchange rate using the table below.
    d. Create a Message Box that presents the result of the money exchange.

27. Create a procedure called "WeightConverter" that helps converting weight. The given table presents the conversion rates. The procedure should do the following. (Refer to worksheet "14.27".)
    a. Ask the user to choose unit to convert from and a unit to convert to.
    b. Ask the user to enter the amount to be converted.
    c. Create a Message Box that presents the results of the conversion.

28. Create a procedure called "Temperature-Converter" that converts temperature from degrees Celsius to Fahrenheit and vise versa.
    a. Ask the user to choose whether to convert from degrees Celsius to Fahrenheit, or vise versa.
    b. Ask the user to enter the temperature to be converted.
    c. Create a Message Box that returns the converted temperature.

29. Create a procedure called "DistanceConverter" that helps converting distance/ length. A given table presents the conversion rates. The procedure should do the following. (Refer to worksheet "14.29".)
    a. Ask the user to choose unit to convert from and a unit to convert to.
    b. Ask the user to enter the amount to be converted.
    c. Create a Message Box that presents the results of the conversion.

30. Create a procedure called "VolumeConverter" that helps converting volume. The given table presents the conversion rates. The procedure should do the following. (Refer to worksheet "14.30".)
    a. Ask the user to choose unit to convert from and a unit to convert to.
    b. Ask the user to enter the amount to be converted.
    c. Create a Message Box that presents the results of the conversion.

CHAPTER *fifteen*

Sub Procedures and Function Procedures

chapter OVERVIEW

15.1 *Introduction*

This chapter discusses how to use sub procedures and function procedures in VBA. This is a useful topic since programs for DSS applications will have several different procedures. These procedures will structure the flow of the DSS: they begin by navigating the user after the first button click and then proceed to gather the user's input data, perform calculations, optimization, or simulation procedures, and end by generating output. Each step of the DSS application will require one or more procedures. We discuss outlining procedures as part of the DSS development process in Chapter 22.

In this chapter, the reader will learn how to:

- Call sub procedures.
- Execute function procedures to return a value.
- Pass variables by reference and by value.
- Work with both private and public procedures.
- Create two applications that work with calling sub procedures and creating function procedures which pass variables.

15.2 *Sub Procedures*

When constructing a large program or DSS, we may perform several different sets of actions. It is important to group these actions into several smaller sub procedures rather than write the entire program in one large sub procedure. This organization increases program efficiency.

15.2.1 Calling Other Procedures

The ideal module structure for our program is to have one *Main()* sub procedure from which other sub procedures are called. To call another sub procedure, we use the command ***Call*** followed by the sub procedure name. (We can also call a procedure just by giving its name. We also do not need to include the parenthesis in the procedure name to call it if there are no variables being passed.) The *Main()* sub procedure can then be assigned (as a macro) to a "Start" button on the "Welcome" worksheet, which the user would see upon opening the workbook. The entire program would begin once the user pushes this button.

For example, let's say we have a program that gathers user input, performs calculations, and creates a report. In this case, we divide these functions into three different sub procedures, called *GetInput()*, *Calculations()*, and *CreateReport()*, respectively. We can then call these three sub procedures from the *Main()* sub procedure as follows:

```
Sub Main()
    Call GetInput
    Call Calculations
    Call CreateReport
End Sub
```

We may need to call other sub procedures from the *GetInput()*, *Calculations()*, or *CreateReport()* procedures if there is a set of actions that must be performed before one of these sub procedures can continue. This set of actions may be long enough to group as another sub procedure. For example, there may be a small sub procedure called *CheckInput()* that must be called to verify the data before the *GetInput()* sub procedure can finish.

15.2.2 Passing Variables in Procedures

We can also pass variables to a procedure when calling the procedure. The default method for passing variables is ***by reference***; we specify ***ByVal*** in the sub argument to pass ***by value***. Passing a variable by reference implies that we are giving the name of the variable to which the procedure can refer to find the current variable value; that is, we are referring to the storage space of that value. This means that the function procedure can actually access and modify the value of the specified variable. Passing a variable by value implies that we are copying the current value of the specified variable and using that value in the procedure. In this case, the function procedure cannot modify the variable, but only use its current value. To pass a variable in VBA, we need to insert the variable as an argument of the sub when it is called. When calling a sub, we use the following structure to pass variables:

```
Call ProcedureName(variable to be passed)
```

If passing by reference, the variable name used as an argument when the sub is called and the variable name used in the sub procedure statement do not need to be the same; however, they must be of the same data type if the data type is specified in the sub statement. For example we could type the following:

```
Dim RangeUser As Range, ColorUser As String
Call FormatCell(RangeUser, ColorUser )

-------------------------
Sub FormatCell(r,c)
        r.Interior.Color = c
End Sub
```

Note that when we pass variables, they must be listed in the same order that they are stated in the called procedure. For example, in the above code, we should not write *Call FormatCell(ColorUser, RangeUser)*; if we did so, then r would be set to the string variable and c would be set to the range variable.

Passing variables in sub procedures can be helpful when performing a task multiple times with changing parameters. As in the above example, we have formatted cells multiple times using different property values specified in the passed values. We can also use subs and variables in this way to perform more complicated tasks.

Subs can also be used to update other variable values. Consider the example below in which we call a sub passing two variables *x* and *y* that are used to update another variable *SumVar*.

```
Dim x as Integer, y as Integer, SumVar as Integer
Call Sum(x, y)

-------------------------
Sub Sum(x, y)
      SumVar = x + y
End Sub
```

While this method is viable, function procedures offer a more efficient way to write this calculation code.

Summary

Sub Procedures:

```
Sub SubName1()
    Dim variable As DataType, x As DataType
        ...
        Call SubName2(variable)
        ...
End Sub
_______________________
Sub SubName2(variable)
        ...
        use variable in a set of actions
        use this variable to update the value of another variable
End Sub
```

15.3 *Function Procedures*

Function procedures are sub procedures that can return values. A function procedure can be called from any sub procedure or any other function procedure by using the *Call* statement. A function procedure can also be called by using the function name directly, as with any variable. A function can be used just like a sub procedure simply by performing a set of actions. However, we discourage using function procedures when a value is not returned.

To return a value in a function procedure, there is not a *return* function in VBA; instead, we simply assign the value to return to the name of the function procedure. Below, we show the different ways in which a function procedure can be used:

```
Call FunctionName(a,b,c)
OR
x = FunctionName(a,b,c)
OR
MsgBox FunctionName(a,b,c)
_______________________
Function FunctionName(a,b,c)
    ...(actions)...
    FunctionName = value
End Function
```

15.3.1 Passing Variables in Functions

Just as with sub procedures, it is not necessary that variables be passed when calling a function. That is, our function may not require any input from the procedure in which it is called, and it may not necessarily return any value. However, most of the time, we will use functions that pass variables and return some value. As with sub procedures, the default method for passing variables is by reference; we can specify *ByVal* in the function argument to pass by value.

We use the following structure to call a function that will not return a value:

Call FunctionName(variable)

We use the following structure to use the result of a function procedure:

x = FunctionName(variable)

If the function receives a variable as input to the function, the function procedure statement must include a variable name as an argument. For example, if we create a function that calculates the sum of two values, we define the function procedure as follows:

```
Function SumVal(a, b)
    SumVal = a + b
End Function
```

The variable name used as an argument when the function is called and the variable name used in the function procedure statement do not need to be the same; however, they must be of the same data type if the data type is specified in the function statement. For example, we could call the above function from another procedure using this statement:

Call SumVal(x, y)

This would imply that we have declared x and y as variables in the procedure from which we call our function. The variables *a* and *b* in this example do not need to be declared; they will be the variables used throughout the function procedure. In this case *a* and *b* will assume the respective data types assigned to *x* and *y*. However, if we had defined our function statement with data types in the argument, we would be restricted to only passing variables of that data type. For example:

Function SumVal(a As Integer, b As Integer)

To return a value from a function in VBA, we assign a value to the name of the function procedure. That is, instead of using a *return* command or variable, we set the function name equal to the value that we want to return. For example, to return the value of the sum in the above function, we would type the following in the function procedure:

```
Function SumVal(a, b)
    SumVal = a + b
End Function
```

Let us return to the comparison of passing by reference (the default in VBA) and passing by value. Consider the following procedures:

```
Sub PerformCalc()
    Dim Val1 As Integer, Val2 As Integer
    Val1 = 5
    Val2 = 10

    MsgBox FindSum(Val1, Val2)
    MsgBox Val1
End Sub
-------------------------
Function FindSum(X, Y)
    FindSum = X + Y
    X = 3
End Function
```

Here, we have passed by reference. The *MsgBox* statement used with the function name will cause the function procedure to be executed. We will see that the value of the function is 10 + 5 = 15 and that the new value of the *Val1* variable is 3. Now let us consider what would be the result of these procedures if we passed by value instead. The modified function procedure is shown below:

```
Function FindSum(ByVal X, ByVal Y)
    FindSum = X + Y
    X = 3
End Function
```

In this case, the function value will still be 10 + 5 = 15, however the value of the variable *Val1* will now be 5. That is, because we used the *ByVal* declaration, the statement X = 3 in the function procedure does not do anything since we are not modifying the original variable *Val1*, but only using its value of 5.

Summary

Function Procedures:

```
Sub SubName()
    Dim variable As DataType, x As DataType
        ...
        x = FunctionName(variable)
        ...
End Sub
_________________________
Function FunctionName(a variable name)
    ...
    FunctionName = value
End Function
```

Note that both sub procedure and function procedure names should not conflict with VBA commands.

An interesting feature about creating function procedures is that they become User-Defined functions in the Excel list of spreadsheet functions. That is, if we create a function procedure, with or without parameters, we can find this function listed in the User-Defined function category in Excel. This is beneficial for enhancing our spreadsheet capabilities by using a small amount of VBA code. (Note: If we do not want users to access VBA-defined functions, we can declare them to be *Private* procedures. We discuss private and public procedures in the next section.)

15.4 Public and Private Procedures

A procedure, like a variable, can also be defined as ***Public*** or ***Private***. We declare a private procedure by putting the word *Private* before the *Sub* or *Function* statement. Private procedures can only be called from procedures in the same module. Private procedures are also not listed when we try to run a macro in Excel.

A public procedure, however, can be called from any other procedure. We can type the word *Public* in front of the *Sub* or *Function* statement, or we can write the *Sub* or *Function* statement without a preceding statement.

Consider four small sub procedures as an example of private and public procedures. Two of these procedures are private: *Test1()* and *Test2()*. Since they are in the same module, they can call one another. For example, suppose these two sub procedures have the following code:

```
Private Sub Test1()
    MsgBox "This is Test1"
    Call Test2
End Sub
-------------------------
Private Sub Test2()
    MsgBox "This is Test2"
End Sub
```

If we run the *Test1()* sub procedure (from the VBE, using the run button), we will see one Message Box that reads "This is Test1," followed by another that reads, "This is Test2."

If we have a third sub procedure called *Test3()* that is public but in another module, we will not be allowed to call either of the private sub procedures in the original module. That is, *Test3()* cannot contain the code *Call Test1* or *Call Test2*. However, we can call this public procedure from one of our private procedures. In other words, we can modify the *Test1()* procedure to say:

```
Private Sub Test1()
    MsgBox "This is Test1"
    Call Test3
End Sub
```

If we now consider a fourth sub procedure called *Test4()*, which is also public and in the same module as *Test1()* and *Test2()*, even though *Test4()* is public, it can still call the private procedures since they are in the same module. Again, it is important to be aware of how we define these procedures.

Summary

Private:	Cannot be called from a procedure that is not in the same module and cannot be found in the macro list when trying to play a macro, or assign a macro to a button in Excel.
Public:	Can be called from any other procedure

15.5 Applications

There are various sub and function procedures that may be useful to create. Many functions are already available to us through Excel formulas and VBA math functions; however, some programs and DSS's require customized functions. In this section, we will demonstrate navigating procedures and some derived math functions.

15.5.1 Navigating Procedures

In many of the case studies that we develop, and as discussed in the GUI design chapter (23), several buttons in our workbook may be used to navigate the user through the different worksheets. Some of these buttons may be called *Continue*, *Next*, *Back*, *Previous*, etc. Each time one of these buttons is clicked, we want to close the current worksheet, that is, hide it, and make the next appropriate worksheet visible. (We want to try to always have only one sheet visible to minimize the user's awareness of background actions being performed in the spreadsheet and code.) If we try to create one sub procedure to associate with these buttons, we find that each time a button is clicked we are not performing completely identical actions.

For example, consider a workbook with several worksheets: "Input," "Step 1," "Step 2," and "Optimization"; the user should view these worksheets in the order listed. If we click a *Next* button on the "Input" worksheet, we want to hide the "Input" sheet and make the "Step 1" sheet visible. Here is the coded sub procedure:

```
Sub NextSheet()
    Worksheet("Step 1").Visible = True
    Worksheet("Input").Visible = False
End Sub
```

(*Note:* We must make the new sheet visible before hiding the current sheet. If we make these statements in the reverse order, we will momentarily have a workbook with no visible worksheets, which will create an error in VBA.)

However, we cannot assign this same macro to the *Next* button found on the "Step 1" worksheet. If we press *Next* on the "Step 1" sheet, we want to make the "Step 2" sheet visible and hide the "Step 1" sheet. Its code is:

```
Sub NextSheet()
    Worksheet("Step 2").Visible = True
    Worksheet("Step 1").Visible = False
End Sub
```

We therefore compare the similarities of these sub procedures to see if we can construct a procedure that works with any of these button types on any worksheet. There are two different worksheet names that we need to know to set the appropriate *Visible* properties: the worksheet that we are hiding and the worksheet that we are showing.

The worksheet that we are hiding is just the current worksheet, or the ActiveSheet. Therefore, we can just use the ActiveSheet object and set the *Visible* property equal to false. Regardless of which sheet has the *Next* button, we can always use the ActiveSheet object to hide it.

The name of the worksheet that we are opening, however, will change each time. Our solution is to create a procedure that passes a worksheet name as its variable; we call this the *NextSheet()* procedure. We can capture the desired worksheet name in each unique sub procedure associated with the buttons on each sheet and then call a procedure to make this worksheet visible and hide the current worksheet. Our procedure can be used as follows:

```
Public name As String
------------------------
Sub InputNext()
    name = "Step 1"
    Call NextSheet(name)
End Sub
------------------------
Sub NextSheet(name)
    Worksheets(name).Visible = True
    ActiveSheet.Visible = False
End Sub
```

(This particular sub procedure would be associated with the *Next* button on the *Input* worksheet; note that we cannot assign procedures to buttons, only macros.)

We use this procedure structure above to assign related macros to the *Next* button on each of the sheets in our workbook. The final code for these sub procedures and the procedure appear in Figure 15.1.

```
Option Explicit

Public name As String

    Sub InputNext()
        name = "Step 1"
        Call NextSheet(name)
    End Sub

     Sub Step1Next()
        name = "Step 2"
        Call NextSheet(name)
    End Sub

     Sub OptimBack()
        name = "Input"
        Call NextSheet(name)
    End Sub

    Function NextSheet(name)
        Worksheets(name).Visible = True
        ActiveSheet.Visible = False
    End Function
```

Figure 15.1 Each sub procedure is associated with a button on each worksheet. The *NextSheet()* procedure receives the name value of the worksheet that it displays.

We may also have a particular sheet that is usually hidden but that can be shown at some point, for example, an "Example" worksheet that the user may refer to at times while using the program. To view this "Example" sheet, there may be a "View Example" button on all the other sheets in the workbook. If the user clicks this button, we want to close the current sheet and show the "Example" sheet. On the "Example" sheet, we may have a "Return to Program" button that should re-open the previously visible sheet.

So we know which sheet to re-open when the user clicks the "Return to Program" button, we need to capture the original worksheet name in which we first click the "Example" button. We accomplish this using a worksheet variable and a navigating procedure; this time we don't need to pass a variable.

Let's consider the same set of worksheets as in the above example with an additional "Example" sheet. We declare a public variable *ws* as a worksheet data type and use a procedure to capture this value and hide the worksheet. When the "Return to Program" button is clicked, this same variable can be used to re-open the appropriate sheet. The code is as follows:

```
Public ws As Worksheet
-------------------------
Sub ViewExample()
    Worksheets("Example").Visible = True
    Call CloseCurrent()
End Sub
-------------------------
Sub CloseCurrent()
    Set ws = ActiveSheet
    ws.Visible = False
End Sub
-------------------------
Sub ReturnToProgram()
    ws.Visible = True
    Worksheets("Example").Visible = False
End Sub
```

These sub procedures are assigned to appropriate buttons in the workbook to implement the navigational tools (see Figure 15.2).

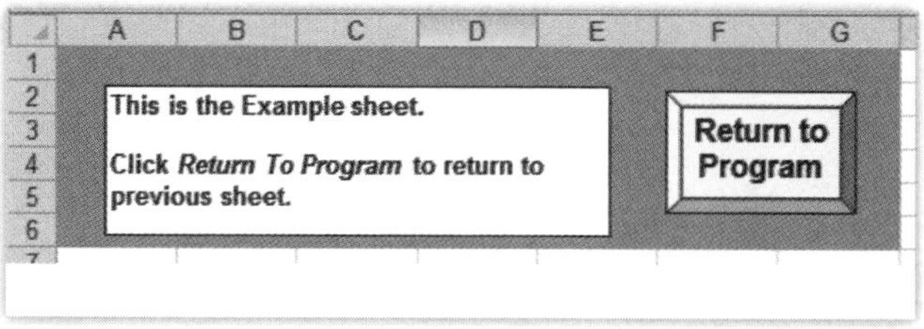

Figure 15.2 The "Return to Program" button takes the user to the previously visible sheet that was captured by the worksheet variable.

To create navigating procedures, we can also use the index value of the worksheets. To find the index value (or tab number) of a worksheet, we can simply use its *Index* property. For example, if we write the code *MsgBox Worksheets("Sheet 1").Index*, a Message Box with the value 1 is shown. Once we know a worksheet's index value, we can simply refer to it by this index (instead of by the worksheet name). For example, instead of writing *Worksheets("Sheet 1"). Visible = True*, we can just write *Worksheets(1).Visible = True.*

15.5.2 Derived Math Functions

As we learned in Chapter 14, the pre-defined VBA math functions and trigonometric functions can be used to derive new functions. To actually create these derived functions in Excel, we create a function procedure and both pass a variable and return some value. For example to create the *Log base n* derived math function, we create the following function:

```
Function LogBaseN(x, n)
    LogBaseN = Log(x) / Log(n)
End Function
```

Prior to calling the function, the values for *x* and *n* would need to have been assigned in the sub procedure that calls this function. In these functions, we may not directly call the function using the *Call* statement; we can instead just refer to the function name, such as in a Message Box or another function. When we refer to this function, it will call the function procedure to determine the return value. Therefore, we should have something like the following code in another sub procedure:

```
Sub FindLog()
    Dim x As Integer, n As Integer
    x = InputBox("Enter x value of Log base n of x function: ")
    n = InputBox("Enter n value of Log base n of x function: ")
    MsgBox "The value of Log base " & n & " of " & x & " is: " & LogBaseN(n, x)
End Sub
```

Note that the variables x and n are declared privately in the sub procedure but can still be passed to the function. It is irrelevant in which order we enter sub procedures and functions into a module. The module does not read the code from procedure to procedure; rather, one particular procedure is run, and only if another procedure is called it is also run.

15.6 Summary

- The ideal module structure for a program is to have one *Main()* sub procedure from which other sub procedures are called.
- To call another sub procedure, use the command *Call* followed by the sub procedure name.
- A sub procedure, like a variable, can also be defined as public or private.
- Declare a private sub procedure by putting the word *Private* before the *Sub* statement. Private sub procedures can only be called from procedures in the same module and are not listed when we try to run a macro in Excel.
- A public sub procedure can be called from any other procedure. The word *Public* can be put in front of the *Sub* statement, or the *Sub* statement can be written without a preceding statement.
- Function procedures are sub procedures that can pass variables or return values. A function procedure can be called from any sub procedure

or any other function procedure, using the *Call* statement.

- Function procedures are similar to sub procedures and follow this basic structure:

  Function FunctionName()

  ...

  End Function

- To pass a variable in VBA, we should insert the variable as an argument/parameter of the function when it is called. Use the following structure to call a function: *Call FunctionName(variable to be passed).*

15.7 Exercises

15.7.1 Review Questions

1. Can a subroutine be called from inside itself?
2. What is the difference between sub procedures and function procedures?
3. What is the default method of passing variables in sub procedures: *by reference* or *by value*?
4. How do we pass a variable by value?
5. An accountant would like to create a program to perform the following tasks. Propose a program structure that would organize these various tasks into appropriate subroutines.
   a. Prepare a Balance Sheet, Income Statement, Statement of Retained Earnings, and Statement of Cash Flows.
   b. Each statement requires a heading including the company name, statement title, date, and unit of monetary measure.
   c. Both the Balance Sheet and the Statement of Cash Flows contain a graph.
   d. After all statements are prepared, they should be printed out as the final Annual Report.

15.7.2 Hands-On Exercises

NOTE: *Please refer to the file "Chapter_15_Exercises.xlsx" for the associated worksheets noted for the hands-on exercises. The file is available at: www.dssbooks.com.*

1. Write a function called *CalculateHypotenuse* that takes variable *Side1* and variable *Side2* as arguments, where *Side1* and *Side2* are the sides of a right triangle. Write a *Main* sub that uses the function to calculate the hypotenuse of the three triangles with given side lengths. (Refer to worksheet "15.1".)

   The *Main* sub should send the side lengths to the function as doubles if they appear as doubles in the table above. For each triangle, the *Main* sub displays in a message the side lengths and the hypotenuse length rounded to two decimal places. *Note:* $(Hypotenuse)^2 = (\text{Side1})^2 + (\text{Side2})^2$.
2. Using the idea of indexing worksheets, create a navigational function for using a *Next* and *Back* button on any worksheet.
3. Create a program that enables the user to compute random numbers from a Normal distribution and graph the corresponding values. This program will ask the user to input the total number of random numbers to be generated, the mean and standard deviation of the distribution. The program will then compute the random values, and display user's input, the random values and the corresponding graph. Below we describe the sub procedures needed to complete this exercise:
   a. The *InputData* sub procedure asks the user to input the total number of random numbers to be generated, the mean and standard deviation of the distribution. This data is then displayed in the worksheet.
   b. The *RandomNr* sub procedure generates and displays the random numbers in the worksheet.
   c. The *Reset* sub procedure clears the current worksheet.
   d. The *Graph* sub procedure graphs the random numbers generated.
   e. The *Main* sub procedure calls the other subroutines in the appropriate order.

   Place a button labeled "Random Values" on the worksheet. Assign the *Main* sub procedure to this button.

4. Create a button on the active worksheet that calls a program to perform the following operations. (Refer to worksheet "15.4".)

  a. Format the given table using one of the preset format styles available in Excel.

  b. Use the data in the table to create a 3-D Column Graph using a function procedure.

5. Create a button that will copy selected data from one worksheet onto another to create a final report. (Refer to worksheet "15.5".)

  a. This report should organize the given data by types of products sold and include only the company name, products sold, and annual sales figures.

  b. Also create a Pie Chart using the annual sales values provided through a function procedure.

6. Modify the original code below so that the main subroutine has the given structure and the sheet has the following layout.

	A	B	C	D
1	Customer	Product	Amount Sold	Final Sale
2	Jane Smith	Computer	1	$2,500.00
3				

Final main subroutine:

```
Dim Customer As String, Product, Amount As
Double, Price As Currency, Sale As Currency


Sub main()
   Call RequestInfo
   Call Calculate(Price, Amount)
   Call PrintReport
End Sub
```

Original code:

```
Dim Customer As String, Product, Amount As
Double, Price As Currency, Sale As Currency


Sub HandsOn6()
   Customer = InputBox("Enter customer name:")
   Product = InputBox("Enter product sold:")
   Amount = InputBox("Enter quantity of " &
                                        Product & " sold:")
   Price = InputBox("Enter unit price of " &
                                        Product & ":")
   Sale = Price * Amount
   Range("A2").Value = Customer
   Range("B2").Value = Product
   Range("C2").Value = Amount
   Range("D2").Value = Sale
   MsgBox "Transaction Complete. Congratulations
   on your sale to" & Customer & "."
End Sub
```

7. Create a procedure which prompts the user for the size of data s/he is interested in generating. Prompt the user for a mean and standard deviation for the Normal distribution; store these in variables. Prompt the user for a lambda value for the Exponential distribution; store this in a variable. Prompt the user for a lower and an upper bound value for the Uniform distribution; store these in variables. Then call the following three functions:

  a. Normal Function: (pass size, mean, stdev) generate a column of random values from the Normal distribution.

  b. Exponential Function: (pass size, lambda) generate another column of random values from the Exponential distribution.

  c. Uniform Function: (pass size, lower and upper bound) generate another column of random values from the Uniform distribution.

8. Modify the *Navigating Functions* application to include the following:

  a. Add *Back* buttons that take the user through the forms in the reverse order.

  b. Create an *Input()* sub procedure that prompts the user to supply an *y* value to be used to compute the hyperbolic sine. This sub procedure should be associated with a button called "Add More Data" that can be clicked multiple times until the user is ready to move on by pressing Next. Print these values in a table on the "Input" sheet.

  c. Create a function that calculates the hyperbolic sine of the values in the data table on the "Input" sheet. (*Hint:* Use the *Exp* function.) Create a new table of this function's results for each value entered in the input table and place it on the "Step 1" sheet.

  d. Make a chart that uses the data from both tables. First copy and paste both tables to form one table on the "Step 2" sheet. Then update your source data with VBA code.

9. Create code that performs the following tasks:

a. Has a *Main()* sub procedure that:

i. calls a procedure to clear previous data;

ii. prompts the user for the size of the data he or she enters;

iii. formats a table for the data of the given size; and

iv. tells the user to enter data into the table.

b. Has a *Done()* procedure that:

i. takes the data and graphs it;

ii. finds the mean and standard deviation of the data; and

iii. calls a procedure to generate a final report on a new sheet.

10. A person preparing his cost sheet wants to review his list of orders and refer to a table with prices to calculate his total bill. Tables of the orders and prices are given. He wants to reference the price for each order item and create a new table with only two columns: one for the item and one for its price. (Refer to worksheet "15.10".)

a. Write a procedure that:

i. captures the value of the selected cell in a variable and

ii. prompts the user to enter the type of item in the list (Book = 1, CD = 2, Movie = 3).

b. Call a function procedure that:

i. is given this number and the variable from part (a);

ii. uses a range and *Offset* or *Cells* to highlight the column of items that contain the item given in part (a) time, in the price list;

iii. uses a match function to find the row of the selected item;

iv. finds the corresponding price for the item; and

v. returns this value that will be stored in a variable in the main procedure.

c. In the procedure, now call another function that:

i. is given the original selected value from part (a) and the price found in part (b) and

ii. copies these to the end of the cost sheet.

11. Create a procedure to convert the temperature from degrees Celsius to degrees Fahrenheit or vise versa. This procedure asks the user to choose whether s/he wants to convert the temperature from degrees Celsius to degrees Fahrenheit or vise versa; calls function procedures that take as input the temperature entered by the user and return the result of the conversion rounding it up 2 decimal points; creates a message box to present the user with the results of the conversion.

12. The given table is part of a library database. Create the following sub procedures that will help to search the database. (Refer to worksheet "15.12".)

a. Search by *BookNr*: the user is prompted to enter the identification number of a book. The information about the selected book is presented using message box.

b. Search by title: the user is prompted to enter the title of a book. The information about the selected book is presented using message box.

c. Search by author: the user is prompted to enter the author name. The title of the books written by the selected author are presented using message box.

d. Search by category: the user is prompted to enter the name of a category. The information about the books in the selected category is presented using message box.

Finally, create a main sub procedure that prompts the user about the type of search to be performed (by title, author name, etc) and depending on the user's choice calls one of the sub procedure created. Assign the main sub procedure to a button titled "Search the Database."

13. Create the following sub procedures to format any table of data.

a. *Format 1*: The font size is 12pt, the font color is red, the font style is italic and the font name is Times New Roman.

b. *Format 2*: The font size is 10pt, the font color is blue, the font style is bold and the font name is Arial.

c. *Format 3*: The font size is 11pt, the font color is green, the font style is italic and bold, and the font name is Tahoma.

Create a main sub procedure that prompts the user to enter the range of data and chooses one of the sub procedures to format the data on the given range.

14. Create the following sub procedures:

a. *Triangle*: Creates a triangle.

b. *Circle*: Creates a circle.

c. *Rectangle*: Creates a rectangle.

d. *Square*: Created a square.

Create a main sub procedure that prompts the user to enter the choice of the shape and calls one of the sub procedures above to create the shape selected by the user.

15. The following sub procedures graph a given set of data. (Refer to worksheet "15.15".)

a. *Line*: Creates a line chart.

b. *XYScatter*: Creates a XY scatter chart.

c. *Pie*: Creates a pie chart.

d. *Column*: Creates a column chart.

Create a main sub procedure that prompts the user to enter the range of data and choose a chart type. The main sub procedure should then call one of the procedures described above to chart the data according to the user's choice.

CHAPTER sixteen Programming Structures

chapter OVERVIEW

16.1 Introduction

This chapter shows the reader how to use several different programming structures in VBA. Programming structures in VBA include *If, Then* statements, several different loop structures, *Select, Case* statements, and exit statements. These structures allow you to place conditions on actions performed in your program, various calculations to perform, and different ways to communicate with the user. We use these structures extensively when building any advanced decision support system.

In this chapter, the reader will learn how to:

- Use *If, Then* statements for conditional programming, logical checks, and error checking.
- Use the VBA *Select, Case* structure.
- Work with *For Loops* and *Do Loops*.
- Use various exit statements and the *End* statement.
- Create a banking account management application using the programming structures described in the chapter.

16.2 *If, Then* Statements

If, Then statements allow us to perform the same conditional actions as the IF function in Excel. A condition is evaluated to be true or false; if it is true, then the subsequent actions are taken. If a condition is evaluated to be false, another set of actions may be performed instead. The general format for the *If, Then* statement is:

```
If condition Then
    action
End If
```

Note that if we only have one action to perform if the condition is true, then we can write the *If, Then* statement in one line of code without the *End If* statement. For example, compare the two statements below:

Several actions:

```
If x > 100 Then
    Range("A1").Value = x
    Range("A2").Value = x – 100
End If
```

One action:

```
If x > 100 Then Range("A1").Value = x
```

The *If, Then* statement defines the action to perform if the condition is false by using the ***Else*** and ***ElseIf*** statements. The *Else* statement allows we to specify the action to be performed if the condition is not met. (If this statement is not included in the *If, Then* statement, then the program will perform no action if the condition is not met.) The general format for using the *Else* statement is:

```
If condition Then
    action1
Else
    action2
End If
```

We can use multiple *If, Then* statements within each other to construct ***nested*** *If* statements. Recall the example from Chapter 4 that used another IF function as the *false* argument of the original IF function. In other words, instead of performing a direct action if the original condition is not met, another *If* condition is considered. The *Else, If* statement is similar in that we can place another condition within our original *If, Then* statement. Note that when we use the *ElseIf* statement, we must type *Then* again. (This step is not necessary for the *Else* statement.) To elucidate this point, Let us look at a brief example:

```
If x < 1000 Then
    MsgBox "Your number is smaller than 1000."
ElseIf x < 2000 Then
    MsgBox "Your number is greater or equal to 1000 but less than 2000."
Else
    MsgBox "Your number is larger than or equal to 2000"
End If
```

Here we use both the *Else* and *ElseIf* statements to create a *nested If* statement. If the first condition is true, the first Message Box will be displayed; if it is false, another *If* condition is listed using the *ElseIf* statement. If this condition is true, the second Message Box will be displayed; if it is false, the *Else* statement runs and the third Message Box is displayed.

We also often use the *If, Then* statement for error checking. We will discuss some error checking functions in a later section in this chapter and in more detail in Appendix B. However, we can now provide some simpler examples of error checking that are most useful. Let us revisit the *MsgBox* and *InputBox* functions.

We have already stated that a response variable can be defined (as a variant data type) and assigned to the *MsgBox* function to capture which button the user has pressed. Then, we may want to perform a different set of actions depending on which button was pressed (the result of the *MsgBox* function). An example of using the result of the *MsgBox* function would be to determine whether or not the user wants to repeat an action that he or she has just completed.

Suppose we have a sub procedure in which we prompt the user to enter an input value. After recording the value, we may ask the user if he or she wants to enter another input value. If the answer is yes, we repeat the sub procedure by calling it recursively (from within itself). If the answer is no, then we simply end the sub. (Note that we specify that a *Yes* and *No* button should be on the Message Box by using the *vbYesNo* value for the button type argument.) The code for this example is:

```
Sub RecordInput()
    Dim inp As String, response As Integer

    inp = InputBox("Please enter the input value.")
    Range("Input Values").End(xlDown).Offset(1,0).Value = inp

    response = MsgBox("Do you want to enter another value?", vbYesNo)
```

```
    If response = vbYes Then
        Call RecordInput
    End If
End Sub
```

An Input Box also has two possible button choices: *OK* and *Cancel.* (These buttons cannot be changed.) There may be a procedure in which you do not want to continue with subsequent actions if a user has pressed the "Cancel" button on an Input Box. For example, in the above procedure, *RecordInput*, we may not want to enter the value to the spreadsheet or perform the other tasks if the user never supplies any input in the Input Box. To determine if a user has pressed *Cancel* on an *Input Box*, we use an *If, Then* statement to check the value of the variable assigned to the *InputBox* function. If this variable is empty, that is, equal to "", then the user has pressed the *Cancel* button. Consider the following modification of the above code:

```
Sub RecordInput()
    Dim inp As String, response As Integer

    inp = InputBox("Please enter the input value.")

    If inp <> "" Then
        Range("Input Values").End(xlDown).Offset(1,0).Value = inp
    Else
        MsgBox "No value was entered."
    End If
End Sub
```

(Note that we use the signs "<>" to mean "not equal to.") We can also use *If, Then* statements to check for the possible problems mentioned when using the *End* property. As we discussed in Chapter 13, the *End* property will not return any range selection if there are no adjacent cell values to the range from which we are searching. Suppose we are entering user input values into a column of data. We always want to enter the newest value at the bottom of the list; therefore, we use the *End(xlDown)* and *Offset(1,0)* properties to find the last value in the list and move one cell down to enter the new value. Consider the following code that prompts the user to enter input in a column that begins with a cell named "DataStart":

```
Dim UserValue As String
UserValue = InputBox("Enter a new value.")

Range("DataStart").End(xlDown).Offset(1,0).Value = UserValue
```

However, if the value that the user enters is the first in the list, the *End* property will not return a range to *Offset* from and so we cannot enter the value. We will therefore add an *If, Then* statement to check if the value is the first added. If it is, then we will enter it directly below the initial cell in the column, "DataStart." Otherwise, we can use the *End* and *Offset* properties as seen above.

```
Dim UserValue As String
UserValue = InputBox("Enter a new value.")

If Range("DataStart").Offset(1, 0).Value = "" Then
    Range("DataStart").Offset(1,0).Value = UserValue
```

```
Else
    Range("DataStart").End(xlDown).Offset(1,0).Value = UserValue
End If
```

We will return to this discussion in a later section in this chapter and in Appendix B.

16.2.1 Logical Checks and Booleans

We can also use *If, Then* statements with logical checks and *Boolean* variables. Logical checks include ***And*** and ***Or*** operators, similar to the *AND* and *OR* functions we learned in Excel (see Chapter 4).

The *And* logical statement requires every condition of the *If, Then* statement to be true in order for the proceeding action to be performed. If only one of the conditions is false, the action will not be performed and the following *Else* or *ElseIf* statement will be read, or the *If, Then* statement will end. This statement structure is as follows:

```
If condition1 And condition2 And condition3 And . . . Then
    action1
Else (or ElseIf)
    action2
End If
```

The *Or* logical statement requires only one condition in the *If, Then* statement to be true in order for the proceeding action to be performed. Every condition would have to be false to skip it and execute the *Else*, *ElseIf*, or *End If* statements. This statement structure is as follows:

```
If condition1 Or condition2 Or condition3 Or . . . Then
    action1
Else (or ElseIf)
    action2
End If
```

Compare these logical checks with the following two *If, Then* statements:

```
If x < 1000 And x > 500 Then
    MsgBox "Your number is between 500 and 1000."
Else
    MsgBox "Your number is smaller than or equal to 500 or greater than or equal to 1000."
End If
```

```
If x >= 1000 Or x <= 500 Then
    MsgBox "Your number is smaller than or equal to 500 or greater than or equal to 1000."
Else
    MsgBox "Your number is between 500 and 1000."
End If
```

(Note that we use the signs "<=" to mean "less than or equal to"; and the signs ">=" to mean "greater than or equal to.") In the first *If, Then* statement, the *And* check requires that both conditions are met. If this is true, then the value of *x* should be between 500 and 1000 (exclusive of 500 and 1000); therefore the program displays the first *Message Box*. However, if either condition is false, then the statement in the second *Message Box* must be true. In the second *If, Then* statement, we can see the difference in using the *Or* logical check. With *Or*, either of the conditions can be true to display the first *Message Box*. That is, either *x* can be less than 500 or greater than 1000. If neither condition is met, then the second *Message Box* must be true.

And and *Or* conditions can also be combined using parenthesis. For example, we could type the following code:

```
If (x < 1000 And x > 500) Or (y < 1000 And y > 500) Then
    MsgBox "One of your numbers is between 500 and 1000."
End If
```

If, Then statements are used with *Boolean* variables to check if their values are *True* or *False*. We can use the following two statements:

```
If variable = True Then
    action1
End If

------------------------
If variable = False Then
    action1
End If
```

(*Else* and *ElseIf* statements are also useable.) To check if a *Boolean* variable is *True*, we simply state the name of the variable; that is, the default value of any *Boolean* variable is *True*. Instead of the first statement above, we could just type:

```
If variable Then
    action1
End If
```

Consider this small example:

```
If found Then
    MsgBox "The solution has been found."
ElseIf found = False Then
    MsgBox "The solution has not been found."
End If
```

(Note that we do not need to use the *ElseIf* statement since the only other alternative to *found = True* is *found = False*.) We can now begin to see how *Boolean* variables will be useful in our programs. We will discuss more uses of *Boolean* variables in the next section.

Summary

Name	Related Terms	Structure

If, Then	**Else, ElseIf, End If nested**
	And, Or
	Boolean variables
		If condition1 Then
		action1
		ElseIf condition2 Then
		action2
		Else
		action3
		End If

16.3 Select, Case

The ***Select, Case*** statement lists possible situations in which certain actions should be performed. The general structure of the *Select, Case* statement gives a particular expression that is to be evaluated and a list of cases of possible values of that expression. For example:

```
Select Case number
    Case 1
        MsgBox "Your number is 1."
    Case 2
        MsgBox "Your number is 2."
End Select
```

The *End Select* statement must be used to close the *Select, Case* structure. The word *Case* always appears before each possible expression value. Note that the cases are mutually exclusive. Here, the possible values we consider are 1 and 2. We can also give a range of values as a case instance. Consider the following example which checks ranges of integer values.

```
Select Case number
    Case 1 To 5
        MsgBox "Your number is in the interval (1, 5)."
    Case 6 To 10
        MsgBox "Your number is in the interval (6, 10)."
    Case 11 To 15
        MsgBox "Your number is in the interval (11, 15)."
End Select
```

We can also use the optional ***Case Else*** statement to specify all other cases that are not listed. The ability to provide a range of values as a case instance using the ***To*** statement can be extended to string values:

```
Select Case name
    Case "Adams" To "Henderson"
        MsgBox "Please look in files A to H."
```

```
    Case "Ignatius" To "Nichols"
        MsgBox "Please look in files I to N."
    Case Else
        MsgBox "Please look in the rest of the files."
End Select
```

Here the range of text is considered alphabetically; string values for the *name* variable are checked on letter intervals. We may also include some conditions as cases, instead of simple instances. This approach is useful in replacing several *ElseIf* statements in an *If, Then* structure. We place a condition on a range of values using the ***Is*** statement. For example:

```
Select Case number
    Case Is < 10
        MsgBox "Your number is less than 10."
    Case Is > 10
        MsgBox "Your number is greater than 10."
    Case Else
        MsgBox "Your number is equal to 10."
End Select
```

This useful structure increases coding efficiency.

Summary

Name	Related Terms	Structure

Select, Case	**To, Is**	*Select Case expression*
		    Case instance
		        action1
		    Case condition
		        action2
		    Case range Is condition
		        action3
		    Case Else
		        action4
		End Select

16.4 Loops

Loops are programming structures that allow us to repeat a set of actions a certain number of times. We can specify the number of loops, or iterations, by counting up to (or down to) a certain value. Otherwise, a loop can run indefinitely while or until a certain condition is met.

16.4.1 For Loops

We can use the ***For, Next*** and ***For Each, Next*** loops to repeat a loop while counting up to or down to a certain number; we refer to both of them generally as ***For Loops***. To count, we can use a simple index variable such as *i* or a counting variable such as *count* or *iteration*; these variables are usually integer data types although they do not need to be. The more common of these two structures is the *For, Next* loop. Its structure is as follows:

```
For i = 1 to n
    actions
Next i
```

Use this structure to count up to a number n, starting at 1. *For, Next* loops can also be nested. Each *Next* statement completes the loops using the counting variable for that loop. Consider the example below (we will see another example of this in Chapter 17 when using arrays).

```
For i = 1 to n
    For j = 1 to m
        actions
    Next j
Next i
```

There is also a ***Step*** parameter with this loop. The *Step* value specifies how much the counter variable (in this case *i*) should increase during each loop. If *Step* is not specified, the default value is 1. Therefore, the above structure would increase *i* by 1, starting at 1 until, and including, n. If we wish to count down to a number, the *Step* value should be negative and the start value should be greater than the end value. For example:

```
For i = n to 1 Step -1
    actions
Next i
```

This loop will count down to 1 starting at n and decreasing *i* by 1 each time. Notice that the increase or decrease in the counter variable by the *Step* amount is part of the loop structure; therefore, the variable does not need to be incremented or decremented in the set of actions as in several other programming languages. Also note that it is not necessary to specify the counter variable name after the *Next* statement, although it is good practice to do so.

The *For Each, Next* loop works almost identically to the *For, Next* loop. The only difference is that *For Each, Next* counts a certain number of objects in a collection of objects; that is objects are counted rather than using a counter variable.

For example, if we want to count the number of worksheets in a current workbook, we declare a worksheet variable *ws* and use the following *For Each, Next* loop with a count variable.

```
For Each ws In ActiveWorkbook.Worksheets
    count = count + 1
Next
```

Note that we do not need to specify the object being counted after *Next*. Here we are not repeating this loop until the counter variable reaches a certain value, but rather until there are no more worksheets to be found in the workbook. When each object in the collection of objects has been examined, the loop ends.

16.4.2 Do Loops

There are two main ***Do Loops: Do, While*** and ***Do, Until***. These *Do Loops* perform a set of actions repeatedly while or until a condition is met. There are two main structures for these loops. Let us consider the *Do, While* loop first. In the structure below, a *While* condition is considered before a set of actions is performed.

```
Do While count < 10
    actions
    count = count + 1
Loop
```

Here, the *While* condition is checked first, a set of actions are performed, and then the count value is increased. In the structure below, the set of actions will be performed, and then the *While* condition will be checked before the actions are repeated.

```
Do
    actions
    count = count + 1
Loop While count < 10
```

In this example, the actions occur first; then the count value is increased, and then the *While* condition is checked. It is important to consider which format is best, depending on whether or not it is appropriate to perform the actions prior to checking the *While* condition. These two structures are also optional for the *Do, Until* loop.

The difference between looping *while* the condition is met and *until* the condition is met is important to note. For the *Do, While* loop, if the condition is true, it signals the loop to repeat the actions. However, for the *Do, Until* loop, if the condition is true, it signals the loop to stop repeating the actions. For example, compare the values generated by the following two loops.

```
Do While count <= 10
    x = 2*x
    count = count + 1
Loop
_______________________
Do Until count = 10
    x = 2*x
    count = count + 1
Loop
```

For the first loop, assuming the value of the *count* variable is initialized at 1, the condition will be met the first time (1 <= 10) and the next 9 times. The action ($x = 2*x$, again assuming x is initially 1) will therefore be repeated 10 times, yielding the final values of $x = 2^{10}$ and *count* = 11. The second loop, however, will stop repeating when *count* reaches 10 (but not including 10), thus yielding final values of $x = 2^9$ and *count* = 10.

These *Do Loops* can also be used with *Boolean* variables. That is, the *Boolean* variable can be used as the condition for the *Do, While* or *Do, Until* loops. These conditions usually imply some nested *If, Then* statements that change the value of the *Boolean* variable once a certain result is found. For example:

```
Do While found = False
    actions
    If x > 100 Then
        found = True
    End If
Loop
```

Here we are performing some actions while a certain result is still not found. Once the *found* variable is set to *True*, the *While* condition is no longer met and the loop ends. We could have also used the *Do, Until* loop by changing the condition to:

```
Do Until found = True
```

We will commonly use *Boolean* variables as conditions for *Do Loops* in our decision support systems. Note that both the *Do, While* and *Do, Until* loops can have nested loops. A *Do, While* loop can contain a *Do, Until* loop and vice versa. Also, as we have shown above, we may often include *If, Then* statements or other programming structures within loops.

(Note that there is also a ***While, Wend*** statement available in VBA; it has the same functionality as the *Do, While* loop. However, since the *Do, While* structure offers more flexibility, we will use it instead of the *While, Wend* statement.)

Summary

Name	Related Terms	Structure
For, Next	**Step**	*For counter = start to end Step step* *actions* *Next counter*
For Each, Next		*For Each object In object collection* *actions* *Next*
Do, While	*Boolean* variables, nested loops	*Do While condition* *actions* *Loop*
Do, Until	*Boolean* variables, nested loops	*Do Until condition* *actions* *Loop*

16.5 *Exit Statements and End*

As we develop and run longer programming structures, such as nested *If, Then* statements and *Do Loops*, we may want a way to exit the current set of actions at any time. We may also want to take advantage of this option while running any sub procedure or function procedure. VBA provides several ***Exit Statements*** that allow current actions to stop. We will usually use these statements with the *If, Then* structure.

16.5.1 Exiting Procedures

To exit a procedure, we use either ***Exit Sub*** or ***Exit Function***, depending on if we are currently running a sub procedure or function procedure, respectively. When *Exit Function* is stated, the function procedure stops executing and the program returns to the point in the code from which the function was called. Note, however, that even when the *Exit Function* statement is used, the last value that the function name was assigned to will still be returned. When we use the *Exit Sub* statement, the sub procedure stops executing, and, if the sub was called from another sub, the program returns to this sub and begins executing the next line of code.

For example, in the two procedures below, we use both the *Exit Function* and *Exit Sub* statements with *If, Then* statements. With a *Divide* function, we perform simple error checking.

```
  Sub Calculations()
     x = InputBox("Enter x value.")
     y = InputBox("Enter y value.")
     value = Divide(x, y)

   If value = "none" Then
       Exit Sub
   End If
   MsgBox "x divided by y is" & value
End Sub

-------------------------
Function Divide(a, b)
   If b = 0 Then
       Divide = "none"
       Exit Function
   End If
   Divide = a / b
End Function
```

If the denominator in the *Divide* function is 0, then we do not continue evaluating the function since we know it will lead to an error; so, we use the *Exit Function* statement. Once the *Exit Function* statement is read, the program returns to the line of code below where the function was called. This line is the *If, Then* statement of the sub procedure. Since we also do not want to display the faulty result of this function, we use *Exit Sub* to exit the sub procedure. Being able to exit a procedure if a specific condition or event occurs saves time and avoids errors when running a code.

16.5.2 Exiting Loops

To exit a loop, we use ***Exit For*** and ***Exit Do***, depending on if we are currently in a *For, Next* or *For Each, Next* loop or in a *Do, While* or *Do, Until* loop. Similar to the above exit statements, *Exit For* stops executing a *For, Next* or *For Each, Next* loop and moves to the line of code after the *Next* statement. The *Exit Do* code stops executing a *Do Loop* and moves to the line of code after the *Loop* statement.

Again, we will usually use an *If, Then* statement to check if a certain condition requires the use of one of these exit statements. An example of using *Exit For* may be as follows:

```
Sub Organize()
    Set StartCell = Range("A1")
    For i = 1 to 100
        StartCell.Offset(i, 0).Value = i * (i – 1)
        If i * (i – 1) > 50 Then
            MsgBox "The calculation values exceed the limit."
            Exit For
        End If
    Next i
End Sub
```

An example of using the *Exit Do* statement in a *Do, Until* loop may be as follows:

```
Do
    x = x^2
    If x mod 5 = 0 Then
        MsgBox "The number " & x & " is divisible by 5."
        Exit Do
    End If
    x = x + 1
Loop Until x >100
```

We may now be interested in finding the first squared number divisible by 5. We again set our *Until* condition to a large value and exit the loop when the first number that meets the *If, Then* condition is found. (Remember, the *Mod* function finds the remainder left after dividing *x* and 5. The general structure for this function is: *number1 Mod number2*. Refer to Chapter 14 for more details.)

These statements can also be used with nested loops. The exit statement applies to the inner most loop in which it is used. For example:

```
For i = 1 to 100
    For j = 1 to 50
        StartCell.Offset(i, j).Value = i + j
        If i + j > 60 Then
            Exit For
        End If
    Next j
Next i
```

Here, the *Exit For* statement ends the inner *For, Next* loop indexed by *j* and moves to the next *i* value in the outer *For, Next* loop.

16.5.3 Ending the Program

We can stop executing the entire program with the ***End*** statement. Just as the *End Sub, End Function, End If,* and *End With* statements end the execution of the enclosed lines of code, the *End* statement stops executing all code and exits all loops and procedures.

End can be a useful function if there is a significant condition or requirement that must be met before the program can function correctly. For example:

```
Sub Main()
    Call Username
    Call FindFile(username)
    If filename = "" Then
        MsgBox "No file was found for this user."
        End
    End If
    Call EditRecord
End Sub
```

In this code, the *Username* sub procedure is called to prompt the user for a *username*. Then, the *FindFile* function procedure is called to find the filename listed for the given *username* in a particular database. If the file is found, then the record for this user can be edited. However, if no file that matches the *username* given is found, then there is no need to continue running the program as this is a necessary requirement for all further actions.

Summary

Name	Action
Exit Sub	Exits the current sub procedure; the program returns to the line of code following that one where the sub procedure was called.
Exit Function	Exits the current function procedure; the program returns to the line of code following that one where the function procedure was called.
Exit For	Exits the current *For* loop (either *For, Next* or *For Each, Next*) and moves the program to the line of code after the loop.
Exit Do	Exits the current *Do* loop (either *Do, While*, or *Do, Until*) and moves the program to the line of code after the loop.
End	Exits the entire program; all procedures and loops are exited.

16.5.4 Basic Error Checking Functions

We discuss error checking and debugging in detail in Appendix B; however, we want to mention here a few error checking functions and tips that can be used with basic programming structures. The intention of these functions is that the program encounters any errors before the user does. It is preferable to have already identified an error and provided the user with a Message Box with clear instructions, rather than have the user be prompted with a VBA Error message and brought to the VBE Code Window.

If a user is prompted to provide some input (whether through an Input Box, as described in this chapter, or through a user form, as described in Chapter 18), this input is usually assigned to a variable. This variable must have been declared previously with a specific data type. Therefore, an error can occur if the data that the user provides as input does not match the data type already assigned to the variable.

One way to avoid this problem is to take advantage of the variant data type. We suggest using a temporary variant data type variable to assign to any input that is provided by the user. We can then employ the conversion functions described above to ensure that this variable has the data type needed for subsequent calculations. Below is an example of this technique:

```
Dim TempInput As Variant, x As Integer

TempInput = InputBox("Please enter a number.")

x = CInt(TempInput)
```

However, there is still a possible error here; if the user supplies a string expression without any numbers (for example, "two"), the *CInt* function will not work as expected. Therefore, we suggest another VBA function to check if a variable is a number or not: ***IsNumeric***. This function returns the value *True* or *False* depending on whether or not the variable or expression is a numeric data type. For example:

```
IsNumeric(1234) = True

IsNumeric("two") = False
```

We can therefore modify the previous code to strengthen the error checking, as follows:

```
Dim TempInput As Variant, x As Integer
TempInput = InputBox("Please enter a number.")

If IsNumeric(TempInput) = True Then
    x = CInt(TempInput)
End If
```

As mentioned before in the conversion functions, *CDate* can only be used on values that can be converted to dates. To determine whether or not a variable value or expression meets the date criteria, we can use a VBA function called ***IsDate***. The result of this function is again either *True* or *False*. Some examples of valid and invalid dates are:

```
IsDate("tomorrow") = False

IsDate("Jan 3") = True
IsDate("1/3/04") = True
```

We could use this function with an *If, Then* statement, as follows:

```
Dim UserDate As String, ActualDate As Date
UserDate = InputBox("Please enter a date")

If IsDate(UserDate) =True Then
    ActualDate = CDate(UserDate)
End If
```

We will discuss more error checking functions in Appendix B.

16.6 *Applications*

We will now develop one application that uses several of the programming structures discussed above.

16.6.1 Banking Account Management

The program that we will be working with stores deposits, withdrawals, and the current balance of a user's banking account. Users can record a new deposit or new withdrawal, or they can sum current deposits or withdrawals. Each time a new deposit or withdrawal is made, the balance is updated. We want to begin enforcing a minimum balance requirement of $100 for this account.

There are only two worksheets for this program: the "Account Welcome" sheet and the "Account" sheet (see Figures 16.1 and 16.2). Like any welcome sheet, the "Account Welcome" sheet has a program title and description. We have also added a ***Start*** button; this button will be associated with a ***Main*** sub procedure, as we recommended in Chapter 15.

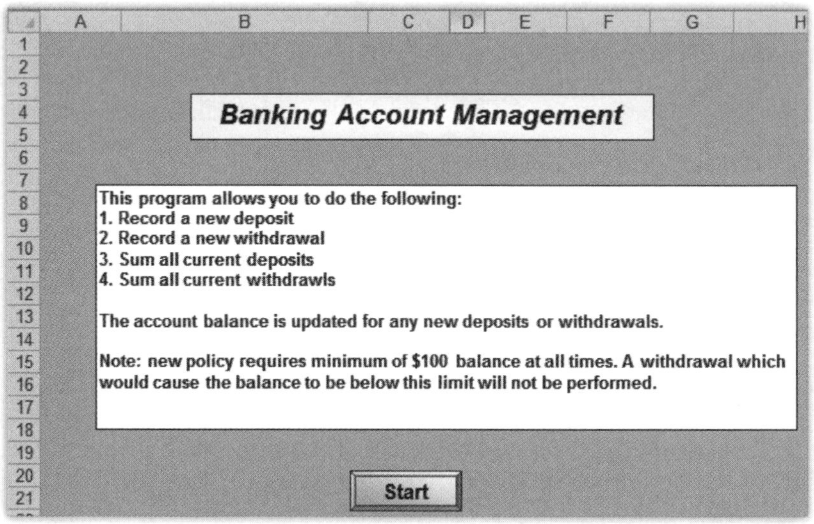

Figure 16.1 The "Account Welcome" sheet contains a program description and the *Start* button.

The "Account" sheet is where the program actions occur. The record of account transactions is displayed with the date and description of each transaction. Withdrawals are shown as negative values in the "Amount" column and deposits are positive entries. The balance is maintained in the "Balance" column. Each button is associated with the action stated in the button caption. The ***Sum*** buttons calculate their respective sums and place them in the cells below each button. The ***Exit*** button, as in all of our applications, brings the user back to the welcome sheet.

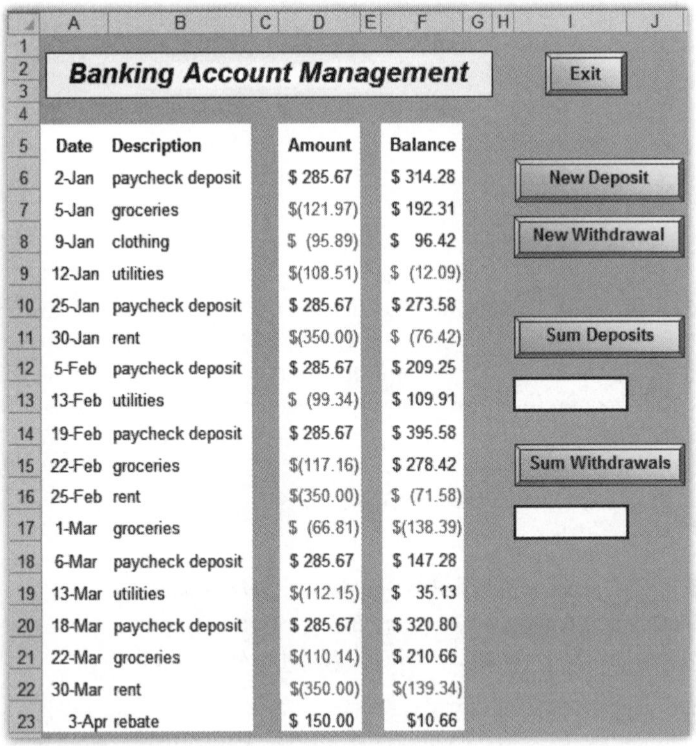

Date	Description	Amount	Balance
2-Jan	paycheck deposit	$ 285.67	$ 314.28
5-Jan	groceries	$(121.97)	$ 192.31
9-Jan	clothing	$ (95.89)	$ 96.42
12-Jan	utilities	$(108.51)	$ (12.09)
25-Jan	paycheck deposit	$ 285.67	$ 273.58
30-Jan	rent	$(350.00)	$ (76.42)
5-Feb	paycheck deposit	$ 285.67	$ 209.25
13-Feb	utilities	$ (99.34)	$ 109.91
19-Feb	paycheck deposit	$ 285.67	$ 395.58
22-Feb	groceries	$(117.16)	$ 278.42
25-Feb	rent	$(350.00)	$ (71.58)
1-Mar	groceries	$ (66.81)	$(138.39)
6-Mar	paycheck deposit	$ 285.67	$ 147.28
13-Mar	utilities	$(112.15)	$ 35.13
18-Mar	paycheck deposit	$ 285.67	$ 320.80
22-Mar	groceries	$(110.14)	$ 210.66
30-Mar	rent	$(350.00)	$(139.34)
3-Apr	rebate	$ 150.00	$10.66

Figure 16.2 The "Account" sheet contains the account record and all program button options.

Let us consider which procedures we need. Clearly, we require a ***NewDeposit*** and ***NewWithdrawal*** procedure associated with the first button options. In each of these procedures, we add a new user-supplied value to the "Amount" column. We also need to update the balance in both procedures. We can therefore create a function procedure, called ***UpdateBalance***, to perform the balance update that can be called from either sub procedure. Finally, we need two summing procedures that we call ***SumDeposits*** and ***SumWithdrawals***.

However, the first, and most important organizational sub procedure is the *Main* sub procedure. This *macro* is assigned to the *Start* button on the welcome sheet. So, let us clear previous sum values from their respective ranges, set any range variables, initialize any other variables if needed, hide the welcome sheet, and bring the user to the "Account" sheet. We will also need to assign a short ***ExitAccount*** procedure to the *Exit* button.

Before we begin typing these procedures, let us create all of the variables we currently know we need. We need a ***deposit*** and ***withdrawal*** variable to insert the new values and update the balance. In order to perform *error checking*, we use a ***value*** variable (declared as a *variant* data type) to receive user input before assigning values to the deposit and withdrawal variables. Additionally, we include ***sumDep*** and ***sumWith*** variables to calculate the respective sums. And we introduce two range variables to identify the "Amount" and "Balance" columns: ***AccountStart*** and ***BalanceStart***. Later, we will use an integer counter ***i*** for our loops and a ***response*** variable (declared as a *variant* data type) in a *MsgBox* function.

Let us again create the *Workbook_Open* event procedure; however, this time we will improve our code by using a worksheet variable, ***ws***, and a *For Each, Next* loop:

```
Private Sub Workbook_Open()
    For Each ws In ActiveWorkbook.Worksheets
        If ws.Name = Account Welcome" Then
            ws.Visible = True
        Else
            ws.Visible = False
        End If
    Next
End Sub
```

In this loop, we examine each worksheet object in the Active Workbook and check its name property. Only if the name is equal to "Account Welcome" do we set the *Visible* property to *True*; otherwise the *Visible* property of all the other worksheets will be set to *False*. (In this case, we only have two worksheets, but for future programs, this new structure will greatly decrease the code's size for this procedure.) Note that we have left the *Private* declaration for this procedure now that we understand its implications.

We define all previously discussed variables, including the worksheet variable, as public variables:

```
Public deposit As Double, withdrawal As Double, sumDep As Double, _
sumWith As Double, AccountStart As Range, BalanceStart As Range, _
ws As Worksheet, Value As Variant, i As Integer, response As Variant
```

Let us begin by creating the *Main* sub procedure. In preparation for coding, we name the two ranges in which the sum values are calculated: "DepositSum" and "WithdrawalSum" respectively. This step makes it easier to clear the values of these cells and place the new values when needed. The code for the *Main* sub procedure is:

```
Sub Main()
    Range("DepositSum").ClearContents
    Range("WithdrawalSum").ClearContents

    Set AccountStart = Worksheets("Account").Range("D5")
    Set BalanceStart = Worksheets("Account").Range("F5")

    sumDep = 0
    sumWith = 0

    Worksheets("Account").Visible = True
    Worksheets("Account Welcome").Visible = False
    Worksheets("Account").Activate
End Sub
```

The first two lines of code clear the sum ranges. The next two lines set the values for the range variables of the table. (See *StartCell* functionality of range variables in Chapter 14.) The next two lines of code initialize the sum variable values as they will be incrementally modified later using a loop. The last lines of code for this procedure are simply navigational; they hide the welcome sheet and display the "Account" sheet. We can now simply state the navigational procedure for the *Exit* button:

```
Sub ExitAccount()
    Worksheets("Account Welcome").Visible = True
    Worksheets("Account").Visible = False
End Sub
```

Now, let us create the sub procedures for the *Sum* buttons. For each button, we step through every entry of the "Amount" column until we reach the end of the column using a *Do, Until* loop. For each entry, we check if the value is a withdrawal or deposit and update our respective sum variables using *If, Then* statements. We opt for the counter variable *i* for the loop; note that with the *Do Loops*, we must increment the counter in the loop (unlike in the *For Loops*). The procedures are:

```
Sub SumDeposits()
    i = 1
    Do Until AccountStart.Offset(i, 0).Value = ""
        If AccountStart.Offset(i, 0).Value > 0 Then
            sumDep = sumDep + AccountStart.Offset(i, 0).Value
        End If
        i = i + 1
    Loop

    Range("DepositSum").Value = sumDep
End Sub
-------------------------
Sub SumWithdrawals()
    i = 1
    Do Until AccountStart.Offset(i, 0).Value = ""
        If AccountStart.Offset(i, 0).Value < 0 Then
            sumWith = sumWith + AccountStart.Offset(i, 0).Value
        End If
        i = i + 1
    Loop

    Range("WithdrawalSum").Value = sumWith
End Sub
```

To search through each entry in the "Amount" column, we use the *AccountStart* range variable and the *Offset* property: *AccountStart.Offset* (*i*, 0). The loop continues until no entry is found: *Do Until AccountStart.Offset* (*i*, 0). *Value* = "". Then, for deposits, we only want to sum positive values; for withdrawals, we only want to sum negative values. So, we use an *If, Then* statement to check if the current entry is greater or less than 0. If the condition is satisfied, we update the sum variable by incrementing it by the current entry value. When the loop ends, we place the final sum value in the appropriately named range.

Now, let us work with the *NewDeposit* sub procedure. The first line of code asks the user for the amount of the new deposit. Temporarily, we set the *value* variable equal to our *InputBox* function so we can perform *error checking* on the input. We use the *InputBox* function with a default value of 150 as shown below.

```
Sub NewDeposit()
    value = InputBox("Please enter amount to deposit.", "New Deposit", 150)
```

To perform the *error checking*, we use the ***IsNumeric*** function with the *value* variable to determine if the user enters a numerical data type. If so, then we can continue running the sub procedure. If not, then we cannot continue with the procedure actions. We therefore inform the user of an error using a simple *Message Box* and then use *Exit Sub*. We perform the *error checking* with an *If, Then* statement:

```
If IsNumeric(value) = False Then
    MsgBox "You have not entered a numerical value. Please try again."
    Exit Sub
End If
```

If the user provides a numeric value, then we assign this value to the *deposit* variable. (Observe that it was necessary to use the *value* variable, which is a *variant* data type, to avoid an immediate error. In other words, if we assign the *deposit* variable, a *double* data type, to the *InputBox* function, and the user does not enter a numeric value, or even a *double* data type, then an immediate VBA error will appear. We want to prevent the user from seeing any errors by VBA. We could also use a *string* variable type with the *InputBox* function.)

We now insert this value into the "Amount" column, using the *AccountStart* range variable and the *End* property. We also format the table's new row by changing the background color of the appropriate cells:

```
With AccountStart.End(xlDown).Offset(1, 0)
    .value = deposit
    .Interior.ColorIndex = 0
End With

Range(AccountStart.End(xlDown).Offset(0, –3), _
    AccountStart.End(xlDown).Offset(0, –2)).Interior.ColorIndex = 0
BalanceStart.End(xlDown).Offset(1, 0).Interior.ColorIndex = 0
```

The only action left to perform is to update the balance by calling the *UpdateBalance* function. (We discuss this in more detail below.) After those actions are complete, we can simply tell the user to enter a date and description for the new entry with a Message Box:

```
Call UpdateBalance(deposit, "D")
MsgBox "You may now enter the date and description of your deposit into the table."
```

With the *MsgBox* function and *response* variable, we can add an additional option to continue adding more new deposits. We prompt the user if he or she wants to enter another deposit and set the Message Box buttons to ***vbYesNo***. The *MsgBox* function is assigned to the *response* variable, so we can now check the value of the *response* variable and perform the related actions. We use another *If, Then* statement to check if the response is "Yes" (which is equal to the *VB Constant* **vbYes**), and, if it is, call the *NewDeposit* sub procedure again. Otherwise, we simply end the sub:

```
response = MsgBox("Would you like to enter another deposit?", vbYesNo, _
        "Another Deposit?")
If response = vbYes Then
        Call NewDeposit
End If
End Sub
```

The *NewWithdrawal* procedure is quite similar. We do not provide the option of creating a new withdrawal here, but we can add it later. The only main changes are that we use the *withdrawal* variable instead of *deposit* and enter the value in the table as a negative number:

```
Sub NewWithdrawal()
    value = InputBox("Please enter amount to withdraw.", "New withdrawal", 150)

    'error checking
    If IsNumeric(value) = False Then
        MsgBox "You have not entered a numerical value. Please try again."
        Exit Sub
    End If

    withdrawal = value

    'insert into table and format new row
    With AccountStart.End(xlDown).Offset(1, 0)
        .value = -withdrawal
        .Interior.ColorIndex = 0
    End With
    Range(AccountStart.End(xlDown).Offset(0, -3), _
            AccountStart.End(xlDown).Offset(0, -2)).Interior.ColorIndex = 0
    BalanceStart.End(xlDown).Offset(1, 0).Interior.ColorIndex = 0

    'update balance
    Call UpdateBalance(withdrawal, "W")
End Sub
```

Let us now discuss the *UpdateBalance* procedure, which has two parameters: the deposit/withdrawal value and a simple letter signifying deposit with "D" and withdrawal with "W." Notice that these variables are passed when the procedure is called from the above two procedures; the procedure declaration refers to these two parameters simply as *x* and *y*. We can then use a *Select, Case* statement to check the value of the *y* parameter. In the case that it is "D," we add the deposit value to the last entry of the "Balance" column. In the case that it is "W," we subtract the withdrawal value from the last entry of the "Balance" column. We must also perform one more check when a withdrawal is made; we must ensure that the $100 balance requirement is still met. We use an *If, Then* statement to check the result of this calculation. If the withdrawal results in a balance less than $100, we do not perform the transaction. The user is then informed that his or her balance is too low, the initial entry to the "Amount" column is cleared, and the procedure is exited using the *Exit Function* statement. However, if the requirement is still met, then we update the balance and tell the user that he or she can enter the date and description for the withdrawal. The final procedure is as follows:

```
Sub UpdateBalance(x, y)
    Select Case y
      Case "D"
          BalanceStart.End(xlDown).Offset(1,0).value = _
              BalanceStart.End(xlDown).value + x
      Case "W"
          If BalanceStart.End(xlDown).value - x < 100 Then
              MsgBox "This withdrawal cannot be made due to the $100 " & _
                  & "balance requirement."
              AccountStart.End(xlDown).ClearContents
              Exit Function
          End If
          BalanceStart.End(xlDown).Offset(1,0).value = _
              BalanceStart.End(xlDown).value - x
          MsgBox "You may now enter the date and description of your " & _
              & "withdrawal into the table."
    End Select
End Sub
```

The procedures are now complete. We assign them to their respective buttons and test the procedures. (Remember, the procedures, or macros, are assigned to buttons by right-clicking on the button, or drawing object, and choosing *Assign Macro* from the drop down menu.) The application is finished.

16.7 Summary

- *If, Then* statements allow we to perform conditional actions. If a condition is met, a certain set of actions is performed; if it is not, another set of actions may be performed instead. The *If, Then* statement defines the action to be performed if the condition is false with the *Else* and *ElseIf* statements. The *ElseIf* statement allows we to construct *nested If* statements.
- *If, Then* statements are also used with logical checks and *Boolean* variables. Logical checks include *And* and *Or* statements. The *And* logical statement requires every condition in the *If, Then* statement to be true in order for the proceeding action to be performed. If only one of the conditions is false, the action will not be performed and the following *Else* or *ElseIf* statement will be read, or the *If, Then* statement will end. The *Or* logical statement requires only one condition in the *If, Then* statement to be true in order for the proceeding action to be performed. Every condition would have to be false to skip it and read the *Else*, *ElseIf*, or *End If* statements.
- Loops are programming structures that allow us to repeat a set of actions a certain number of times. We can use the *For, Next* and *For Each, Next* loops to repeat a loop while counting up to or down to a certain number. The *Step* parameter used with this loop specifies how much the counter variable, in this case *i*, should increase during each loop.

- The *For Each, Next* loop works almost identically to the *For, Next* loop. The only difference is that *For Each, Next* counts a certain number of objects in a collection of objects; that is objects are counted rather than using a counter variable.
- There are two main *Do Loops: Do, While* and *Do, Until*. They perform a set of actions repeatedly while or until a condition is met. For the *Do, While* loop, if the condition is true, the loop repeats the actions. However, for the *Do, Until* loop, if the condition is true, the loop stops repeating the actions.
- *Do Loops* can also be used with *Boolean* variables. The *Boolean* variable can be used as the condition for the *Do, While* or *Do, Until* loops. These conditions usually imply some nested *If, Then* statements that change the value of the *Boolean* variable once a certain result is found.
- Use the *Select, Case* statement to list possible situations in which certain actions should be performed. The general structure of the *Select, Case* statement presents a particular expression that is to be evaluated as well as a list of cases of that expression's possible values. There is also an optional *Case Else* statement that specifies all other unlisted cases.
- The ability to give a range of values as a case instance using the *To* statement can be extended to string values. We can place a condition on a range of values using the *Is* statement.
- VBA provides several *Exit Statements* that allow current actions to stop and moves the program to ensuing code. We usually use these statements with the *If, Then* structure.
- To exit a procedure, use either *Exit Sub* or *Exit Function*, depending on if we are running a sub procedure or function procedure, respectively. The program then returns to the line of code following that where the sub procedure was called.
- To exit a loop, use *Exit For* and *Exit Do*, depending on if we are in a *For, Next* or *For Each, Next* loop or in a *Do, While* or *Do, Until* loop. These statements then move the program to the line of code after the loop.
- To stop executing an entire program, use the *End* statement. Just as the *End Sub, End Function, End If,* and *End With* statements end the execution of the enclosed lines of code, the *End* statement stops executing all code and exits all loops and procedures.

16.8 Exercises

16.8.1 Review Questions

1. What is the difference between *Do . . . Loop While* and *Do While . . . Loop*?
2. Give an example of the possible difference in outcome using a *Do, While* loop as opposed to a *Do, Until* loop.
3. What function should you use with an *If, Then* statement to check if a variable value is a number?
4. How do you check if a user has clicked the *Cancel* button on an *Input Box*?
5. How would you check if multiple conditions are all met?
6. When do you use the *Is* statement in a *Select, Case* structure?
7. Can you use an *Exit Sub* statement in a *For, Next* loop, or do you have to use an *Exit For* statement first?
8. Write a short program that asks the user to enter a letter. Using *Select, Case*, determine which position the given letter has in your first name. If the letter is not in your name, tell the user.
9. Write a program that counts down from a given user value to 1 using a Message Box. For example, if the user specifies to start the countdown at 10, then the first box should appear as follows:

Clicking *OK* should continue the countdown to 1.

10. What will the output of this program be, given the following table (where the word "Product" is in cell "A9")?

```
Sub counter()
Dim i As Integer, n As Integer, p1 As Integer
Dim p2 As Integer, p3 As Integer

    p1 = 0
    p2 = 0
    p3 = 0

    For i = 1 To 10
        n = Range("A1").Offset(i, 0).Value
        Select Case n
            Case 1
                p1 = p1 + 1
            Case 2
                p2 = p2 + 1
            Case 3
                p3 = p3 + 1
        End Select
    Next i

    MsgBox "Product 1 occured " & p1 & " times, " & vbCrLf & _
    "Product 2 occured " & p2 & " times, " & vbCrLf & _
    "Product 3 occured " & p1 & " times."
End Sub
```

16.8.2 Hands-On Exercises

NOTE: Please refer to the file "Chapter_16_Exercises .xlsx" for the associated worksheets noted for the hands-on exercises. The file is available at: *www .dssbooks.com*.

1. Write a sub that asks a user to input a string with exactly three letters followed by three integers or vise versa three integers followed by three letters. Prompt the user to input a string until the entered string contains exactly three letters followed by three integers or vise versa.
2. A number is prime if and only if the number is divisible by no other number than itself and one. Write a function called *DetermineIfPrime* that determines whether a number is prime. Write a sub called *Main* that determines whether or not the number in each cell in a selected range is prime. Apply a *For Each* loop and use the function for each cell. If a number is prime, change the background color of the cell and bold the cell. Try to optimize the running time of your program by limiting the number of iterations in a loop that are required to determine if a number is prime.
3. The Least Common Multiple (LCM) of two positive integers *a* and *b* is the smallest positive integer that is divisible by both *a* and *b*. The Greatest Common Divisor (GCD) of two positive integers *a* and *b* is the largest integer *c* that divides both *a* and *b*. It may help to know that for two positive integers a and b: ab = LCM(a,b) * GCD(a,b).
    a. Write a function called *CalculateLCM* that calculates the LCM of two positive integers.
    b. Write a function called CalculateGCD that calculates the GCD of two positive integers.
    c. Write a sub called *Main* that obtains two positive integers from the user using *Input Boxes*. As appropriate, display the LCD and GCD of the two numbers to the user in a message.
4. Write a logic loop that assigns grade letters to the students in the given table based on the grade scale of 90–100 = A, 80–89 = B, 70–79 = C, 60–69 = D, 0–59 = F. (*Note:* assume each Exam is weighted the same.) (Refer to worksheet "16.4".)
   Using the same grade sheet as the above example, create a logic loop that increases the grade of the first exam by 5 points and then assigns a final grade based on 40% of Exam1 grade and 60% of Exam2 grade.
5. Write a program that evaluates given sales information. The program should also print a sales report that displays a total of all units sold of each product as well as a Message Box that reports the final sales figure for the given data. The following information is given: a pricing matrix gives the unit price of each product, and a discount matrix provides the percent discount given to customers based on their order quantity. Determine the total value of sales. (Refer to worksheet "16.5".)
6. Write a program that plays the game "Paper-Rock-Scissors" with the user. The rules for

the game are that the user will be prompted to choose paper, rock or scissors. The computer will then randomly generate a value. Values less than .3 = paper, between .3 and .6 = rock, and above .6 = scissors. If the user's choice matches the computer's choice, the user is a winner.

7. Write a program that converts military time into the 12-hour time equivalent. For example, if the user enters 2045 into the InputBox when prompted for the time, the MessageBox should appear informing the user that the time is 8:45 PM.

8. Perform the following extensions to the Banking Account Management application. (Refer to worksheet "16.8".)
   - **a.** Receive as input from the user the date and description of the transaction and insert this into the table appropriately [*Hint:* define another range variable].
   - **b.** Perform one of these additional calculations:
     - **i.** Sum the total deposits and withdrawals for a given month. Prompt the user for the month.
     - **ii.** Sum the deposits or withdrawals of a particular transaction type. Prompt the user for a transaction description.

9. Perform the following error checking tasks:
   - **a.** Prompt the user for the total number of input values they want to enter in the spreadsheet and check the validity of the entry.
   - **b.** Given the total number of entries provided in part (a), prompt the user to enter the values. The values should be entered as dates. For each value entered check its validity and convert it to the VBA date format. Only the values in VBA format are entered in the spreadsheet. Note that, the total number of correct entries should be equal to the number of entries specified in part (a).
   - **c.** This process should be repeated and all values entered are in one column. That is, if the user wants to make a new entry, the new values entered will be attached to the existing values in the spreadsheet. (*Hint:* use the End property and the necessary error checking.)

10. A dating program has a list of users stored and corresponding personal information. Each user has a username and a password. Create a button that enables the users to sign-in. The new users should be prompted to enter the following information in the database: username, password, age, etc. Returning users should enter their username and password to access the data. If the username and the password entered are not found in the database, the user should be prompted to try again. The existing users should be able to edit their information. For this purpose use InputBox. Set the default value of the InputBox to the current user's information. (Refer to worksheet "16.10".)

11. Create a procedure that generates a random month and day using a *Select, Case* statement. The user should be prompted on how many dates he or she wants to generate. Repeat the procedure this many times. Then check if any of the dates are equal.

12. Create a diagram of a bill of materials (BOM).
   - **a.** Ask the user for the name of the end product. Create a shape and label it with this name.
   - **b.** Ask the user how many primary components this end product has. Create this many shapes under the end product shape. Repeatedly ask him or her for the name of each component. (Title your Input Box accordingly.) Label each shape with the corresponding name given.
   - **c.** For each primary component, ask the user if there are any secondary components, and if so, how many. Repeat part (b) for the secondary components.

13. Create a fast food ordering system using the provided data. (Refer to worksheet "16.13".)
   - **a.** Prompt the user if he or she would like to order a value meal, sandwich, salad, and/or drink.
   - **b.** Depending on the answer, provide the user with a list of options. (*Hint:* Use a Select, Case statement. Prepare a list of items for each category on the spreadsheet. Depending on the answer, gather the values in the appropriate list and display them in one Message Box.)
   - **c.** Once the user has selected an item, reveal the current price and ask if he or she would like to order another item. (Find the price from your spreadsheet list using a lookup function.)
   - **d.** If the user answers "yes," begin the entire program again by prompting from which category he or she would like to place an order.

e. If the user answers no, calculate the total price and display it.

14. **Card guessing game:** Given an Ace, and two Kings, randomly shuffle them so that the user can guess which card is the Ace.
    a. Name three ranges on the spreadsheet for the three different positions.
    b. Create three shapes (or use three images) for the Ace, King1, and King2.
    c. Show the user all three card values, then fill the shapes a black color to hide their values.
    d. Prompt the user how many times he or she wants to shuffle the cards. Then call a shuffling procedure this many times. The shuffling procedure should randomly assign a position (from the three available positions) to each card. Ensure that no two cards are assigned to the same position.
    e. When the shuffling ends, ask the user which card he or she thinks is the Ace (first, second, or third).
    f. Reveal the card values (change fill black to white or none) and tell the use if he or she won or lost.

15. Create a quality control program in which you are checking to see which, if any, items from a production line should be rejected.
    a. Prompt the user for the number of items produced.
    b. Ask the user which distribution the production follows: Normal or Exponential.
    c. Based on the answer, ask the user for the corresponding parameter values and generate the given number of item values (for example, diameter sizes of x widgets).
    d. Find the mean and standard deviation of these values. Graph the data with a mean line and +/– standard deviation lines.
    e. Then review all of the data points and highlight the items that are above or below the standard deviation. Count these items and display this value to the user.

16. Create a sub procedure that determines if a number is even or odd. The procedure prompts the user to enter the number. Use the *If, Then* statement to ensure that a numerical value is entered. If the value entered is not numerical, prompt the user if s/he wants to enter a new value.

17. Create a sub procedure that sorts a list of numbers. Prompt the user to enter the range of numbers to sort. Use the Do While loop and If statement in your visual basic code. Do not use the sorting function of Excel.

18. Create a sub procedure that prompts the user to enter a year and determines if this is a leap year.

19. Create a sub procedure that asks the user to enter her/his birthday and returns user's age.

20. A given table presents information about flight reservations of an airline company. Use Do While Loop and If statements to perform the following tasks. (Refer to worksheet "16.20".)
    a. Create a sub procedure that adds a new reservation in the table below. The TktNo should be automatically assigned to each reservation, while the rest of the information required (CustomerId, FlightNo, etc) should be entered by the user. Check user's input for the following errors: the length of CustomerId should be exactly 4; FlightNr is an integer; Class should either be Economy, Business or Class; TravelDate should be greater than or equal to BookingDate; PaymentMode should either be Check, Cash or Credit Card.
    b. Create a sub procedure that calculates the average amount of payments made by check, cash and credit card.
    c. Create a sub procedure that prompts for a travel date and returns the identification number of the customers traveling that date.

CHAPTER

seventeen Arrays

chapter OVERVIEW

17.1 Introduction

This chapter explains how to use ***arrays*** in VBA. Arrays are useful programming structures which store several data using a single variable name. We can use arrays to manipulate several values using one entity. This chapter shows how to define, resize, and sort arrays in VBA. We use these structures in various DSS applications for storing data values. One example of using arrays is for storing arrival and service times of customers in the Queuing Simulation application. We store these values in arrays and then loop through the values to execute the simulation. As arrays are very useful structures, they will be commonly used in developing DSS applications.

In this chapter, the reader will learn how to:

- Use arrays and how they are beneficial.
- Define one-dimensional and multi-dimensional arrays.
- Modify the indexing standard for arrays in VBA.
- Work with dynamic arrays.
- Sort arrays.
- Work through an application that uses several arrays.

17.2 When and Why to Use Arrays

Arrays store series of data using one variable name for reference. The values in an array must all be of the same data type. We can refer to the array as a whole, or we can refer to its individual elements by an index value.

Arrays can be very efficient tools for programming systems with multiple series of data. However, we should also compare the benefit of using arrays with the option of printing values to a spreadsheet for storage in a table. As we have seen earlier, in some cases there is no need to store data in an array variable. However, arrays offer an alternative that may be quite useful in many situations and are often more efficient to use.

17.3 Defining Arrays

To define an array, we can use the *Dim*, *Private*, or *Public* variable declarations. There is not an array data type, but a data type is assigned to all of the elements in an array. By our declaring an array variable name with a set of parentheses, VBA recognizes that a variable is an array and not a scalar variable. Instead of *data* as the variable name, we write *data()* with parentheses. If we know the size of the array, we can put this value in the parentheses in the array variable declaration. Here is a quick example of defining an array variable named *data* with 10 elements, all of *double* data type:

```
Dim data(10) As Double
```

To insert values into an array, we can use the *Array* function. The array function allows us to list values for each array element. For example, to insert 10 values into the *data* array, we type the following:

```
Dim data() As Variant

data = Array(12.3, 13.4, 16.5, 13.8, 7, 2.9, 24.2, 5.5, 8, 9.1)
```

(Note that the *Array* function returns a *variant* containing an array; therefore the data array should be declared as a variant.) To set the value of a specific element of the array, we use an index. The default initial index value is 0; however, to keep in line with our example, let us assume the initial index is 1. (We discuss indices in a later section.) For example, if we want to change the third value in the above data array from 16.5 to 10.5, we type the following:

```
data(3) = 10.5
```

To enter multiple element values using indices, we usually use a *For, Next* loop with a counter variable. For example, if we want to set each element in the *data* array as its index number, we type the following:

```
For i = 1 to 10
    data(i) = i
Next i
```

17.3.1 Multi-Dimensional Arrays

As illustrated in the above example, a single number is all that is necessary to specify the size of a one-dimensional array. To define ***multi-dimensional arrays***, we need to specify the size of each dimension, separated by a comma. For example, if we want to define a two-dimensional array of size 5 by 10 (number of rows by number of columns), we type the following:

```
Dim data(5, 10) As Double
```

A multi-dimensional array can be defined for up to 60 dimensions in VBA. To insert values into a multi-dimensional array or to search for a value, we will use nested *For, Next* loops with different counter variables. For example, to set the value of each element in the above two-dimensional array equal to the product of its index numbers, we type the following:

```
For i = 1 to 5
    For j = 1 to 10
        data(i, j) = i*j
    Next j
Next i
```

This code would create the following values for the *data* array:

1	2	3	4	5	6	7	8	9	10
2	4	6	8	10	12	14	16	18	20
3	6	9	12	15	18	21	24	27	30
4	8	12	16	20	24	28	32	36	40
5	10	15	20	25	30	35	40	45	50

This is another example where the value of each element of the two-dimensional array shows the order in which it is generated. For example, the value 25, which corresponds to the 3rd row and 5th column of this array, is the 25th value generated.

```
For i = 1 to 5
    For j = 1 to 10
        data(i, j) =( i-1)*10 + j
    Next j
Next i
```

This code would create the following values for the *data* array:

1	2	3	4	5	6	7	8	9	10
11	12	13	14	15	16	17	18	19	20
21	22	23	24	25	26	27	28	29	30
31	32	33	34	35	36	37	38	39	40
41	42	43	44	45	46	47	48	49	50

17.3.2 Indexing

As previously mentioned, the default initial index value of arrays in VBA is 0. However, to change the initial index value of all arrays in our module to 1, we simply type ***Option Base 1*** at the top of the module. If we want to keep the default initial index as 0 but have a specific array start indexing at 1, we can specify the starting index value in the array declaration as *(1 to arraysize)*. As a comparison, in the example below, we use *Option Base 1*.

```
Option Base 1

Dim data(10) As Double, results(12) As Double
```

Here, both the *data* and *results* arrays have an initial index of 1 (as will any other array that we later define in this module). Below we do not specify the *Option Base* setting, but instead, we change the index of one of the arrays:

```
Dim data(1 to 10) As Double, results(12) As Double
```

Now, the *data* array begins with an index of 1, but the *results* array begins with an index of 0. We recommend choosing one general initial index for all arrays in the module in order to avoid mistakes or confusion. However, there may be situations in which specific arrays require different indexing bounds. In these cases, we can start the index at any value; we just have to be aware of the size of the array (size = upper index bound – lower index bound + 1). For example:

```
Dim results(2 to 13) As Double
```

The *results* array is still of size 12; it is just indexed starting with 2. In this case, we need to coordinate the initial index value that we chose with the counter variable used in *For, Next* loops. That is, if we want to insert a value into each element of the *results* array indexed starting with 2, we need to set our initial counter variable equal to 2.

```
For i = 2 to 13
    results(i) = value
Next i
```

Here, for example, *results(1)* would cause an error since there is no such index for the array.

17.4 *Dynamic Arrays*

If we are unsure of the size an array should or will be depending on some user input or other dynamic programming reasons, we can define a ***dynamic*** array. (*Fixed-size* arrays are those whose size is known.) When declaring a *dynamic* array, we do not specify the size; that is, we leave the parentheses empty. For example:

```
Dim input() As Double
```

However, before we can use this array or refer to any of its elements, we need to know its size. To set or change the size of a *dynamic* array at some later point in the code, we use the ***ReDim*** statement.

Let us suppose that we want to ask the users to insert some input values, which we will store in an *input* array, but we are unsure how many values the users want to insert. We first assign a variable to an *Input Box* that asks for the number of values. Then, we insert the value of each element using a *For, Next* loop. The code is as follows:

```
size = InputBox("How many values will you enter as input?")

ReDim input(1 to size) As Double

For i = 1 to size
    input(i) = InputBox("Please enter value for element " & i )
Next i
```

Another important command that we can use with the *ReDim* statement is ***Preserve***. Using the complete statement *ReDim Preserve* with an array changes the array size but keeps any values that were previously assigned. For example, suppose we have completed the code shown above in which users specified the number of elements in the *input* array and then provided a value for each element. Now, we prompt the users to see if there are more elements they want to add. If so, we want to keep, or preserve, the array we used previously but increase its size to account for the new elements. The next set of code is as follows:

```
size2 = InputBox("How many MORE elements to you want to add?")

ReDim Preserve input(1 to size + size2)

For i = size+1 to size2
    input(i) = InputBox("Please enter value for element " & i)
Next i
```

We learn that the number of additional elements to add to the array is *size2*. We can then increase the original size of the array, which is *size*, by the number of new elements: *size + size2*. We use the *Preserve* statement in order to retain the values for the initial elements. We then use a *For, Next* loop to assign values to only the new set of elements; that is why we loop from *size + 1* to *size2*. The *ReDim Preserve* statement is a valuable element of dynamic programming.

Summary

Arrays	Store series of data that we can manipulate or refer to later. Sets of values stored in an array must all be of the same data type.
Array Function	Uses the entire array variable to set values for each array element. arrayname = Array(*element1 value, element2 value, . . .)*
Multi-Dimensional Arrays	Specify the size of each dimension, separated by a comma.
Option Base 1	Changes the initial index value of all arrays in a module (from default of 0) to 1; declared at top of module.
Dynamic Arrays	Size is not specified; we leave the parentheses empty in array declaration.
ReDim	Used to set the size of a dynamic array at some later point in the code; can also be used to set or change the number of dimensions and the indexing bounds.
ReDim Preserve	Used to reset the size of a previously defined array while maintaining the values of the previously assigned elements.

17.5 Sorting Arrays

Usually sorting arrays requires some advanced algorithms. In this section, we provide one such algorithm, the Bubble Sort algorithm, for future use. However, aside from coding algorithms in VBA, there are also simpler ways to sort arrays by using the Excel spreadsheet features. To perform a simple sort, we can take advantage of Excel's spreadsheet sorting function. Suppose we have the following array of size 10:

```
Dim data() as Variant

data() = Array(5, 2, 8, 3, 7, 1, 9, 6, 10, 4)
```

To sort this array in increasing order using the Excel sort function, we can simply output this array to a range in the spreadsheet, sort it in this range, and then input it back into the array. The code for this is as follows (Here we use a range named "ArrayStart" as the reference for our output.):

```
Sub ExcelSort()
    For i = 1 to 10
        Range("ArrayStart").Offset(i, 0).Value = data(i)
    Next i

    Range(Range("ArrayStart").Offset(1,0), Range("ArrayStart").Offset(10,0))
        .Sort Key1:=Range("ArrayStart"), Order1:=xlAscending

    For i = 1 to 10
        data(i) = Range("ArrayStart").Offset(i,0).Value
    Next i
End Sub
```

Another way to sort an array is by using the ***Bubble Sort*** algorithm, which performs passes over the elements to be sorted. In each pass, it considers an element, say *p*, in order and compares it with the next element, say *q*. If $p > q$ (and we are trying to sort the list in ascending order), then the two elements are switched since they are out of order. A pass ends when each element has been compared with the next element and switched (if it is out of order). The algorithm terminates when in one complete pass no two elements are out of order, that is, when all elements have been sorted.

Let us consider the *data* array defined above: (*5, 2, 8, 3, 7, 1, 9, 6, 10, 4*). In the first pass of the *Bubble Sort* algorithm, the element 5 would be selected. We first compare 5 with 2 and find that 5 is larger, so we switch the two elements. We now compare 5 with 8 and find that 5 is smaller, so we now select 8 and continue our comparisons. We compare 8 with 3 and find that 8 is bigger, so we switch the elements. We then compare 8 with 7 and find that 8 is bigger, so we again switch the elements. We compare 8 with 1 and again switch the elements. Then, we compare 8 with 9 and find that 9 is bigger, so we now select 9 and continue our comparisons. We compare 9 with 6 and find that 9 is bigger, so we switch the elements. We compare 9 with 10, and 10 is bigger, so we now select 10. We compare 10 with 4 and switch the elements since 10 is bigger. We have now reached the end of the array and have completed the first pass of the algorithm. The current state of the array is as follows:

```
data() = Array(2, 5, 3, 7, 1, 8, 6, 9, 4, 10)
```

We repeat this process until no switches are performed. To code the *Bubble Sort* algorithm in VBA, we want to use a *Do, While* loop. We define a *Boolean* variable which we will use to determine when to stop running the algorithm. We know the array is sorted when no switches have been made; therefore, we keep track of the number of switches made in each loop with a counter variable, *switches*. In order to perform a switch, we use a temporary variable to hold the place of the value being switched.

The last note about the Bubble Sort procedure is that we can reduce the number of loops needed by noting that in each pass, one element is correctly placed. Therefore, instead of checking each element, say from 1 to 10, we can reduce the number of elements we check by one each time. That is, we can use some counting variable, say *j*, in order to write the loop as *For i = 1 to j*. We will initialize *j* to the size of the array and then decrease the value of *j* in each loop. The complete Bubble Sort procedure is given below.

```
Sub BubbleSort()
    Dim sorted As Boolean, temp

    j = 10
    Do
        sorted = True
        For i = 1 To j – 1
            If data(i) > data (i + 1) Then
                temp = data (i)
                data (i) = data (i + 1)
                data (i + 1) = temp
                sorted = False
            End If
        Next i
```

```
    j = j - 1
    Loop While sorted = False
End Sub
```

Note: We can use arrays with function procedures as well. We can pass the name of an array to a function procedure in order to manipulate some or all of its elements. Also, we can pass elements of an array to a function procedure to manipulate. We can also create a new array using a function procedure by using the function procedure to populate the array and returning this value. It may be useful to create a function procedure for one of the sorting methods explained above. That is, we could use *Function BubbleSort*(Array*Name*) to pass an array to the *BubbleSort* procedure and sort it. Refer to Chapter 15 for more on function procedures.

17.6 Applications

Let us now develop a phonebook application which uses dynamic arrays.

17.6.1 Phonebook

This application allows users to search, add new entries to, and view all listings in a phonebook. The phonebook stores a name and number for each entry.

There are only two worksheets for this program: "Phonebook Welcome" and "Phone Data." The "Phonebook Welcome" sheet is the basic welcome sheet with a problem description. The button options appear on this sheet as well (see Figure 17.1). (Refer to Hands-On Exercise 9 to add a *Start* button to this sheet.) The "Phone Data" sheet contains a table with the name and number of each entry in the phonebook. There is also a button to return to the "Phonebook Welcome" sheet (see Figure 17.2).

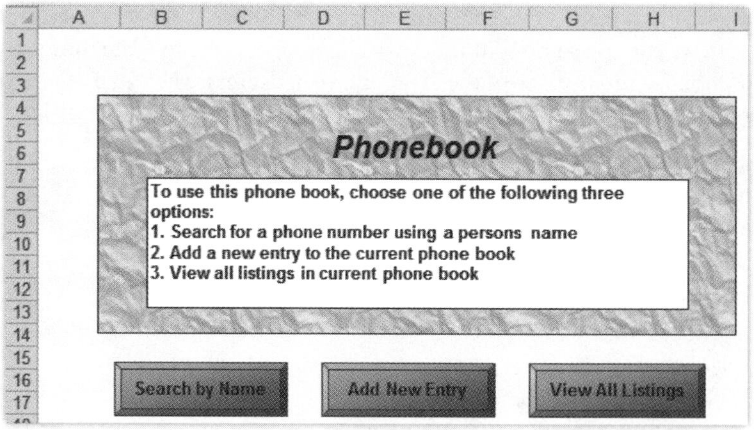

Figure 17.1 Welcome sheet for the phonebook application.

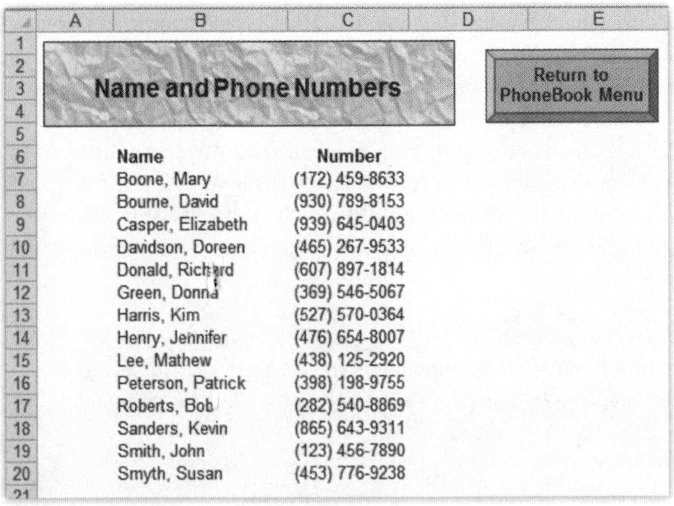

Figure 17.2 Data sheet with all the phonebook entries.

In this case, we only need two main sub procedures. We need a ***Search*** procedure to search for an entry in the phonebook by name and a ***NewEntry*** procedure to enter a new name and number into the phonebook. There will also be two navigational procedures, one to take the users from the welcome sheet to view all listings and one to return the users to the welcome sheet or the phonebook menu. In the *Search* procedure, we call a ***Create****Array* procedure to put all the names and numbers from the "Phone Data" sheet into two arrays from which to search.

We also need some counting variables, two array variables (one for the names and one for the numbers), two range variables (for the two columns of data in the phonebook table), and two variables to capture the name and number for searching or adding a new entry. We declare these variables as follows:

```
Public i As Integer, n As Integer, PhoneName() As String,_
PhoneNumber() As Double, NewName As String, NewNumber As Double,_
NameStart As Range, NumStart As Range
```

We can quickly create the navigational procedures as follows:

```
Sub ViewBook()
    Worksheets("Phone Data").Visible = True
    Worksheets("Phonebook Welcome").Visible = False
End Sub

------------------------
Sub ViewMenu()
    Worksheets("Phonebook Welcome").Visible = True
    Worksheets("Phone Data").Visible = False
End Sub
```

These procedures are assigned to the "View All Listings" and "Return to PhoneBook Menu" buttons, respectively.

Let us now discuss the *Search* sub procedure. The first action is to ask the users for the name that they want to search for in the phonebook. We assign the ***NewName*** variable to the *InputBox* function and provide a default value. Next, we call the *Create*Array procedure to create an array of all current names, ***PhoneName***, and numbers, ***PhoneNumber***, in the phonebook. (We will discuss this procedure later.) This course of action makes our search easier since now we can just use a *For, Next* loop to check if any of the array elements is equal to the *NewName* value.

If a match is found, the corresponding element (i.e., the same index number) from the *PhoneNumber* array is assigned to the ***NewNumber*** variable, and the result of the search appears. If no match is found, we consider that the *NewNumber* variable was never changed from its default value of 0. Therefore, using this check, we can tell the users that no match was found. The code is as follows:

```
Sub Search()
    NewName = InputBox("Please enter name you wish to search for using " &_
        & " the following format: Last, First:", "Name Search", "Smith, John")

    Call CreateArray
    NewNumber = 0
    For i = 1 To n
        If PhoneName(i) = NewName Then
            NewNumber = PhoneNumber(i)
            MsgBox "The phone number for " & NewName & " is " &_
                Format(NewNumber, "(###) ###-####")
        End If
    Next i

    If NewNumber = 0 Then
        MsgBox "There was no phonebook entry by that name."
    End If
End Sub
```

We have used the *Format* function to display the *NewNumber* value as a standard 10-digit phone number. In this case, the expression is the value of the *NewNumber.*

We need the users to enter the phone number as a standard set of 10 digits since *NewNumber* is defined as a *double* data type, and it can be easier to compare a *double* value than a *string.* If we had not used the Format function, we may have wanted the numbers to be defined as a *string* in order to use the parentheses and dashes. We also format the cells on the phonebook list to this custom format using Excel format cells options (on the spreadsheet, not in the code).

We can now discuss the *Create*Array procedure. Notice in our variable declarations the two arrays, *PhoneName* and *PhoneNumber,* were defined as *dynamic* arrays. Now we need to find the size of these arrays and use the *ReDim* statement. To find the size of the arrays, we can use range variables and the *End* property to count the number of values currently in the phonebook table. To count the number of values in this range, we use the *Rows* property and the *Count* sub property.

[*Note*: If we use the *Count* property directly on the range instead of as a sub property to *Rows*, we will count the total number of cells in the entire range. If there is only one column or one row of data, this is inconsequential; however, if there are multiple rows or columns, we will need to ensure what we are counting: the number of rows (using *Rows*), number of columns (using *Columns*), or number of cells (using the range directly).]

Next, we use a *For, Next* loop to enter each value in the table as an element in one of our arrays. The code is as follows:

```
Sub CreateArray()
    With NameStart
        n = Range(.Offset(1, 0), .End(xlDown)).Rows.Count
    End With

    ReDim PhoneName(n)
    ReDim PhoneNumber(n)

    For i = 1 To n
        PhoneName(i) = NameStart.Offset(i, 0)
        PhoneNumber(i) = NumStart.Offset(i, 0)
    Next i
End Sub
```

(Note that the range variables are initialized in the *Workbook_Open event procedure.* We also use the *For Each, Next* loop to hide and show necessary sheets. See Chapter 16 on applications.)

The last procedure that we need to create is *NewEntry.* In this procedure, we begin by prompting the users for both a name and a number to add to the phonebook. We assign *Input Boxes* to the *NewName* and *NewNumber* variables. We also add error checking at this point. To ensure that a non-empty string is entered as a name, we use an *If, Then* statement with the condition *NewName* = "". If this condition is true, then the sub will be exited and the users will be prompted to re-enter a name. (Another way to create an *error checking* statement for the *NewNumber* variable is to temporarily use a variant variable before assigning a value to *NewNumber*; see Chapter 16 on applications).

Using the ***Len*** function in VBA, we also add an *error checking* statement to ensure that the phone number entered is 10-digits in length. The *Len* function takes any string expression or variable name as input and counts the number of characters or digits. Therefore, to check if the number entered by the users is 10 digits, we can just check if the *Len* function, when applied to this value, returns 10.

We then call the *Create*Array procedure again to search all names in the current list and avoid duplicate entries. If the *NewName* value is found in the *PhoneName* array, the users are told that this entry already exists. If no match is found, the program proceeds by adding the new entry to the table; we do this using range variables. Now, we select our modified table and sort all of the values using the *Sort* method. (Notice that the *NameStart* range variable can be used as the Key argument.)

We also use the *ScreenUpdating* property of the Application object to ensure that the users do not see this background work on the "Phone Data" sheet. Once the new entry is added, the users are told that the new name has been added. (Note that we assume each name in the phonebook is unique.) The code for this procedure is as follows:

```
Sub NewEntry()
    Application.ScreenUpdating = False
    Worksheets("Phone Data").Activate
```

```
    NewName = InputBox("Please enter the new entry name using the " & _
                & "following format: Last, First", "New Name", "Smith, John")
    If NewName = "" Then
        MsgBox "Please enter a name."
        Exit Sub
    End If

    NewNumber = InputBox("Please enter the 10-digit phone number for " & _
                NewName & " using the following format: 1234567890", _
        "New Number", 1234567890)
    If Len(NewNumber) <> 10 Then
        MsgBox "Please enter a 10-digit number."
        Exit Sub
    End If

    Call CreateArray
    For i = 1 To n
        If PhoneName(i) = NewName Then
            MsgBox "There is already an entry for this person in the phonebook."
        Exit Sub
        End If
    Next i

    NameStart.Offset(n, 0).value = NewName
    NumStart.Offset(n, 0).value = NewNumber

    Range(NameStart, NumStart.Offset(n, 0)).Select
    Selection.Sort Key1:=NameStart, Order1:=xlAscending

    Worksheets("Phonebook Welcome").Activate
    Application.ScreenUpdating = True

    MsgBox NewName & " has been added to the phonebook."
End Sub
```

The application is now complete. We assign the procedures to the respective buttons and check the functionality of the program.

Summary

Format()	This function applies a specified format to a variable value or expression. *Format(Expression, Format) Format(NewNumber, "(###)###-####")*
Count	We can apply this property directly to a range to count the number of cells in the range. We can also apply it to the *Rows* property of a range to count the number of rows or to the *Columns* property to count the number of columns.

17.7 Summary

- Arrays store series of data that we can manipulate or refer to later. The set of values stored in an array must all be of the same data type. We can refer to the array as a whole, or we can refer to its individual elements by an index value.
- To define an array, use the *Dim, Private*, or *Public* variable declarations. The data type will be assigned to all of the elements in that array. VBA will recognize that the variable is an array and not a scalar variable because we must specify the size of the array in the variable declaration.
- To insert values into an array, use the entire array variable and the array function. The array function allows us to list values for each array element.
- To enter multiple element values using indices, use a *For, Next* loop with a counter variable.
- For a one-dimensional array, we just need a single number to specify the size. To define *multi-dimensional* arrays, we must specify the size of each dimension, separated by a comma.
- To insert values into a *multi-dimensional* array or to search for a value, use nested *For, Next* loops with different counter variables.
- The default initial index value of arrays in VBA is 0. However, to change the initial index value of all arrays in our module to 1, we simply type *Option Base 1* at the top of the module.
- If we want to keep the default initial index as 0 but have a specific array that we want to index starting at 1, we can specify the starting index value in the array declaration as *(1 to* array*size)*.
- We can start the index at any value; just be aware of the size of the array (size = upper index bound – lower index bound + 1).
- If we are not sure what size an array should or will be, depending on the users or other dynamic programming reasons, we can define a *dynamic* array. When declaring a *dynamic* array, we do not specify the size; we leave the parentheses empty.
- To set the size of a *dynamic* array at some later point in the code, use the *ReDim* statement. We can also use it to set or change the number of dimensions and the indexing bounds. The *ReDim Preserve* statement accomplishes the same function as the *ReDim* statement but retains any previously assigned element values.
- Use the *Format* function to apply a custom format to an expression or variable value.
- We can apply the *Count* property directly to a range to count the number of cells in the range. We can also apply it to the *Rows* property of a range to count the number of rows or to the *Columns* property to count the number of columns.
- The *Len* function counts the number of characters or digits in a string expression or variable value.

17.8 Exercises

17.8.1 Review Questions

1. What would happen if you assigned entry *i* equal to entry *j* in the same array? For example, List() is an array of integer values. What does it mean to assign List(4) = List(10)?
2. What is the difference between defining a variable and defining an array of variables?
3. Why are multi-dimensional arrays beneficial? How many elements are in a multi-dimensional array?
4. Using *Option Base 0*, what is the last index of a variable array of size *N*? Using *Option Base 1*?
5. How do you define a public variable array with a size of integer variable *N*?
6. Is there a way to re-dimension an array without losing the data already in the array? If so, explain and then discuss any restrictions.
7. How do you find the length of an expression or variable value? Can this function be used on any variable data type?
8. Can arrays be passed to function procedures?
9. How do you format information in a *Message* Box?
10. How do you find the number of columns in a range?

17.8.2 Hands-On Exercises

NOTE: *Please refer to the file "Chapter_17_Exercises. xlsx" for the associated worksheets noted for the hands-on exercises. The file is available at:* www.dssbooks.com.

1. Complete the following code so that the user's input is used to define the size of the array:

```
Dim NewArray() As String, UserInput As Integer

Sub DefineArraySize()
    UserInput = InputBox("Enter the require array size: ")
End Sub
```

2. Based on a set of given data, what will the output be for the program below? (Refer to worksheet "17.2".)

```
Dim i As Integer, Data(11) As Integer, DataValue As Double
Sub Review()
    'copy and manipulate data to array
    With Range("A1")
        For i = 1 To 11
            DataValue = .Offset(i, 0).Value
            Data(i) = Int(DataValue)
        Next i
    End With
    'print out the 5th entry
    MsgBox Data(5)
End Sub
```

3. Write a small program that copies each element of an array variable into another array variable. Both arrays should have the same size.
4. Write a program that reads data from a table into a multi-dimensional array and then sorts the array entries from smallest to largest based on the measurement values. (Note: Do not use the sort function for this problem. Instead, use the *BubbleSort()* algorithm we describe above.) (Refer to worksheet "17.4".)
5. Write a visual basic code that calculates A + B and A x B, where A and B are two-dimensional arrays.(Do not use the Excel spreadsheet functions to calculate A + B or A x B. Use *For Next* loops to perform the operations.) In writing the code, consider the following. (Refer to worksheet "17.5".)
   - **a.** Ask the users whether they want to use the data given below to test the code or use their own data. If the users choose to read the data from the table, copy this data in two two-dimensional arrays A and B. Otherwise, ask the users to enter the size of each array and the corresponding elements.
   - **b.** Ask the users whether they want to perform the A + B or A x B operation. Prompt the users if the size of the arrays is not suitable for the chosen operation.
6. Write a program that asks the users to enter 5 numbers and then outputs these values in reverse order on a spreadsheet.
7. Create a two-dimensional array that stores dates and prices for purchases made by users. Search through this array and sum the values of the prices for each month. Report these prices to the users.
8. Using VBA functions (including the Application object) and arrays, perform the following:
   - **a.** Define an array of size 20.
   - **b.** Populate the array with a set of random numbers between 1 and 100.
   - **c.** Find the maximum value of the array.
   - **d.** Find the minimum value of the array.
   - **e.** Create a new array of size 20 and populate it with random numbers from a normal distribution with mean and standard deviations equal to mean and standard deviations of the random numbers generated in part (b).
9. Reorganize a list of names.
   - **a.** Create an array of size 25 with random numbers from 1 to 10.
   - **b.** For each number, create a unique name. Replace the values of this array with the corresponding names.
   - **c.** Sort this array in alphabetical order.
10. **Creating Subsets:** Create an array of size 50 with random numbers from 1 to 20. Loop through these values to check necessary conditions to find the following subsets:
    - **a.** An array called Odd with only odd numbers.
    - **b.** An array called Even with only even numbers.
    - **c.** An array called Five with numbers that are multiples of five.

d. An array listing all the numbers that were repeated in the original array.

11. The sales of a product follow a normal distribution with different parameters for each quarter. Create a program that computes sales figures for five years using the distribution parameters for each quarter. The program should perform the following actions:

a. Ask the users to enter the parameters for each quarter using *Input Boxes*.

b. Store the parameters in a two-dimensional array, "parameters."

c. Create a two-dimensional array, "sales," that stores the sales of each quarter for five years.

d. Use nested For loops and the "parameters" array to compute random sales values in the "sales" array.

e. Use nested For loops and the "sales" array to list all sales values in order on a worksheet in two columns. The first column contains the year and quarter, such as "2003 Qtr 1," and the second column contains the sales values.

f. Display a line chart with the sales information.

12. Create an array named *Birthdays*() that contains randomly generated birthdays. Present the number of pairs of matching birthdays in the array. The following steps should be considered in building the visual basic code:

a. Prompt the users to enter the number of birthdays to generate and re-dimension the Birthdays() array.

b. Prompt the users to enter a range of years within which the birthdays should be created. Verify that the latter year is greater than the former year. If not, inform the users that the latter year must be greater and repeat part (b).

c. Randomly generate birthdays, assuming thirty days in a month. *Note:* Use the DateSerial() function in visual basic.

d. Compare and count the number of pairs of matching birthdays. *Note:* If there are three matching birthdays, then they should count for three pairs of birthdays that match.

e. Display the number of pairs of matching birthdays.

13. A building construction manager is trying to keep track of her subcontractors. She has ten subcontractors who have each been assigned a projected completion date for their tasks. As the subcontractors complete their tasks, they report to the construction manager, who updates her records in a table with the actual completion dates and checks to see what is left to be done. (Refer to worksheet "17.13".)

a. Create a two-dimensional array called SubC of size 10 which stores the name and projected completion date of each contractor. Randomly generate dates within the current year. Assume that a month has 30 days. *Note:* Use the DateSerial() function in visual basic.

b. Sort this array by the date values so that the earliest date is first.

c. Prompt the users for the name of a subcontractor whose dates they want to update. Search the SubC array for this name, and then report the corresponding date to the users as the default value of an Input Box.

d. The users can then change this date value or leave it as it is. Update the SubC array and resort it.

e. Output the ordered array to the spreadsheet.

14. Playing the Lottery: There are several different levels in winning the lottery. If your ticket matches every number of the lottery ticket, you win the grand prize. If your ticket has the same numbers, but in a different order, you win the second prize. If your ticket has half of the matching numbers in the correct order, you win the third prize. Create a program in which the winners can play the lottery and see what they won.

a. Randomly generate each number of the lottery ticket between 1 and 10. Store the lottery numbers in an array of size 10 called LotteryTicket.

b. Ask the users if they want to buy a ticket with random numbers or if they want to choose their own. If they want a random ticket, repeat part (a) in an array called "UserTicket." If they want to choose their own, then prompt them for ten different values, and put them in the "UserTicket" array.

c. Check for each of the three winning conditions above and tell the users what, if anything, they have won. Ask the users if they want to play again.

15. Task Manager: Create a program which allows users to store and maintain a list of tasks with a corresponding description and due date. Create the following sub procedures and assign each to a command button. (Refer to worksheet "17.15".)

a. Create array: Copy the information stored in the Excel spreadsheet to a two-dimensional array, called Tasks.

b. Add a new task: Prompt the users to enter the name, description, and due date of a new task. Check to ensure this task was not previously in the list. Update the spreadsheet and Tasks array.

c. Delete a completed task: Prompt the users for the name of the task, find it in the Tasks array, delete it, and update the array and the Excel spreadsheet.

d. List the tasks that are completed: Sort the Tasks array by the due date. Use a message box to present the tasks that have already been completed. When sorting the tasks, do not use the Excel function.

16. Perform the following extensions to the *Phonebook* application. (Refer to worksheet "17.16".)

a. Update the arrays as entries are added. In other words, new entries should not only be added to the spreadsheet but also inserted into the array.

b. Add error checking to ensure that a value has been entered for the NewNumber Input Box. (*Hint:* Refer to the application in Chapter 16.)

c. Create a button and sub procedure to *Delete* an entry. This should be similar to the *Search* procedure. Make sure you update your arrays.

17. Help Herman, a vacuum salesman, to determine which route is best for him if he visits 10 cities.

a. Create a two dimensional array called "Distance" that stores random distances between cities i and j. (Ensure that the distance between a city and itself is 0.)

b. Create an array called "Order" that stores the order in which the cities should be visited. (It can store either the city names or numbers.)

c. Create an array called "Visited" that stores Boolean values to determine if a city has already been visited. (Herman does not wish to visit any city twice.)

d. Create a For, Next loop that begins at city i = 1, and check the distances from this city to the other cities in order to find the city with the minimum distance. (Ensure that you do not check the distance to a city that has already been visited. Also make sure that you do not check the distance to the city itself, as that would be 0 and a false minimum.)

e. Place this city in the "Order" array, and update its "Visited" array value to True.

f. Continue this process and keep track of the total distance traveled.

g. Report to Herman the order in which he should visit the cities and the total distance he can expect to travel.

18. Write a visual basic code that calculates average, standard deviation, and minimum and maximum of a range of data. Build the program following these steps:

a. Prompt the users for the starting and ending cell of the range where the data is saved.

b. Copy the data into a one-dimensional array called Data().

c. Calculate the average, standard deviation, and minimum and maximum of the data saved in the array. Do not use the Excel functions. Use For Next loops and If statements to calculate these statistics.

d. Use a message box to present the results to the users.

19. The Northwest corner rule for the transportation problem: The transportation problem is concerned with finding the minimum-cost distribution plan for shipping products from plants to warehouses. We will describe the steps to be followed in order to find a feasible solution to this problem.

The data required for this problem is the unit transportation costs from each plant to each warehouse, the available capacity at each plant, and the demand at each warehouse. A given table provides the unit transportation costs as well as demand in each warehouse and available capacity in each plant for a transportation problem with four plants and five warehouses. (Refer to worksheet "17.19".)

a. Prompt the users to choose whether they want to solve the transportation problem using the data given in the table above or use their own data. If the users choose to use the data given in this problem, read the data from the Excel spreadsheet to a two-dimensional array called Data(). Otherwise, prompt the users to enter the number of warehouses and the number of plants. Use this information to re-dimension the array Data(). Prompt the users to enter the unit transportation costs, demands, and available capacities.

b. A feasible solution to the transportation problem is found using this simple heuristic, known as the *Northwest corner heuristic*: Start with the upper-left corner of the cost matrix corresponding to Plant 1 and W 1. Ship as much as possible from the plant to the warehouse (Min(Demand W1, Available Capacity Plant 1)). Reduce the demand at W1 and available capacity at Plant 1 by the amount shipped. If the available capacity at W1 is zero and demand at Plant 1 is positive, move to W2. If the available capacity at W1 is positive and demand at Plant 1 is zero, move to Plant 2. Follow these steps until the demand in each warehouse is satisfied.

c. Create a two-dimensional array that presents the amount shipped from the plants to the warehouses. Print this array in an Excel spreadsheet. Print also the remaining demand and available capacity.

d. Calculate the total transportation costs.

20. Improve the Northwest corner heuristic for the transportation problem described in Hands-On Exercise 19, updating part (b) as follows: Start with the combination (Plant, W) that has the minimum unit transportation cost. Ship as much as possible from the plant to the warehouse (*Min*(Demand of Warehouse, Available Capacity at Plant)). Reduce the demand at Warehouse and available capacity at Plant by the amount shipped. If the demand of Warehouse is positive, look for the next plant that has available capacity and has the best unit costs. Continue this way until the demand in each warehouse is satisfied. Calculate the total transportation cost. Compare this cost to the one calculated in Hands-On Exercise 19. (Refer to worksheet "17.20".)

CHAPTER

eighteen User Interface

chapter OVERVIEW

18.1 *Introduction*

This chapter explains the user interface development in VBA. This interface includes user forms, controls on the spreadsheet, and overall spreadsheet appearance. The user interface is a very important part of a DSS. It is what guides the users through the application and allows them to communicate with the program. The users may use a button to start the program, a form to enter input or simulation parameters, and controls on the spreadsheet to resolve their problem by modifying some input or parameter values. Good graphical user interface (GUI) design principles are discussed in detail in Appendix B. We have developed a variety of user interfaces in all of our DSS applications.

In this chapter, the reader will learn how to:

- Create a user form with various controls.
- Set the properties of these controls and work with common events.
- Code in form modules using event procedures, variable scope, and error checking.
- Create a professional appearance for the workbook interface.
- Create two user interface applications: one with controls on the spreadsheet and one with several user forms.

18.2 *User Form Controls*

Designing a good user interface is one of the most important parts of having a good decision-support system. After ensuring that all mathematical models are correct and the VBA code functionality is working correctly, we have to ensure that the users can then use the program we have developed. One of the best tools in VBA for Excel which helps us communicate with the user is ***user forms***.

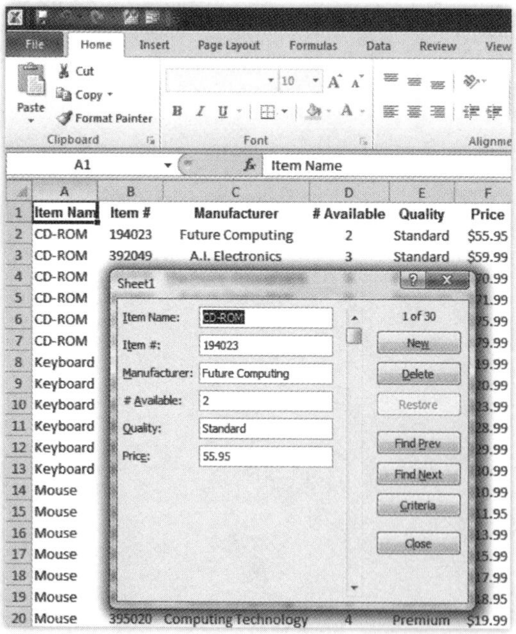

Figure 18.1 This is a user form created using Excel's new Form command. The *Control Toolbox* provides available controls which can be placed on the form.

Excel offers a simple way to build a user form (see Figure 18.1) using the *Form* command in *Quick Access toolbar*. To create this form, select a cell of the table in A1:F20, and then click on the *Form* button. We can use the form for data-entry and -editing. To create this form using VBA you can type this simple VBA code

```
Sub DataForm()
    Range("A1").Select
    ActiveSheet.ShowDataForm
End Sub
```

[*Note*: *Form* command is not listed in the Ribbon, therefore to add the command to *Quick Access toolbar*, we right-click on the *Quick Access toolbar* and select the *Customize Quick Access toolbar* option. In the *Excel Options* dialog box that appears, select *Commands Not in the Ribbon* from the *Choose commands from* drop-down list on the left. In the list box in the left select *Form* and click the *Add* button.]

The built-in data form of Excel is easy to create. However, we cannot modify its appearance and functionalities to make it a better fit for our specific application. ***User forms*** in VBA enable us to develop an application specific, and user friendly Excel interface. To add a user form to our program, we simply use *Insert > User Form* from the menu in the Visual Basic Environment (VBE); we could also use the insert icon for user forms, similar to using the insert icon for inserting modules. We will then see a blank form and the ***Control Toolbox*** (as we saw earlier in Chapter 12). This time, however, we will use the *Control Toolbox* to add necessary controls to the user form (see Figure 18.2). Each of these controls is described in the following sections (see Figure 18.3 for a demonstration of how each of these controls appears on the user form).

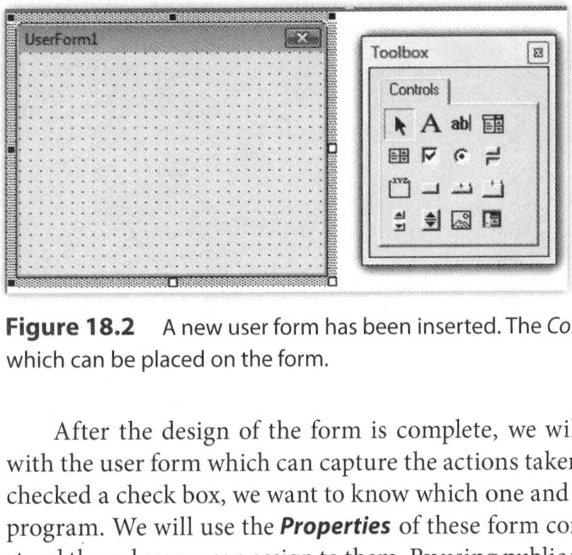

Figure 18.2 A new user form has been inserted. The *Control Toolbox* provides available controls which can be placed on the form.

After the design of the form is complete, we will need to create some code associated with the user form which can capture the actions taken by the users. For example, if they have checked a check box, we want to know which one and how that affects the next actions of our program. We will use the ***Properties*** of these form controls to name each control and understand the values we can assign to them. By using public variables, we will then be able to transfer actions performed on the user form to the main code of our program.

The most important property which we will use for all user form controls is the ***Name*** property. The name of a control from a user form is treated as an object in the code. We recommend that the beginning of the user form control name identify which type of control it is. User form will also have name property values. For example, the name of a form may begin with "frm" followed by some descriptive name: a form which gives the user some basic menu options might be called "frmMenu." Note that the *Name* property can be set in the code for the form as we have seen with other Excel objects. However, we usually recommend using the *Properties window* to enter the name without coding (See Figure 18.4).

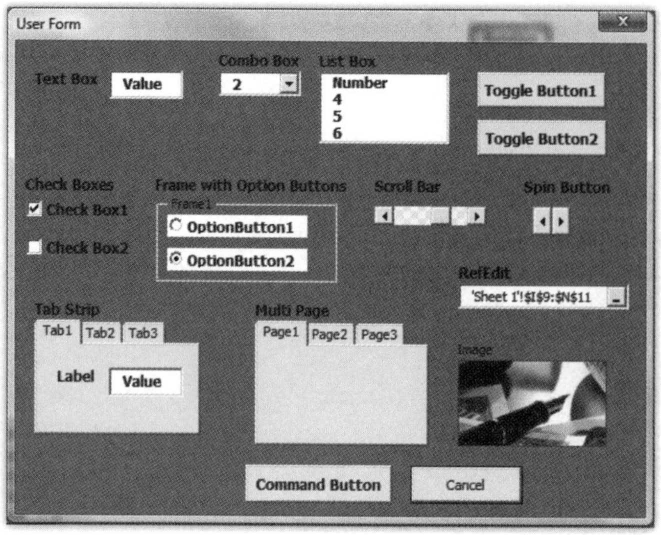

Figure 18.3 Each of the possible user form controls is labeled on this form.

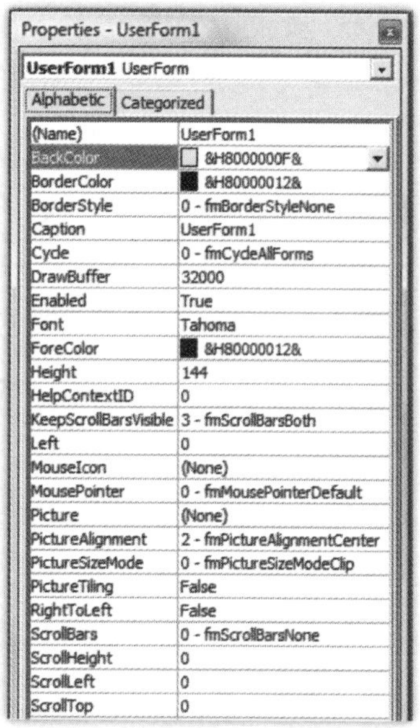

Figure 18.4 The Properties window lists the properties for the selected control on the user form.

If we are writing code associated with the user form which contains the object we want to manipulate, we only have to enter the name of the object directly and then use any property or method available. To manipulate a user form object while in another user form code or in any other module, we just type the name of the form first followed by a period and the name of the object; for example, *frmMenu.lblQuantity.*

To view the code of our current user form or to view the form design of our current form code, we use the *View Code* and *View Object* buttons, respectively (see Figure 18.5).

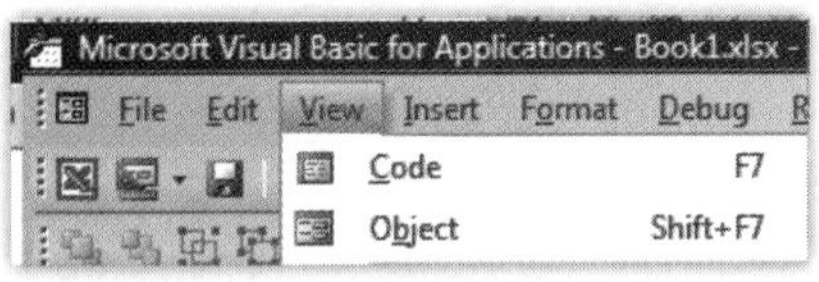

Figure 18.5 The *View Code* and *View Object* buttons allow us to view the code and form design of the selected user form.

Summary

User form:	Form which contains any control or controls which receive user input.
Control Toolbox:	Set of all controls available to insert on the user form.
Properties Window:	View properties associated with any selected control.
Name property:	Used to identify controls in the code.

18.2.1 Labels and Textboxes

Labels and textboxes will be the most commonly used form controls.

We use a ***label*** to give a description to any control on the form (as used in Figure 18.3). We can also use labels to give the form a general description or to specify instructions to the users. (Note that if we want to enter a new line of text in a label, we press Shift+Enter.) To insert a label on our form, we use the A icon from the *Control Toolbox*.

The name of a label should begin with "lbl" followed by some descriptive name. For example, a label for a textbox which takes the value of some quantity might be "lblQuantity." (Note that we usually do not name labels unless we intend to manipulate them later.)

The only manipulation of labels that we use in developing applications is with the ***Caption*** property and the ***Visible*** property. We use the Caption property to change the text displayed in the label. The Visible property takes True/False values, and we can use it with all other user form controls as well. We can set the Visible property in the code for the form; for example, to hide the "lblQuantity" label, we would type the following:

lblQuantity.Visible = False

Summary

Form Object	**Suggested Name Prefix**
Label	Lbl
Common Properties	
Visible	True/False
Caption	Text value in label

We use a ***textbox*** to allow the users to enter some value. This value may be a string or number; the label next to the textbox should specify the kind of value the users should enter. Note than any non-numerical value the users enter will be considered as a string. Therefore, if we want the users to enter a date or other data type which we may use later in our code, we may need to take advantage of the conversion functions discussed in Chapter 14 (such as CDate). Textboxes are usually accompanied by a label control to describe what value should be entered into the textbox.

To insert a textbox, use the ab| icon from the *Control Toolbox*. The textbox should appear as seen in Figure 18.6.

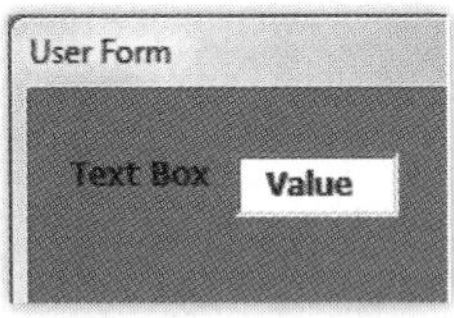

Figure 18.6 Example of a textbox.

The name given to a textbox in the *Properties* window should begin with "txt" and be followed by some descriptive name. For example, a textbox which will hold a quantity value may be named "txtQuantity."

We usually want to assign the value of a textbox object to some variable in our code; we do this using the ***Value*** property. For example, if there were a *quantity* variable in our code to which we wanted to assign the "txtQuantity" textbox value, we would type the following:

```
quantity = txtQuantity.Value
```

Summary

Form Object	Suggested Name Prefix
Textbox	Txt
Common Properties	
Value	Value entered by user or initialized in code

18.2.2 Combo Boxes and List Boxes

Combo boxes and list boxes are used to give the users a list of options from which they can select one control. The main difference between combo boxes and list boxes is the way in which the data is displayed.

A ***combo box*** will list the first entry next to a drop-down button. When the button is pressed, all other controls in the list are shown. The users can also enter a value into the combo box as with a textbox if they do not wish to select a control from the list. To insert a combo box in our form, we use the icon from the *Control Toolbox*. The combo box should appear as shown in Figure 18.7 (note that we also have a label control in this figure).

Figure 18.7 An example of a combo box.

The name given to a combo box should begin with "cmb" followed by a descriptive name. For example, if we had a combo box which listed some controls, it could be called "cmbControls."

There are several important properties associated with combo boxes. The main property we use to capture the users' selection is the *Value* property. Similar to textboxes, this value can be assigned to some variable in our code. For example, if we have the variable *usercontrol* which is associated with the users' selection from the combo box of controls called "cmbControls," we could use the following code to assign a value to our variable:

```
usercontrol = cmbControls.Value
```

To specify the values to be listed in the combo box, we use the ***RowSource*** property. This property can have a value equal to a specified range in a worksheet or a range name (both should be entered as a string). For example, if the range *A5:B10* has five rows and two columns of data which we want to show in the combo box, we would set the *RowSource* property as follows:

```
Worksheets("Sheet1").Range("A5:B10").Name = "Options"
cmbItmes.RowSource = "Options"
```

Related to the *RowSource* property is the ***ControlSource*** property. This property allows us to output directly to the spreadsheet the selection made by the users. The value of the *ControlSource* property must be a range name, just as with the *RowSource* property. For example, to output the selection of the combo box *cmbControls* to the cell A20, we would set the *ControlSource* property as follows:

```
cmbControls.ControlSource = "A20"
```

The combo box will be initialized to show the value in the *ControlSource* range, and the final value the users select will be displayed in this range. Even though this is a nice feature, we usually assign the value of the combo box to a variable and therefore do not use this feature often.

If the *RowSource* of a combo box has more than one column, we can use several other properties. The first is the ***BoundColumn*** property. This property determines which column of the multicolumn data will contain the value which will be captured with the *Value* property. That is, for the above example, if we set the *BoundColumn* to 1, then regardless of what row of data is selected, only the data from column A will be stored in the *Value* property. (*Note:* the columns are indexed beginning with 1.) We would type the following:

```
cmbControls.BoundColumn = 1
```

Another useful property for multicolumn data is ***ColumnCount***. We use *ColumnCount* to set how many columns of the *RowSource* data should be displayed in the combo box. If this value is 0, no columns are displayed; if it is –1, all columns are displayed; we can use any other number less than 10 to display the corresponding number of columns from the data.

We may, however, want to show non-adjacent columns in the combo box. In our example, the data in column A may have some ID numbers for controls for sale while column B may have control names; in this case, it may be more useful to only display the control names to the users. We still have to set the *ColumnCount* property to 2 in order to make both columns of data available. However, we use another property to hide the first column: this is the ***ColumnWidths*** property. If we set the column width of column A to 0, and set column B to some non-zero width value, then only column B will be displayed. We enter the column widths in quotation marks for all columns; we can enter the width values using a VBA point system or with any specified unit of measure. We would type the following:

```
cmbControls.ColumnCount = 2
cmbControls.ColumnWidths = "0", "1"
```

Another useful property is the ***ColumnHeads*** property. This property can be set to *True* if there are column headings in the data which we want to display in the combo box. The row which contains the column headings does not need to be included in the *RowSource* data. The users cannot select these column headings.

There are some formatting properties specific to combo boxes, such as ***ListRows*** and ***Style***. We use *ListRows* to specify the number of rows that should appear in the combo box. If there are more rows of data than are set by the *ListRows* property, a scroll bar will automatically appear in the combo box. The *Style* property has two main options: ***fmStyleDropDownCombo*** and ***fmStyleDropDownList***. The *Combo* option allows the users to type a value into the combo box, and the *List* option does not.

Two other useful properties of the combo box are ***ListIndex*** and ***List***. The *ListIndex* property will return the index value of the control that was selected (the index for combo boxes begins at 1; the index for list boxes begins at 0). We can use the *List* property with the index of a control to select a particular control from the list. For example, to initialize a combo box to show the first control in the list to be selected, we would type:

```
cmbControls.Value = cmbQuantity.List(1)
```

Summary

Form Object	**Suggested Name Prefix**
Combo Box	cmb
Common Properties	
RowSource	Specifies the values to be listed
ControlSource	Outputs directly to the spreadsheet the selection made by the users
BoundColumn	Determines which column of the multicolumn data will contain the value which will be captured with the Value property
ColumnCount	Sets how many columns of the RowSource data should be displayed
ColumnWidths	Enter widths in quotation marks for all columns
ColumnHeads	True/False to show/hide column headings
ListRows	Specifies the number of rows that should appear
List	Used with the index of a control to select a particular control from the list
ListIndex	Return the index value of the control that was selected (the index for combo boxes begins at 1)
Style	Allows or disallows the user to type a value into the combo box
Value	selected control

A ***list box*** has basically the same functionality and several similar properties as a combo box. A list box will list all controls to be selected in a single box (that is, there is no drop-down button as with combo boxes). The users cannot, therefore, enter a value into the list box. To insert a list box in our form, we use the icon from the *Control Toolbox*. The *list box* should appear as shown in Figure 18.8 (note that a label control is also shown with the list box).

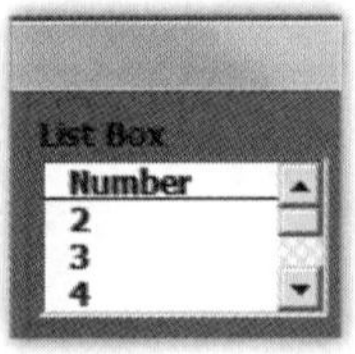

Figure 18.8 An example of a list box.

The name we give to a list box should begin with "lst" followed by a descriptive name. For example, if we had a list box which listed some controls, it could be called "lstControls."

List boxes also use the *RowSource*, *ControlSource*, *BoundColumn*, *ColumnCount*, *ColumnWidths*, *ColumnHeads*, *ListRows*, *ListIndex*, and *List* properties as described above. (Note that the *ControlSource* property used with the list box displays the value of the index of the selected control rather than the value of the selected control.)

In addition to these properties, the list box has a unique property called ***MultiSelect***. The *MultiSelect* property determines if users can select more than one control from the list box. There are three possible values for this property: ***fmMultiSelectSingle***, ***fmMultiSelectMulti***, and ***fmMultiSelectExtended***. The *Single* option is the default and allows the users to select only one control at a time. The *Multi* option allows the users to select more than one control by clicking on several from the list. The *Extended* option allows the users to select a section of controls from the list box by clicking the first control in the section they want and then pressing the Shift key and selecting the last control in the section they want; this method requires the section of controls to be adjacent. The users can also select multiple, non-adjacent controls by pressing the CTRL key and clicking from the list.

Summary

Form Object	**Suggested Name Prefix**
List Box	lst
Common Properties	
MultiSelect	Determines if users can select more than one control from the list box
ListIndex	Returns the index value of the control that was selected (the index for list boxes begins at 0)
RowSource, ControlSource, BoundColumn, ColumnCount, ColumnWidths, ColumnHeads, ListRows, List, Value	

18.2.3 Check Boxes, Option Buttons and Toggle Buttons

We use check boxes and option buttons to create *Boolean* selection options for the users. We can use frames to group these controls or other related controls.

Check boxes imply a positive selection (that is, a *yes*, *true*, *on*, etc. value) when checked; the opposite is true if they are unchecked or de-checked. To insert a check box into our form, we use the icon from the *Control Toolbox*. The check boxes should appear as shown in Figure 18.9.

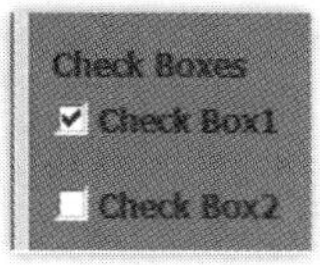

Figure 18.9 An example of two check boxes.

The name given to a check box should begin with "chk" followed by a descriptive name. For example, if we have two check boxes, one of which is associated with searching some database of textbooks by author name and the other with searching by book title, we could name them "chkAuthor" and "chkTitle," respectively.

We can use the *Value* property of check boxes as with *Boolean* variables. That is, we can state either of the following lines of code to see if one of the above check boxes is true:

```
If chkAuthor.Value = True Then
    actions1...
End If
-------------------------
If chkAuthor Then
    actions2...
End If
```

We also use the ***Caption*** property to give a brief description to each check box. This is important as it will describe the selection being made if the check box is checked.

Summary

Form Object	**Suggested Name Prefix**
Check Box	chk
Common Properties	
Value	True/False
Caption	Text description of check box (no label control needed)

Option buttons imply a positive selection (that is, a *yes*, *true*, *on* value) when selected; the opposite is true if they are de-selected. To insert an option button into our form, we use the icon from the *Control Toolbox*. The option buttons should appear as shown in Figure 18.10 (even without the frame).

The name we give to an option button should begin with "opt" followed by a descriptive name. For example, if we have two option buttons, one of which is associated with buying and the other with selling, we could name them "optBuy" and "optSell," respectively.

We can use the *Value* property of option buttons as with *Boolean* variables. That is, we can state either of the following lines of code to see if one of the above option buttons is true:

```
If optBuy.Value = True Then
    actions1...
End If
-------------------------
If optBuy Then
    actions2...
End If
```

We also use the *Caption* property to give a brief description of each option button. This is important as it will describe the selection being made if the option button is selected.

Summary

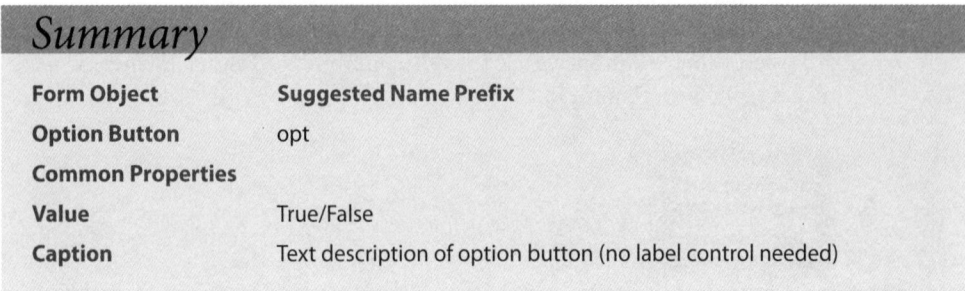

Form Object	Suggested Name Prefix
Option Button	opt
Common Properties	
Value	True/False
Caption	Text description of option button (no label control needed)

We can also use option buttons with a ***frame***. A frame groups similar controls together. For example, we can use it to group textboxes which contain related data or check boxes which apply to the same category. To insert a frame into the user form, we use the icon from the *Control Toolbox*. A frame which groups two option buttons is shown in Figure 18.10.

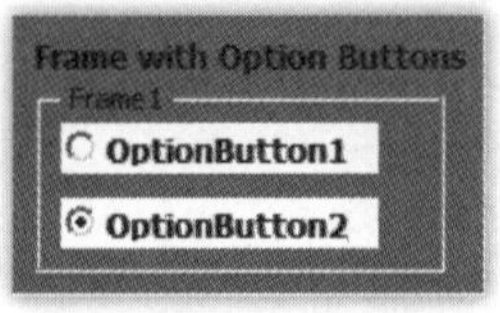

Figure 18.10 An example of a frame with two option buttons.

The name of a frame should begin with "fra" followed by a descriptive name. For example, if we have a frame which contains the buy/sell option buttons, we may name it "fraBuySell."

Frames primarily use the *Caption* property and *Visible* property. We can use the *Visible* property of a frame to set the *Visible* property of a group of controls. For example, if we have three textboxes in one frame, to make all of the textboxes not visible, we can just set the *Visible* property of the frame to *False*.

Frames become more interesting when applied to option buttons as this makes the option buttons mutually exclusive. That is, when we use option buttons without a frame, users can select more than one (as with check boxes). However, when we place option buttons inside a frame, the user can select only one at a time. This feature is only true for option buttons (not for check boxes or toggle buttons). This may be applicable in our buy/sell example above; users may only be allowed to buy or sell a selected control; both actions cannot be simultaneously performed.

Summary

Form Object	Suggested Name Prefix
Frame	fra
Common Properties	
Caption	Text value for title of frame
Visible	True/False

Toggle buttons are similar to check boxes and option buttons in that they imply a positive selection (that is, a *yes*, *true*, *on* value) when clicked; the opposite is true if they are un-clicked. To insert a toggle button, we use the icon from the *Control Toolbox*. The toggle button appears as shown in Figure 18.11.

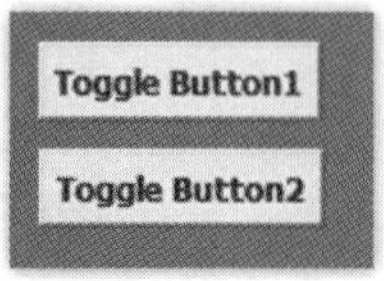

Figure 18.11 An example of a toggle button.

A toggle button name should begin with "tgl" followed by a descriptive name. For example, if we want to view data that is grouped by years, we may have several different toggle buttons associated with each year of data; we could then name those toggle buttons "tglYear1," "tglYear2," etc.

Toggle buttons also have values similar to those of *Boolean* variables. We can check the value of a toggle button by typing either of the following codes:

```
If tglYear1.Value = True Then
    actions1...
End If

-------------------------
If tglYear1 Then
    actions2......
End If
```

Toggle buttons also use the *Caption* property to give a brief description of what the toggle button will select. The caption appears directly on the button. We can also group toggle buttons in a frame; however, they do not become mutually exclusive.

Summary

Form Object	Suggested Name Prefix
Toggle Button	tgl
Common Properties	
Value	True/False
Caption	Text description of check box (no label control needed)

18.2.4 Command Buttons

We will use ***command buttons***, unlike the controls we have learned so far, for their associated event procedures more than for their properties. The only property we will use often with this control, aside from *Visible* possibly, is the *Caption* property (as with toggle buttons, the caption will appear directly on the button). To insert a command button, we use the icon from the *Control Toolbox*. The command button should appear as shown in Figure 18.12.

Figure 18.12 An example of a command button.

Command buttons should be named starting with "cmd" followed by some descriptive name. The two command buttons we will use most often will be called "cmdOK" and "cmdCancel."

Summary

Form Object	**Suggested Name Prefix**
Command Button	cmd
Common Properties	
Caption	Text displayed on button

18.2.5 Tab Strips and Multipage

Tab strips and multipage controls allow us to organize user input options.

Tab strips group data into different sections of this one control; all sections or ***tabs*** have the same layout. That is, one tab strip will have a set of controls which will appear on each tab. Each tab can be associated with a group of data to which the tab strip information belongs. For example, consider a customer contact database: each tab may have the textbox values for name, phone number, and address, but each tab title may be associated with a different customer.

To insert a tab strip, we use the icon from the Control Toolbox. The tab strip should appear as shown in Figure 18.13.

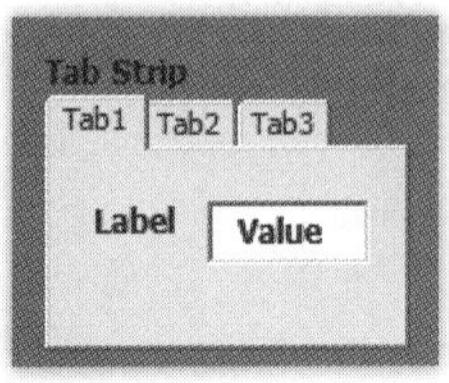

Figure 18.13 An example of a tab strip with two tabs.

A tab strip should be named starting with "tab" followed by a descriptive name. For example, if a tab strip contains tabs of information for different customers, it might be called "tabCustomers."

Since a tab strip is a collection of tab objects, different properties of tabs can be considered sub properties of a tab strip. To refer to a specific tab, say a specific customer in the above example, we can type:

tabCustomers.Tab(customer1)

The main property used with tab strips is to capture a selected value is ***SelectedControl***. We can find the number of tabs in the selected tab strip by using the ***Count*** method. To add a new tab to the tab strip, we simply right-click on the tab strip in the design view of the user form in the VBE and choose "new page" from the list of options.

The important characteristic to remember about tabs is that each tab contains the same set of controls. These control values can be changed or recorded based on the tab index which is selected by the users. Let us consider an example:

Suppose we have a form which displays the home, office, and cell phone numbers of a contact using a tab strip (see Figure 18.14). Each tab has only one textbox; however, the values of the textbox can change depending on which tab is selected. In the figure below, a different phone number is displayed when the Home Phone tab is selected (a) than when the Cell Phone tab is selected (b), but the same textbox control is used.

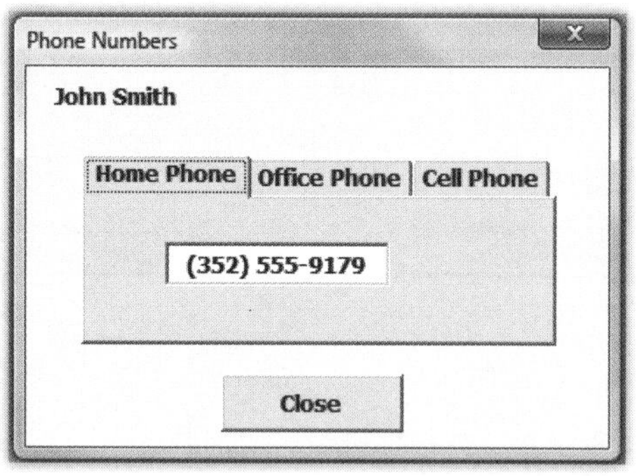

(a)

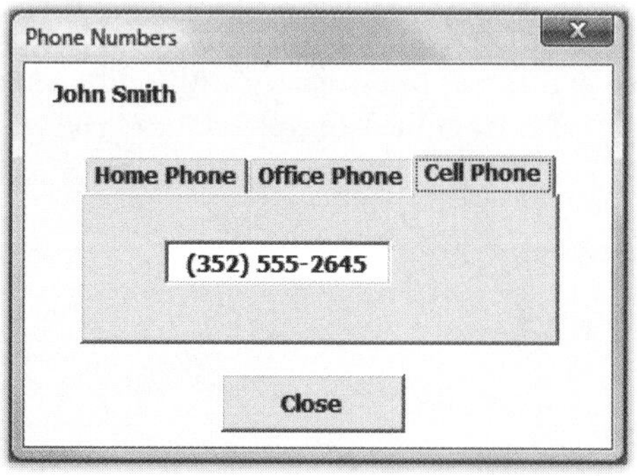

(b)

Figure 18.14 The tabs have the same *textbox* control, but different values are shown for different tabs.

To change the value of the textbox, we need to determine which tab the users have selected. Each tab has a numerical index which is stored as the tab strip value. In this example, the Home Phone tab is 0, Office Phone tab is 1, and Cell Phone tab is 2. We use the ***Change*** event procedure of the tab strip and a *Select Case* statement to check the value of the tab strip (see Figure 18.15). Depending on this value (0, 1, or 2), we update the textbox value accordingly.

```
Private Sub tabPhones_Change()

    Select Case tabPhones.Value
        Case 0
            txtPhNum.Value = "(352) 555-9179"
        Case 1
            txtPhNum.Value = "(352) 555-1293"
        Case 2
            txtPhNum.Value = "(352) 555-2645"
    End Select
End Sub
```

Figure 18.15 The *Change* event procedure for the tab strip.

Summary

Form Object	Suggested Name Prefix
Tab Strip	tab
Common Properties	
Value	Tab index
SelectedControl	
Count	

A ***multipage*** control, on the other hand, can be considered a collection of individual form objects, or ***pages***. Each page can have a different layout and is treated as a separate form. To insert a multipage, use the icon from the *Control Toolbox*. An example of a multipage control is shown in Figure 18.16.

Figure 18.16 An example of a multipage with three pages.

A multipage should be named starting with "mpg" followed by a descriptive name. We use the *Value* property with multipages to denote the index of the particular page.

It is important to remember that multipages are different from tab strips in that they have a unique set of controls per page. That is, in the tab strip example above, we had one textbox named *txtPhNum* which appeared on each tab. However, if we had used multipages in this example, the textbox on each page would be unique; for example, *txtPhNumHome, txtPhNumOffice, txtPhNumCell.*

Let us consider an example of a multipage. Suppose we are now not only keeping track of a contact's phone numbers, but mailing address, email address, and other notes as well (see Figure 18.17). In this case, we would want to use a multipage control instead of a tab strip because each category of information, that is, each page, requires a different set of controls. For example, for the Mailing Address page, we use several textboxes (a), whereas for the Notes page, we use combo boxes and option buttons (b).

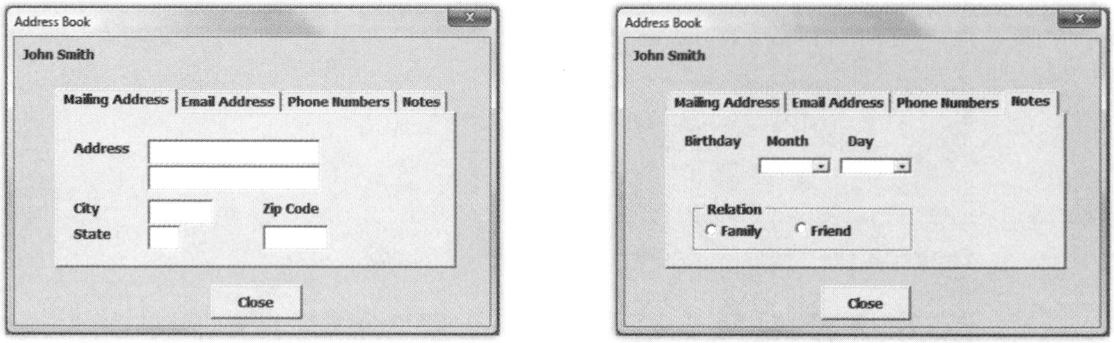

(a) (b)

Figure18.17 Each page of a multipage has a unique set of controls.

Since each control is unique, values can be changed or recorded for any control at any time. We can also use the *Change* event with multipages if we want to change some control values or properties when a page is selected.

Summary

Form Object	**Suggested Name Prefix**
Multipage	mpg
Common Properties	
Value	Page index

18.2.6 Scroll Bar and Spin Buttons

We use scroll bars and spin buttons to update values of other controls using event procedures.

Scroll bars can change text, numerical values, or other values of associated controls. To insert a scroll bar, we use the  icon from the *Control Toolbox*. An example of a scroll bar is shown in Figure 18.18.

Figure 18.18 An example of a scroll bar.

A scroll bar should be named starting with "scr" followed by a descriptive name. For example, if a scroll bar is associated with a textbox which displays some size value, it may be called "scrSize."

We can capture the value of the scroll bar, which is numerical, using the *Value* property. There are also the ***Min*** and ***Max*** properties, which we can set for the scroll bar values, along with a ***SmallChange*** and ***LargeChange*** property to specify how much the scroll bar value should change for each change in the scroll bar position. The *SmallChange* value is added or subtracted from the scroll bar value when the arrows are clicked; the *LargeChange* value is used when the bar is clicked. There is also an ***Orientation*** property, which we can use to set the scroll bar position to vertical or horizontal.

Summary

Form Object	**Suggested Name Prefix**
Scroll Bar	scr
Common Properties	
Min, Max	The minimum and maximum value possible
Small Change	The amount the value changes on the click of an arrow
Large Change	The amount the value changes on the click of the bar
Orientation	Either horizontal or vertical
Value	Numerical value

Spin buttons are similar to scroll bars, except that they only increment or decrement numerical values of other controls. To insert a spin button, we use the icon from the *Control Toolbox*. An example of a spin button is shown in Figure 18.19.

Figure 18.19 An example of a spin button.

A spin button name should start with "spn" followed by a descriptive name. For example, if we have a spin button associated with inserting the height of different subjects in some research, it may be called "spnHeight."

We also use the *Value* property and *Min, Max*, and *SmallChange* properties. We can also apply the *Orientation* property to spin buttons.

Summary

Form Object	**Suggested Name Prefix**
Spin Button	spn
Common Properties	
Min, Max	The minimum and maximum value possible
Small Change	The amount the value changes on the click of an arrow
Orientation	Either horizontal or vertical
Value	Numerical value

18.2.7 Images and RefEdit

Images allow us to display a picture in the form. To insert an image, we use the icon from the *Control Toolbox*. An example of an image window is shown in Figure 18.20.

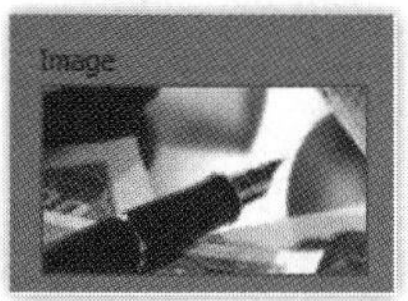

Figure 18.20 An example of an image window.

An image can be named starting with "img" and the picture name. To assign an image to the image window, we use the ***Picture*** property and *Browse* options. We can use the ***PictureAlignment*** and ***PictureSizeMode*** properties to adjust the alignment and size of our image (all other editing should be done outside Excel).

Summary

Form Object	**Suggested Name Prefix**
Image	img
Common Properties	
Picture	Picture assigned to the window
PictureAlignment	Alignment of image
PictureSizeMode	Size of image

We use ***RefEdit*** to select or enter a worksheet range. There is a button, similar to what is used in Excel dialog boxes, which allows the users to collapse the form while they select a range directly from the worksheet. To insert a RefEdit control, we use the icon from the *Control Toolbox*. An example of a RefEdit control is shown in Figure 18.21.

Figure 18.21 An example of a RefEdit control.

The name for RefEdit should begin with "ref" followed by a descriptive name. For example, we could name the RefEdit control "refOutput" if we plan to store some output range in this control value. To capture the range the users have selected, we use the *Value* property; this value will be a *string variable* type and so can only be assigned to a string variable. [*Note:* Right click on the *Control Toolbox* and select *Additional Controls* from the short-cut menu to add additional controls to the toolbox.]

Summary

Form Object	Suggested Name Prefix
RefEdit	ref
Common Properties	
Value	Selected range

18.3 User Form Options

There are some properties associated with the user form itself which can be useful. There are several ***Position*** properties that can be modified. To view these, we use the ***Categorized*** tab of the *Properties Window* and scroll to the *Position* category. The values of these positions are relative to the left and top margins of the worksheet and are measured with Excel's point system. To align several controls on the form, we can select them (by dragging our cursor around the controls or holding down Shift and clicking them) and then right-click and choose ***Align*** from the list of drop-down options. We will then see several choices on how to align the controls.

Another property of the user form is ***ShowModal***. When set to *True*, the form must be completed (and/or some command button which closes the form should be clicked) before the users can return to the program or use any worksheets. However, when this property is set to *False*, the form becomes *modeless*, or a ***floating form***. When the user form is modeless, actions can occur on the worksheet and the program can continue while the form is still showing. This can be useful for navigational purposes or to have a constant set of options always available to the users. We use floating forms in some of our case studies. [*Note:* There are some restrictions applied to modeless forms; for example the RefEdit control cannot be used on modeless forms.]

There are some general properties that apply to the user form as well as to most controls. These include general formatting properties such as ***Font***, ***BackColor***, ***ForeColor***, etc. As we have mentioned already, some other common properties found for most if not all controls are *Name*, *Caption*, and *Visible*. There are three other important common properties used with most/all controls: ***TabIndex***, ***TabStop***, and ***Locked***.

TabIndex and *TabStop* control the tabbing order in which the users can move through controls on the user form with the *Tab* button of their keyboard. The *TabIndex* property takes a numerical value from 1 to the number of controls on the user form, 1 being the first control visited when *Tab* is pressed. We can set the *TabStop* property to *True* or *False* depending on whether or not we want the users to be able to select a certain control.

Similar to *TabStop*, the *Locked* property takes *True* or *False* values and allows us to prevent the users from entering or changing any values of a control. This may be useful if, for example, we want to have sequential forms and to show some of the data entered on the first form in a form or forms which follow. The control will appear darkened, and its value, if any, will be displayed, but the users will not be able to modify the control value if the *Locked* property is set to *True*.

Another useful property of the controls on a user form is ***ControlTipText***. This property allows us to enter some text to serve as brief instructions to the users to explain what a particular control will do. For example, we could enter the *ControlTipText* "Click here when you are done" for a command button. This text will appear when users bring their cursor over the control. This property is available on all form controls.

Summary

Form Object	Suggested Name Prefix
User Form	frm
Common Properties	
Position	Relative to the left and top margins of the worksheet
Align	Used to align several controls on the form
ShowModal	True/False; False creates a floating form
Misc Form Properties	
Font, BackColor, ForeColor	
TabIndex	Index of tab order
TabStop	True/False to allow users to stop or not stop at this control by tabbing
Locked	True/False to allow users to be able to modify or not modify a control value
ControlTipText	Text displayed when users bring cursor over control

18.4 Event Procedures

Event procedures are code procedures which are associated with an event or action that occurs on a control. (We have seen event procedures in Chapter 12 and the *Workbook_Open* procedure in Chapter 13.) There are many event procedures that can be associated with the action of the user form controls. To find the unique list of events for each control, we simply select the name of the control from the upper-left drop-down list of the code view of a particular form. For example, in Figure 18.22, we have selected the option button *optChoice1* from the list of controls on a previously created form.

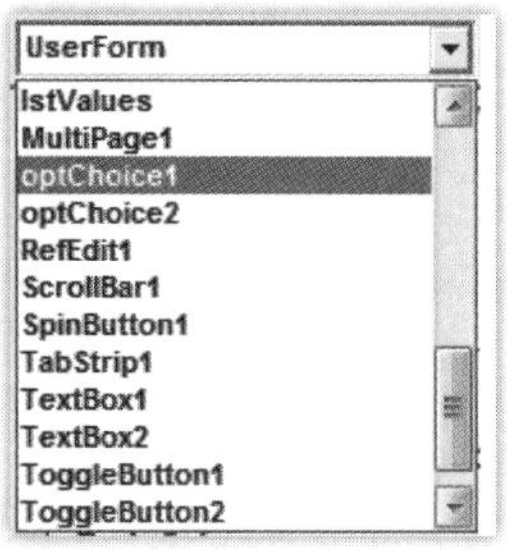

Figure 18.22 Select a control from the list in the code view of a created form.

Once we have selected a control, the drop-down list in the upper right-hand corner of the code window will have a list of events, or actions, associated with that particular control. For example, after selecting *optChoice* from the list of controls, we see the list of associated events in Figure 18.23.

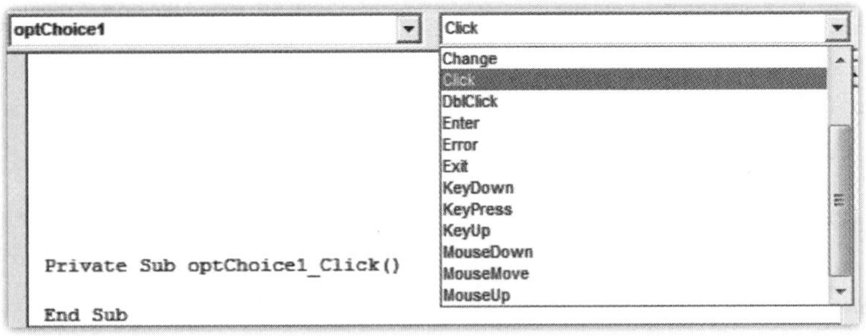

Figure 18.23 Each control has a list of associated events.

Although there are several events available for each control, we will explain a few of the more common ones. The first event procedure that will commonly be used in a form, is the ***Initialize*** procedure of the user form. This procedure will run when the form is first opened. It is a good idea to set default values for textboxes in this code. This is also the procedure in which we would set the *RowSource* of a combo box or list box. We may also set some controls to be visible or not visible in this code. It is important to have default values for the users so that they are further informed on the type of input we want from them. (It also helps to make trial runs quicker when debugging if there are already some values in the form.) However, remember that we can set many initial values using the properties window of each control (*Value*, *Visible*, *RowSource*, etc). We recommend only coding the dynamic properties of the controls in this initialization procedure.

The main event procedure associated with command buttons is the ***Click*** event. For the "cmdOK" button, for example, the event procedure associated with this button would be where we may assign variables to textbox values or create an *If, Then* statement with some option buttons.

We may want to show another form after the users have finished filling out the current form. To do this, we use the ***Show*** method of the form object. We simply state the name of the user form we want to show next followed by the *Show* method.

We will almost always close the current form at the end of this event procedure. To do this, we use the ***Unload Me*** statement. *Me* refers to the current form object; we can use *Unload* with any form object name. The event procedure associated with the "cmdCancel" button will usually just have this line of code and the *End* statement. Examples of these event procedures may be as follows:

```
Sub cmdOK_Click()
    quantity = txtQuantity.Value

    With fraBuySell
        If .optBuyThen
            actions1...
        ElseIf .optSell Then
            actions2....
        End If
    End With
```

```
    Unload Me
    frmMenu.Show
End Sub
_________________________
Sub cmdCancel_Click()
    Unload Me
    End
End Sub
```

We most commonly use the ***Change***, or ***Scroll***, event procedures to associate the change in the scroll bar values with an effect on another control value. We may have the following code associated with the *Change* event of the "scrSize" scroll bar which affects the value of a textbox called "txtSize":

```
Sub scrSize_Change()
    scrSize.Min = 1
    scrSize.Max = 30
    scrSize.SmallChange = 1

    Select Case scrSize.Value
        Case 1 to 5
            txtSize.Value = "too small"
        Case 6 to 15
            txtSize.Value = "small range, but good"
        Case 16 to 25
            txtSize.Value = "large range, but good"
        Case 26 to 30
            txtSize.Value = "too large"
        End Select
End Sub
```

Spin buttons also use the *Change* event procedure primarily to associate its values with the values of another control. An example of transferring the "spnHeight" values to a textbox called "txtHeight" might be as follows:

```
Sub spnHeight_Change()
    spnHeight.Min = 4.5
    spnHeightMax = 7.0
    spnHeight.SmallChange = 0.25

    txtHeight.Value = spnHeight.Value
End Sub
```

One more common event procedure is the *After Update* procedure. We can use this with textboxes to perform some actions immediately after the users enter a value. For example, we may ask users to enter a date in one textbox, called *txtDate*, and want to display to them the day for this date in another textbox, called *txtDay*. We may therefore write an event procedure as follows:

```
Sub txtDate_AfterUpdate()
    txtDay.Value = FindDay(txtDate.Value)
End Sub
```

Here we have referred to a function called *FindDay* to find the corresponding day for the date given by the users. (How would we write this function? *Hint*: we use an Excel spreadsheet function.)

For option buttons and check boxes, we most commonly use the *Click* and *Change* events. If the *Click* event occurs, then the users have clicked on the option button or check box. This event does not imply the value of the option button or check box; that is, we will need to check if it is true or false. The *Change* event implies that the value of the option button or check box has changed. That is, if we know that the control was initialized to be true, then if the *Change* event occurs, we know it is now false.

Summary

Form Object	Common Events
User Form	Initialize
Command Button	Click
Scroll Bar	Change, Scroll
Spin Button	Change
Textbox	After Update
Tab Strip	Change
Multipage	Change
Options Buttons and Check Boxes	Click, Change

18.5 *Variable Scope*

We should now understand the scope of the variables used in the form code window, which we can refer to as the form module. Remember the general variable scope rules discussed in Chapter 14: a variable declared within a procedure can only be used within that procedure, but a variable declared as a public variable in a module can be used in any procedure in that module or in any other module, including the form module. Any variable declared within a form module, however, can only be used directly in the procedures for that particular form. Even if a variable is declared as a public variable within a form module, it is public only in that module. Consider the following code within the *frmMain* module:

```
Public UserInput As Integer

Sub cmdOK_Click()
    UserInput = txtInput.Value

    Unload Me
End Sub
```

Even though the integer variable *UserInput* has been declared as a public variable in the form module, we cannot refer to it directly in any other module. That is, if we wanted to use the input value the users gave in the *txtInput* textbox on the form in another module in the application, we could not use the *UserInput* variable as is.

In order to refer to a public form variable outside of the form module, we have to provide the name of the form before the variable name. (*Note:* this is only true for public variables.) That is, to refer to the *UserInput* variable outside of the *frmMain* code, we must type the following:

```
frmMain.UserInput
```

In the same way, we can use the form name to refer to any of its controls outside of the form module. That is, to change the property of a form control in another module, we might type the following:

```
frmMain.lblQuantity.Visible = True
```

However, it is important to keep in mind that all form control values are reset when we use the *Unload Me* statement. Therefore, if we are intending to refer to a control value, that is any input users have entered or selected on a form, in a later procedure in another module, we must call that procedure before making the *Unload Me* statement in the form code. For example, to use the value entered by users for the textbox *txtInput* in a later procedure, called *Calculations*, we would have to type the following:

```
Sub cmdOK_Click()
    'txtInput.Value has been entered by user

    Call Calculations
    Unload Me
End Sub
```

However, we must keep in mind that we also use the *Unload Me* statement to close the form. That is, we do not want to bring the users through the rest of the application with the initial input form still displayed. We therefore generally recommend assigning form control values to variables defined as public variables outside of the form module. This allows us to make the *Unload Me* statement without losing the variable values. To rewrite the code in the example above, we would type the following (assume we have declared *UserInput* as a public variable in another module):

```
Sub cmdOK_Click()
    UserInput = txtInput.Value

    Unload Me
    Call Calculations
End Sub
```

18.6 *Error Checking*

As we discussed with Input Boxes in Chapter 14, any time we are receiving something from the users, we have to check for errors. We showed several simple error-checking methods in Chapter 16 using *If, Then* statements and some functions to check if user values are the same data type as the variables we are assigning to them. We can also use these structures and functions to check the values given in forms. We can simply check the control value's data type before assigning it to a variable.

Another important thing to check in forms is if the users entered values for multiple controls. For example, if we have three textboxes for input, we may want to make sure that they completely fill the form. There are a few special statements that we can use to loop through all of the structures in our form. Let us first look at the final code and then explain each part. In the code below, we are checking all of the textboxes in the forms to ensure that the users have provided numerical values:

```
Dim ctl As Control
For Each ctl In Me.Controls
    If TypeName(ctl) = "TextBox" Then
        If ctl.Value = "" or IsNumeric(ctl) = False Then
            MsgBox "Please enter a numeric value in all textboxes."
            ctl.SetFocus
            End Sub
        End If
    End If
Next
```

The first thing we do in this code is define a variable as a ***Control*** data type. The *Control* data type is another example of an object data type; this is similar to our usage of the worksheet data type in the *Workbook_Open* procedure. We then use a *For Each, Next* loop to check all of the controls in our form. The statement *Me* always refers to the form itself; therefore ***Me.Controls*** refers to the set of controls in the current form. (This is again similar to how we loop through all worksheets in the current workbook using the statement *ActiveWorkbook.Worksheets.*) We now want to find out if the control is a textbox or not; that is, we do not need to check the values of the command buttons or other controls that may not interest us at this point. To determine the type of control, we use the ***TypeName*** function with an *If,Then* statement. If we have found a "TextBox," then we check if the value of the textbox is empty or non-numeric. If this is the case, we display a message to the users to clarify that all textboxes should have numeric values. Before ending the procedure, we make the statement ***ctl.SetFocus***. Setting the focus will select the control we found to cause an error so that the users' cursor is in the first place where an error was found.

We can use this structure to check if textboxes intended to hold dates actually have date values if at least one check box or option button has been selected and if at least one control from a list box or combo box has been selected. We usually place this simple error-checking code at the beginning of our *cmdOK_Click* procedures if there are multiple inputs from the users.

Summary

Control	An object data type which refers to a form control.
Me.Controls	*Me* refers to the current form. *Me.Controls* refers to the set of controls in the current form.
TypeName	This function determines the type of control ("TextBox," "ComboBox," "CheckBox," etc.).
ctl.SetFocus	*SetFocus* selects the current control so that the users' cursor is brought to the location of the error.

18.7 *Importing and Exporting Forms*

Any form we create can be exported or saved as a template. This is very helpful if we are creating an application with many similar forms or if we are creating many applications with some basic form similarities. For example, we may want to create a standard form template with an introductory label and two command buttons for OK and Cancel (see Figure 18.24); we could also save some basic coding with the form. To save a form as a template, we simply right-click on the form name in the *Project Explorer* and choose **Export File** from the list of options. (We can also go to *File > Export File* if the form we want to save is currently selected in the code window.) We will then save our form as a ".frm" file type. Note that any time we try to remove a form (by right-clicking on the form and selecting *Remove Form*), we will be prompted to export the form first.

To use a form template or import a form, we can again select any form from the *Project Explorer* window and right-click. This time we choose **Import File** from the list of options. (We can also go to *File > Import File* at any time.) Then, we simply select the form we want to import. Note, however, that we cannot import a form which is already in use in another application. To avoid this error, we simply change the name of the form that is already in use and then import our template. For example, if we have a standard form template which we named *frmBasic*, we may want to import it several times within the same application. To do this without causing an error, we simply change the name of the form (using the *Properties* window) after each import.

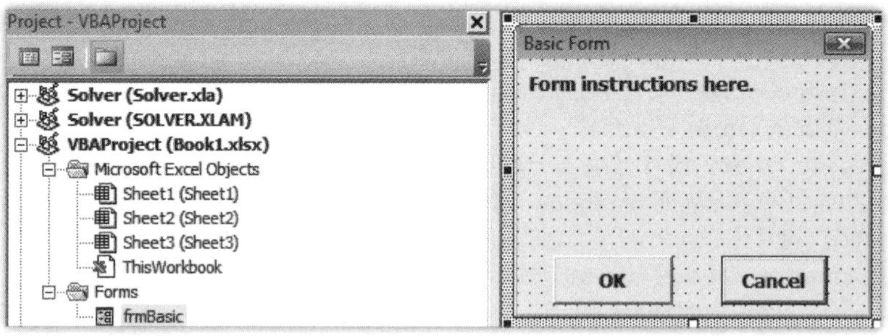

Figure 18.24 Basic form template.

18.8 *Navigating*

We have already discussed some navigational techniques to help the users move through the program as needed. These techniques are all part of designing a good user interface.

Buttons, or shapes, on the spreadsheet are usually a great tool for navigating the users not only through different sheets of the program, but also through different steps or actions. We might label some of these buttons "Next," "Back," "Exit," "Start," or "View Example." We should place them at the top of the worksheet in a visible spot. The code for these macros can be identical or call an identical function (as seen in Chapter 15). Thus these navigational tools can be beneficial to the users without adding too much code to the program.

A useful property of these buttons, or shape objects, is the *Visible* property. By naming these buttons appropriately, we can use the *Shape* object and *Visible* property to hide and show different buttons. This is a good way to prevent users from being confused or overwhelmed by too many options. For example, we may initially only show some instructions on a worksheet and a "Done" button. Then, after the users press the "Done" button and the users' actions have been recorded by an assigned macro, a "Next" button can appear, and the "Done" button can disappear. This lets the users know that they should now move on to the next worksheet.

As we explained in Chapter 15, we can also use the index value of worksheets in creating navigating procedures. To find the index value (or tab number) of a worksheet, we can simply use its Index property. For example, if we write the code *MsgBox Worksheets("Sheet 1").Index*, a Message Box with the value 1 would be shown. Once we know a worksheet's index value, we can simply refer to it by this index (instead of by the worksheet name). For example, instead of writing *Worksheets("Sheet 1").Visible = True*, we could write *Worksheets(1).Visible = True.*

18.9 Professional Appearance

Part of developing a good user interface involves creating a user-friendly environment. Our application should give clear instructions to the users on what to do and what not to do. There should not be too many options to overwhelm the users, and the users should not be able to accidentally cause many errors with our program. There are a few simple options available in Excel which can bring our application to a more professional level and create a more user-friendly environment.

18.9.1 Protecting the Worksheet

To prevent users from changing formatting or title values in any worksheet tables or other features, we can protect the worksheet. To do this, we use the ***Locked*** property of a range of cells. For any cells in which the users will need to enter values or in which the program may enter values, we set the value of the *Locked* property to *False*. Then, we leave the *Locked* property of all other cells to the *True* default value. Any cell which is locked cannot be modified.

After we lock and unlock the appropriate cells, we click on *Home > Cells > Format* command from the Ribbon. From the drop-down list, we select *Protect Sheet* option. We will be prompted to enter a protection password, and then we can set the specific options which the users will no longer be able to perform with locked cells.

This can be a very useful tool for creating the finished version of our program. However, we must be aware that any cells whose values are also modified by the code (read from or written to) will have to be unlocked in the code when necessary and locked again if needed. For example, if a particular input range is locked, but we want to input new data via some code (using input either from an Input Box or user form), we might type the following:

```
With Range("Input")
    .Locked = False
    .Value = UserInput
    .Locked = True
End With
```

Another way to prevent users from modifying cell values is to hide rows or columns in our worksheet. We can do this using the ***Hidden*** property; this property takes the values *True* or *False* (see Chapter 13). We simply specify some cell or range of cells and then use the *Hidden* property with the *Rows* or *Columns* property of the *Range* object. For example, to hide the rows containing the range *A1:B4*, we would type the following:

```
Range("A1:B4").Rows.Hidden = True
```

Aside from hiding or protecting ranges in our spreadsheets, we may also want to protect our VBA code. To do this, we select the name of our project in the Project Window and right-click. We select ***VBAProject Properties*** from the drop-down list. A window will appear allowing us to enter *General* summary information for our project (name, description, etc). If we click on the *Protection* tab, we can then choose to "Lock project for viewing." We can then specify a password to use in order to unlock and view our code.

18.9.2 Sheet Options

There are some other options which we can set for each worksheet in our program to finalize the version which the users will see. These are not necessary nor do they affect the program performance; they can, however, make our program look more professional.

To view these options, we select the *View* tab from the *Ribbon*. For example, the *View* > *Show* group on the *Ribbon* lists options to hide *gridlines*, hide the *formula bar*, and hide row/column *headings*. The *View* > *Workbook Views* > *Full Screen* command when active, hides the *Ribbon*. We recommend not selecting these options until after we have performed all final debugging and testing so that editing is easier.

18.10 Applications

18.10.1 Real Estate Search Spreadsheet Application

As we mentioned in Chapter 12, we can also place controls on the spreadsheet. This application uses the properties and events of the controls explained above in a small spreadsheet application for real estate search. Note that when we use controls on the spreadsheet, all of the code associated with the controls placed on the spreadsheet is located in the code window for the spreadsheet object in the Project Window.

Let us consider a real estate search application in which users can search for houses based on certain criteria. This search is performed on an Excel database of real estate data, as shown in Figure 18.25. The criteria for this search include a maximum price, minimum area (square feet), minimum number of bedrooms, minimum number of bathrooms, and location in the city. Figure 18.26 shows the application with the result of one search made using the selected criteria.

Address	Agent	Price	Area	Bedrooms	Bathrooms	Location
6743 NW 13th St	S. Jones	$110,000	1126	2	1	Northwest
1234 NW 32nd Ave	P. Macon	$130,000	1346	2	2	Northwest
498 SE 37th Ave	P. Macon	$145,000	1541	2	2	Southeast
234 NE 14th Ave	P. Macon	$157,000	1616	3	2	Northeast
3621 NE 12th Ave	S. Jones	$168,000	1713	4	2	Northeast
453 SE 34th St	E. Amber	$170,000	1766	4	3	Southeast
687 NE 12th Ave	S. Jones	$175,000	1828	5	2	Northeast
378 NE 13th St	E. Amber	$180,000	1834	5	3	Northeast
4213 SW 4th St	E. Amber	$125,000	1200	3	2	Southwest

Figure 18.25 The real estate Excel database.

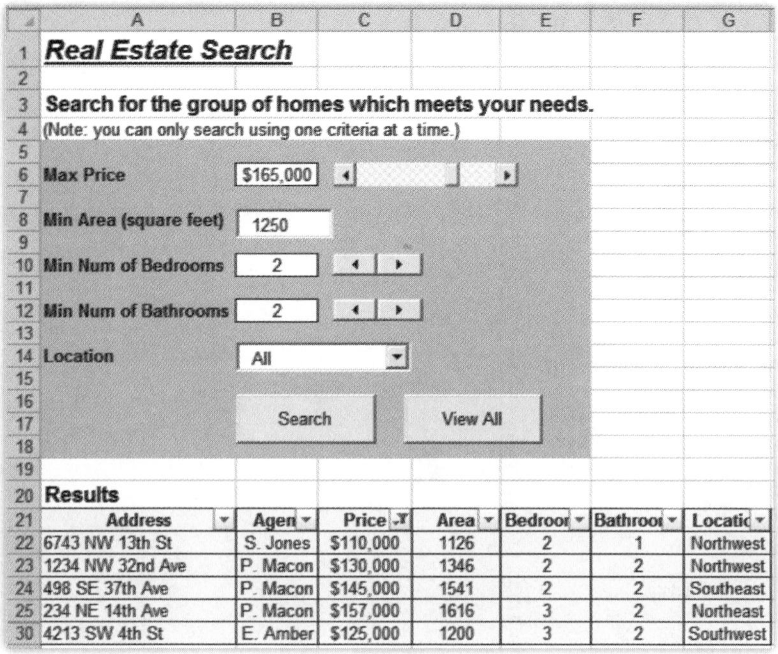
Real Estate Search
Search for the group of homes which meets your needs.
(Note: you can only search using one criteria at a time.)
Max Price
$165,000
Min Area (square feet)
1250
Min Num of Bedrooms
2
Min Num of Bathrooms
2
Location
All
Search
View All
Results
Address
Agen
Price
Area
Bedroor
Bathroor
Locatic
6743 NW 13th St
S. Jones
$110,000
1126
2
1
Northwest
1234 NW 32nd Ave
P. Macon
$130,000
1346
2
2
Northwest
498 SE 37th Ave
P. Macon
$145,000
1541
2
2
Southeast
234 NE 14th Ave
P. Macon
$157,000
1616
3
2
Northeast
4213 SW 4th St
E. Amber
$125,000
1200
3
2
Southwest

Figure 18.26 The real estate search application.

Let us first understand the design of the application by looking at the controls and their properties. We use five different control types in the criteria section of the spreadsheet: a scroll bar, a textbox, two spin buttons, a combo box, and two command buttons. These controls, used in the spreadsheet, have almost exactly the same set of properties that they do when used in the form. We will specify different properties which are important.

We first use a scroll bar to determine the max price criteria. We place the scroll bar on the spreadsheet using *ActiveX Controls* toolbox that appears on the click of *Developer > Controls > Insert* command from the *Ribbon. We use* the *Properties* dialog box (see Figure 18.27) to change the value of a number of properties of the scroll bar. We begin by naming the control *scrPrice*. As mentioned in above sections, the most important properties of the scroll bar are its *Max* and *Min* values and its *SmallChange* and *LargeChange* values. We set the *Max* value at 200,000 and the *Min* value at 75,000 to model the price range of the houses available. We then set the *SmallChange value* to 1,000 and *LargeChange* values to 10,000. As we explained above with event procedures, we will usually connect a scroll bar to a textbox to display the value of the scroll bar. However, when using controls on the spreadsheet, there is an extra property which relieves the need for this procedure: this is the ***LinkedCell*** property. The *LinkedCell* property holds the value of a cell name in which the value of the control will be displayed. In this application, we set the *LinkedCell* property of the scroll bar to *B6*. We then format this cell as currency so that whenever the scroll bar value changes, the price is shown in the cell.

We insert a textbox for the users to specify the minimum area criteria. We name the control *txtArea* and do not set any other property values.

The next two controls are spin buttons. We use these to determine the minimum number of bedrooms and bathrooms in the criteria. We name them *spnBed* and *spnBath*, respectively. The most important properties for spin buttons are *Max*, *Min*, and *SmallChange*. For *spnBed*, we set the value of these properties equal to 5, 1, and 1, respectively. For *spnBath* we set the value of these properties equal to 3, 1, and 1, respectively. We also use the *LinkedCell* property for both of these controls in order to display the values of the spin buttons. For *spnBed*, we set the *LinkedCell* property to *B10*. For *spnBath*, we set the *LinkedCell* property to *B12*.

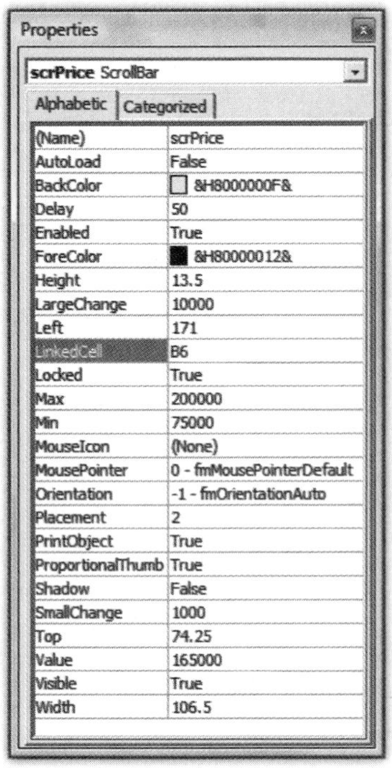
Properties
scrPrice ScrollBar
Alphabetic
Categorized
(Name) scrPrice
AutoLoad False
BackColor &H8000000F&
Delay 50
Enabled True
ForeColor &H80000012&
Height 13.5
LargeChange 10000
Left 171
LinkedCell B6
Locked True
Max 200000
Min 75000
MouseIcon (None)
MousePointer 0 - fmMousePointerDefault
Orientation -1 - fmOrientationAuto
Placement 2
PrintObject True
ProportionalThumb True
Shadow False
SmallChange 1000
Top 74.25
Value 165000
Visible True
Width 106.5

Figure 18.27 The properties for the scroll bar.

The last criteria control is a combo box which we use to specify the location of the house. We name this combo box *cmbLocation*. As explained above, the most relevant property of a combo box or list box is the *RowSource* property. This property sets the range of values which will be listed in the box. When using a combo box or list box on the spreadsheet, the *RowSource* property is called the ***ListFillRange***. In cells *I5:I8*, we list the names of the four regions, or locations, where houses can be found: *Northwest, Southwest, Northeast*, and *Southeast*. We also have *All* listed as an option to view all locations. We name this range "Location," as shown in Figure 18.28. We then hide the column which contains these cells so that the users do not see them when running the application. To do this, we can simply right-click on the column heading and choose *Hide* from the list of options.

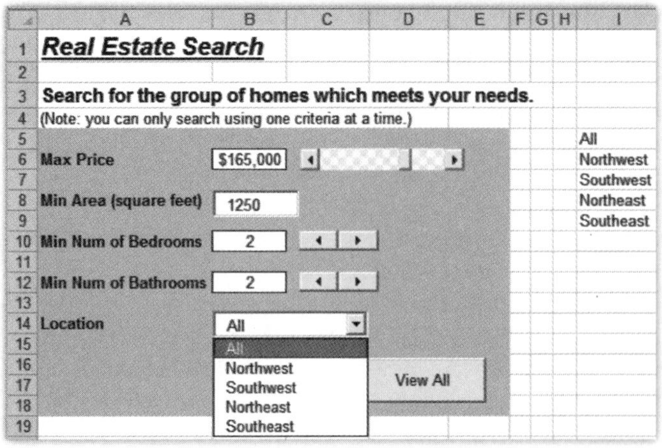

Figure 18.28 Hidden columns contain the data for the combo box.

The last controls we place on the spreadsheet are the two command buttons. We first create a "Search" button, named *cmdSearch*, which we will use to capture the current values of all the controls as search criteria. We then create a "View All" button, named *cmdReset*, which we will use to reset any filtering done and show the original database.

After completing the design and formatting of the criteria section of the spreadsheet, we are ready to code. We will use the *Click* event procedure of the *cmdSearch* button to filter the house information based on the criteria specified. In order to filter the house data, we will be using the *AutoFilter* method (see Chapter 12). Since we will always be filtering the same range of data, which is the original Excel database, we will name this range "Houses" for easier reference. For the price and area criteria, we will also be using a custom filter since we are not searching based on known values from the data, but rather from user-provided values. The general structure of the filter method using a custom filter is as follows:

Range("Houses").AutoFilter Field:=(number), Criteria:= "(inequality)" (value), Operator:=xlAnd

We remember that when filtering data, each field refers to a column (see Chapter 10). The field numbers we will use are based on the following matching: Address = 1, Agent = 2, Price = 3, Area = 4, Bedrooms = 5, Bathrooms = 6, Location = 7. For the price criteria, the inequality will be "<=". For the area criteria, the inequality will be ">=". For the number of bedrooms and number of bathrooms, the inequality will also be ">=". For the location criteria, we can ignore the inequality and just give the value (we can also ignore the Operator argument). The values for each criterion will be the value of the control which is involved in the criterion. The code is shown in Figure 18.29.

```
Private Sub cmdSearch_Click()
    ShowAll
    'price
    Range("Houses").AutoFilter field:=3, Criteria1:="<=" & scrPrice.Value, Operator:=xlAnd
    'area
    Range("Houses").AutoFilter field:=4, Criteria1:=">=" & txtArea.Value, Operator:=xlAnd
    'bedrooms
    Range("Houses").AutoFilter field:=5, Criteria1:=">=" & spnBed.Value
    'bathrooms
    Range("Houses").AutoFilter field:=6, Criteria1:=">=" & spnBath.Value
    'location
    If cmbLocation.Value <> "All" Then
        Range("Houses").AutoFilter field:=7, Criteria1:=cmbLocation.Value
    End If
End Sub
```

Figure 18.29 Code window for all five Change event procedures.

We will now write code for the *cmdReset* button. This will also be a *Click* event procedure. In this event we want to remove all filtering from the data. To remove any filtering, we simply type the *AutoFilter* method without any fields or criteria:

Range("Houses").AutoFilter

The event procedure for the cmdReset command button is shown in Figure 18.30.

```
Private Sub cmdReset_Click()
    Range("Houses").AutoFilter
End Sub
```

Figure 18.30 Command button *Click* event procedure.

We are almost finished at this point. However, we notice that if we run our code as is, there is a slight problem with the filtering: whatever filtering is done first remains as multiple criteria are specified. This means that if the users first specify a 2-bedroom house and then click to see what 3-bathroom houses are available, we will filter for 2 bedroom houses with 3 bathrooms instead of for all houses with 3 bathrooms. Therefore, before each criterion's filtering is done, we must first reset our data to be unfiltered. We know this code from the *cmdReset_Click* event procedure above. We could simply enter this line of code in each previously created event procedure, or we can create a small function procedure to call multiple times. In Figure 18.31, we have created a function procedure called *ShowAll*, which we call from each event procedure, including the *cmdReset_Click* event procedure.

```
Sub ShowAll()
    Application.ScreenUpdating = False
    For i = 3 To 7
        Range("Houses").AutoFilter field:=i
    Next i
    Application.ScreenUpdating = True
End Sub
```

Figure 18.31 Final code with the *ShowAll* function procedure.

There is one last event procedure to write which is equivalent to *Userform_Initialize*; this is the *Worksheet_Activate* procedure (see Figure 18.32). We could use this procedure to call the *ShowAll* function to ensure that the entire house data is displayed when the users first open the application. We can also ensure that the row source of the combo box is initialized; again, we use the *ListFillRange* property of the spreadsheet combo box to do this. The application is now complete.

```
Private Sub Worksheet_Activate()
    ShowAll
    cmbLocation.ListFillRange = "Location"
End Sub
```

Figure 18.32 We use the *Worksheet_Activate* event procedure to reset the database and set the row source of the combo box.

18.10.2 Product Search Form

In this application, we are designing a search form for a product in a computer product database. The program finds a product based on certain search priorities and search criteria.

There are only two sheets needed for this application: "Products Search" and "Products Database." The "Products Search" sheet is the welcome sheet (see Figure 18.33). We give a brief description of the application, and there is a *Start* button.

The "Products Database" sheet contains the Excel database through which we search for products which meet the users' criteria. The users, however, never see this sheet (see Figure 18.34).

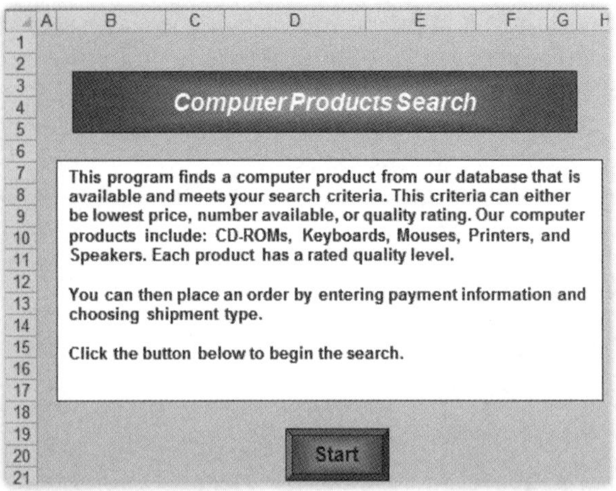

Figure 18.33 The welcome sheet is called "Products Search."

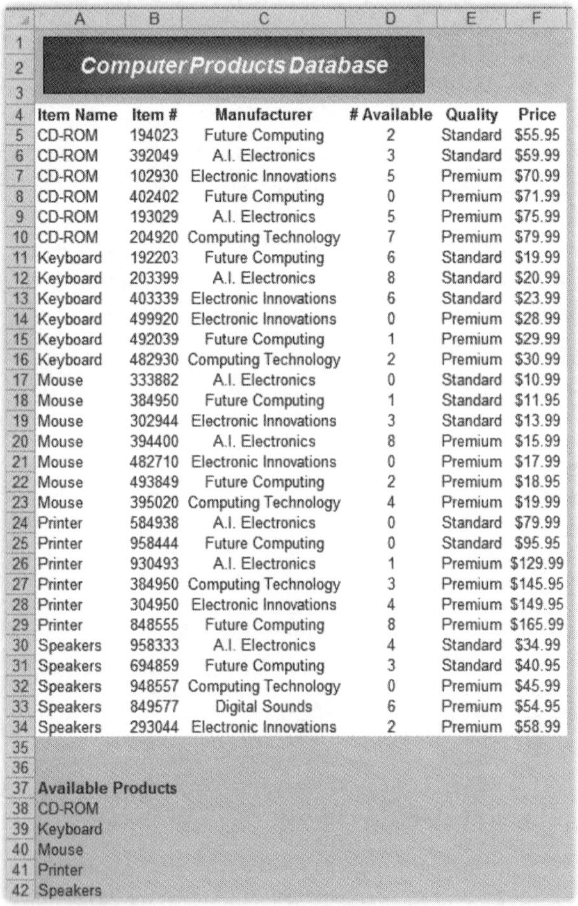

Item Name	Item #	Manufacturer	# Available	Quality	Price
CD-ROM	194023	Future Computing	2	Standard	$55.95
CD-ROM	392049	A.I. Electronics	3	Standard	$59.99
CD-ROM	102930	Electronic Innovations	5	Premium	$70.99
CD-ROM	402402	Future Computing	0	Premium	$71.99
CD-ROM	193029	A.I. Electronics	5	Premium	$75.99
CD-ROM	204920	Computing Technology	7	Premium	$79.99
Keyboard	192203	Future Computing	6	Standard	$19.99
Keyboard	203399	A.I. Electronics	8	Standard	$20.99
Keyboard	403339	Electronic Innovations	6	Standard	$23.99
Keyboard	499920	Electronic Innovations	0	Premium	$28.99
Keyboard	492039	Future Computing	1	Premium	$29.99
Keyboard	482930	Computing Technology	2	Premium	$30.99
Mouse	333882	A.I. Electronics	0	Standard	$10.99
Mouse	384950	Future Computing	1	Standard	$11.95
Mouse	302944	Electronic Innovations	3	Standard	$13.99
Mouse	394400	A.I. Electronics	8	Premium	$15.99
Mouse	482710	Electronic Innovations	0	Premium	$17.99
Mouse	493849	Future Computing	2	Premium	$18.95
Mouse	395020	Computing Technology	4	Premium	$19.99
Printer	584938	A.I. Electronics	0	Standard	$79.99
Printer	958444	Future Computing	0	Standard	$95.95
Printer	930493	A.I. Electronics	1	Premium	$129.99
Printer	384950	Computing Technology	3	Premium	$145.95
Printer	304950	Electronic Innovations	4	Premium	$149.95
Printer	848555	Future Computing	8	Premium	$165.99
Speakers	958333	A.I. Electronics	4	Standard	$34.99
Speakers	694859	Future Computing	3	Standard	$40.95
Speakers	948557	Computing Technology	0	Premium	$45.99
Speakers	849577	Digital Sounds	6	Premium	$54.95
Speakers	293044	Electronic Innovations	2	Premium	$58.99

Available Products
CD-ROM
Keyboard
Mouse
Printer
Speakers

Figure 18.34 The data is kept on the "Products Database" sheet.

There are two forms for this application: one to ask about the search priority, and one to ask about the search criteria. The search priority form determines if the users want to search for a product based on lowest price or quality level. This form should have only these options, and the users should select only one of these options. We therefore use a frame with two option buttons to give the users these options. We give a description label along with the two typical command buttons: OK and Cancel (see Figure 18.35).

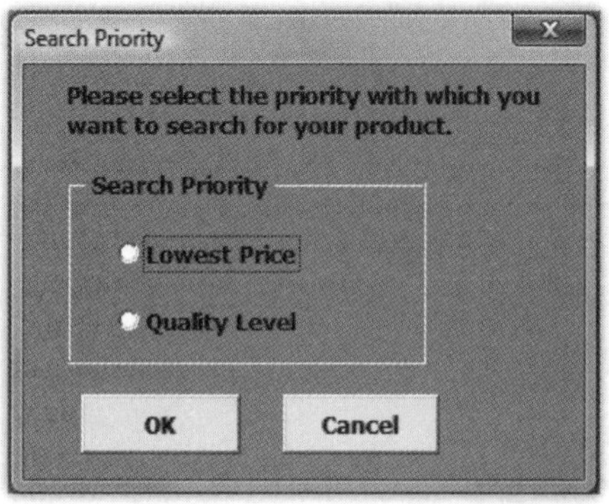

Figure 18.35 This form prompts the users to select their search priority.

When the users press OK, we need to capture which option button they have selected. These options will be associated with public *Boolean* variables which will determine how the search is performed later in our code. In the form which follows, the search criteria form, we also have some frames related to the selected search priority which may or may not be visible depending on what the users select in this form. We will explain these shortly. Figure 18.36 gives the code associated with the OK button of this search priority form. The only code associated with the Cancel button is to unload the form.

```
Option Explicit

Private Sub cmdCancel_Click()
    Unload Me
    End
End Sub

Private Sub cmdOK_Click()
    If optPrice Then
         Price = True
         frmProductSearch.fraQuality.Visible = False
         frmProductSearch.fraPriceLimit.Visible = True
     ElseIf optQuality Then
         QualityLevel = True
         frmProductSearch.fraQuality.Visible = True
         frmProductSearch.fraPriceLimit.Visible = False
     End If

    Unload Me
    frmProductSearch.Show
End Sub
```

Figure 18.36 Based on the option button selected, *Boolean* variable values are given and appropriate updates are made to the frames on the next form.

The second form, the search criteria form, takes additional input from the users to determine which product they are searching for and what other criteria they are searching by (see

Figures 18.37 and 18.38). This form uses frames to group some controls together. We name the OK button on this form *cmdFindProduct*. Some of these labels and frames may not appear depending on the users' choice in the search priority form.

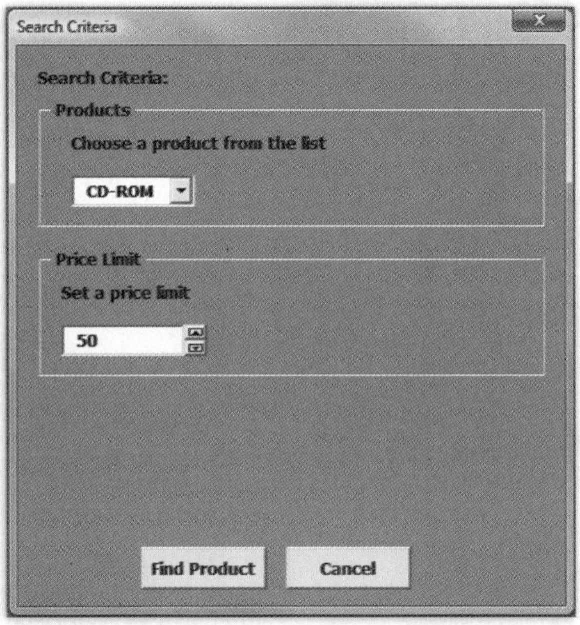

Figure 18.37 The search criteria form options when the search priority is lowest price.

The "Products" combo box lists the main product types in the database. We only search for products within this matching product category. To set the *RowSource* of the combo box, we create a small table below our main database with the names of the product categories. We name this range "ProdList" in Excel and assign this range name to the *RowSource* property. The initialization code for this form is as follows:

```
Private Sub UserForm_Initialize()
    cmbProducts.RowSource = "ProdList"
    chkStandard = True
    chkPremium = True
    txtPriceLimit.Value = 100
End Sub
```

The "Quality" information will appear only if "Quality" is a search priority. These two check boxes will determine which quality product the users want. If both are checked, either of the two quality levels will be acceptable. The "Price Limit" option allows the users to limit the search to be below a certain price level. This option is not provided if the users are searching by lowest price. The spin button is associated with the adjacent textbox. The code for this spin button is as follows:

```
Private Sub spnPriceLimit_Change()
    txtPriceLimit = spnPriceLimit.Value
End Sub
```

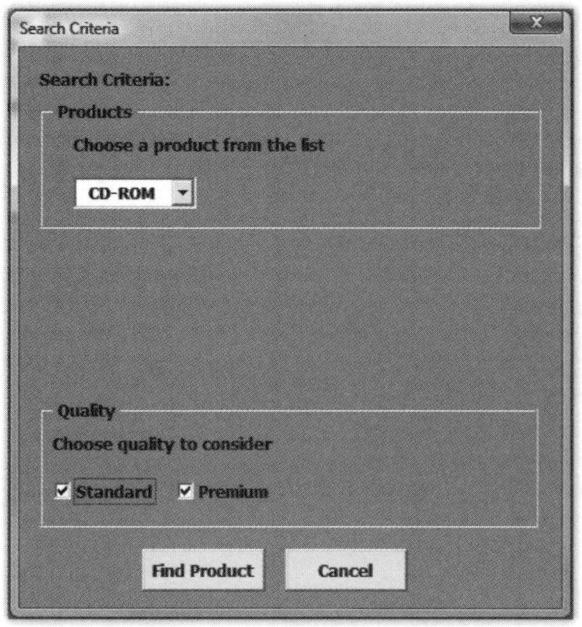

Figure 18.38 The search criteria form options when the search priority is quality level.

If the users checked "Quality" on the first form, then we want to capture which quality level check box they marked. Since the users are not required to use the price limit option, we need to check if there is a value in the corresponding textbox before capturing its value; we do this using the ***IsNull*** function. We also tell the users that if this value is set to 0, we will ignore it. The final action to take in the code associated with the *Find Product* button is to call the sub procedure which searches for the data. The code is as shown below:

```
Private Sub cmdFindProduct_Click()
    Product = cmbProducts.Value

    If QualityLevel Then
        If chkStandard And chkPremium Then
            Quality = "Any"
        ElseIf chkStandard Then
            Quality = "Standard"
        ElseIf chkPremium Then
            Quality = "Premium"
        End If
    End If

    If IsNull(txtPriceLimit.Value) = False And txtPriceLimit.Value > 0 Then
        BestPrice = txtPriceLimit.Value
    Else
        BestPrice = 0
    End If
```

```
        Unload Me
        Call FindProduct
    End Sub
```

This *FindProduct* sub procedure will first sort the entire database depending on the product selected and then by the search criteria. We name this database "Database" in Excel to make the code easier to write. We use a counting variable *i* to search each row in the database and two variables called *RowStart* and *RowEnd* to capture the row values which contain the control meeting the users' criteria.

If the users have selected lowest price as their search priority, then once we find the desired product in the database list, we check the price column to see if the price is lower than the price limit specified in the search criteria. Once we find a price value greater than this limit, called *BestPrice*, we record the final row which matched the criteria so that we can copy the results later.

```
i = 1
RowStart = 0
RowEnd = 0

If Price Then
    'sort by product and then by price
    Range("Database").Sort Key1:=Range("Product"), Order1:=xlAscending,
    key2:=Range("Price"), order2:=xlAscending
    With Range("Database")
        Do While .Cells(i, 1) <> ""
            If .Cells(i, 1) = Product Then
                RowStart = i
                Do While .Cells(i, 1).Value = Product
                    If .Cells(i, 6).Value > BestPrice Then
                        RowEnd = i – 1
                        Exit Do
                    End If
                    i = i + 1
                Loop
                RowEnd = i – 1
                Exit Do
            End If
            i = i + 1
        Loop
    End With
```

If the users have selected quality level as their search priority, then once we find the desired product in the database list, we check the quality column to see if it matches the criteria specified by the users. Since the quality level criteria were given with check boxes, the users could have selected both; therefore, we first check if the quality level was "Any." In that case, we select all of the listings for the product. Otherwise, we check the quality column until the value is no longer equal to the users' selection. We again use the *RowStart* and *RowEnd* variables to store the location of these values, which we will copy later.

```
ElseIf QualityLevel Then
    'sort by product and then by quality
    Range("Database").Sort Key1:=Range("Product"), Order1:=xlAscending,
        key2:=Range("Qual"), order2:=xlAscending
    With Range("Database")
        Do While .Cells(i, 1) <> ""
            If .Cells(i, 1) = Product Then
                If Quality = "Any" Then
                    RowStart = i
                    Do While .Cells(i, 1).Value = Product
                        i = i + 1
                    Loop
                    RowEnd = i - 1
                    Exit Do
                ElseIf .Cells(i, 5) = Quality Then
                    RowStart = i
                    Do While .Cells(i, 1).Value = Product
                        If .Cells(i, 5).Value <> Quality Then
                            RowEnd = i - 1
                            Exit Do
                        End If
                        i = i + 1
                    Loop
                    RowEnd = i - 1
                    Exit Do
                End If
            End If
            i = i + 1
        Loop
    End With
End If
```

We use the *Application.ScreenUpdating* code at the beginning and end of this procedure. We also activate the appropriate sheets and ensure the welcome sheet is showing at the end. When we are done searching for the data, we call a *DisplayProduct* procedure which will copy on the welcome sheet all the data for the corresponding controls we found.

We use a range variable and name another range on the spreadsheet to perform these actions. The code is below:

```
Sub DisplayProduct()
    Results.Value = "Search Results"
    Results.Font.Bold = True
    Range("Titles").Copy
```

```
        Results.Offset(1, 0).PasteSpecial

        With Range("Database")
            If RowStart = 0 Then
                Results.Offset(2, 0).Value = "No product in the database matches your criteria."
            Else
                Range(.Cells(RowStart, 1), .Cells(RowEnd, 6)).Copy
                Results.Offset(2, 0).PasteSpecial
            End If
        End With

        Range(Results.Offset(2, 0), Results.Offset(2, 5)).Interior.ColorIndex = 0
    End Sub
```

The last procedure we need to be sure to write is the *Main* sub procedure. This code will be associated with the *Start* button on the welcome sheet. This code simply initializes the range variable, clears all previous search results, performs some formatting, and then shows the first form.

```
    Sub Main()
        Set Results = Worksheets("Products Search").Range("B25")

        Range(Results, Results.Offset(20, 5)).Clear
        Range(Results, Results.Offset(20, 5)).Interior.ColorIndex = 40

        frmSearchPriority.Show
    End Sub
```

These are all the worksheets, forms, and procedures necessary to build this application.

18.11 Summary

- The most important property which we will use for all user form controls is the *Name* property. The name of a control from a user form is treated as an object in the code.
- A label is used to give a description to any control on the form (as used in Figure 18.3). A textbox is used to allow the users to enter some value. This value may be a string or number.
- A combo box will list the first entry next to a drop-down button. When the users press the button, all other controls in the list are shown. A list box has basically the same functionality and several similar properties as a combo box. A list box will list all controls to be selected in a single box (that is, there is no drop-down button as with combo boxes).
- Check boxes imply a positive selection (that is, a *yes*, *true*, *on*, etc. value) when checked; the opposite is true if they are unchecked or de-checked. Option buttons imply a positive selection (that is, a *yes*, *true*, *on*, etc. value) when selected; the opposite is true if they are de-selected. We can also use option buttons with a frame. Toggle buttons are similar to check boxes and option buttons in that they imply a positive selection (that is, a *yes*, *true*, *on*, etc. value) when clicked; the opposite is true if they are un-clicked.
- We will use command buttons, unlike the controls we have learned so far, for their associated event procedures more than for their properties. The main event procedure associated with command buttons is the *Click* event. To show another form

after the users have finished filling the current form, we use the *Show* method. To close the current form at the end of this event procedure, we use the *Unload Me* statement.

- Tab strips group data into different sections of this one control; all sections or tabs have the same layout. That is, one tab strip will have a set of controls which will appear on each tab. Each tab can be associated with a group of data to which the tab strip information belongs. A multipage control, on the other hand, can be considered a collection of individual form objects, or pages. Each page can have a different layout and is treated as a separate form.
- Scroll bars can change text, numerical values, or other values of associated controls. We most commonly use the *Change*, or *Scroll*, event procedures to associate the change in the scroll bar values with an effect on another control value. Spin buttons are similar to scroll bars, except that they only increment or decrement numerical values of other controls. Spin buttons also use the *Change* event procedure primarily to associate its values with the values of another control.
- Images allow us to display a picture in the form. We use RefEdit to select or enter a worksheet range.
- There are some properties associated with the user form itself which can be useful. There are several *Position* properties that can be modified. To view these, we use the *Categorized* tab of the *Properties Window*. Another property of the user form is *ShowModal*. When set to *True*, the form must be completed (and/or some command button which closes the form should be clicked) before the users can return to the program or use any worksheet. However, when this property is set to *False*, the form becomes modeless, or a floating form.
- Buttons are usually a great tool for navigating the users not only through different sheets of the program, but also through different steps or actions. The code for these macros can be identical or call an identical function. A useful property of these buttons, or shape objects, is the *Visible* property. By naming these buttons appropriately, we can use the *Shape* object and *Visible* property to hide and show different buttons.
- To prevent users from changing formatting or title values in any worksheet tables or other features, we can protect the worksheet. To do this, we use the *Locked* property of a range of cells.
- There are some other options which we can set for each worksheet in our program to finalize the version which the users will see. To view these options, we select *View* > *Show* and *View* > *Workbook Views* groups from the Ribbon.

18.12 Exercises

18.12.1 Review Questions

1. List five user form controls available in the VBA toolbox.
2. What is the purpose of the Frame control? (What is its relationship to Option Buttons?)
3. Write the *FindDay* function explained at the end of Section 18.1.9.
4. What data type does the RefEdit control return?
5. What data type is stored in a textbox?
6. How do you create a floating form?
7. Which control has unique pages, Tab Strips or Multipages?
8. Can you attach code to a Toggle Button which performs a set of actions?
9. What is the default event of a Scroll Bar?
10. What is the default event of a Check Box?
11. How do you check which Option Button in a Frame has been selected?
12. Are Check Boxes placed in a Frame mutually exclusive?
13. List some basic error-checking done with forms.
14. How do you ensure that the program will not continue when the Cancel button is pressed?
15. How do you enter values into a cell in VBA after a worksheet has been protected?

18.12.2 Hands-On Exercises

NOTE: Please refer to the file "Chapter_18_Exercises .xlsx" for the associated worksheets noted for the hands-on exercises. The file is available at: www .dssbooks.com.

1. The following user form allows the users to input the current temperature using either a scroll bar or a textbox as shown below:

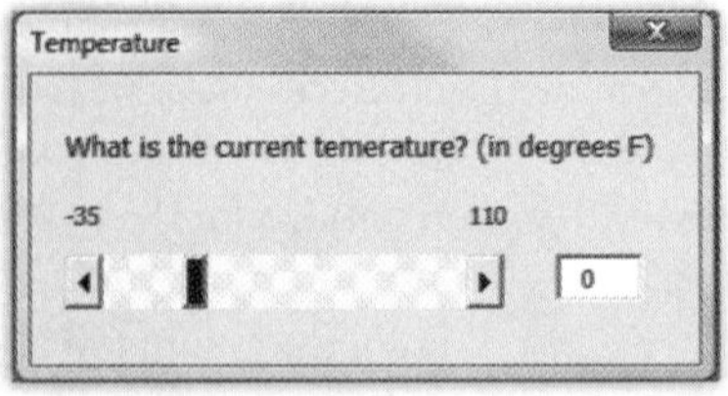

The following code currently modifies the value of the scroll bar when users type a new value into the textbox. Write a similar line of code which will update the value of the textbox if users use the scroll bar.

```
Private Sub TextBox1_Change()
ScrollBar1.Value = TextBox1.Value
End Sub
```

2. Create a user form that does not permit you to open a worksheet until you enter the password "go gators."
3. Create a user form that allows the users to select a range of cells using the RefEdit control. Allow the users to change the background color, font color, and the font style of the selected range. Give the users at least three different color choices. The different font styles available should include regular, bold, italic, and underline. Users should be able to choose any combination of bold, italic, and underline.
4. Create a paint program.
   - **a.** Create several shapes on the spreadsheet and name them. List these names on the spreadsheet.
   - **b.** Create a form which has a list box of the shapes you have created. The users should be able to select one or more shape names and then color them.
   - **c.** To color the shapes, ask the users to select a color from a frame of option buttons.
   - **d.** Give the users the option to change the size of the selected shape(s) as well. Do this using a scroll bar with a percentage scale.
5. Create a conversion program based on the following user form example. Include at least two units for each category.

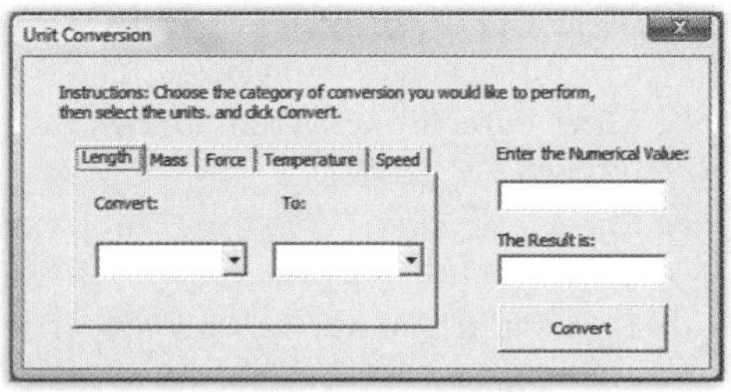

6. Create a user form to build a bill of materials (BOM).
   - **a.** Begin with an end product form. Ask the users for the name of the end product.
   - **b.** Enter this name in a list on the spreadsheet. You will be adding more to this list.
   - **c.** Next show the users a component form. Ask the users if the component is secondary or primary. Ask them also for the name of the component. Then, ask them to select the predecessor of the component from a combo box. This combo box will initially have only the name of the end product which was written to the spreadsheet in part (b).
   - **d.** Update the spreadsheet list with this component name. Update the list for the predecessor combo box.
   - **e.** Allow the users to fill this component form again by pressing an *Add New Component* button. This should repeat parts (c) and (d).
7. Develop a program which allows users to enter data which will be analyzed to determine if any trends exist.
   - **a.** Create a form which asks the users for the size of the data.
   - **b.** Format a table in the spreadsheet where they can enter their data.
   - **c.** Also ask the users which trendline they would like to add. Use option buttons for Normal, Exponential, and Linear curves.
   - **d.** Generate data from the distribution given, and graph both data together.
   - **e.** Tell the users the mean error, and ask if they would like to try another trendline. If they do, store the mean error result and distribution type of the previous trendline(s).
   - **f.** Make a comparison of which trendline was the most accurate.

8. Create a conference registration form. Your form should include the following:
   a. Option buttons to determine registrant type: student, professor, or retired. (Each should have different registration fees.)
   b. Check boxes listing sessions to attend: A through F.
   c. Check boxes listing events and tours offered. (Each should have a different price.)
   d. Toggle button for whether or not they are bringing a guest. (There should be an additional guest fee.)

   Based on these values, calculate the total price for the registration. Then provide the users with the following (either on a different form or in a frame below which is updated after the above information is entered):
   e. Combo box listing accepted credit cards.
   f. Textbox for credit card amount.

   Then create a final report on the spreadsheet summarizing the information given by the users and creating a confirmation number.
9. Apartment guides allow users to search for an apartment in their area based on their preferences. Create a user form-based program that allows the users to search the area for apartments based on a given table providing available housing options. (Refer to worksheet "18.9".)
10. A database is kept in an Excel spreadsheet with employee information. The employees' names, gender, starting date, ending date, and position in the company are recorded. Allow an employer to update this database by doing the following. (Refer to worksheet "18.10".)
    a. Create a form which displays the entire database from the spreadsheet. All five columns should be displayed.
    b. Give the users the option to modify the database. There should be a button which says Modify on this form.
    c. Once this button is pressed, show the users a new form with a combo box of only the names from the database.
    d. Once a name is selected, show the users a new form with all of the data for this particular name only.
    e. Then provide textboxes for the ending date and position. There should be an Update button which will change the database only if a value(s) has been entered in one of the textboxes.
    f. Tell the users that the database has been updated and return them to part (a).
11. **Loan Manager:** Help users determine what their monthly payments would be based on the amount they need from a loan and for how long they need the loan. Assume the users can choose between two loans: the first has a 7.9% APR with an annual fee of $20, and the second has a 15% APR, but no annual fee. Create a user interface on the spreadsheet with the following:
    a. A frame with option buttons for the two loan choices.
    b. A scroll bar to represent the amount of the loan.
    c. A spin button to represent the time (this should be 12, 18, 24, ..., 60 months).
    d. Use Excel functions to calculate the different payment amounts depending on the criteria specified by the users. This calculation should be done when a button is pressed.
    e. Repeat parts (a) through (d) with a user form and VBA functions instead.
12. Create a portfolio selection form.
    a. Create a user form with tabs. Label each tab with a stock category (Energy, Technology, etc.).
    b. On each tab have a list box with the names of stocks in each category.
    c. Create a list box below the tabs called Portfolio. This list box should show the stock names and share amounts of the portfolio.
    d. Put two command buttons between the tabs and the list box below. One should Add/Buy a selected stock to the Portfolio list box. The other button should Remove/Sell the selected stock from the Portfolio. Next to the command button should be a textbox where the users will enter the number of shares to buy or sell.
    e. Make sure that stocks are not added more than once. If users want to add more shares of a stock that was already bought, simply update the share value rather than adding the stock to the list again.
13. **Text Search:** Using the list of sections from this chapter entered on a spreadsheet, perform the following. (Refer to worksheet "18.13".)

a. Create a user form which asks the users to enter some text value(s) to search for among these quotes/readings.
b. After they enter this information into a textbox on the form and press a Search button, you will search for the text.
c. If you find the text, you will return all of the chapters/section numbers where the text was found. Show these in a list box.
d. The users can then select one of these to see the full text of the corresponding chapter/section number displayed in a label below.

To search for text in ranges, you can use the ***Find*** method. The Find method requires one parameter which is the value for which you are searching. There are several other optional parameters such as the starting position of the search and whether or not to match the case. The format of the Find method is as follows:

Range("name").Find(value)

This method returns a range where the value was found. If no value was found, the range will be set to Nothing. You can use a loop such as what is shown below to check if text has been found:

```
For i = 1 To 3
    If Not Range("Text").Cells(i).Find("hello") Is
        Nothing Then
            MsgBox "Text found in row " & i
        End If
Next i
```

If you want to search for text using some wildcard symbol such as *, use the ***Like*** comparison statement. The format of this statement is shown in the example below:

```
For i = 1 To 3
    If Range("Text").Cells(i).Value Like "hel*" Then
        MsgBox "Text found in row " & i & " using
        Like"
    End if
Next i
```

14. Airlines use forms to search for flights that meet the travel needs of their customers. Based on these online forms, generate a user form, and reference the supporting data so that users can search for a flight. Based on their inputs, display all flights that meet their criteria on a worksheet. Use the given flight schedule. (*Note:* Assume all flights depart daily.) (Refer to worksheet "18.14".)

Here is an example of an online travel form:

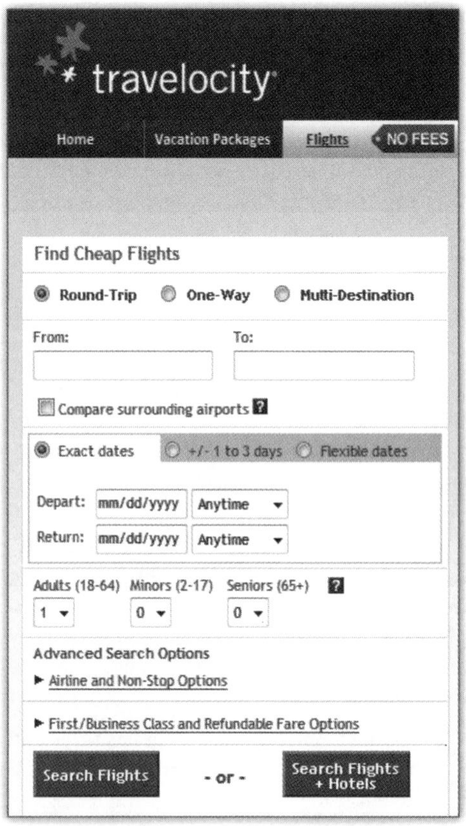

15. ***Quality Control***: A company keeps track of product deliveries made by various suppliers. Each product has a different measure for quality from 1 to 10, 10 being best. The promised delivery amount and date are also stored for each product along with the actual delivery amount and date. (Refer to worksheet "18.15".)

Create the following user form:

a. Ask users if they want to examine quality per product or per supplier. Use option buttons.
b. Based on the answer in part (a), display a combo box with a list of products or suppliers.
c. Ask the users if they want to examine quality measure, quality in amount delivered, or quality in time delivered. Use check boxes.
d. Based on the values selected, review the table given and find the average quality. That is, if the users checked to view the time quality for supplier B, search the table and measure the time difference between promised date and actual date for each delivery made by supplier B.

16. Create a user form that enables the user to generate random data from different distributions. The form should include the following.

   a. A combo box that lists the distributions the user can choose from. Upon the selection of a distribution from the combo box, textboxes appear where the user enters the parameters of the selected distribution. For example, if the exponential distribution is selected, a textbox appears where the user types-in the value of lambda; if the normal distribution is selected two textboxes appear where the user types-in the mean and standard deviation.

   b. Two textboxes, one where the user specifies how many numbers to generate and one where the user specifies the starting cell of the range where the numbers will be displayed.

   c. A command button to submit the data and generate the random numbers in the spreadsheet.

17. Create a user form to search a library database. The form should include the following. (Refer to worksheet "18.17".)

   a. Create a welcome form that has three command buttons. Each command button takes the user to one of the following forms.

   b. Create a form that enables the user to search the database by author name, book title, or subject. Include a "Submit" and a "Go back" command button in this form. The results of the search are presented to the user in a list box.

   c. Create a form that enables the user to add a new item in the database. Use textboxes to enable the user to enter the data. Make sure that you are not adding an item that already exists in the database. Include a "Submit" and a "Go back" command button in this form.

   d. Create a form that enables the user to delete an item from the database. Include a "Submit" and a "Go back" command button in this form

18. Create a data analysis form. Insert a RefEdit box where the user can enter a selected range of cells. Insert a frame that has five option buttons. These buttons enable the user to select whether s/he wants to find the mean, median, standard deviation, minimum, or maximum value of the data selected. Insert a textbox to display the result. (Refer to worksheet "18.18".)

19. Create a user form to search a database of a university. The form should include the following. (Refer to worksheet "18.19".)

   a. A frame that has two option buttons. The option buttons enable the user to search the database for classes based on the course number or course name. Insert a combo box that displays the course number/name. Insert a list box to display the results of the search and a command button that when clicked-on checks the database and lists information about the selected class.

   b. A frame that includes combo box and a list box. The combo box presents the name of the professors. Upon the selection of a name from the combo box, the list box presents the classes taught by the selected professor.

   c. A frame that includes a combo box and a list box. The combo box presents the dates a class was offered. Upon selection of a date, the classes offered are listed on the list box.

20. Create a user form for a running club. The form will help to manage members' information. The form should include the following. (Refer to worksheet "18.20".)

   a. A multipage with two pages. The first page presents members' contact information. The second page presents a list of events the member has participated on and the corresponding results.

   b. A frame that includes two check boxes. The check boxes enable the user to choose a particular event, half marathon, a marathon or both. Include a command button that when clicked-on a lists (on a list box) the members that have participated on the selected events.

   c. A frame that has two option buttons. The option buttons enable the user to choose whether to search for the fastest long distance (marathon) runner and the fastest short distance (3 Mile) runner. Insert a command button that when clicked-on presents the results. Use textboxes to present the results.

CHAPTER

nineteen

Mathematical Programming Revisited

chapter OVERVIEW

19.1 Introduction

This chapter shows how to create, modify, and solve an optimization problem using the Visual Basic for Applications *commands*. Because many decision support system applications may involve optimization, it is important to know how to set up and run the Risk Solver Platform from VBA. Using the Solver with VBA allows us to create a dynamic environment in which optimization parameters can be modified and the problem can be resolved. The users may become involved in setting the objective function as a minimization or maximization problem, changing the number of variables, and including or ignoring any constraints. The Solver can also be run as part of a loop, such as in an application in which optimization and simulation are combined. We have developed several DSS applications that use the Solver dynamically through VBA commands. Some examples are Portfolio Management and Optimization, Beta of Stocks, Sales Force Allocation, and Option Pricing.

In this chapter, we will discuss how to use the *object-oriented Application Programming Interface (API)* in the Risk Solver Platform. The object-oriented API is convenient and very powerful optimization and simulation tool. The Risk Solver Platform also supports the "traditional" VBA functions (see Appendix A). These functions are used to manipulate the standard Excel Solver through VBA.

In this chapter, the reader will learn how to:

- Prepare an optimization problem to be solved by the Risk Solver Platform.
- Prepare and run the Risk Solver Platform using object-oriented API.
- Create a dynamic optimization application using object-oriented API.

19.2 Review of Chapter 8

In Chapter 8, we described how to transform a problem into a mathematical model and then use the Risk Solver Platform to solve it. In this chapter, we learn that the Solver can be manipulated using VBA code to solve the same types of mathematical models. Before learning the VBA code, which applies to manipulating and running the Solver, let's review the main parts of a mathematical model and the Solver preparation steps. These are important steps that take place in the Excel spreadsheet before we use the Solver.

Using the Solver requires a short sequence of steps: (1) reading and interpreting the problem, (2) preparing the spreadsheet, and (3) solving the model and reviewing the results. In the interpretation of the problem, we define the mathematical model; that is, we must define our decision variables, objective function, and constraints via mathematical representation.

19.2.1 Understanding the Problem

Mathematical models transform a word problem into a set of equations that clearly define the values we are seeking given the limitations of the problem. There are three main parts of a mathematical model: *decision variables, objective function*, and *constraints.*

Decision variables are variables that are assigned to a quantity or response that we must determine in the problem. They can be defined as *negative, non-negative*, or *unrestricted* variables. An unrestricted variable can be either negative or non-negative. We use these variables to represent all other relationships in the model, including the objective function and constraints.

The *objective function* is an equation that states the goal, or objective, of the model. Objective functions are either maximized or minimized; most applications involve maximizing profit or minimizing cost.

The *constraints* are the limitations of the problem. In most realistic problems there are certain limitations, or constraints, that we must satisfy. Constraints can be a limited amount of resources, labor, or requirements for a particular demand. We write these constraints as equations in terms of the decision variables.

We saw an example in Chapter 8 of the Product Mix problem. A company produces six different types of products. It wants to schedule its production to determine how much of each product type it should produce in order to maximize its profits. Production of each product type requires labor and raw materials, but the company is limited by the amount of resources available. There is also a limited demand for each product, and the company can produce no more than this demand per product type. Input tables for the necessary resources and the demand are given. This is a linear programming problem, as the constraints and objective function are linear with respect to the decision variables, as we will see later. We therefore use the *Risk Solver Platform to solve the problem.*

We can perform the first step of using the Solver by reading this problem description and determining the model parts. The decision variables are the amounts to produce of each product. There are three constraints: labor, raw materials, and demand. The objective function is to maximize the total profit.

19.2.2 Preparing the Spreadsheet

The second step is equally important: preparing the spreadsheet. We must translate and clearly define each part of our model in the spreadsheet. The Solver will then interpret our model according to how we have declared the decision variables, objective function, and constraints in the spreadsheet. We use referencing and formulas to mathematically represent the model in the spreadsheet cells.

To enter the decision variables, we list them in individual cells (with some verbal description such as *x1, x2* or *item1, item2*) with an empty cell next to each one. The Solver will place values in these cells for each decision variable as it solves the model. All other equations (for the objective function and constraints) will reference these cells.

To enter the objective function, we place our objective function equation in a cell with an adjacent description. We should enter this equation as a formula that references the decision variable cells. As the Solver changes the decision variable values in the decision variable cells, the objective function value will automatically be updated.

To enter the constraints, we place the constraint equations in the spreadsheet. We list the equations separately with a description next to each constraint. The most important part of setting up the constraint table is expressing the left side of our equations as formulas. As each constraint is in terms of the decision variables, all of these formulas must be in terms of the decision variable cells that the Solver uses. These equations should reference the decision variable cells so that as the Solver places values in these cells, the constraint values will automatically be calculated. Another important consideration when laying out the constraints in preparation for the Solver is that the RHS (right-hand side) value of each constraint should be in individual cells to the right of these equations. We use these values to enter constraints into the Solver. We should also place all inequality signs in their own cells. This organization is necessary for the Solver to interpret our model.

Another advantageous way to keep our constraints organized as we use the Solver is to name our cells. Using the methods discussed in Chapter 3, we can name the ranges for the decision variables and the cell that holds the objective function equation. We can also name ranges of constraint equations that are in a similar category of constraints or that have similar inequality signs. This makes inserting these model parts into the Solver easier when using both Excel and VBA code.

The spreadsheet is now prepared for Solver with all three parts of the model clearly displayed. Let's refer to the example used in Chapter 8 to show how the spreadsheet should appear after this preparation step is complete. In Figure 19.1, we see the overall spreadsheet layout. We organize our cells by input, decision variables, constraints, and objective function. The input table was given. We calculate the Unit Profit row by subtracting the Variable Cost from the Unit Price.

	A	B	C	D	E	F	G	H	I
1	**Product Mix**								
2									
3	Input		Product Type 1	Product Type 2	Product Type 3	Product Type 4	Product Type 5	Product Type 6	Available
4		Labor	6	5	4	3	2.5	1.5	4500
5		Raw Material	3.2	2.6	1.5	0.8	0.7	0.3	1600
6		Unit price	$12.50	$11.00	$9.00	$7.00	$6.00	$3.00	
7		Variable cost	$6.50	$5.70	$3.60	$2.80	$2.20	$1.20	
8									
9		Unit profit cont.	$6.00	$5.30	$5.40	$4.20	$3.80	$1.80	
10									
11									
12	Decision Variables		Product Type 1	Product Type 2	Product Type 3	Product Type 4	Product Type 5	Product Type 6	
13		Amount produced							
14			<=	<=	<=	<=	<=	<=	
15		Demand	960	928	1041	977	1084	1055	
16									
17	Constraints				Available				
18		Labor Used	0.00	<=	4500				
19		Raw Material Used	0.00	<=	1600				
20									
21	Objective Function								
22		Profit	$0.00						

Figure 19.1 Spreadsheet layout for product mix.

We also name some ranges on the spreadsheet. We name the Decision Variable range "PMDecVar," the Labor resource requirement row "PMLabor," the Raw Material resource requirement row "PMRawMat," and the Unit Profit row "PMUnitProfit." These names will be helpful in writing the constraint and objective function formulas as well as for inserting cell references in the Solver.

19.2.3 Solving the Model

After appropriately preparing the cells, we use the Risk Solver Platform to find our solution. In Figure 19.2, we show the Risk Solver task pane. We set the objective to the location of the objective function formula; we set the variables to the empty decision variable cells, which we name "PMDecVar"; and the constraints show the left and right sides of the constraint equations with the corresponding inequalities. The labor and raw material constraints are listed as normal constraints. Demand constraints are listed as the bound constraints because they set an upper limit on the value that the decision variables can take. We set the *Assume Non-Negative property of the model to True.*

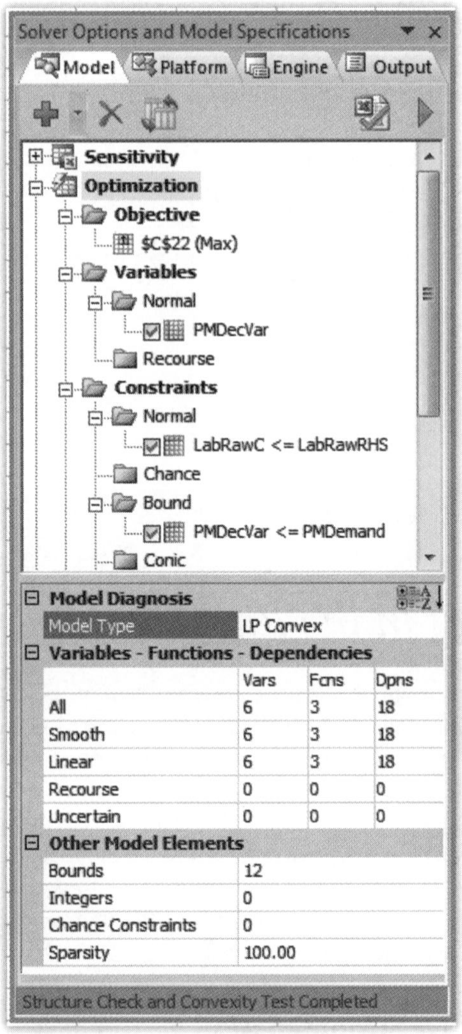

Figure 19.2 The final Risk Solver task pane lists decision variables, constraints, and the objective function of our model.

The final results are shown in Figure 19.3. Notice that all constraints are met. The company now knows how much to produce of each product type and what its maximum profit will be.

	A	B	C	D	E	F	G	H	I
1	**Product Mix**								
2									
3	Input		Product Type 1	Product Type 2	Product Type 3	Product Type 4	Product Type 5	Product Type 6	Available
4		Labor	6	5	4	3	2.5	1.5	4500
5		Raw Material	3.2	2.6	1.5	0.8	0.7	0.3	1600
6		Unit price	$12.50	$11.00	$9.00	$7.00	$6.00	$3.00	
7		Variable cost	$6.50	$5.70	$3.60	$2.80	$2.20	$1.20	
8									
9		Unit profit cont.	$6.00	$5.30	$5.40	$4.20	$3.80	$1.80	
10									
11									
12	Decision Variables		Product Type 1	Product Type 2	Product Type 3	Product Type 4	Product Type 5	Product Type 6	
13		Amount produced	0.00	0.00	0.00	596.67	1084.00	0.00	
14			<=	<=	<=	<=	<=	<=	
15		Demand	960	928	1041	977	1084	1055	
16									
17	Constraints				Available				
18		Labor Used	4500.00	<=	4500				
19		Raw Material Used	1236.13	<=	1600				
20									
21	Objective Function								
22		Profit	$6,625.20						

Figure 19.3 The final Solver solution is shown.

19.3 *Object-Oriented API in the Risk Solver Platform*

We will now discuss how to use object-oriented API to create a problem initially, and then add the decision variables, objective function, and constraints. We will also learn how to manipulate Engine parameters, and optimize the problem using VBA commands. Finally, we will see how to access the results of the optimization, such as objective function value, optimal solution, dual variables, etc.

(**Note:** To use the object-oriented API in VBA, we must reference the Risk Solver Platform type library from the VBE. To do this, we go to *Tools > References* and choose R*isk Solver Platform xx Type Library* from the list. This is different from *Solver*, which is the reference added in order to use the "traditional" VBA functions.)

19.3.1 Building a Problem Using Object-Oriented API

We start by creating an instance of the ***Problem*** object. The *Problem* object represents the whole optimization problem. We declare this object variable using the *Dim* statement as follows:

Dim MyProb As New RSP.Problem

The ***SolverType*** property of the ***Solver*** object allows us to specify whether the problem should be optimized or simulated. For optimization problems, this property also allows us to specify if the objective function of our problem will be maximized or minimized, or if the problem should be solved to find a feasible solution. The values that the SolverType property can take are Solver_Type_FindFeas (find a feasible solution), Solver_Type_Maximize (maximize),

Solver_Type_Minimize (minimize), and Solver_Type_Simulate (simulate). For example, to identify *MyProb* as an optimization problem whose objective function should be maximized, we would type the following:

```
MyProb.Solver.SolverType = Solver_Type_Maximize
```

Previously, when using the Risk Solver Platform in Excel, we added the cells that contain the decision variables, objective function, and constraint equations in the *Solver task pane* using the *decision variables*, *objective*, and *constraints* commands listed on the *ribbon*. Let's now learn how to use VBA in order to identify these parts of the model as Solver input, and have them appear in the *task pane model tab*.

To add new decision variables to MyProb, we create a *variable* object, initialize the object, set its properties, and then add this object to the *variable collection* of the problem. We use the *Init* method to specify the range that contains the decision variables. This range of cells should not have any formulas; these cells should be blank or have some temporary values. There may be descriptive cells adjacent to the empty decision variable cells. We add these decision variables to the problem using *Variables.Add* method. Once the variables are added to the problem, we have no more use for the variable object. At this point, it is a good practice to set the value of the variable object to *Nothing*, so Excel will not be reserving unnecessary memory. We create the decision variables of MyProb using this VBA code as follows:

```
Dim MyVar As New Variable
  MyVar.Init Range("DecissionVariables")
  MyVar.NonNegative
  MyProb.Variables.Add MyVar
  Set MyVar = Nothing
```

To add an objective function to MyProb, we create a *function* object, initialize this object, set its properties, add it to the *function collection* of the problem, and finally set its value to Nothing. We use the *Init* method to specify the range of the objective function. This cell should contain the formula of the objective function that references the decision variable cells. We use the *FunctionType* property to identify the type of the function that is being added to the problem. This property takes the value *Function_Type_Objective* for the objective function, and *Function_Type_Constraint* for normal constraints. We add the objective function to MyProb using this VBA code as follows:

```
Dim MyObj As New RSP.Function
  MyObj.Init Range("ProdObjFunc")
  MyObj.FunctionType = Function_Type_Objective
  MyProb.Functions.Add MyObj
  Set MyObj = Nothing
```

We now show how to create and add a set of constraints to MyProb. We use a ***For Next*** loop to add each individual constraint. We create an array of *function* objects using the ***Dim*** statement. The size of this array is set to the total number of constraints. We use the ***Init*** method, which specifies the range that contains a constraint equation. This equation should reference the decision variable cells. The *Relation* method allows us to specify the relation (<=, =, or >=) and the RHS value of the constraints. The constants Cons_Rel_EQ (=), Cons_Rel_GE (>=) or Cons_Rel_LE (<=) are used to specify the relation. The *Add* method is used to add each individual constraint to the end of the function collection of the problem. We would create and add the constraints of MyProb using this VBA code as follows:

```
Dim MyConstraints(NumCons) As New RSP.Function

For i = 1 To NumCons
  MyConstraints (i).Init Range("A1").Offset(i – 1, 0)
  MyConstraints (i).Relation Cons_Rel_GE, Range("B1").Offset(i – 1, 0).Value
  MyConstraints (i).FunctionType = Function_Type_Constraint
  MyProb.Functions.Add MyConstraints (i)
  Set MyConstraints (i) = Nothing
Next
```

Another method that we frequently use is the *Remove* method. This method allows us to delete constraints from the problem formulation. The only parameter of this function is the index of the constraint that will be removed. For example, the index of the last constraint of MyProb is *NumCons*. To remove this constraint we would type the following:

```
MyProb.Functions.Remove NumCons
```

Note that, the formulas referenced in the objective function and constraints of the problem as well as the values of the RHS are stored in an excel spreadsheet. Therefore, we should activate the appropriate worksheet if we want to specify the ranges without the preceding worksheet name. It is also recommended to use the *Application.ScreenUpdating* statement before and after running the Solver.

19.3.2 Identifying Solver Engine and Parameters

Prior to solving an optimization problem, we should specify the appropriate *Solver Engine* to use. For an optimization problem, the *Engine object* represents the *LP/Quadratic*, the *Standard Evolutionary*, or the *GRG Nonlinear Solver* depending on the type of the problem we are solving. When the *Solver.Optimize* method is then called, this engine will run.

A collection of *Engine objects* is automatically created when we declare a new *Problem object*. We can then reference a particular engine using this object. For example, if the problem we are working with is a linear program, we will select the *LP/Quadratic Solver* using the following code.

```
MyProb.Engine = MyProb.Engines("Standard LP/Quadratic")
```

Each *Solver Engine* has a number of parameters. We have seen previously in Chapter 8 how to modify these parameters using the *task pane Engine tab* of the *Risk Solver Platform*. We recommend that prior to modifying the Solver Engine parameters, you should reset all the parameters to their default value by using the *ParamReset* method. You can then specify changes to these default values.

```
MyProb.Engine.ParamReset
```

There are a large number of problem parameters for a particular Solver Engine. For example, there are 62 parameters for the LP/Quadratic Solver engine. You can use the *Name* property to identify the name and the index of a parameter of interest. Then use this index to access and modify the corresponding parameter. For example, we can set the number of iterations to 100 using the following code.

```
For i = 0 To MyProb.Engine.Params.Count – 1
    If MyProb.Engine.Params(i).Name = "Iterations" Then
        MyProb.Engine.Params(i).Value = 100
    End If
Next i
```

Or, if you would like to set the value of *AssumeNonneg* parameter to True, then you can use the following statement in your code:

```
MyProb.Engine.Params("AssumeNonneg").Value = True
```

19.3.3 Running the Solver

After we have created the problem and identified the *Solver Engine* and corresponding parameters to use, we are ready to run the *Solver*. To run the *Solver* through VBA, we use the *Solver.Optimize* method. This method has one argument and is written as follows:

```
MyProb.Solver.Optimize (Solve_Type)
```

The ***Solve_Type_Analyze*** value of *Solve_Type* argument is used to perform a model analysis without actually solving the problem, and the ***Solve_Type_Solve*** value is used to solve the optimization problem.

The ***OptimizeStauts*** property of the Solver object returns an integer value classifying the result of the optimization. The value 0, 1, or 2 signifies a successful run in which a solution has been found. The value 4 implies that there was no convergence, and the value 5 implies that no feasible solution could be found. It can be useful to assign the value of *OptimizeStatus* property to an integer variable, and then check the value of this variable in order to display an appropriate Message Box to the users if needed. For example:

```
Dim result As Integer
result = MyProb.Solver.OptimizeStatus
If result = 5 Then
    MsgBox "Your problem was infeasible. Please modify your model."
End If
```

We would like to note that *Solver.Optimize* is the only command needed to actually run the Solver. That is, if we have already set up the Solver in the spreadsheet or in some initial part of the VBA code, at execution time, we need to write only the *Solver.Optimize* command. This may be convenient for combining optimization with a simulation in which we may be performing several loops where we are running the Solver and storing the results. In such a scenario, only the *Solver.Optimize* command would need to appear in a simulation loop. We discuss this more in Chapter 20 with simulation in VBA.

19.3.4 Accessing Optimization Results

We can access the results of the optimization by using the ***value*** property of *variable* object, or ***FinalValue***, ***DualValue***, and ***Slack*** properties of the *function* object. We can also automate in VBA the process of generating the solution reports listed in the Report drop-down menu of the ribbon.

The *Size* property of *VarDecision object* identifies the total number of the decision variables in a problem. We use this number in *a For, Next* loop that prints the value of each decision variables as shown in the following lines of code.

```
For i = 0 To MyProb.VarDecision.Size – 1
   MsgBox MyProb.VarDecision.Value(i)
Next i
```

The *Count* property of *functions object* identifies the total number of functions in the *problem object*. The last function counted is the objective function. Therefore, in order to print the objective function value you can write:

```
MsgBox MyProb.Functions(MyProb.Functions.Count – 1).Value(0)
```

To print the dual variables for problem constraints, we would write.

```
For i = 0 To MyProb.Functions.Count - 2
    MsgBox MyProb.Functions(i).DualValue(0)
Next i
```

Prior to running the Solver we can decide whether or not we want to generate any optimization reports. If we decide to generate the reports, then we need to set the value of ***Bypass Solver Reports*** engine parameter to True. After the Solver has finished running, we can access the reports using the following statement.

```
Solver.Report ReportName
```

In this statement the *ReportName* is one of the following strings *"Answer," "Feasibility," "Linearity," "Limits,"* "Population," *"Sensitivity," "Scaling," and "Solution."* The *Report* method generates a report in the form of an Excel worksheet and inserts it into the active workbook. For example, to create an *Answer* report we would type.

```
MyProb.Solver.Report "Answer"
```

We will now comment briefly on three other methods that correspond to saving a problem. These are *Init, Save,* and *Load*. The ***Init*** method instantiates a problem using a named model or worksheet. This method creates the variable and function objects using an optimization problem already defined in the worksheet. You can use the ***Save*** method in order to save model specifications in a cell range, or as a text string model name. The ***Load*** method is then used to load model specifications. ***Format*** is one of the parameters required by this method. This parameter is a constant which takes one of the following two values: *File_Format_XLStd* or *File_Format_XLPSI*. The constant *File_Format_XLPSI* is used for problems that call the PSI function. For example, one would use the following lines of code to initiate a problem using a model already defined in an existing worksheet, save problem parameters, solve the problem, and display the corresponding objective function value.

```
Sub Init_Save_Prob_Methods()
Dim prob As New RSP.Problem
    prob.Init Worksheets("Prob_Setup")
    prob.Save Worksheets("Prob_Save").Range("A1")
    prob.Solver.Optimize
```

```
    MsgBox prob.Functions(prob.Functions.Count – 1).Value(0)
End Sub
```

Using the following lines of code you can load the model you already saved, optimize the problem, and display the corresponding objective function value.

```
Sub Load_Prob_Method()
Dim prob As New RSP.Problem, Param as Range
    Set Param = Worksheets("Prob_Save").Range(Range("A1"),Range("A1").End(xlDown))
    prob.Load Param, File_Format_XLStd
    prob.Solver.Optimize

    MsgBox prob.Functions(prob.Functions.Count – 1).Value(0)
End Sub
```

Summary

Objects	**Properties**	**Values**	**Methods**	**Arguments**
Problem	Engine	Standard LP/Quadratic	Init	Worksheet
		GRG Nonlinear	Functions.Add	Function
	Functions.Count	Integer	Functions().DualValue()	Double
	Solver.OptimizeStatus	Integer	Functions.Remove	Index
			Load	RangeOrModel
				Format
			Save	Range
				Format
			Solver.Optimize	Solve_Type
			Solver.Report	String
			Variables.Add	Variable
			VarDecision.Value()	Double
Variable	NonNegative	True/False	Init	Range
Function	FunctionType	FunctionType_Constraint	Init	Range
		FunctionType_Objective	Relation	RelationType
				Value
Solver	SolverType	SolverType_FindFeas	Optimize	Solve_Type
		SolverType_Maximize	Simulate	Simulate_Type
		SolverType_Minimize		
		SolverType_SimulateSimulate		
	Optimize_Status	Optimize_Status_Optimal		
		Optimize_Status_Unbounded		
		Optimize_Status_Unfeasible		

19.4 Applications

19.4.1 Dynamic Production Problem

We consider a production problem in which we are trying to determine how much of different items to produce in order to maximize profit. Each item has a given weight, space requirement, profit value, quota to satisfy, and limit on production. Each item must meet its quota but be less than its limit. There is also a total weight requirement and space requirement for shipping, which will limit the production. We have prepared our spreadsheet as shown in Figure 19.4. We have used the SUMPRODUCT function in calculating the total weight and space constraints as well as the total profit in the objective function.

However, we want this production problem to be dynamic. That is, we want the users to decide how many items to consider in the problem and to provide the input for each item. We limit these dynamic options to five possible items and prepare the spreadsheet for the maximum number possible. This way, if the users provide input for all five items, there is space allocated on the spreadsheet, but if they choose to solve the problem for only three items, then the extra two rows will be left empty for the input and constraints.

To make this problem dynamic, we develop a user interface. We place a button on the spreadsheet called *Solve Dynamic Problem,* which the users can press to begin solving the problem (see Figure 19.4).

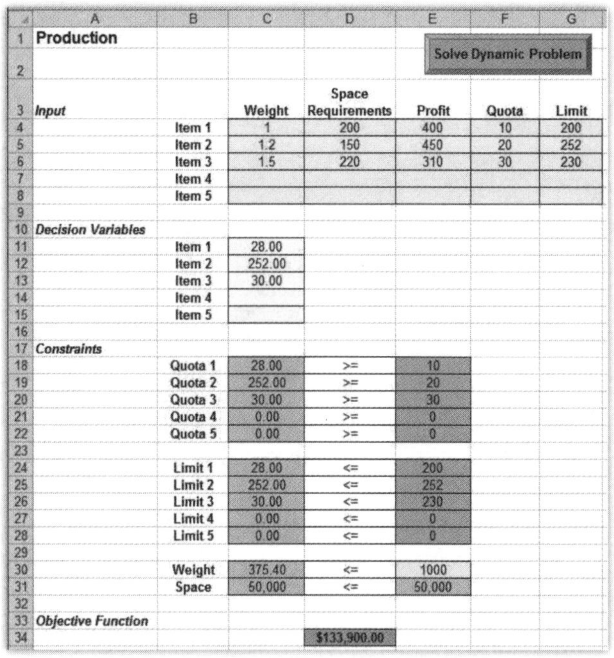

	A	B	C	D	E	F	G
1	Production				Solve Dynamic Problem		
2							
3	Input		Weight	Space Requirements	Profit	Quota	Limit
4		Item 1	1	200	400	10	200
5		Item 2	1.2	150	450	20	252
6		Item 3	1.5	220	310	30	230
7		Item 4					
8		Item 5					
9							
10	Decision Variables						
11		Item 1	28.00				
12		Item 2	252.00				
13		Item 3	30.00				
14		Item 4					
15		Item 5					
16							
17	Constraints						
18		Quota 1	28.00	>=	10		
19		Quota 2	252.00	>=	20		
20		Quota 3	30.00	>=	30		
21		Quota 4	0.00	>=	0		
22		Quota 5	0.00	>=	0		
23							
24		Limit 1	28.00	<=	200		
25		Limit 2	252.00	<=	252		
26		Limit 3	30.00	<=	230		
27		Limit 4	0.00	<=	0		
28		Limit 5	0.00	<=	0		
29							
30		Weight	375.40	<=	1000		
31		Space	50,000	<=	50,000		
32							
33	Objective Function						
34				$133,900.00			

Figure 19.4 Spreadsheet for the Dynamic Production problem.

We then bring the users to a form that asks them to specify the number of items, or decision variables, for which they want to solve the problem (see Figure 19.5). We use a spin button on this form to limit the value of this input from 1 to 5.

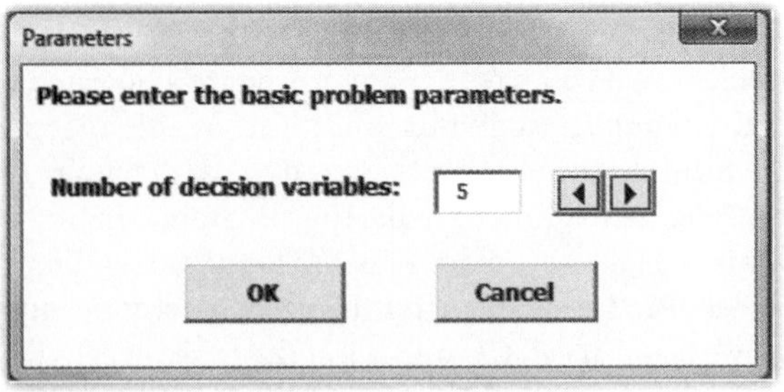

Figure 19.5 The parameters form asks the users for the number of decision variables.

We then bring the users to another form that allows them to enter the total weight and space limits for the final production as well as all input values for each item (see Figure 19.6). This is a dynamic form. Depending on the value entered in the first form, the users should only enter input values for the same number of items on this form. To accomplish this for each item, we create a frame containing text boxes for each input value. We then use the visible property of these frames to only show the frames for the number of items specified by the users.

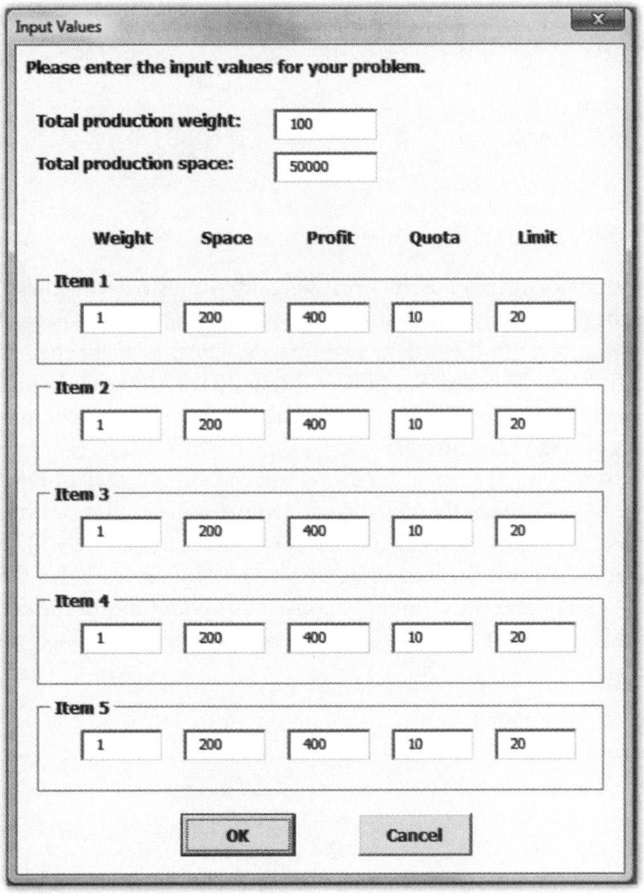

Figure 19.6 The input form is dynamic in that it allows the users to enter input values for the number of items they specified in the parameters form.

Let's now discuss the necessary code to show these forms to the users, record the dynamic information, and solve the problem. We will have a main procedure associated with the *Solve Dynamic Problem* button called *SetParameters*. In this procedure, we initialize some variables, clear previous values, show the forms to the user, and respond to the dynamic values.

The important issue to consider here is how to make this program dynamic without making it too complicated. To do this, we take advantage of using range names. Our first dynamic range is for the decision variables "ProdDecVar." After the users specify the number of items for which to solve the problem, we begin at cell *C11* and select the range of cells below it accordingly. We use a range variable *DVRg* to set to cell *C11*.

The next set of dynamic ranges is for the input values "Weight," "Space," "Profit," "Quota," and "Limit." We also use range variables to accordingly select the range of cells equal in size to the number of items specified by the users. We use the variables *WtRg*, *SpRg*, *PrRg*, *QuRg*, and *LmRg*, respectively, and set them equal to the cells in the first row of the input table: *C4* through *G4*. Redefining these four ranges plus the decision variable range is the only action necessary in the code to solve this problem dynamically.

For our formulas in the spreadsheet, for the constraints and objective function, we have used these range names:

Total Weight Constraint:
= SUMPRODUCT(Weight,ProdDecVar)

Total Space Constraint:
= SUMPRODUCT(Space,ProdDecVar)

Objective Function:
= SUMPRODUCT(Profit,ProdDecVar)

In order to prevent major changes in the worksheet, we simply redefine these range names in our code to make the problem dynamic; no change to these formulas is necessary. We have also given range names to refer to the cells containing these formulas for the constraints and objective function defined in the code: "WeightC," "WeightRHS," "SpaceC," "SpaceRHS," and "ProdObjFunc." These ranges are not dynamic, for they do not change size in respect to the number of items being solved in the problem.

In Figure 19.7, we show the variable declarations and code for the *SetParameters* procedure and a *ClearPrev* procedure. In the *SetParameters* procedure, we initialize our range variables, call the *ClearPrev* procedure, show the users the first form (the second form will be shown from the first form code), and then redefine our dynamic ranges. We set the value for the number of decision variables *NumDV* and the number of constraints *NumCons* in the code of the first form. At the end of this procedure, we call the *SolveProb* procedure in which we will use the Solver code statements.

```
Option Explicit
Option Base 1

Public Weight(5) As Control, Space(5) As Control, Profit(5) As Control, _
Quota(5) As Control, Limit(5) As Control, Frames(5) As Control

Public NumDV As Integer, NumCons As Integer, DVRg As Range, WtRg As Range, SpRg As Range, _
PrRg As Range, QuRg As Range, LmRg As Range, result As Integer, i As Integer

Sub SetParameters()
    Worksheets("Production").Activate
    Set DVRg = Range("C11")
    Set WtRg = Range("C4")
    Set SpRg = Range("D4")
    Set PrRg = Range("E4")
    Set QuRg = Range("F4")
    Set LmRg = Range("G4")
    Call ClearPrev

    'show parameters form and input form
    Set Frames(1) = frmInput.fraItem1
    Set Frames(2) = frmInput.fraItem2
    Set Frames(3) = frmInput.fraItem3
    Set Frames(4) = frmInput.fraItem4
    Set Frames(5) = frmInput.fraItem5
    frmParam.Show

    'rename ranges
    Range(DVRg, DVRg.Offset(NumDV - 1)).Name = "ProdDecVar"
    Range(WtRg, WtRg.Offset(NumDV - 1)).Name = "Weight"
    Range(SpRg, SpRg.Offset(NumDV - 1)).Name = "Space"
    Range(PrRg, PrRg.Offset(NumDV - 1)).Name = "Profit"
    Range(QuRg, QuRg.Offset(NumDV - 1)).Name = "Quota"
    Range(LmRg, LmRg.Offset(NumDV - 1)).Name = "Limit"

    Call SolveProb
End Sub

Sub ClearPrev()
    Range(DVRg, DVRg.End(xlDown)).ClearContents
    Range(WtRg, WtRg.End(xlDown)).ClearContents
    Range(SpRg, SpRg.End(xlDown)).ClearContents
    Range(PrRg, PrRg.End(xlDown)).ClearContents
    Range(QuRg, QuRg.End(xlDown)).ClearContents
    Range(LmRg, LmRg.End(xlDown)).ClearContents
End Sub
```

Figure 19.7 *SetParameters* code, *ClearPrev* code, and variable declarations and initializations.

Notice here that we have also defined and initialized some array variables. Since our *input* form involves five frames, each with parallel text boxes, we declare an array of *control* data type for these controls in order to reduce coding (refer to Figures 19.6 and 19.9). We define *Weight(5)* as an array of *Controls* for the weight text boxes, *Space(5)* as an array of *Controls* for the space text boxes, and, similarly, *Profit(5)*, *Quota(5)*, and *Limit(5)* for the corresponding set of text boxes. The advantage of using these arrays will become clear in the form code procedures. We also define an array *Frames(5)* of *Controls* for each frame on the *Input* form. We initialize this array in the *SetParameters* code by setting each index to a frame from the *Input* form (for example: *Set Frames(1) = frmInput.fraItem1).*

Let's now discuss the code used in the two forms. In the first form, the parameters form, our main objective is to record the number of decision variables specified by the users. We do this by setting our *NumDV* variable equal to the text box control value (we could also do this using the spin button control value). The total number of constraints *NumCons* is also calculated. The only other task is to display the next form, the *input* form. However, this second form is dynamic in that we only want to show the frames, with the corresponding text boxes, for the number of items the users specified. We therefore loop through our *frame* array to set the *visible* property to *True* for the number of decision variables specified by the users. Note that we have initialized the *visible* property of each frame to be *False* in the *UserForm_Initialize* code. The complete code for this form is shown in Figure 19.8.

```
Private Sub cmdCancel_Click()
    Unload Me
End Sub

Private Sub cmdOK_Click()
    NumDV = txtDV.Value
    NumCons = 2 * NumDV + 2

    For i = 1 To NumDV
        Frames(i).Visible = True
    Next i

    'optional: also hide the rows
    'on the spreadsheet for the unused dec var
    Unload Me
    frmInput.Show
End Sub

Private Sub spnDV_Change()
    txtDV.Value = spnDV.Value
End Sub

Private Sub UserForm_Initialize()
    For i = 1 To 5
        Frames(i).Visible = False
    Next i
End Sub
```

Figure 19.8 The code for the parameters form.

(***Note:*** We could have also made the spreadsheet more dynamic by hiding the rows of the unused items. How would this be done? ***Hint:*** See Chapter 13.)

The code for the *input* form is now fairly simple. We simply need to record the values given in the text boxes for each visible frame. We therefore again loop through our frame array. We check if the frame is visible; if it is, then we can record the value of each text box onto the corresponding range in the spreadsheet (see Figure 19.9). Notice that here we use the arrays of text box controls to record the values. This has become a very simple procedure because of our arrays.

```
Private Sub cmdCancel_Click()
    Unload Me
End Sub

Private Sub cmdOK_Click()
    Range("WeightRHS").Value = txtProdWt.Value
    Range("SpaceRHS").Value = txtProdSp.Value

    For i = 1 To 5
        If Frames(i).Visible = True Then
            WtRg.Offset(i - 1, 0).Value = Weight(i).Value
            SpRg.Offset(i - 1, 0).Value = Space(i).Value
            PrRg.Offset(i - 1, 0).Value = Profit(i).Value
            QuRg.Offset(i - 1, 0).Value = Quota(i).Value
            LmRg.Offset(i - 1, 0).Value = Limit(i).Value
        End If
    Next i

    Unload Me
End Sub
```

Figure 19.9 The code for the nput form.

Before using the arrays of text box controls, we have to set them to the appropriate text boxes; we do this in the *UserForm_Initialize* procedure. We also give some default values to each text box for all frames when we open this form. After initializing the text box arrays, it is easy to set these default values simply by looping through each array (see Figure 19.10).

```
Private Sub UserForm_Initialize()
    Set Weight(1) = txtWeight1
    Set Weight(2) = txtWeight2
    Set Weight(3) = txtWeight3
    Set Weight(4) = txtWeight4
    Set Weight(5) = txtWeight5

    Set Space(1) = txtSpace1
    Set Space(2) = txtSpace2
    Set Space(3) = txtSpace3
    Set Space(4) = txtSpace4
    Set Space(5) = txtSpace5

    Set Profit(1) = txtProfit1
    Set Profit(2) = txtProfit2
    Set Profit(3) = txtProfit3
    Set Profit(4) = txtProfit4
    Set Profit(5) = txtProfit5

    Set Quota(1) = txtQuota1
    Set Quota(2) = txtQuota2
    Set Quota(3) = txtQuota3
    Set Quota(4) = txtQuota4
    Set Quota(5) = txtQuota5

    Set Limit(1) = txtLimit1
    Set Limit(2) = txtLimit2
    Set Limit(3) = txtLimit3
    Set Limit(4) = txtLimit4
    Set Limit(5) = txtLimit5

    txtProdWt.Value = 100
    txtProdSp.Value = 50000

    For i = 1 To 5
        Weight(i).Value = 1
        Space(i).Value = 200
        Profit(i).Value = 400
        Quota(i).Value = 10
        Limit(i).Value = 20
    Next i

End Sub
```

Figure 19.10 All text boxes are given default values.

Let's now return to our module to discuss the final code that takes place in the *SolveProb* procedure. In this procedure, we need to input all model parts into the Solver using the objects and corresponding methods and properties as defined in this chapter. We begin by using the *Clear* method, which removes all variables and constraints from the problem object. We then initialize the decision variables, set the non-negative property to True, and add these variables to the problem object. We initialize the objective function, set its function type property to *Function_Type_Objective*, and add this function to the problem object. We initialize the left-hand side, set the function type property to *Function_Type_Constraint*, set the relation type and the right-hand side value, and finally add each constraint to the problem object. Figure 19.11 presents the code that we use to create the optimization problem.

```
Dim i As Integer, prob As New RSP.Problem, myVar As New Variable
Dim constraints() As New RSP.Function, obj As New RSP.Function

Sub SolveProb()
    Application.ScreenUpdating = False
    'clear problem variables and constraints
    prob.Variables.Clear
    prob.Functions.Clear

    'Variables
    myVar.Init Range("ProdDecVar")
    myVar.NonNegative
    prob.Variables.Add myVar

   'Objective Function
    obj.Init Range("ProdObjFunc")
    obj.FunctionType = Function_Type_Objective
    prob.Functions.Add obj

    'Create the constraints array
    ReDim constraints(NumCons) As New RSP.Function

    'Add the quota & limit constraints
    For i = 1 To NumDV
        constraints(i).Init DVRg.Offset(i - 1, 0)
        constraints(i).FunctionType = Function_Type_Constraint
        constraints(i).Relation Cons_Rel_GE, QuRg.Offset(i - 1, 0).Value
        prob.Functions.Add constraints(i)

        constraints(NumDV + i).Init DVRg.Offset(i - 1, 0)
        constraints(NumDV + i).FunctionType = Function_Type_Constraint
        constraints(NumDV + i).Relation Cons_Rel_LE, LmRg.Offset(i - 1, 0).Value
        prob.Functions.Add constraints(NumDV + i)
    Next

    'Add the weight constraint
    constraints(NumCons - 1).Init Range("WeightC")
    constraints(NumCons - 1).FunctionType = Function_Type_Constraint
    constraints(NumCons - 1).Relation Cons_Rel_LE, Range("WeightRHS").Value
    prob.Functions.Add constraints(NumCons - 1)

    'Add the space constraint
    constraints(NumCons).Init Range("SpaceC")
    constraints(NumCons).FunctionType = Function_Type_Constraint
    constraints(NumCons).Relation Cons_Rel_LE, Range("SpaceRHS").Value
    prob.Functions.Add constraints(NumCons)
```

Figure 19.11 This part of *SolveProb* procedure creates a problem instance and adds the corresponding decision variables, constraints, and objective function.

The rest of the code for the *SolveProb* procedure is shown in Figure 19.12. This code sets the *Standard LP/Quadratic* as the engine for solving the problem, resets engine parameters to their default values, sets the number of iterations to 100, sets the solver type to *Solver_Type_Maximize*, and, finally, optimizes the problem. We can now solve this problem multiple times using the *Solve Dynamic Problem* button and varying the number of items for which the problem is solved. If the result is infeasible, we can simply modify the input values and solve it again. If the problem has a solution, then we call *ViewResults* procedure (Figure 19.13) in order to see the final value of the decision variables, the value of the dual variables, and the objective function value. The *ClearProb* procedure clears the memory we allocated to problem, variable, and function objects.

```
    'Identify the solver engine
    prob.Engine = prob.Engines("Standard LP/Quadratic")
    prob.Engine.ParamReset

    'Set the engine
    For i = 0 To prob.Engine.Params.Count - 1
        If prob.Engine.Params(i).Name = "Iterations" Then
            prob.Engine.Params(i).Value = 100
        End If
    Next i

    'Solve the problem
    prob.Solver.SolverType = Solver_Type_Maximize
    prob.Solver.Optimize Solve_Type_Solve

    Application.ScreenUpdating = True

    If prob.Solver.OptimizeStatus = 5 Then
        MsgBox "This problem is infeasible. Please enter new input values."
    Else
        Call ViewResults
    End If

    Call ClearProb
End Sub
```

Figure 19.12 This part of *SolveProb* procedure selects an engine, sets engine parameters, and solves the problem.

```
Sub ClearProb()
    Set myVar = Nothing
    Set obj = Nothing
    For i = 1 To NumCons
        Set constraints(i) = Nothing
    Next
    Set prob = Nothing
End Sub
```

```
Sub ViewResults()

  For i = 0 To prob.VarDecision.Size - 1
        MsgBox "The value of " & i + 1 & " th decision variable is: " _
            & prob.VarDecision.Value(i)
  Next i

  For i = 0 To prob.Functions.Count - 2
         MsgBox "The value of " & i + 1 & " th dual variable is: " _
            & prob.Functions(i).DualValue(0)
  Next i

  MsgBox "The objective function value is: " & _
    prob.Functions(prob.Functions.Count - 1).Value(0)

End Sub
```

Figure 19.13 The *ClearProb* procedure frees the memory allocated to problem, variable, and function objects. The *ViewResults* procedure prints the value of the decision variables, dual variables, and the objective function value.

Notice that we use range names previously defined to initiate variables and function objects. There is no extra code necessary in the Solver statements to make this problem dynamic since we have already redefined range names.

19.5 *Summary*

- There are three main parts of an optimization model: *decision variables*, *objective function*, and *constraints*.
- *Decision variables* are variables whose respective values are to be determined in the problem. We use these variables to represent all other relationships in the model, including the objective function and constraints.
- The *objective function* is an equation that states the goal, or objective, of the model. Objective functions are either maximized or minimized.
- The *constraints* are the limitations of the problem. We write these constraints as equations in terms of the decision variables.
- Using the Risk Solver Platform requires a short sequence of steps: (1) reading and interpreting the problem, (2) preparing the spreadsheet, and (3) solving the model and reviewing the results.
- In the interpretation of the problem, we define the mathematical model; that is, we must define our decision variables, objective function, and constraints via mathematical representation.
- In preparing the spreadsheet, we must translate and clearly define each part of our model in the spreadsheet. We use referencing and formulas to mathematically represent the model in the spreadsheet cells.
- To enter the decision variables, we list them in individual cells with an empty cell next to each one. We then enter the objective function and constraints in different ranges with formulas which reference these decision variable cells.
- Remember that it is a good idea to name ranges of the model parts in the spreadsheet to help with coding efficiency later.
- We use object-oriented API in the Risk Solver Platform to create an instance of an optimization problem, and add to this problem the corresponding decision variables, constraints, and objective function.
- We use *Variables.Add* and *Functions.Add* methods to add the decision variables, constraints and objective function to the problem object. We can use the *Functions.Remove* method to remove existing constraints from the problem.
- Before adding variables and constraints to the problem, we use the *Variables.Clear* and *Functions.Clear* methods of the problem object. These methods remove all the existing variables and constraints from the problem.
- To select an engine for solving the problem, we use the *Engine* property of the problem object. The *Standard LP/Quadratic* engine is used to solve linear programming and quadratic programming problems. The *GRG Nonlinear* engine is used to solve nonlinear programming problems. It is a good practice to initially set the engine parameters to their default values, and later on make changes to the parameters as seen necessary.
- To solve an optimization problem, we use the *Solver.Optimze* method. There is one argument for this method: *Solve_Type*.
- We use the *Solver.OptimizeStatus* property of the problem object to keep or ignore the Solver results.
- We use the *Solver.Report* method of the problem object to generate solution reports. There is one argument for this method: *ReportName*.
- We use the *Init*, *Save*, and *Load* methods of the problem object to initialize a problem instance, save, and load a optimization problem.

19.6 *Exercises*

19.6.1 Review Questions

1. What library must be referenced by the VBE in order to use *object-oriented API* in the *Risk Solver Platform* to create, modify, and solve optimization problems?
2. Assume that the code below is part of a program that is correctly implemented. What are the possible values of *result* after running the code? What do the possible values tell you about the solution of the optimization problem?

```
Dim Result as Integer
Result = Prob.Solver.OptimizeStatus
```

3. Which property of the *problem* object allows us to specify if the objective function should be maximized or minimized?

4. Explain how to add an objective function to an instance of the *problem* object.
5. What are the parameters for *Relation*, a method of *functions* object? What values do these parameters take?
6. Write a VBA code that sets the parameter *AssumeNonneg* of the *Engine* object to True.
7. Write a VBA code that displays the final value of the *decision variables* of a *problem* object.
8. Write a VBA code that displays the *Limits* Report generated by the Solver.
9. Explain the purpose of *Init*, *Save*, and *Load* methods of the problem object.
10. How can arrays be set to *control* data types? How do you initialize them?

19.6.2 Hands-On Exercises

*(**Note:** Please refer to the file "Chapter_19_Exercises .xlsx" for the associated worksheets noted for the hands-on exercises. The file is available at: www.dssbooks.com.)*

1. Add the optional code to the *frmParam* form *cmdOK_Click* procedure in the *Dynamic Production problem* application. This code should hide rows on the spreadsheet based on the number of decision variables chosen by the users.
2. A farmer has 100 acres of land for crops and must decide how many acres to devote to three different crops: cotton, peanuts, and soybean. The number of acres to devote must be a multiple of four. Information about cost per acre and revenue per acre is provided in a table. Set up the model of this problem and write a procedure in VBA to find the number of acres to devote to each crop that maximizes profit. (Refer to worksheet 19.2.)
3. Imagine that you are a production manager for an automobile manufacturing facility, and you must choose the best combination of paints that minimizes cost without requiring more time for painting than is available. Each car must be painted with primer, then a base coat, and finally a clear coat. The cost and time per car is given for the available paints. The cheaper paints require more drying time. (Refer to worksheet 19.3.)
   a. Set up a worksheet to use the Risk Solver Platform for optimization.
   b. Create a procedure that uses the Solver to find the combination of paints that minimizes the total cost of painting one vehicle in no more than 12 minutes.
4. As the manager of a retail store, you must decide on the number of each product to order so that you maximize expected total profit. Each week, you forecast the demand for each product for the following week. You must order each product in batches of five products. For example, if you forecast demand to be six, then you must order two batches to meet the expected demand. After meeting the expected demand, any remaining products have an inventory cost of $6 per unit. The purchase cost per unit for each product depends on the quantity purchased and decreases as quantity increases. Information for each product is given in a table. Assume that the beginning inventory level is zero for all products. Set up the model of this problem in a worksheet to use the Risk Solver Platform for optimization. Write a procedure that performs the following actions. (Refer to worksheet 19.4.)
   a. Asks the users to enter the expected demand for each product.
   b. Displays the current inventory in a user form and allows the users to modify the inventory if necessary.
   c. Optimizes the quantity of each product to order using the Solver commands.
   d. Displays a message giving the optimal order quantity of each product and the expected profit.
5. A semiconductor company has three manufacturing facilities and four distribution centers throughout its sales region. A given table contains the distance between each manufacturing facility and each distribution center. It also provides information on the required number of shipments (demand) needed at each distribution center and available shipment amounts at the manufacturing facility (supply). Based on this information, create a VBA program that uses the Risk Solver Platform to find an optimal solution. (Refer to worksheet 19.5.)
6. Let's see how we can use the data given in worksheet 19.6 to optimize the production schedule of a company. The situation is as follows: The data within the chart are referred to as the "Hours Required per Unit Made." This

means, for product 1, that in order to make one unit, Dan must work 1 hour, Kathy must work 4 hours, and Ashley must work 2 hours. The "Hours Available" column lists the maximum number of hours each worker can be scheduled to work. The "Profit per Unit" row provides information on the company's profits earned for each unit of product produced. Write a procedure that maximizes company profits given the hourly constraints of the workers and the time required to produce one unit of each product.

7. An assignment problem involves the decision of allocating tasks to available resources. For example, if an employer has three machines and five products to be manufactured, he would need to assign products to each machine that would allow for their successful completion. The first diagram is a breakdown of the cost/unit to produce each product on each machine and the production requirements for each product. The second diagram uses the data provided in the first chart, including the information about the machine capacity (supply). Based on these data, create the final chart required and assign ranges to the data appropriately so that the Solver can be used to solve this problem. Create a VBA procedure that will solve this assignment problem. (***Note:*** The demand values in the second chart are all equal to 1 since each machine will be assigned to manufacture the entire products' daily production requirements, and the supply values are equal to either 1 or 2 based on the machines' capability to manufacture more than one product.) (Refer to worksheet 19.7.)

8. Read the following scenario and determine the objective, constraints, and decision variables in the problem:

A coffee shop would like to order 5 lbs of coffee beans this week and 9 lbs of coffee beans next week to keep up with customer demand. Two suppliers have been approved to sell the beans. The first supplier has an inventory of 7 lbs and is willing to charge $5.70/lb this week and $7.20/lb next week. The second supplier has 12 lbs of beans in inventory and its prices for this week and next week are $7.35 and $7.90, respectively. The coffee shop needs to determine how many pounds of coffee to order from each supplier to minimize costs.

Write a VBA procedure to solve the problem. (Refer to worksheet 19.8.)

9. The state police department needs 12, 8, 6, and 15 officers to work each of the 6-hour periods in a day, respectively. Officers are hired to work in 12-hour or 18-hour shifts. They are paid $25/hour for the first 12 hours they work and then $27/hour for each hour over that.

a. Formulate a scheduling LP problem to minimize the cost of the police department.

b. Prepare the spreadsheet for this problem and then use object-oriented API in VBA to solve it.

c. Make this problem dynamic by allowing the users to modify the input values for the following:

i. number of officers needed per 6-hour period

ii. pay for first 12 hours

iii. pay for each hour over 12 hours

10. A young investor can invest up to $2,000. She wants to invest her money in stocks and loans. Each dollar invested in stocks yields a 15-cent profit and each dollar invested in loans yields a 20-cent profit. At least 25% of all the money invested must be in stocks, and at least $350 must be invested in loans.

a. Formulate a capital budgeting LP problem to maximize her profits.

b. Prepare a spreadsheet and write a VBA procedure to solve this problem.

c. Design a user form that does the following:

i. allows the user to change her available investment amount in a text box

ii. has a scroll bar to determine percent that can be invested in stocks and another scroll bar for percent to be invested in loans

11. A company knows its demands and production costs for the next three periods (see table below). It also has a holding cost of $2/unit for all units not sold at the end of each period. At the beginning of the first period, it has 5 units on hand. Assume that only one-half of the units produced during a period can be used to meet the current period's demand.

	A	B	C	D	E
1		Period 1	Period 2	Period 3	Period 4
2	Demand	30	15	25	30
3	Production Unit Cost	$10	$11	$12	$4

a. Formulate a multiperiod financial LP problem to minimize the cost of meeting demands for these three periods.
b. Prepare a spreadsheet and write a VBA procedure to solve this problem.
c. Design a user form that allows the users to enter another period worth of data (demand and production cost). Make your program adjustable so that necessary constraints are added and the objective function is updated.

12. A hospital needs to purchase 3 gallons of a perishable medicine to use during the current month and 4 gallons to use during the next month. Each medicine has an expiration time of one month. Two companies are selling this medicine. The medicine is in short supply, however, so the hospital is limited to buying a maximum of 5 gallons from each company. The prices charged by each company are given in worksheet 19.12.
    a. Formulate a transportation problem to minimize the cost of purchasing the medicines.
    b. Prepare a spreadsheet and write a VBA procedure to solve this problem.
    c. Make the problem dynamic by allowing the users to do the following:
        i. Change the medicine demand per month for the hospital.
        ii. Change the limited amount per company (these limits to not have to be the same for each company).
        iii. Change the number of companies.
        iv. Change the number of months (and give demand for new months and company prices for new months).
13. A manufacturer can sell product 1 at a profit of \$3/unit and product 2 at a profit of \$7/unit. Three units of raw material are needed to manufacture 1 unit of product 1 and 6 units of raw material are needed to manufacture 1 unit of product 2. A total of 120 units of raw material are available. If any of product 1 is produced, a setup cost of \$10 is incurred, and if any of product 2 is produced, a setup cost of \$20 is incurred.
    a. Formulate an IP problem to maximize profits.
    b. Prepare a spreadsheet and use VBA Solver commands to solve this problem.
    c. Allow the users to modify the input (profit, raw materials, setup cost) per product.
    d. Allow the users to change the number of products.
14. A product can be produced on four different machines. Each machine has a fixed setup cost, variable production costs, and a production capacity. A total of 2,000 units of the product must be produced. (Refer to worksheet 19.14.)
    a. Formulate an IP problem to minimize total costs.
    b. Prepare a spreadsheet and write a VBA procedure to solve this problem.
    c. Allow the user to change the number of machine and the requirements per machine.
15. Read Chapter 8, Hands-On Exercise 8. Create a user form that does the following:
    a. Allows the user to modify the amount of time required in each workstation to produce one batch of nuts or bolts.
    b. Allows the user to modify the cost of manufacturing a batch of nuts or bolts.
    c. Allows the user to change the minimum amount of nuts/bolts required.
    d. Allows the user to change the number of workstations allocated to producing nuts and bolts.
    e. Solves the corresponding mathematical formulation of the problem and presents the optimal objective function value and solution to the user.
16. Read Chapter 8, Hands-On Exercise 4. Create a user form that does the following:
    a. Allows the user to modify the unit production cost, sales price, labor hours, and machine hours required for each product.
    b. Solves the corresponding linear programming problem and presents the corresponding objective function value and solution to the user.
17. Read Chapter 8, Hands-On Exercise 12. Create a user form that does the following. (Refer to worksheet 19.17.)
    a. Allows the user to modify the hourly salary and the number of employees working everyday of the week.
    b. Solves the corresponding integer programming problem and presents the objective function value (salary expenses) and solution to the user.

18. Read Chapter 8, Hands-On Exercise 17. Create a user form that does the following. (Refer to worksheet 19.18.)

a. Allows the user to modify the unit cost from each warehouse to the customers.

b. Allows the user to modify the capacity of each warehouse and customer demand.

c. Allows the user to increase the number of customers (up to 6). For this purpose use a spinbutton.

d. Solves the corresponding linear programming problem and presents the objective function value to the user.

19. Read Chapter 8, Hands-On Exercise 20. Create a sub-procedure that uses the Risk Solver Platform to solve this vendor selection problem.

20. Read Chapter 8, Hands-On Exercise 22. Create a sub-procedure that uses the Risk Solver Platform to find the shortest path in the network.

CHAPTER

twenty
Simulation Revisited

chapter OVERVIEW

20.1 *Introduction*

This chapter illustrates how a dynamic simulation can be performed and enhanced in Excel using Visual Basic for Applications. We will learn how to use the object-oriented API in the Risk Solver Platform to create and solve a simulation model under the control of our customized user forms built in VBA. We will also discuss how to collect and analyze data from the simulation, and add animation to our application. Many DSS applications may involve simulation. We use simulation in our Birthday Simulation, Reliability Analysis, Queuing Simulation, and Retirement Planning cases.

In this chapter, the reader will learn how to:

- Create and modify a simulation problem using object-oriented API.
- Perform dynamic simulation runs using VBA.
- Create simulation animation using VBA.
- Perform dynamic analysis using histograms and VBA.
- Create a full dynamic simulation application with animation.

20.2 *Review of Chapter 9*

In Chapter 9, we defined simulation and discussed how to create simulation models in Excel using the Risk Solver Platform. In this chapter, we will show some parallel functionality that we can accomplish using the object-oriented API in VBA. First, let's review how simulation is defined and how to create a simulation model in Excel.

20.2.1 Defining Simulation

Simulation is a modeling tool that we use to imitate a real-world process or system in order to understand its behavior. The true behavior of a system is estimated using distributions. We use simulation to evaluate multiple strategies and predict the future performance of the system. Simulation is a useful tool in that it helps us make observations from trial and error without the cost of materials, labor, and time that would be necessary to observe the same results on the original process or system. Simulation differs from optimization in that instead of seeking to optimize an objective function value, it simulates the behavior of a system to assess its performance under several scenarios.

20.2.2 Simulation Using Risk Solver Platform

The Risk Solver Platform is a useful tool to build simulation models in Excel. We will now review a few important things we need to keep in mind when we create and simulate a model.

The first step in building a simulation model using the Risk Solver Platform is to set up our Excel worksheet. Remember that simulation is a higher level what-if scenario analysis. Therefore, we should design our worksheet accordingly by identifying model *inputs* and corresponding *outputs*.

In a simulation model there is at least one problem input that is stochastic in nature. We model stochasticity by generating random numbers from a particular distribution function. We have already discussed how to use the *RAND* function of Excel and *Psi Distribution* functions of the Risk Solver Platform to generate numbers from a given distribution. In order to access the galleries of *Psi* functions, we click the *Risk Solver Platform > Simulation Model > Distributions* command on the *Ribbon*. Some of the most useful distribution functions are *PsiNormal(mean, std dev)*, *PsiDiscrete(values, weights)*, *PsiExponential(mean)*, *PsiTriangular(min, mean, max)*, etc. The *Model* tab of the of the Risk Solver's task pane lists all problem inputs, which are referred to as *Uncertain Variables*.

The values that problem *outputs* take depend on the value of the stochastic problem inputs. Problem outputs are functions that use problem inputs to perform certain calculations. Usually, we are interested only in some problem outputs. To make this choice clear to the Risk Solver Platform, we add "*+PsiOutput()*" to the existing formula of an output cell. The Risk Solver Platform lists problem outputs in the *Model* tab of the *task pane*. Problem outputs are referred to as *Uncertain Functions*.

During simulation, a number of simulation trials are performed. We are interested in calculating summary statistics about problem outputs. To accomplish this, we use functions such as *PsiMean()*, *PsiStdDev()*, *PsiMax()*, etc. These functions are listed as *Statistic Functions* in the *Model* tab of the *task pane*. The single argument of these functions is the address of the problem output cell.

Finally, we set the value of *Trials per Simulation* property at the *Platform* tab of the *task pane* and run the simulation. The Risk Solver Platform generates a wide variety of simulation reports. We double click on an output cell to activate the *Simulations Results* dialog box, which summarizes the results of the simulation. The Risk Solver Platform provides tools to perform sensitivity analysis with respect to different problem parameters.

Summary

Simulation:	A modeling tool that is used to imitate a real-world process or system in order to understand its behavior.
Uncertain variables:	Simulation problem inputs of stochastic nature. We randomly generate their values using Psi distribution functions of the Risk Solver Platform.
Uncertain functions:	Simulation problem outputs. These functions use problem inputs to perform certain calculations.
Statistic functions:	Calculation of summary statistics of problem outputs over all simulation trials.

20.3 Simulation Using Object-Oriented API in the Risk Solver Platform

The Risk Solver Platform tab on the Ribbon provides a user-friendly interface to build and analyze advanced *Monte Carlo* simulation models. Therefore, it is recommended to initially build your simulation model using the Risk Solver Platform in Excel, and then use object-oriented API in VBA to control Solver engine parameters, perform a simulation, and collect simulation statistics as demonstrated in the following sections. We will also discuss how to use VBA to add animation to our simulations. To learn more about using object-oriented API in the Risk Solver Platform, readers should refer to the User Guide and Reference Manual that come with the Risk Solver Platform software.

20.3.1 Creating a Simulation Problem

Suppose that we have already created a simulation model of a process or system in the current workbook. We use object-oriented API in VBA to create an instance of the *problem* object. The *problem* object represents the whole simulation problem. We declare a *problem* object variable using the *Dim* statement as follows:

```
Dim MyProb As New RSP.Problem
```

We next use the *Init* method to initialize an instance of the problem object using the simulation model in the current workbook. We type the following in VBA.

```
MyProb.Init ActiveWorkbook
```

Upon initializing our problem, a collection of *variable* objects and a collection of *function* objects are created automatically. Each variable object corresponds to a range of one or more cells that contain *Psi Distribution* functions. Each *function* object corresponds to an output (formula) cell that contains an Excel function that manipulates problem variables, and references the *PsiOutput()* function. Note that when uncertain variables lie in contiguous cells, then one single variable object is created to represent all the cells in the range. For example, suppose we have created a simulation model in which the problem inputs are randomly generated using some Psi Distribution function. These inputs are located in cells A1:A10 and D1:G1. Two variable objects are created, one for each range of inputs. *Variables(0)* refers to range A1:A10. In order to display the random values generated in cell A2 during the i-th simulation trial, we type the following:

```
MyProb.Variables(0).AllTrials(1,i-1)
```

AllTrials is a property of *variable and function* objects. It allows us to access the value that the variable cells take during each simulation trial. The *AllTrials* property yields a *DoubleMatrix* object that takes two subscripts, the index of the cell in the range represented by the *Variables(0)* object (A2 is the 2nd cell in this range), and the index *i* of the simulation trial.

Similarly, when uncertain functions lie in contiguous cells, then one single function object is created to represent all the cells in the range. For example, if cells B1:B10 and F1:H1 contain uncertain functions, we type the following VBA code to access the function value in cell H1 during the i-th simulation trial:

```
MyProb.Functions(1).AllTrials(2,i-1)
```

We can make changes to the uncertain variables and functions of an existing simulation problem by overriding the corresponding formulas in the Excel worksheet. We can add a new uncertain variable by typing a formula to a cell. For example, we use the following VBA code to add one additional variable (cell A11) to the existing model.

```
Range("A11"). Formula = "=PsiExponential(10)"
```

We can also add an uncertain function to an existing model. Suppose that in cell B11 we have already typed a formula that manipulates some problem inputs. In order to turn this cell into an uncertain function of our model, we use this VBA code.

```
Range("B11").Formula = Range("B11").Formula + "+PsiOutput()"
```

20.3.2 Making Runs and Collecting Data

Prior to running the simulation model we should set Solver and Engine parameters, such as the number of simulations to run, the number of trials per simulation, the sampling method, and random seed to use. Next, we present a procedure that can be used to initialize a problem, set Solver and Engine parameters, and simulate the problem.

```
Sub Simulate()
    Dim MyProb as New RSP.Problem
    MyProb.Init ActiveWorkbook

    MyProb.Solver.NumTrials = 5000
    MyProb.Engine.Params("SamplingMethod") = 2
    MyProb.Engine.Params("RandomSeed") = 12

    MyProb.Solver.Simulate
    Set MyProb = Nothing
End Sub
```

The number of simulation trials, or sampling method and random seed to use in the simulation model, can come as an input from the user. To accomplish this, we can use input boxes. We can also create a user form, and use textboxes to get users' input. We demonstrate how to use input boxes and user forms through the application presented in section 20.4.

The Risk Solver Platform automatically generates summary statistics for each problem output that we have identified. We can use *For, Next* loops to access these statistics. The *Count* property of *FunctionCollection* object identifies the total number of function blocks in the problem. The *Size* property of *Function* object identifies the number of cells in the range, and its other properties (Mean(), Min(), Max(), etc.) are indexed to access statistics of individual cells.

```
Sub Simulate()
    Dim MyProb as New RSP.Problem, i as Integer, j as Integer
    MyProb.Init ActiveWorkbook
    MyProb.Solver.Simulate

    For i = 0 To MyProb.Functions.Count -1
        For j = 0 To MyProb.Functions(i).Size -1
            MsgBox MyProb.Functions(i).Statistics.Min(j)
            MsgBox MyProb.Functions(i).Statistics.Mean(j)
            MsgBox MyProb.Functions(i).Statistics.Max(j)
            MsgBox MyProb.Functions(i).Statistics.StdDev(j)
        Next j
    Next i
End Sub
```

As seen in the code above, we can use *For, Next* loops to collect statistics about the minimum, maximum, mean, and standard deviation of an output cell over all simulation trials. We can calculate similar statistics by using the VBA code. Suppose that cell A1 references PsiOutput() function, and we want to display in cells B1 and B2 statistics related to cell A1. Then we use the following VBA code to display these statistics.

```
Range ("B1").Formula = "=PsiMean(A1)"
Range ("B2").Formula = "=PsiMin(A1)"
```

Sometimes, however, instead of the summary statistics, we want to know exactly the value of an output cell during each simulation trial. We then need to determine if we will be storing this data in *arrays* or in a *worksheet.* When multiple calculations of data are needed, and they do not require Excel functions, arrays can be easier structures to work with. They are easier in the sense that we do not have to define range names and use extra worksheet space. If, however, we need to use some other Excel functions, such as distribution functions, with the generated data, it may be better to store these data in a worksheet. We now show how to use the *AllTrials* property of *function* object to access the value that output cells take during each simulation trial. The following VBA code displays the values taken by all output cells during each simulation trial. The values taken by *Functions(1)* block overall simulation trials are stored in an Excel worksheet for the user to see.

```
For i = 0 To MyProb.Functions.Count – 1
   For j = 0 To MyProb.Functions(i).Size – 1
      For k = 0 to MyProb.Solver.NumTrials – 1
         MsgBox MyProb.Functions(i).AllTrials(j, k)
         If (i = 1) then
               Range("D1").Offset(k,j).Value= MyProb.Functions(i).AllTrials(j, k)
         End if
         Next k
   Next j
Next i
```

We can store other input and/or output of a simulation in a spreadsheet for the users to see. However, for some simulation models, it will be unnecessary to store or show the users the input values; analysis of the output is usually of most importance to the users.

Summary

Objects	Properties	Methods	Arguments
Engine	Params		
Function	AllTrials		
Problem	Engine Size	Init	Workbook
	FunctionCollection	Count	
Variable	AllTrials		
Solver	SolverType	Simulate	None
	NumTrials		
Statistics	Max		
	Mean		
	Min		
	StdDev		

20.3.3 Animation

The two VBA methods that we often use to create a simulation program are the ***ScreenUpdating*** and ***Wait*** methods of the Application object (as discussed in Chapter 13). The *ScreenUpdating* method should be set to *False* before the simulation begins. This reduces screen flickering while the program runs and increases efficiency (due to decreased running time) if the screen is not updated after every action in the code. It should be set to *True* when the simulation has been completed.

We use the *Wait* method to create some animation of the simulation. Let's now use a simple example to demonstrate how to animate a production line. For example, consider a production line where several parts are received and shipped from different workstations. Every morning a batch of parts arrive at the beginning of the production line. These parts move from one workstation to the next until they are all processed by the end of the working day. Each workstation has a different distribution for processing time. We use the *PsiLogNormal()* function to randomly generate the time it takes for a part to be processed at Workstation 1. Processing time at Workstation 1 is presented in our model by the first group of the *Variable* object—that is, *Variables(0)*. We would like to animate the fourth simulation trial of this model. We collect the processing time at Workstation 1 using *AllTrials* property of the Variable object. We set the second subscript of *AllTrials* property equal to 3 to ensure that we are collecting the values from the fourth simulation trial. We then use the following loop to collect the randomly generated data about processing time at Workstation 1.

```
ReDim Workstation1(BatchSize) As Double

For i = 0 To BatchSize - 1
    Workstation1(i) = MyProb.Variables(0).AllTrials(i, 3)
Next i
```

Here, BatchSize presents the total number of parts that we are simulating that is equal to the number of parts that pass through Workstation 1 during a workday. We can consider each value of our Workstation1 array to be a time value. We can then create a cumulative time array using the following:

```
ReDim CumWork1(BatchSize) As Double

CumWork1 (0) = 0
For i = 1 To BatchSize - 1
    CumWork1(i) = WorkStation1(i) + WorkStation1(i - 1)
Next i
```

Now we can run a loop to show that a product leaves Workstation 1 at each time value. To do this, we may highlight some cell that changes position, or disappears and reappears, every time this action occurs. To create this action, we would pick some range to highlight (by changing the color with the *Interior* property), and each time we loop through a run, we un-highlight this cell and highlight the next cell (using the *Offset* property). However, to ensure that the users see a delay between these actions, we use the *Wait* method. (Note that we will now need to move the *ScreenUpdating* statement inside the loop so that the users see the highlighted cell in each iteration.) It may be a good idea to display the time of each event as well. The corresponding code would be as follows:

```
For i = 0 To BatchSize – 1
    Application.ScreenUpdating = False
    Range("Time").Value = CumWork1(i)
    Range("A1").Offset(i, 0).Interior.ColorIndex = 0
    Range("A1").Offset(i+1, 0).Interior.ColorIndex = 5
    Application.Wait(Now + TimeValue("0:0:03"))
    Application.ScreenUpdating = True
Next i
```

Running this code will create an animated simulation that appears to move a product from one cell to the next at each iteration. We can modify this idea to create an animation that better reflects any particular system.

20.3.4 Analysis

The motivation for using simulation is, of course, to conduct some analysis to understand the behavior of the system. There are several ways to analyze the results of a simulation. As we discussed in section 20.3.2, the Risk Solver Platform automatically generates a wide variety of statistics related to a problem's uncertain variables and functions. Figure 20.1 presents properties and methods of *Statistics* object which is a child of the *Variable* and *Function* objects.

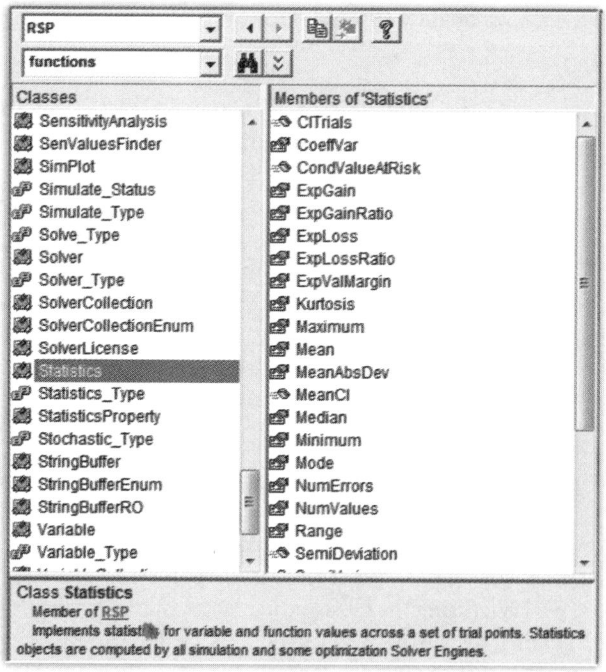

Figure 20.1 Properties and methods of Statistics object. This object is a child of the Variable and Function objects.

In addition to collecting summary statistics that are generated by the Risk Solver Platform, we can collect problem inputs and outputs from each simulation trial, and use the data to create a graph, find the maximum or minimum, etc. We can accomplish these actions using the Chart object as seen in Chapter 13 or any of the mathematical functions shown in Chapter 14.

Another powerful analysis tool available in Excel is the Data Analysis Toolpak. We discussed some of the analysis tools available in this Add-In file in Chapter 7; the tool we discussed in most detail was the histogram. Histograms calculate the number of occurrences, or frequency, in which values in a data set fall into various intervals. When we created histograms in Excel using the Data Analysis Toolpak, we had to provide several parameters: an input range of data, a range for bin values (optional), and an output range for the histogram results. We also had to check if we wanted to show data labels, create a Pareto chart, calculate cumulative values, and display a chart of the histogram results. The bin range is used to specify the location of the bin values, where bins are the intervals into which values can fall. If no bin range is specified, Excel automatically calculates a set of evenly distributed bins.

To create a histogram using VBA, we will use the ***Application*** object and the ***Run*** method. We use the Run method to specify the Add-In file from which we will be running the analysis. The arguments for this method include all of the parameters we specified when creating a histogram in Excel:

Application.Run "ATPVBAEN.XLAM!Histogram", InputRange, OutputRange, BinRange, Labels, Pareto, Cumulative, Chart

The values for the *InputRange*, *OutputRange*, and *BinRange* parameters should be ranges. These ranges can be named in Excel or they can be range variables in VBA. The *Labels*, *Pareto*, *Cumulative*, and *Chart* parameters all take *True/False* values.

We can use this simple line of code on dynamic input ranges to create a histogram for different sets of user data. Note, however, that if we run this code multiple times with the *Chart* parameter set to *True*, we will have multiple charts created on the spreadsheet.

For better code efficiency, we recommend creating a histogram in Excel first (as we have seen with some Chart applications) and then modifying our code so that all of the chart option parameters are set to *False*. As we repeat this code to run a histogram analysis on different sets of input values, we may see a warning message that our output range will be overwritten. We therefore recommend adding a line of code to clear this output range of cells before creating the histogram multiple times.

Other analysis from the Analysis Toolpak may be useful to our application. To discover the particular code and parameters for each analysis tool, we record a macro first in Excel (most analysis tools will still run an extension of the *ATPVBAEN.XLAM* file).

Summary

Animating simulation with VBA:
Application.ScreenUpdating
Application.Wait(Now() + TimeValue("00:00:01""))

Analysis using histograms:
Application.Run "ATPVBAEN.XLAM!Histogram," InputRange, OutputRange, BinRange, Labels, Pareto, Cumulative, Chart

20.4 *Applications*

20.4.1 Single Server Queuing Problem Revisited

In Chapter 9, we described how to simulate a Single Server Queuing problem using the Risk Solver Platform. The purpose of building the simulation model is to mimic the behavior of an ATM system to determine the expected customer waiting time and the expected total time in the system. The ATM system consists of the ATM and its queue. Upon the customer arrival in the system, if the queue is empty, the customer is served by the ATM machine; otherwise, the customer waits. In the worksheet model we created, the interarrival time of customers in the system and the corresponding service time were randomly generated using Psi functions. We used interarrival and service time to calculate the waiting time in queue and time in the system for each customer. Simulation tools available in the Risk Solver Platform were used to simulate the model and analyze the results.

We will now rebuild this simulation using VBA. The VBA model, similar to using the Risk Solver Platform in Excel, will allow us to perform the simulation and analyze the results. In addition, we use VBA to create a user-friendly interface for this problem and animate the queue. Figure 20.2 presents the worksheet model we created in Chapter 9 to simulate this problem. The user does not see this worksheet.

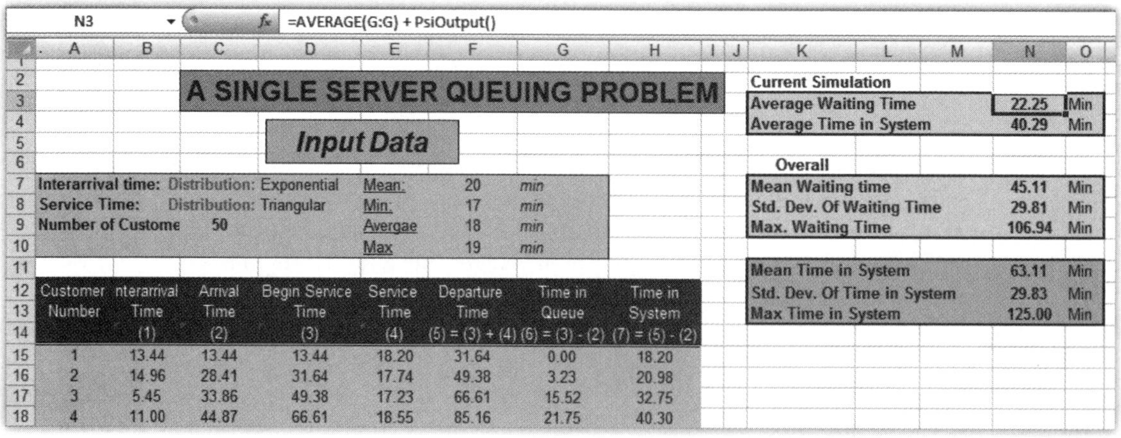

Figure 20.2 Simulation model spreadsheet setup in Excel.

Figure 20.3 (a) presents a form we have created to get the user's input about the total number of customers to simulate in each simulation trial, the mean interarrival time, and the minimum, maximum, and average service time at the ATM. We also use an input box (see Figure 20.3 (b)) to get the user's input about the total number of simulation trials.

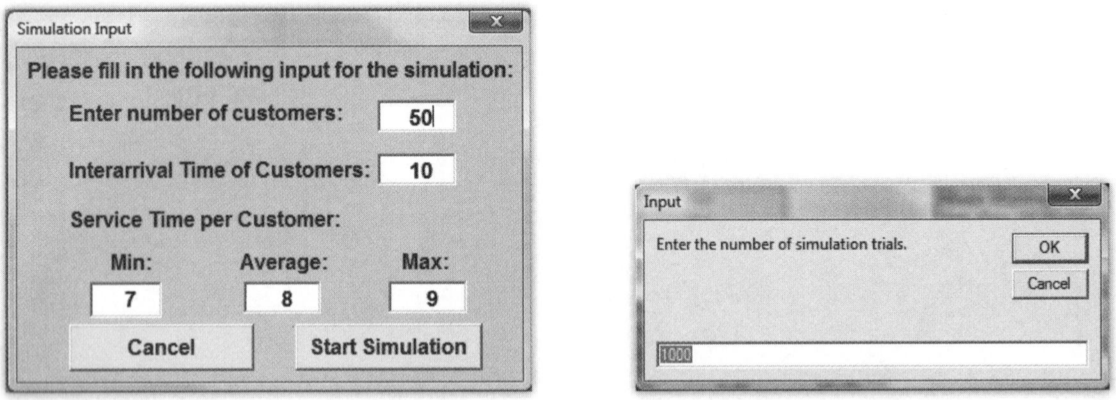

(a) Simulation input form.

(b) Input box to enter the number of simulation trials.

Figure 20.3 User interface designed in VBA for the single server queuing problem.

We animate the activities at the ATM and at the queue to visualize and better understand system's behavior. Figure 20.4 presents the spreadsheet setup for animation. In this spreadsheet, the yellow cell represents the customer being served. Customers arrive at a queue line; if the server is "Idle," then the customer begins service; if the server is "Busy," the customers stay in the queue until the server becomes "Idle" again.

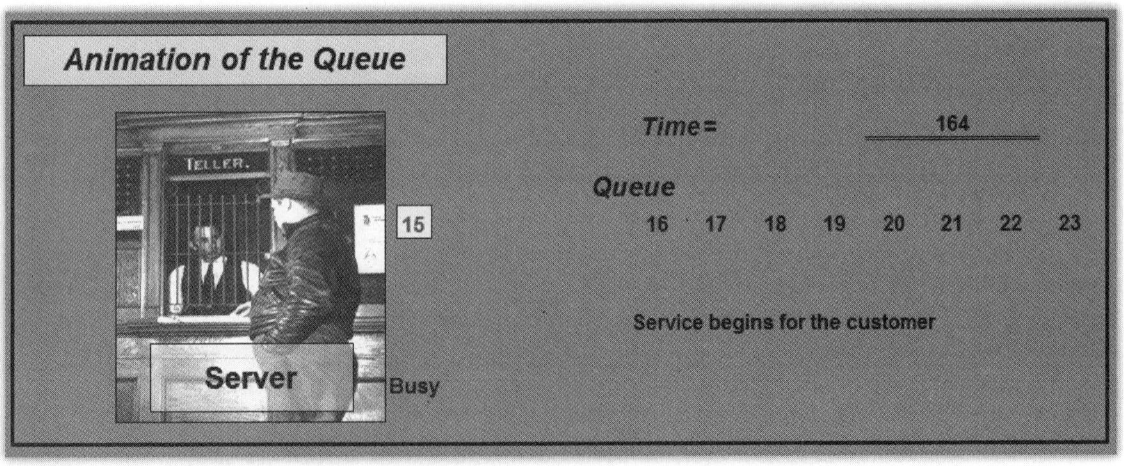

Figure 20.4 Simulation animation in the simulation sheet.

In the end of the simulation, we present to the user a number of related statistics, such as, the expected mean waiting time in the queue, standard deviation of the mean waiting time, maximum waiting time, etc. (see Figure 20.5). We use the mean waiting time from all simulation trials to create a histogram: the frequency with which users wait in the queue up to 13 minutes, or 13 to 26 minutes, etc. We specify the number of bins to use, and corresponding bin range when creating the histogram (this range is hidden on the spreadsheet).

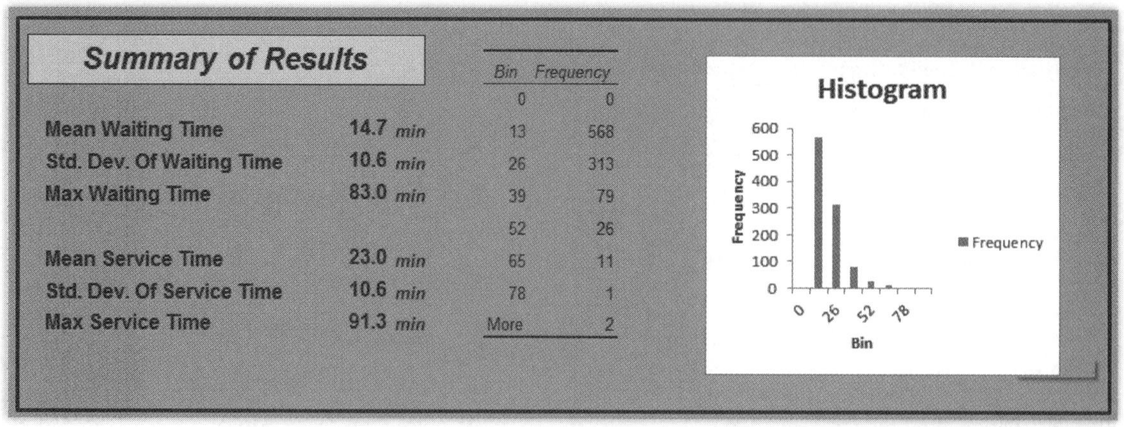

Figure 20.5 Summary of results collected during the simulation.

Let's now take a look at the code. We begin with the *Main* procedure. We use this procedure to call the user input frame, and subroutines to clear previous values, create the simulation model in Excel, simulate the model using the Risk Solver Platform, present simulation results, and animate the model (see Figure 20.6).

The *ClearAll* procedure clears the data in the Excel spreadsheet model, the results from the simulation, and the data used to create the histogram.

```
Public i As Integer, NCust As Integer, InterArrivMean As Double
Public ServerMin As Double, ServerAvg As Double, ServerMax As Double
Dim SingleS As New RSP.Problem

Sub Main()

    Call ClearAll
    frmInput.Show
    Call ExcelSimModel
    Call SimulateSS
    Call SimultaionResults
    Call Animate

End Sub
Sub ClearAll()
    On Error Resume Next
    Application.ScreenUpdating = False
    Range("SimTable", Range("SimTable").Offset(0, 6).End(xlDown)).ClearContents
    Range("SimData", Range("SimData").Offset(0, 8).End(xlDown)).ClearContents
    Range("HistData").ClearContents
    Range("Hist", Range("Hist").Offset(0, 1).End(xlDown)).ClearContents
    Range("Results", Range("Results").End(xlDown)).ClearContents
    Application.ScreenUpdating = True
End Sub
```

Figure 20.6 The *Main*, and *ClearAll* procedures.

We use the form *frmInput* to get the user's input about the total number of customers, customer mean interarrival time in the system, and the minimum, average, and maximum service time at the ATM. We assign the values entered in corresponding textboxes to public variables (see Figure 20.7). This way, the values entered by the user will not be lost when we unload the form. The *ExcelSimModel* procedure (see Figure 20.8) assigns the values of these public variables to cells in the input data area of the Simulation worksheet (Figure 20.2). We make this worksheet not visible to the user since it contains the core simulation model for this application, and we do not want the user to make any changes to this model. Every time we run this application, the *ClearAll* procedure clears all the data of this table, other than the two first rows. These two rows contain formulas used to calculate waiting time in queue and time in the system. In the *ExcelSimModel* procedure, we copy the formulas of the second row to the rest of the table. The table has as many rows as the number of customers arriving in the system.

```
Sub cmdCancel_Click()
    Unload Me
End Sub

Sub cmdOK_Click()

    'error checking for text boxes
    Dim ctl As Control
    For Each ctl In Me.Controls
        If TypeName(ctl) = "TextBox" Then
            If ctl.Value = "" Then
                MsgBox "Please make sure all textboxes are filled in."
                ctl.SetFocus
                Exit Sub
            End If
        End If
    Next

    NCust = txtNumCust
    InterArrivMean = txtInterArriv
    ServerMin = txtServerMin
    ServerAvg = txtServerAvg
    ServerMax = txtServerMax
    Unload Me

End Sub
```

Figure 20.7 The VBA procedures for OK and Cancel buttons of frmInput.

```
Sub ExcelSimModel()     'create simulation data
  With Worksheets("Simulation")
    .Range("C9").Value = NCust
    .Range("F7").Value = InterArrivMean
    .Range("F8").Value = ServerMin
    .Range("F9").Value = ServerAvg
    .Range("F10").Value = ServerMax

    .Range(Range("SimTable").Offset(-1, 0), _
        Range("SimTable").Offset(-1, 6)).Copy
    .Range("SimTable", Range("SimTable").Offset(NCust - 3, 6)). _
        PasteSpecial xlPasteAll
  End With
End Sub

Sub SimulateSS()
Dim trials As Variant

'Initialize the Simulation Model
SingleS.Init ActiveWorkbook
SingleS.Engine.Params("SamplingMethod") = 2
SingleS.Engine.Params("RandomSeed") = 12

trials = InputBox("Enter the number of simulation trials.", _
        "Input!", 1000)

If IsNumeric(trials) Then
    SingleS.Solver.NumTrials = Int(trials)
Else
    MsgBox "Enter a numerical value!"
    End
End If

'Simulate the model
SingleS.Solver.Simulate
End Sub
```

Figure 20.8 Procedures for Single Server model setup in Excel, and for problem simulation using the Risk Solver Platform.

We are ready now to simulate the model using the *SimulateSS* procedure (Figure 20.8). We declare SingleS as an RSP.Problem variable in the beginning of this module. We initialize SingleS using the Excel model we already created using the ExcelSimModel procedure. We set the value of different engine parameters, and ask the user to input the total number of simulation trials. Finally, we simulate the model and are now ready to collect the corresponding statistics.

```
Sub SimultaionResults()
'Statistics related to waiting time & time in system
With Range("Results")
    .Value = SingleS.Functions(0).Statistics.Mean(0)
    .Offset(1, 0).Value = SingleS.Functions(0).Statistics.StdDev(0)
    .Offset(2, 0).Value = SingleS.Functions(0).Statistics.Maximum(0)
    .Offset(4, 0).Value = SingleS.Functions(0).Statistics.Mean(1)
    .Offset(5, 0).Value = SingleS.Functions(0).Statistics.StdDev(1)
    .Offset(6, 0).Value = SingleS.Functions(0).Statistics.Maximum(1)
End With


'HISTOGRAM OF WAITING TIME DURING SIMULATION
    'Extract waiting time per trial
    Worksheets("SingleServerApp").Activate
    For i = 0 To SingleS.Solver.NumTrials - 1
        Range("AY33").Offset(i, 1).Value = SingleS.Functions(0).AllTrials(0, i)
    Next i
    'Create bins and histogram for wait times
    Range("AY33").Name = "WaitBinStart"
    Range("AZ33", Range("AZ33").End(xlDown)).Name = "HistData"

    Range("WaitBinStart").Value = 0
    For i = 1 To 6
        Range("WaitBinStart").Offset(i, 0).Value = _
            Int(Range("WaitBinStart").Offset(i - 1, 0).Value + (Range("K24").Value / 6))
    Next i
    Range(Range("WaitBinStart"), Range("WaitBinStart").End(xlDown)).Name = "WaitBins"
    Application.AlertBeforeOverwriting = False
    Application.Run "ATPVBAEN.XLAM!Histogram", Range("HistData"), Range("Hist"), _
            Range("WaitBins"), False, False, False, False
    Range("Hist", Range("Hist").Offset(10, 1)).Font.Color = RGB(0, 0, 0)
    Range("Hist", Range("Hist").Offset(10, 1)).Interior.Color = RGB(141, 180, 226)
    Range("A1").Select
End Sub
```

Figure 20.9 Simulation Results procedure.

The SimulationResults procedure (see Figure 20.9) prints the results of the simulation in Excel, and creates a histogram of customer waiting time in the queue. Let's first discuss how we access the result from the simulation. In the Simulation worksheet, we type the following formula in cells N3 and N4 to calculate the expected waiting time and service time in the system:

=AVERAGE(G:G) + PsiOutput()

=AVERAGE(H:H) + PsiOutput()

The *PsiOutput()* function identifies these as output cells of the simulation model. Since N3 and N4 are adjacent to each other, a single *Functions* object is created to represent both cells. We use *SingleS.Functions(0)* object to refer to this group of uncertain functions. The *Statistics* object is then used to access statistics (such as mean, standard deviation, and maximum value) of each cell. For example,

SingleS.Functions(0).Statistics.Mean(0)

calculates the mean waiting time over all simulation trials. This is equivalent to using *PsiMean(N3)* function in the worksheet. Similarly,

SingleS.Functions(0).Statistics.Mean(1)

calculates the mean time in the system over all simulation trials, equivalent to using *PsiMean(N4)* function in the worksheet. We use the *AllTrials* property of Functions object within a *For, Next* loop to access the value of cell N3 in each trial of this simulation, as follows.

```
For i = 0 To SingleS.Solver.NumTrials – 1
    Range("AY33").Offset(i, 1).Value = SingleS.Functions(0).AllTrials(0, i)
Next i
```

Note that cell N3 is the first cell in the range N3:N4; therefore, the first subscript of AllTrials property is zero. The simulation results are used to calculate bins and the data needed to build the histogram shown in Figure 20.5. We create the histogram by using the *Application. Run "ATPVBAEN.XLAM!Histogram"* statement. The arguments for this statement are input range, output range, bin range, and some options for creating labels, charts, Pareto, and cumulative values. The input ranges are named "HistData" and we use the "Hist" range to locate the output range. We have created a range called "WaitBins," hidden on the worksheet, which contains the corresponding bin values for the histogram. We use this bin range to forçe the frequency calculations done by the histogram. As we recommend when using charts, we will not re-create the histogram charts in the code. We have already run the histogram program once in the spreadsheet to create the initial chart. We have formatted the histogram and given it an appropriate title. We can therefore set all the histogram options to *False*, as the histogram output range will not change, and so the chart will be updated each time.

The last procedure for this application is the *Animate* procedure. This procedure imitates the movement of customers through the queue to the server. Initially, we use the data generated by the simulation model presented in Figure 20.2 to create a table with the timeline of the events that are happening during the simulation. The VBA code in Figure 20.11 generates the timeline table shown in Figure 20.10. The second part of the *Animate* procedure (Figure 20.12) browses through the timeline table. For each time value, we check the corresponding event description: "Arrival," "Begin Service," and "End Service." As customers arrive in the system, we check the status of the server. If the server is "Idle," then the customer moves to the server to begin service; if the server is "Busy," the customer stays in the queue until the server is "Idle" again. Queue length is also recorded for each time period. We use the *Application.Wait* method to cause a slight delay to enhance the animation.

	W	X
1		
2	2.728	Arrival
3	2.728	BeginService
4	3.886	Arrival
5	10.939	EndService
6	10.939	BeginService
7	18.181	Arrival
8	18.900	EndService
9	18.900	BeginService
10	22.558	Arrival
11	22.564	Arrival
12	27.043	EndService
13	27.043	BeginService
14	35.836	EndService
15	35.836	BeginService
16	36.073	Arrival

Figure 20.10 The hidden data sheet with the simulation timeline.

```
Sub Animate()
Dim NCust As Integer, QueueLength As Integer, Customer As Integer

    Application.ScreenUpdating = False
    Worksheets("Simulation").Activate
    NCust = Range(Range("C15"), Range("C15").End(xlDown)).Count
    Range(Range("C15"), Range("C15").Offset(NCust, 3)).Copy
    Range(Range("SimData").Offset(0, 2), Range("SimData").Offset(NCust, 2)). _
        PasteSpecial xlPasteValues

    Range("SimData", Range("SimData").Offset(3 * NCust - 1, 1)).Name = "TimeLine"
    For i = 1 To NCust
        Range("TimeLine").Cells(i, 1) = Range("SimData").Offset(i - 1, 2).Value
        Range("TimeLine").Cells(i, 2) = "Arrival"
    Next i
    For i = i To 2 * NCust
        Range("TimeLine").Cells(i, 1) = Range("SimData").Offset(i - 1 - NCust, 5).Value
        Range("TimeLine").Cells(i, 2) = "EndService"
    Next i
    For i = i To 3 * NCust
        Range("TimeLine").Cells(i, 1) = Range("SimData").Offset(i - 1 - 2 * NCust, 3).Value
        Range("TimeLine").Cells(i, 2) = "BeginService"
    Next i

    'sort the timeline by times
    Range("TimeLine").Sort Key1:=Range("W:W"), Order1:=xlAscending
    Range("TimeLine").NumberFormat = "0"

    QueueLength = 0
    Customer = 0

    'step through "timeline" data
    'perform animation and record queue length
```

Figure 20.11 Simulation Animation procedure: Create simulation timeline table.

```
    'step through "timeline" data
    'perform animation and record queue length

    Application.ScreenUpdating = True
    Worksheets("SingleServerApp").Activate
    For i = 1 To 3 * NCust
        Application.ScreenUpdating = False
        With Range("TimeLine")
            Select Case .Cells(i, 2)
                'arrival: customer number inc, queue length inc
                Case "Arrival"
                    Customer = Customer + 1
                    Range("Action") = "Customer arrives in the queue"
                    QueueLength = QueueLength + 1
                    Range("Queue").Offset(0, QueueLength) = Customer
                'begin serve: customer moves to server, queue length dec
                Case "BeginService"
                    Range("Status") = "Busy"
                    Range("Action") = "Service begins for the customer"
                    Range("BeingServed") = Range("Queue").Offset(0, 1)
                    Range("Queue").Offset(0, 1).Delete (xlToLeft)
                    Range("X9").Interior.Color = RGB(141, 180, 226)
                    QueueLength = QueueLength - 1
                'end serve: server free, customer leaves
                Case "EndService"
                    If QueueLength = 0 Then
                        Range("Status") = "Idle"
                    End If
                    Range("Action") = "Service is finished"
                    Range("BeingServed").ClearContents
            End Select
            Range("Time") = .Cells(i, 1)    'update system time
        End With
        Application.Wait (Now + TimeValue("0:0:01") / 2)
        Application.ScreenUpdating = True
    Next i
End Sub
```

Figure 20.12 Simulation Animation procedure: Perform the animation.

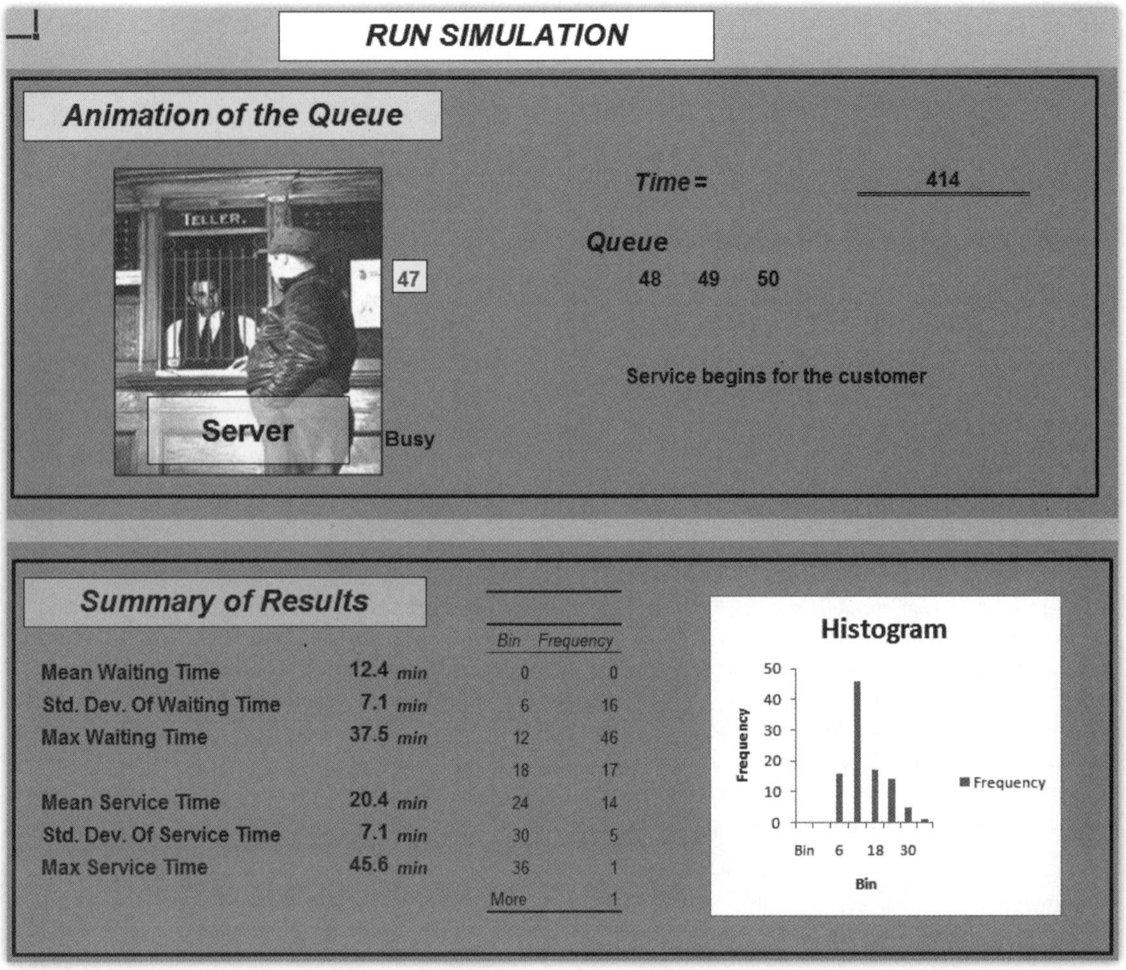

Figure 20.13 Complete Single Server Queuing application interface.

The application is now complete. We can start the code by assigning the Main procedure to the RUN SIMULATION button (Figure 20.13).

20.5 Summary

- *Simulation* is a modeling tool that we use to imitate a real-world process to understand its behavior.
- The three most important parts of a simulation model created using the Risk Solver Platform are the uncertain variables, uncertain functions, and statistic functions. Uncertain variables are problem inputs. Uncertain functions are problem outputs. Statistic functions are summary statistics of problem outputs overall simulation trials of a simulation run.
- In a simulation model at least one input variables or parameters is stochastic in nature. We model stochasticity by generating random numbers using distribution functions.
- We use the *RAND* function of Excel and the galleries of *Psi Distribution* functions provided by the Risk Solver Platform to generate the input data for a simulation model.
- A problem output cell uses Excel functions to manipulate problem inputs. Many cells in a worksheet may use problem inputs to perform some

calculations. To make our choice of problem outputs clear to the Risk Solver Platform, we add "+ PsiOutput()" to the existing formula of an output cell.

- We use functions such as PsiMean(), PsiMin(), PsiMax(), and PsiStdDev() to calculate summary statistics about problem outputs. The single argument of these functions is the address of a problem output cell.
- We use the *Dim* statement to declare a *Problem* variable instance in *VBA*. Next, we use the *Init* method to initialize the problem using an existing simulation model in the current workbook.
- We use the *AllTrials* property within *For, Next* loops to collect data about problem uncertain variables and functions.
- We use the *Simulate* method of *Solver* object to run a simulation using object-oriented API in VBA. We use *Params* property of the *Engine* object to set engine parameters such as sampling method and random seed. We use *NumTrials* property of the *Solver* object to set the total number of simulation trials.
- When building a simulation model, we often need to determine if the data and the results of the specified calculations will be stored in *arrays* or in a *worksheet*. When multiple calculations of data are needed, and do not require Excel functions, arrays can be easier structures to work with. If, however, we will need to use some other Excel functions, such as distribution functions, with the generated data, it may be better to store this data in a worksheet.
- We should set the *ScreenUpdating* method to *False* before the simulation runs begin. It should be set to *True* when the runs have been completed.
- We can use the *Wait* method to create some animation of the simulation. This method ensures that the user sees a delay between actions during simulation.
- We can use the *Analysis Toolpak* to perform many types of analysis with the data collected during simulation. This Add-In can be run in VBA using the Application object.
- Histograms calculate the number of occurrences of values in a particular interval. There are four main parts to creating a histogram: input, bins, output, and charts options.
- We use the Application object and the *Run* method in VBA to specify the Add-In file from which we will be running the analysis. The arguments for this method include all of the parameters of the analysis tool.

20.6 *Exercises*

20.6.1 Review Questions

1. How do you generate random numbers from a uniform distribution between 5 and 15?
2. Suppose the range A1:A5 presents some of the input cells of our simulation model. In cell A6 we have typed the following "=SUM(A1:A5)." Is A6 a simulation output cell? If yes, explain why. If not, how can we transform this into an output cell?
3. Suppose the range A1:A5 presents output cells of our simulation model. We want to calculate the mean of the values that each of these cells takes during all simulation trials. We will store the corresponding mean values in range B1:B5. What functions should we type in each cell of range B1:B5?
4. Suppose that simulation output cells are located in the range A1:A5 and D1:D5. Write a VBA code that stores in an array called Data the value that the output cell A4 calculates during each simulation trial.
5. What is the code used to deactivate and reactivate the screen updating functionality in VBA? Give an example of when this code would be useful.
6. Write the VBA code to delay a VBA program for 10 seconds.
7. Discuss how the *Wait* method and *ScreenUpdating* property are useful in simulation programs.
8. How can animation be an important part of a simulation program?
9. Write a VBA code that sets the number of simulation trials of a simulation problem based on user's input. Use an input box.
10. What is the code to generate a histogram?

20.6.2 Hands-On Exercises

Note: *Please refer to the file "Chapter_20_Exercises.xlsx" for the associated worksheets noted for the hands-on exercises. The file is available at www.dssbooks.com.*

1. Simulate the following experiment. The experiment involves two urns. Urn 1 contains two white balls and one black ball. Urn 2 contains one white ball. A ball is drawn from Urn 1 and placed in Urn 2. Then a ball is drawn from Urn 2. The theoretical probability that the ball drawn from Urn 2 is white is 5/6. Based on this simulation, what percentage of the time the ball drawn from Urn 2 is white? Run the simulation for 100, 1,000 and 10,000 iterations. Present and comment on the corresponding results.
2. Consider a production line that has three workstations. There is only one queue in this system, which is located at the beginning of the production line. Once the processing on an item at Workstation 1 is finished, the item moves to Workstation 2. However, since there is no queue between the two stations, the item will keep Workstation 1 busy until Workstation 2 becomes idle. Similarly, there is no waiting queue between Workstations 2 and 3. The processing time at Workstation 1 is normally distributed with a mean of 15 minutes and a standard deviation of 5 minutes. The processing time at Workstation 2 is exponentially distributed with a mean of 11 minutes. The processing time at Workstation 3 is lognormal distributed with a mean of 12 minutes and a standard deviation of 2 minutes. In the beginning of the day, a batch of 30 items arrives in this production line. Simulate this system to identify the probability that all the items will have been processed by the end of an 8-hour workday. What should be the batch size arriving in the beginning of the day to ensure that 90% of the time all the items will be processed by the end of an 8-hour workday?
3. A basketball player hits 75% of his free throws. When playing two throws in a row, the possible events and their corresponding probabilities are:

Outcome of throw	Outcome of 2nd throw	Probability
Hit	Hit	0.56
Hit	Miss	0.19
Miss	Hit	0.19
Miss	Miss	0.06

Simulate this experiment (two throws of the ball). Run the simulation for 100, 1,000, and 10,000 iterations. Using the results from the simulation, report the proportion of times each event happened.

4. Consider the Single Server Queuing model presented in section 20.4. We are now interested in calculating the utilization of the ATM machine. Update the code we discussed in this section to calculate the expected ATM utilization, the maximum utilization, and the corresponding standard deviation. Plot a histogram of ATM utilization during different simulation trials.
5. Consider the Single Server Queuing model presented in section 20.4. Suppose that the management has decided to add a second identical ATM machine just next to the existing ATM. Simulate the new system considering these two queuing models:
   - **a.** One single queue serves both ATM machines. In this case, if both machines are busy, the customer waits in the queue. He will be served by the first available ATM.
   - **b.** One queue for each ATM machine. In this case, if both machines are busy, the customer waits in the queue that is the shortest.

   For each model calculate the mean waiting time in the queue. Which model performs better?
6. Create a program that allows users to control the movements of an object on a worksheet from cell to cell. The program should perform the following actions:
   - **a.** Initializes an object with a background color and a border around it and locates it approximately in the center of a worksheet.
   - **b.** Asks the users for a string of letters that give the directions for moving the object. The following letters give the corresponding direction of movement: "U" is Up, "D" is Down, "L" is Left, and "R" is Right. Any other character does not cause the object to move. Here is an example of an input and the resulting movements.

     Input: "DLLDR UR"

     Movements: Down, Left, Left, Down, Right, No Movement, Up, Right
   - **c.** Moves the object according to the users' input until finished or the object cannot move in the given direction. Use a one-second delay between characters.
   - **d.** Displays an appropriate message.

7. **Dice Statistics:** Suppose we toss an ordinary die 5 times. A 4-straight occurs if exactly 4 (not 5) of our rolls are consecutive integers. For example, if we roll 1, 2, 3, 4, 6, we have a 4-straight.
   a. Run a simulation for 100, 1,000, and 2,000 trials.
   b. For each simulation, find a 95% confidence interval for tossing a 4-straight.
   c. Repeat parts (a) and (b) for a 3-of-a-kind (Example: 1, 1, 1, 2, 3)
8. Create a VBA program that allows users to simulate buying and selling shares of Finch Mutual Fund. Users may choose to buy or sell shares or to simulate the next day without any transaction. When making a decision to buy or sell shares, users provide the number of shares and then push either a "Buy" button or a "Sell" button. The transaction takes place before the next close of trading. The share price at the time of transaction differs from the previous closing price according to a Uniform distribution with a lower bound of $0.30 and an upper bound of $0.50. The share price has an equal chance of either increasing or decreasing. The closing price for each day is calculated the same way. The volume traded each day follows a Uniform distribution with a lower bound of 200 shares and an upper bound of 250 shares. Build two charts for the users to view the closing share price and volume traded for the past 30 business days as each day is simulated.

   Use one table to keep information on the closing share price and volume for the past 30 business days. Use another table to record transactions: shares traded, bought, or sold; total shares held after transaction; and any profits or losses. The initial share price is $42.
9. Create a program that allows users to simulate a production facility for Micro Circuits, Inc., which produces circuit boards for computers. The program will simulate 12-hour workdays for one month. The probability of a production failure occurring during a workday increases each day according to an exponential distribution with an average of 0.75%. When a failure occurs, required maintenance is performed the same day. Preventive maintenance is performed twice a month, on days 1 and 15. Use a worksheet to keep records for each day: day number, number of failures, maintenance costs, maintenance time, number of hours in production, number of circuit boards produced, and predicted profit for circuit boards produced.

   Simulate this model using object-oriented API in VBA. Set the number of simulation trials to 1,000. Use a histogram to plot the frequency of total failures per month during all simulation trials. Use histograms to plot the frequency of the total number of circuit boards produced per month and to predict monthly profit during the simulation. Assume a production rate of 30 circuit boards per hour and an expected profit of $35.00 per circuit board. (Refer to worksheet 20.9.)
10. Six months before its regional conference, the Institute of Industrial Engineers (IIE) must determine how many rooms to reserve for students in the university hotel. At this time, IIE can reserve rooms at a cost of $50/room. The professional organization must pay the $50 room cost even if the room is not occupied. IIE believes that the number of students attending the conference will be anywhere between 4,000 and 5,000. If the number of people attending the conference exceeds the number of rooms reserved, IIE must reserve extra rooms at a cost of $80/room.
    a. Use object-oriented API in VBA to simulate and optimize the problem of determining the number of rooms that should be reserved to minimize the expected cost to IIE.
    b. Create a graph of expected costs for different numbers of rooms reserved to ensure that the number of rooms identified in part (a) minimizes expected costs.
    c. Consider that the number of participating students will increase the next year. This increase is expected to be anywhere between 500 and 1,000. How many rooms should IIE reserve to minimize the expected costs?
11. Jones and Smith are the best players of the current year's tennis tournament. There is a probability of 0.9 that Jones or Smith will defeat any other player at the tournament. The tournament has 8 players. The tournament is organized in such a way that players meet each other just once. For example, in the first round, Player 1 plays against Player 2; 3 plays against 4; 5 plays against 6; and Player 7 plays against 8. In the second round, the winner of Players 1 and 2 plays

against the winner of Players 3 and 4. Assume that the 8 players are randomly assigned to one of the 8 starting positions. The goal is to estimate the probability that Jones and Smith will meet each other in the final game. Simulate this system 1,000 times and present the results.

12. The game *Try Your Luck* is played as follows: The user chooses a number between 1 and 6 and tosses three dice. If the number does not appear, the user loses $1. If the number appears x times, the user wins $x. (Refer to worksheet 20.12.)

a. Develop an animated program for this game. Create a small user form with a spin button to allow the user to choose his/her number. Use dice images to illustrate the random toss of three dice.

b. Determine, on the average, how much money the user will win or lose on each play of the game.

13. A soda company, KOOLOFF, is giving away a prize by selling bottles with letters under the bottle caps. To win the prize, you must collect caps with letters that spell the company name. In production, letters are randomly selected and placed on the bottle caps. Create a VBA program and complete the following:

a. **Select** bottle cap letters until all six of the necessary letters have been collected. (Letters are randomly and independently selected from the alphabet to be inserted into the bottle caps.)

b. Perform this simulation several times (without the animation) to determine, on the average, how many sodas need to be bought in order to win the prize.

c. How much would the prize need to be worth in order to play the game without losing money on all the sodas bought? (Assume that each soda costs $1.00.)

14. A manufacturer is trying to determine its annual profit. It estimates that it is equally likely that annual unit sales will be low or high. If sales are low (less than 75,000 units), the company can sell the product for $10/unit. If sales are high (between 75,000 and 100,000 units), a competitor will enter the market and the company can sell the product for only $8/unit. The variable cost per unit has a 25% chance of being $6, a 50% chance of being $7.50, and a 25% chance of being $9. Annual fixed costs are $30,000.

a. Use simulation to determine the expected annual profit. Set the number of simulation trials to 1,000.

b. Make this program dynamic by allowing users to do the following:

i. Try a different estimate on sales. (It is currently estimated to follow a Uniform distribution between 60,000 and 100,000 units.)

ii. Try different variable costs for 25%, 50%, and 25% of the time.

iii. Try different variable costs and different probabilities (ensure that these probabilities values sum to 1.)

15. Two leading pharmacy stores, EZ and WD, are competing to be top in the market. Each week, usual pharmacy store shoppers go to EZ once or WD once. If the shoppers' last visit was to EZ, then their next purchase will be at EZ with a probability of 0.9; otherwise, they will go to WD. Similarly, if the shoppers' last visit was to WD, then their next purchase will be at WD with a probability of 0.8; otherwise, they will go to EZ. Currently, half of the pharmacy store-shopping population visit EZ and half visit WD.

a. Simulate one year of sales, and estimate each store's average weekly market share. Assume that the total market size is 1,000 customers. (*Hint:* Use the Binomial distribution.)

b. Animate this simulation by having an image for each store and keeping track of the number of weekly visitors to the store below it.

16. The daily sales at a small restaurant has a probability distribution that is approximately normal with a mean equal to $530 per day and a standard deviation equal to $120.

The manager of the restaurant is planning to extend the business. For that reason he is interested to know how often in a month sales are expected to exceed $700 per day. The restaurant currently must have at least $300 sales per day to break even. The manager is interested to know the proportion of the days in a month that the restaurant will not break even.

Simulate the system and collect necessary data to answer the questions posed by the manager. Create a user form that would enable the manager to update the information about the demand distribution and the break-even point.

17. Every three years a textbook publisher revises its inventory. It has been two years since the best-selling book *Developing Spreadsheet-Based Decision Support Systems* has been revised. At present, 1,000 copies of the book are in the inventory. The publisher must determine how many copies of the book should be printed for the next year. The sales department believes that sales during the next year will be governed by the distribution in the table presented in worksheet 20.20. Each copy of the book is sold for $40. Any copy left at the end of the year cannot be sold for the full price, but can be sold for $5 to a local bookstore. There is a fixed cost of $50,000 for printing the books plus a $15 for each book printed. (Refer to worksheet 20.17.)

Use object-oriented API in VBA to simulate the model and estimate the number of copies to be printed so that the profits would be maximized. Create a user form for this exercise that enables the user to update the information about the demand, inventory, costs and price.

18. A doctor's office schedules patients at 15-minutes intervals beginning at 9 AM and ending at 4:00 PM. Patients are equally likely to arrive at any time within 5 minutes of their appointment. A nurse initiates a patient's visits by asking a number of questions related to the patient's health. The nurse takes 5 to 10 minutes to complete her checkup. Next, the doctor visits with the patient. The number of minutes the doctor spends with a patient varies based on a normal distribution with a mean of 10 minutes and a standard deviation of 3 minutes. There are two nurses and one doctor in the office.

Simulate this system. Estimate the probability that the doctor will be able to leave by 5:00 PM. Estimate the expected waiting time to meet with the doctor. Create a user form that enables the user to update the distribution's parameters of the arrival time and time with the doctor, as well as the scheduled time between arrivals.

19. A manufacturing company produces a variety of computer components. The demand for processors fluctuates each day between 150 and 200, with any demand in this range being equally likely. The company likes to keep its production level at 170 units per day, but this also may fluctuate because of variations in labor availability, defect rates, material delays, and so on. In about 4 of every 10 days production falls to 140 units and about 10% of the time 190 units are produced. The company likes to maintain an inventory level of at least 250 units. If inventory falls below 250 units, 200 extra units are produced using overtime.

The management is interested to know how often overtime is necessary. Simulate the system to enable the user to answer this question. Create a user form to enable the user to update problem parameters.

20. An electronics retailer store has observed that daily demand for a product is related to the number of units in the shelf. The store manager believes that customers buy more if the shelf is full. The table in worksheet 20.20 presents the probability for different sales levels, given the number of units on the shelf for a product. (Refer to worksheet 20.20.)

At most, 100 units can be stored in the shelf and no other storage area is available. The profit per unit sold is $30, ordering costs to replenish the shelf is $17, and demand is not backordered (demand over available units are lost). The cost of a lost sale is estimated to be $35/unit. Currently there are 70 units on the shelf. Evaluate the following inventory policies with a 30-day simulation.

Policy 1: Send an order for 80 (shelf capacity – 20) more units whenever the number of units on the shelf drops below 21.

Policy 2: Send an order every 3 days with whatever amount is needed to bring the amount of units on the shelf up to 100 (shelf capacity).

Create a user form that enables the user to update the parameters used in this problem.

CHAPTER

twenty-one

Working with Large Data Using VBA

chapter OVERVIEW

21.1 Introduction

This chapter explains how large amounts of data can be imported, exported, manipulated, and searched using VBA. These functions are very useful for developing DSS applications in industry settings as most of the data is large and stored in text files or databases. They are also useful for performing dynamic web queries for a live portfolio DSS or other similar business applications. This chapter will also explain how to use VBA to dynamically create a pivot table as an output in a DSS application. Although working with databases may be useful for developing a DSS, we do not teach databases in this text. We do give a review of some SQL commands that are used in database queries, but we expect the reader to have some previous knowledge of databases or to refer to another text. Other texts which discuss databases and SQL in more detail include the following: *Database Systems: A Practical Approach to Design, Implementation, and Management* by Thomas Connolly and Carolyn Begg, *Fundamentals of Database Systems* by Ramez Elmasri and Shamkant B. Navathe, *SQL: The Complete Reference* by James R Groff and Paul N. Weinberg, and *Developing Web-Enabled Decision Support Systems* by Abhijit Pol and Ravindra Ahuja. In Part III of this book, we develop several DSS applications which allow the user to import text files for historical data such as Stochastic Customer Forecasting and Inventory Management. Our Supply Chain Management application creates pivot tables dynamically using VBA as part of the program output. We also illustrate a DSS application which uses a database, called the University Information Systems DSS.

In this chapter, the reader will learn how to:

- Create pivot tables using VBA.
- Import data from text files or webpages using VBA.
- Import data from databases.
- Create basic queries using the SQL programming language.
- Export data using VBA.
- Create an application which allows a user to query a database from Excel.

21.2 Creating Pivot Tables with VBA

As we have seen, VBA can be applied to many of the Excel tools we have already reviewed in order to allow these tools to become more dynamic through automation. This also applies to pivot tables and pivot charts. In Chapter 6, we learned how to create pivot tables and pivot charts using the *Insert > Tables > Pivot Table* command on the Ribbon. We learned how to filter large data by specifying row fields, column fields, report fields, and value fields. We also learned how to create calculated fields, include sub totals and grand totals, and manipulate the pivot table options. We will now learn the properties and methods in VBA that will allow us to perform these tasks dynamically via VBA procedures.

First, we will review the pivot table example used in Chapter 6 to use as a reference. In this example, we dealt with/showed/listed/looked at the shipping costs for varying maximum weights and days to arrive for two different shipping companies (see Figure 21.1).

In the pivot table we created, the row fields were "Days to Arrive" and "Max Weight, lbs," the column field was "Shipping Companies," and the data field was "Cost." In this pivot table, we also added a calculated field for minimum costs (see Figure 21.2).

	A	B	C	D	E
1					
2		**Compare Shipping Companies**			
3		**Shipping Companies**	**Max Weight, lbs**	**Days to Arrive**	**Costs**
4		United Carrier	5	1	$5.00
5		United Carrier	5	2	$3.00
6		United Carrier	5	4	$1.00
7		United Carrier	5	8	$0.50
8		United Carrier	20	1	$25.00
9		United Carrier	20	2	$15.00
10		United Carrier	20	4	$10.00
11		United Carrier	20	8	$5.00
12		United Carrier	20+	1	$45.00
13		United Carrier	20+	2	$35.00
14		United Carrier	20+	4	$25.00
15		United Carrier	20+	8	$20.00
16		International Route	5	1	$4.00
17		International Route	5	2	$3.00
18		International Route	5	4	$1.00
19		International Route	5	8	$0.50
20		International Route	20	1	$23.00
21		International Route	20	2	$14.00
22		International Route	20	4	$10.00
23		International Route	20	8	$5.00
24		International Route	20+	1	$40.00
25		International Route	20+	2	$34.00
26		International Route	20+	4	$23.00
27		International Route	20+	8	$19.00

Figure 21.1 The shipping pivot table data is in the "Data-Shipping" worksheet.

	A	B	C	D	E
1					
2					
3	Min of Costs		Shipping Companies		
4	Max Weight, lbs	Days to Arrive	International Route	United Carrier	Min Cost
5	⊟5				
6		1	$4.00	$5.00	$4.00
7		2	$3.00	$3.00	$3.00
8		4	$1.00	$1.00	$1.00
9		8	$0.50	$0.50	$0.50
10	⊟20				
11		1	$23.00	$25.00	$23.00
12		2	$14.00	$15.00	$14.00
13		4	$10.00	$10.00	$10.00
14		8	$5.00	$5.00	$5.00
15	⊟20+				
16		1	$40.00	$45.00	$40.00
17		2	$34.00	$35.00	$34.00
18		4	$23.00	$25.00	$23.00
19		8	$19.00	$20.00	$19.00
20	**Min Cost**		**$0.50**	**$0.50**	**$0.50**

Figure 21.2 The pivot table for the shipping data is in the "Pivot-Shipping" worksheet.

Now, let us discuss the pivot table objects used in VBA. The two main objects we use to create and manipulate pivot tables are the ***PivotCaches*** and ***PivotTables*** collection. *PivotCaches* is a collection of PivotCache objects on a Workbook object. A PivotCache is the memory cache where the data used by a pivot table is stored. The first step in creating a pivot table is creating the corresponding cache. We declare a PivotCache object variable by using the *Dim* statement. For example, to declare *MyCache* as a new variable, we would type the following:

```
Dim MyCache As PivotCache
```

We will use the *Create* method to create a cache object, and then use the *Set* statement to assign this object to *MyCache* variable. The *Create* method has three arguments: ***SourceType***, ***SourceData***, and ***Version***. The *SourceType* argument specifies if the data comes from the spreadsheet (xlDatabase), an external source (xlExternal), or multiple ranges (xlConsolidation). We will primarily use data from spreadsheets and external databases. The SourceData argument is used to specify the specific data from this source type. For example, if we are using data from a spreadsheet, the *SourceData* argument value would be the range of values from the spreadsheet we are using. The Version argument specifies the version of the pivot table. The values that this argument takes are *xlPivotTableVersion2000* for Excel 2000, *xlPivotTableVersion10* for Excel 2002, *xlPivotTableVersion11* for Excel 2003, *xlPivotTableVersion12* for Excel 2007 and *xlPivotTableVersion14* for Excel 2010. This argument ensures that the tables we create are compatible on the version of Excel we have specified. To create a pivot cache object and assign it to *MyCache* variable, we would type the following:

```
Set MyCache = ActiveWorkbook.PivotCaches.Create(xlDatabase,_ Worksheets("Data_Shipping").
Range("B3:E27"), xlPivotTableVersion14)
```

PivotTables is a collection of pivot table objects on a particular Worksheet object. We declare a *PivotTable* object variable by using the *Dim* statement. For example, to declare *MyPT* as a new variable, we would type the following:

```
Dim MyPT As PivotTable
```

We use the *Add* method to create a new *PivotTable* object, and then use the *Set* statement to assign this object to *MyPT* variable. The *Add* method has three arguments: *PivotCache*, *TableDestination* and *TableName*. The *PivotCache* argument specifies the cache for this table. The *TableDestination* argument specifies a range where the table should be placed, and the *TableName* argument is used to give a name to this table, such as "PivotTable1." We use the following code to declare the variable and set its value.

```
Set MyPT = ActiveSheet.PivotTables.Add(MyCache, Range("G3"), "Pivot Table1")
```

Once the pivot table has been created, we must specify its layout; that is, the row fields, column fields, and data field. We use the *PivotField.Orientation* property in order to set row fields, column fields, and page fields of the pivot table. This property takes the values ***xlDataField***, ***xlRowField***, ***xlColumnField***, and ***xlPageField*** for the respective fields. For example, to specify the row and column fields of MyPT pivot table, we type the following code.

```
With MyPT
    .PivotFields("Shipping Companies").Orientation = xlColumnField
    .PivotFields("Max Weight, lbs").Orientation = xlRowField
```

```
    .PivotFields("Days to Arrive").Orientation = xlRowField
    .PivotFields("Costs").Orientation = xlDataField
End With
```

One of the possible values for the Orientation property is ***xlHidden***. This will hide all of the values of the specified field. This property can be useful not only to set the data field, but also to change any previously set fields to be different field types or to be removed from the pivot table altogether.

We can to refer to the items in a particular field of the pivot table using the *PivotItems* method. For example to refer to item "4" in the field "Days to Arrive" we would type the following:

```
MyPT.PivotFields("Days to Arrive").PivotItems("4")
```

Each of the objects we presented, PivotCache, PivotTables, PivotFields, and PivotItems, have their own set of properties and methods which can be used to create or modify a pivot table. We have selected a few properties and methods which we feel are most important.

The *RefreshOnFileOpen* is one PivotCache property that is used frequently. For example, to refresh the data on "Pivot Table1" located on worksheet "Data_Shipping" every time that the workbook is open, we set the value of this property to true by typing the following:

```
Worksheets("Data_Shipping").PivotTables("Pivot Table1").PivotCashe.RefreshOnFileOpen = True
```

For the *PivotTables* object, there are several other properties and methods to discuss. We will begin with the *RowGrand* and *ColumnGrand* properties. These properties specify whether or not grand totals should be calculated for row or column fields, respectively. The possible values for these properties are *True* or *False*. For example, in the above pivot table, to remove the cost totals for the row fields "Max Weight, lbs" and "Days to Arrive," we would type the following:

```
MyPT.RowGrand = False
```

Similarly, we use *MyPT.ColumnGrand = False* in order to remove the cost total for the column field "Shipping Companies."

A useful method of the PivotTables object is the ***RefreshTable*** method. This method is equivalent to pressing the Refresh command icon on the PivotTable Tools tab. If any changes are made to the data from which the pivot table was created, refreshing the data will update the pivot table data. There are no arguments for this method; just simply type the following:

```
MyPT.RefreshTable
```

One useful method of the PivotTables object is ***GetPivotData***. This method has the same functionality as the GETPIVOTDATA function defined in Chapter 6. For a specific item in a given row or column field, this method will find the corresponding value from the data field. The format of this method is as follows:

```
GetPivotData("DataFieldName", "RoworColumnFieldName", "ItemName")
```

If only one row or column field is given with a paired item name, then this method will return a grand or sub total value from the data field. However, if more than one row or column field is given, then the method will narrow down the search as much as possible to return the specific value from the data field. For example, in the above pivot table, to find the minimum cost for shipping with the company International Route for a package whose maximum weight is five pounds, we would type the following:

```
MyPT.GetPivotData ("Costs", "Shipping Companies", "International Route", "Max Weight, lbs", "5")
```

Since our pivot table calculated fields are currently set to find the minimum costs, the value returned from this statement would be $0.50 (the minimum cost in the International Route column for a Max Weight of 5 pounds).

We can use two properties to make calculations (sum, average, min, max, etc): the ***Function*** property and the ***SubTotals*** property. The *Function* property is used for data fields. To use this property, we simply specify the type of calculation we want to make on the named field. For example, in the above pivot table, to create the Minimum Cost calculated field, which shows the minimum of each row of costs, we would type the following:

```
MyPT.PivotFields("Sum of Costs").Function = xlMin
```

We use the *SubTotals* property for non-data fields. With this property, we must specify an index number or numbers, which represent the type of sub totals we want to show for the given field. These index values are 2 = sum, 3 = count, 4 = average, 5 = max, 6 = min, and others. For example, to show the minimum cost for each "Max Weight, lbs" value, we would type the following:

```
MyPT.PivotFields("Max Weight, lbs").SubTotals(6) = True
```

These properties are very useful for identifying important values in a pivot table. The last object we would like to discuss is *PivotItems*. The main property we use often with this object is the ***Visible*** property. Using this property is similar to clicking on the drop-down list of values for a field in a pivot table and checking or un-checking the values which we want to be displayed. The values for this property are *True* and *False*, much like we have seen in uses of the *Visible* property with other objects. For example, in the above pivot table, if we only want to see the costs for "Days To Arrive" values 1 and 8, we would type the following:

```
With MyPT
  .PivotFields("Days To Arrive").PivotItems("1").Visible = True
  .PivotFields("Days To Arrive").PivotItems("8").Visible = True
  .PivotFields("Days To Arrive").PivotItems("2").Visible = False
  .PivotFields("Days To Arrive").PivotItems("4").Visible = False
End With
```

Note that, pivot tables are used similarly to the Chart and Shape objects in that we must use the ActiveSheet object before specifying a PivotTables object. For example, to refer to a pivot table named "Pivot Table1" that we have already created using some other subroutine, we would use the following:

```
ActiveSheet.PivotTables("PivotTable1")
```

From this PivotTables object, we can further specify ***PivotFields***, and from PivotFields we can specify ***PivotItems***. For example, in the pivot table above, to refer to the "Days to Arrive" field, we would type the following:

```
ActiveSheet.PivotTables("PivotTable1").PivotFields("Days to Arrive")
```

Likewise, to refer to the item "4" in that particular field, we would type the following:

ActiveSheet.PivotTables("PivotTable1").PivotFields("Days to Arrive").PivotItems("4")

Note that instead of using the ActiveSheet object, we can also use the Worksheets object to specify different sheets. For example:

Worksheets("Data_Shipping").PivotTables("Pivot Table1")

One last useful property is the ***ShowPivotTableFieldList*** property, which we use with a Workbook object. This property has True or False values which we can set to show or hide the pivot table field list of the pivot tables in the workbook. For example, we may type the following:

ActiveWorkbook.ShowPivotTableFieldList = True

A complete procedure for creating the shipping costs pivot table is shown in Figure 21.3. In this procedure, we have created the pivot table, specified the layout (row fields, column fields, and data field), opted to show row grand totals, applied formatting, added a min cost sub total, used the GetPivotData function, and hidden the fields list. Other options may be set using the properties and methods explained above.

```
Sub CreatePivot()
Dim MyCache As PivotCache
Dim MyPT As PivotTable

    'CREATE PIVOT TABLE
    Set MyCache = ActiveWorkbook.PivotCaches.Create(xlDatabase, Worksheets _
        ("Data_Shipping").Range("B3:E27"), xlPivotTableVersion14)

    Set MyPT = Worksheets("Data_Shipping").PivotTables.Add(MyCache, _
        Range("G3"), "Pivot Table1")

    'PIVOT TABLE LAYOUT
    With MyPT
        .PivotFields("Shipping Companies").Orientation = xlColumnField
        .PivotFields("Max Weight, lbs").Orientation = xlRowField
        .PivotFields("Days to Arrive").Orientation = xlRowField
        .PivotFields("Costs").Orientation = xlDataField
        .PivotFields("Sum of Costs").Function = xlMin
    End With

    'GRAND TOTALS
    MyPT.RowGrand = False
    MyPT.ColumnGrand = False

    'SUBTOTALS
    MyPT.PivotFields("Max Weight, lbs").Subtotals(6) = True
    MyPT.PivotFields("Days to Arrive").Subtotals(6) = True

    'USE GETPIVOTDATA FUNCTION
    MsgBox MyPT.GetPivotData("Costs", "Shipping Companies", "International Route", _
        "Max Weight, lbs", "5")

    'PIVOT TABLE OPTIONS
    ActiveWorkbook.ShowPivotTableFieldList = True

    With MyPT
        .PivotFields("Days To Arrive").PivotItems("1").Visible = True
        .PivotFields("Days To Arrive").PivotItems("8").Visible = True
        .PivotFields("Days To Arrive").PivotItems("2").Visible = False
        .PivotFields("Days To Arrive").PivotItems("4").Visible = False
    End With

End Sub
```

Figure 21.3 A procedure to create the shipping costs pivot table.

Again, there are several other properties and methods for these pivot table objects. However, we feel the ones we have discussed here are the most useful for developing applications.

Summary

Object	Property/Method	Values/Arguments
PivotChaches	Create	SourceType, SourceData, Version
	RefreshOnFileOpen	True/False
PivotTables	Add	PivotCache, TableDestination, TableName
	ColumnGrand	True/False
	RowGrand	True/False
	RefreshTable	
	GetPivotData	Data Field, Row or Column Field, Item
PivotFields	Orientation	xlDataField, xlHidden
	Function	xlAverage, xlMax, xlMin, more
	SubTotals	2 = Sum, 3 = Count, 4 = Average, 5 = Max, 6 = Min, more
PivotItems	Visible	True/False
Workbook	ShowPivotTable	True/False FieldList

To create a pivot chart in VBA, we simply use the Chart object and the *Add* method. After adding a new chart, we set the source data to the created pivot table range instead of the original data range used to create the pivot table. For example, in the above pivot table, the data used and the corresponding pivot table are in the worksheet "Data_Shipping." However, the pivot table is in a different range of cells: G3:I19. To create a pivot chart after creating the pivot table, we would type the following:

```
Charts.Add
ActiveChart.SetSourceData Source:=Worksheets("Data_Shipping").Range("G3:I19")
```

Pivot charts are very useful and are easily created in VBA. We can then use previously discussed Chart properties and methods to further edit the pivot chart.

21.3 *Using External Data*

As we saw in Chapter 10, data can be imported to Excel. This data can be from a text file, webpage, or database. If this data is from a database, it can also be queried as it is imported. In Chapter 10, we saw how to use the Query Wizard to specify the tables and/or queries whose data we want to use, to place some criteria on this data by filtering it, and to sort the filtered data. We can perform all of these tasks, importing, and querying data in VBA to allow for more automated data manipulation.

21.3.1 Importing Data

Text Files and Webpages We will first describe how to import data from text files and webpages in VBA. We will use an object called ***QueryTables***. This object is referred to using a Worksheet object. For example:

ActiveSheet.QueryTables

To import data, we will simply add a QueryTable object using the ***Add*** method. The *Add* method has two arguments: ***Connection*** and ***Destination***. The Connection argument requires the type of data being imported and the actual location of the data. It is by using this argument that we will clarify if we are importing data from a text file or a webpage. If we are importing data from a text file, we would define the *Connection* argument as follows:

Connection:= "TEXT; path"

Here, the *path* is the actual location of the text file on our computer given by some string value. For example, the *path* could be *C:\MyDocuments\textfile.txt*. The path value can also be given dynamically by prompting the user for the path value and storing the path name in a string variable. This path value would have to be concatenated with the TEXT specification. For example, we may use the following code to specify a dynamic value for the Connection argument:

```
Dim UserPath As String
UserPath = InputBox("Enter path of text file.")

Connection:= "TEXT; " & UserPath & "
```

In creating dynamic imports, we may prefer to let the users browse for a file rather than enter the path. To display an explorer browse window, we use the ***GetOpenFilename*** method associated with the Application object. This method presents the users with a browse window and allows them to select a file. The name of the file is returned as a string value. This method has the following format:

Application.GetOpenFilename(FileFilter, FilterIndex, Title, ButtonText, MultiSelect)

The ***FileFilter*** argument gives us the option of limiting the type of file the users can select. For example, since we may be using this method to allow the users to select a text file to import, we may want to limit their browsing to text files only. To do this, we would set the *FileFilter* value to "Text Files (*.txt), *.txt". We will ignore the *FilterIndex* and *ButtonText* arguments. The ***Title*** argument allows us to give a title to the browse window that will appear. For example, we may want to title the window, "Select a file to import." The ***MultiSelect*** has the values *True* or *False* to determine if users can select more than one or only one value, respectively. Consider now the code below as an alternative to finding the path value for a user text file to import.

```
Dim UserPath As String
UserPath = Application.GetOpenFilename("Text Files (*.txt), *.txt", , "Select a file to import.", ,
False)

Connection:= "TEXT; " & UserPath & "
```

If we are importing data from a webpage, we would define the Connection argument as follows:

Connection:= "URL; actual URL"

Here, the *actual URL* is the URL of the website. For example, the URL might be *http://www.ise.ufl.edu*. Again, this value could be taken from the user dynamically.

The *Destination* argument is the location on the spreadsheet where we would like to place the imported data; the value for this argument is simply a range. Columns and rows will be created for the data appropriately. The output range for the entire table of data will begin in the *Destination* range. For example, to import and output a text file to a range beginning at cell A1, we would define the *Destination* argument as follows:

Destination:=Range("A1")

When using the *Add* method for importing text files and webpages, we must also define a few properties for the import to be complete. These properties differ for importing a text file and a webpage.

The necessary properties for importing a text file basically describe how the text is organized in the file so that the values are imported correctly. The first property to set is the ***Name*** property; this simply gives a name to our imported file so that we can refer to it for future modification if necessary. The next two properties are ***FieldNames*** and ***RowNumbers***. These properties take *True/False* values to determine whether or not there are field names in the first row or enumerations in the first column which should be ignored when the data is imported; these values will be ignored if the value of these properties is set to *True*.

The next four properties determine how the text data is organized. The first of these is the ***TextFileStartRow*** property. This value should be equivalent to the row number on which the data we want to import begins. The next property is ***TextFileParseType***. The value for this property is either ***xlDelimited*** or ***xlFixedWidth***. We will normally work with delimited files. When working with delimited files, the next two properties apply: ***TextFileTextQualifier*** and ***TextFile__Delimiter***. We will usually set the text qualifier to ***xlTextQualifierDoubleQuote***. The *TextFile__Delimiter* property can be one of the following properties: ***TextFileConsecutiveDelimiter, TextFileSemicolonDelimiter, TextFileCommaDelimiter, TextFileSpaceDelimiter, TextFileTabDelimiter***. Each of these properties takes *True/False* values. The default values for these properties is *False*, so it is only necessary to specify the property which we want to set to *True*; that is, we only need to specify which delimiter we are using.

There is also one method that we must define to complete the import. This is the ***Refresh*** method. This method has one required argument called ***BackgroundQuery*** which takes the values True/False. We will usually set this argument to *False*, implying that the background query (in this case, the text file) does not need to be refreshed when changes are made to the imported data. Below is the complete code necessary to import a text file. We have used a comma delimiter for this example.

```
With ActiveSheet.QueryTables.Add
    (Connection:="TEXT;C:\MyDocuments\textfile.txt", Destination:=Range("A1"))
      .Name = "ImportTextFile"

       .FieldNames = True
       .RowNumbers = False

       .TextFileStartRow = 1
       .TextFileParseType = xlDelimited
       .TextFileTextQualifier = xlTextQualifierDoubleQuote
       .TextFileCommaDelimiter = True

       .Refresh BackgroundQuery:=False
End With
```

Let us consider a simple example. Suppose we have a text file of numerical data separated by commas (see Figure 21.4). To import this text to Excel, we can use the code given above. We have specified the path appropriately and noted that we intend to use commas as the delimiter (see Figure 21.5).

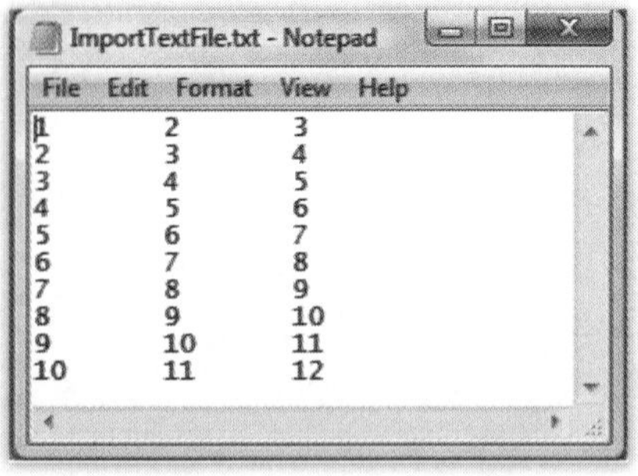

Figure 21.4 Text file to import to Excel.

```
Sub ImportText()
    With ActiveSheet.QueryTables.Add(Connection:= _
        "TEXT;C:\My Documents\ImportTextFile.txt" _
        , Destination:=Range("A1"))

        .Name = "ImportTextFile"

        .FieldNames = True
        .RowNumbers = False

        .TextFileStartRow = 1
        .TextFileParseType = xlDelimited
        .TextFileTextQualifier = xlTextQualifierDoubleQuote
        .TextFileCommaDelimiter = True

        .Refresh BackgroundQuery:=False
    End With
End Sub
```

Figure 21.5 Code to import text file using QueryTable object.

The imported text is then separated into columns respective of the comma locations in the original text file. The resulting table (see Figure 21.6) begins in the range specified in the *Destination* argument; here, cell A1.

	A	B	C
1	1	2	3
2	2	3	4
3	3	4	5
4	4	5	6
5	5	6	7
6	6	7	8
7	7	8	9
8	8	9	10
9	9	10	11
10	10	11	12

Figure 21.6 Imported data in Excel.

Summary

Importing Text Files with the QueryTables object

Property/Method	Values/Arguments
Add	Connection:="TEXT; path", Destination
Name	name of query
FieldNames	True/False
RowNumbers	True/False
TextFileStartRow	row number of text file from which to start importing
TextFileParseType	xlDelimited
TextFileTextQualifier	xlTextQualifierDoubleQuote
TextFile___Delimiter	delimiter type, True/False
Refresh	BackgroundQuery:=False

Dynamic path value:

Application.GetOpenFilename(FileFilter, , Title, , MultiSelect)

The basic properties needed for importing a webpage also include *Name*, *FieldNames*, and *RowNumbers* as described above. There is then a set of five properties specific to importing data from a webpage. The first of these is ***WebSelectionType***. We use this property to determine how the data is organized on the webpage. We usually use the value *xlSpecifiedTables*. The next property is ***WebFormatting***. We usually set this property value to *xlWebFormattingNone* so that the formatting from the webpage is not transferred to the spreadsheet. We can ignore this property if we want the webpage formatting to be imported with the data.

The next property is ***WebTables***. This property is the most important to specify as it determines which table of data from the webpage will be imported. As we saw in Chapter 10, when importing data from a webpage, several areas are blocked as possible "tables" for importing; these areas are marked with yellow arrows. In VBA, we have to specify which arrow we want to click, that is, which area we want to select for importing. We will have to research this ahead of time by either recording a macro or counting the areas shown in the wizard for importing webpages. This may seem to hinder the functionality of importing a webpage in VBA; however, that is not necessarily the case. We can use the VBA code for importing webpages to refresh a previously made import with the latest data. That is, we may create the first webpage import, check the *WebTable* value, set the formatting for the import area, and make other preparation steps. Then, when we run our VBA procedure for refreshing the import, we can add a line of code which clears the contents of the initial area and imports the most current data from the same webpage table.

The next property is ***WebPreFormattedTextToColumns***. We set this property to *True* to ensure that the formatted text from the webpage is imported into columns on the spreadsheet. The last property is ***WebConsecutiveDelimitersAsOne***. We also set this property to *True* to inherit any delimiters used on the webpage for separation of the data. We end the code for the webpage import with the *Refresh* method as used above in the text file import code, *Refresh BackgroundQuery:=False*. The complete code is below:

```
With ActiveSheet.QueryTables.Add
    (Connection:= "URL;http://www.webpage.com", Destination:=Range("C1"))

    .Name = "WebpageQuery1"

    .FieldNames = True
    .RowNumbers = False

    .WebSelectionType = xlSpecifiedTables
    .WebFormatting = xlWebFormattingNone
    .WebTables = "1"
    .WebPreFormattedTextToColumns = True
    .WebConsecutiveDelimitersAsOne = True

    .Refresh BackgroundQuery:=False
End With
```

Let us consider an example. Suppose we wish to import into Excel the most recent mortgage rates quoted by CNN Money. We use the "money.cnn" webpage shown in Figure 21.7.

We write a procedure using the code given above. We specify the WebTables value to be "1" based on the desired area of information we wish to import (again, we find this by running a temporary query using the import wizards in Excel). See Figure 21.8 for the importing procedure.

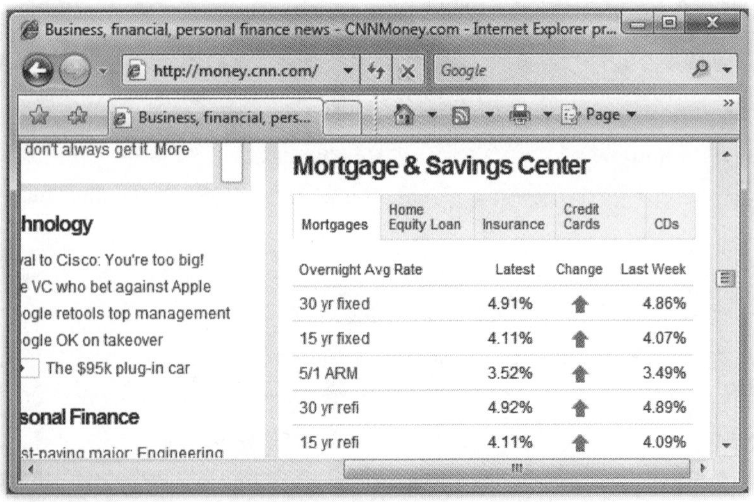

Figure 21.7 CNN Money webpage data on mortgage rates.

The imported data is separated into columns according to the delimiters used on the webpage (see Figure 21.9). This table begins in the range specified as the Destination argument value; here, this is cell C1. This query can be run multiple times to retrieve the most current stock values from this webpage.

```
Sub ImportWebpage()

    With ActiveSheet.QueryTables.Add(Connection:= _
        "URL;http://money.cnn.com/", Destination:=Range("C1"))

        .Name = "WebImport1"

        .FieldNames = True
        .RowNumbers = False

        .WebSelectionType = xlSpecifiedTables
        .WebFormatting = xlWebFormattingNone
        .WebTables = "1"
        .WebPreFormattedTextToColumns = True
        .WebConsecutiveDelimitersAsOne = True

        .Refresh BackgroundQuery:=False
    End With
End Sub
```

Figure 21.8 Code to import webpage data using the QueryTables object.

	A	B	C	D	E	F
1			Overnight Avg Rate	Latest	Change	Last Week
2			30 yr fixed	4.91%		4.86%
3			15 yr fixed	4.11%		4.07%
4			5/1 ARM	3.52%		3.49%
5			30 yr refi	4.92%		4.89%
6			15 yr refi	4.11%		4.09%

Figure 21.9 Imported data in Excel columns.

Summary

Importing Webpages with the QueryTables object

Property/Method	**Values/Arguments**
Add	Connection:="URL; actual URL," Destination
Name	name of query
FieldNames	True/False
RowNumbers	True/False
WebSelectionType	xlSpecifiedTables
WebFormatting	xlWebFormattingNone
WebTables	table number from webpage
WebPreFormattedText ToColumns	True/False; True will convert text into columns when imported to Excel
WebCosecutuvie DelimetersAsOne	True/False; True will detect delimiter from webpage text and use to import into Excel
Refresh	BackgroundQuery:=False

Databases Let us now discuss how to import data from a database. There are two main systems used in VBA for communicating with databases as external data sources. One such system is called ***Data Access Object*** (DAO). We use this set of objects to import and manipulate data, primarily from databases. To use DAO, we must first reference it in the VBE using the Tools > References menu options. The second system for using external data is called ***ActiveX Data Objects*** (ADO), which also imports and manipulates data from databases. Both ADO and DAO use ***Object Database Connectivity*** (ODBC) to securely access data from databases. We have found that ADO objects are much simpler to use than DAO objects; therefore, we only discuss ADO in detail.

There are two main ADO objects used to import data: ***Connection*** and ***Recordset***. The Connection object establishes the communication to a particular database. There are two main methods used with this object: ***Open*** and ***Close***. The *Open* method uses a ***ConnectionString*** argument to define the path to the database. The *Close* method does not have any arguments. A Connection should be opened and closed every time a query or import is made from the database.

To define a Connection object variable, we use a data type called ***ADODB.Connection***. This object variable is similar to the *Range* data type variables discussed in Chapter 14; we declared a variable as a *Range* data type and then used the *Set* statement to define the range value of this variable. For Connections, we declare the variable as an *ADODB.Connection* data type and then use the *Set* statement to define the connection value of our variable. We can refer to a previously created connection; however, in most cases we will define our connections to be new connections using the ***New*** statement. We could create a new Connection object variable called *MyConnection* as follows:

```
Dim cntMyConnection As ADODB.Connection
Set cntMyConnection = New ADODB.Connection
```

Note: Similar to working with User Form objects, we recommend using some initial variable name letters to denote the type of object the variable represents; here we name our Connections starting with "cnt". Now, we need to define the data provider, or database type, and data source, or filename, of this connection. These values will be given to the *ConnectionString* argument of the *Open* method. We can define the data provider we will usually use as, "Microsoft.Jet.OLEDB.4.0". The data source should be the filename of the database plus the path of the file. We can either type the entire path as a string value, for example, "C:\MyDocuments\Databases\MyDatabase.mdb", or we can use a string filename value and the ***Path*** property of the Workbook object, more specifically ***ThisWorkbook*** object. For example, here we define a String variable and create the entire data source value:

```
Dim dbMyDatabase As String
dbMyDatabase = ThisWorkbook.Path & "\MyDatabase.mdb"
```

Notice again that we use some variable name which denotes that a database path is represented, "db". Now we have the data provider and data source; we can either assign these values directly to the *ConnectionString* argument or we can use a String variable. The *ConnectionString* argument value has two sub arguments named ***Provider*** and ***Data Source*** for the data provider and data source, respectively. The default *Provider* we use is "Microsoft.ACE.OLEDB.12.0", however we may connect to other database providers such as "SQLServer" or "Oracle". We will use these sub arguments in the value of our String variable, which we will then use in the ConnectionString argument; notice that we are using the data source variable we defined above:

```
Dim CnctSource As String
CnctSource = "Provider=Microsoft.ACE.OLEDB.12.0; Data Source=" &
        dbMyDatabase & ";"
```

Now we have defined our Connection and *ConnectionString* argument for the *Open* method using data source and connection string variables. We can now apply the *Open* method as follows:

```
cntMyConnection.Open ConnectionString:=CnctSource
```

To close a Connection, simply use the *Close* method with the Connection variable. We would close the Connection we defined as follows:

```
cntMyConnection.Close
```

We use the *Set* statement again after closing a Connection to clear the Connection value; this time however, we set the Connection to ***Nothing***.

```
Set cntMyConnection = Nothing
```

To summarize, at the beginning of each procedure in which we are connecting to a database to import or manipulate data, we should type the following lines of code:

```
Dim cntMyConnection As ADODB.Connection, dbMyDatabase As String,
            CnctSource As String
Set cntMyConnection = New ADODB.Connection
dbMyDatabase = ThisWorkbook.Path & "\MyDatabase.mdb"
CnctSource = "Provider=Microsoft.ACE.OLEDB.12.0; Data Source=" &
            dbMyDatabase & ";"

cntMyConnection.Open ConnectionString:=CnctSource
```

At the end of each procedure in which we have used a database connection, we should type the following lines of code:

```
cntMyConnection.Close
Set cntMyConnection = Nothing
```

Summary

Procedure code for defining, opening, and closing a Connection object

```
Dim cntMyConnection As ADODB.Connection, dbMyDatabase As String, CnctSource As String

Set cntMyConnection = New ADODB.Connection
dbMyDatabase = ThisWorkbook.Path & "\MyDatabase.mdb"
CnctSource = "Provider=Microsoft.ACE.OLEDB.12.0; Data Source=" & dbMyDatabase & ";"
cntMyConnection.Open ConnectionString:=CnctSource

cntMyConnection.Close
Set cntMyConnection = Nothing
```

We can now discuss the second main object in ADO, the Recordset object. We use the Recordset object to define a particular selection of data from the database that we are importing or manipulating. We will again use a variable to represent this object throughout the code; to define Recordset object variables, we use the ***ADODB.Recordset*** data type. We again use the Set statement to assign the value to this variable as a *New* Recordset.

```
Dim rstFirstRecordset As ADODB.Recordset
Set rstFirstRecordset = New ADODB.Recordset
```

Notice that we use the letters "rst" for the Recordset variable name. Similarly to the Connection object, the Recordset should be opened before it is used; we do this using the *Open* method. The arguments for the *Open* method of the Recordset object are ***Source*** and ***ActiveConnection***. The Source argument defines the data that should be imported. The Source value is a string which contains some SQL commands; we define and discuss SQL in the next section. Similarly to the data source value and *ConnectionString* value discussed above, we can use a String variable to define these SQL commands to use as the value of the *Source* argument. For example, we may type the following:

```
Dim Src As String
Src = "SELECT * FROM tblTable1"
```

Again, we will discuss the SQL commands in the next section. The *ActiveConnection* argument value is the name of the open Connection object we have previously defined. To open the Recordset we defined above using the previously defined Connection, we would type the following:

```
rstFirstRecordset.Open Source:=Src; ActiveConnection:=cntMyConnection
```

Using the Open method of the Recordset object only selects the data that should be imported (or queried upon importing using SQL). To copy this data to the Excel spreadsheet, we use the Range object and a new method: ***CopyFromRecordset***. This method only needs to be followed by the name of the Recordset variable we have just opened. For example, to copy the data from the Recordset defined above to a range in our spreadsheet, we can type the following:

```
Range("A1").CopyFromRecordset rstFirstRecordset
```

In each procedure where we are importing or manipulating data from a database, we type the following:

```
Dim rstFirstRecordset As ADODB.Recordset, Src As String
Set rstFirstRecordset = New ADODB.Recordset

Src = "SELECT * FROM tblTable1"
rstFirstRecordset.Open Source:=Src; ActiveConnection:=cntMyConnection
Range("A1").CopyFromRecordset rstFirstRecordset
```

When we are done using this Recordset, we should clear its values; we do this using the *Set* statement with the value *Nothing*. For example, to clear the above Recordset values, we would type the following:

```
Set rstFirstRecordset = Nothing
```

We may use different Recordset variable names in each procedure, even though the Connection variable names can remain the same for all procedures if we are using the same database (cntMyConnection, dbMyDatabase). The string variable values can also remain the same throughout the module (CnctSource, Src).

Summary

Procedure code for defining and using a Recordset object

```
Dim rstFirstRecordset As ADODB.Recordset, Src As String
Set rstFirstRecordset = New ADODB.Recordset

Src = "SELECT * FROM tblTable1"
rstFirstRecordset.Open Source:=Src; ActiveConnection:=cntMyConnection
Range("A1").CopyFromRecordset rstFirstRecordset

Set rstFirstRecordset = Nothing
```

In applications where we plan to make multiple queries to a database, we recommend creating a function procedure to perform the above code. Since every query requires an opened Connection and a new Recordset, we can place this code in one function rather than in several procedures. All we need to pass to this function is the Source value, or SQL query, and output range for the Recordset. If we define the SQL statement as a string variable, such as *Src*, as shown above, then we can simply pass this variable to the function; that is, in every procedure with a query, we will define the *Src* variable value and then call the function. We can also use a string variable or value for the output range. We have defined this function, which we call *QueryData*, below:

```
Function QueryData(Src, OutputRange)
    dbUnivInfo = ThisWorkbook.Path & "\UniversityInformationSystem.mdb"
    Set cntStudConnection = New ADODB.Connection
    CnctSource = "Provider=Microsoft.ACE.OLEDB.12.0;Data Source=" & dbUnivInfo & ";"
    cntStudConnection.Open ConnectionString:=CnctSource

    Set rstNewQuery = New ADODB.Recordset
    rstNewQuery.Open Source:=Src, ActiveConnection:=cntStudConnection
    Range(OutputRange).CopyFromRecordset rstNewQuery

    Set rstNewQuery = Nothing
    cntStudConnection.Close
    Set cntStudConnection = Nothing
End Function
```

21.3.2 Performing Queries with SQL

Structured Query Language (SQL) is the code used to perform queries or filter the data which is imported. As mentioned above, SQL statements are used to define the *Source* argument of the *Open* method with the Recordset object. We can define the *Source* to be all values in a particular database table or pre-defined query (which is basically a direct import of data), or we can create a query as the value of the *Source* argument.

SQL is a complex language. Many books explain using this language to perform advanced queries and manipulating Access objects. In this section, we aim to give only a brief overview of how SQL can be used to create simple queries.

For the definitions and examples in this section, we will use a table from a University System database. This table, called *tblStudents*, contains student names, IDs, and GPAs.

tblStudents

StudentID	StudentNam	GPA
1	A. Berkely	3.7
2	C. Dorth	3.2
3	E. Farris	2.9
4	G. Henderson	3.3
5	I. Jones	3.5
6	K. Lennox	3.6
7	M. Nichols	3.4
8	O. Peterson	3.3
9	R. Stevens	3.2
10	T. Underhill	3.1
11	V. Walace	3.8
12	Y. Zaals	3.7

Figure 21.10 The table *tblStudents* contains student IDs, names, and GPAs.

The basic structure of SQL commands is this: a statement which specifies an action to perform, a statement which specifies the location of the data on which to perform the action, and a statement which specifies the criteria the data must meet in order for the action to be performed. Some basic action statements are SELECT, CREATE, and INSERT. There are others which we have included in a table below. For now, we will just discuss the ***SELECT*** statement.

The SELECT statement selects a specific group of data items from a table or query in the database. (The SELECT statement can also be used to retrieve data from more than one table or query using the "join" feature; however, we do not discuss this in our textbook. Again, please refer to the other database or SQL texts referenced above.) In the format of the SELECT statement, the phrase appearing immediately after the word SELECT is the name or names of the fields which should be selected.

SELECT field_name FROM table_name

For example, if we want to select the names of all the students in the table above, we would use the SELECT statement followed by the field in which the names are stored, in this case "StudentName". We would type:

SELECT StudentName FROM tblStudents

This query would return all student names shown in the table (refer to Figure 21.10). Note: To select everything in a table, that is, all fields, use the asterisk mark (*) after the SELECT statement. We must also specify the location of this field, that is, the table or query title from the database. We do this using the ***FROM*** statement. In our example, we are selecting the student names from *tblStudents*.

Note also that no quotation marks are used for the field and table names. We can also include a criteria filtering in the query. The most common criteria statement is ***WHERE***. The WHERE statement can use sub statements such as <, > , = for value evaluations, or ***BETWEEN***, ***LIKE***, ***AND***, ***OR***, and ***NOT*** for other comparisons (see table below for examples). In the same example above, suppose we only want the names of students who have GPAs greater than 3.5. We can therefore specify our criteria using the WHERE statement and > sub statement as follows:

SELECT StudentName FROM tblStudents WHERE GPA > 3.5

Here GPA is the name of the field which contains GPA values. This query would return only the student names which match the criteria (from the figure shown, these names would be A. Berkely, K. Lennox, V. Walace, and Y. Zaals).

Summary

WHERE Sub Statements

<, >, =, <=, >=	... WHERE GPA > 3.5, ... WHERE Price <= 100
BETWEEN	... WHERE GPA BETWEEN 3.5 AND 3.9, ... WHERE Population BETWEEN 1000 AND 5000
LIKE	... WHERE Customer LIKE "Smith", ... WHERE Customer LIKE "Jo*"
AND	... WHERE Price <= 100 AND Customer LIKE "Smith"
OR	... WHERE Price <= 100 OR Customer LIKE "Smith"
NOT	... WHERE Customer NOT "Smith"

Other criteria statements include GROUP BY and ORDER BY. ***ORDER BY*** can be used with the WHERE statement to sort the selected data; this data can be sorted in ascending or descending order using the statements ***ASC*** or ***DESC***, respectively. For example, if we had selected both the name field and GPA field of the "tblStudent" table, we may want to sort the final data by names alphabetically or by GPA values. Below, we type the statement to sort the data by GPA values in descending order:

SELECT StudentName, GPA FROM tblStudents WHERE GPA > 3.0 ORDER BY GPA DESC

In a SELECT statement, we can also perform a simple aggregate function. Simply type the name of the function after the SELECT statement and list the field names which apply to the function statement in parentheses. One common function statement is ***COUNT***. Using SELECT COUNT will return the number of items (matching any given criteria) instead of the items themselves. For example, the following command would return the number of students with a GPA greater than 3.5:

SELECT COUNT (StudentName) FROM tblStudents WHERE GPA > 3.5

For the table shown in Figure 21.10, the result of this query would be 4. Other functions, such as ***MIN***, ***MAX***, and ***AVG***, work in a similar manner. For example, to find the average GPA of the list of students in the given table, we would type the following:

SELECT AVG (GPA) FROM tblStudents

The result of this query would be 3.34. There are many other SQL statements that can be used to filter or manipulate the data. Again, we do not discuss these in detail in this book. We will discuss next how we can use these SQL statements to make our queries dynamic. We accomplish this by incorporating variables into the SQL statements.

Summary

Action	Location	Criteria
SELECT	FROM	WHERE
COUNT, MIN, MAX, AVG, AS		GROUP BY HAVING ORDER BY

In VBA, SQL statements always appear as a string; that is, they are enclosed by quotation marks. If our criteria checks for a particular string value, we must use single quotation marks to state that value. For example, say we wanted to find the social security number of a student from the "tblStudents" table if we know the name. If the field name of the social security number is SSN and the name of the student is "John Doe,",we would type the following (notice that the student name, a string value, is enclosed in single quotation marks):

```
="SELECT GPA FROM tblStudents WHERE StudentName = 'John Doe' "
```

Now suppose instead of specifying our own criteria, we want the users to determine which name to search for. We can use an Input Box and a variable, in this example called "*StudName*," to prompt the users for this value. Then we can include this variable in place of the criteria value in the SQL statement. This would be the new statement:

```
="SELECT SSN FROM tblStudents WHERE StudentName = '" & StudName &" '"
```

Note that we have to include the single quotation marks around the criteria value; therefore, we have concatenated the variable name followed by the ending single quotation mark.

Now let us incorporate these SQL statements into our database query code. As mentioned in the previous section, we will use a string variable to assign the value of the SQL commands. We will then use this variable in the *Source* argument of the *Open* method of the Recordset object. For example, let us search for John Doe's social security number as the value of the Recordset defined previously.

```
Src = "SELECT GPA FROM tblStudents WHERE StudentName = 'O. Peterson"

rstFirstRecordset.Open Source:=Src; ActiveConnection:=cntMyConnection
Range("A1").CopyFromRecordset rstFirstRecordset
```

The value in range *A1* would now be the GPA value of O. Peterson from the *tblStudents* table in the database used in our Connection. To make this query dynamic, we can use the variable described above with an Input Box as follows:

```
Dim StudName As String
StudName = InputBox("Please enter name of student whose GPA you want."

Src = "SELECT GPA FROM tblStudents WHERE StudentName = '" & StudName & "'"
```

rstFirstRecordset.Open Source:=Src; ActiveConnection:=cntMyConnection
Range("A1").CopyFromRecordset rstFirstRecordset

We can use variables to make queries dynamic with Input Boxes, User Forms, or simply by taking values the users have entered to a spreadsheet. We can then place these variables in the statements of SQL commands in the code to search for the users' criteria.

21.4 Exporting Data

We can place data into a previously created Access database using the ***CREATE*** and ***INSERT*** SQL commands. We can use the CREATE statement to create a new table in the database. The corresponding location statement for the CREATE command is TABLE. The name of the new table is given after the ***TABLE*** statement. The name of the table is followed by the name of the fields for the new table; these are listed in parentheses with a description of the data type the field should hold. We must also include a ***CONSTRAINT*** command to specify the primary key of the table (where the primary key is the unique value which identifies each item). We would give a name to this key, specify that it is the PRIMARY KEY, and then list the selected field. For example, to create a new table for course information, called tblCourses, we may write the following SQL statement:

="CREATE TABLE tblCourses (CourseName TEXT, CourseNumber NUMBER, FacultyAssigned TEXT) CONSTRAINT CourseID PRIMARY KEY (CourseNumber)"

Once we have created a table, we can use the INSERT statement to enter values for each field. The INSERT statement is always followed by the ***INTO*** location statement. The name of the table into which we are entering values is listed after the INTO statement. The field names for which we are entering values should then be listed in parentheses; that is, we may not want to enter values for all fields. Then the values are listed after a ***VALUES*** statement in the same order in which the corresponding fields were listed. For example, if we wanted to enter new values into the table tblCourses created above, we may type:

="INSERT INTO tblCourses (CourseName, CourseNumber, FacultyAssigned) VALUES ('DSS', 234, 'J. Smith')"

Using the INSERT command, we can loop over several user values from a spreadsheet or from an array value and insert each set of values into the fields of a new or previously created table. This is the best way to export data to a database from Excel.

Note: We can also use the ***UPDATE*** statement to change values in a previously created table. The UPDATE statement uses the ***SET*** location statement and the same criteria statements used with the SELECT command. For example, to update the GPA value for the student Y. Zaals, we could type the following:

="UPDATE tblStudents SET GPA = 3.9 WHERE StudentName = 'Y. Zaals'"

Summary

Action	Location	Criteria
create	table	constraint
insert	into	values
update	set	where
		group by
		having
		ORDER BY

A chart can be exported as an image file using VBA. There is a method of the Chart object called ***Export*** which allows this to happen. The *Export* method has three arguments: ***FileName***, ***FilterName***, and ***Interactive***. The *FileName* argument is the name we wish to give to the exported image file. The *FilterName* is the type of image file: "GIF", "JPG", etc. The *Interactive* argument decides whether or not to display a dialog box in which filter options can be specified. The values for this argument are *True* or *False*; the default value is *False*. For example, to export a chart created in Excel as an image file, we would type the following:

Worksheets("Sheet1").ChartObjects(1).Chart.Export FileName:="Chart1", FilterName:="GIF"

21.5 Applications

21.5.1 Transcript Query

We will develop an application which performs dynamic database queries using a pre-developed Access database. This database contains information on students, faculty, courses, sections, and grades; there are six tables and one query (see Figure 21.11).

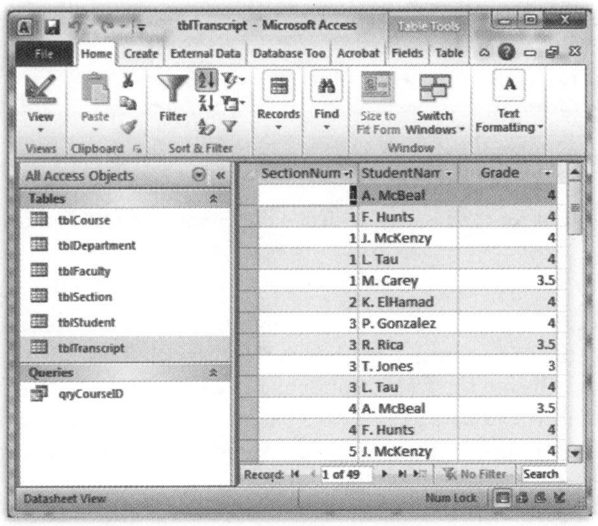

Figure 21.11 The Access database "UniversityInformationSystem" has six tables and one query.

In this application, we will allow the users to query the database to retrieve transcript data for a particular student. This transcript data will include every course the student has taken with the details of the course and section as well as the grade earned. We will then evaluate all grades to calculate the selected student's overall GPA. An example of a result of this query is shown in Figure 21.12.

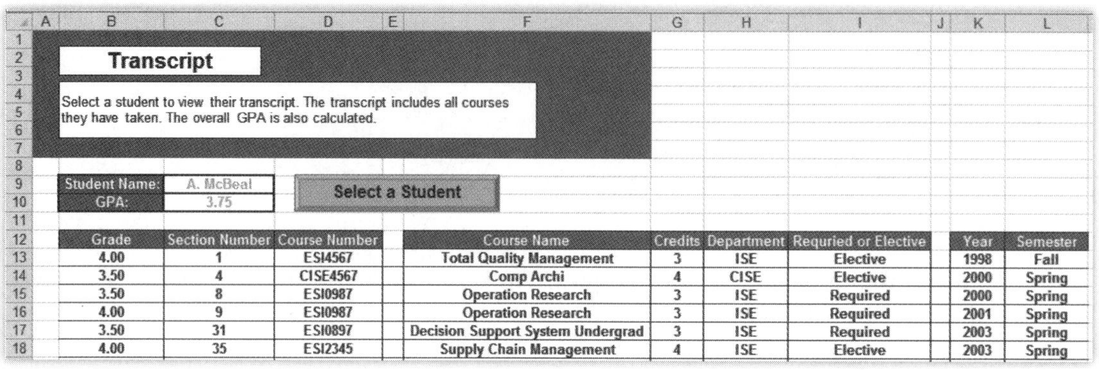
Transcript
Select a student to view their transcript. The transcript includes all courses they have taken. The overall GPA is also calculated.
Student Name: A. McBeal
GPA: 3.75
Select a Student

Grade	Section Number	Course Number	Course Name	Credits	Department	Requried or Elective	Year	Semester
4.00	1	ESI4567	Total Quality Management	3	ISE	Elective	1998	Fall
3.50	4	CISE4567	Comp Archi	4	CISE	Elective	2000	Spring
3.50	8	ESI0987	Operation Research	3	ISE	Required	2000	Spring
4.00	9	ESI0987	Operation Research	3	ISE	Required	2001	Spring
3.50	31	ESI0897	Decision Support System Undergrad	3	ISE	Required	2003	Spring
4.00	35	ESI2345	Supply Chain Management	4	ISE	Elective	2003	Spring

Figure 21.12 The transcript query shows the course and grade information for a selected student.

We will use the query function described above to define the Connection and Recordset objects used in the query; we call this function *QueryData* (see Figure 21.13). We have added two more parameters, *i* and *j*, to this function, which are used with the Offset method for the output range. The need for these extra parameters will become clear when we discuss the central transcript query code.

```
Function QueryData(Src, OutputRange, i, j)

    dbUnivInfo = ThisWorkbook.Path & "\UniversityInformationSystem.mdb"
    Set cntStudConnection = New ADODB.Connection
    CnctSource = "Provider=Microsoft.ACE.OLEDB.12.0; Data Source=" & dbUnivInfo & ";"
    cntStudConnection.Open ConnectionString:=CnctSource

    Set rstNewQuery = New ADODB.Recordset
    rstNewQuery.Open Source:=Src, ActiveConnection:=cntStudConnection
    Range(OutputRange).Offset(i, j).CopyFromRecordset rstNewQuery

    Set rstNewQuery = Nothing
    cntStudConnection.Close
    Set cntStudConnection = Nothing

End Function
```

Figure 21.13 The QueryData function is used to define the Connection and Recordset for each query.

Let us now look at our *Main* sub procedure (see Figure 21.14). In this procedure, we will clear previous data, show the users a form from which they can select a student, and then call another procedure which will find the transcript data and calculate the GPA for the selected student. Before we can show the users a form with a list of students, we need to make a query to the database to find the names of all the students. We do this using the *CreateStudentList* procedure (see Figure 21.14).

```
Option Explicit

Public i As Integer, j As Integer, dbUnivInfo As String, CnctSource As String, _
Src As String, OutputRange As String, cntStudConnection As ADODB.Connection, _
rstNewQuery As ADODB.Recordset, StudName As String, GPA As Double

Sub Main()
    Call CreateStudentList

    Worksheets("StudentTranscript").Activate
    Range(Range("TransTBL"), Range("TransTBL").Offset(0, 10).End(xlDown)).ClearContents
    frmStudentChoice.Show

    Call Transcript
End Sub

Sub CreateStudentList()
    Application.ScreenUpdating = False
    Worksheets("Temp").Activate
    Worksheets("Temp").Cells.ClearContents

    Src = "SELECT Name FROM tblStudent"
    OutputRange = "A1"
    Call QueryData(Src, OutputRange, 0, 0)

    Range(Range("A1"), Range("A1").End(xlDown)).Name = "StudList"
    Application.ScreenUpdating = True
End Sub
```

Figure 21.14 The *Main* and *CreateStudentList* procedures.

We will query the database in the *tblStudent* table which contains the complete list of student names (see Figure 21.15).

tblStudent

Name	Department	StudentType	Email	Address	DateEntered	Nationality	Gender
A. Castanza	DIS	Undergrad	acas@ufl.edu	562 43rd St	1/1/2002	American	Male
A. McBeal	ISE	Undergrad	amcb@ufl.edu	12 South Dorm	8/1/1999	American	Male
C. Iceman	DIS	Undergrad	cice@ufl.edu	18 Hume Hall	8/1/2000	American	Male
F. Hunts	ISE	Undergrad	fhunts@ufl.ed	13 New Hall	1/1/2001	Hispanic	Female
F. Johnson	ISE	Undergrad	fjohn@ufl.edu	12 New Hall	8/1/2000	African Americ	Male
J. McKenzy	CISE	Grad	jmck@ufl.edu	54 20th Ave	1/1/2000	Turkish	Male
K. ElHamad	CISE	Grad	kelham@ufl.e	78 University A	8/1/1998	Russian	Male
L. Tau	ISE	Undergrad	ltau@ufl.edu	32 16th St	8/1/2001	Chinese	Female
M. Carey	DIS	Undergrad	mcar@ufl.edu	30 New Hall	1/1/2001	Indian	Female
M. Henderson	ISE	Grad	mhen@ufl.edu	45 6th Ave	8/1/2002	American	Female
O. Smith	ISE	Grad	osmit@ufl.edu	621 15th St	8/1/2001	Turkish	Male
P. Gonzalez	ISE	Grad	pgon@ufl.edu	44 13th St	8/1/2000	Hispanic	Male
R. Rica	CISE	Undergrad	rrica@ufl.edu	37 North Dorm	8/1/2001	Hispanic	Male
T. Jones	ISE	Undergrad	tj@ufl.edu	500 34th St	1/1/2000	American	Female

Record: 1 of 14 No Filter Search

Figure 21.15 The table "tblStudent" contains the list of the names of each student.

This is the SQL statement for this query:

"SELECT Name FROM tblStudent"

We will output the result of this query to a temporary sheet called "Temp" in the first cell, A1. We therefore define the *Src* and *OutputRange* variables accordingly and then call our *QueryData* function; the *i* and *j* parameters are set to 0 for this query. Once the query has output the list of names to the "Temp" sheet, we will select the entire list, using the *End* property, and name it "StudList". We can then use this range name to define the *RowSource* of the combo box on the user form (see Figure 21.16).

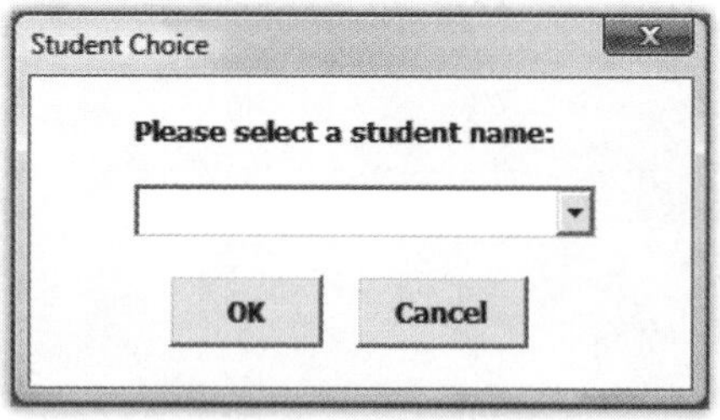

Figure 21.16 This form contains a combo box with a list of all students in the database.

In the code for the form, we use the *Initialize* event of the *UserForm* to set the *RowSource* to "StudList" (see Figure 21.17). For the *cmdOK_Click* procedure, we do a simple error check to ensure the user has made a selection, and then we set the selected student name to the string variable *StudName*.

```
Option Explicit

Sub cmdCancel_Click()
    Unload Me
    End
End Sub

Sub cmdOK_Click()
    If cmbStudent.Value = "" Then
      MsgBox "Please select a student."
      Exit Sub
    End If

    StudName = cmbStudent.Value
    Unload Me
End Sub

Sub UserForm_Initialize()
    cmbStudent.RowSource = "StudList"
End Sub
```

Figure 21.17 The code for the user form.

The combo box will now contain the current list of students from the database (see Figure 21.18). This query is important to make each time the user wants to see a new transcript to ensure that the list of students reflects the current data in the database. This way, if any changes are made to the database, the form will always have the most up-to-date list of students.

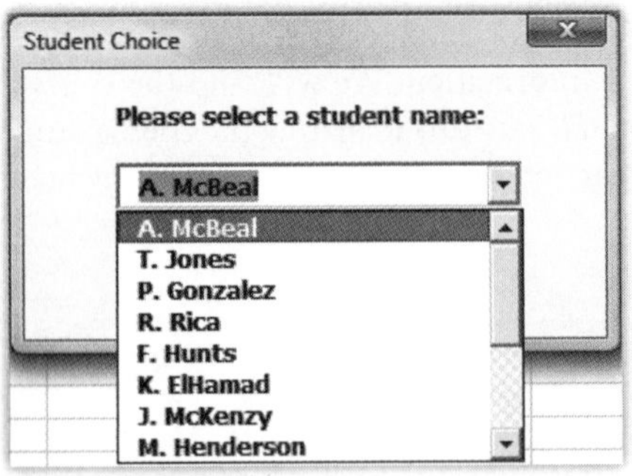

Figure 21.18 The combo box list of students is the most current list from the database.

The only code remaining now is the main transcript query, which we have placed in a procedure called *Transcript* (see Figure 21.14). The first sets of values we will collect from the database are the students' grades and section numbers for each course they have taken, found in *qryCourseID* (see Figure 21.19).

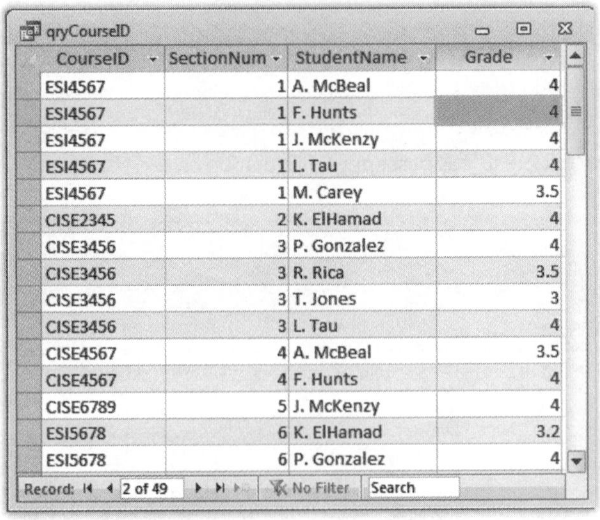
qryCourseID

CourseID	SectionNum	StudentName	Grade
ESI4567	1	A. McBeal	4
ESI4567	1	F. Hunts	4
ESI4567	1	J. McKenzy	4
ESI4567	1	L. Tau	4
ESI4567	1	M. Carey	3.5
CISE2345	2	K. ElHamad	4
CISE3456	3	P. Gonzalez	4
CISE3456	3	R. Rica	3.5
CISE3456	3	T. Jones	3
CISE3456	3	L. Tau	4
CISE4567	4	A. McBeal	3.5
CISE4567	4	F. Hunts	4
CISE6789	5	J. McKenzy	4
ESI5678	6	K. ElHamad	3.2
ESI5678	6	P. Gonzalez	4

Record: 2 of 49 No Filter Search

Figure 21.19 The query "qryCourseID" has the course ID and section number for all the courses each student has taken.

This is the SQL statement for this query:

"SELECT Grade, SectionNum, CourseID FROM qryCourseID
WHERE StudentName = '" & StudName & "'"

This is a dynamic query in that we are using criteria dependent upon the users' input. That is, we are searching for the grade, section number, and course information from the *qryCourseID* in each case where the student name value is equal to the name selected by the user from the form.

We will output this query to the first section of the result table, in a cell we have named "TransTBL" (see Figure 21.12). We again perform this query using our *QueryData* function; the *i* and *j* parameters are again set to 0.

Now that we have recorded all of the section numbers and course numbers taken by the student, we can query for the remaining information. We will find the course name, credit hours, department, and course type from *tblCourse* by matching the course numbers recorded (see Figure 21.20); and we will find the year and semester from *tblSection* by matching the section numbers (see Figure 21.21).

tblCourse

CourseID	Department	CourseName	Description	CreditHours	CourseType
CISE1234	CISE	Comp Programming 1		3	Required
CISE2345	CISE	C++		3	Required
CISE3456	CISE	DataBase Management		3	Elective
CISE4567	CISE	Comp Archi		4	Elective
CISE5678	CISE	Comp Simulation		4	Required
CISE6789	ECE	Comp Graphics		3	Required
ECE3456	ECE	Computer Animation		3	Elective
ECE5412	ECE	Artificial Intelligence		3	Required
ESI0897	ISE	Decision Support System Undergrad		3	Required
ESI0987	ISE	Operation Research		3	Required
ESI1234	ISE	Digital Simulation		4	Required
ESI2345	ISE	Supply Chain Management		4	Elective
ESI3456	ISE	Network Analysis		4	Elective
ESI4567	ISE	Total Quality Management		3	Elective
ESI5678	ISE	Manufacturing Management		3	Required
ESI6789	ISE	Decision Support System Grad		4	Required
MAN3423	DIS	Production and Logistics		3	Required
MAN5621	DIS	International Logistics		3	Elective
MAN6784	DIS	Operations Management		3	Required

Record: 1 of 19 No Filter Search

Figure 21.20 The table "tblCourse" has descriptive information on each course.

tblSection

SectionNum	CourseID	FacultyName	Year	Semester	YearSem	Day	Time	RoomNumb	Capacity	Evaluati
1	ESI4567	D. Henry	1998	Fall	1998 Fall	MWF	12:00 PM	WEIL 270	30	4.5
3	CISE3456	E. Richards	1999	Fall	1999 Fall	T R	12:00 PM	FLG 260	50	4.8
13	ESI4567	E. Richards	1999	Spring	1999 Spring	MWF	3:00 PM	FLG 270	50	4.5
2	CISE2345	E. Aleman	1999	Spring	1999 Spring	MWF	12:00 PM	WEIMER 1060	40	4.3
10	ESI4567	E. Aleman	1999	Spring	1999 Spring	MWF	12:00 PM	WEIL 273	30	4.7
7	ESI1234	E. Richards	1999	Summer	1999 Summer	MTWRF	11:00 AM	WEIL 321	30	4.6
16	CISE3456	R. Abherto	2000	Fall	2000 Fall	T R	12:00 PM	FLG 270	50	4.3
5	CISE6789	S. Balow	2000	Fall	2000 Fall	MWF	3:00 PM	FLG 280	50	4.7
15	CISE2345	E. Richards	2000	Spring	2000 Spring	MWF	3:00 PM	WEIMER 1060	40	4.6
18	CISE5678	D. Henry	2000	Spring	2000 Spring	MWF	10:00 AM	WEIL 270	50	4.8
24	ECE5412	R. Abherto	2000	Spring	2000 Spring	T R	9:00 AM	NEB 200	40	4.7
25	MAN5621	S. Edwards	2000	Spring	2000 Spring	MWF	12:00 PM	STZ 100	45	4.8
4	CISE4567	R. Abherto	2000	Spring	2000 Spring	T R	2:00 PM	WEIL 273	40	4.7
8	ESI0987	R. Abherto	2000	Spring	2000 Spring	MWF	1:00 PM	WEIMER 1084	40	4.5
12	ESI3456	R. Abherto	2000	Summer	2000 Summer	MTWRF	8:00 AM	WEIL 273	30	4.3
33	ESI1234	E. Aleman	2000	Summer	2000 Summer	T R	9:00 AM	FLG 270	40	4.6

Record: 1 of 36 No Filter Search

Figure 21.21 The table "tblSection" has detailed information on each section.

However, these queries will be repeated multiple times since we want to find this information for each course in our initial query result. We will therefore use a Do Until loop will the following basic structure:

```
i = 0
Do Until Range("TransTBL").Offset(i, 0).Value = ""
    (query from tblCourse)
    (query from tblSection)
    i = i + 1
Loop
```

Since we are repeating these queries for each course in our initial query result, our output range will have to shift down one row each time. This is why we have added the *i* and *j* parameters to the *QueryData* function. The output range will be offset by the same *i* value used in the loop. (In this case, the *j* value will always be 0; however, for later applications it may be used.)

This is the SQL statement for the first query:

"SELECT CourseName, CreditHours, DepartmentID, CourseType FROM tblCourse WHERE CourseID = '" & Range("TransTBL").Offset(i, 2).Value & "'"

Here the criterion is the course number which can be found from the initial query results in "TransTBL". The output range for this query will be in the second section of the result table, the first cell of which we have named "CourseTBL".

This is the SQL statement for the second query:

"SELECT Year, Semester FROM tblSection WHERE SectionNum = " & Range("TransTBL").Offset(i, 1).Value

(Notice here that we do not end this SQL statement with another & "'". This is because the section number value is numeric and therefore does not need to be included in single quotation marks.) The output range for this query will be in the third section of the result table, the first cell of which we have named "SectTBL".

As we loop through the courses taken by the student to perform these two queries, we also keep track of the sum of the grades so that we can calculate the GPA when the loop has ended. We do this using a *GPA* variable as follows:

GPA = GPA + Range("TransTBL").Offset(i, 0).Value

When the loop has ended, we find the GPA value by dividing the *GPA* variable by the last value of *i* (*i* was initialized to be 0). We then sort the entire result table by the year value. The final code is shown in Figure 21.22.

```
Sub Transcript()
    Application.ScreenUpdating = False
    Range("TStudent").Value = StudName

    Src = "SELECT Grade, SectionNum, CourseID FROM qryCourseID WHERE StudentName = '" & StudName & "'"
    OutputRange = "TransTBL"
    Call QueryData(Src, OutputRange, 0, 0)

    i = 0
    GPA = 0
    Do Until Range("TransTBL").Offset(i, 0).Value = ""
            Src = "SELECT CourseName, CreditHours, DepartmentID, CourseType FROM tblCourse WHERE CourseID = '" _
                & Range("TransTBL").Offset(i, 2).Value & "'"
            OutputRange = "CourseTBL"
            Call QueryData(Src, OutputRange, i, 0)

            Src = "SELECT Year, Semester FROM tblSection WHERE SectionNum = " & Range("TransTBL"). _
                Offset(i, 1).Value
            OutputRange = "SectTBL"
            Call QueryData(Src, OutputRange, i, 0)

            GPA = GPA + Range("TransTBL").Offset(i, 0).Value
            i = i + 1
    Loop

    Range("GPA").Value = GPA / i

    Range(Range("TransTBL"), Range("TransTBL").Offset(i - 1, 10)).Sort key1:=Range("TransTBL"). _
        Offset(0, 9), order1:=xlAscending

    Application.ScreenUpdating = True

End Sub
```

Figure 21.22 The Transcript procedure contains the main query code.

21.6 *Summary*

- The two main objects we use to create a pivot table are PivotCaches and PivotTables. We must use the ActiveWorkbook object to refer to an existing PivotChaches object. We must use the ActiveSheet object to refer to an existing PivotTables object.
- To create a pivot chart in VBA simply use the Chart object. After adding a new chart, set the source data to the created pivot table instead of the original data used to create the pivot table.
- There are two main systems used in VBA for communicating with external data sources: DAO and ADO. We use ADO as we feel it is less complicated. There are two main ADO objects used to import data: Connection and Recordset.
- The Connection object establishes the communication to a particular database. To define a Connection object variable, we use a data type called *ADODB.Connection*. There are two main methods used with this object: *Open* and *Close*. The *Open* method uses a *ConnectionString* argument to define the path to the database. To define the data source value of this argument, we use the string filename value and the *Path* property of the *ThisWorkbook* object.
- To define Recordset object variables, we use the *ADODB.Recordset* data type. The arguments for the *Open* method of the Recordset object are *Source* and *ActiveConnection*. The *Source* argument defines the data that should be imported. The *ActiveConnection* argument value is the name of the open Connection object we have previously defined.
- To copy this Recordset-defined data to the Excel spreadsheet, use the Range object and the method *CopyFromRecordset*.
- *Structured Query Language* (SQL) is the code used to perform queries or filter the data which is imported. The basic structure of SQL commands is as follows: an action to perform, the location of the data on which to perform the action, and the criteria the data must meet in order for the action to be performed.
- The SELECT statement selects a specific group of data items from a table or query in the database. The phrase appearing immediately after the SELECT statement is the name or names of the fields which should be selected.
- The FROM statement is followed by the name of the table or query in the database from which the information is being selected.
- The most common statement to implement the filtering step of the query is WHERE. The WHERE statement can use sub statements such as <, >, = for value evaluations or BETWEEN, LIKE, IN, AND, OR, and NOT for other comparisons.
- ORDER BY is another statement; it can be used with the WHERE statement to sort the selected data. This data can be sorted in ascending or descending order using the statements ASC or DESC, respectively.
- Variables can be used to make queries dynamic with Input Boxes, User Forms, or by simply taking values the user has entered in a spreadsheet. These variables can then be placed in the statements of SQL commands in the code to search for the user's criteria.
- To export data from Excel we can use Charts. Use the *Export* method with the Chart object. The *Export* method has three arguments: *FileName*, *FilterName*, and *Interactive*.

21.7 *Exercises*

21.7.1 Review Questions

1. What method is used to create a pivot table?
2. How do you set grand totals for pivot tables using VBA code?
3. What is the equivalent for the GETPIVOTDATA in VBA?
4. How do you set the row, column, and data fields of a pivot table in VBA?
5. What object is used to import text and webpages?
6. In which argument of which method are *TEXT* and *URL* given to specify the source type of the import?
7. How do you specify to use a space delimiter when importing text in VBA?
8. What property is used to set the delimiters when importing a webpage in VBA?

9. What is the difference between *DAO* and *ADO* objects?
10. What are the two main objects used when importing databases?

21.7.2 Hands-On Exercises

NOTE: *Please refer to the files "Chapter_10_Exercises.xlsx", "UniversityInformationSystem.mdb", and "AirlineSystem.mdb" for the associated worksheets or databases noted for the hands-on exercises. The file is available at: www.dssbooks.com.*

1. Create a user form for importing data.
   a. Give the users the option to import from a text file or webpage using option buttons.
   b. Below the option buttons, have a text box in which the users should provide the path of the text file or URL of the webpage. An appropriate label should appear above the text box depending on the option button selected by the users in part (a).
   c. Ask the users to specify the range on the spreadsheet where they want the date to be imported. They should select this range using a RefEdit control.
   d. Import the text or webpage to this location using VBA commands.
2. The website *http://www.x-rates.com* has current exchange rates between the U.S. Dollar and several other country currencies. Import this data and make a button on the spreadsheet that will allow the users to refresh the query at any time. Each time the query is refreshed, report which country has the strongest currency.
3. The URL *http://www.nba.com/***/stats* contains player statistics for any NBA team. The name of the team would be in the place of "***"; for example, the statistics for the Indiana Pacers would be at: *http://www.nba.com/pacers/stats*. Create a program which does the following:
   a. Displays a user form with a combo box listing several NBA teams.
   b. The form should also have several check boxes for possible analysis to perform on the available statistics, such as Team Average Points Per Game, Top Five Players (based on Points Per Game), etc.
   c. Import the data for the selected team and perform the checked analysis on the imported statistics.
   d. Create another user form which allows the users to compare overall statistics among three teams. They should be able to select three teams from the list of teams. The comparison should be made on Average Team Points Per Game, Average Team Free Throws Made, and Average Team 3-Pointers Made. Make a chart for this comparison with each set of values as a series.

Use the tables and queries from the MS Access database "UniversityInformationSystem.mdb" to complete the following three exercises.

4. Write an SQL query to do the following:
   a. Import a list of all student names from the ISE Department.
   b. Count how many students are male and how many are female.
   c. Find the average course evaluation for the professor E. Aleman.
5. Suppose you want to create a small user form which lists all department names in a combo box (refer to the course list form in Figures 21.8 and 21.10 from the application). Write a procedure to do this. (You may use the *QueryData* function developed in the chapter.)
6. Create a procedure called Audit which lists all the courses affiliated with a selected department. Each course should have its ID and name listed. The credit hours should also be listed for each course along with whether it is "required" or an "elective". The department should be selected from a small user form with a combo box listing all departments from the database (refer to exercise 5 above).

Use the MS Access database "AirlineSystem.mdb" to complete the following three exercises. There are four tables, tblAircraft, tblFlightLeg, tblLegInstance, and tblPassenger.

- Table "tblAircraft" gives information for each plane, or aircraft, including: plane ID (CraftID), maximum number of seats (MaxSeats), manufacturing company (ManfCompany), and plane type (Type).
- Table "tblFlightLeg" gives information on each flight number (FlightNo). It shows the

arrival airport (ArrivalAirportCode), departing airport (DepartingAirportCode), and the arrival and departing times (ArrivalTime and DepartTime, respectively).

- Table "tblLegInstance" gives information for each flight based on a unique Instance ID. The flight number (FlightNo), date (Date), plane ID (CraftID), fare (Fare), and seats available (SeatAvailable) are recorded.
- The table "tblPassenger" gives a unique passenger ID (PassID), the passenger name (PassName), passenger phone number (PassPhone), and the flight they have reserved (FlightRes).

7. Write the SQL code needed to do the following:
   a. Count the number of passengers on flight AA103.
   b. Find the average fare associated with flight AA102.
   c. Find the number of flights which leave from Orlando, FL (ORL).
   d. Find the average number of seats on Boeing manufactured planes.
8. Create a user form which will list the different plane manufacturers in a combo box. Based on a selection from this list, show another form which lists all the planes made by that manufacturer (again in a combo box).
9. Create a user form in which a Passenger Name is selected from a list. Based on this selection, display the passenger's ID, phone number, and flight reservation.
10. Create a procedure which will report detailed information for each flight. The users should select a flight from a combo box in a user form. After the flight has been selected, check the Leg Instance table to find each plane assigned to that flight. Report the maximum seats on this type of plane and the seats available on this particular flight instance. Report to and from which city this flight is traveling. Also report the date of the flight instance.
11. Refer to the table "tblCourse" from the "UniversityInformationSystem.mdb" database. Create the following pivot tables using VBE:
   a. For each department present the total number of courses offered. Present also the total number of courses offered in the University.
   b. For each department present the total number of 3 and 4 credit hour courses offered. Present also the total number of 3 and 4 credit hour courses offered in the University.
   c. For each department present the total number of required and elective courses offered. Present also the total number of required and elective courses offered in the University.
12. A given table presents detailed information about the faculty of a University. The administration of this University is concerned about minority rights' issues and therefore is interested to know the following. (Refer to worksheet "21.12".)
   a. The total number of female and male faculty per department.
   b. The total number of female and male faculty per faculty status (assistant, chair, etc).
   c. The total number of white and African American faculty per department.
   d. The total number of white and African American faculty per faculty statues (assistant, chair, etc).

   Create pivot tables using VBE to answer these questions.
13. "Italian Pizzeria" is a family-owned pizza restaurant in a small town. While many of the customers dine-in, about 80% of their business depends on delivery service. Recently, one of the well-known pizza chains has opened a restaurant in the city. The new competitor is attracting customers as they guarantee the delivery of an order within 30 minutes. If the order is not delivered on time, the customer receives the order without charge.

   The owner of the "Italian Pizzeria" is planning to offer a similar guarantee in order to remain competitive. He plans to offer a guarantee of 29 minutes or less delivery time. In order to see if the restaurant is able to offer such a deal, the owner collected data from the last 7 days. Five observations are taken per hour, from 2pm to 10pm. (Refer to worksheet "21.13".)

   Create pivot tables using VBE to answer the following:
   a. Present the number of times, for each day, that a delivery was on time, and the number of times that the delivery was not on time. This table will help the owner to understand whether the day of the week had an effect on delivery time.

b. Present the number of times, for each hour, that a delivery was on time, and the number of times that the delivery was not on time. This table will help the owner to understand whether the time of the day had an effect on delivery time.

c. The owner of the restaurant believes that the waiting time for an order to be picked-up by a delivery employee should not be more than 3 min. He wants to know how many times in a particular day, the waiting time is more than 3 min, and how many times in a particular hour the waiting time is more than 3 min. This information would help in deciding whether more delivery employees should be hired.

Note: For the purpose of this exercise randomly generate the prep time, wait time and travel time.

14. "Greg's Bicycles" is a company that manufactures mountain bicycles. As their business is growing, the company is interested in advertising their products to reach potential customers. For this purpose, the management decided to collect relevant data that would help identify the particular market segment that is more likely to buy their bicycles. A table presents the data collected. (Refer to worksheet "21.14".)

Create pivot tables using VBE to answer the following:

a. For each product, present the total number of female and male buyers.

b. For each product, present the total number of married and single buyers.

c. For each product, present the average miles/wk performed by its buyers.

d. For each product, present the average fitness level of its buyers.

e. For each product, present the average education level of its buyers.

Note that in the table above gender is equal to 1 if the customer is male and 2 if female; education = 1 if the customer has no high-school diploma, education = 2 if the customer has high-school diploma, education = 3 if the customer has a college degree and education = 4 if the customer has graduate degree; marital status = 1 for single and 2 for married; fitness level varies from 1 = poor to 5 = excellent. For the purpose of this exercise randomly generate the data.

15. Create the form presented below which enables the user to dynamically create the pivot tables given in Hands-On Exercise 21.14.

The form includes the following:

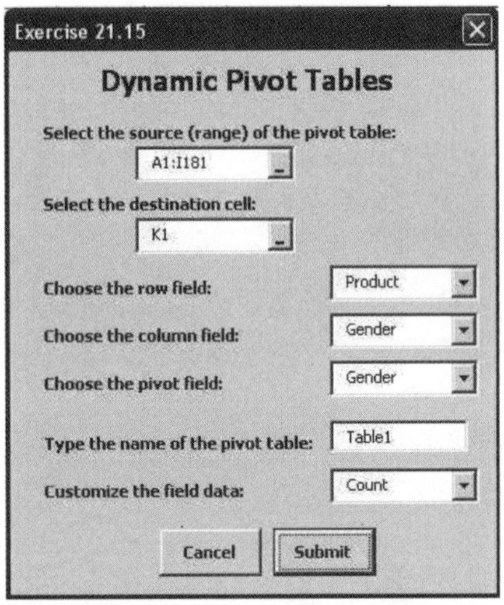

a. A RefEdit that enables the user to select the range of the source data and a RefEdit for the destination cell.

b. Four combo boxes that enable the user to choose the row field, column field, the pivot field, as well as to choose an option (sum, count, average, min or max) on how to customize the field data.

c. A textbox to enter the name of the pivot table.

d. The cancel command button that closes the form and the submit command button that when clicked-on takes the information provided from the user as input and creates the corresponding pivot table in an excel spreadsheet.

Check the performance of the code by using it to build the pivot tables described in Hands-On Exercise 14.

CHAPTER

twenty-two

The DSS Development Process

chapter OVERVIEW

22.1 *Defining the DSS Development Process*

Now that we have discussed in great detail the components of a spreadsheet-based decision support system (DSS), we need to learn the process of putting these components together to build a complete DSS application. Before entering formulas into Excel or coding procedures in VBA, it is necessary to plan the overall layout for the DSS and give some thought to the design and implementation of the application. We propose six basic steps for developing a DSS: 1) ***Application Overview and Model Development***, which creates a layout of the entire application, designing the flow from the user input to the model calculations to the output, and outlining the model details; 2) ***Worksheets***, which determine how many worksheets the programmers require to best handle input, calculations, and output; 3) ***User Interface***, which outlines what interface the programmers require to receive input from the users and navigate them through the application; 4) ***Procedures***, which outline what sub and/or function procedures the programmers require in the code to receive input, perform calculations, and display output; 5) ***Re-solve Options***, which decide what re-solve options the users may have, and 6) ***Testing and Final Packaging***, which ensures the application is working properly and has a professional appearance which is clear for the users.

These steps have been our guidelines in developing decision support systems. We do not claim that they are necessary to follow but, rather, consider them helpful guidelines when developing a DSS application. In this chapter, we provide several examples from case studies that we have developed using these proposed steps. The following chapters offer a more detailed explanation of each case study's development using these six steps. We wish to illustrate the variety and consistencies that are possible when developing DSS applications.

22.2 *Application Overview and Model Development*

The *Application Overview and Model Development* step is the most important step in developing a DSS. In this step, we consider the entire flow of the application and the details for the DSS model. In preparing the model, we must consider the input, output, any necessary assumptions, and all calculations. The calculations may involve optimization or simulation (using Risk Solver Platform) with some decision analysis. For these calculations, the DSS developers should start thinking which formulas and functions can be used from the Excel worksheet and which will be done dynamically in the code.

22.2.1 Input

We should first consider if and how the users will provide input. Determining the type of input for the model will guide us in designing the input interface (sheet, forms, and other controls). For example, if we only need one or two pieces of information from the users, we may not even need a form or an entire sheet for input; instead, we can use an Input Box. In some applications, we may need large sets of data for our analysis. In that case, we may just prompt the users to import data from a text file or a database to a worksheet. Once we have decided which method is most appropriate for the application, we may need to spend more time designing the interface (We will return to this task in the *User Interface* step.). It is important to complete the *Application Overview and Model Development* step before designing the interface so that we have a clear idea of what the entire application will incorporate.

We have used various types of input in our case study applications (see Part III of the book). For example, in our Forecasting Methods application, we ask the users for historical data. This data is entered directly in an input worksheet. In our Warehouse Layout application, the users enter the warehouse dimensions, number of docks, and number of products in a user form. They then enter more specific input such as dock usage frequency and product demand, in the appropriate input worksheets. In our Portfolio Optimization application, the user input includes the stock selection for their portfolio as well as the optimization-related input. The users select the stocks from a list on an input worksheet, and they enter the optimization-related input on a user form. The input and input interface will depend on our application's model and end user design.

22.2.2 Model and Calculations

We should now have an overview of what is required for our model calculations. We may need to determine the model formulation before we can finish deciding what the user input will be. First, we must decide if the DSS will compute simple calculations, perform an optimization, or run a simulation. This general model outline will help us to determine the details of our worksheet, user interface, and procedure designs.

For example, in our Inventory Management application, we use three different models: basic EOQ, EOQ with backorders, and Reorder Point method. For each model, we have some general input, which is used for all models, and some specific input. We have designed our input interface such that the general input is asked at the beginning of the application and the specific input is only asked when a particular model is selected. Outlining these models and their individual input requirements was an important step in developing the application.

22.2.3 Output

Once input is received and the model calculations are performed, we need to determine what output is displayed to the users: charts, graphs, histograms or tables. Does some of the input need to be re-displayed to the users? Again, these options depend on the application. It is important to consider the output, as it is a driving force in establishing why the users are using the DSS. It is worthwhile to check if we are computing everything that the users may be interested in.

The type of output we display will vary with each application. For example, in our Portfolio Management and Optimization application, we display several output tables and charts to the users. We graph portfolio's efficient frontier to help the user understand the risk that s/he would be taking if seeking higher returns. In our Queuing Models: Single Server application, the output consists of several histograms which show the users the distribution of server utilization and waiting times in the queue. We also use a graph to show how the queue length changes during a simulation run. It is important to consider what results our model calculations will yield and then determine what analysis of these results will be most useful to present to the users.

Summary

Welcome Sheet	Flow begins; introduction to what DSS is and how to begin using it.
Input	Provided by the user via a set of forms, an input worksheet, or Input Boxes.
Model Calculations	Formulation of objectives and necessary input; decide if computing simple calculations, performing an optimization, or running a simulation.
Output	A driving force in why the users are using the DSS.
Re-solve Options	Resolve options; modify input; redefine constraints or objectives.

22.3 *Worksheets*

Worksheet design is an important part of the DSS development process. The developers should consider how many sheets they will use in their application and what worksheet features they will include. Since we are developing spreadsheet-based DSS applications, we usually take advantage of the worksheet features to aid us in retrieving user input, performing calculations, and displaying output. It is beneficial to use Excel's spreadsheet features as much as possible and then save more complicated or dynamic tasks for VBA code. Therefore, we encourage the developers to design the worksheets before creating the code-based interface.

22.3.1 Welcome Sheet

There may be two to several sheets in a DSS application. The first sheet should always be the "Welcome" sheet, as we discussed above. For example, in Figure 22.1, we display the "Welcome" sheet for a case study that we developed for a "Portfolio Management and Optimization" DSS. In it, we describe the DSS and the model assumptions. We also reference the source of our model formulation and include some images related to portfolios. Then, we introduce a "Start" button, which the users can press to begin the application.

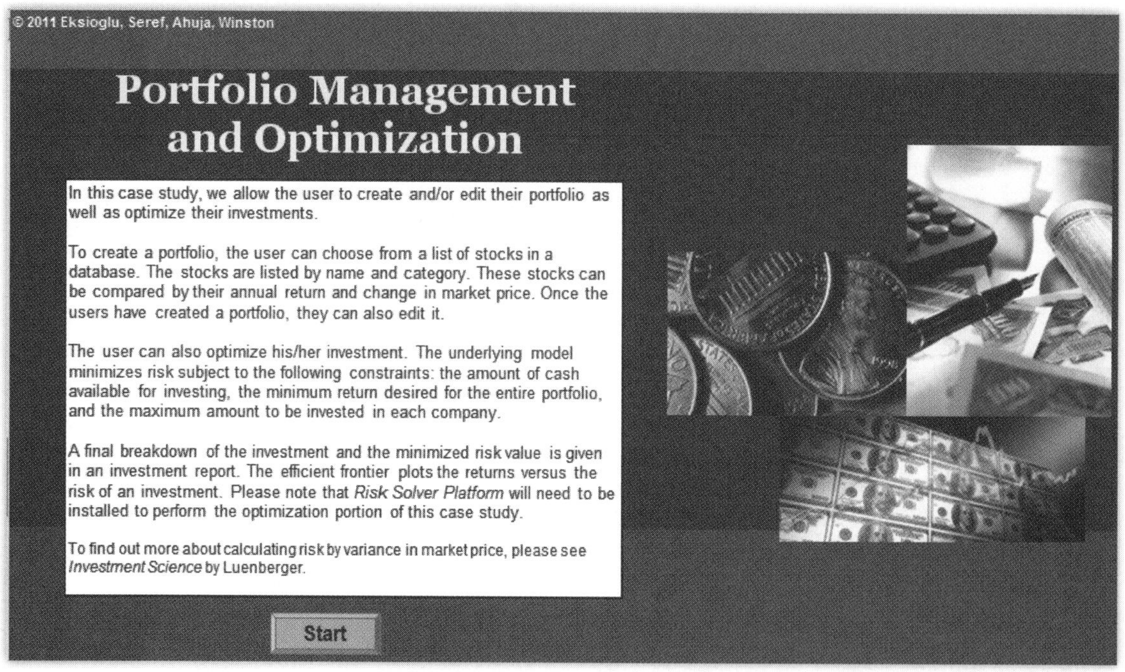

Figure 22.1 An example of a "Welcome" sheet.

22.3.2 Input Sheet

The remaining sheets are for input, calculations, and output. Each can be a separate sheet, or some elements can be combined onto fewer sheets. Let us first consider the input sheet. We can prepare the sheet by using appropriate labels for tables or input locations. We may also name some ranges at this point; this step will help us later when coding. Below is an example from a case study that we developed for the "Critical Path Method" (see Figure 22.2). In this application, we take the users through several input sheets. In each sheet, a table for a set of input values appears. In some cases, a worksheet may be a better user interface than forms for receiving input; we discuss this in more detail in the next section.

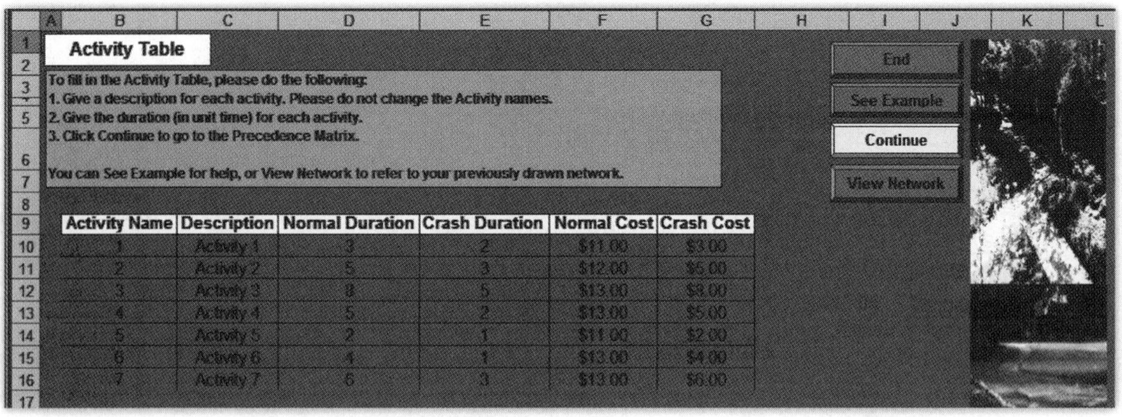

Figure 22.2 Using worksheets to receive input from a user.

We may also have an application that requires a large set of data. Users may import this data from a text file or a database, or may input it directly to the spreadsheet. Figure 22.3 displays an input sheet from a "Stochastic Customer Forecasting" case study. This sheet contains the historical data that is used to make future forecasts. In this application, we give the users the option to enter this data manually or to import it from a text file.

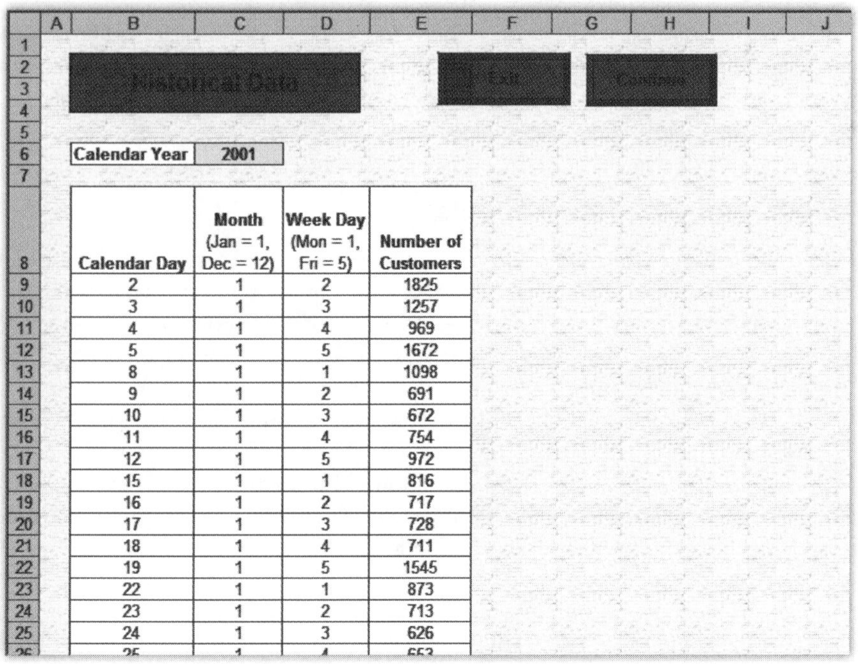

Figure 22.3 An example of a large set of data imported from a text file.

We may not require an input sheet for every application. Let us consider the case in which we can combine the input sheet with the calculations sheet or output sheet. For example, the figure below displays a sheet from a "Technical Analysis" case study in which the input, calculations, and output are all on one sheet (see Figure 22.4). Here, the users can modify the input using worksheet controls and press the "Re-solve" button to update the calculations in the table. A small table on the right of the screen summarizes the output.

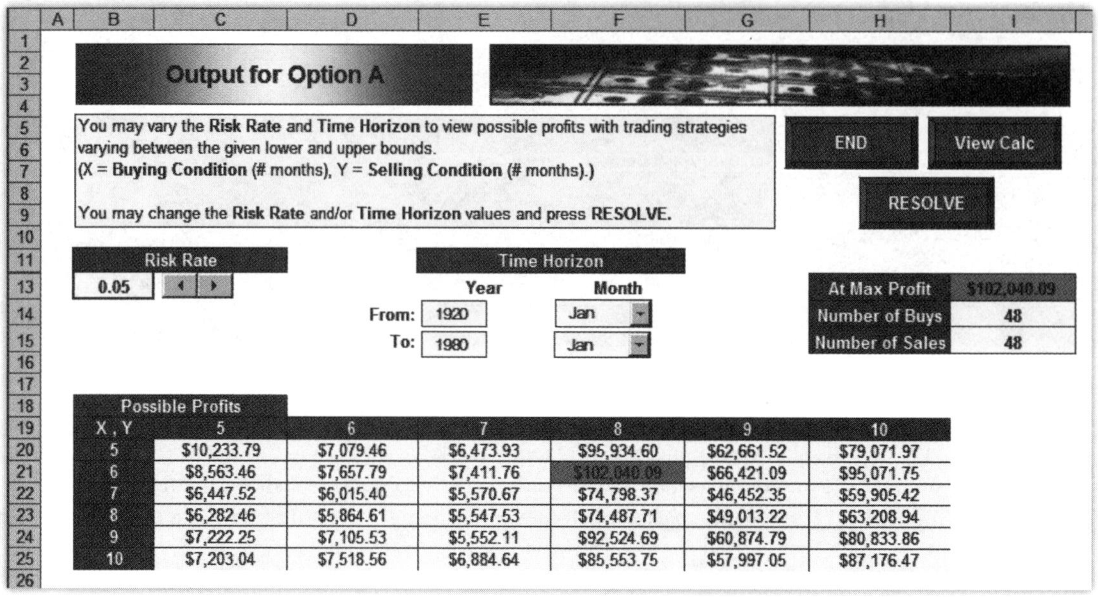

Figure 22.4 An example of input, calculations, and output on the same sheet.

Again, we may not even use a sheet at all for the input. We may simply obtain input from a user form and then use that directly in a calculations sheet or in some calculations procedures and take the user directly to the output sheet.

22.3.3 Model and Calculation Sheets

Let us now discuss the model and calculations sheets. These sheets or sheet may be viewed by or, in most cases, hidden from the users. A model or calculations sheet should be hidden if the intended users may not be familiar with the details of the calculations but are solely interested in the results. Figure 22.5 displays a complicated calculations sheet from a simulation performed in a "Retirement Planning" case study. In the sheet, there are several worksheet functions and formulas as well as some input cells whose values have been updated after the users have completed an input form. Since the sheet calculations are somewhat complicated, we do not show this sheet to the users during the normal flow of the application; however, we do give the users the option to view the calculations if desired. Normally, we take the users directly from the input form to the output sheet in this application.

It is possible to have some additional hidden sheets related to the calculations. For example, when a problem uses simulation tools of Risk Solver Platform, we usually build the model in a spreadsheet and use Psi distribution function to randomly generate the input data; we store the results of the runs for creating histograms or other summary reports. We should hide this sheet with simulation details from the users in the application flow, but we can make it available for viewing if the users are interested. With the *Application.ScreenUpdating* method and the *Worksheets.Visible* property, we can prevent the users from seeing these calculation sheets while they are operating for the model calculations.

END BACK

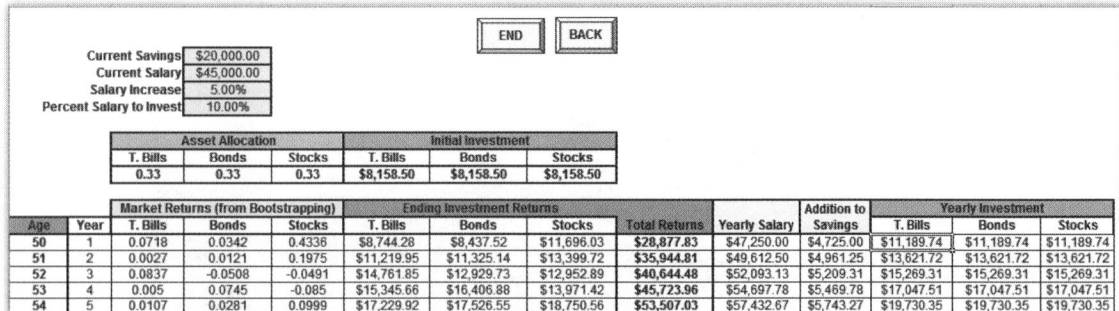

Current Savings	$20,000.00
Current Salary	$45,000.00
Salary Increase	5.00%
Percent Salary to Invest	10.00%

Asset Allocation			Initial Investment		
T. Bills	Bonds	Stocks	T. Bills	Bonds	Stocks
0.33	0.33	0.33	$8,158.50	$8,158.50	$8,158.50

		Market Returns (from Bootstrapping)			Ending Investment Returns					Addition to	Yearly Investment		
Age	Year	T. Bills	Bonds	Stocks	T. Bills	Bonds	Stocks	Total Returns	Yearly Salary	Savings	T. Bills	Bonds	Stocks
50	1	0.0718	0.0342	0.4336	$8,744.28	$8,437.52	$11,696.03	**$28,877.83**	$47,250.00	$4,725.00	$11,189.74	$11,189.74	$11,189.74
51	2	0.0027	0.0121	0.1975	$11,219.95	$11,325.14	$13,399.72	**$35,944.81**	$49,612.50	$4,961.25	$13,621.72	$13,621.72	$13,621.72
52	3	0.0837	-0.0508	-0.0491	$14,761.85	$12,929.73	$12,952.89	**$40,644.48**	$52,093.13	$5,209.31	$15,269.31	$15,269.31	$15,269.31
53	4	0.005	0.0745	-0.085	$15,345.66	$16,406.88	$13,971.42	**$45,723.96**	$54,697.78	$5,469.78	$17,047.51	$17,047.51	$17,047.51
54	5	0.0107	0.0281	0.0999	$17,229.92	$17,526.55	$18,750.56	**$53,507.03**	$57,432.67	$5,743.27	$19,730.35	$19,730.35	$19,730.35

Figure 22.5 An example of a complicated calculations sheet.

22.3.4 Output Sheet

Probably the most important sheet for the users is the output sheet. This sheet should clearly summarize the results of the calculations so the users can understand the behavior of whatever system they were modeling or analyzing. It is usually a good idea to include some graphical results as part of the output sheet. For example, in Figure 22.6, the results sheet from an "Inventory Management" case study illustrates the ordering strategy found by the model calculations. There are also some tables that summarize the numerical results of the solution.

Results END RESOLVE

The costs and order strategy for the selected method are shown. A set of example data has been generated for a few months to illustrate the inventory levels.
You can press the **Resolve** button to select a different method and resolve the problem.

Average Costs (per year)	
Total Annual Cost	$2,059.13
Annual Order Cost	$1,029.56
Annual Holding Cost	$1,029.56
Annual Shortage Cost	$0.00

Strategy	
Order Quantity	102.96
Number of Orders (per year)	20.59
Time Between Orders	0.05
ReOrder Point	60.00

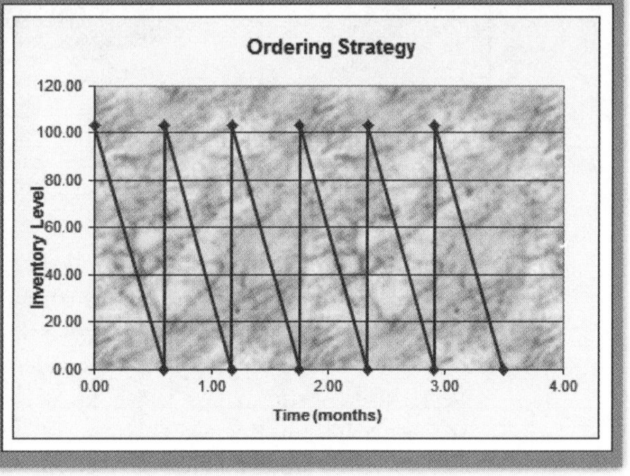

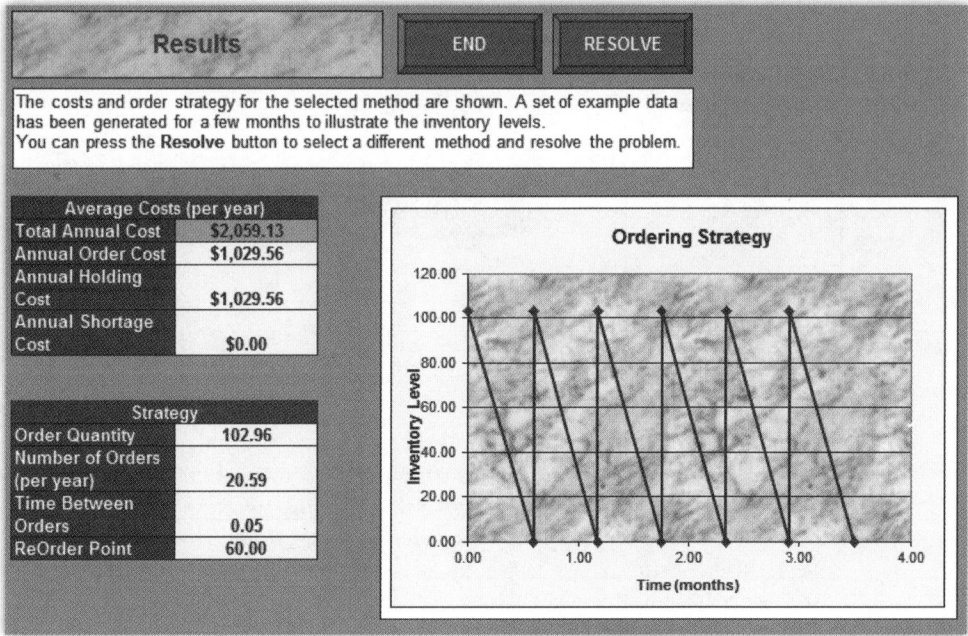

Figure 22.6 Using a graph to illustrate results in an output sheet.

In DSS application using simulation, it is usually important to include some histograms as part of the output sheet. Figure 22.7 displays some histograms that summarize the results of a "Reliability Analysis" case study. One histogram illustrates the frequency of various system failure time values with a bar graph and an overlaid scatter plot; these figures convey the cumulative probability of each value. Below that, another histogram, in the form of a pie chart, represents the frequency with which different machine types have caused system failure. We provide the users with several options from this output sheet; these include returning to and rerunning the simulation and returning to the initial input phase to re-solve the problem.

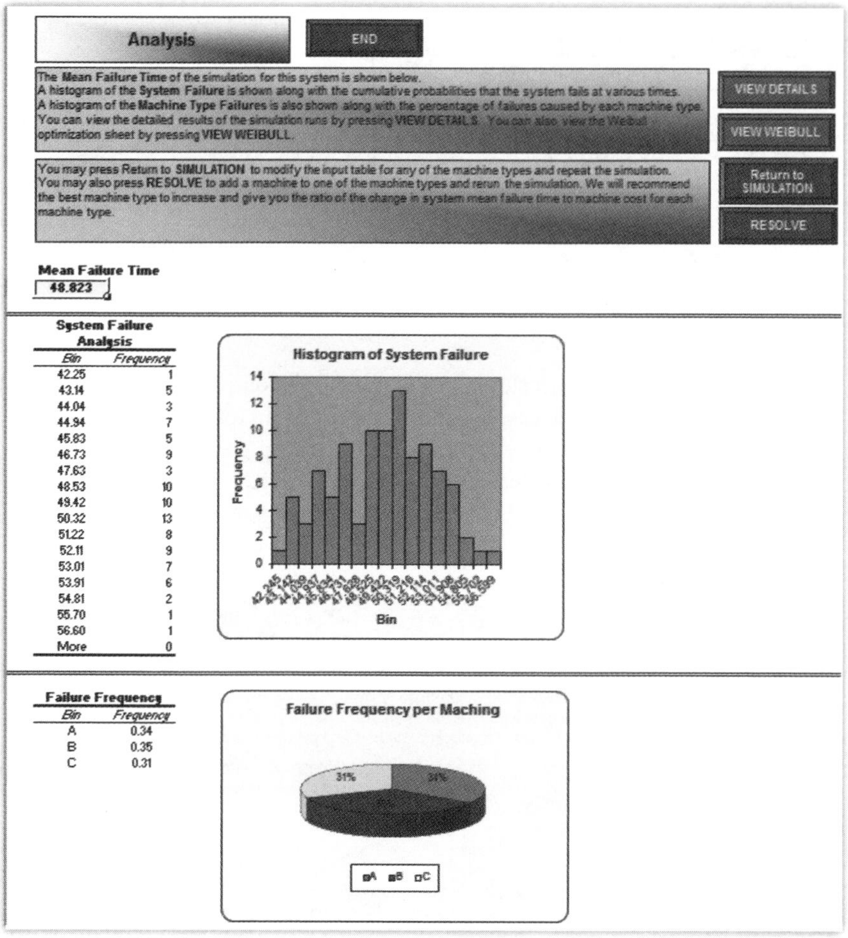

Figure 22.7 Histograms in the output sheet of a simulation-based DSS.

In some cases, we may have several charts or large summary tables that may not fit into one output sheet. In that case, we recommend making a navigational output sheet that will allow the users to view these individual reports. For example, In Figure 22.8, we show a navigational output sheet from a "Supply Chain Management" case study. This sheet allows the users to view several different summary pivot tables (see Figure 22.9). From these pivot tables, the users can also view corresponding pivot charts displayed as separate chart sheets (see Figure 22.10). The users can always return to the navigational output sheet from any of these reports.

Whichever results are relevant to our application, we should ensure that they are clearly presented in the output sheet. "End" and "Re-solve" options should also be included in the output sheet as well as options to "View" the input or the calculation sheets.

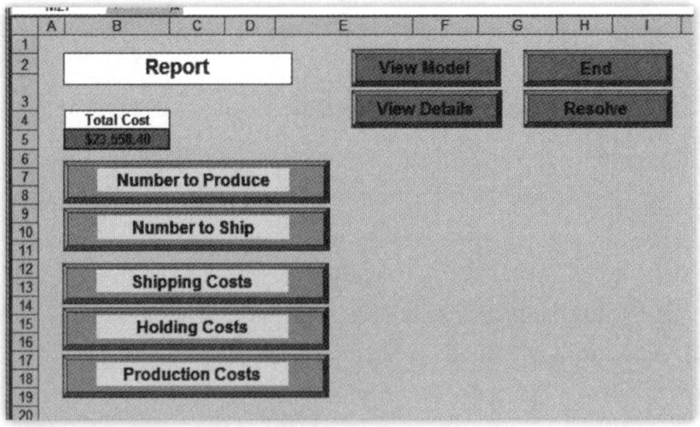

Figure 22.8 A navigational output sheet.

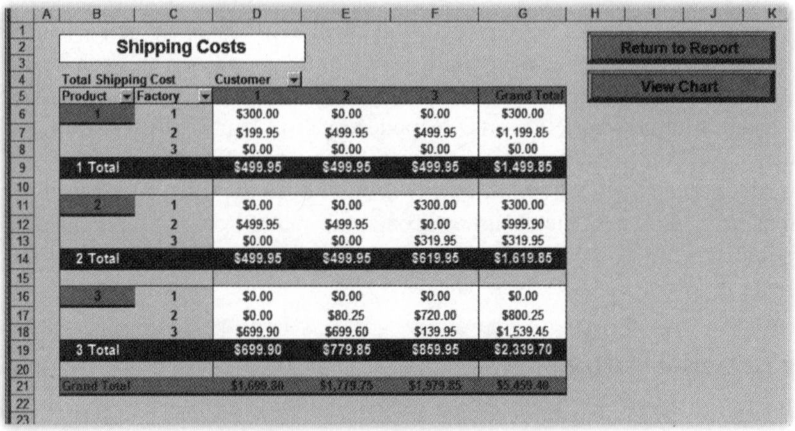

Total Shipping Cost		Customer			
Product	Factory	1	2	3	Grand Total
1	1	$300.00	$0.00	$0.00	$300.00
	2	$199.95	$499.95	$499.95	$1,199.85
	3	$0.00	$0.00	$0.00	$0.00
1 Total		$499.95	$499.95	$499.95	$1,499.85
2	1	$0.00	$0.00	$300.00	$300.00
	2	$499.95	$499.95	$0.00	$999.90
	3	$0.00	$0.00	$319.95	$319.95
2 Total		$499.95	$499.95	$619.95	$1,619.85
3	1	$0.00	$0.00	$0.00	$0.00
	2	$0.00	$80.25	$720.00	$800.25
	3	$699.90	$699.60	$139.95	$1,539.45
3 Total		$699.90	$779.85	$859.95	$2,339.70
Grand Total		$1,699.80	$1,779.75	$1,979.85	$5,459.40

Figure 22.9 A pivot table report sheet is one of the output sheets.

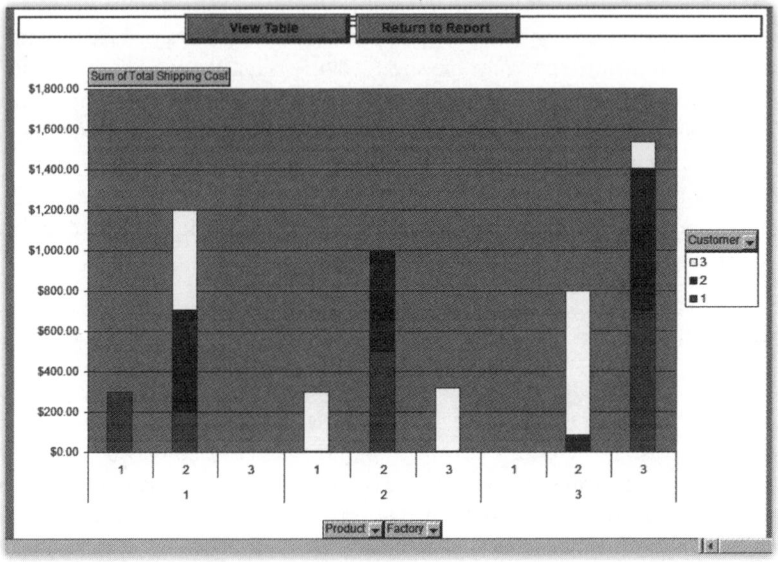

Figure 22.10 The corresponding pivot chart is another report sheet.

Summary

Welcome Sheet	Title and description of the DSS; images; "Start" button.
Input Sheet	User input; large data input; can be combined with other sheets.
Model and Calculations Sheets	Worksheet calculations; simulation results; usually hidden from users.
Output Sheet	Summary tables and reports; graphs, charts or histograms; navigational output buttons; "End", "Resolve", and "View" buttons.

22.4 *User Interface*

Designing a user interface is an important element of developing a user-friendly DSS. We will discuss effective graphical user interface (GUI) design in the next chapter; for now, let us focus on what role the user interface plays in DSS development. We have discussed four main types of user interface in spreadsheet-based DSS applications in Chapter 18: user forms, form controls on the worksheet, functional buttons on the worksheet, and navigational buttons on the worksheet. When developing the DSS, we must think about how to use these interface options to perform the following tasks: navigate the users through the application, receive input, allow the users to set parameters for the model and calculations, and allow the users to begin the calculations and then repeat them or re-solve the model.

22.4.1 Navigational Buttons

Let us begin by discussing the development of the DSS navigational interface. As we have already mentioned, the first navigational button we should create is the "Start" button, which is located on the "Welcome" sheet (see Figure 22.1). We should assign this button to a macro that brings the users to the input interface. On all other sheets (input, calculation, and output sheets) there should at least be an "End" or "Exit" button. The users should always have the option to quit the application and return to the Welcome sheet. (Note: Whether you use "End" or "Exit" or any other phrase for this action, be sure that you are consistent across all sheets in the application. We will discuss consistency in user interface design more in Chapter 23 on GUI design.)

We may also include navigational buttons such as "Next," "Continue," or "Back" if we intend for the users to be able to step through the sheets or to revisit sheets. These buttons are especially important if we have hidden the sheet tabs or are only making one sheet visible at a time, which we recommend for a more professional presentation.

22.4.2 Receiving Input

The next important interface is for receiving user input. The type of user interface we select will depend on the type of input we are receiving (refer to the examples mentioned in Section 22.2.1). For example, historical data for a Forecasting Management DSS may be input directly to cells on an input worksheet, whereas input interface for a Warehouse Layout DSS may be better with a user form. As we saw in Chapter 18, two main types of user interface are form controls on a worksheet and user forms. Let us explore which interface is best for which types of input.

Form Controls on the Worksheet: We may use form controls on the worksheet to receive user input or to allow the users to set or change model parameters. Refer to Figure 22.4 to see an example of text boxes and combo boxes on a worksheet in which input was taken from the users on the same sheet where calculations and output were displayed. Another example appears in Figure 22.11. This example is from the "Inventory Management" case study. Here, three option buttons represent different methods that find the best order strategy. These option buttons are mutually exclusive, and two of them also have dynamic features. The bottom two buttons have some associated cells for extra input; they are shaded darker when unmarked and made lighter when marked (see Figure 22.11(b)).

Form controls on the worksheet are useful when there are many re-solve options in the application. In this case, we want to provide the users with easy access to the input so they can change it multiple times. It is important to retain the clarity of the worksheet layout when placing form controls adjacent to other input cells, calculations, or output. We will return to these interface design issues in a later section.

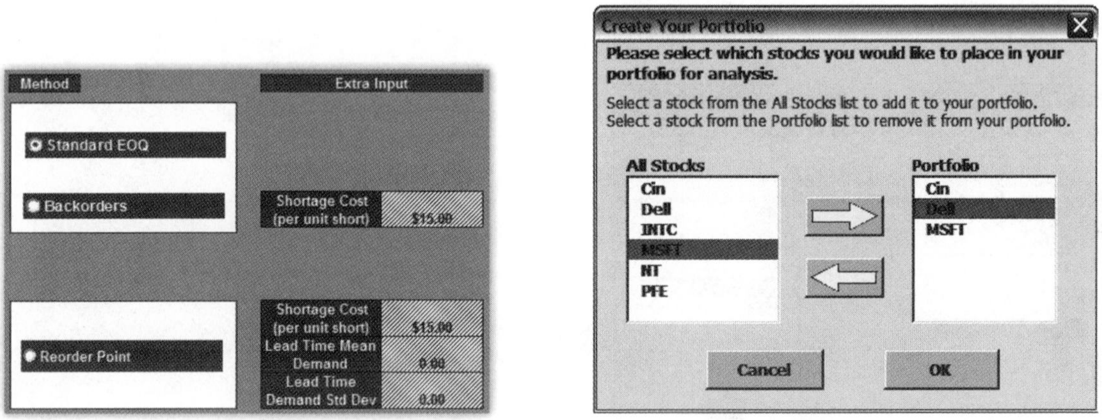

(a) (b)

Figure 22.11 Dynamic form controls on a worksheet.

User Forms: Creating a user form is another good option for user input interface. In some cases, there may be a tradeoff between using functional buttons or form controls on a worksheet and creating a user form. For example, in Figure 22.12(a), we have used two functional buttons to allow users to "Add" and "Remove" stocks to and from their portfolios in the "Portfolio Management and Optimization" case study. In this particular case study, we have put this functionality on the worksheet because it is a feature that the users may use often. The users may go to a new sheet to view stock comparisons and then return to edit the portfolio; they may also go to an optimization sheet to view investment strategy results and then return to edit the portfolio and re-solve.

However, if the users do not need to create or edit their portfolios multiple times, we may choose to create a user form to perform this functionality. In Figure 22.12(b), we provide an example of such a form for a "Beta of Stocks" case study. In this case, the users only select their portfolios once.

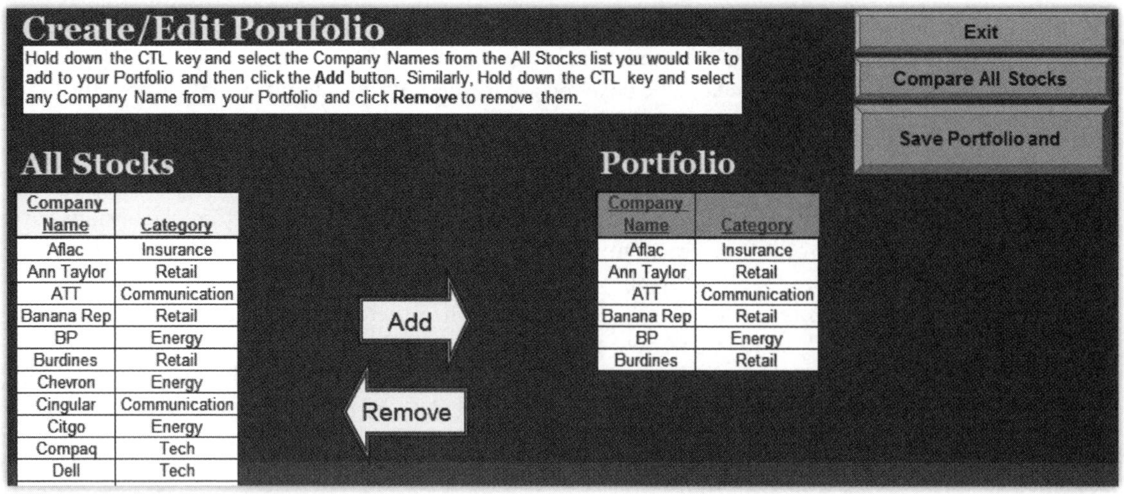

(a)

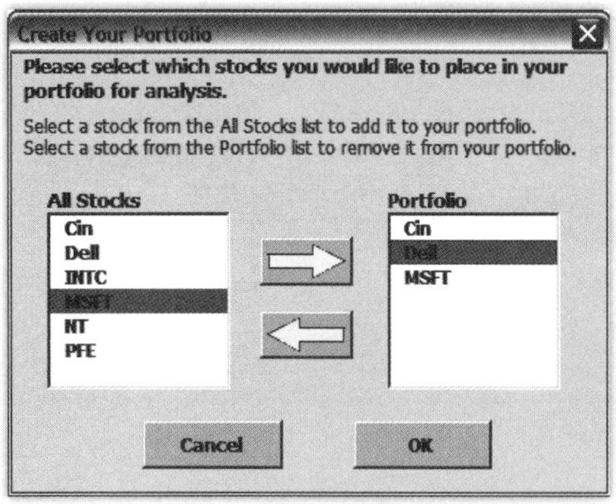

(b)

Figure 22.12 An example of controls on a form and worksheet.

In most DSS applications, if there is a large enough set of input required from the users, we suggest creating user forms. User forms can be advantageous in that there are many options for placing and manipulating controls on them. The controls can also be more clearly displayed, as they do not interfere with other cells on the worksheet. Another advantage of user forms is that they can be displayed to the users at any time; that is, they are not attached to a specific worksheet. This feature can be especially useful for re-solve options. If the users wish to re-solve the problem and press a "Re-solve" button on an output sheet, the input form can be directly redisplayed without moving to a new sheet.

Figure 22.13 displays a user form from a "Retirement Planning" case study. This form is dynamic in that the first frame below the text boxes may change depending on a previously selected option. In Figure 22.13(a), the users provide values for "Desired Savings at Retirement" and "Confidence Interval for Returns," whereas in Figure 22.13(b), this frame changes to prompt the users for the "Age to Retire." The second frame on this form, for "Asset Allocation," is also dynamic. In Figure 22.13(a), the users are prompted to enter this information, but in Figure 22.13(b), the textboxes are grayed and locked since the information is not relevant for this option.

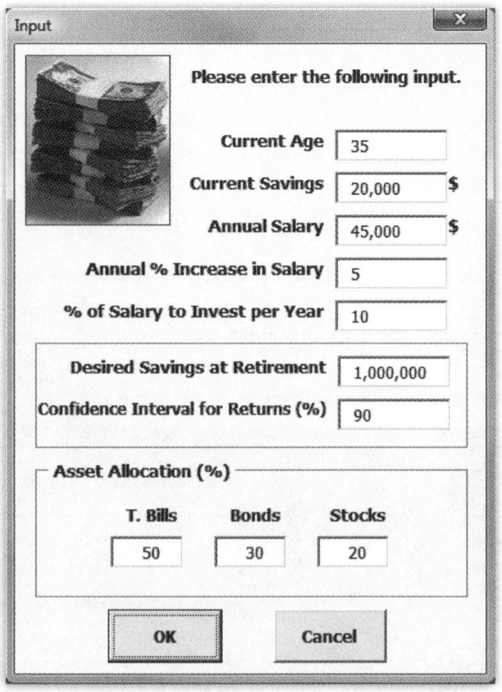

(a)

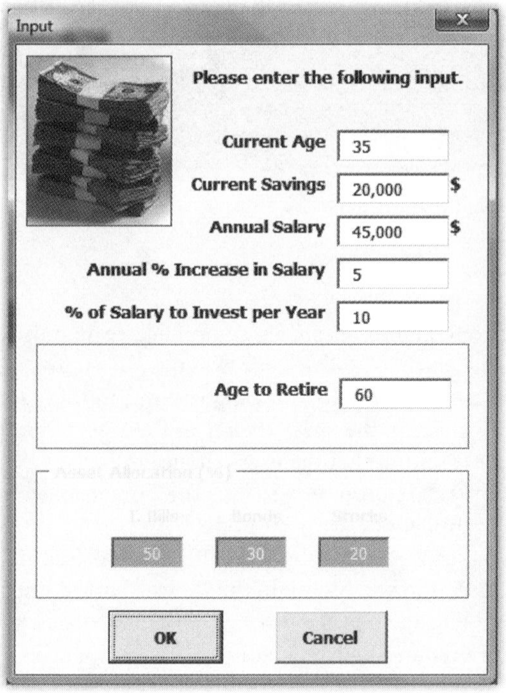

(b)

Figure 22.13 An example of dynamic form controls.

Another way to employ user forms for a situation in which the users may need to modify input multiple times is to create a "floating" form (or non-modal form; refer to Chapter 18). The advantage of this type of user form is that the users can select or modify cells in the worksheet without having to close the form first. In Figure 22.14, there is an example of a floating form from a case study for "Animating the Simplex Method." This form allows the users to select the entering variable for each iteration from the tableau on the worksheet; then, they can view the results for that scenario on the floating form. The form is hidden when the users move to another sheet.

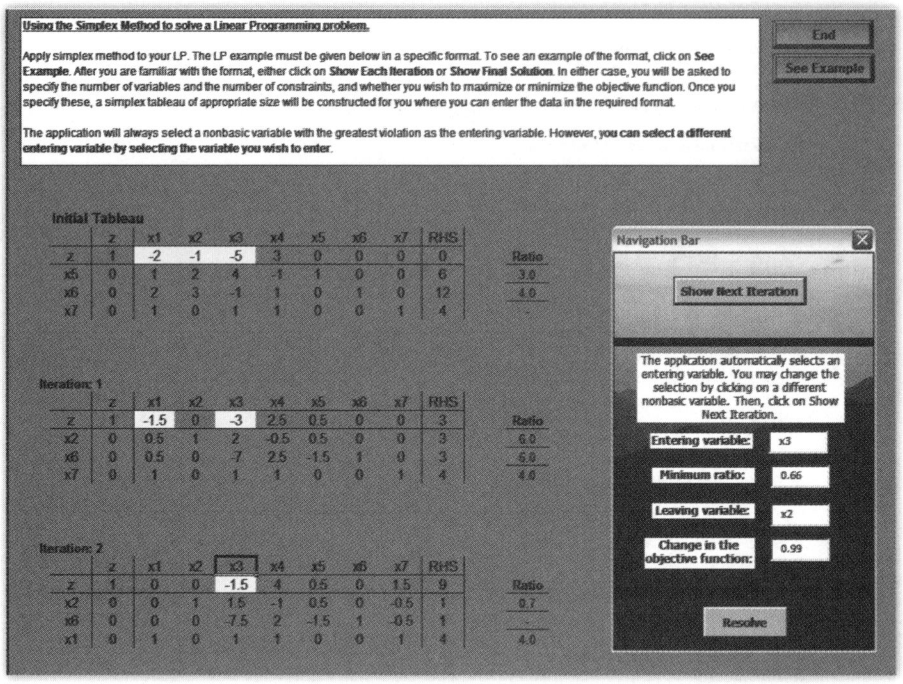

Figure 22.14 An example of a "floating" form.

22.4.3 Functional Buttons

In the case in which input, calculations, and/or output are combined, we may also include some functional buttons on the worksheet, such as "Solve." For example, in Figure 22.15, one such sheet is in a case study on the "Animation of the Kruskal Algorithm." In this case, we take the users directly from the "Welcome" sheet to the sheet shown in the figure. We highlight the "Create Table" button as it is the next button that the users should press (see Figure 22.15(a)). When the users press this button, they are prompted to give the dimensions of the network; then, a table with a corresponding number of rows is created.

After the table is created, we make visible a new button called "Solve" (see Figure 22.15(b)). We un-highlight the "Create Table" button and highlight the "Solve" button since it is the next button the users should click. This button runs the procedure that animates Kruskal's algorithms and determines the minimum spanning tree solution.

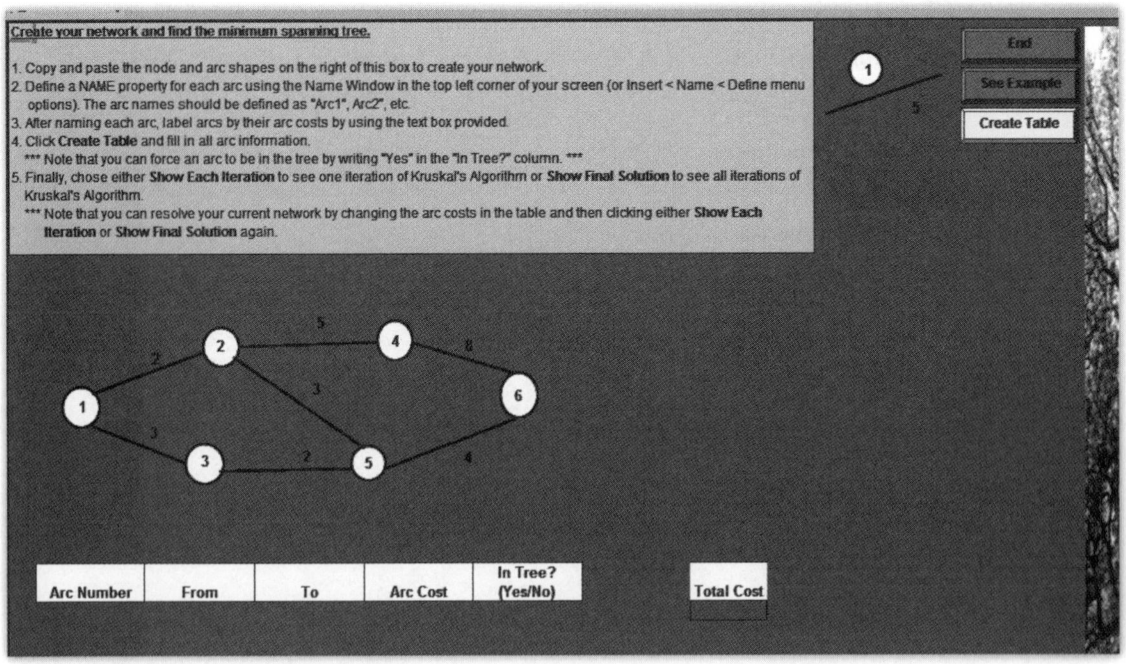

(a)

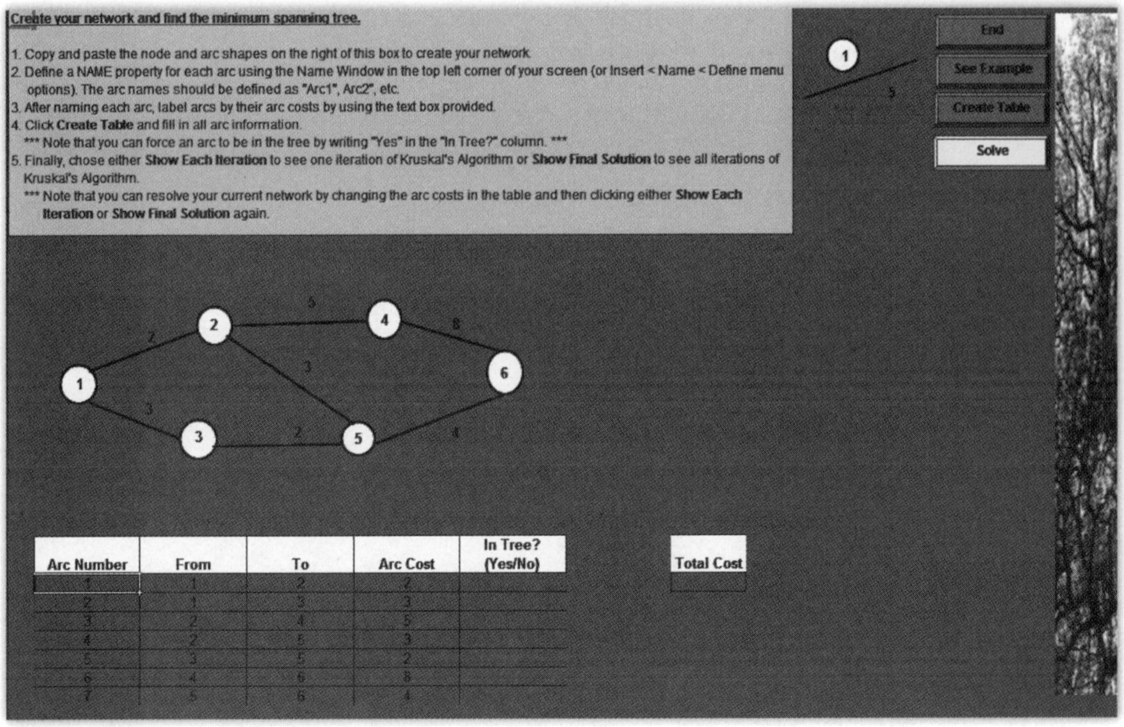

(b)

Figure 22.15 An example of worksheet buttons to work with input and calculations.

There are many options available for creating a user interface for an Excel DSS. Choosing between functional buttons, form controls on the worksheet, or a user form depends on the application and what options the users should have in providing and changing input values.

Summary

Navigational Buttons	These buttons, such as "Start," "Next," "Back," or "End," should be on every sheet to navigate the users through the application.
Functional Buttons	These buttons, such as "Create Table" and "Solve", may be used if multiple functions occur on one sheet.
Controls on the	Placing controls on a worksheet allows users to easily modify input for **Worksheet** multiple solution calculations.
User Forms	Quite advantageous, user forms are most commonly used when large amounts of input are needed.

22.5 *Procedures*

The next step in developing a DSS application is to create an outline of what procedures we need in order to conduct the flow and execute the calculations. As discussed in Chapter 15, we recommend organizing the code into several smaller procedures that may be called from other main procedures or associated with buttons on the worksheet. We also recommend drawing up an outline of these procedures in the code before beginning the details of the implementation. This outline should include procedure names and documentation via comments in the code. The comments should outline the general purpose of each procedure as well as specific tasks performed within the procedure.

We always begin our applications with a *Main* sub procedure that is associated with the "Start" button on the "Welcome" sheet. From the *Main* procedure, we usually clear all previous data and initializing variables by calling a *ClearPrevious* procedure. We then either take the users to an input sheet or display an input form. For example:

```
Sub Main()
    Call ClearPrevious

    frmInput.Show
    Worksheets("Input").Visible = True
    Worksheets("Welcome").Visible = False
End Sub
—————————————————
Sub ClearPrevious()
    'clear ranges on other sheets
    Worksheets("Calc").Range("InputValues").ClearContents
    Worksheets("Output").Range("Results").ClearContents
    'initialize variables
    Set InputRange = Worksheets("Input").Range("InputStart")
End Sub
```

22.5.1 Receiving Input

There should then be a procedure that receives the users' input. If we are applying user forms as the interface for receiving input, then this code would be in the forms' event procedures. For example:

```
Sub cmdOK_Click()
    'set variables equal to control values
    NrTrials = txtNumTrials.Value
    InputSize = txtInputSize.Value

    ReDim InputArray(InputSize)

    Unload Me
End Sub
```

22.5.2 Model and Calculations

Once the input is received, the calculations should be ready to perform. These calculations may involve running a simulation with a loop structure or evoking the solver with the Risk Solver Platform commands. We may call the calculation procedure(s) when the users click the "OK" button on a user form, or we may assign it to a "Solve" or "Continue" button on an input worksheet. For example:

```
Sub DoSimulation()
Dim MyProb as New RSP.Problem
     MyProb.Init ActiveWorkbook
     MyProb.Engine.Params("...")
MyProb.Solver.NumTrials = NrTrials
MyProb.Solver.Simulate
End Sub
—————————————————
Sub DoOptimization()
Dim MyProb as New RSP.Problem
    'clear problem variables and constraints
    'create and add the decision variables
'create and add the objective function
For i = 1 to NumCons
        'create and add problem constraints
    Next i
    MyProb.Engine = MyProb.Engines("...")
    MyProb.Solver.Optimize Solve_Type_Solve
End Sub
```

22.5.3 Output Analysis and Display

The next procedure we will outline is related to displaying the solution on the output sheet. If there is a chart, we may need to update the source data. If a simulation took place, we may want to create some histograms. In any case, we want to put the solution values in a report table on the output sheet. We may call the procedure to create the output from the calculation procedures or from another functional or navigational button on the calculation worksheet. For example:

```
Sub CreateReport()
    'place solutions in report table
    'update chart source data
    ActiveSheet.ChartObjects(1).Select
    ActiveChart.SetSourceData Source:= ...

    'create histogram
    Application.Run "ATPVBAEN.XLAM!Histogram", Input, Output, Bin, Labels, Pareto,
Cumulative, Chart
    Worksheets("Output").Visible = True
End Sub
```

These procedures should outline the overall flow of the application from user input to calculations to output.

22.5.4 Navigational

In addition to these procedures, we should also include any required navigational procedures for "End," "Next," "Back," or "View" buttons. For example:

```
Sub EndProgram()
    Worksheets("Welcome").Visible = True
    ActiveSheet.Visible = False
End Sub
```

We must also ensure that we declare all variables and that we declare any variables we use in multiple procedures as Public variables at the top of the module.

Summary

Main	Call the ClearPrevious procedure. Show the input form or take the users to the input sheet.
Clear Previous	Clear previous ranges of input or solution values. Initialize the variables.
Receive Input	Store the values from form controls or input cells to corresponding variables. Record these values to the appropriate cells in the calculation sheet.
Perform Calculations	Perform calculations using function procedures, simulations loops, or Solver commands.
Generate Output	Display solution values to report the table, update chart source data, or create histograms.
Navigational	Change Visible property of worksheets for "End", "Next", "Back", or "View" button functionality.
Variables	Make sure to declare all variables and to declare variables used in more than one procedure as Public variables at the top of the module.

22.6 Re-solve Options

In Chapter 1, we defined in detail what comprises a DSS. These components include the model base and user interface discussed above. However, a DSS should also provide re-solve options for the users. The users should be able to change some of their initial input values and re-solve the problem. The users may also want to add some constraints to an optimization or redefine the objective function. We suggest that these re-solve options be made available on the output sheet.

In developing the re-solve options, we may ask the following questions:

1. Can the users easily modify the input to re-solve the problem without having to re-enter all the input from scratch? We should ensure that this is possible by confirming that the users' initial input values are preserved when re-displaying a user form or input sheet. We must make sure that we do not call a ClearPrevious procedure unless the users have indeed restarted the entire application. Also, we do not want the default values to overwrite the users' last input values when re-showing a user form. This revision allows users to quickly modify one or several parts of the input and re-solve the calculations to compare results.
2. Can the users change other parts of the calculations or the model when re-solving? In other words, we do not want the users to be limited to only modifying input values when re-solving. The users should be able to change some constraints or objectives as well. We therefore try to keep our application dynamic so users can experiment with different problem dimensions. This may not be possible or applicable for every DSS, but when it is, we should make it available to the users. If certain dynamic options are not available to the users, we state our assumptions clearly on the "Welcome" sheet to say so.

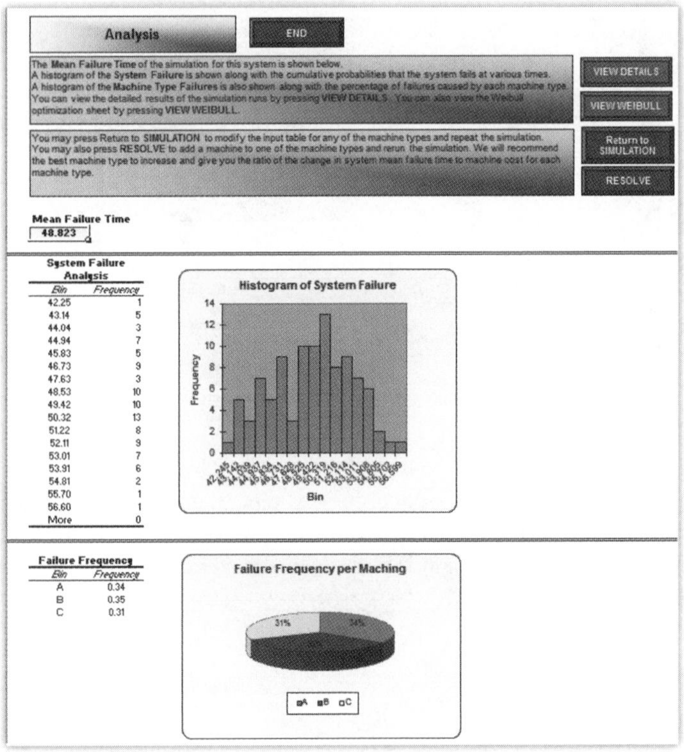

Figure 22.16 The output sheet for the "Reliability Analysis" case study.

With re-solve options, we may want to provide the users with a way to compare various results or scenarios. We may also want to store multiple solutions for this comparison or sensitivity analysis. So, we consider what the users are really interested in learning from our DSS, recalling that a DSS is designed to aid a decision-maker in making a decision. We double-check that the results of the application are indeed beneficial to this decision- making process.

We will now provide a few examples from our case studies; a detailed description of the DSS components can be found in each case study chapter in this part of the book. Let us first consider the "Reliability Analysis" case study, in which the users analyze a parallel series system of three machine types. After the users provide the necessary input, a simulation runs to determine the mean failure time of the system and how often a particular machine type caused system failure. Figure 22.16 displays the output sheet for this study.

This case presents two re-solve options to the users. The first option is to return to the simulation sheet and modify the initial input values in a given table (see Figure 22.17). The users can then re-run the simulation and view the updated results.

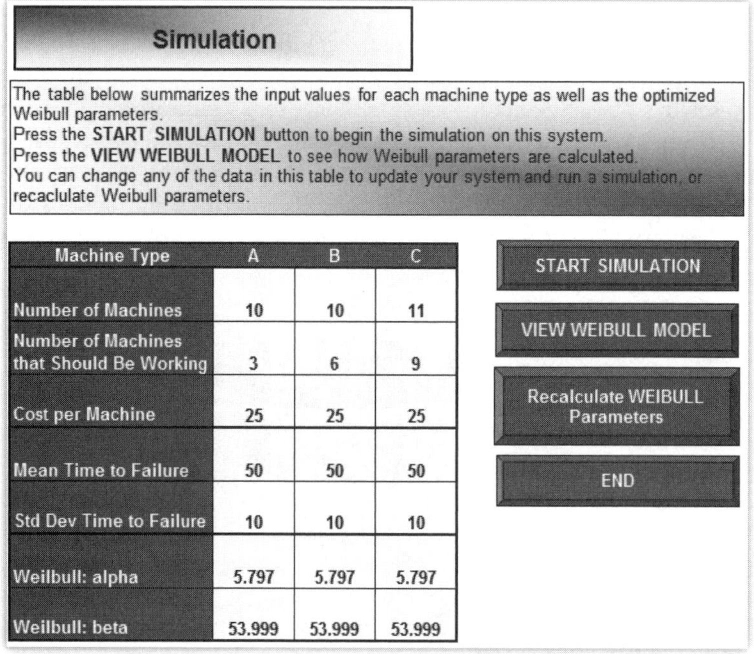
Simulation
The table below summarizes the input values for each machine type as well as the optimized Weibull parameters.
Press the START SIMULATION button to begin the simulation on this system.
Press the VIEW WEIBULL MODEL to see how Weibull parameters are calculated.
You can change any of the data in this table to update your system and run a simulation, or recaclulate Weibull parameters.
Machine Type | A | B | C
Number of Machines | 10 | 10 | 11
Number of Machines that Should Be Working | 3 | 6 | 9
Cost per Machine | 25 | 25 | 25
Mean Time to Failure | 50 | 50 | 50
Std Dev Time to Failure | 10 | 10 | 10
Weilbull: alpha | 5.797 | 5.797 | 5.797
Weilbull: beta | 53.999 | 53.999 | 53.999
START SIMULATION
VIEW WEIBULL MODEL
Recalculate WEIBULL Parameters
END

Figure 22.17 The first re-solve option: Modify input in table and re-run simulation.

The second option is for the users to improve the system by adding one machine of a particular machine type. To aid the users, or decision-makers, in deciding which machine type to add, we first run an optimization in the background and suggest the optimal choice. We do not enforce this decision, but instead try to aid the decision- makers. This information is presented on a user form (see Figure 22.18).

After the users select a machine type, one machine of this type is added and the simulation is re-run. The updated results then appear.

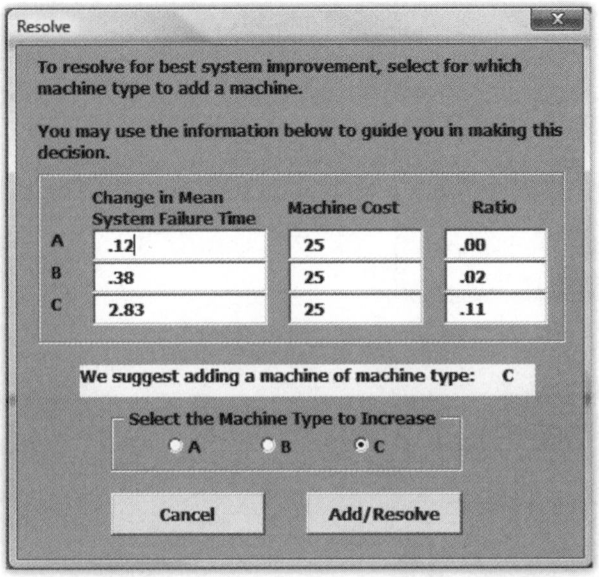

Figure 22.18 The second re-solve option: Making a suggestion to aid the decision-maker.

Another example is from the "Inventory Management" case study (see Figure 22.11(a)). In this case, the users can actually change the model base along with the input each time the application is re-solved. The users can decide which inventory model to use: Standard EOQ, Backorders, or Reorder Point. There is also an input table, which can be modified, on the same sheet.

In another example, the "Portfolio Management" case study (see Figure 22.12), after users have created their portfolios, they can optimize their investment strategy by minimizing risk (see Figure 22.19).

After the users fill the input in the user form for the optimization (Figure 22.19(a)), the resulting optimized investment strategy displays on an output sheet (Figure 22.19(b)). However, if the optimization is infeasible or if the users want to experiment with different values, they can either return to the input form to experiment with different values (by pressing the "Modify Input" button) or return to the portfolio sheet to modify their stock selection (by pressing the "Modify Portfolio" button). An extension to this case study may be to allow users to modify their objective in optimizing their investment strategy; currently, we assume that we minimize risk, but users may also want to maximize returns.

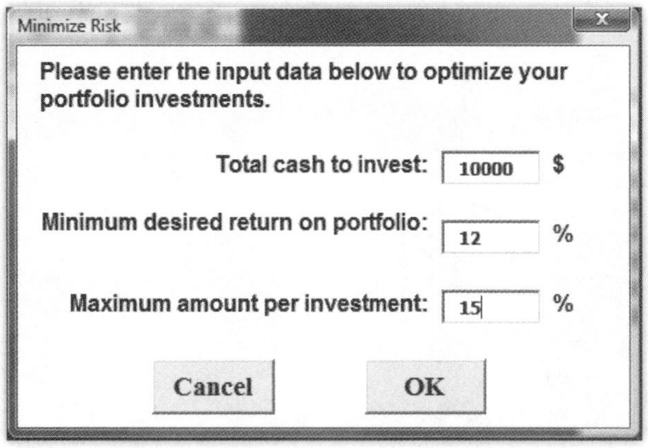

(a)

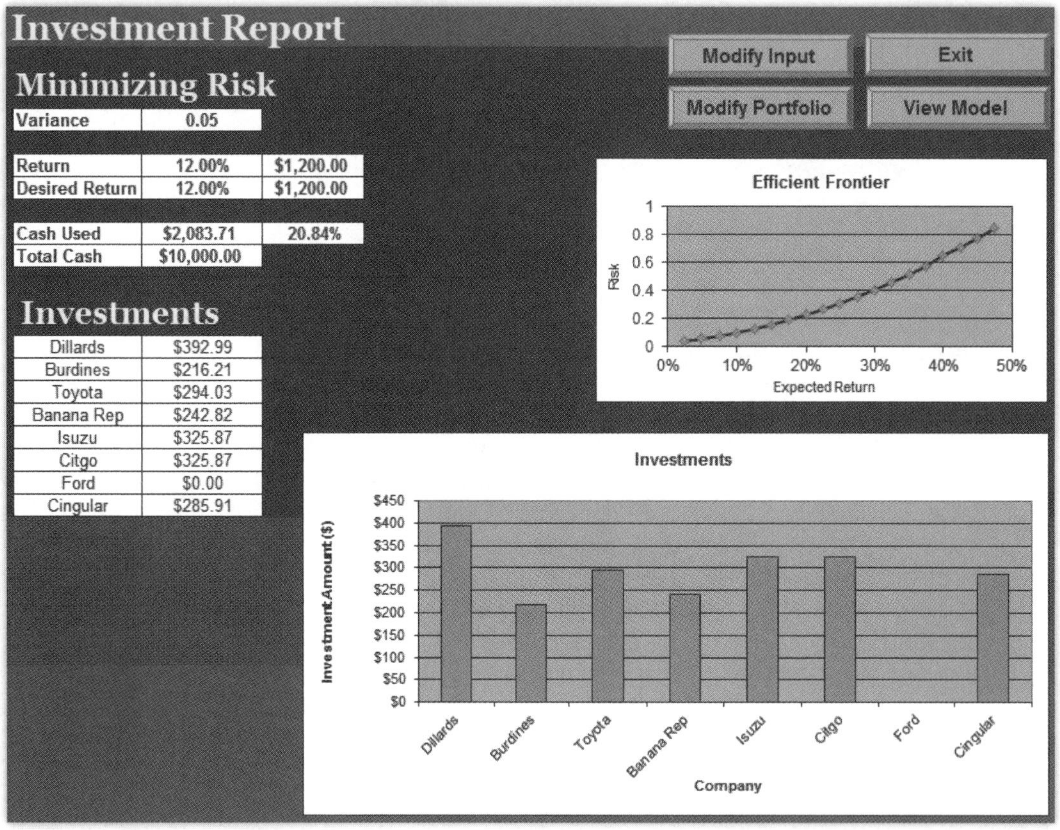

(b)

Figure 22.19 The two "Modify" buttons give the users different re-solve options.

Re-solve options are important DSS components. To ensure that the DSS is aiding the decision-makers, we allow the users to modify inputs or calculation options.

Summary

Re-solve Options	Modify inputs, calculation options, constraints, objectives; aid the decision-makers in making the best decision.

22.7 *Testing and Final Packaging*

The final step of the DSS development process is *Testing and Final Packaging.* Testing is an important final step which ensures that the DSS performs as intended. We should test for smooth navigation as well as for calculation correctness. To test navigation, we can simply check all navigational options in each step of the application. Each navigational button should bring the users to the appropriate worksheet and close the current worksheet. We may consider having an unbiased user test our program by clicking through all the navigational buttons and other interface to catch any unexpected user errors.

To test calculation correctness, we use a simple set of input values and check the calculation results. We find the calculation results with another method outside our application to compare the result values. If this testing shows that there are some errors in our application, then we return to our calculation sheet and procedures to find the error (refer to Appendix B). Then we repeat the testing. If the testing shows that all calculations are correct, then we may keep this test data in any user forms or input sheets as the default values.

The final packaging should ensure that our DSS has a professional appearance. The Welcome sheet should have nice formatting and a clear description of the application. All sheets should have clear instructions for the user options. All forms and other interface should also be clear and nicely formatted. We check that the output sheet is also easy to read and formatted professionally. Refer to Chapters 18 and 23 for more on interface clarity. Once all testing and final packaging is complete, our DSS application should be ready for the end users.

22.8 *Summary*

- There are six basic steps to develop a DSS application: Application Overview, Worksheets, User Interface, Procedures, and DSS Components.
- The outline of the worksheets in the DSS should include Welcome Sheet, Input sheet, Calculations sheet, and Output sheet.
- The worksheet user interface includes Navigational Buttons, Functional Buttons, Controls on the Worksheet, and User Forms.
- The outline of the procedures in the application should include a Main procedure, a Clear Previous procedure, a procedure to receive input, some procedures and functions to perform calculations, and a procedure to generate output. There may also be some Navigational procedures. Ensure that we also outline what Variables we may need and if they are public or private.
- In designing the re-solve options, the developers should check that the users are able to modify inputs, calculation options, constraints, and objectives. Aid the decision-makers in making the best decision.
- The testing and final packaging step ensures that the DSS application works correctly and has a professional appearance for the end users.

22.9 Exercises

22.9.1 Review Questions

1. What are the six main steps in developing a DSS application?
2. What are some various interfaces used to receive input from the users?
3. What are some examples of re-solve options?

CHAPTER

twenty-three

GUI Design

chapter

OVERVIEW

23.1 GUI Design

A graphical user interface (GUI) is the "graphical representation of, and interaction with, programs, data, and objects on a computer screen" (Mandel). It presents a visual display of information and objects that can present visual feedback to users. Part of the definition of a DSS is that it is designed to be easy to use; user friendliness, graphical capabilities, and an interactive human-machine interface greatly increase the effectiveness of a DSS (see Chapter 1). Therefore, it is very important to design a user interface such that the users find it straightforward to understand and use. If the user interface is not well designed, then the application's functionality may be diminished. In this section, we will discuss the theory behind proficient GUI design and provide some examples of effective and ineffective user interfaces.

23.2 The Theory Behind Effective GUI Design

Many GUI design books list several different principles and guidelines for effective GUI design, such as *GUI Bloopers* by Johnson and *Elements of User Interface* by Mandel. We present here a summarized version of what we feel are the most important theoretical points when working in spreadsheet-based DSS applications: know the users and their tasks and goals, maintain clarity, and stay consistent.

23.2.1 Users, Tasks, and Goals

It is important to know who the users of our application are. For example, are they managers? If so, how deep is their understanding of the problem? Do they know the model or algorithms being used to perform the calculations? What terminology do they use to discuss the problem? If the users do not possess a highly technical understanding of the application's topic, then we should try to avoid overwhelming them with the details of the model or calculations. An effective way to do so is to hide the calculation sheet. Additionally, we provide instructions and label the input without relying on technical terminology. For example, instead of labeling inputs, "C" or "D," we should assign meaningful descriptions such as, "Annual Cost" or "Annual Demand." In the case that our users do have a more technical understanding, we should present and explain the calculations and assumptions. We may also want to provide more details with the terminology that they are familiar with. While programming, we must always remember: know the users.

We must also remember that the users are using our application to complete a task(s) and to achieve a goal. It is important to ensure that the user interface is an aid to the users in completing these tasks so that they feel that the DSS has served its purpose efficiently.

The users' task domain includes "the data that users manipulate, the manner in which that data is divided ... and the nature of the manipulation that users perform on the data." Remember that the users' tasks are already necessary without the help of a DSS; therefore, we must ensure that our DSS application aids them in completing these tasks in the domain that they are familiar with. These tasks should be organized on some priority or hierarchy base in order to create a flow for the application. This flow influences the outline of the entire application, as we discussed in the first section. Our interface should guide the users so that they can work with the data in their task domain in the order in which it needs to be completed.

For example, suppose that the users' task domain involves researching some historical data, then computing a mean and standard deviation of this data, and finally entering these values into a forecasting model. Based on the result of the model, the users must determine the forecast demand for the next month and place an order of that size. When constructing the interface for a forecasting DSS, we ensure that these tasks are presented to the users in the same order. First, we ask them to enter the historical data. If they usually get this data as a text file from a coworker, then we do not ask them to enter it manually; instead, we prompt them to import the text file. Next, we automatically calculate the mean and standard deviation and display the figures to the users. Afterwards, we ask for some extra input for the forecasting model, but we try not to get too technical. We then clearly display what their order amount should be, based on this forecast. Because our users would find the DSS hard to understand, we do not try to reorganize their tasks. We keep our task presentation simple so our users experience an element of familiarity.

Summary

- What does the user understand about the problem and the model calculations?
- What terminology is the user familiar with?
- Define the user's task domain to determine the application flow.

23.2.2 Clarity

A user interface is the communication between the users and the application; therefore, if we want the users to use our application correctly, we must communicate clearly to them how to use it. Most importantly, we need to make sure that there is a clear description of what is involved on every spreadsheet and every form. For example, in Figure 23.1, we display the calculation sheet for a "Sales Force Allocation" case study. We ask the users to enter bound values for the optimization constraints. We then give them two calculation options. We explain the users' tasks in a text box at the top of the sheet. We have bolded the button names and column names in the text to help the users quickly identify the location of the tasks on the sheet.

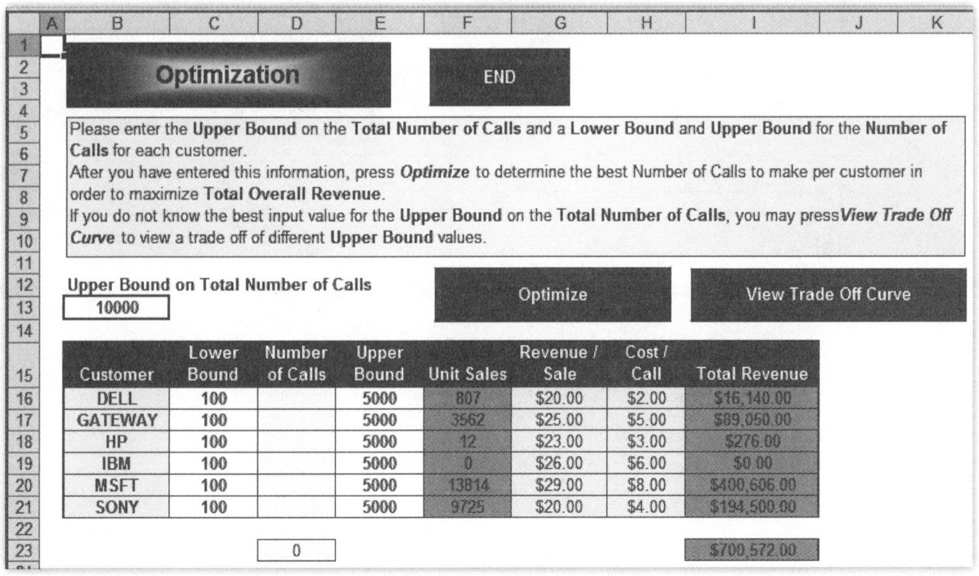

Figure 23.1 Giving clear instructions and descriptions on each sheet and form.

The functionality of any button or control should be clear to the users. On spreadsheets, we try to create some separation between navigational buttons and functional buttons. For example, if the buttons "End," "Back," and "Solve" appear on an input sheet, it is better to keep the navigational buttons "End" and "Back" together and to place the "Solve" button somewhere else on the sheet.

(a) (b)

Figure 23.2 (a) The buttons are mixed, so functionality may be unclear. (b) Buttons are clearly separated into navigation and calculation groups.

Likewise, on user forms, we ensure that functional buttons are separate from the "OK" and "Cancel" buttons.

In addition to buttons and command button controls, all other controls should also be clearly labeled so that their functionality is understood. We never leave a text box unlabeled or assume that the users know what to enter. Likewise, we ensure that list boxes and combo boxes are labeled so the users know what the list contains. Frames containing grouped items should also be labeled to signify the grouping. The clearer the controls are, the quicker the users can learn their functionality, and the easier it is for them to use the application. For example, compare Figure 23.3(a) and Figure 23.3(b); without clear control labels, users have to hesitate and guess what information we are asking for.

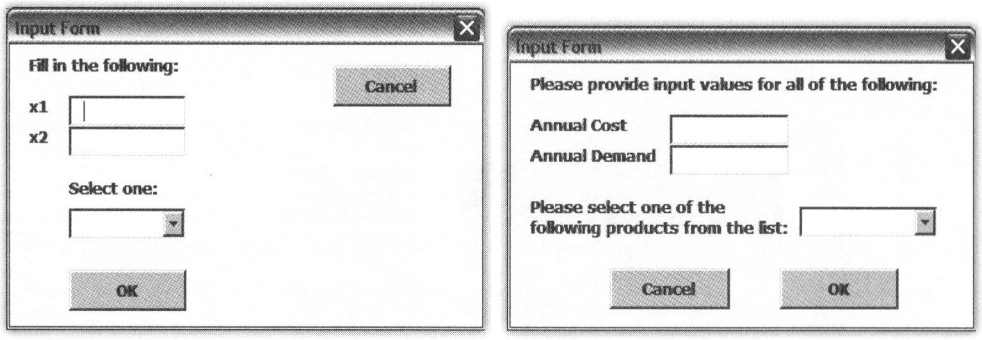

(a) (b)

Figure 23.3 (a) Control functionality is not clear. (b) Labels clearly designate control functionality.

Another way to clarify control functionality is by creating control tip messages; these provide more detailed instructions without cluttering the form. For example, Figure 23.4 illustrates a control tip for a combo box. When the users place the cursor over the combo box, the text reads, "This list contains all products in the system."

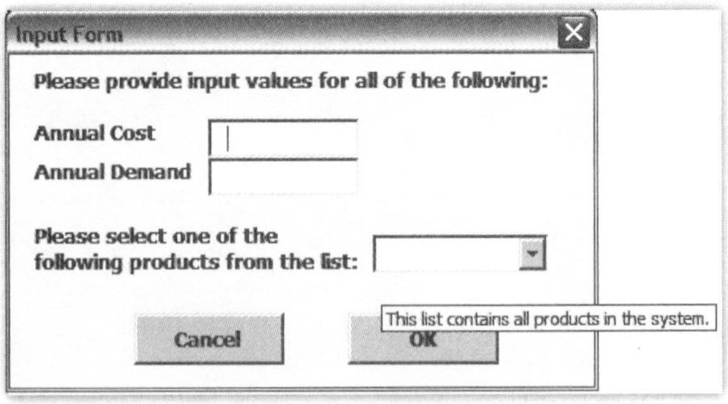

Figure 23.4 Control tips are also useful for clarifying control functionality.

Another benefit to clarifying user interface functionality is that it can reduce the errors encountered by users. The most frequent user errors involve inputting values in an incorrect format or type or choosing a selection or command button at an inappropriate time. Even though error checking can be done, as discussed in Chapter 22, developing a better designed user interface can reduce this extra coding. In addition to clearly labeling controls, we can also assign a default value as an example of what kind of input the users should enter. We may also guide the users to assist with proper formatting issues.

For example, referring to Figure 23.3(b), if the users are supposed to enter a cost, they may enter "$20,000" or "20,000" or "20000." If we do not want the users to enter a dollar sign, comma, or other punctuation marks, then we convey this to them on the interface design; we either write more specific instructions or guide them with default values (see Figure 23.5). Otherwise, we should conduct error checking in our code to ensure that a data type error does not occur when we try to perform an operation on the users' input values.

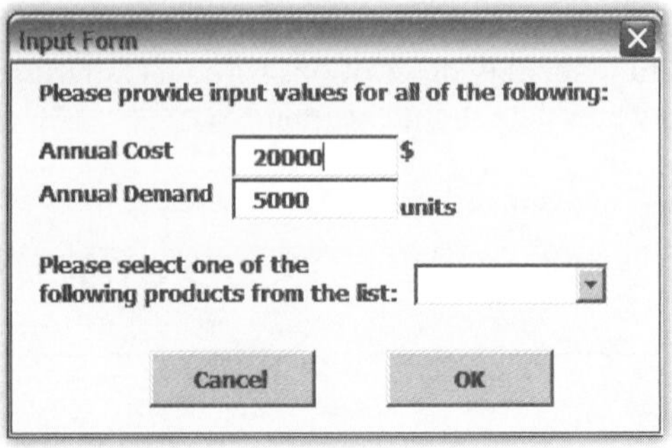

Figure 23.5 Providing default values and formatting guidelines.

Some other common formatting examples include those for numeric input such as social security numbers and telephone numbers. In Figure 23.6(a), we show that the users may input these values in various formats. This may cause errors when storing, searching for, or performing operations with the data. Figure 23.6(b) has clarified the formatting issues so that the users only enter numerical values without extra punctuation.

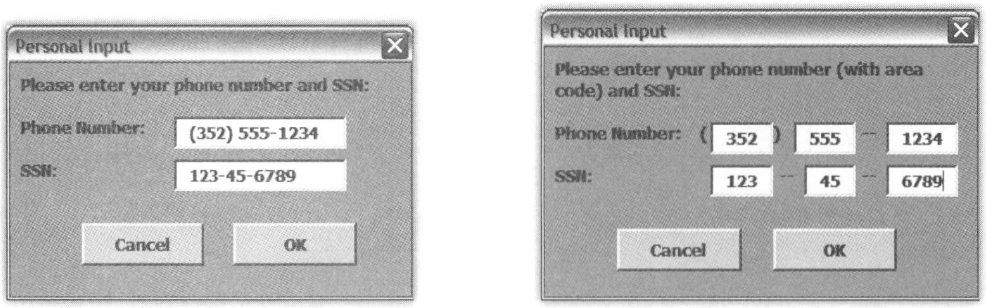

(a) (b)

Figure 23.6 (a) Unclear formatting. (b) Clear formatting with default values.

If there is still a user error while using an input interface, we make sure that a clear error message is provided to the users. The users should understand what they did wrong and what they need to do to correct the problem. For example, the error message "Incorrect input!" is not helpful to users. However, a message such as "You may not enter negative numbers. Please enter a positive number." Redirects the users to correct the error. Errors should be hard to make and easy to correct.

Overall, clarity is very important in effective GUI design. It is essential to check sheet and form instructions, control labels, and data input guidelines to ensure that the users can clearly understand what to do.

Summary

- Provide clear instructions at the top of each spreadsheet and each form.
- Label controls clearly so that their functionality is understandable.
- Control tips can add detail to functionality descriptions without cluttering the form.
- Provide default values to clarify how data should be inputted.
- Make formatting issues clear.
- Clear GUI design can help users avoid making errors.
- If user errors are made, give clear error messages to redirect the users to correct their error.

23.2.3 Consistency

The last theoretical method by which to achieve effective GUI design is consistency. Users are inclined to interact with an interface according to their expectations. In other words, they may expect an input prompt, button locations, and viewable options based on their familiarity with working with the problem or with other interfaces. It is important that within our application, or across similar applications, we keep certain features of the user interface consistent.

The first place to design for consistency is on the spreadsheets. On each sheet in the application, we try to keep the title, sheet description, and instructions all in the same location. This way, if users are looking for an explanation of what is included on a particular sheet, they can always refer to the same location on the sheet. In our applications, we tend to keep sheet titles and descriptions at the top left of each sheet layout. Also, we ensure that the navigational buttons, especially the "End" button, are in the same location on each sheet. Users should not have to search through the sheet to try to exit the application. Compare the clarity of the button positioning in the forms presented in Figure 23.7. We should also consider consistency in the sheet layout for input cells and charts. For example, if we have multiple output sheets, each with a chart, the charts should all be in the same position on each sheet.

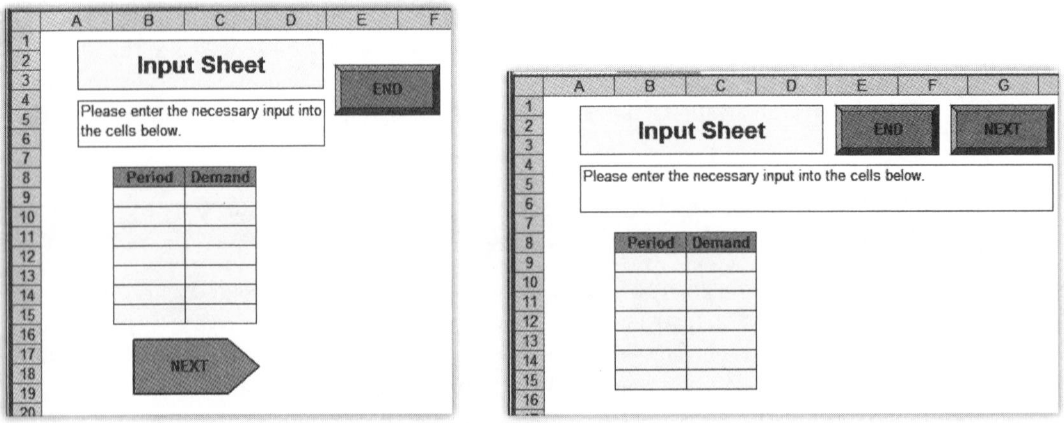

(a) (b)

Figure 23.7 (a) The buttons are different shapes and different colors. The navigational buttons are in different locations on the sheet. (b) The navigational buttons are together and consistent.

When designing user forms, we can maintain consistency in several ways. First of all, as with sheets, we ensure that a description label is always at the top of the form. Also, we keep navigational command buttons such as "OK" and "Cancel" in the same position on all forms. If "OK" is on the bottom right of a form and "Cancel" is on the bottom left, we do not switch them on subsequent forms. Users should not feel tricked into pressing the wrong button.

Regarding form controls, the alignment and size features can also improve the form layout. So, we try to keep text box sizes the same throughout the form and align them equally. We keep all buttons the same size as well. Similarly, we try to be consistent with punctuation, such as colons. Compare the forms presented in Figure 23.8.

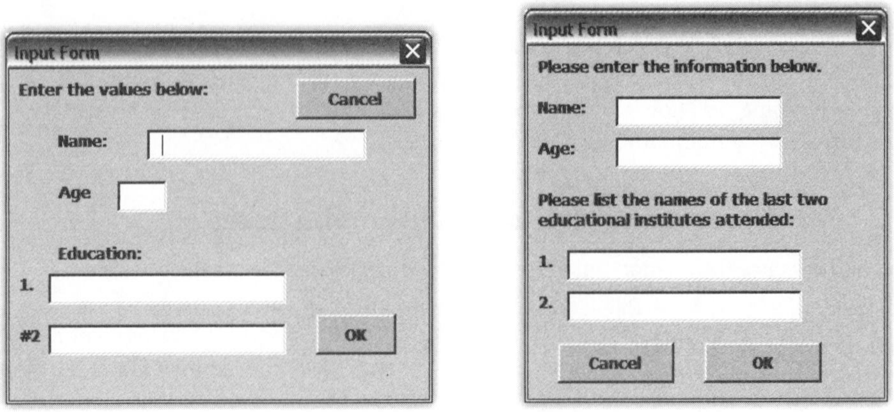

(a) (b)

Figure 23.8 (a) Buttons are different in size and in different locations. Colons are used inconsistently. Textbox sizes differ. Numbers in the list are formatted differently. (b) Grouped textboxes are of the same size. Colons are consistent. The numbers in the list are consistent. Instructions are clearer.

If a form instruction label and command buttons are consistent in our application's forms, we can save interface development time by saving the first form we create and importing it multiple times. (Refer to Chapter 18 for detailed instructions on how to do this.)

Another feature of form consistency that can aid the users in moving quickly through the interface is the tab order of the form. We ensure that the tab order takes the users from the top of the form down to the "OK" button and finally to the "Cancel" button. Again, the idea is to help the users feel that the user interface is easy to learn and easy to use. Keeping the forms consistent throughout an application aids the users in accomplishing their tasks more quickly and efficiently.

Summary

- Consistency is important in helping the users move quickly through the user interface.
- Keep sheet titles and instructions in the same location.
- Keep navigational buttons, especially the "End" button, in the same location per sheet.
- Keep input cells and charts in the same locations for similar sheets.
- Keep form instructions and command buttons in the same location for each form.
- Make controls consistent by using alignment and same size features.
- Set tab order to take users from top of form to "OK" to "Cancel" buttons.

23.3 *Effective and Ineffective GUI Designs*

We would now like to provide several examples of effective and ineffective GUI designs. We have grouped these examples by different control types and a few more general categories that apply to the entire user form.

23.3.1 Buttons

As previously stated, buttons should always be of the same size and shape. We also try to keep buttons the same color unless highlighting a particular function button to guide the users. Grouping functional buttons together and navigational buttons together is also a highly effective way to maintain interface consistency.

23.3.2 Text Boxes versus List Boxes and Combo Boxes

To reduce the memorization requirements of the users, we replace text boxes with list boxes or combo boxes when possible. This technique also reduces the possibility for errors. For example, if users are asked to enter a student name for their class grades, using a combo box would prevent them from entering the name of a student who is not in their class or from misspelling a student's name. Compare the forms in Figure 23.9.

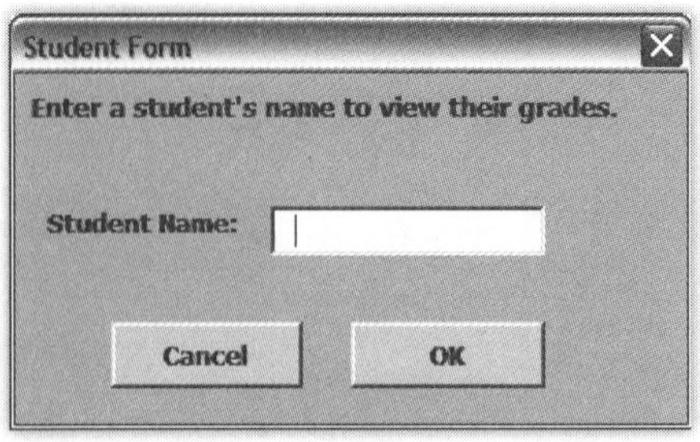

(a)

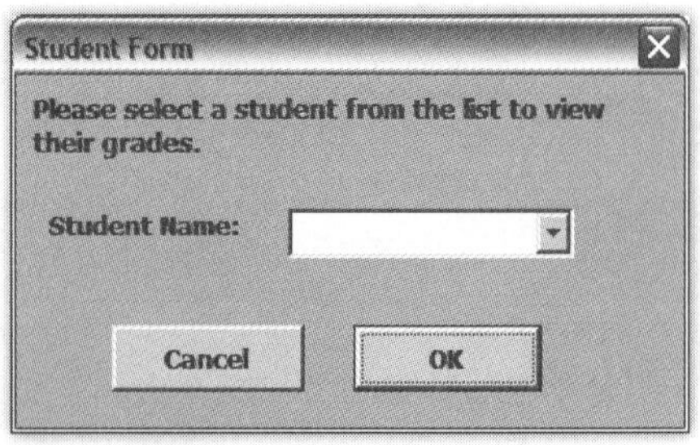

(b)

Figure 23.9 (a) Using a text box forces the users to remember all the names and to spell them correctly. (b) Using a combo box reduces user memorization and the chance for errors.

23.3.3 Tab Strips and Multi Pages

When applying tab strips or multi pages, we try to minimize the number of tabs. Too many tabs can cause tab positions to shift when clicked, or the users may not see all of the tabs and leave an input blank. So, we reorganize our input needs into multiple forms or combine tab information to reduce the total number of tabs. Compare the forms in Figure 23.10.

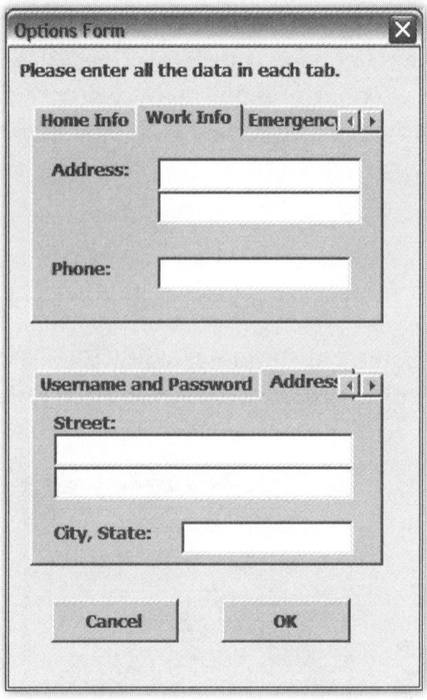

(a)

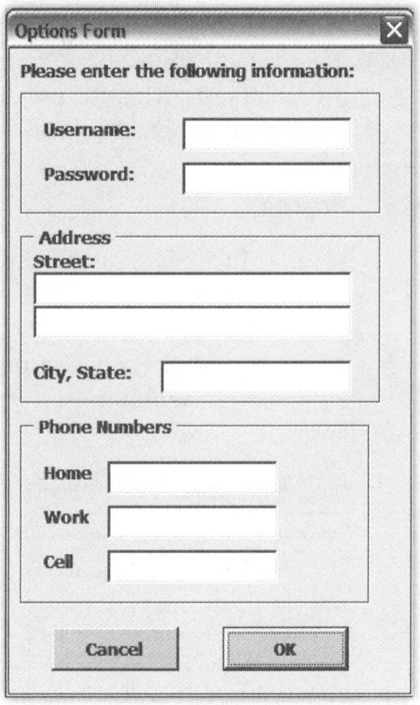

(b)

Figure 23.10 (a) Too many tabs. (b) Combining the tab strip and multi page into one form with several text boxes.

23.3.4 Check Boxes versus Option Buttons

Option buttons should be used for mutually exclusive input. Even though option buttons can also be used for non-mutually exclusive input, if they are not grouped in a frame, we recommend check boxes for this purpose instead. We must be consistent in our use of check boxes and option buttons for these respective purposes. Compare the forms in Figure 23.11.

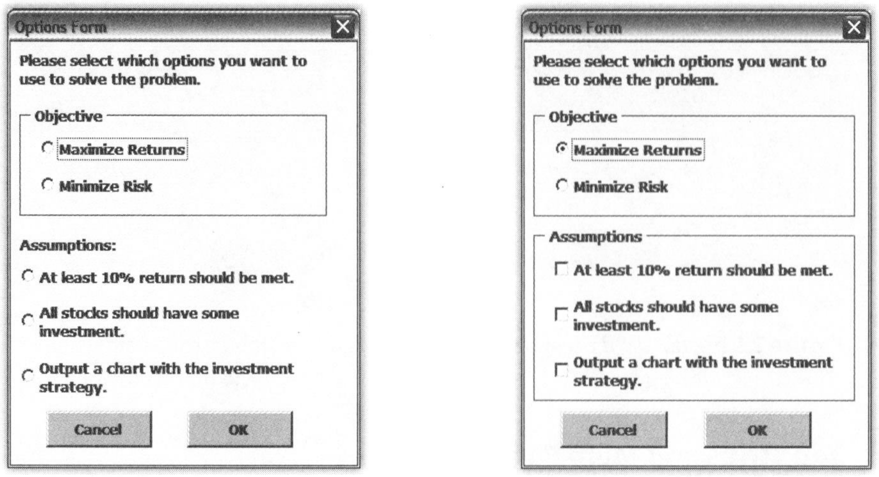

(a) (b)

Figure 23.11 (a) Option buttons are used inconsistently. (b) Option buttons are used for mutually exclusive options and check boxes are used for other options.

When using option buttons, we should always have more than one option grouped in a frame. If there is only one option, then we treat it as an "on/off" option and use a check box. Another way to modify only one option is to create another option with an opposite value. For example, instead of just giving the users an "on/off" option for "Assume non-negative values," we could create another option, such as "Do not assume non-negative values" or "Allow positive values."

23.3.5 Frames

Frames can group similar items. We should therefore always have at least two controls in a frame. However, if we have more than one frame on a form or sheet, to separate different groups of controls we may end up with only one control in one of the frames. We should still avoid including all frames with only one control or only one frame with only one control. Compare the forms in Figure 23.12. Additionally, to apply frames with controls on the spreadsheet, we can use shape boxes.

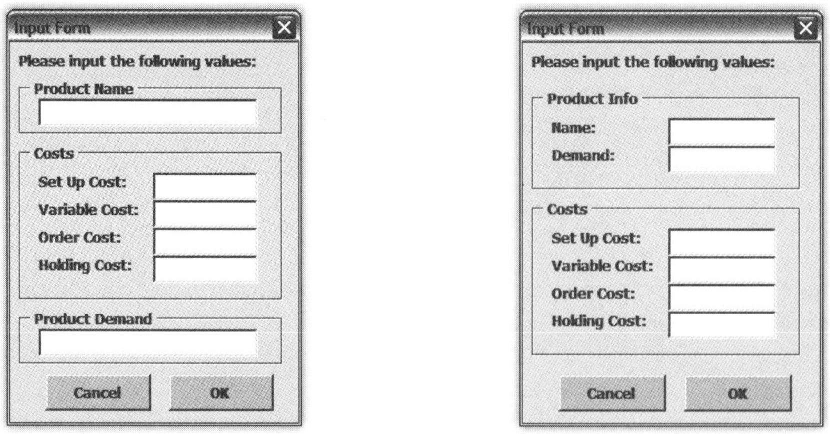

(a) (b)

Figure 23.12 (a) Using frames as labels. Two of the frames only have one control. (b) The two frames have more than one control each.

23.3.6 Labels versus Text Boxes

Labels should be used for read-only information. We do not use a text box to present information to users when they should not be able to modify it. For example, suppose a form receives input for three machine types in a production system. We may use a loop to display the same form to the users three times to receive the input for each machine type. We can reveal the machine type number to the users, but we do not want them to modify it; therefore, we use a label, not a text box (see Figure 23.13).

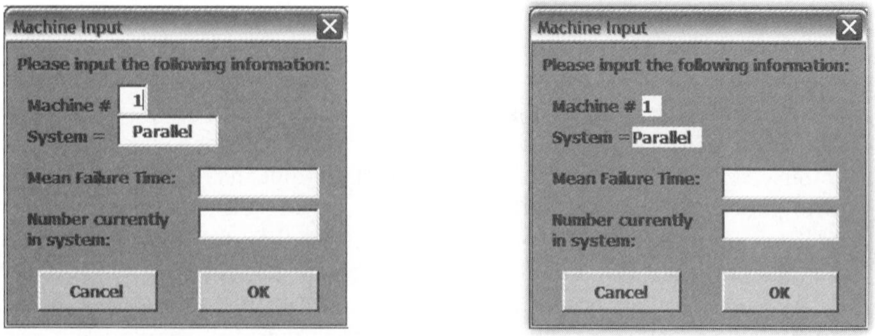

(a) (b)

Figure 23.13 (a) Users should not change the "Machine #" and "System" values, so they should not be in text boxes. (b) Using labels instead. The labels are a different color in order to demonstrate that their values have been set.

23.3.7 Dynamic Controls

When using dynamic controls, we may make some controls visible or not visible, or we may keep them visible but make them inactive. To make a control inactive, we must gray it out to an extent that users are not confused about whether or not they can change the value in the inactive control (see Figure 23.14). We recommend making dynamic controls inactive rather than hiding them so that the users are always aware of all options. We should also lock inactive controls so they cannot be modified. If a control becomes inactive, we should also set the Tab Stop property to "False."

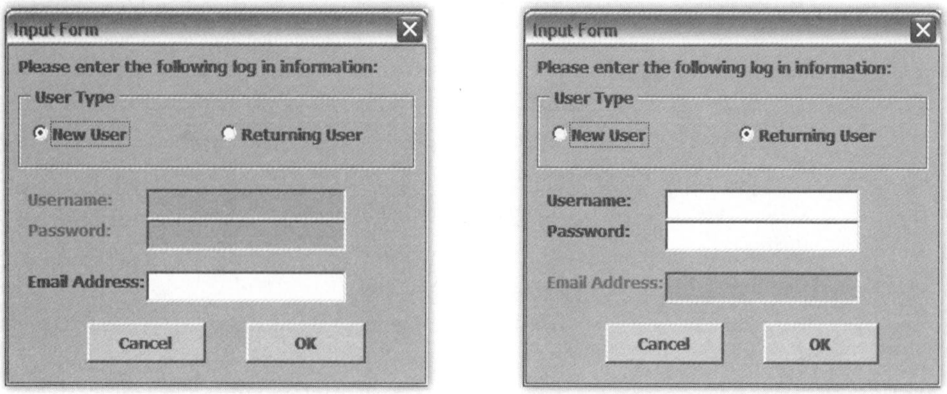

(a) (b)

Figure 23.14 (a) The "Username" and "Password" are inactive since "New User" is selected. (b) The "Email Address" is inactive since "Returning User" is selected.

23.3.8 Multiple Forms

When using multiple forms, we must hide or unload sequential forms so there is no layering on the screen. The only time a layering may occur is if there is a sub form that must be filled before a main form can be completed. However, we should try to avoid such situations.

23.3.9 Event Procedures

Associating actions with event procedures can be confusing to users. For example, when using command buttons, it is better to apply the Click event rather than the MouseDown event. Otherwise, users may press the mouse down, not see a result, and think that the form is not working.

When using text boxes, it is more efficient to use the AfterUpdate event rather than the Change event, which may cause errors if certain formatting or values have been enforced. For example, suppose we error-check to ensure that a number has been entered in a text box. If the users are deleting a previous value to enter a new one, then when the text box changes from one value to empty, the error will occur. Instead, we use the AfterUpdate event so we only check the value of the text box once the new value is completely entered.

When using check boxes, we recommend applying the Change event instead of the Click event. However, with mutually exclusive option buttons, the Change event may be triggered often, so the Click event may be more desirable.

Summary

Command Buttons	Display in similar shapes, sizes, colors, and locations. Separate functional and navigational buttons.
Text Boxes versus	Minimize user memorization with list boxes or combo boxes instead of text boxes.
List Boxes and Combo Boxes	This may also minimize user error.
Tab Strips and Multi Pages	Only use a few tabs. Ensure that tabs are not hidden.
Check Boxes versus	Use option buttons for mutually exclusive options; use check boxes otherwise.
Option Buttons	Use check boxes for "on/off" options or create an opposite option for option buttons.
Frames	Try to have more than one control per frame and more than one frame per form.
Labels versus Text Boxes	Apply labels for read-only information.
Dynamic Controls	Make inactive controls grayed and locked. Also change their tab order.
Multiple Forms	Be sure to close sequential forms. Avoid layering if possible.
Event Procedures	Command buttons: Click is better than MouseDown. Text boxes: AfterUpdate is better than Change. Check boxes: Change is better than Click. Option buttons: Click is better than Change.

23.4 Summary

- Designing an effective GUI involves the following points: knowing the users and their tasks and goals, being clear, and being consistent.
- There are many effective and ineffective GUI designs for each control type.
- Make dynamic controls inactive rather than hiding them so that the users are always aware of all options.
- Be aware of GUI design considerations when using multiple forms and event procedures.

23.5 Exercises

23.5.1 Review Questions

1. What are some of the common errors made with option buttons?
2. Should you have only one control in a frame?
3. What are some ways to maintain clarity in a user interface?
4. How do you define the users' goals and tasks?
5. Give some examples of consistent and inconsistent use of navigational and functional buttons in a DSS.

CHAPTER

twenty-four

Programming Principles

chapter

OVERVIEW

24.1 *Programming Practices*

There are many books on programming practices and coding standards. We summarize here what we feel are some important issues when coding in VBA for spreadsheet-based DSS development. We categorize these issues as follows: coding with a consistent style; using naming standards; having clear comments; and increasing coding efficiency. We refer to the Microsoft Standards Document online and the following books: *The Practice of Programming* by Kernighan and Pike and *Programming Pearls* by Bently.

24.2 *Clarity*

Clarity is probably the most important programming practice to implement. It is important to have a clear, readable, and understandable code. Clarity is helpful for code maintenance and evolvement. If your code is written clearly, it is easier to correct and also more likely to be correct in the first place. Clear code can also be given to another developer to more comfortably understand or augment your code. We consider three main components of programming clarity: consistent style, naming, and documentation.

24.2.1 Consistent Style

Your code should reflect a consistent style; that is, it should appear that the same person has developed all of the code. Spacing, indenting, line length, and other formatting should be consistent. We recommend keeping procedures and functions spaced far enough apart so that it is easy to scan through the code. We also recommend indenting to signify the beginning and end of a loop or logical structure. Consider the two examples below:

No indenting:

```
If A is True Then
  'actions 1
ElseIf B is True Then
  'actions 2
End If
```

....

Clear indenting:

```
If A is True Then
 'actions 1
ElseIf B is True Then
 'actions 2
End If
```

We also recommend being consistent with the code's line length. It is better not to have to scroll back and forth through a module to read various lines of code. So, we try to break lines at logical places, while keeping line length as consistent as possible. Coding style can also be observed in the naming standards and commenting style, which we will discuss in later sections.

Another area where style should be consistent is in error checking. We must be sure that we do not check input from one form but not another or check input from an Input Box but not a form. Whatever methods we use for error checking, we try to apply them to all of our error checking routines, if possible. In general, when we are outlining our procedures, we ensure that there is consistency in our coding approach.

24.2.2 Naming

We apply naming standards to both variables and procedures, working to avoid redundancies. For example, in a procedure named "MinProfit," we would not define a variable "MinProf," A useful alternative is to abbreviate names, while ensuring that they are clear and not easily confused with other meanings. For example, the variable name "NumFac" could represent "number of facilities," "number of faculty," or "number of factories." When there is more than one word in a name, we suggest capitalizing the beginning of each word. We try to create descriptive names that aren't lengthy; for example: "MinValue," "SumProfit," or "MaxPrice." Variables used for loops, aside from "i" and "j" and other small indices, can be descriptive of the loop count. For example, we may use "iter" to count the number of iterations in a loop; or "run" to count the number of runs in a simulation.

Some other common naming standards refer to control names. We provide a list of the prefixes for various controls in Chapter 18. For example, the name of a text box should begin with "txt;" the name of a form should begin with "frm." For Boolean variables, we recommend starting the variable name with "Is" or "Do"; for example, "IsDone" or "DoAnimation." For constants, we recommend writing the names in all uppercase, such as "PI" or "INFINITY." Refer to Chapter 14 for more on variable declarations.

It is also a good practice to make procedure names clear. For example, instead of "Calc," we use a more descriptive name, such as "CalcReturn." For function procedures, we may also use names that signify the returned value; for example, "FindMinCost" or "GetUserInfo." In general, we use names that are not easily confused. This strategy helps to avoid coding errors and ease debugging.

24.2.3 Documentation

Documentation is an important part of any programming project. We accomplish documentation by placing comments throughout our code. Comments help clarify what we have done and why we have done it. They also benefit another programmer who may look through our code later. So, we keep our comments up-to-date as we make changes or updates to the code.

We should have a comment at the beginning of each procedure to provide an overview of what the sub or function does. We avoid abbreviations in these comments as we want to ensure that they are clear. We should also have comments before loops or logical checks to explain the flow of the code.

Using comments organizes our code and makes it easier to read. However, we must be careful not to overdo it; we do not want to include unnecessary comments that only add length to the code.

24.3 *Efficiency*

Another important programming issue is code efficiency. We should continuously be working to improve our code by reducing the complexity of the logic and the time required. If our code includes several nested loops, we go back and investigate if we can simplify the structure; for example, a Select, Case structure might be better than multiple levels of If, Then. We check if we are unnecessarily repeating certain actions. Are we clearing values before overwriting them? Are we unnecessarily reformatting a range? Are we repeating a calculation that has previously been computed? As we are writing comments to explain our code, we first check if we could improve it.

Another way to improve code efficiency is to ensure that extra memory is not being used. For example, there is no need to declare a counting variable "i" as a *Double*; it only requires the memory of an *Integer* data type. We also ensure that arrays are dimensioned for the needed storage space with the *ReDim Preserve* statement.

We should also write our code to be dynamic for future extensions or updates. For example, for bound variables, array sizes, or range values, we may want to use variables instead of values. Consider the following examples:

Static structure:

```
For i = 1 to 10
 'do actions
Next i
..............
```

Dynamic structure:

```
For i = 1 to NumProducts
 'do actions
Next i
..............
```

Static structure:

```
Dim CostArray(10) as Double
..............
```

Dynamic structure:

```
Dim CostArray() As Double, CostSize As Integer
ReDim CostArray(CostSize)
..............
```

Static structure:

```
'paste in output table
Range("A1").PasteSpecial
..............
```

Dynamic structure:

```
Dim OutputTable As Range
Set OutputTable = Range("A1")
OutputTable.PasteSpecial
```

In the dynamic structures in the above examples, it is easy to modify the code by assigning a new value to the extra variable; whereas in the static structures, we would have to make multiple modifications throughout the code.

For spreadsheet-based DSS applications, we can also improve code efficiency by balancing what needs to be done in code with what can be done in the spreadsheet. For example, some calculations can be prepared with Excel functions on a spreadsheet instead of computing them with a function procedure or a loop in the code. Likewise, much formatting can be done in the spreadsheet instead of in the code. There is a tradeoff between program functionality and intricacy; it is more important that the application model performs correctly. The better the coding, the better the quality and performance of the application.

Summary

Clarity	The most important programming practice: keep your code clear. Clarity involves consistent style, naming, and documentation.
Consistent Style	Use a consistent style for formatting, organizing, and commenting your code.
Naming	Use naming standards for variables and procedures. Naming standards also apply to control names and specific data types, such as Boolean.
Documentation	Make comments clear throughout the code. Describe procedure functionality and loop and logical flow.
Efficiency	Always look for ways to improve your coding efficiency. Avoid redundancies and unnecessary code.

24.4 *Summary*

- The most important programming principles are writing with a consistent style, using naming standards, including clear comments, and improving code efficiency.
- It is important to have a clear, readable, and understandable code.
- Documentation is an important part of any programming project. We accomplish documentation by placing comments throughout our code.
- We should continuously be working to improve our code by reducing the complexity of the logic and the time required.

24.5 *Exercises*

24.5.1 Review Questions

1. What are the main programming principles?
2. How is consistent style implemented as a programming practice?
3. How would you name a variable which will store an array of stock prices?
4. Where should you place documentation in your code?
5. Give an example of a code before and after its efficiency has been improved.

CASE STUDY

one Birthday Simulation

chapter OVERVIEW

CS1.1 Application Overview and Model Development

This is a simple application that demonstrates the validity of the statistical claim that there is a 50 percent chance that out of 23 students in a classroom, two or more students have the same birthday. We can confirm this claim by manually performing several trials of collecting or generating birthdays until two match. Or, we can perform a simulation that automates these trials and creates an accurate analysis using graphs and statistical functions.

CS1.1.1 Model Definition and Assumptions

We provide the users with four options to perform trials of generating birthdays until two or more match. The first option allows the users to enter a birthday manually. We define birthdays to be the combination of a month number (1 to 12) and a day number (1 to 31). All birthdays entered are displayed to the users on a calendar. The second option allows the users to generate a random birthday. We do so by generating a month number randomly (an integer between 1 and 12) first. Then, depending on this month number, we generate a day number. We use a "Select Case" structure to determine the maximum number of days per month in order to define the upper bound of the random day number.

The third option allows the users to generate multiple random birthdays until a match, or a hit, is found. This option repeatedly performs the previous process, checking after each random birthday generation whether or not the birthday month and day are repeated. We perform this check using animation; however, we can also perform it with arrays or other methods. When a match is found, the number of birthdays generated is displayed to the users. For example, if 20 birthdays were generated until a match was found, the number 20 would be displayed to the users.

The fourth option allows the users to perform a simulation. We use a simple spreadsheet model that randomly generates birthdays (months and days) with the PsiIntUniform() function of Risk Solver Platform, and checks the dates to see if there is a match. We run 49 simulations, one simulation for each class size (sizes 2 to 50). We use Risk Solver Platform to complete each simulation run. Before the simulation begins, the user specifies the number of simulation trials for each simulation run. We use this input to set the NumTrials property of the problem object variable. Figure CS1.1 presents the simulation worksheet. The following are the formulas we use in this worksheet to complete each simulation run, and calculate the probability of a match. Note that during the simulation, we copy formulas in cells B3:G3 on the range B4:G52. Cell I5 is the simulation output cell. The value in this cell changes during each simulation trial. It takes the value 1 if a match is found and 0 otherwise. The formula in cell I7 present the mean value of cell I5 during all simulation trials; that is the number of times a match is found. In other words, it presents the probability of a match during a simulation run.

Cell B3: =PsiIntUniform(1,12)
Cell C3: =IF(OR(B3=1,B3=3,B3=5,B3=7,B3=8,B3=10,B3=12), PsiIntUniform(1,31),0)
Cell D3: =IF(B3=2, PsiIntUniform(1,28),0)
Cell E3: =IF(OR(B3=4,B3=6,B3=9,B3=11), PsiIntUniform(1,30),0)
Cell F3: =CONCATENATE(B3,C3,D3,E3)
Cell G3: =IFERROR(MATCH(F3,F4:$F$52,0),0)

Cell I2: =COUNTIF(G3:G51,">0")
Cell I5: =IF(I2>0,1,0) + PsiOutput()
Cell I7: =PsiMean(I5)

	Brd.	The Dayof Bday						
Class Size	Month	Months: 1, 3, 5, 7, 8, 10, 12	Month: 2	Months: 4, 6, 9, 11	Concatenate Results	Is there a match?	Nr. of matches:	5
1	1	18	0	0	11800	0		
2	6	0	0	15	60015	0	Prob. of a match	
3	8	4	0	0	8400	0		100.00%
4	1	14	0	0	11400	26		
5	5	28	0	0	52800	0	Overall mean:	96.00%
6	9	0	0	20	90020	42		
7	8	8	0	0	8800	0		
8	4	0	0	2	4002	0		
9	6	0	0	12	60012	0		
10	11	0	0	17	110017	0		

Figure CS1.1 The simulation sheet.

When the simulation is complete, the users can review the created table, which displays the probability of two students having the same birthday in a class of size 2 to 50. For a more detailed analysis, the users can click on a button to go to the analysis sheet in which a graph is created using the data from the simulation. Note that, the larger the number of simulation trials per simulation run, the closer these result will get to the theoretical probabilities. For example, the results from Figure CS1.2 show that there is a 52.10% probability that a match will be found in a class with 23 students (see Figure CS1.2). The number of trials for this simulation was set to 1,000. The fourth option is the clearest for validating the statistical claim that, on average, there is a 50% probability that a match will be found when 23 birthdays are generated.

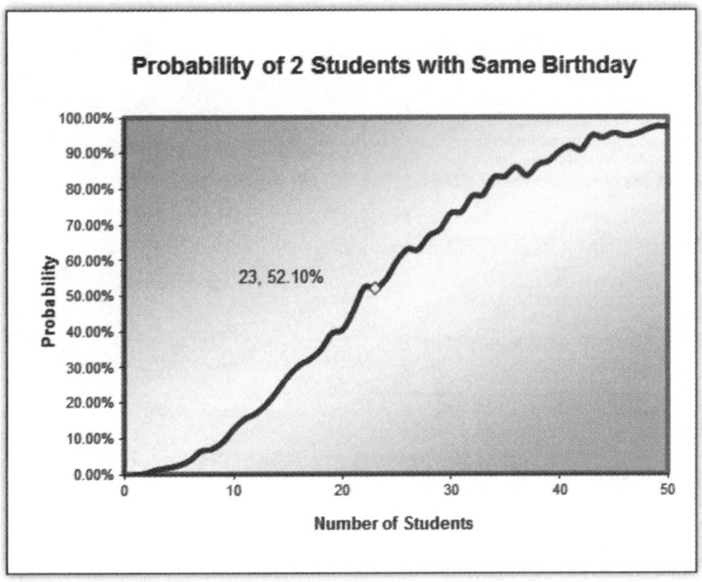

Figure CS1.2 The relationship between class size and the probability that 2 students have the same birthday.

CS1.1.2 Input

Since three of the four birthday generation options involve obtaining random birthdays with VBA, only the first option requires user input. The total number of simulation trials is used for simulation using Risk Solver Platform.

- The month number (1 through 12)
- The day number (1 through 31, depending on the given month)
- The number of simulation trials

CS1.1.3 Output

The outputs from this application are:

- The number of birthdays generated until a match is found
- A simulation table with the probability of a match in a class of size 2 to 50
- A graph that displays the probability of a match for different class sizes

CS1.2 *Worksheets*

This application requires four worksheets: the welcome sheet, an input sheet, an output sheet and the simulation sheet. The welcome sheet includes the title, the description of the application, and an image. (See Figure CS1.3.) The "Start" button on the welcome sheet brings the users to the input sheet.

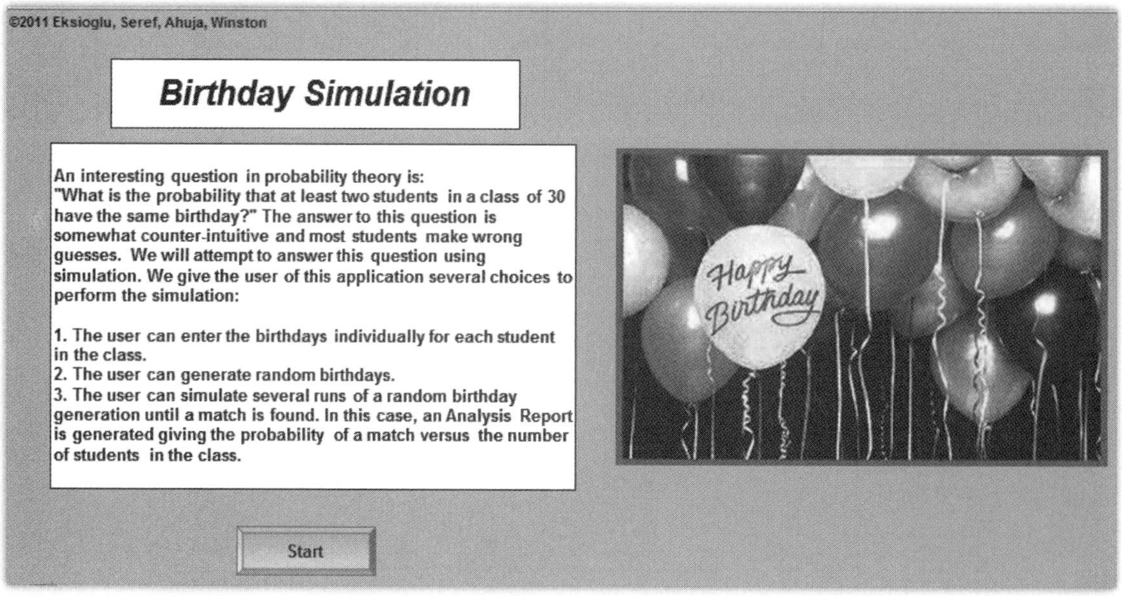

Figure CS1.3 The welcome sheet.

The input sheet is the main worksheet of the application. (See Figure CS1.4.) It has an interface in which the users can choose from the four options to generate birthdays. It also includes a calendar that animates the birthdays generated, and there is an area on the right in which the output is displayed. A box on the right displays the number of birthdays generated until a match is found. For the simulation, a table with the probability of a match for classes of different size is displayed. (See Figure CS1.3.) The animation is off during simulation. Notice that another button appears after the simulation is performed to allow the users to proceed to the output sheet.

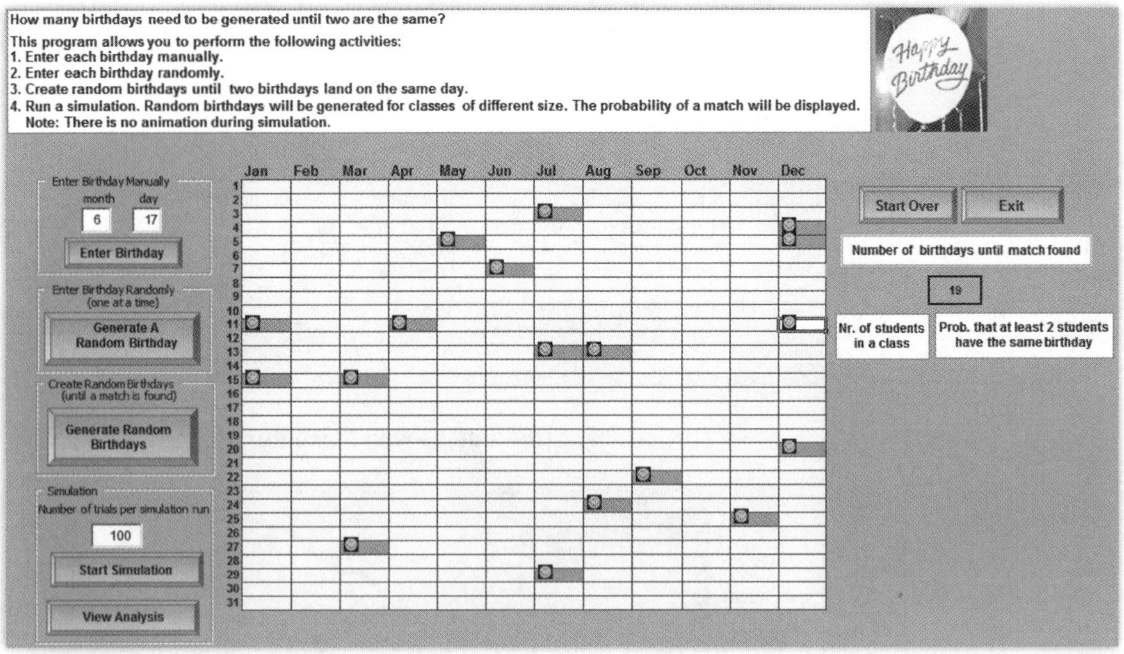

Figure CS1.4 The input sheet.

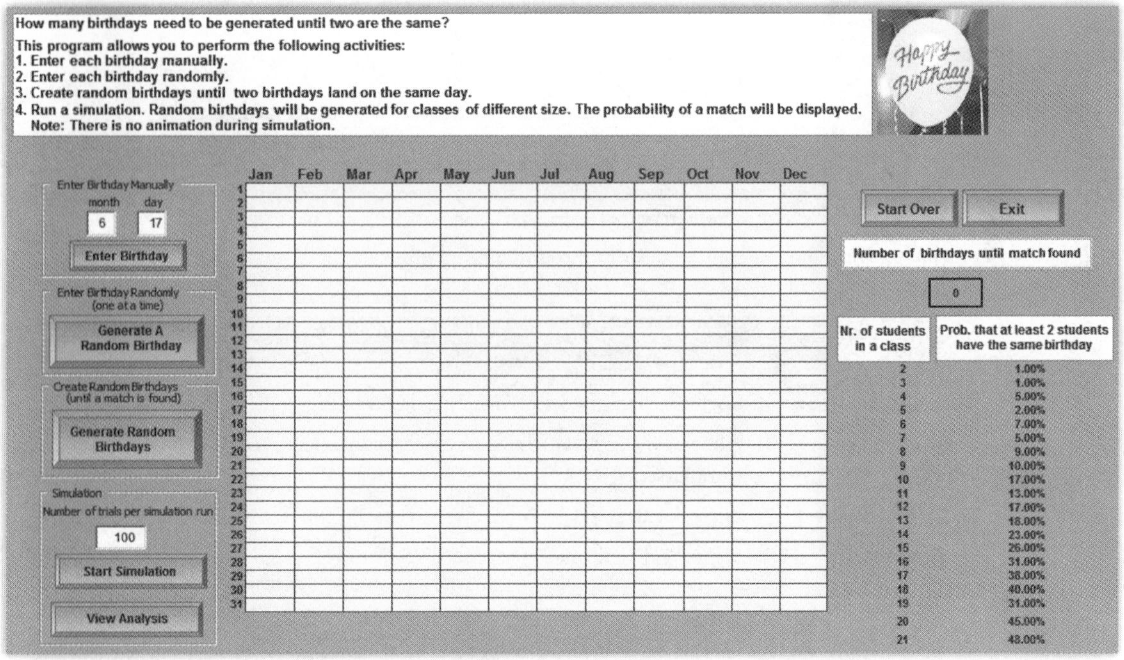

Figure CS1.5 The input sheet after simulation.

The output sheet contains the simulation analysis, primarily the graph. (See Figure CS1.6.) This graph reveals the probability of a match for a class with 2 to 50 students. The data used to create this graph appears in the table on the left of the sheet. Details about the simulation sheet are presented in section CS1.1.1. This sheet is hidden.

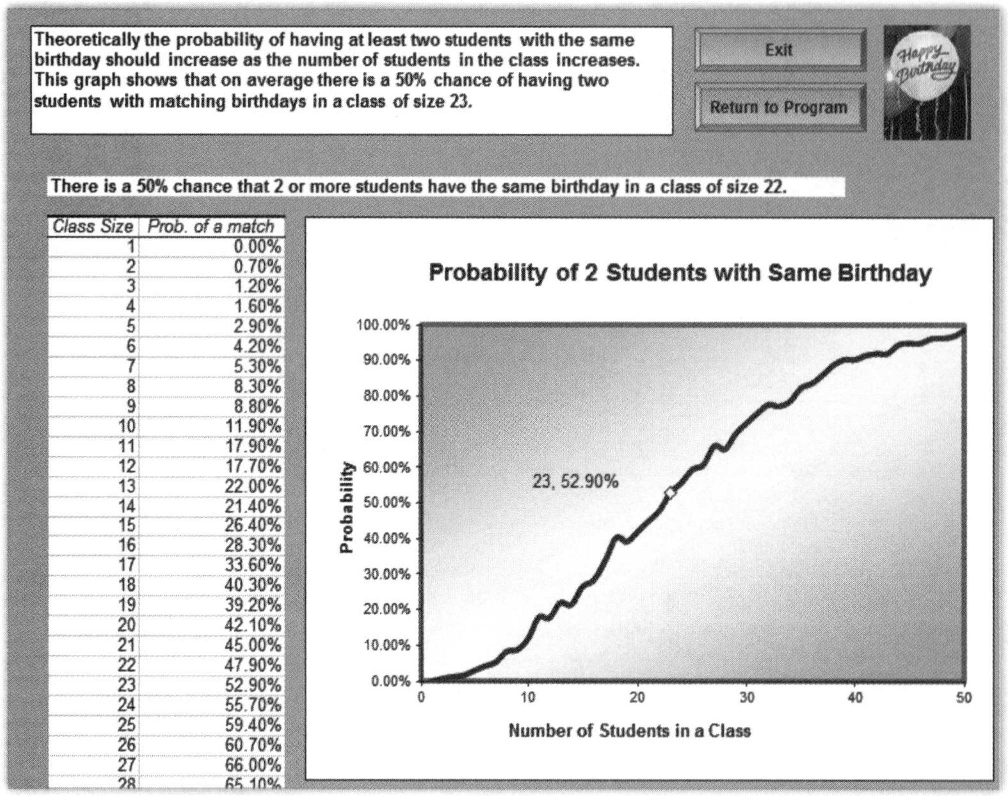

Figure CS1.6 The output sheet contains analysis of the simulation option.

Summary

Welcome sheet	Includes an application description and a "Start" button.
Input sheet	The main sheet, which includes a user interface, animation, and simulation.
Output sheet	Includes the simulation analysis, a graph, and a table.
Simulation sheet	Includes the simulation spreadsheet model.

CS1.3 *User Interface*

For this application's user interface, we include buttons and several controls on the worksheet. On the welcome sheet, the "Start" button brings the users to the input sheet, which contains the largest set of user interface controls. These controls correspond to the four options we give the users for generating birthdays. (See Figure CS1.4.)

The first option uses two text boxes on the worksheet and the "Enter Birthday" button to receive the month number and the day number for entering a manual birthday. The second and third options use the "Generate a Random Birthday" and "Generate Random Birthdays" buttons to generate random birthdays. The fourth option uses a text box and the "Start Simulation" button to receive the number of trials for the simulation and to begin the simulation. The "View Analysis" button appears when the simulation is complete and allows the users to view the output sheet.

This sheet also includes the "Exit" button, which allows the users to quit the application and return to the "Welcome" sheet, and the "Start Over" button, which clears the calendar and resets the value of the number of birthdays generated until a match was found. The output sheet contains another "Exit" button as well as a "Return to Program" button, which brings the users back to the input sheet.

Summary

Manual birthday	Two text boxes and one button.
Random birthday	A button.
Multiple random birthdays	A button.
Simulation	A text box and a button.
Navigational	Buttons on all the sheets.

CS1.4 *Procedures*

Let us now outline the procedures for this application, starting with the initial sub procedure and the variable definitions. (See Figure CS1.7.) The "Main" procedure begins by calling the "ClearPrevious" procedure; it then takes the users to the input sheet and sets default values for the controls located on the input sheet.

```
Option Explicit
Public hit As Boolean, Bdays As Integer, i As Integer, DrwObj As Object, _
CellAdd As String, UserMonth As Integer, UserDay As Integer, _
simulation As Boolean, BrdSimProb As New RSP.Problem

Sub MAIN()   'called from START button
    Call ClearPrevious

    Worksheets("Birthdays").Visible = True
    Worksheets("Welcome").Visible = False
    ActiveSheet.Shapes("ViewButton").Visible = False

    'set default values
    With Worksheets("Birthdays")
      .txtDay.Value = "17"
      .txtMonth.Value = "6"
      .txtRuns.Value = "50"
    End With
End Sub
```

Figure CS1.7 The "Main" procedure.

The "ClearPrevious" procedure clears the previous values from all the sheets. (See Figure CS1.8.) For this application, we animate all the birthdays generated on a range of cells that form a calendar. We do so by changing the color of the cells in the calendar range that represent the dates on which a birthday has been generated and pasting an image for each birthday. Therefore, the "ClearPrevious" procedure must not only clear the previous values but also reset the cell colors and delete the images in the calendar range. We also use this procedure to clear the simulation table and the simulation spreadsheet.

```
Sub ClearPrevious()
    Worksheets("Birthdays").Activate
    Application.ScreenUpdating = False

    For Each DrwObj In ActiveSheet.DrawingObjects
        'Count number of Smile face objects on calendar
        If DrwObj.Name = "Smiley" Then
            Bdays = Bdays + 1
        End If
    Next DrwObj

    'Delete each Smile face
    For i = 1 To Bdays
        ActiveSheet.Pictures("Smiley").Delete
    Next i
    Bdays = 0

    'Clear colored cells in calendar
    Range("Calendar").Interior.ColorIndex = 36

    Range("HitRes").Value = 0
    'clear simulation table and simulation worksheet
    If simulation = False Then
        Range("S26", "U100").ClearContents
    Else
        Worksheets("Simulation").Range("B4:G53").ClearContents
    End If
    Range("A1").Select
    Application.ScreenUpdating = True
End Sub
```

Figure CS1.8 The "ClearPrevious" procedure.

The next two procedures correspond to the users' first two options for generating a birthday. The first procedure is the "ManualBday" procedure. (See Figure CS1.9.), which allows the users to enter a birthday manually. It begins by recording the month number and the day number the users have entered on the worksheet controls. It then performs some simple error checking to ensure that both values were entered as numbers. Finally, it calls the "CheckBday" procedure.

Several procedures call the "CheckBday" procedure to check whether or not a matching birthday has been generated. (See Figure CS1.10.) The "CheckBday" procedure selects the cell in the calendar range that corresponds to the month and day numbers passed to the procedure; in other words, it selects the cell in the calendar range that corresponds to the birthday that was just generated. We check to see if a match, or a hit, was found by looking at the color index of the cell. We use this method since we are already animating the birthdays by changing the color of the cells in the calendar. If the cell color has already been changed, then we know that this birthday has already been generated and a match has been found. If the selected cell still has its original color index, then this is the first time this birthday has been generated and there is no match. In this case, we change the color of the cell to reflect that a birthday has been generated to update the calendar for the next check. Notice that we also copy and paste an image into the cell representing a generated birthday. This procedure ends by updating the birthday counter, which is displayed to the right of the calendar.

```
Sub ManualBday()     'This procedure enters a birthday manually
    'take day and month from text boxes on sheet
    UserDay = Worksheets("Birthdays").txtDay.Value
    UserMonth = Worksheets("Birthdays").txtMonth.Value

    'error check to ensure day and month are numbers
    If IsNumeric(UserMonth) = False Or IsNumeric(UserDay) = False Then
        MsgBox "Please fill in the numeric month and date of the birthday."
    Else
        'Add birthday and check for hit
        Call CheckBday(UserMonth, UserDay)
        If hit = True Then
            MsgBox "A match is found!"
        End If
    End If

End Sub
```

```
Sub RandBday()       'This procedure generates one random birthday
    'randomly select month
    UserMonth = Int(12 * Rnd() + 1)

    'randomly select day depending on what month was selected
    Select Case UserMonth
        Case 2
            'month is Feb, so randomly select day from 1-28
            UserDay = Int(28 * Rnd() + 1)
        Case 1, 3, 5, 7, 8, 10, 12
            'month is Jan, Mar, May, July, Aug, Oct, or Dec, so randomly select day from 1-31
            UserDay = Int(31 * Rnd() + 1)
        Case 4, 6, 9, 11
            'month is Sept, April, June, or Nov, so randomly select day from 1-30
            UserDay = Int(30 * Rnd() + 1)
    End Select

    'Add birthday and check for hit
    Call CheckBday(UserMonth, UserDay)
    If hit = True Then
            MsgBox "A match is found!"
    End If
End Sub
```

Figure CS1.9 The "ManualBday" and "RandBday" procedures.

The "RandBday" procedure is very similar to the "ManualBday" procedure except that it generates a random birthday instead of recording a birthday the users have entered. (See Figure CS1.9.) The procedure generates a random month number by selecting a number between 1 and 12. Then, depending on the generated month number, the procedure generates a random day number. We use a "Select Case" structure to determine the maximum number of days per month to define the upper bound of the random day number. The procedure ends by calling the "CheckBday" procedure, passing the newly generated birthday month and day values.

The "MultRandBday" procedure corresponds to the users' third option for generating birthdays. It calls the "RandBday" procedure repeatedly until a matching birthday is generated. (See Figure CS1.11.) Using the "CheckBday" procedure's "Hit" Boolean variable, we form a loop.

```
Sub CheckBday(ByVal UserMonth, ByVal UserDay)
    'This procedure checks a date to see if there is a hit
    hit = False

    'Given the day and month of new birthday, the corresponding cell is selected
    Range("E13").Offset(UserDay, UserMonth).Select

    With ActiveCell
        'If the cell is already colored, this is the second birthday on that day
        If .Interior.ColorIndex = 38 Then
            'Change cell color to indicate a hit
            .Interior.ColorIndex = 2
            hit = True
        Else
            'Change cell to indicate a birthday now falls on the day
            .Interior.ColorIndex = 38
            CellAdd = ActiveCell.Address
            Worksheets("Smile Picture").Activate
            ActiveSheet.Shapes("Smiley").Copy
            Worksheets("Birthdays").Activate
            Range(CellAdd).Select
            ActiveSheet.Paste

            'center picture in cell
            Selection.ShapeRange.IncrementLeft 3.25
            Selection.ShapeRange.IncrementTop -2.25
            Range("F6").Select
        End If

        'Increment counter to show that another date has been added
        Range("HitRes").Value = Range("HitRes").Value + 1
    End With
End Sub
```

Figure CS1.10 The "CheckBday" procedure.

```
Sub MultRandBday()        'generate random birthdays until there is a hit
    Call ClearPrevious
    Application.ScreenUpdating = False

    Do
        'Continue to randomly select birthdays until a hit is found
        Call RandBday
    Loop While hit = False

    Application.ScreenUpdating = True

End Sub
```

Figure CS1.11 The "MultRandBday" procedure.

The "MultRuns" procedure performs the simulation, which is the fourth input option. (See Figure CS1.12.) This procedure uses the simulation spreadsheet model to initiate a new instance of the *BrdSimProb*, a Risk Solver Platform problem object variable. We run 49 simulations of the problem. The number of trials per simulation run is an input from the user. In each successive simulation run, the size of the problem increases to reflect a different class size. We use the *Solver. Simulate* method to simulate the problem, and the *Statistics* object to display the results. For each simulation run, the subroutine records the probability of a match (mean value of the simulation output cell) on the table to the right of the calendar and on the output sheet. The graph on the output sheet is dynamic, so as we update the data on the table next to the graph, the corresponding values appear on the graph. We then update the output sheet by displaying the number of birthdays needed to have a 50% chance of finding a match.

```
Sub MultRuns() 'perform simulation to proof the theoritical results
Dim PtVal As Double

    MsgBox "Note: Animation is off during simulation!"
    simulation = True
    Call ClearPrevious
    Application.ScreenUpdating = False
    'Initiate and simulate the simulation problem
    BrdSimProb.Init ActiveWorkbook
    BrdSimProb.Model.Params("Interpreter") = 2
    BrdSimProb.Solver.NumTrials = Worksheets("Birthdays").txtRuns.Value

    For i = 2 To 50
        Worksheets("Simulation").Range("B3:G3").Offset(i - 2).Copy
        Worksheets("Simulation").Range("B3").Offset(i - 1).PasteSpecial xlPasteAll
        BrdSimProb.Solver.Simulate
        Worksheets("Birthdays").Range("S27").Offset(i - 2).Value = i
        Worksheets("Birthdays").Range("U27").Offset(i - 2).Value = _
            BrdSimProb.Functions(0).Statistics.Mean(0)
        Worksheets("Analysis").Range("D13").Offset(i - 2).Value = _
            BrdSimProb.Functions(0).Statistics.Mean(0)
     Next i
    Set BrdSimProb = Nothing

    'report 50% value
    PtVal = Application.WorksheetFunction.Match(0.5, Worksheets("Analysis").Range("D12:D62"), 1)
    Range("ProbRes").Value = "There is a 50% chance that 2 or more stuents have " & _
        "the same birthday in a class of size " & PtVal & "."

    Application.ScreenUpdating = True
    MsgBox "Simulation is complete."
    simulation = False
    ActiveSheet.Shapes("ViewButton").Visible = True
End Sub
```

Figure CS1.12 The "MultRuns" procedure.

The navigational procedures correspond to the "Exit," "View Analysis," and "Return to Program" buttons. (See Figure CS1.13.) We assign the "Start" button to the "Main" procedure, and we assign the "Start Over" button to the "ClearPrevious" procedure.

```
Sub ReturnToProg()
    Worksheets("Birthdays").Visible = True
    Worksheets("Analysis").Visible = False
End Sub

Sub ExitProg()
    Worksheets("Welcome").Visible = True
    ActiveSheet.Visible = False
End Sub

Sub ViewAnalysis()
    Worksheets("Analysis").Visible = True
    Worksheets("Birthdays").Visible = False
End Sub
```

Figure CS1.13 The navigational procedures.

Summary

Main	Initializes the application and takes the users to the input sheet.
ClearPrevious	Initializes the variables, clears the previous values, and clears the animation formatting.
ManualBday	Records the month and day entered by the users and checks for a match.
RandBday	Generates a random month and day and checks for a match.
CheckBday	The procedure called to check for a matching birthday.
MultRandBdays	Repeats "RandBday" until a match is found.
MultRuns	Uses Risk Solver Platform to simulate the problem.
Navigational	For the "Exit," "View Analysis," and "Return to Program" buttons.

CS1.5 Re-solve Options

The users have several re-solve options for this application. Basically, all four of the input options can re-solve the application. The users can press the "Start Over" button to clear the calendar and then choose one of the four input options. Once the simulation is complete, the users can view the output sheet and then re-run the simulation by pressing the "Return to Program" button on the output sheet and then pressing the "Start Over" button on the input sheet.

Summary

"Start Over"	Clears the calendar for a new birthday generation.
"Return to Program"	Brings the users back from the output sheet to re-run the simulation or to select other input option.

CS1.6 Summary

- The birthday simulation application demonstrates the validity of the statistical claim that states that there is a 50 percent chance that out of only 23 students in a classroom, two or more students have the same birthday.
- This application requires four worksheets: the welcome sheet, the input sheet, the simulation sheet, and the output sheet.
- We use several buttons in the application and place several controls on the input sheet that correspond to the users' input options.
- This application consists of several procedures that allow the users to generate birthdays and check for a match.
- This application uses Risk Solver Platform to simulate the problem.
- The users can repeatedly use any of the input options as re-solve options and can return to the program from the output sheet to repeat the simulation with a different number of trials.

CS1.7 *Extensions*

1. Add error checking to the user input: ensure that the user can only enter month numbers from 1 to 12 and day numbers restricted to that month (for example, month 2 with day 30 would be invalid).
2. Create an alternate "CheckBday" procedure that uses arrays to check for a match instead of the calendar cells' color index.
3. Create a different user interface for the input sheet. What improvements does your new interface make?
4. Name another statistical claim that can be verified using a simulation application similar to this one. Can further statistical analysis be performed for this new application?
5. Suppose that you do not have access to Risk Solver Platform. How will you change the MultRuns() subroutine to complete the simulations?

CASE STUDY

two Eight Queens

chapter OVERVIEW

CS2.1 Application Overview and Model Development

The eight-queens problem consists of placing eight queens on a regular eight-by-eight chessboard so that none of them is in the line of attack of any other queen. The line of attack of a queen is anywhere in its column and row and anywhere in a diagonal direction from its location. (See Figure CS2.1.)

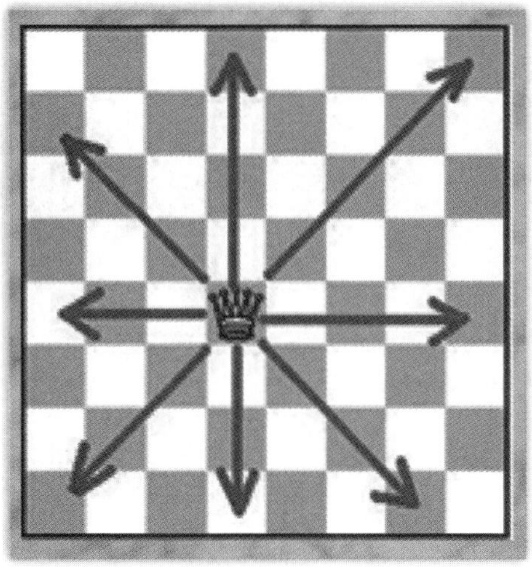

Figure CS2.1 An illustration of the permissible movements of a queen on a chessboard.

CS2.1.1 Model Definition and Assumptions

The eight-queens problem has 92 distinct solutions. If we exclude symmetry, it has 23 distinct solutions. We could generalize this problem into an *N* queens problem, which would involve an *N*N* board and require us to place *N* queens so that none of them were in the line of attack of any other queen. However, for this application, we assume the chessboard size is fixed at eight-by-eight.

To generate each solution, we use a simple algorithm. We must determine how to place eight queens on the board so that none of them can attack another. In other words, no queen can be in the same row, in the same column, or on the same diagonal as another. We know we can only place one queen on each row of the chessboard; therefore, we examine each row at a time to determine on which cell in that row, or in which column, a queen is placed. For each placed queen, we keep track of its row and column index. We will use these indices to check that no two queens have the same column index, have the same row index, or lie on the same diagonal.

As we examine each row, we initially place a queen in the first "legal" cell. That is, if we begin by examining the first row of the board to determine where to place the first queen, we find that the first cell, or the first column, is "legal" since no other queens have been placed. We therefore place the first queen in this first cell of the board's first row. We can then continue to the second row of the board and find that the first column is "illegal" since the first queen has already been placed there. The second column is also illegal since it conflicts with the first queen's diagonal. However, the third column is legal; therefore, we place the second queen in the third column of the second row since it is the first legal cell we find. (See Figure CS2.2.)

We continue using this method for all the rows of the board. However, we may find a row in which no cell, or no column, qualifies as a legal placement for the queen currently being placed.

In other words, depending on the locations of the previously placed queens, we may not find an available column or cell that does not conflict with the diagonal of another queen. In that case we must "backtrack." We do not place the current queen, but move back to the previously examined row and then move that already-placed queen to a different legal cell. For example, if we have placed queens in rows 1 through 4 but cannot find a legal placement for the queen in row 5, then we would return to row 4 and try to move that queen.

Since we are initially always placing the queens in the first legal cells, we may have ignored other legal options. For example, the second queen we placed in Figure CS2.2 could have also been placed in columns 4 through 8 of the second row. Therefore, we try a different legal position for the queen placed in the row above the queen for which we could not find a legal placement.

After moving the queen above it, we return to the queen that we were positioning and see if a legal position has now become available. For example, suppose we revisited row 4 and moved the queen to a new legal position; we would then return to row 5 and try to place the queen we left. If there is still no available legal position, then we continue backtracking until shifting a queen in some previously examined row eventually opens a legal position for the current queen. We may continue using this backtracking technique until we return to row 1 and have tried all possible legal positions for the queen in this row. Once all positions have been tried, we can declare that all the possible solutions have been generated. An example of a complete solution appears in Figure CS2.3. The *Place* and *IsLegal* procedures are used to implement this algorithm; refer to Section CS2.4.

Since there are many possible solutions, 92 for the symmetric eight-by-eight board scenario to be exact, we allow the users several options to view these solutions. The first allows the users to generate one solution at a time. We assume that the solutions are unique; in other words, none is repeated. The second option allows the users to generate several solutions at a time. For example, they may generate five solutions at once. The third option allows the users to generate all the possible solutions.

Figure CS2.2 Placing the first two queens on the board.

Figure CS2.3 A solution for the eight-queens problem.

CS2.1.2 Input

The only input for this application is the number of solutions to generate if the users choose the second option for viewing the solutions.

- Number of solutions to generate

CS2.1.3 Output

The output for this application is the solution set of the eight-queens problem.

- Chessboard with queen placements for each possible solution

CS2.2 *Worksheets*

This application requires two worksheets: the welcome sheet and the solution sheet. The welcome sheet contains the title and the description of the application as well as an image. (See Figure CS2.4.) The "Start" button on the welcome sheet brings the users to the solution sheet.

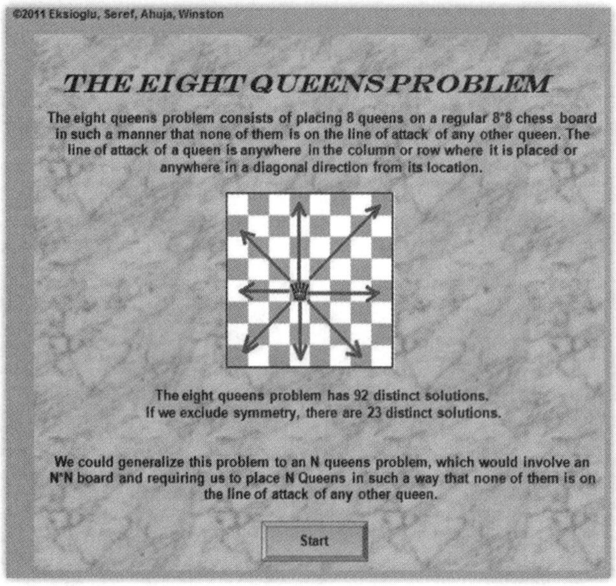

Figure CS2.4 The welcome sheet.

The solution sheet displays all of the possible solutions to the users. (See Figure CS2.5). These solutions are displayed as chessboards with images of queen pieces in the placements generated by the solution. The users can select among the three options for viewing these solutions using a floating form visible on the solutions sheet. We will discuss this form in more detail in the next section.

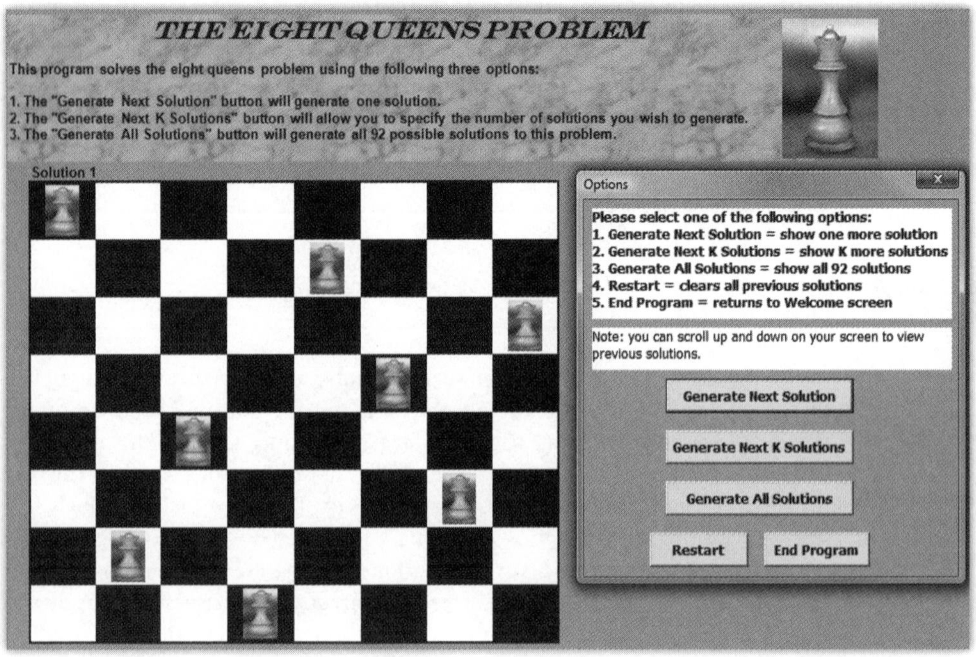

Figure CS2.5 The solutions sheet.

Since these placements are unique, a new chessboard is shown for each solution. All of the solutions that the users generate are stored sequentially on the sheet so the users can compare them. (See Figure CS2.6.)

Figure CS2.6 Multiple solutions on the solution sheet.

Summary

Welcome sheet Includes an application description and a "Start" button.

Solution sheet Displays all of the solutions to the users using multiple chessboards with queen images.

CS2.3 *User Interface*

For this application's user interface, we use buttons, a user form, and an input box. On the welcome sheet, the "Start" button brings the users to the solutions sheet. On the solutions sheet, we include a user form for all user interface. (See Figure CS2.7.) This user form is a floating form; it is always available to the users and does not have to be closed for the users to scroll up and down the various solutions on the worksheet. The form includes labels to give the users clear descriptions of their options, which are indicated by the following five buttons: "Generate Next Solution," "Generate Next K Solutions," "Generate All Solutions," "Restart," and "End Program." The first three buttons correspond directly to the users' options of viewing the solutions. The "Restart" button clears all of the solutions displayed, and the "End Program" button brings the users back to the welcome sheet.

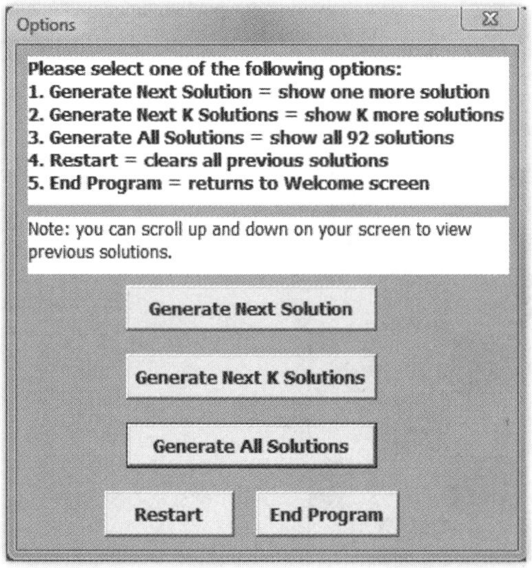

Figure CS2.7 The "Options" user form, which is a floating form on the solutions sheet.

If the users select to generate several solutions at a time by pressing the "Generate Next K Solutions" button on the form, an input box appears. This input box prompts the users for the number of solutions that they want to generate. In other words, the input box prompts the users for the value of K. (See Figure CS2.8.)

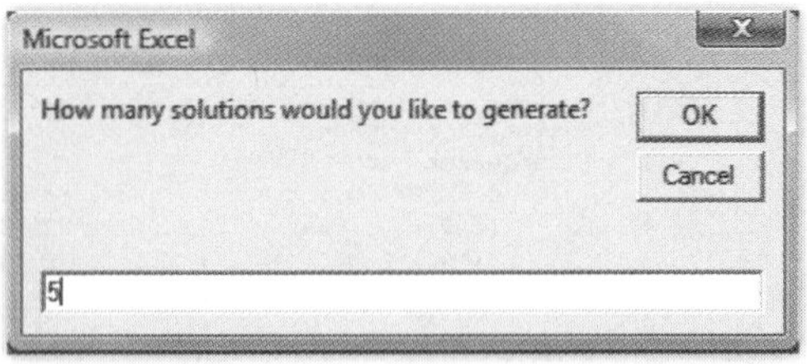

Figure CS2.8 The input box used for generating multiple solutions.

Summary

Navigational Buttons	The "Start" button on the welcome sheet
User Form	A floating form that gives the users viewing options as well as "Restart" and "End Program" options.
Input Box	Prompts the users for the number of solutions to generate.

CS2.4 *Procedures*

We will now outline the procedures for this application, beginning with the initial sub procedure and the variable definitions. (See Figure CS2.9.) The "Main" procedure initializes the variables and calls the "ClearPrevious" procedure; it then takes the users to the solutions sheet and displays the "Options" form.

```
Option Explicit

Public Const SIZE As Integer = 8

Public column(1 To SIZE) As Integer, x As Integer, NumQueens As Integer, _
i As Integer, j As Integer, CellAdd As String, k As Integer, _
Iterations As Integer, Answer As Integer, row As Integer, col As Integer, _
DrwObj As Object, y As Integer, StartCell As Range, response As String, _
BoardNum As Integer

Sub MAIN() ' This is called from the start button on the Welcome Sheet
    Set StartCell = Worksheets("Queen Program").Range("B4")
    BoardNum = 1

    Call ClearPrevious

    Worksheets("Queen Program").Activate
    Worksheets("Queen Program").Visible = True
End Sub
```

Figure CS2.9 The "Main" procedure and the variable declarations.

The "ClearPrevious" procedure initializes some variables and clears the solutions sheet. (See Figure CS2.10.) Resetting the cell colors and borders clears the chessboards from the previously displayed solutions. The "ClearQueens" procedure clears the queen images by looping over all the drawing objects on the sheet to count the number of queens and then deleting the queen image that many times. (See Figure CS2.11.)

```
Sub ClearPrevious()
    x = 1
    Application.ScreenUpdating = False
    Worksheets("Queen Program").Activate
    Call ClearQueens
    With Worksheets("Queen Program").Cells
        .Interior.ColorIndex = 15
        .Borders(xlInsideVertical).LineStyle = xlNone
        .Borders(xlInsideHorizontal).LineStyle = xlNone
        .ClearContents
    End With
    Application.ScreenUpdating = True

    BoardNum = 1
    Set StartCell = Range("B4")
    StartCell.Select
End Sub
```

Figure CS2.10 The "ClearPrevious" procedure.

```
Function ClearQueens()
    NumQueens = 0
    For Each DrwObj In ActiveSheet.DrawingObjects
        If DrwObj.name = "QueenPic2" Then
        'Count number of Queen picture objects
            NumQueens = NumQueens + 1
        End If
    Next DrwObj

    For i = 1 To NumQueens
    'Delete all Queens pictures
        ActiveSheet.Shapes("QueenPic2").Delete
    Next i
End Function
```

Figure CS2.11 The "ClearQueens" procedure.

The users are now on the solutions sheet and can use the "Options" form for the user interface. Figure CS2.12 outlines the procedures associated with each of the buttons on this form. The "cmdRestart_Click" procedure simply calls the "ClearPrevious" procedure to clear the solutions sheet. The "cmdEndProg_Click" procedure calls the "ClearPrevious" procedure and returns the users to the welcome sheet. Finally, the "cmdAllSoln_Click," "cmdKSoln_Click," and "cmdNextSoln_Click" procedures all call their corresponding procedure in the main module: "AllSolns," "KSolns," and "NextSoln," respectively. (See Figure CS2.13.)

```
Option Explicit

Sub cmdAllSoln_Click()
    Call AllSolns
End Sub

Sub cmdEndProg_Click()
    Call ClearPrevious

    Worksheets("Welcome").Visible = True
    Worksheets("Queen Program").Visible = False

    Unload Me
End Sub

Sub cmdKSoln_Click()
    Call KSolns
End Sub

Sub cmdNext_Click()
    Call NextSoln
End Sub

Sub cmdRestart_Click()
    Call ClearPrevious
End Sub
```

Figure CS2.12 The procedures for the "Options" form.

These three main procedures, "AllSolns," "KSolns," and "NextSoln," all call the "Place" procedure, which executes the algorithm for placing the queens. (Refer to Section CS2.1.1.) This procedure requires that an iteration value be passed to it. From the "NextSoln" procedure, we pass an iteration value of 1; from the "AllSolns" procedure, we pass an iteration value of 100 (or any number >= 92); and from the "KSolns" procedure, we pass an iteration value of K. To find K, we prompt the users with the input box described in Section CS2.3. To ensure that the users enter a numeric value for the number of solutions to generate, we use some error checking. If the users press the "Cancel" button on the input box, we bring them back to the welcome sheet.

The "Place" procedure generates the number of solutions specified by the iterations value it receives when called. (See Figure CS2.14.) This iteration value is used as the counter in the main "For, Next" loop. The outer "Do, While" loop performs the algorithm to generate one solution. This "While" condition checks that the row number, x, remains less than the size of the board, in this case 8. For each row, the queen position is shifted to all possible columns (from left to right, or 1 to 8), checking each time if the position is legal. The "isLegal" function performs this check. (See Figure CS2.15.)

```
Sub AllSolns()
'iteration should be >= 92 for SIZE = 8
    Call Place(100)
End Sub

Sub KSolns()
    response = InputBox("How many solutions would " & _
            "you like to generate?")
    If response = "" Then
        'user has pressed Cancel button
        Worksheets("Welcome").Activate
        Worksheets("Welcome").Visible = True
        Worksheets("Queen Program").Visible = False
        Unload frmOptions
        Exit Sub
    ElseIf IsNumeric(response) = False Then
          MsgBox "Please enter an integer."
          Exit Sub
    Else
        k = Int(response)
        Call Place(k)
    End If
End Sub

Sub NextSoln()
    Call Place(1)
End Sub
```

Figure CS2.13 The procedures for the three options for viewing solutions.

```
Sub Place(ByVal Iterations)
    'Iterations = Number of solutions desired
    'place a queen on the board
    'must check all possible locations using loop and IsLegal function

     For i = 1 To Iterations
        'Loop to find a legal position
        Do While x <= SIZE
            Do
                column(x) = column(x) + 1
                If column(x) > SIZE Then Exit Do
            Loop While Not isLegal(x, column(x))
            'Check if we need backtrack.
            'Backtracking to previously visited rows is necessary if
            'a conflict has been found and no other possibilities
            'exist for placement on the current row.
            If column(x) > SIZE Then
                column(x) = 0
                x = x - 1
                If x < 1 Then Exit Do 'There are no more solutions.
            Else
                'We have found a legal position. Proceed to next row.
                x = x + 1
            End If
        Loop

        x = x - 1
        'check if all possible solutions have been found
        If x < 0 Then
            MsgBox "All possible solutions have been generated."
            Exit Sub
        End If

        Call Display
    Next i
End Sub
```

Figure CS2.14 The "Place" procedure.

The "isLegal" function receives the row and column value of the queen currently being placed. The column value passed is checked to determine if it is a value position or if it should be shifted once more. If the row value, x, is 1, then the position is legal. Even if we are backtracking, we assume that any location of the first queen on row 1 is valid. Otherwise, we compare the columns and diagonals of all queens placed in the previous rows to determine if there is a conflict with the queen currently being placed. We check the columns by comparing the passed column value for the queen we are currently placing to the column array value (*column(j)*) of each of the other queens (*j*). We check the diagonals by comparing the absolute difference between the current row number (*x*) and each queen number (*j*) with the absolute difference between the passed column number (*y*) and the column array value of each queen. A Boolean value is set to true to indicate that the passed column value of the current queen is a legal position if no conflicts are found.

```
Function isLegal(ByVal x, ByVal y) As Boolean
    'this function checks if a queen placement is "legal"

    'If this is the first row on which a queen is placed,
    'then there should not be any conflict since other rows
    'have not been visited
    If x = 1 Then
        isLegal = True
        Exit Function
    End If

    'otherwise, we must check column and diagonal of
    'current queen placement, to see if other queens
    'have already been placed in a conflicting position
    For j = 1 To SIZE
        If j <> x And column(j) <> 0 Then
            If y = column(j) Then          'Check column
                isLegal = False
                Exit Function
            End If
            If Abs(x - j) = Abs(y - column(j)) Then
            'Check Diagonals
                isLegal = False
                Exit Function
            End If
        End If
    Next j

    isLegal = True
End Function
```

Figure CS2.15 The "isLegal" function procedure.

After this part of the "Place" procedure is done, we check to ensure that the queen was placed in a legal position. If the column location of the queen is greater than the size of the board, then we know no legal position was found. In that case, we backtrack by re-initializing the illegal queen's column and resetting the row count by one. The main "Do, While" loop now repeats. If all the rows have been revisited in the backtracking and no legal position was found for row 1, then we can declare that all the possible solutions have been generated. If legal positions were found for each queen, then our row value exceeds the board size and the main "Do, While" loop is exited. We then decrease the row counter by one again to ensure that the next time the "Place" procedure is called, we begin by backtracking. This step ensures that all the solutions generated are unique.

Next, we call the "Display" procedure. (See Figure CS2.16.) This procedure displays a new chessboard for the generated solution and copies an image of a queen piece onto each position for the current solution. A solution number also appears above the displayed solution.

```
Sub Display()
    Application.ScreenUpdating = False
    Worksheets("Queen Picture").Range("C2:J9").Copy 'copy chess board
    Worksheets("Queen Program").Activate
    ActiveSheet.Paste Destination:=StartCell.Offset(1, 1)
    Worksheets("Queen Picture").Activate
    ActiveSheet.Shapes("QueenPic2").Copy    'copy queen picture
    Worksheets("Queen Program").Activate

    'paste the queen picture for each queen appropriately
    For row = 1 To SIZE
        For col = 1 To SIZE
            If column(row) = col Then
              ActiveSheet.Paste Destination:=StartCell.Offset(row, col)
            End If                      'Goto next column
        Next col                        'Goto starting cell of next row
    Next row
    Application.ScreenUpdating = True

    'show solution number
    StartCell.Offset(0, 1).Value = "Solution " & BoardNum
    BoardNum = BoardNum + 1
    StartCell.Offset(5, -1).Select

    'Move StartCell a few rows down for next solution
    Set StartCell = StartCell.Offset(SIZE + 2, 0)
End Sub
```

Figure CS2.16 The "Display" procedure.

Summary

Main	Initializes the application and takes the users to the input sheet.
ClearPrevious	Initializes the variables, clears the previous values, and clears the animation formatting.
ClearQueens	Counts and deletes all the queen images.
Options Form Procedures	Used for the "Reset," "End Program," and solution viewing options.
AllSolns	Calls the "Place" procedure for 100 iterations.
KSolns	Calls the "Place" procedure for K iterations. K is received from the users through an input box.
NextSoln	Calls the "Place" procedure for 1 iteration.
Place	Executes the algorithm to generate each solution.
isLegal	The function called by the "Place" procedure to check if a column position is legal for the current queen.
Display	Displays a chessboard and queen images for each solution generated.

CS2.5 *Re-solve Options*

The users can re-solve this application by selecting the "Restart" button on the options form or by switching between any of the options for viewing the solutions. However, we have also created a more complex re-solve option that allows users to fix certain queens before generating solutions. This means that users can specify a particular position for 1 to 7 queens on the chessboard and then see what solutions are possible when these fixed positions never change.

Figure CS2.17 displays a new sheet in which the users can specify which queens to fix. To let the users fix the queens, we use a "Worksheet_SelectionChange" event procedure. (See Figure CS2.18.) This procedure checks the location of the selected cell to ensure that it is inside the board area. If so, then it checks to make sure no other queen has been placed there previously. If this is also true, then a queen image is copied and pasted onto the selected cell.

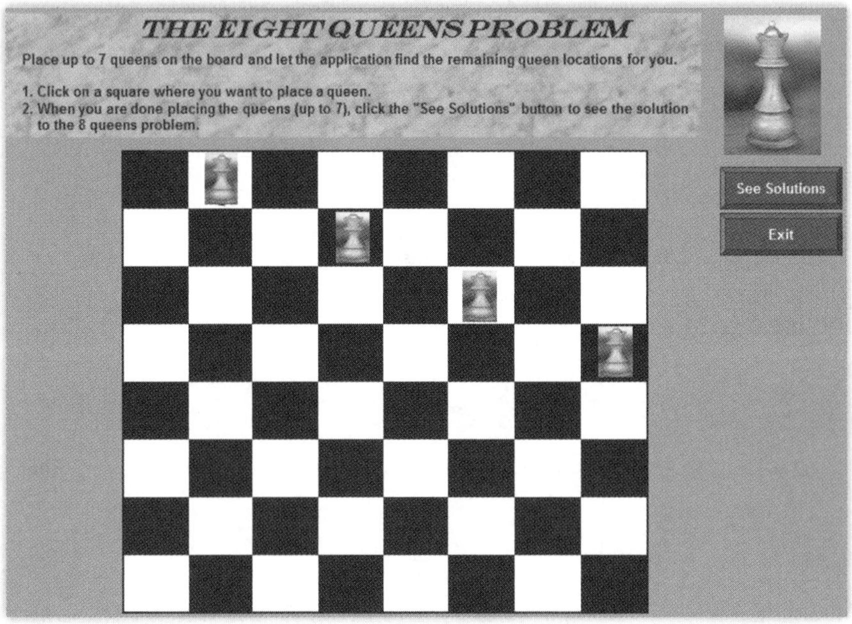

Figure CS2.17 The new sheet for fixing queens.

When the users are finished fixing the queens, they press the "See Solutions" button, which is assigned to a new procedure, the "UserProgram" procedure. (See Figure CS2.19.) This procedure records which queens are fixed by noting the column and row numbers. A new array also stores a Boolean variable of whether or not a row has a fixed queen. When the algorithm is executed, this array will be checked so that the rows with fixed queens are skipped. The "UserProgram" procedure then performs a quick error check to ensure that the users did not place queens in illegal positions. Finally, the users are taken to the solutions sheet, and the "Options" form appears.

```
Option Explicit

Private Sub Worksheet_SelectionChange(ByVal Target As Range)
    Application.ScreenUpdating = False

     If Application.Union(ActiveCell, Range("Board")).Address = _
        Range("Board").Address And ActiveCell.Value <> "Q" Then
            Worksheets("Queen Picture").Activate
            ActiveSheet.Shapes("QueenPic2").Copy
            Worksheets("User").Activate
            ActiveSheet.Paste Destination:=ActiveCell

            ActiveCell.Value = "Q"
     End If

    Application.ScreenUpdating = True
End Sub
```

Figure CS2.18 The "Worksheet_SelectionChange" procedure for the new sheet.

```
Sub UserProgram()     'called for fixing queens option

    'record where fixed queens are
    For row = 1 To SIZE
        For col = 1 To SIZE
            If Range("Board").Cells(row, col).Value = "Q" Then
                column(row) = col
                UserPlaced(row) = True
            End If
        Next col
    Next row

    'check that fixed queens obey rules
    For x = 1 To SIZE
        If UserPlaced(x) = True Then
            If Not isLegal(x, column(x)) Then
                MsgBox "Your initial queen placement " & _
                        "does not follow the " & vbCrLf & _
                    "Eight Queens Problem rules."
                Call ClearPrevious
                Exit Sub
            End If
        End If
    Next x

    x = 1
    Worksheets("Queen Program").Visible = True
    Worksheets("User").Visible = False
    frmOptions.Show

End Sub
```

Figure CS2.19 The "UserProgram" procedure.

Now, when the users return to the solutions sheet, any solutions generated highlight the fixed queens. (See Figure CS2.20.) The users still have the same three options for viewing the solutions. Notice, however, that the "Generate All Solutions" option now generates fewer than 92 solutions. Also note that in some cases no solutions are possible, given the positions of the fixed queens.

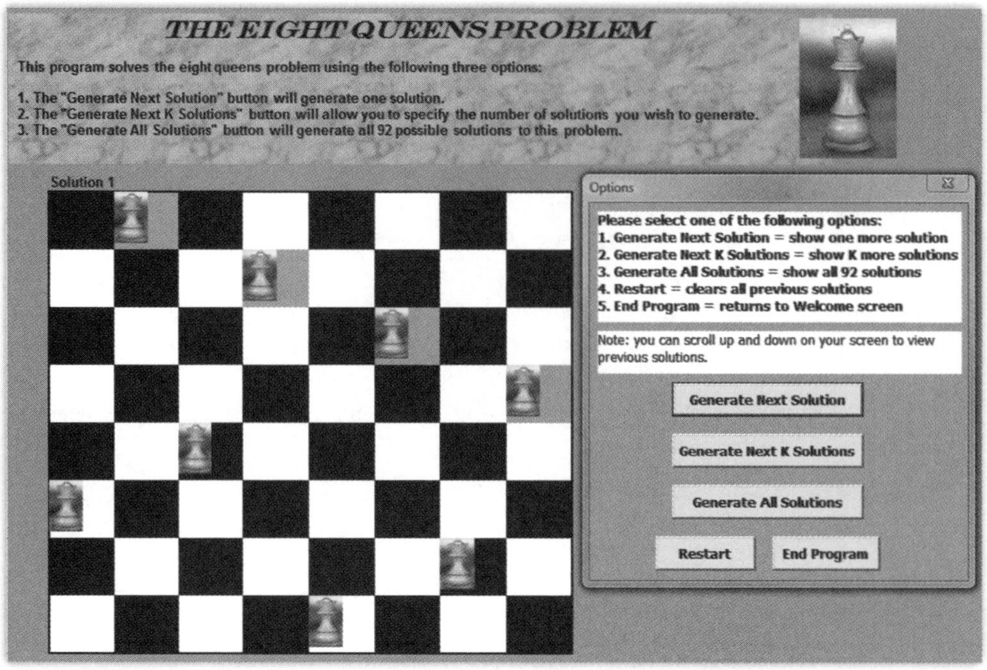

Figure CS2.20 The fixed queens are highlighted in all the generated solutions.

We have also added one more user form that gives the users the option of generating all the solutions with or without fixing some queens first. (See Figure CS2.21.) This form is now shown when the users click the "Start" button on the welcome sheet. The procedures for this new form simply determine whether or not to take the users to the new sheet for fixing the queens or to the solutions sheet. (See Figure CS2.22.) If the users are taken to the solutions sheet, then the "Options" form also appears.

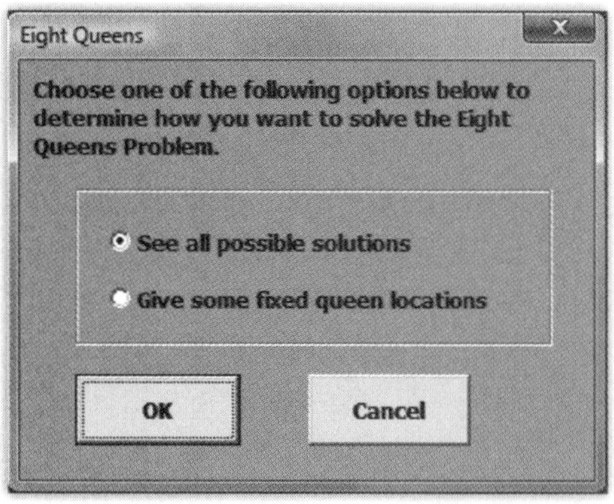

Figure CS2.21 The new user form that allows users to fix queens.

```
Private Sub cmdCancel_Click()
    Unload Me
End Sub

Private Sub cmdOK_Click()
    If optUser Then
        Worksheets("User").Visible = True
        Worksheets("User").Activate
        Worksheets("Welcome").Visible = False

        Unload Me
    ElseIf optReg Then
        Worksheets("Queen Program").Activate
        Worksheets("Queen Program").Visible = True
        Worksheets("Welcome").Visible = False

        Unload Me
        frmOptions.Show
    End If
End Sub
```

Figure CS2.22 The procedures for the new user form.

We have also made a few modifications to the procedures. As mentioned above, the new form is now called from the "Start" button on the welcome sheet. In other words, we have modified the "Main" procedure to display this new form instead of taking the users directly to the user form and showing the "Options" form. (See Figure CS2.23.) The new Boolean array for storing fixed queens is also initialized in this procedure.

```
Sub MAIN() ' This is called from the start button on the Welcome Sheet
    Set StartCell = Worksheets("Queen Program").Range("B4")
    BoardNum = 1

    'initialize for fixing queens option
    For i = 1 To SIZE
        UserPlaced(i) = False
    Next i

    Call ClearPrevious
    frmMain.Show
End Sub
```

Figure CS2.23 Modifying the "Main" procedure.

We also modify the "ClearPrevious" procedure. (See Figure CS2.24.) Additionally, we clear the board and queen images from the new sheet. Notice that the Boolean array for the fixed queens is checked when re-initializing the columns record so the fixed queens' positions are not lost; this is a factor when the "Reset" button is pressed.

```
Sub ClearPrevious()
    x = 1
    For i = 1 To SIZE
    'Reset Column Array
        If UserPlaced(i) = False Then
            column(i) = 0
        End If
    Next i

    Application.ScreenUpdating = False
    'fixed queens option sheet
    With Worksheets("User").Cells
        .Interior.ColorIndex = 15
        .Borders(xlInsideVertical).LineStyle = xlNone
        .Borders(xlInsideHorizontal).LineStyle = xlNone
        .ClearContents
    End With
    'copy chess board
    Worksheets("Queen Picture").Range("C2:J9").Copy

    Worksheets("User").Activate
    ActiveSheet.Paste Destination:=Range("Board")
    Range("Board").HorizontalAlignment = xlCenter
    Call ClearQueens

    'main queens position sheet
    Worksheets("Queen Program").Activate
    Call ClearQueens
    With Worksheets("Queen Program").Cells
        .Interior.ColorIndex = 15
        .Borders(xlInsideVertical).LineStyle = xlNone
        .Borders(xlInsideHorizontal).LineStyle = xlNone
        .ClearContents
    End With
    Application.ScreenUpdating = True

    BoardNum = 1
    Set StartCell = Range("B4")
    StartCell.Select
End Sub
```

Figure CS2.24 Modifying the "ClearPrevious" procedure.

We also modify the "Place" procedure. (See Figure CS2.25.) Now is when we use the new Boolean array to determine whether or not the algorithm should skip a row in which a queen has been fixed. We also check this array to ensure that a row with a fixed queen is not re-examined during the backtracking loop. In the end of the procedure, we check if the first iteration was able to generate a solution. If it was not able to, then we inform the users that the positions of their fixed queens were too constrained to find a possible solution.

```
Sub ClearPrevious()
    x = 1
    For i = 1 To SIZE
    'Reset Column Array
        If UserPlaced(i) = False Then
            column(i) = 0
        End If
    Next i

    Application.ScreenUpdating = False
    'fixed queens option sheet
    With Worksheets("User").Cells
        .Interior.ColorIndex = 15
        .Borders(xlInsideVertical).LineStyle = xlNone
        .Borders(xlInsideHorizontal).LineStyle = xlNone
        .ClearContents
    End With
    'copy chess board
    Worksheets("Queen Picture").Range("C2:J9").Copy

    Worksheets("User").Activate
    ActiveSheet.Paste Destination:=Range("Board")
    Range("Board").HorizontalAlignment = xlCenter
    Call ClearQueens

    'main queens position sheet
    Worksheets("Queen Program").Activate
    Call ClearQueens
    With Worksheets("Queen Program").Cells
        .Interior.ColorIndex = 15
        .Borders(xlInsideVertical).LineStyle = xlNone
        .Borders(xlInsideHorizontal).LineStyle = xlNone
        .ClearContents
    End With
    Application.ScreenUpdating = True

    BoardNum = 1
    Set StartCell = Range("B4")
    StartCell.Select
End Sub
```

Figure CS2.25 Modifying the "Place" procedure.

We modify the "Display" procedure (See Figure CS2.26.) Again, we use the new Boolean array to check if users fixed a queen position. If they did, then we not only paste a queen image, but we also highlight the cell to indicate to the users that it is a fixed queen.

```
Sub Display()
    Application.ScreenUpdating = False
    Worksheets("Queen Picture").Range("C2:J9").Copy 'copy chess board
    Worksheets("Queen Program").Activate
    ActiveSheet.Paste Destination:=StartCell.Offset(1, 1)
    Worksheets("Queen Picture").Activate
    ActiveSheet.Shapes("QueenPic2").Copy    'copy queen picture
    Worksheets("Queen Program").Activate

    'paste the queen picture for each queen appropriately
    For row = 1 To SIZE
        For col = 1 To SIZE
            If column(row) = col Then
              ActiveSheet.Paste Destination:=StartCell.Offset(row, col)
              If UserPlaced(row) = True Then
                'indicate that this is a fixed queen position
                StartCell.Offset(row, col).Interior.ColorIndex = 37
              End If
            End If                      'Goto next column
        Next col                        'Goto starting cell of next row
    Next row
    Application.ScreenUpdating = True

    'show solution number
    StartCell.Offset(0, 1).Value = "Solution " & BoardNum
    BoardNum = BoardNum + 1
    StartCell.Offset(5, -1).Select

    'Move StartCell a few rows down for next solution
    Set StartCell = StartCell.Offset(SIZE + 2, 0)
End Sub
```

Figure CS2.26 Modifying the "Display" procedure.

The last procedure we modify is "cmdRestart_Click." (See CS2.27.) We use a *For Next* loop to set the value of the Boolean array to False. This is necessary to clear any prior solution that the user may have fixed, and restart the application.

```
Sub cmdRestart_Click()
    For i = 1 To SIZE
        UserPlaced(i) = False
    Next i
    Call ClearPrevious
End Sub
```

Figure CS2.27 Modifying the "cmdRestart_Click" procedure.

Summary

"Reset"	Clears the solutions sheet.
New sheet	Allows the users to fix the queens' positions before generating solutions.
New form	Gives the users the option of fixing queens before viewing solutions.
New procedure	The "UserProgram" procedure records the row and column of the fixed queens and performs some error checking.
Modified procedures	Some of the procedures now have slight modifications to incorporate the fixed queens option.

CS2.6 *Summary*

- The eight-queens problem consists of placing eight queens on a regular eight-by-eight chessboard so that none of them is in the line of attack of any other queen.
- This application requires two worksheets: the welcome sheet and the solution sheet. (Note that a new sheet is added with the re-solve option.)
- For this application's user interface, we use buttons, a user form, and an input box.
- There are several procedures for this application that execute the algorithm for generating possible solutions.
- The users can re-solve the application by using the "Restart" button on the "Options" form or by switching among any of the options for viewing the solutions. There is also a more complex re-solve option that allows users to fix certain queens before generating solutions.

CS2.7 *Extensions*

1. Generalize this problem to an N-queens problem, which can use an N*N board, and place N queens so that none of them is in the line of attack of any other queen. Prompt the users for the value of N before beginning the application.
2. Design an alternative user interface for the solutions sheet. Can you use a control that allows the users to scroll through the multiple solutions on the sheet without using the worksheet's scroll bars?
3. **Knights Trail Problem:** You are given a chessboard and a knight as well as the knight's starting position. The problem is to visit each square of the chessboard (exactly once) with a minimum number of moves. In other words, the trail left by the knight should be the shortest one possible. Develop a system that solves this problem.
4. **Queen Domination Problem:** Determine the least number of queens that can be placed on a chessboard so that each square either contains a queen or can be attacked by one.
5. **Crowded Board Problem:** You are given a chessboard along with 8 queens, 8 rooks, 21 knights, and 14 bishops. The problem is to place these 51 pieces on the chessboard so that no queen can attack another queen, no rook can attack another rook, no bishop can attack another bishop, and no knight can attack another knight. Ignore the intercession of pieces of another type from the one under consideration. In other words, two queens can still attack each other even if there is a bishop, a rook, or a knight between them. Develop a system to solve the above problem.

CASE STUDY

three Inventory Management

chapter OVERVIEW

CS3.1 *Application Overview and Model Development*

This application allows the users to plan an inventory ordering strategy using either the Standard EOQ, the EOQ with Backorders, or the Reorder Point method. The EOQ methods are deterministic and require the following input: the order cost, the holding cost, the lead time, and the mean demand. The EOQ with Backorders also requires a shortage cost input. The Reorder Point method is stochastic and requires the additional input of shortage cost and demand standard deviation. The application determines the order quantity, the number of orders, the time between orders, the reorder point, and the total costs, which consist of order costs, holding costs, and shortage costs.

CS3.1.1 Model Definition and Assumptions

For all model descriptions, we will use the following notation: Q = order quantity, K = order cost, h = holding cost, C = unit cost, S = shortage cost, D = mean demand. For each model, we are trying to determine the optimal order quantity that minimizes the total cost. The total cost, TC, is the sum of the order costs, holding costs, unit costs, and shortage cost.

$$TC = CD + hC(Q/2) + K(D/Q) + S(D - Q)$$

The EOQ model finds the optimal order quantity by solving the first order conditions of the total cost equation. Here, we do not assume a shortage cost; therefore, the total cost equation is simply the following:

$$TC = CD + hC(Q/2) + K(D/Q)$$

The optimal value for Q can be determined from the following result:

$$Q = \sqrt{\frac{2DK}{hC}}$$

The EOQ model with Backorders does consider a shortage cost. The first order conditions can then be solved to find Q, as follows:

$$Q = \sqrt{\frac{2KD}{hC}} * \sqrt{\frac{h+S}{S}}$$

The Reorder Point model considers a shortage cost, and, more importantly, it assumes that the demand is stochastic. Therefore, instead of assuming a constant demand equal to the mean demand D, it uses a normal distribution with the mean and standard deviation, V, of demand. We use this mean and standard deviation to compute the mean and standard deviation of the demand during lead time, L. We represent the mean demand during lead time with ? and the standard deviation of demand during lead time with σ. We compute these values as follows:

$$\mu = L * D$$

$$\sigma = \sqrt{V}$$

We perform a sequence of calculations to determine the optimal order quantity Q as well as the reorder point R. We begin by using the Standard EOQ method to find an estimate of Q. We then use this value to calculate the probability of reordering. Next, we standardize this probability to calculate the reorder point. We then use the reorder point in the loss function to estimate the expected number of shortages. The loss function is defined as an integral of the standard normal distribution where $\phi(t)$ is the density function of the standard normal distribution:

$$Loss(z) = \int_z^{\infty} (t - z)\phi(t)dt$$

With this value, we calculate Q in the next iteration. We perform three iterations of these calculations (we assume convergence after three iterations for simplicity):

1. $Q = \sqrt{\frac{2DK}{hC}}$
2. $P(Reorder) = \frac{hC * Q}{S * D}$
3. $z = F^{-1}$ (1–P(Reorder)), where $F(x)$ is the normal distribution function
4. $R = \sigma * z + \mu$
5. $E(Shortage) = \sigma * Loss(z)$
6. $Q = \sqrt{2D * \frac{K + S * E(Shortage)}{hC}}$

For more details on these methods, please refer to *Supply Chain Management: Strategy, Planning, and Operations* by Chopra and Miendl and *Production and Operations Analysis* by Nahmias.

CS3.1.2 Input

The input for this application is the following:

- The general input: order cost, holding cost, lead time, and mean demand. (The mean demand is either directly provided by the users or calculated from historical data provided by the users.)
- The standard EOQ method: only the general input.
- The EOQ with Backorders method: the general input and the shortage cost.
- The Reorder Point method: the general input, the shortage cost, and the standard deviation of demand.

CS3.1.3 Output

The output for this application is the following:

- Costs: Annual total costs, order costs, holding costs, and shortage costs
- Strategy: Order quantity, number of orders, time between orders, and reorder point
- Chart and table of inventory values for an example year using the solution strategy

CS3.2 Worksheets

This application requires four worksheets: the welcome sheet, the historical data sheet, the input sheet, and the results sheet. The welcome sheet contains the title, the description of the application, and the "Start" button. (See Figure CS3.1.) The "Start" button shows the users a form to determine how the demand information will be provided. If the users select to provide historical data, then the historical data sheet appears. The "Run Demo" button takes the users to the historical data sheet and enters demo historical data.

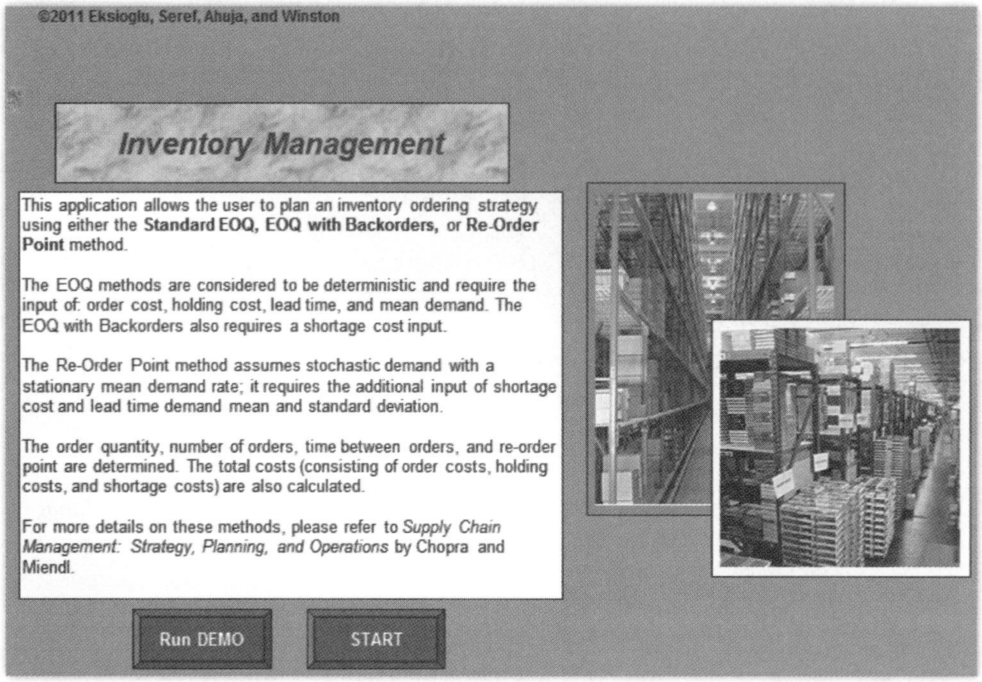

©2011 Eksioglu, Seref, Ahuja, and Winston
Inventory Management
This application allows the user to plan an inventory ordering strategy using either the Standard EOQ, EOQ with Backorders, or Re-Order Point method.
The EOQ methods are considered to be deterministic and require the input of: order cost, holding cost, lead time, and mean demand. The EOQ with Backorders also requires a shortage cost input.
The Re-Order Point method assumes stochastic demand with a stationary mean demand rate; it requires the additional input of shortage cost and lead time demand mean and standard deviation.
The order quantity, number of orders, time between orders, and re-order point are determined. The total costs (consisting of order costs, holding costs, and shortage costs) are also calculated.
For more details on these methods, please refer to Supply Chain Management: Strategy, Planning, and Operations by Chopra and Miendl.
Run DEMO
START

Figure CS3.1 The welcome sheet.

The historical data sheet allows the users to enter several demand values for past periods. (See Figure CS3.2.) We use these values to calculate the mean and standard deviation for the demand. We use the mean demand for the deterministic methods (EOQ and EOQ with backorders), and we use the standard deviation of the demand for the stochastic method (Reorder Point).

When the users are finished entering the historical demand or if they directly gave the mean demand on the welcome sheet's form, the input sheet next appears. The input sheet is the main sheet of the application. (See Figure CS3.3.) On this sheet, the users must enter the remaining general input: the order cost, the holding cost, and the lead time. They must then select the method to find the optimal inventory ordering strategy. If the users select the EOQ method, then no more input is necessary; they can see the solution by pressing the "Solve" button. If the users choose the EOQ with Backorders method, then the application requires a shortage cost before solving. If the users select the Reorder Point method, then the application requires a shortage cost and the demand standard deviation before solving. Note that even though the calculated mean and the standard deviation are shown in their respective input cells on this sheet, the users can overwrite or change them at any time.

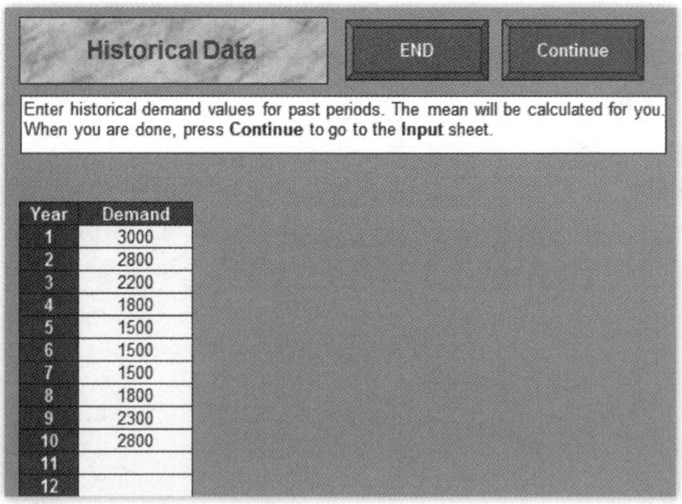

Figure CS3.2 The historical data sheet.

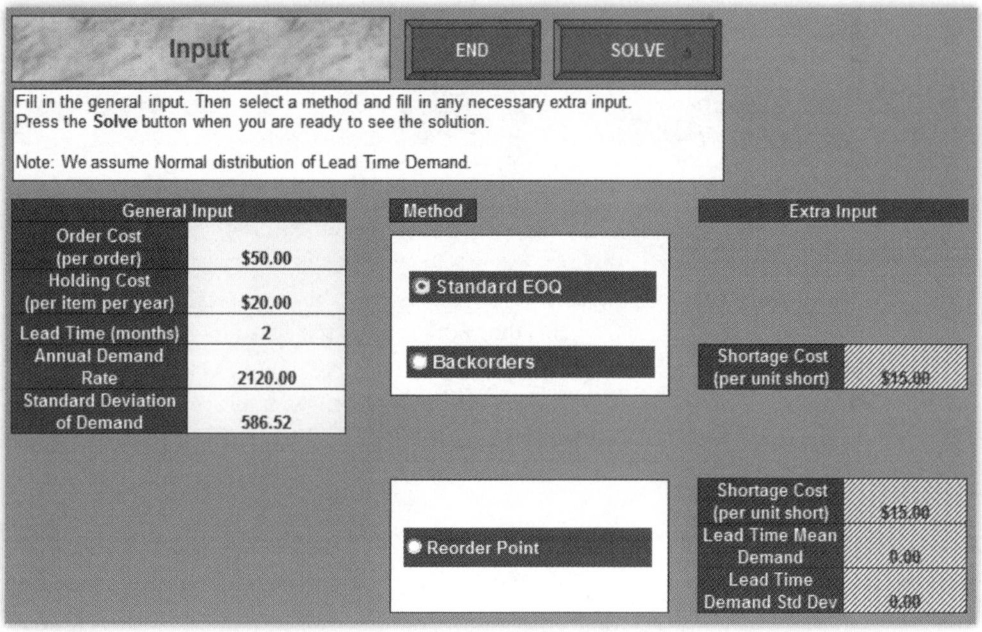

Figure CS3.3 The input sheet.

Once the problem has been solved, the users are taken to the results sheet. (See Figure CS3.4.) This sheet displays the costs and inventory ordering strategy for the found solution. The costs include the total annual cost, the annual ordering cost, the annual holding cost, and the annual shortage cost. The ordering strategy includes the order quantity, the number of orders, the time between orders, and the reorder point. A chart and table show the inventory levels for an example year of data following the solution strategy.

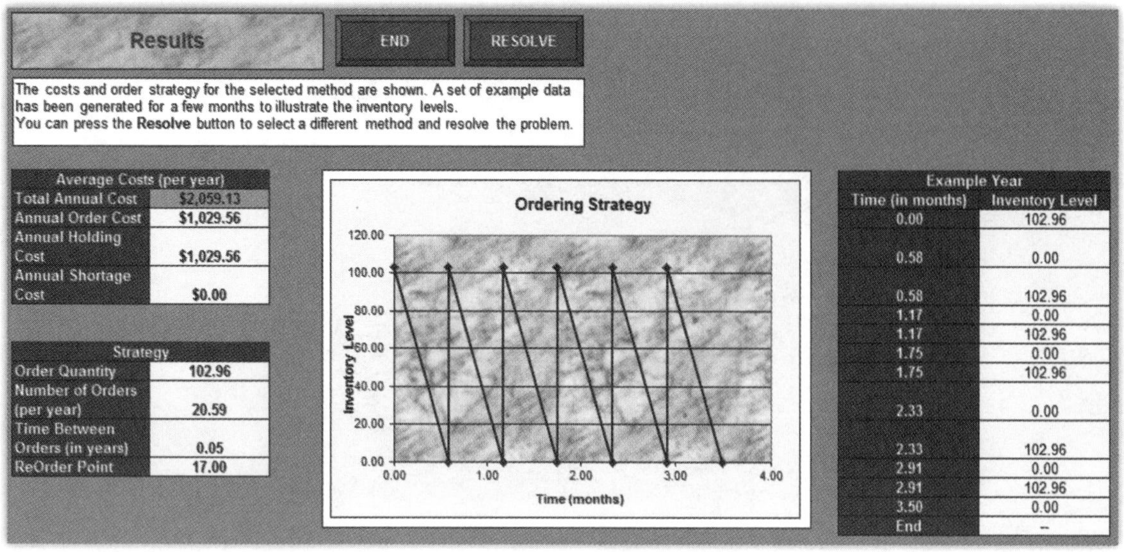

Figure CS3.4 The results sheet.

Summary

Welcome sheet	Contains the application description and the "Start" button.
Historical data sheet	Where the users can enter the historical demand data from which a mean and standard deviation are calculated.
Input sheet	Where the users provide all the necessary input and select the method that they wish to use to solve the problem.
Results sheet	Where the costs, the order strategy from the solution, and the chart of the inventory levels for the example year are displayed.

CS3.3 *User Interface*

For this application's user interface, we use navigational and functional buttons, controls on the worksheet, and a user form. On the welcome sheet, the "Start" button displays the data form. This form allows the users to decide if they will provide historical demand data (from which the mean and standard deviation are calculated) or a mean demand value directly. [See Figure CS3.5(a) and (b).]

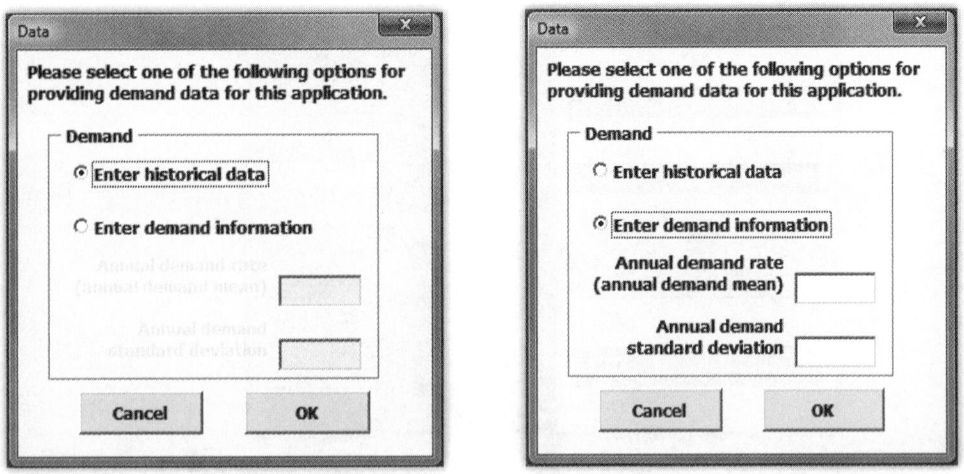

(a) (b)

Figure CS3.5 The data form.

On the input sheet, three option buttons allow the users to select the method to solve the problem. If they select the Standard EOQ option, then no further input is required. (See Figure CS3.6.) If they select the EOQ with the Backorders option, then the input cell for the shortage cost becomes available. (See Figure CS3.7.) If they select the Reorder Point option, then the input cells for the shortage cost and demand standard deviation become available. (See Figure CS3.8.)

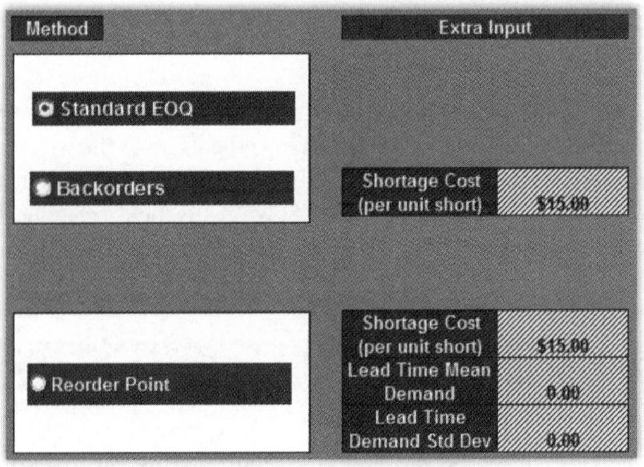

Figure CS3.6 Selecting the standard EOQ option button.

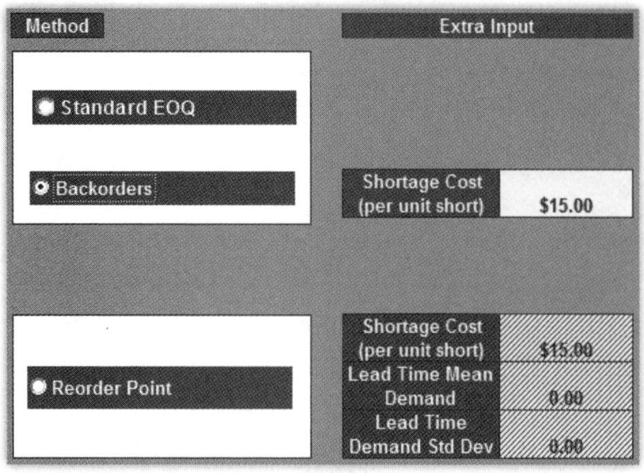

Figure CS3.7 Selecting the EOQ with the Backorders option button.

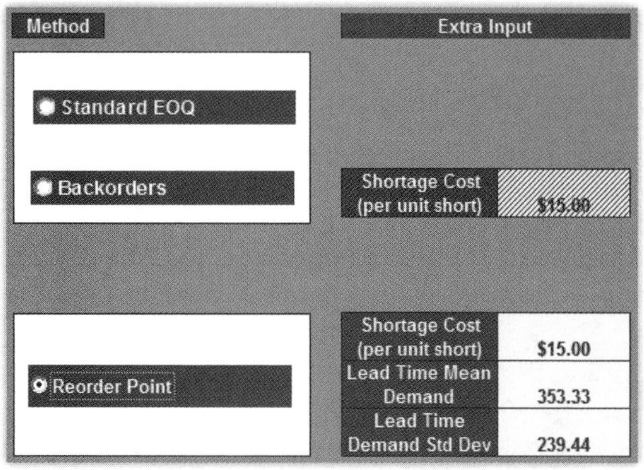

Figure CS3.8 Selecting the Reorder Point option button.

The "End" button is a navigational button that brings the users to the welcome sheet. The "Continue" and "Solve" buttons are both functional buttons. "Continue" calculates the mean and standard deviation of the historical demand, and "Solve" calls the corresponding procedure for the method the users have selected. We will discuss the "Re-solve" button, a navigational button, in Section CS3.5.

Summary

Navigational buttons	"Start" and "Run Demo" on the welcome sheet; "End" on all the sheets; "Re-solve" on the results sheet.
Functional buttons	"Solve" on the input sheet; "Continue" on the historical data sheet.
Controls on the worksheet	Option buttons on the input sheet allow the users to select the method to solve the problem.
Data form	Allows the users to select whether to provide historical demand data or give the mean demand directly.

CS3.4 Procedures

We will now outline the procedures for this application beginning with the initial sub procedures and variable definitions. (See Figure CS3.9.) The *Main* procedure, which is called from the "Start" button, calls the *ClearPrev* procedure and displays the data form. The *RunDemo* procedure also calls the *ClearPrev* procedure and copies and pastes the demo historical data to the historical data sheet; it then takes the users to the historical data sheet. The *ClearPrev* procedure clears any previous historical data and initializes several variables.

```
Option Explicit
Const pi = 3.14
Public i As Integer, OrdCost As Double, HoldCost As Double, LeadTime As Double, _
MeanDem As Double, ShortCost As Double, StdevDem As Double, OrdQuan As Double, _
OrdTime As Double, DoEOQ As Boolean, DoBackOrder As Boolean, DoReOrder As Boolean, _
EstDem As Double, VarCon As Double, EOQ As Double, ReOrderPt As Double, _
OrderTime As Double, MaxShort As Double, MeanLeadDem As Double, _
StdDevLeadDem As Double, ProbReOrder As Double, MeanNumShort As Double, _
ProbNumShort As Double, z As Double, StationaryCheck As Boolean

Sub Main()  'called from the Start button
    Call ClearPrev
    frmData.Show
End Sub

Sub RunDemo()   'called from the Run Demo button
    Call ClearPrev

    'copy and paste demo data
    Worksheets("DemoData").Range("DemoData").Copy
    Worksheets("HistData").Range("HistDemand").PasteSpecial xlPasteValues
    Application.CutCopyMode = False

    Worksheets("HistData").Visible = True
    Worksheets("Welcome").Visible = False
    Range("A1").Select
    MsgBox "The historical data has been entered for you."
End Sub

Sub ClearPrev() 'clears previous data values on historical demand sheet
    Worksheets("HistData").Range(Range("HistDemand"), Range("HistDemand"). _
            End(xlDown)).ClearContents

    DoEOQ = False
    DoBackOrder = False
    DoReOrder = False
    StationaryCheck = True
End Sub
```

Figure CS3.9 The variable declarations and the *Main*, *RunDemo*, and *ClearPrev* procedures.

The procedures for the data form record which option the users have selected. (See Figure CS3.10.) If the users choose to enter historical data, then the historical data sheet appears. If the users choose to provide the mean demand, then the mean demand is recorded and the users view the input sheet. Since this form is dynamic in that it only shows the mean demand text box if the corresponding option button is selected, there is also some small code to change the colors of this text box and label when the second option button is clicked.

```
Private Sub cmdCancel_Click()
    End
End Sub

Private Sub cmdOK_Click()
    If optHist Then
        Worksheets("HistData").Visible = True
    ElseIf optMean Then
        MeanDem = txtMean.Value
        StdevDem = txtStdev.Value
        Range("DemandMean").Value = MeanDem
        Range("DemandStdDev").Value = StdevDem
        Worksheets("Input").Visible = True
    End If

    Worksheets("Welcome").Visible = False
    Unload Me
End Sub

Private Sub optHist_Click()
    If optHist Then
        txtMean.BackColor = &H8000000B
        txtStdev.BackColor = &H8000000B
        lblMean.ForeColor = &H8000000B
        lblStdev.ForeColor = &H8000000B
    End If
End Sub

Private Sub optMean_Click()
    If optMean Then
        txtMean.BackColor = &HFFFFFF
        txtStdev.BackColor = &HFFFFFF
        lblMean.ForeColor = &H80000012
        lblStdev.ForeColor = &H80000012
    End If
End Sub
```

Figure CS3.10 The data form procedures.

If the users opt to enter historical data, then they press the "Continue" button to proceed to the input sheet. We assign this button to the *Continue* procedure. (See Figure CS3.11.) The *Continue* procedure calculates the mean and standard deviation of the provided demand values. Note that we require the user to have entered at least two values to ensure these calculations can be performed. The *DataCheck* function procedure is then called to check if the data is stationary. (See Figure CS3.15.) This check is necessary before assuming a constant demand when using the EOQ and EOQ with Backorders methods. The *Continue* procedure then initializes the input cells on the input sheet and takes the users to this sheet.

The *UserInput* procedure is called from the "Solve" button on the input sheet. (See Figure CS3.11.) It records the input values and then calls the corresponding procedure for the method the users have selected.

```
Sub Continue()  'called from Continue button on historical demand sheet
    'ensure values were entered
    If Application.WorksheetFunction.CountA(Range(Range("HistDemand"), _
    Range("HistDemand").End(xlDown))) < 2 Then
        MsgBox "Please enter at least 2 values."
        Exit Sub
    End If

    'calc mean and stdev
    Range(Range("HistDemand"), Range("HistDemand"). _
            End(xlDown)).Name = "Demands"
    MeanDem = Application.WorksheetFunction.Average(Range("Demands"))
    StdevDem = Application.WorksheetFunction.StDev(Range("Demands"))
    Range("DemandMean").Value = MeanDem
    Range("DemandStdDev").Value = StdevDem

    'initialize input sheet
    Range(Range("BackShort"), Range("BackShort").Offset(0, -1)). _
            Interior.Pattern = xlLightUp
    Range(Range("ReShort").Offset(0, -1), Range("LTDemandS")). _
            Interior.Pattern = xlLightUp
    Call DataCheck

    Worksheets("Input").Visible = True
    Worksheets("HistData").Visible = False
End Sub
```

```
Sub UserInput() 'called from Solve button on input sheet
    'record General Input
    OrdCost = Range("OrderCost").Value
    HoldCost = Range("HoldCost").Value
    LeadTime = Range("LeadTime").Value
    MeanDem = Range("DemandMean").Value
    StdevDem = Range("DemandStdDev").Value

    'Depending on method, record Extra Input and call
    'appropriate Solve procedure
    If DoEOQ Then
        Call SolveEOQ
    ElseIf DoBackOrder Then
        ShortCost = Range("BackShort").Value
        Call SolveBackOrder
    ElseIf DoReOrder Then
        ShortCost = Range("ReShort").Value
        MeanLeadDem = Range("LTDemandM").Value
        StdDevLeadDem = Range("LTDemandS").Value
        Call SolveReOrder
    End If
End Sub
```

Figure CS3.11 The *Continue* and *UserInput* procedures.

The *SolveEOQ* procedure is called to use the Standard EOQ method. (See Figure CS3.12.) This procedure begins by ensuring that the demand is stationary (by checking the variable set in the *DataCheck* function). If it is, then the EOQ and total costs are calculated. The application then displays the costs and strategy on the results sheet. Next, the *Results* procedure is called.

```
Sub SolveEOQ()  'Solve procedure for Standard EOQ method
    'check if data is stationary
    If StationaryCheck = False Then
        MsgBox "Your historical data is not stationary and " & _
            "constant demand cannot be assumed." & vbCrLf & _
            "Please either select another method to user " & _
            "or enter new historical data."
        Exit Sub
    End If

    'calculate EOQ and costs
    EOQ = Sqr((2 * OrdCost * MeanDem) / HoldCost)
    Range("AnnOrdCost").Value = OrdCost * MeanDem / EOQ
    Range("AnnHoldCost").Value = HoldCost * EOQ / 2
    Range("AnnShortCost").Value = 0

    'display strategy results
    Range("EOQ").Value = EOQ
    Range("NumOrd").Value = MeanDem / EOQ
    Range("TimeBtwn").Value = EOQ / MeanDem
    'Range("ReOrderPt").Value = "--"

    'calculate and display lead time
    If LeadTime * MeanDem <= EOQ Then
        Range("ReOrderPt").Value = LeadTime * MeanDem
    ElseIf LeadTime * MeanDem > EOQ Then
        Range("ReOrderPt").Value = (LeadTime * MeanDem) Mod EOQ
    End If

    'update results sheet
    Call Results
End Sub
```

Figure CS3.12 The *SolveEOQ* procedure.

The *SolveBackOrder* procedure is called to use the EOQ with Backorders method. (See Figure CS3.13.) The procedure begins by ensuring that the demand is stationary (again, by using the variable set in the *DataCheck* function). If it is, the application then calculates the EOQ and costs. The costs and strategy appear on the results sheet, and the *Results* procedure is then called.

```
Sub SolveBackOrder()    'Solve procedure for EOQ with Backorders method
    'check if data is stationary
    If StationaryCheck = False Then
        MsgBox "Your historical data is not stationary and constant demand cannot be assumed." & _
        vbCrLf & "Please either select another method to user or enter new historical data."
        Exit Sub
    End If

    'calculate EOQ and costs
    EOQ = (Sqr((2 * OrdCost * MeanDem) / HoldCost)) * Sqr((HoldCost + ShortCost) / ShortCost)
    MaxShort = (Sqr((2 * OrdCost * MeanDem) / HoldCost)) * Sqr(ShortCost / (HoldCost + ShortCost))
    Range("AnnOrdCost").Value = OrdCost * MeanDem / EOQ
    Range("AnnHoldCost").Value = (MaxShort ^ 2 * HoldCost) / (2 * EOQ)
    Range("AnnShortCost").Value = (((EOQ - MaxShort) ^ 2) * ShortCost) / (2 * EOQ)

    'display strategy results
    Range("EOQ").Value = EOQ
    Range("NumOrd").Value = MeanDem / EOQ
    Range("TimeBtwn").Value = EOQ / MeanDem
    'Range("ReOrderPt").Value = "--"

    'calculate and display lead time
    If LeadTime * MeanDem <= EOQ Then
        Range("ReOrderPt").Value = LeadTime * MeanDem
    ElseIf LeadTime * MeanDem > EOQ Then
        Range("ReOrderPt").Value = (LeadTime * MeanDem) Mod EOQ
    End If

    'update results sheet
    Call Results
End Sub
```

Figure CS3.13 The *SolveBackOrder* procedure

The application calls the *SolveReOrder* procedure to use the Reorder Point method. (See Figure CS3.14.) This procedure begins by finding the best order quantity and reorder point. To do so, we perform three iterations of these calculations in order to ensure accuracy by calling the *ReOrderIteration* procedure. The first iteration employs the standard EOQ method to find the order quantity, which is then used to find the probability of reordering. Next, this probability is standardized and used to find the reorder point; we use the *ZCheck* function to standardize the probability. The application then uses the reorder point with the loss function to find the expected number of shortages. This value is then employed to find the order quantity in the next iteration.

```
Sub SolveReOrder()
    'iterate to find best Q* and R
    'Q* = EOQ independent of lead time
    EOQ = Sqr((2 * OrdCost * MeanDem) / HoldCost)
    Call ReOrderIteration(EOQ)
    'update Q* using ProbNumShort
    EOQ = Sqr(2 * MeanDem * (OrdCost + ShortCost * ProbNumShort) / HoldCost)
    Call ReOrderIteration(EOQ)
    'last iteration
    EOQ = Sqr(2 * MeanDem * (OrdCost + ShortCost * ProbNumShort) / HoldCost)
    Call ReOrderIteration(EOQ)

    MeanNumShort = StdDevLeadDem * _
        (Application.WorksheetFunction.NormDist(ProbNumShort, 0, 1, False) - _
        ProbNumShort * (1 - Application.WorksheetFunction.NormSDist(ProbNumShort)))
    'check validity
    If (HoldCost * EOQ) / (ShortCost * MeanDem) > 1 Then
        MsgBox "The holding cost is too high relative to the shortage cost."
        Exit Sub
    End If

    Range("AnnOrdCost").Value = OrdCost * MeanDem / EOQ
    Range("AnnHoldCost").Value = HoldCost * (EOQ / 2 + ReOrderPt - MeanLeadDem)
    Range("AnnShortCost").Value = (ShortCost * MeanNumShort * MeanDem) / EOQ

    'display strategy results
    Range("EOQ").Value = EOQ
    Range("NumOrd").Value = MeanDem / EOQ
    Range("TimeBtwn").Value = EOQ / MeanDem
    Range("ReOrderPt").Value = ReOrderPt

    'update results sheet
    Call Results
End Sub
```

```
Sub ReOrderIteration(EOQ)
    ProbReOrder = (HoldCost * EOQ) / (ShortCost * MeanDem)
    Call ZCheck(ProbReOrder)
    ReOrderPt = StdDevLeadDem * z + MeanLeadDem
    ProbNumShort = StdDevLeadDem * LossFunc(z)
End Sub
```

Figure CS3.14 The *SolveReOrder* and *ReOrderIteration* procedures.

To use the loss function, we call the *LossFunc* function procedure by passing the standardized probability of reordering. This function finds the partial integration of the standard normal curve for this value. (See Figure CS3.15.)

```
Function DataCheck()
    'called to check if demand is stationary for deterministic methods
    'calculate estimated demand mean and variance
    i = 0
    Do While Range("HistDemand").Offset(i, 0).Value <> ""
        EstDem = (Range("HistDemand").Offset(i, 0).Value) ^ 2 - MeanDem ^ 2
        i = i + 1
    Loop
    EstDem = EstDem / i
    VarCon = EstDem / (MeanDem ^ 2)

    'if variance between estimated mean and actual mena is small then
    'demand is stationary
    If VarCon <= 0.2 Then
        StationaryCheck = True
    Else
        StationaryCheck = False
    End If
End Function
```

```
Function LossFunc(x)
    Dim Sum As Double, j As Double
    Sum = 0
    For j = x To 10 Step 0.01
        Sum = Sum + (Abs(j - x) * ((1 / Sqr(2 * pi)) * exp(-(j ^ 2) / 2)) * 0.01)
    Next j
    LossFunc = Sum
End Function
```

```
Function ZCheck(ProbReOrder)
    If ProbReOrder > 1 Then
        MsgBox "Please try a different lead time value or mean demand value " & _
               "to use this solution method."
        Worksheets("Input").optEOQ = True
        Worksheets("Input").optBackOrder = False
        Worksheets("Input").optReOrder = False
        End
    Else
        z = Application.WorksheetFunction.NormSInv(1 - ProbReOrder)
    End If
End Function
```

Figure CS3.15 The *DataCheck*, *LossFunc*, and *ZCheck* function procedures.

The application calls the *Results* procedure to update the results sheet after the selected method is completed. (See Figure CS3.16.) It generates example data and updates the chart to illustrate the inventory order strategy to the users. The results sheet is then displayed.

```
Sub Results()    'update results sheet
    'create chart data for set of example months
    Range("ChartStart").Offset(1, 0).Value = 0
    If DoReOrder Then
        Range("ChartSTart").Offset(1, 1).Value = EOQ + ReOrderPt
    Else
        Range("ChartSTart").Offset(1, 1).Value = EOQ
    End If
    i = 2
    OrderTime = 0
    Do While Range("ChartSTart").Offset(i, 0).Value <> "End"
        If Range("ChartStart").Offset(i - 1, 1).Value <= Range("ReOrderPt").Value Then
            Range("ChartStart").Offset(i, 1).Value = Range("ChartStart").Offset(i - 1, 1).Value + EOQ
            Range("ChartStart").Offset(i, 0).Value = Range("ChartStart").Offset(i - 1, 0).Value
        Else
            Range("ChartStart").Offset(i, 1).Value = Range("ChartStart").Offset(i - 1, 1).Value _
                                                     - MeanDem * Range("TimeBtwn").Value
            Range("ChartStart").Offset(i, 0).Value = Range("ChartStart").Offset(i - 1, 0).Value _
                                                     + Range("TimeBtwn").Value * 12
        End If
        i = i + 1
    Loop

    Worksheets("Results").Visible = True
    Worksheets("Input").Visible = False
End Sub
```

Figure CS3.16 The *Results* procedure.

The navigational procedures apply to the "End" and "Re-solve" buttons. (See Figure CS3.17.)

```
Sub Resolve()
    Worksheets("Input").Visible = True
    Worksheets("Results").Visible = False
    Worksheets("Input").Activate
End Sub
```

```
Sub EndProg()
    Worksheets("Welcome").Visible = True
    ActiveSheet.Visible = False
End Sub
```

Figure CS3.17 The navigational procedures.

Summary

Main	Initializes the application and displays the data form.
RunDemo	Copies the demo historical data and takes the users to the historical data sheet.
ClearPrev	Clears the previous historical data values and initializes the variables.
Data form procedures	Perform dynamic form formatting; record the users' option and either take the users to the historical data sheet or record the mean and display the input sheet.
Continue	Calculates the mean and standard deviation of the historical demand; calls the *DataCheck* function; takes the users to the input sheet.
UserInput	Records the input values and calls the procedure for the corresponding method the users have selected.
SolveEOQ	Performs calculations for the Standard EOQ method.
SolveBackOrder	Performs calculations for the EOQ with Backorders method.
SolveReOrder	Performs calculations for the Reorder Point method.
DataCheck	Checks if the data is stationary for the constant demand assumption for the deterministic methods.
LossFunc	Performs the integration of the loss function.
Results	Creates example data for the chart of the inventory levels for the solution strategy.
Navigational procedures	Apply to the "End" and "Re-solve" buttons.

CS3.5 Re-solve Options

The users can re-solve this application by pressing the "Re-solve" button on the results sheet. This takes the users back to the input sheet where they can modify any input values, including the mean demand. The users may also change the method for solving the problem. For example, compare the results of the demo data in Figures CS3.18, CS3.19, and CS3.20. The solutions vary for the Standard EOQ, EOQ with Backorders, and Reorder Point methods (shown respectively).

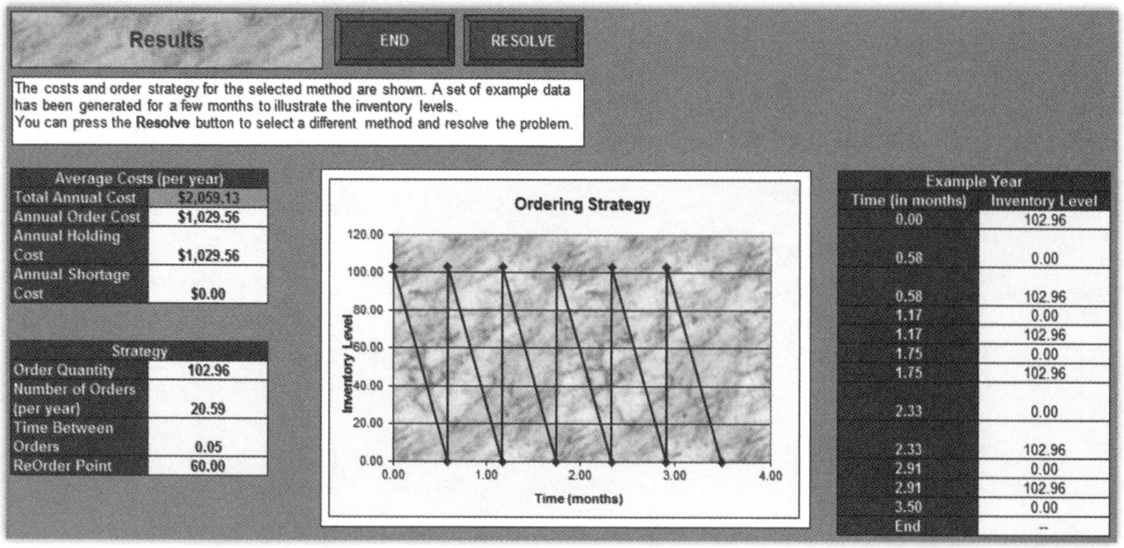

Figure CS3.18 The standard EOQ method results.

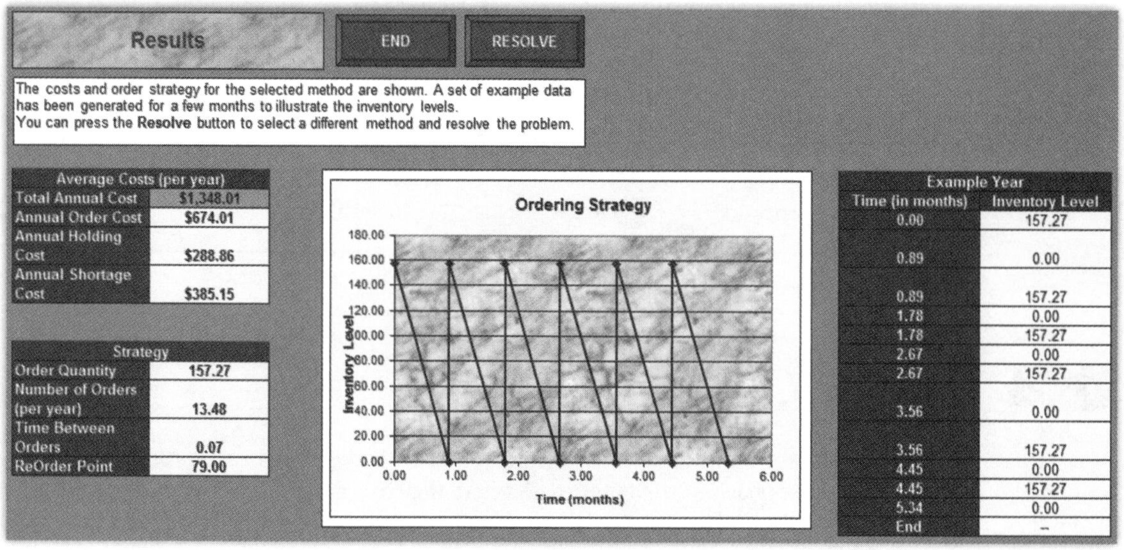

Figure CS3.19 The EOQ with Backorders method results.

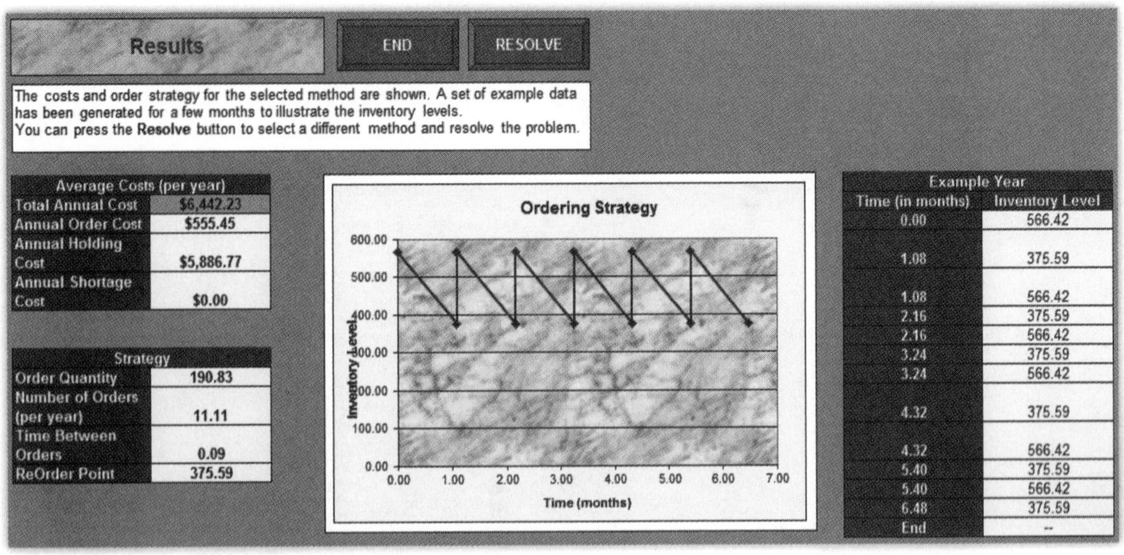

Figure CS3.20 The Reorder Point method results.

Summary

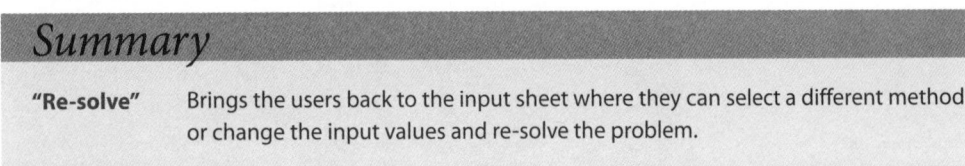

"Re-solve" Brings the users back to the input sheet where they can select a different method or change the input values and re-solve the problem.

CS3.6 Summary

- The Inventory Management application allows the users to plan an inventory ordering strategy using either the Standard EOQ, EOQ with Backorders, or Reorder Point method.
- This application requires four worksheets: the welcome sheet, the historical data sheet, the input sheet, and the results sheet.
- The user interface requires navigational and functional buttons, controls on the worksheet, and a user form.
- Several procedures in this application record the input values and perform the calculations using the selected method.
- The users can re-solve the application by pressing the "Re-solve" button on the results sheet to return to the input sheet. There, they can select a different method or change the input values and re-solve the problem.

CS3.7 Extensions

1. For the Reorder Point method, add the calculation of the safety stock. Ensure that this value is now also displayed on the results sheet.
2. Add a new method option for managing the inventory when Quantity Discounts are available. What procedures are affected? Is any new input needed? Are any new results displayed?
3. Add another re-solve option that allows the users to return to the historical data sheet to append more data and re-solve the problem with the same general input values. Ensure that the mean and standard deviation of the demand are updated.

CASE STUDY

four Warehouse Layout

chapter OVERVIEW

CS4.1 Application Overview and Model Development

This case study is a DSS application of the warehouse layout problem. The warehouse layout problem is to subdivide the floor area of a warehouse into storage areas for several product types so the total material handling cost between the storage areas and the warehouse docks is minimal.

CS4.1.1 Model Definition and Assumptions

For simplicity, we discretize the warehouse floor area into A unit grids, called bays; here, A represents the total warehouse area. We are seeking to allocate these bays to various product types. We will now describe this problem in greater detail. However, we will present some notations first for the three entities in the problem: the warehouse bays, the docks, and the product types.

- *Bays:* We decompose the warehouse floor area into A bays, indexed by $k = 1, 2, \ldots, A$.
- *Docks:* The warehouse has n docks indexed by $j = 1, 2, \ldots, n$. Products are brought into the warehouse and travel out of the warehouse by way of these docks. We represent the distance between each bay and each dock with d_{kj}.
- *Product types:* The warehouse layout problem has m product types indexed by $i = 1, 2, \ldots, m$. A product i requires an area of A_i bays in the warehouse. We assume that the warehouse has enough floor area to store all of the product types:

$$\sum_{i=1}^{m} A_i \leq A$$

In Figure CS4.1 we construct an example with five product types and two docks.

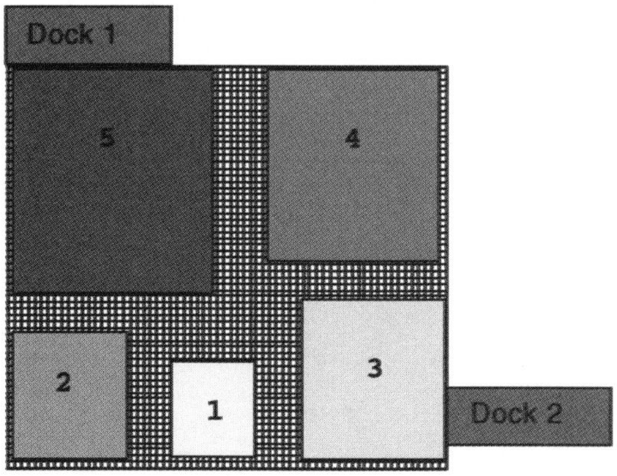

Figure CS4.1 Five different product types with different areas must be assigned to the warehouse area. Two docks are adjacent to the warehouse area.

Each product type i has a demand D_i. We assume that the demand for each product type i is uniformly divided over the entire storage area that the product type requires. Since product type i is stored on A_i bays, the total demand of product i per storage bay is D_i / A_i.

Each product type also interacts with the docks at a different frequency. The frequency is the fraction of the demand that travels in or out of the warehouse through a particular dock. We define these frequencies as F_{ij}. The sum of the frequencies over all docks for each product type should be 1:

$$\sum_{j=1}^{n} F_{ij} = 1, \quad \text{for all } i$$

We are seeking to assign product types to the warehouse area such that those with the highest demand per storage bay are situated closest to the docks with which they have the highest frequency. To enforce this policy during assignment, we define a weight W_{ij} to represent the amount of a particular product type i per storage bay that travels to and from a particular dock j. These weights are defined as follows:

$$W_{ij} = F_{ij} * D_i / A_i$$

Therefore, if product type i is stored at bay k, then the total material handling cost with dock j due to this storage is $d_{kj} * W_{ij}$. We define the assignment decision variables x_{ki} as binary variables to represent whether or not product type i is assigned to bay k:

x_{ki} = {1, if assignment was made; 0, if no assignment was made}

We can now formulate the warehouse layout problem as the following integer programming (IP) problem:

$$\text{(1) } \textit{Minimize} \quad \sum_{i=1}^{m} \sum_{j=1}^{n} \sum_{k=1}^{A} x_{ki} d_{kj} W_{ij}$$

Subject to:

$$\text{(1a) } \sum_{k=1}^{A} x_{ki} = A_i, \quad \text{for all } i$$

$$\text{(1b) } \sum_{i=1}^{m} x_{ki} \leq 1, \quad \text{for all } k$$

(1c) $x_{ki} = \{1, 0\}$, for all i and all k

This objective seeks to minimize the material handling cost between the assigned storage areas and the warehouse docks over all product types. The constraint (1a) states that only A_i bays are assigned for each product type i. Constraint (1b) states that only one product type can be assigned per bay.

This formulation is an IP problem and can be solved with an IP algorithm. (For more details, please see "Facility Layout and Location" by Francis and White.) In this application, however, we will consider a special case of the objective function (1) that can be solved very efficiently using a greedy method.

Recall that W_{ij} represents the amount of a particular product type i per storage bay that travels to and from a particular dock j. We assume that the m by n matrix $W = \{W_{ij}\}$ factors; that is, there exist numbers α_i and β_j, such that, as follows:

$$W_{ij} = \alpha_i * \beta_j \quad \text{for all } i \text{ and all } j$$

We may point out that not every matrix W factors; only some do. When a matrix W factors, we can provide an intuitive explanation to the factors α_i and β_j. Let α_i denote the total demand of product type i per storage bay over all docks, and let β_j denote the frequency with which each dock is used:

$$\alpha_i = D_i / A_i$$

$$\beta_j = F_j$$

We now have the following:

$$W_{ij} = \alpha_i * \beta_j = D_i/A_i * F_j$$

The factoring assumption implies that each product type has the same dock frequency for a dock j as any other product type. This frequency, formerly noted as F_{ij}, is now noted as F_j or β_j. For example, if there are two docks with frequencies $\beta_1 = 0.4$ and $\beta_2 = 0.6$, then the factoring assumption implies that each product type sends 40% of its demand per storage area through dock 1 and 60% of it through dock 2.

In this case, when the matrix W factors, we can restate the objective function of the warehouse layout problem as follows:

$$\text{(2) Minimize} \quad \sum_{i=1}^{m} \sum_{k=1}^{A} x_{ki} \alpha_i \left(\sum_{j=1}^{n} d_{kj} \beta_j \right)$$

We can now observe that since α_i denotes the total demand of product type i per storage bay over all docks, the greater the value of α_i for any product type, the greater the interaction this product will have with the docks. Therefore, we want to ensure that these product types with the highest α_i values are assigned to the bays with the minimum distance from the docks.

We also observe that for any bay k, $\Sigma_j\, d_{kj} * \beta_j$ denotes the average distance traveled per unit demand for any product type stored at that bay; in other words, with probability β_j, the assigned product type will travel to dock j incurring the distance d_{kj}. We now define the value y_k to denote the weighted distances between each bay k and each dock j as follows:

$$y_k = \sum_{j=1}^{n} d_{kj} \beta_j, \quad \text{for all } k$$

It should now be intuitively clear that to minimize the total material handling cost, product types with high priority weight values should be assigned to bays with small distance weights. This intuition suggests the following greedy algorithm for the warehouse layout problem:

1. Sort the weighted distances y_k in ascending order for each bay k.
2. Sort the product type weights α_i in descending order for each product type i.
3. Assign the highest weighted product type i to the first A_i bays from the sorted weighted distance list.

This algorithm ensures that the product types with the highest weight are assigned to the bays with the smallest distance weights. Therefore, the overall distance traveled by each product type to each dock should be minimized.

Let us now illustrate this algorithm with a small numerical example. Consider a warehouse of area $A = 100$ and two docks (see Figure CS4.2).

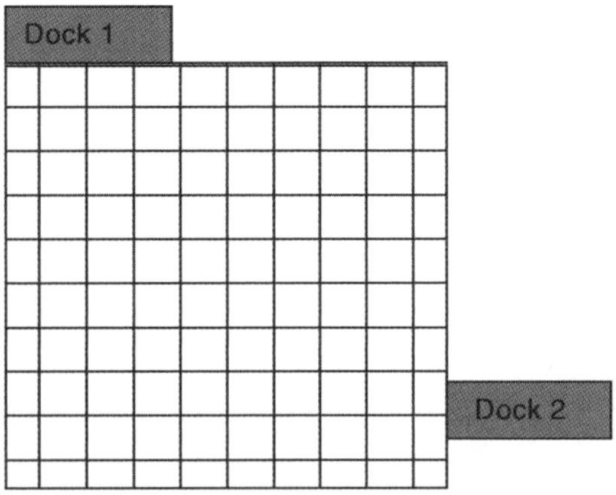

Figure CS4.2 The warehouse area is discretized into bay areas of value 1.

We assume that there are five product types. The product type area requirements and demands are as follows:

Product Type: *i*	Area: *Ai*	Demand: *Di*
1	10	300
2	15	250
3	20	400
4	25	500
5	30	450

Assuming that dock frequencies are the same for all product types, we use the following frequency values for the two docks:

$F_1 = 35\%$

$F_2 = 65\%$

With these values, we can now calculate the α_i values for each product type i and the y_k values for each bay k. If we sort the product types in descending order of their α_i values and the bays in ascending order of their y_k values, applying the greedy algorithm yields the following bay assignments:

Product type	α_i	y_k for assigned bays k	Total area assigned
1	300 / 10 = 30	2, 5, 7, 9, 12, 15, 18, 19, 23, 28	10
3	400 / 20 = 20	30, 32, 34, 36, 38, 39, 40, 43, 44, 46, 48, 49, 50, 54, 57, 59, 62, 64, 67, 68	20
4	500 / 25 = 20	73, 76, 78, 79, 80, 83, 85, 87, 88, 89, 92, 93, 95, 97, 101, 104, 107, 109, 111, 114, 115, 116, 118, 119, 122	25
5	450 / 25 = 18	125, 127, 129, 131, 135, 137, 138, 139, 142, 143, 145, 147, 148, 152, 156, 157, 159, 160, 163, 164, 167, 168, 169, 173, 178, 179, 182, 184, 187, 189	30
2	250 / 15 = 16.67	191, 193, 194, 197, 198, 201, 204, 205, 206, 208, 210, 214, 215, 217, 218	15

Notice that the total number of bays assigned to each product type is equal to the product type areas A_i. See Figure CS4.3 for the final layout for this example.

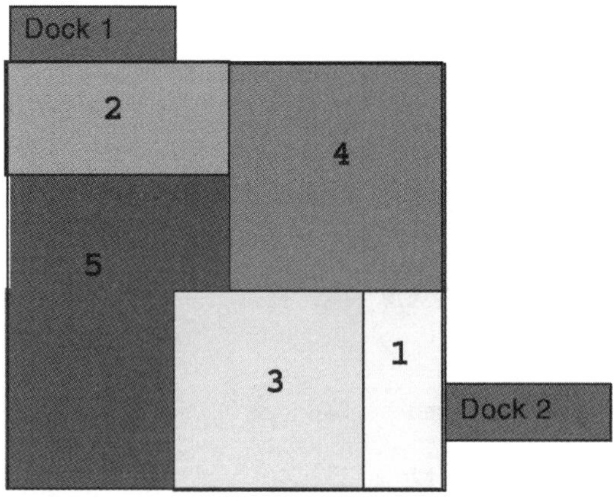

Figure CS4.3 The final warehouse layout for five products and two docks.

Summary

Algorithm

1. Sort the bays in ascending order of their weighted distances.
2. Sort the product types in descending order of their weights.
3. Assign the highest weighted product type to the first bays from the sorted weighted distance list until the product type area requirement is satisfied.

CS4.1.2 Input

Using the model described in the above section, we can define the following input:

- The area of the warehouse
- The number of docks
- The dock locations
- The dock frequencies
- The number of product types
- The area required per product type
- The demand per product type

We consider the area of the warehouse as the total number of bays available for assignment. The area required per product type is basically the number of bays to assign per product type.

We use one user form and two input sheets in this application to receive these input values from the users. We do not place any bounds on these inputs. We do provide default values for a warehouse area of 30: 3 product types and 2 docks. However, the users may change these values.

CS4.1.3 Output

Our main output is the warehouse layout. We present this output to the users using different color cells to represent the different product types. The product type color representation is summarized in a legend next to the warehouse grid. The docks are also displayed in their specified locations adjacent to the grid. We include several navigational buttons as well as some re-solve options, which we will discuss in more detail later.

CS4.2 *Worksheets*

We use four worksheets in this application: a welcome sheet, two input sheets, and an output sheet. In the welcome sheet, we describe the warehouse layout problem and provide an overview of what the users will input and what output will be displayed (see Figure CS4.4). We also include some images of a warehouse and a "Start" button. The "Start" button is assigned to our Main sub procedure, which we will discuss later.

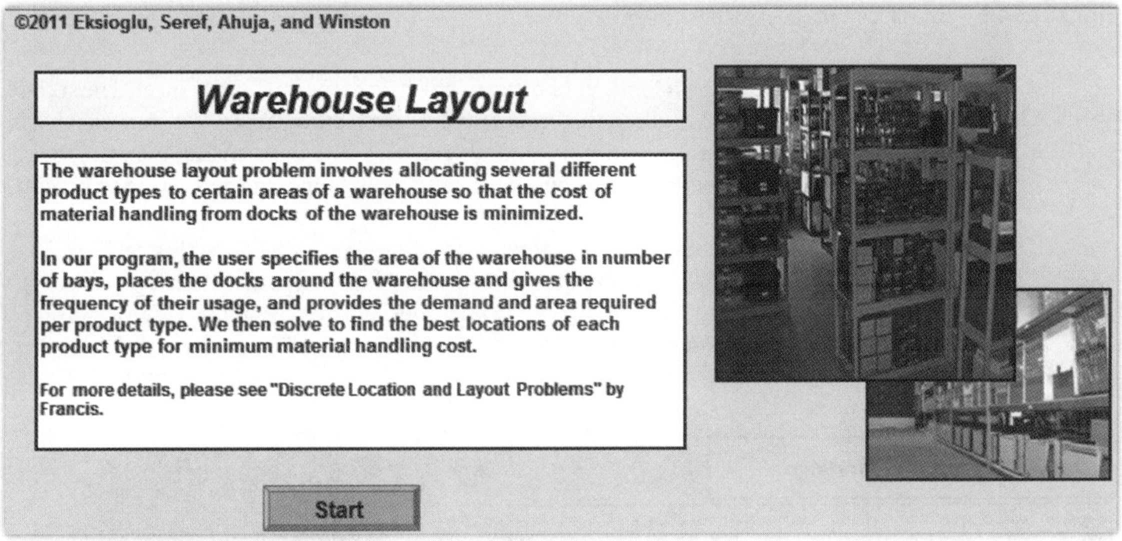

Figure CS4.4 The welcome sheet.

The next worksheet that the users see is the first of two input sheets. Before the users arrive at this sheet, they will complete a user form with the area of the warehouse, the number of product types, and the number of docks. (We will discuss the form in more detail in the next section.) From this information, we create a grid representing the warehouse area on the first input sheet. The first input sheet allows the users to place the docks adjacent to the warehouse grid. There are some event procedures associated with the worksheet that allow the users to simply click on the location of a dock to reveal the dock number and formatting. We will discuss the details of these procedures later.

We also create a table, which the users must complete, for the dock information. Based on the placement of the docks adjacent to the warehouse grid, the users must enter the number of the bay that each dock is adjacent to. This information will help us determine the distance from each bay to each dock. The users must also enter the dock frequencies at this point. The frequencies should sum to 100%. In Figure CS4.5, we present an example with two docks located near bays 1 and 19 with frequencies 20% and 80%, respectively.

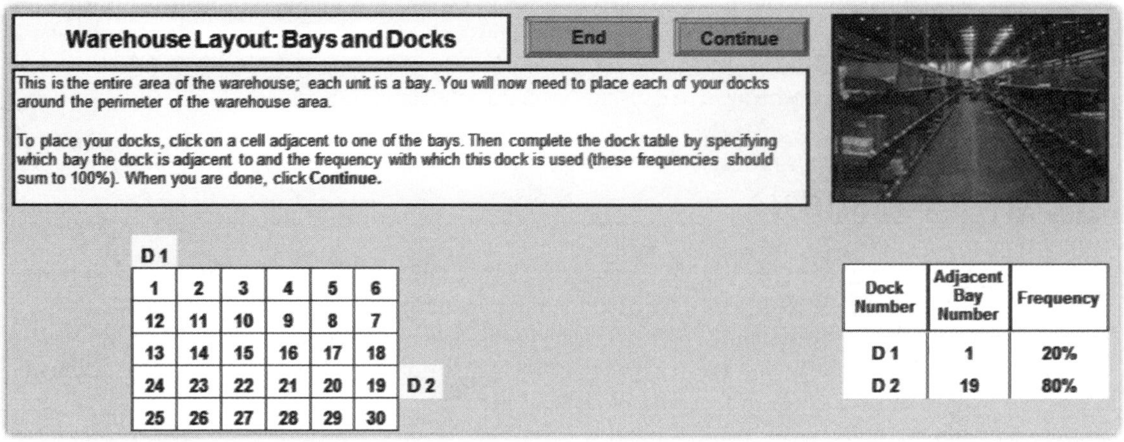

Figure CS4.5 The first input sheet for dock information.

The users then press the "Continue" button to navigate to the next input sheet. The second input sheet is for information about the product types (see Figure CS4.6). We create a table in which the users enter the area requirement (number of bays) and the demand for each product type. The sum of the number of bays required over all product types must be less than or equal to the available number of bays in the warehouse.

In Figure CS4.6, we continue the example shown in Figure CS4.5. In this case, we have three product types with area requirements of 2, 4, and 7 bays, respectively. The product type demands are 300, 500, and 600, respectively. We may note here that the weights for each product type are 150, 125, and 85.7, respectively ($\alpha_i = D_i / A_i$). Therefore, product type 1 has the highest priority, then product type 2, then product type 3.

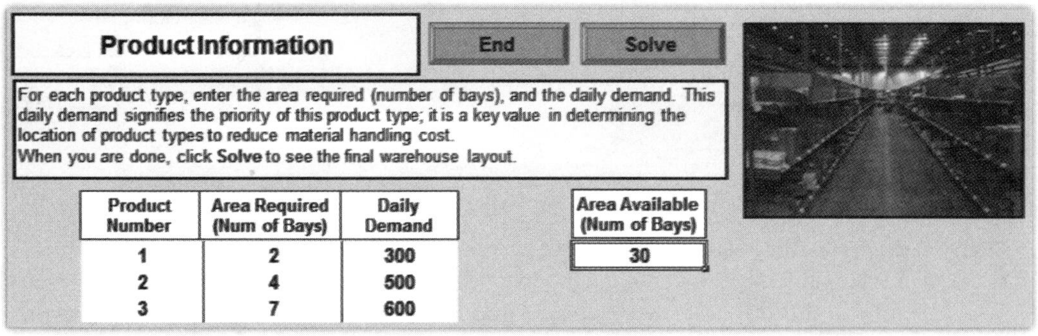

Figure CS4.6 The second input sheet for product information.

The users then press the "Solve" button to run the main calculation procedures and perform the greedy algorithm. The output sheet then appears (see Figure CS4.7). The output sheet reveals the final layout for all of the product types in the warehouse area. We color each product type differently and provide a legend for this representation. In Figure CS4.7, we can observe that product type 1 (which had the highest priority) was assigned to the bays closest to the second dock (which had the highest frequency).

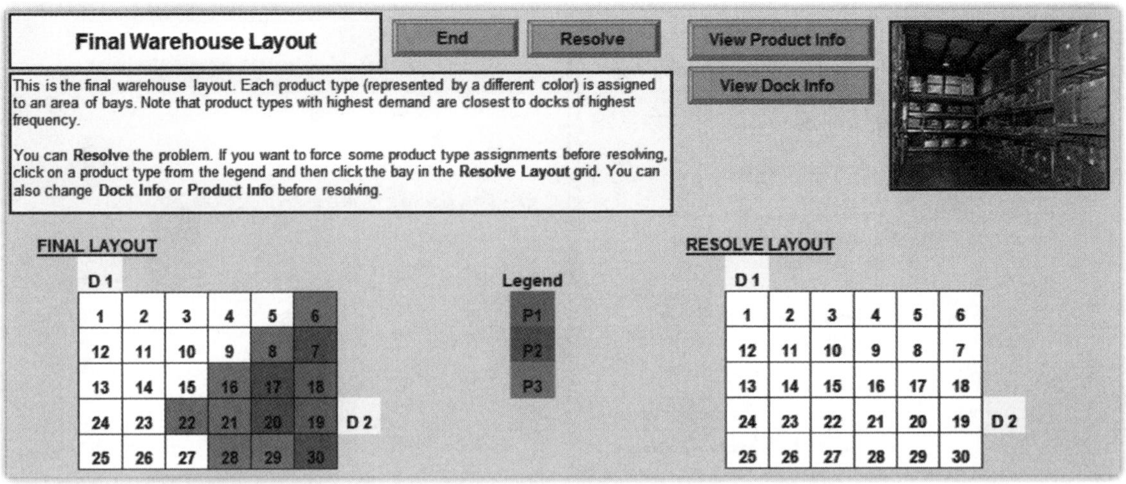

Figure CS4.7 The output sheet with its navigational buttons and re-solve options.

There are some re-solve options and navigational buttons here as well. We will discuss these in more detail in a later section.

Summary

Welcome sheet	Problem description and "Start" button.
First input sheet	Dock input table, initial layout for dock placements, "End" and "Continue" buttons.
Second input sheet	Product type input table, "End," and "Solve" buttons.
Output sheet	Final layout with product type bay assignment, legend for product type colors, re-solve layout area, "End," "Re-solve," "View Product Info," and "View Dock Info" buttons.

CS4.3 *User Interface*

For this application, we include several navigational buttons, some functional buttons, one user form, and two input sheets. We begin the application by displaying the user form after the users press the "Start" button from the welcome sheet. The form prompts the users for the number of product types, the number of docks, and the area of the warehouse. We ask the users to define the area of the warehouse by its dimensions; that is, by the number of rows and columns needed to construct the warehouse area assuming each bay is represented by one row by one column. The form is shown in Figure CS4.8.

We employ two frames to group similar text boxes together. The first frame contains the text boxes for the number of product types and number of docks. The second frame contains the warehouse dimensions values: the number of rows and the number of columns. We have entered default values for three product types, two docks, and a warehouse area of 30 bays. The "Cancel" button simply unloads the form, leaving the users at the welcome sheet. The "OK" button performs some error checking and assigns the input values to corresponding variables. It then takes the users to the first input sheet.

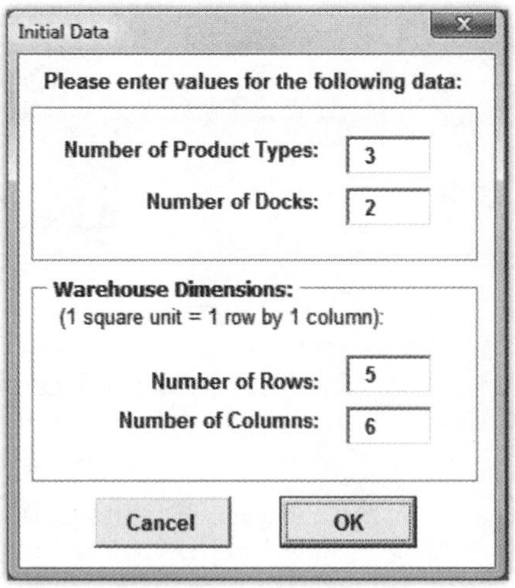

Figure CS4.8 The user form asks for the first input values.

The first input sheet, discussed in the previous section, has two buttons: "End" and "Continue" (see Figure CS4.5). The "End" button closes the sheet and returns the users to the welcome sheet. The "Continue" button performs some error checking, records the dock information that the users have entered in the table, closes the sheet, and takes the users to the next input sheet.

On the second input sheet, also discussed in the previous section, there are two buttons: "End" and "Solve" (see Figure CS4.6). The "End" button has the same functionality as in the previous sheet. The "Solve" button performs some error checking, records the product type information the users have entered in the table, and then calls the main procedures to perform the greedy algorithm. It then closes the sheet and takes the users to the output sheet.

The output sheet has a few more buttons (see Figure CS4.7). The "End" button is again the same as the others. There are then two navigational buttons, which allow the users to revisit the input sheets: "View Product Info" and "View Dock Info." These buttons simply close the output sheet and take the users to the respective input sheet. When the users revisit an input sheet, a new button appears to "Go Back" to the output sheet. This "Go Back" button replaces the "Continue" and "Solve" buttons.

There is also a "Re-solve" button on the output sheet. This button is used to record any changes that the users have made to either of the input sheets or to the "Re-solve Layout" and then re-solves the problem. We will discuss the meaning of the "Re-solve Layout" and other re-solve functions in a later section.

Summary

Input Form	Number of products, number of docks, warehouse dimensions in number of rows and columns.
First Input Sheet	Dock location in terms of adjacent bay, dock frequencies.
Second Input Sheet	Required area and demand per product type.
Navigational Buttons	"End," "View Product Info," "View Dock Info," "Go Back."
Functional Buttons	"Start," "Continue," "Solve," "Re-solve."

CS4.4 Procedures

We will now outline the procedures for this application. We begin with the Main sub procedure and the variable definitions (see Figure CS4.8). We define several variables as public variables since they will be used in multiple procedures. We have variables to represent the problem dimensions, such as the number of product types and the number of docks. We also include some counting variables for loops, several arrays for the preparation calculations, and several variables to be used in the algorithm.

The *Main* procedure begins by calling the *ClearPrevious* procedure, which clears the cell values and all the sheets' formatting in the application (see Figure CS4.9 and CS4.10). It also ensures that the original buttons on the input sheets are visible and hides the "Go Back" buttons. Lastly, it initializes some variables.

```
Option Explicit
Option Base 1

Public NProds As Integer, NRows As Integer, NCols As Integer, _
NDocks As Integer, NBays As Integer, i As Integer, j As Integer, _
k As Integer, XCoord() As Integer, YCoord() As Integer, ACoord() As Integer, _
BCoord() As Integer, Area() As Integer, Demand() As Integer, _
DFreq() As Double, WtDist() As Double, ItemOrder() As Integer, _
BayOrder() As Integer, Sum As Double, DockCount As Integer, _
ProdColor() As Integer, PColor As Integer, FixedBay() As Boolean, _
PIndex As Integer, UserReady1 As Boolean, UserReady2 As Boolean, _
ResolveCalled As Boolean, FixedProd() As Integer

Sub MAIN()
'Assigned to the "Start" button on the "Welcome" sheet

    Call ClearPrevious
    frmInitialData.Show

    'reset any previous resolve conditions (no assignements are enforced)
    NBays = NRows * NCols
    ReDim FixedProd(NProds), FixedBay(NBays)
    For i = 1 To NProds
        FixedProd(i) = 0
    Next i
    For k = 1 To NBays
        FixedBay(k) = False
    Next k

    'assign product colors
    Dim BayCol As Integer
    ReDim ProdColor(NProds)
    BayCol = 7
    For i = 1 To NProds
        ProdColor(i) = BayCol
        BayCol = BayCol + 5
    Next i

    Call NumberingBay
    UserReady1 = True

    Worksheets("Layout").Visible = True
    Worksheets("Welcome").Visible = False
    Worksheets("Layout").Activate
    Range("A1").Select
End Sub
```

Figure CS4.9 The *Main* procedure and public variable declarations.

The *Main* procedure then displays the input form (see Figure CS4.8). The main code associated with this form is in the *Click* event procedure of the "OK" button (see Figure CS4.11). This procedure performs some error checking to ensure that all of the input values have been provided. It then assigns the input values to their corresponding variables. At this point, we know the number of product types, the number of docks, and the area of the warehouse. We refer to the area of the warehouse by the number of bays, which is equal to the number of rows multiplied by the number of columns, as provided by the users.

```
Sub ClearPrevious()
'Called from the Main procedure; clears previous values,
'resets formatting, and initializes some variables

    Application.ScreenUpdating = False
    Dim ws As Worksheet
    For Each ws In ActiveWorkbook.Sheets
        If ws.Name <> "Welcome" Then
            ws.Cells.ClearContents
            ws.Cells.Borders.LineStyle = xlNone
            ws.Cells.Interior.ColorIndex = xlNone
        End If
    Next

    Worksheets("Layout").Shapes("ReturnLayout").Visible = False
    Worksheets("Layout").Shapes("ContLay").Visible = True

    Worksheets("ProductInfo").Shapes("ReturnLayout").Visible = False
    Worksheets("ProductInfo").Shapes("ContProd").Visible = True

    ResolveCalled = False
    UserReady1 = False
    UserReady2 = False
    DockCount = 1

    Application.ScreenUpdating = True
End Sub
```

Figure CS4.10 The *ClearPrevious* procedure clears the values and the formatting on all sheets; it also initializes some variables.

```
Sub cmdCancel_Click()
'close the form

    Unload Me
    End
End Sub
```

```
Sub cmdOK_Click()
'error checking that all input given;
'record values to corresponding variables

    Dim ctl As Control
    For Each ctl In Me.Controls
        If TypeName(ctl) = "TextBox" Then
            If ctl.Value = "" Then
                MsgBox "Please make sure " & _
                    "all textboxes are filled in."
                ctl.SetFocus
                Exit Sub
            End If
        End If
    Next

    NProds = txtNumProd.Value
    NRows = txtNumRows.Value
    NCols = txtNumCols.Value
    NDocks = txtNumDocks.Value

    Unload Me
End Sub
```

Figure CS4.11 The *cmdOK_Click* procedure assigns the input values to their corresponding variables.

The *Main* procedure continues by resetting some arrays used for the re-solve options and then assigning colors to the product types. Then, we call the *NumberingBay* procedure, which numbers the warehouse grid and computes the X and Y coordinates of each bay (see Figure CS4.12).

The procedure begins by creating the initial warehouse layout. We move from row 1 to the number of rows and from column 1 to the number of columns and then back to column 1 and so forth, labeling each bay in the warehouse area. We set the X and Y coordinates equal to the row and column values of each created bay. These coordinates are stored in two arrays.

The *NumberingBay* procedure continues by preparing the input tables for the docks and the product types based on the input users have provided in the input form. The dock table is created on the first input sheet while the product type table is created on the second input sheet. The total number of bay areas is also recorded on the second input sheet. Returning to the *Main* procedure, we now simply take the users to the first input sheet.

```
Sub NumberingBay()
'Called from the Main procedure; creates the warehouse area Bay;
'computes X and Y coord for each bay; creates dock table,
'creates product information table

    Application.ScreenUpdating = False
    ReDim XCoord(NBays), YCoord(NBays)
    Dim u As Integer, v As Integer, increment As Integer

    u = 1
    v = 1
    increment = 1

    'number bays and calculate x and y coordinates
    For k = 1 To NBays
        XCoord(k) = u
        YCoord(k) = v
        With Range("Layout").Offset(v, u)
            .Value = k
            .Interior.ColorIndex = 2
            .BorderAround Weight:=xlThin
        End With

        u = u + increment
        'ensure that dimensions of warehouse area are honored
        If u > NCols Then
            u = NCols
            v = v + 1
            increment = -increment
        ElseIf u = 0 Then
            u = 1
            v = v + 1
            increment = -increment
        End If
    Next k

    'ranges named for interface on first input sheet
    Range(Range("Layout").Offset(1, 1), Range("Layout").Offset(NRows, NCols)).Name = "BayArea"
    Range(Range("Layout"), Range("Layout").Offset(NRows + 1, NCols + 1)).Name = "DockArea"
```

(a)

```
    'tables are created
    For j = 1 To NDocks
        With Range(Range("Docks").Offset(j, 0), Range("Docks").Offset(j, 2))
            .Interior.ColorIndex = 2
            .Borders(xlInsideVertical).Weight = xlThin
        End With
        Range("Docks").Offset(j, 0).Value = "D " & j
    Next j

    For i = 1 To NProds
        With Range(Range("Products").Offset(i, 0), Range("Products").Offset(i, 2))
            .Interior.ColorIndex = 2
            .Borders(xlInsideVertical).Weight = xlThin
        End With
        Range("Products").Offset(i, 0).Value = i
    Next i

    With Range("ProdArea")
        .Value = NBays
        .Interior.ColorIndex = 2
        .BorderAround Weight:=xlThin
    End With

    Application.ScreenUpdating = True
End Sub
```

(b)

Figure CS4.12 The *NumberingBay* procedure defines the initial warehouse layout. (a) The beginning of the procedure. (b) The procedure continued.

On this sheet, the users are able to place the docks around the warehouse area simply by clicking on a cell. To enable this feature, we have written an event procedure for the *Selection-Change* event of the worksheet (see Figure CS4.13). We first check if the active cell is in a range where the docks are allowed to be placed. This range can be defined as the intersection of the warehouse area with an additional one-unit circumference and all other cells. We define this intersection with a logical check and two *Union* worksheet functions.

Once we ensure that the users have clicked a cell in the allowable dock location area, we check that they have not already placed all of the docks. If this condition is false, then we label the cell with "D" and the current dock number.

```
Private Sub Worksheet_SelectionChange(ByVal Target As Range)
'allows user to place docks adjacent to warehouse area

    If UserReady1 Then
    'check that selected cell is in the possible dock placement area
        If Application.Union(ActiveCell, Range("DockArea")).Address _
                = Range("DockArea").Address And _
            Application.Union(ActiveCell, Range("BayArea")).Address _
                <> Range("BayArea").Address Then

            'check that number of docks placed is less than or
            'equal to total number of docks
            If ActiveCell.Value = "" And DockCount <= NDocks Then
                ActiveCell.Value = "D " & DockCount
                DockCount = DockCount + 1
                ActiveCell.Interior.ColorIndex = 36
            ElseIf ActiveCell.Value <> "" Then
                ActiveCell.ClearContents
                ActiveCell.Interior.ColorIndex = xlNone
                DockCount = DockCount - 1
            End If
        End If
    End If

End Sub
```

Figure CS4.13 The *SelectionChange* event procedure enables the users to click on the sheet to place the docks.

We assign the next procedure, *DockInfo*, (see Figure CS4.14) to the "Continue" button on the first input sheet. The procedure begins with two error checks to ensure that the dock table has been completely filled and that the dock frequencies sum to 100 percent. We then determine the X and Y coordinates for each dock.

Knowing that the docks are placed adjacent to the warehouse area and given the bay numbers to which each dock is adjacent, we can find the dock coordinates by determining which border the adjacent bay is on. If the adjacent bay is on the top or bottom border of the warehouse area (that is, on the first or last row), then the X coordinate is zero or one more than the number of rows, respectively. The Y coordinate is the same as the Y coordinate of the adjacent bay. If the adjacent bay is on the left or right border of the warehouse area (that is, on the first or last column), then the Y coordinate is zero or one more than the number of columns, respectively. The X coordinate is the same as that of the adjacent bay.

We also record the dock frequencies into an array. Finally, we take the users to the second input sheet.

```
Sub DockInfo()
'Assigned to the "Continue" button on the first input sheet;
'records the dock locations; computes dock X and Y coord;
'records dock frequencies

    'error checking that dock table was filled
    If Range("Docks").Offset(1, 0).Value = "" Or _
            Range("Docks").Offset(1, 1).Value = "" Then
        MsgBox "You have not completely filled out this sheet."
        Exit Sub
    End If

    Application.ScreenUpdating = False
    ReDim ACoord(NDocks), BCoord(NDocks), DFreq(NDocks)

    'error checking that sum of frequencies is 100 percent
    Sum = 0
    For j = 1 To NDocks
        Sum = Sum + Range("Docks").Offset(j, 2)
    Next j
    If Sum <> 1 Then
        MsgBox "The sum of dock frequencies should be 100 percent." & _
                "Please correct your data and press Next again."
        Exit Sub
    End If

    'X and Y coord of docks calculated based on adjacent bays
    For j = 1 To NDocks
       k = Range("Docks").Offset(j, 1).Value
       If XCoord(k) = NCols Then
            ACoord(j) = NCols + 1
            BCoord(j) = YCoord(k)
        ElseIf XCoord(k) = 1 Then
            ACoord(j) = 0
            BCoord(j) = YCoord(k)
        ElseIf YCoord(k) = NRows Then
            BCoord(j) = NRows + 1
            ACoord(j) = XCoord(k)
        ElseIf YCoord(k) = 1 Then
            BCoord(j) = 0
            ACoord(j) = XCoord(k)
        End If

        DFreq(j) = Range("Docks").Offset(j, 2).Value
    Next j

    Range("A1").Select
    Worksheets("ProductInfo").Visible = True
    Worksheets("Layout").Visible = False
    Application.ScreenUpdating = True
End Sub
```

Figure CS4.14 The *DockInfo* procedure records the dock information.

The *FinalSteps* procedure performs the main calculations and calls the procedures that execute the algorithm (see Figure CS4.15). We assign this procedure to the "Solve" button on the second input sheet. The procedure begins with two error checks to ensure that the product type table has been completely filled and that the sum of the required bays is less than or equal to the total number of bays in the warehouse.

```
Sub FinalSteps()
'Assigned to "Solve" button on second input sheet
'records product type information; calls other calcuation procedures

    Application.ScreenUpdating = False
    'error checking that product table was filled
    If Range("Products").Offset(1, 1).Value = "" _
            Or Range("Products").Offset(1, 2).Value = "" Then
        MsgBox "You have not completely filled out this sheet."
        Exit Sub
    End If

    'error checking that total bay area does not exceed total number of bays
    Sum = 0
    For i = 1 To NProds
        Sum = Sum + Range("Products").Offset(i, 1)
    Next i
    If Sum > NBays Then
        MsgBox "The sum of product areas exceeds the total " & _
                "number of bays in the warehouse." & _
                "Please correct your area data and press Solve again."
        Exit Sub
    End If

    'record product type info
    ReDim Area(NProds), Demand(NProds)
    For i = 1 To NProds
        Area(i) = Range("Products").Offset(i, 1).Value
        Demand(i) = Range("Products").Offset(i, 2).Value
    Next i

    'begin algorithm
    Call ComputeF
    Call SortItems
    Call SortBays
    Call Assign

    Worksheets("FinalLayout").Visible = True
    Worksheets("ProductInfo").Visible = False
    Range("A1").Select
    UserReady2 = True
    Application.ScreenUpdating = True
End Sub
```

Figure CS4.15 The *FinalSteps* procedure performs the main calculations and calls the procedures that execute the algorithm.

Next, we call the *ComputeF* procedure (see Figure CS4.16). It computes the weighted distances with the recorded dock frequencies. These distance weights are equivalent to the y_k values described in the model. We define $y_k = \Sigma_j\, d_{kj} * F_j$ and so compute these values using a loop over each bay with their respective X and Y coordinates and a sub loop over each dock with their respective frequency values and X and Y coordinates.

```
Sub ComputeF()
'called from Final Steps procedure;
'computes the weighted distances for each bay (gamma-k values)

    ReDim WtDist(NBays)
    For k = 1 To NBays
        Sum = 0
        For j = 1 To NDocks
            Sum = Sum + DFreq(j) * (Abs(XCoord(k) - ACoord(j)) + Abs(YCoord(k) - BCoord(j)))
        Next j
        WtDist(k) = Sum
    Next k
End Sub
```

Figure CS4.16 The *ComputeF* procedure computes the weighted distances based on the dock frequencies.

The next procedure called from the *FinalSteps* procedure is *SortItems* (see Figure CS4.17). The first step of the algorithm, this procedure calculates the product type weights and uses these values to sort the product types in a descending order of importance. The product type weights are equivalent to the α_i values described in the model. We define $\alpha_i = D_i \,/\, A_i$ and so compute these values using the recorded demand and area values; the weights are stored in a Ratio array.

We then sort the product types according to these Ratio values. We perform the sort on an array called *ItemOrder* and initialize this array such that each product type *i* has an *ItemOrder* value *i*. We then search for the largest Ratio value and move this product type to the front of the list; in other words, we exchange its *ItemOrder* value with the product type that has an *ItemOrder* value equal to 1. We continue this process but examine one less value each time. Eventually, the *ItemOrder* array signifies the sorted order of the product types.

```
Sub SortItems()
'called from Final Steps procedure; first step of algorithm;
'calculates product type weights (alpha-i values);
'sorts in descending order using arrays

    Dim q As Integer, Ratio() As Integer, _
    Max As Double, MaxIndex As Integer, MaxOrder As Integer

    ReDim ItemOrder(NProds), Ratio(NProds)
    'ratio = alpha-i values
    For i = 1 To NProds
        ItemOrder(i) = i
        Ratio(i) = Demand(i) / Area(i)
    Next i

    'sort arrays by moving max to beginning and shifting beginning by one
    Max = 0
    For i = 1 To (NProds - 1)
        For q = i To NProds
            If Ratio(ItemOrder(q)) > Max Then
                Max = Ratio(ItemOrder(q))
                MaxIndex = q
                MaxOrder = ItemOrder(q)
            End If
        Next q

        ItemOrder(MaxIndex) = ItemOrder(i)
        ItemOrder(i) = MaxOrder
        Max = 0
    Next i
End Sub
```

Figure CS4.17 The *SortItems* procedure calculates the product type weights and sorts them.

The next procedure that we call is the *SortBays* procedure (see Figure CS4.18); this is the second step of the algorithm. *SortBays* sorts the bays in descending order of their distance weights that were computed in the *ComputeF* procedure. The sorting is done in the same manner in which the product types were sorted. This time, however, we search for the minimum weight value in each pass. We use an array called *BayOrder* to store the bay order.

```
Sub SortBays()
'called from Final Steps procedure; second step of algorithm;
'sorts bays in ascending order of weighted distances

    Dim q As Integer, Min As Double, MinIndex As Integer, MinOrder As Integer
    ReDim BayOrder(NBays)

    For k = 1 To NBays
        BayOrder(k) = k
    Next k

    'sort arrays by moving min to beginning and shifting beginning by one
    Min = 100000
    For k = 1 To (NBays - 1)
        For q = k To NBays
            If WtDist(BayOrder(q)) < Min Then
                Min = WtDist(BayOrder(q))
                MinIndex = q
                MinOrder = BayOrder(q)
            End If
        Next q

        BayOrder(MinIndex) = BayOrder(k)
        BayOrder(k) = MinOrder
        Min = 100000
    Next k
End Sub
```

Figure CS4.18 The *SortBays* algorithm sorts the bays in ascending order of their distance weights.

The final procedure called from the *FinalSteps* procedure is the *Assign* procedure (see Figure CS4.19). The last step of the algorithm, this procedure completes the assignment of bays to each product type and creates the final layout.

The procedure begins with the final layout's formatting. There is then a small section of code that is related to the re-solve options; we will discuss this in more detail in the next section. The assignment loop then begins. We loop through the sorted list of product types in descending order of their weight values found in the *SortItems* procedure. We then assign bays to each product by looping through the list of sorted bays until the area requirement for the product type has been met. To reflect that an assignment has been made, we format the assigned bay with the color of the product type. When the assignment is finished for the product type, we also update our legend with the product type's color and index.

```
Sub Assign()
'called from Final Steps procedure; final step of algorithm

    Dim AssignedBay As Integer, AssignStart As Integer, _
        AssignedProd As Integer, Assigned As Integer
    'copy layout to output sheet
    Range(Range("Layout"), Range("Layout").Offset(NRows + 1, NCols + 1)).Copy
    Range("A1").Select
    Range("FinalLayout").PasteSpecial xlPasteAll
    Range("FinalLayout").Offset(-1, 0).Value = "FINAL LAYOUT"
    Range("FinalLayout").Offset(-1, 0).HorizontalAlignment = xlLeft

    For i = 1 To NProds
        Area(i) = Area(i) - FixedProd(i)
    Next i

    AssignStart = 1
    k = AssignStart

    'assign bays with lowest weight to products of highest weight
    For i = 1 To NProds
        AssignedProd = ItemOrder(i)
        Assigned = 0

        'assign bays until the area requirement has been satisfied
        Do While Assigned < Area(AssignedProd)
            If FixedBay(BayOrder(k)) = False Then
                AssignedBay = BayOrder(k)
                With Range("FinalLayout").Offset(YCoord(AssignedBay), XCoord(AssignedBay))
                    .Interior.ColorIndex = ProdColor(AssignedProd)
                End With
                Assigned = Assigned + 1
            End If
            k = k + 1
        Loop

        With Range("FinalLayout").Offset(i, NCols + 5)
            .Value = "P" & AssignedProd
            .Interior.ColorIndex = ProdColor(AssignedProd)
        End With
        AssignStart = k
    Next i
```

(a)

```
    Range("FinalLayout").Offset(0, NCols + 5).Name = "Legend"
    Range("Legend").Value = "Legend"
    Range(Range("Legend").Offset(1, 0), Range("Legend").End(xlDown)).Name = "LegendArea"

    Range(Range("FinalLayout"), Range("FinalLayout").Offset(NRows + 1, NCols + 1)).Copy
    Range("Legend").Offset(0, 4).Name = "ResolveLayout"
    Range("ResolveLayout").PasteSpecial
    Range("ResolveLayout").Offset(-1, 0).Value = "RESOLVE LAYOUT"
    Range("ResolveLayout").Offset(-1, 0).HorizontalAlignment = xlLeft
    Range(Range("ResolveLayout").Offset(1, 1), _
        Range("ResolveLayout").Offset(NRows, NCols)).Name = "ResolveArea"
    Range("ResolveArea").Interior.ColorIndex = 2
    Application.CutCopyMode = False
End Sub
```

(b)

Figure CS4.19 The *Assign* array completes the last step of the assignment algorithm. (a) The first part of the procedure. (b) The last part of the procedure.

The last part of this procedure simply formats the resulting layout and creates a "Re-solve Layout" which we will discuss in the next section. We now return to the *FinalSteps* procedure, which takes the users to the output sheet.

The only remaining procedures are for the navigational buttons (see CS4.20). These include the "End" button, the "View Product Info" button, the "View Dock Info" button, and the "Go Back" buttons. Each procedure simply hides and shows the appropriate sheets.

```
Sub ExitProg()
'assigned to "End" button on all sheets
    Worksheets("Welcome").Visible = True
    ActiveSheet.Visible = False
End Sub

Sub ViewProd()
'assigned to "View Product Info" button on output sheet
    Worksheets("ProductInfo").Visible = True
    Worksheets("ProductInfo").Shapes("ReturnLayout").Visible = True
    Worksheets("ProductInfo").Shapes("ContProd").Visible = False
    ActiveSheet.Visible = False
End Sub

Sub ViewDock()
'assigned to "View Dock Info" button on output sheet
    Worksheets("Layout").Visible = True
    Worksheets("Layout").Shapes("ReturnLayout").Visible = True
    Worksheets("Layout").Shapes("ContLay").Visible = False
    ActiveSheet.Visible = False
    Range("A1").Select
End Sub

Sub FinLayout()
'assigned to "Go Back" buttons on both input sheets
    Worksheets("FinalLayout").Visible = True
    ActiveSheet.Visible = False
End Sub
```

Figure CS4.20 The navigational procedures.

Summary

Main	Initializes the application, displays the input form, calls *ClearPrevious* and *NumberingBays*, takes the users to the first input sheet.
ClearPrevious	Clears the values and formatting on all sheets, initializes the variables.
cmdOK_Click	Does some error checking, assigns the input values to corresponding variables.
NumberingBays	Creates the initial layout, determines the X and Y coordinates for all bays, creates the dock and product type tables.
Worksheet_ SelectionChange	Allows users to place docks adjacent to the warehouse area, keeps track of the number of docks added.
DockInfo	Does some error checking, determines X and Y coordinates for the docks based on adjacent bays, records dock frequencies.
FinalSteps	Does some error checking, records product type areas and demands, calls *ComputeF*, *SortItems*, *SortBays*, and *Assign*, takes the users to the output sheet.
ComputeF	Computes the bay distance weights based on dock frequencies and bay X and Y coordinates.
SortItems	Computes the product type weights based on the ratio between their demands and areas, sorts the product types in descending order of these weights.
SortBays	Sorts the bays in ascending order of their distance weights.
Assign	Creates the final layout by assigning products to bays in their sorted orders until all product type area requirements are satisfied.

CS4.5 Re-solve Options

There are two main re-solve options for this DSS. The first allows the users to revisit the input sheets and change previously entered values. For this option, the users can use the navigational buttons on the output sheet to return to either of the input sheets. Suppose, for example, that the users return to the first input sheet (see Figure CS4.21). Here, they may change the location of the docks or the frequencies of the docks. In Figure CS4.21, we have changed the frequencies from 20% and 80% to 50% and 50%, respectively. The users can then press the "Go Back" button to return to the output sheet.

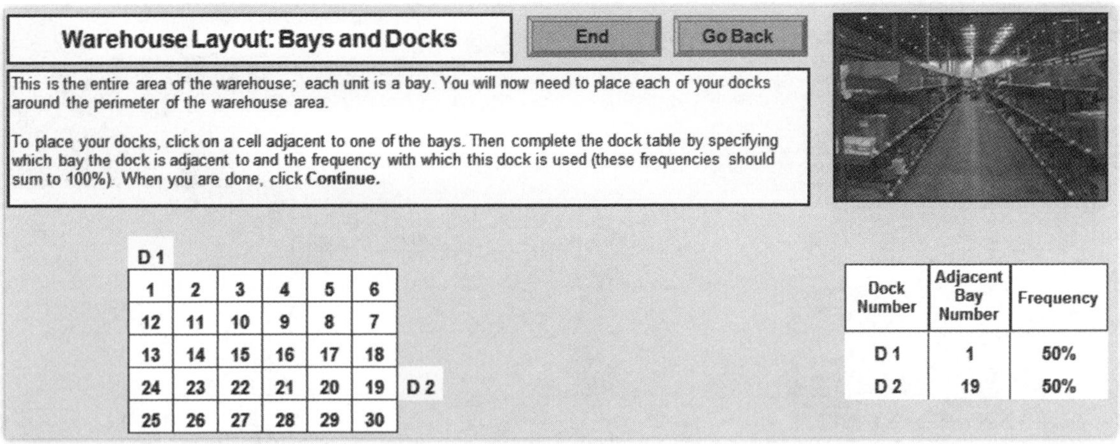

Figure CS4.21 Revisiting the first input sheet and changing some of the dock information.

At this point, the users can press the "Re-solve" button to observe the new layout with the changed dock information. Orthey can choose the other navigational button to revisit the second input sheet. Let us suppose the users also revisit the second input sheet to modify the product type information. In Figure CS4.22, we have changed the area requirements for the product types from 2, 4, and 7 to 4, 10, and 10, respectively. We have also changed the demand values from 300, 500, and 600 to 500, 600, and 800, respectively. The users can again use the "Go Back" button to return to the output sheet.

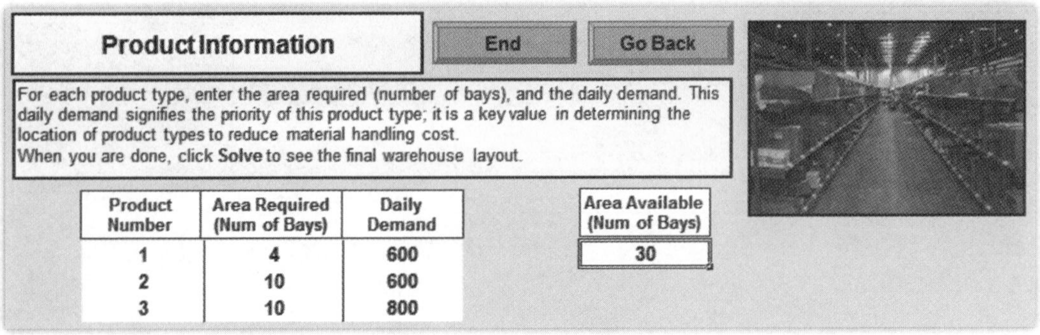

Figure CS4.22 Revisiting the second input sheet and changing the product type information.

If the users now press the "Re-solve" button, the main procedures will be re-run and a new layout will be displayed. In Figure CS4.23, we reveal the result of the re-solved layout after making the above changes to the dock and product type information.

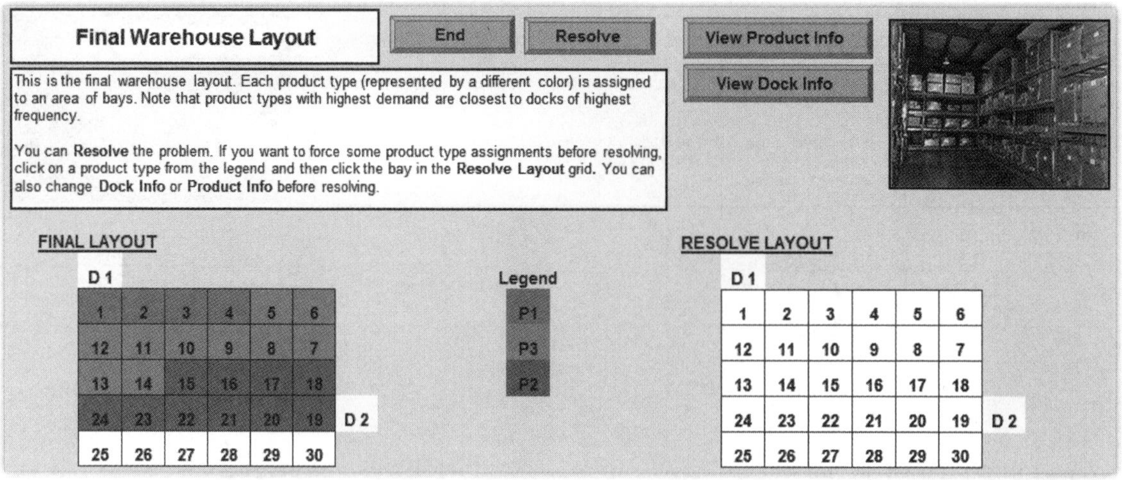

Figure CS4.23 The new layout is displayed after pressing the "Re-solve" button.

The second re-solve option allows the users to enforce bay assignments for any of the product types. To do so, they can select the product type that they wish to enforce from the legend. Then, they can click on the desired bay assignments in the "Re-solve Layout" table. For example, suppose the users want to enforce the bay assignments for all of the bays required for product type 2. The users would click on the "P2" cell in the legend and then select the desired assignment bays in the "Re-solve Layout" table (see Figure CS4.24).

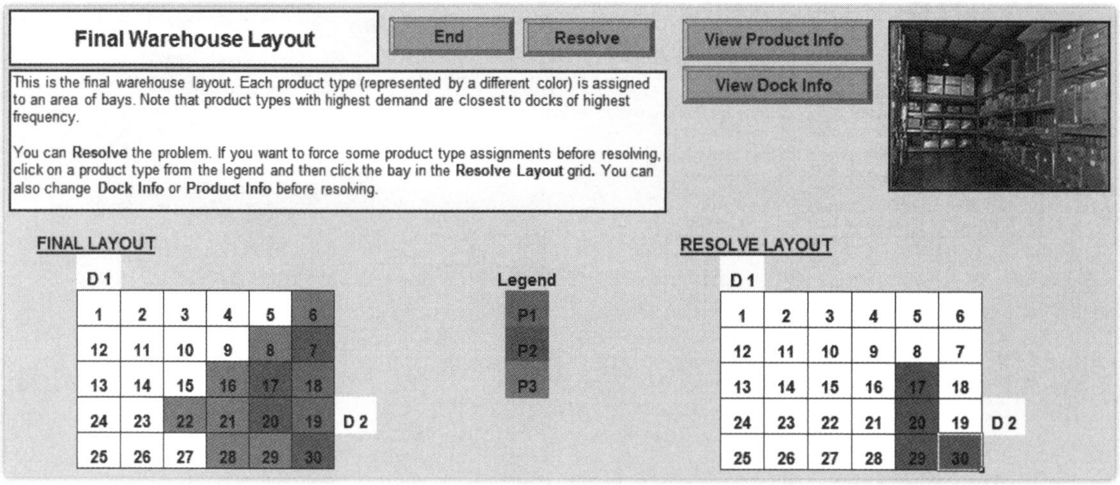

Figure CS4.24 The re-solve options allow the users to specify a particular product's layout on the Re-solve Layout grid.

The users can then press the "Re-solve" button to observe the updated layout with these enforced assignments. In Figure CS4.25, we display the modified layout after enforcing the bay assignments for product type 2. The other assignments are now made given that product type 2 will be assigned to the specified bays.

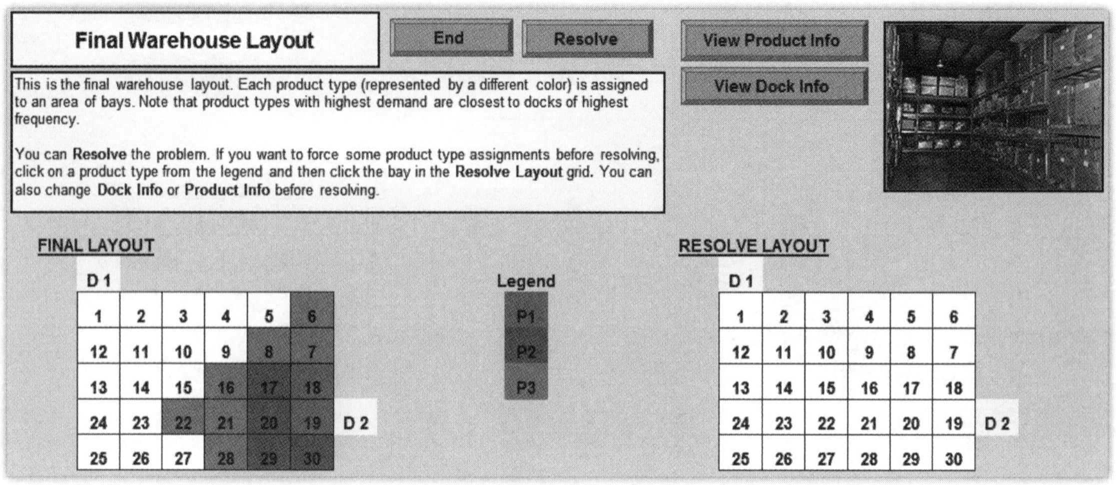

Figure CS4.25 The layout has been re-solved with the users' specifications enforced.

Not all of the required bays for any product type need to be enforced. For example, instead of enforcing all four of the required bays for product 2, the users could have only enforced the assignment of two of the bays. Multiple product types can also be enforced at once. In Figure CS4.26, we enforce the same bay assignments for product type 2 as well as six of the seven required bays for product type 3.

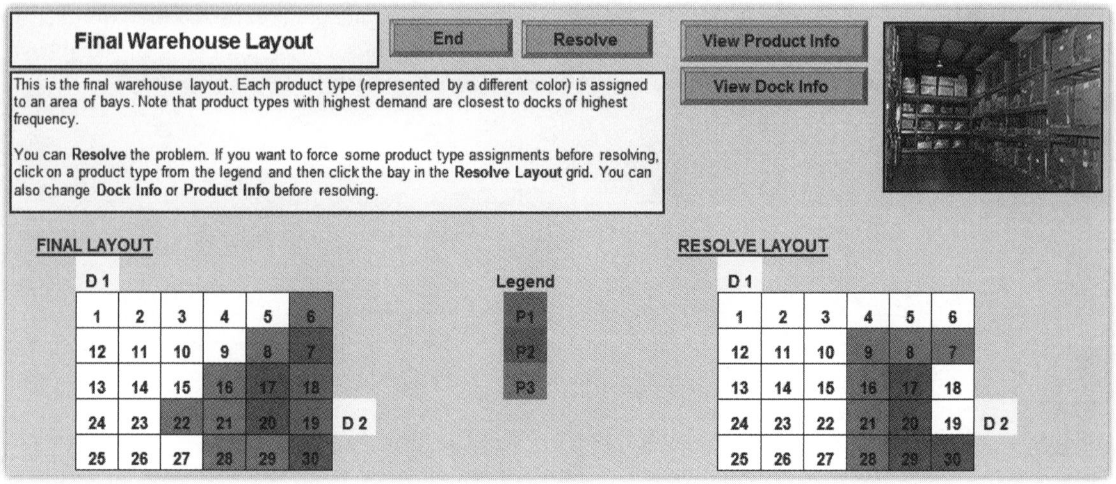

Figure CS4.26 Enforcing bay assignments for multiple product types.

The layout after the "Re-solve" button has been pressed appears in Figure CS4.27.

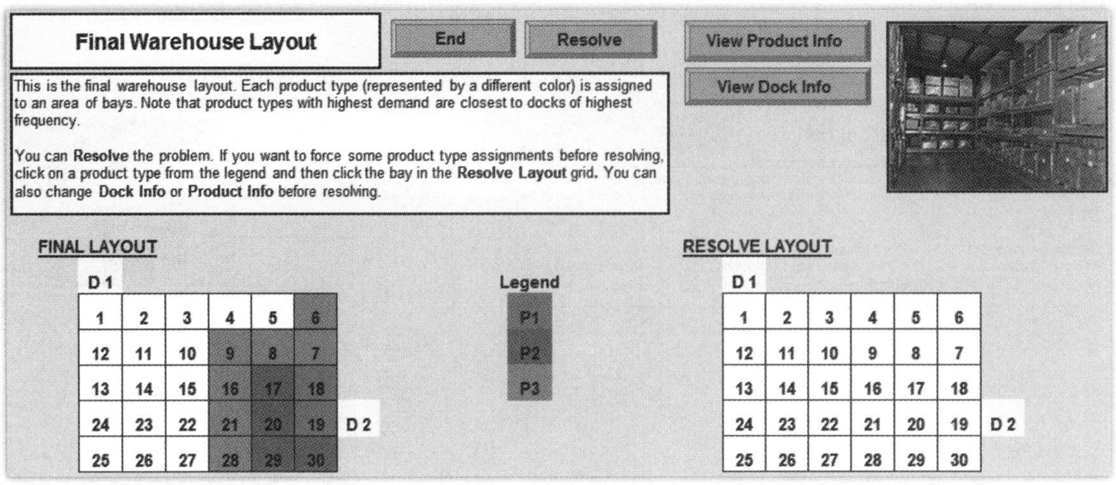

Figure CS4.27 The final layout is modified to honor the enforced bay assignments.

To allow the users to enforce bay assignments with this interface, we have written a *SelectChange* event procedure that is associated with the output sheet (see Figure CS4.28). This procedure is similar to the *SelectChange* event procedure associated with the first input sheet in that we have to first verify the location of the selected cell using *Union* functions.

We first check if the users have clicked in the legend area. If so, then we record the product type that they had selected. Once a product type is selected, the users may click in the "Resolve Layout" area to specify the enforced assignments. We confirm that the next cell clicked is indeed in this layout area and reformat the selected cell with the product type's color.

We also record that the selected bay has been fixed in a Boolean array called *FixedBay*. We must ensure that the users do not specify more bay assignments than the required number of bays for the selected product type. We do so by keeping track of the number of bays that have been assigned for the selected product type in a *FixedProd* array.

```
Private Sub Worksheet_SelectionChange(ByVal Target As Range)
'allows user to enforce bay assignments for selected product types

  If UserReady2 = True Then
    'check if user has made selection from the legend
    If Application.Union(ActiveCell, Range("LegendArea")).Address = _
        Range("LegendArea").Address Then
        'determine which product type was selected
        For i = 1 To NProds
            If ActiveCell.Value = "P" & i Then
                PIndex = i
                PColor = ProdColor(i)
            End If
        Next i

    'check that user is making bay assignment enforcements in "Resolve Layout"
    ElseIf Application.Union(ActiveCell, Range("ResolveArea")).Address = _
        Range("ResolveArea").Address Then
        FixedBay(ActiveCell.Value) = True
        ActiveCell.Interior.ColorIndex = PColor
        'make sure user assigns less than or
        'equal to the required number of bays for the selected product
        If FixedProd(PIndex) + 1 > Area(PIndex) Then
            MsgBox "You cannot fix more units than the available area for this product."
            Range("ResolveArea").Interior.ColorIndex = 2
            For i = 1 To NProds
                FixedProd(i) = 0
            Next i
            Exit Sub
        Else
            'note the number of bays that have been enforced
            FixedProd(PIndex) = FixedProd(PIndex) + 1
        End If
    End If
  End If
End Sub
```

Figure CS4.28 The *SelectChange* event procedure allows the users to enforce particular bay assignments for selected product types.

We can now discuss the *Re-solve* procedure that re-performs the calculations and re-runs the algorithm for either of these two re-solve options (see Figure CS4.29). Since we have stored which bay assignments are fixed, we will skip those bays when we reach the *Assign* procedure. Therefore, we begin the procedure by copying the "Re-solve Layout" to capture the users' assignments.

We then clear the output sheet and recall the *DockInfo* and *FinalSteps* procedures. These procedures re-record the information from the dock table and the product type table on the input sheets to capture any changes that the users have made to the input values. The assignment algorithm is then executed; this time, it ignores the bays that have already been fixed. The resulting layout reflects the users' enforced assignments. We then reset the *FixedProd* and *FixedBay* arrays.

```
Sub Resolve()
'assigned to "Resolve" button on output sheet;
'records any changes to dock or product info;
'recalculates layout by recalling algorithm steps

    ResolveCalled = True
    UserReady1 = False
    UserReady2 = False

    'copy "Resolve Layout" to first input sheet
    Range("ResolveArea").Copy
    Range("Layout").Offset(1, 1).PasteSpecial
    Range(Range("Layout").Offset(1, 1), _
        Range("Layout").Offset(NRows, NCols)).Name = "BayArea"
    Range(Range("Layout"), _
        Range("Layout").Offset(NRows + 1, NCols + 1)).Name = "DockArea"

    'clear previous solution
    With Worksheets("FinalLayout").Cells
        .ClearContents
        .Borders.LineStyle = xlNone
        .Interior.ColorIndex = xlNone
    End With

    Call DockInfo
    Call FinalSteps

    'reset any previous resolve conditions
    For i = 1 To NProds
        FixedProd(i) = 0
    Next i
    For k = 1 To NBays
        FixedBay(k) = False
    Next k
End Sub
```

Figure CS4.29 The *Re-solve* procedure records changes made to input values and honors enforced bay assignments.

Summary

First re-solve option	Use view buttons to return to input sheets and modify values; then, press the "Re-solve" button to see the new layout.
Second re-solve option	Enforce some product type bay assignments by clicking on a product type from the legend and specifying enforced assignments on "Re-solve Lay-out"; then, press the "Re-solve" button to see the new layout.
Worksheet_ SelectionChange	Event procedure to allow users to make assignment enforcements; it records which bays are fixed and how many bays have been fixed for each product type.
Re-solve	Copies the "Re-solve Layout" and recalls the *DockInfo* and *FinalSteps* procedures; reassigns bays ignoring those that users have fixed.

CS4.6 Summary

- The warehouse layout model assigns bays of a warehouse to different product types in such a way that the total distance traveled to docks is minimized given the weighting of the docks to bay distances and the product demand to area ratio. This assignment is accomplished using a greedy algorithm.
- There are four main worksheets: welcome, first input sheet, second input sheet, and output sheet.
- The user interface includes an input form, two input sheets, and several navigational and functional buttons.
- There are several procedures for this application. They guide the users through the input sheets and implement the greedy algorithm to make the assignment.
- The DSS components include two re-solve options: the users can either modify input values and re-solve or enforce some product type bay assignments (or both).

CS4.7 Extensions

1. Create a procedure which will automatically determine the adjacent bay number for each dock according to the user's placement of the docks on the "Warehouse Layout: Bays and Docks" worksheet. Fill these bay numbers in the table on the worksheet.
2. Create an alternative method for sorting the items and bays according to their weights. *Hint:* You do not have to use arrays.
3. How could you enforce adjacent bay assignments within a product type? Create a small procedure that would enforce this.
4. What are some other problems similar to the warehouse layout problem in which this DSS may be reused with slight modifications?

CASE STUDY *five*

Forecasting Methods

chapter OVERVIEW

CS5.1 Application Overview and Model Development

Forecasting is a tool for observing historical demand and predicting future demand. This application allows the users to enter historical data as demand per period and to compare forecasts for this data using the following methods: Moving Averages, Exponential Smoothing, Holt's Method for Trends, and Winter's Method for Seasonality. Since there is always an element of error in any forecast, the mean square error (MSE) is also calculated for each method as a measure of the forecast's accuracy. In this application, we only use the MSE if the forecast was made over the same periods as the given historical data; in this way, we can compare the forecast data to the actual historical data. The users can also forecast for future periods, but the MSE is only calculated for the forecasts over the historical periods. The application then determines the best forecasting method for the users' data by comparing the MSE values for each method and choosing the method that yields the minimum MSE.

CS5.1.1 Model Definition and Assumptions

In this section, we describe the parameters and models for performing the following adaptive methods for forecasting calculations: Moving Averages, Exponential Smoothing, Holt's Method for Trends, and Winter's Method for Seasonality.

The Moving Averages method forecasts the demand in a period t to be the average of the previous N periods of historical data. We use this method when the historical data does not seem to follow any trend or seasonality. The parameters for this method are the initial period to begin forecasting, t_i, the final period to forecast, t_f, and the number of historical periods to use, N, in finding the average demand for the next period. The users must enter an initial period, t_i, greater than the number of historical periods used in the calculations, N.

A demand base, or level, for a period t is calculated as follows:

$$L_t = (\sum_{i=1}^{N} D_i) / N$$

The forecasted demand F for period $t+1$ is then as follows:

$$F_{t+1} = L_t$$

The Exponential Smoothing method, which we also employ when the historical data does not seem to follow any trend or seasonality, forecasts demand by using the average demand over all historical periods, n. The parameters for this method are the initial period to begin forecasting, t_i, the final period to forecast, t_f, and a smoothing constant α between 0 and 1.

The initial demand base is determined as follows:

$$L_0 = \frac{1}{n}\sum_{i=1}^{n} D_i$$

The demand base is updated using the smoothing constant α for each period t:

$$L_{t+1} = \alpha D_{t+1} + (1-\alpha)L_t$$

The forecast can then be calculated with the following:

$$F_{t+1} = L_t$$

We use Holt's Method for Trends when the historical demand data seems to follow a trend. The user input for this method is the initial period to begin forecasting, t_i, the final period to forecast, t_f, a smoothing constant α, and a smoothing constant β. Both α and β must be between 0 and 1.

We determine an initial estimate of the base and trend by performing a linear regression on the relationship between the demand D and each period t. We perform this regression in Excel with the INTERCEPT and SLOPE functions in order to find the initial base and initial trend values, respectively.

$$D_t = L_0 + T_0 t$$

The base and trend values are then updated using the smoothing constants α and β:

$$L_{t+1} = \alpha D_{t+1} + (1-\alpha)(L_t + T_t)$$

$$T_{t+1} = \beta(L_{t+1} - L_t) + (1-\beta)T_t$$

The forecast can then be calculated with the following:

$$F_{t+1} = L_t + T_t$$

Note that with this method, forecasts for future periods are made with the following:

$$F_{t+n} = L_t + nT_t$$

We use Winter's Method for Seasonality when the historical demand seems to follow both trend and seasonality. The user input for this method is the initial period to begin forecasting, t_i, the final period to forecast, t_f, the number of periods per season, p, a smoothing constant α, a smoothing constant β, and a smoothing constant γ. All constants α, β, and γ must be between 0 and 1.

In this method, we also want to determine the initial base and trend estimates through linear regression. However, since there is seasonality, we must first deseasonalize the demand before using a linear regression. To deseasonalize the demand, we find the values $\bar{D}_t$:

$$\bar{D}_t = (D_{t-(p/2)} + D_{t+(p/2)} + \sum_{i=t+1-(p/2)}^{t-1+(p/2)} 2D_i) / 2p, \text{ for } p \text{ even}$$

$$\bar{D}_t = \sum_{i=t-\lfloor p/2 \rfloor}^{t+(\lfloor p/2 \rfloor)} D_i / p, \text{ for } p \text{ odd}$$

Now, we can estimate the initial base and trend values:

$$\bar{D}_t = L_0 + T_0 t$$

Once we determine these estimates, we recalculate the deseasonalized demand for all historical data periods ($t = 1$ to n) with the same equation. With this deseasonalized demand, we can also calculate estimates for the seasonal factors, $\bar{S}_t$:

$$\bar{S}_t = D_t / \bar{D}_t$$

Using these seasonal factor estimates for all historical data periods, we can then find the seasonal factors for each period of seasonality. Here, we use r as the number of seasonal cycles in the historical data, or $r = n / p$:

$$S_i = (\sum_{j=0}^{r-1} \bar{S}_{jp+i}) / r$$

We then update the base, trend, and seasonal factors using the smoothing constants α, β, and γ, as follows:

$$L_{t+1} = \alpha(D_{t+1} / S_{t+1}) + (1-\alpha)(L_t + T_t)$$

$$T_{t+1} = \beta(L_{t+1} - L_t) + (1-\beta)T_t$$

$$S_{t+p+1} = \gamma(D_{t+1} / L_{t+1}) + (1-\gamma)S_{t+1}$$

The forecast can then be calculated as follows:

$$F_{t+1} = (L_t + T_t)S_{t+1}$$

Note that with this method, forecasts for future periods are made with the following:

$$F_{t+n} = (L_t + nT_t)S_{t+n}$$

Please see *Supply Chain Management: Strategy, Planning, and Operations* by Chopra and Meindl for more details.

CS5.1.2 Input

The input for this application is the parameters for each forecasting method.

- Moving Averages: initial period, final period, and number of historical periods to use.
- Exponential Smoothing: initial period, final period, and smoothing constant α.
- Holt's Method for Trends: initial period, final period, smoothing constant α, and smoothing constant β.
- Winter's Method for Seasonality: initial period, final period, periods per season, smoothing constant α, smoothing constant β, and smoothing constant γ.

CS5.1.3 Output

The output for this application is the MSE for each forecasting method and the best method that has the minimum MSE.

- MSE for each forecasting method.
- Chart of forecast versus historical data for each method.
- Best method with minimum MSE.
- Parameters and forecast chart for best method.

CS5.2 *Worksheets*

This application requires four worksheets: the welcome sheet, the historical data sheet, the compare methods sheet, and the best method sheet. The welcome sheet contains the title, the description of the application, an image, a "Run Demo" button, and a "Start" button. (See Figure CS5.1.) The "Run Demo" button enters the historical data for the users, and the "Start" button allows the users to enter their own historical data. They both bring the users to the historical data sheet.

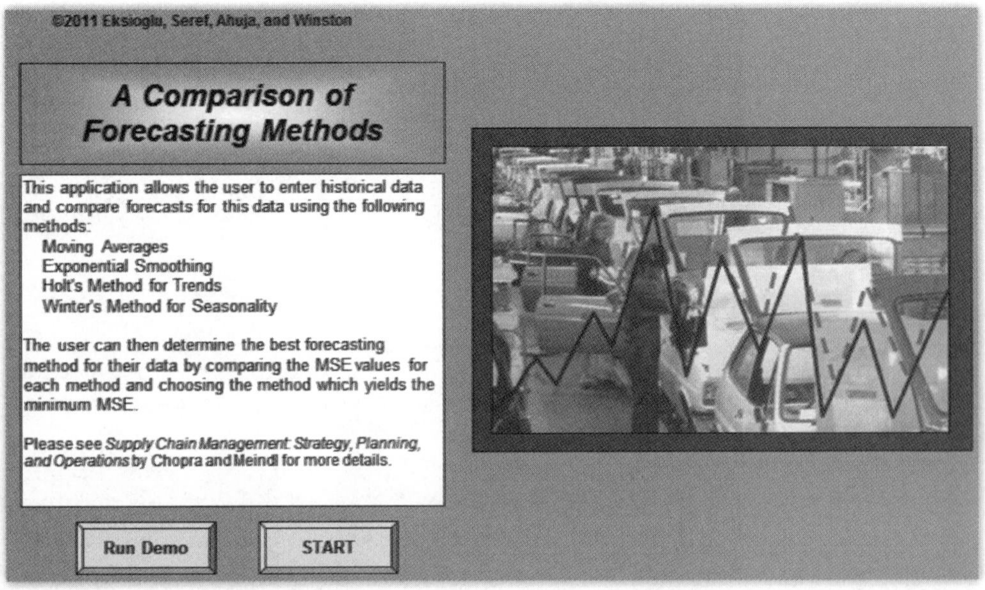

Figure CS5.1 The welcome sheet.

The historical data sheet stores the users' historical data, which is indicated as the demand period. (See Figure CS5.2.) When the users have finished entering or modifying the historical data, they can press the "Continue" button to go to the compare methods sheet.

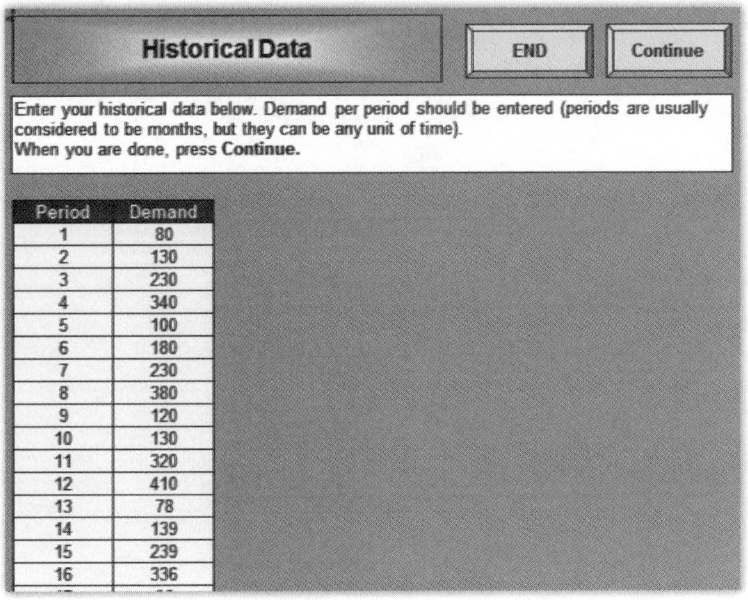

Period	Demand
1	80
2	130
3	230
4	340
5	100
6	180
7	230
8	380
9	120
10	130
11	320
12	410
13	78
14	139
15	239
16	336

Figure CS5.2 The historical data sheet.

The compare methods sheet is the main sheet of the application where the users can select a forecasting method with the check boxes. (See Figure CS5.3.) A box of corresponding parameter controls is displayed for the selected method. The users can enter or modify these parameters and then press the "Forecast" button to see a forecast of the data, which is charted with the historical data. The MSE for the selected method with the given parameters is then calculated and displayed in the table on the bottom of the sheet. The users can press the "Find Best Method" button to proceed to the best method sheet.

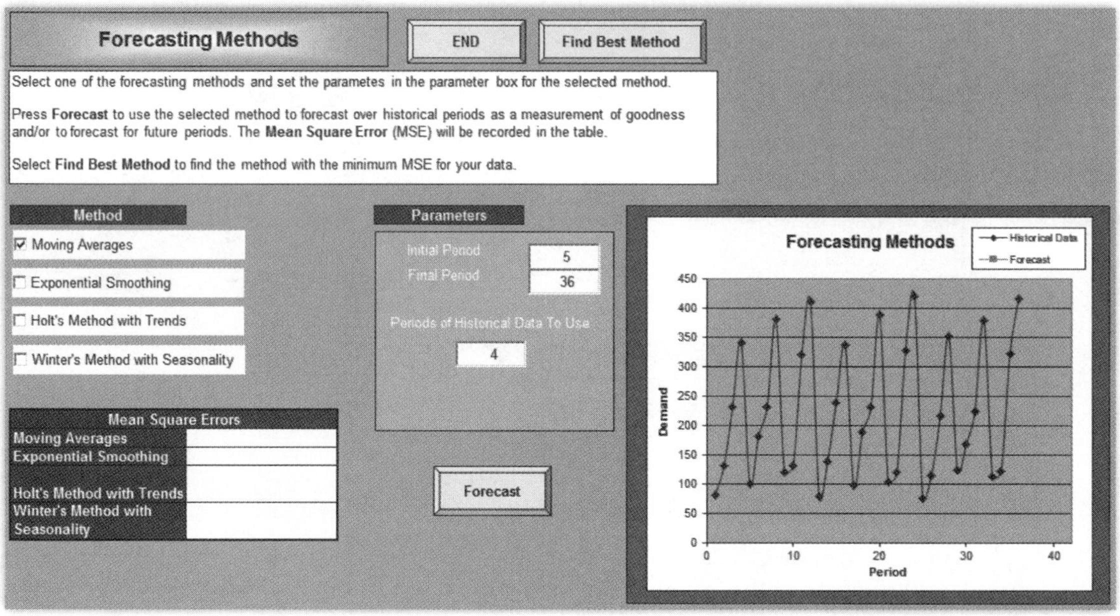

Figure CS5.3 The compare methods sheet.

The best method sheet displays the name, parameters, and MSE value for the best forecasting method. (See Figure CS5.4.) This method is determined by finding the minimum MSE value among all the forecasting methods with the given parameters. The sheet also contains a chart with the historical data and the forecast data of this method.

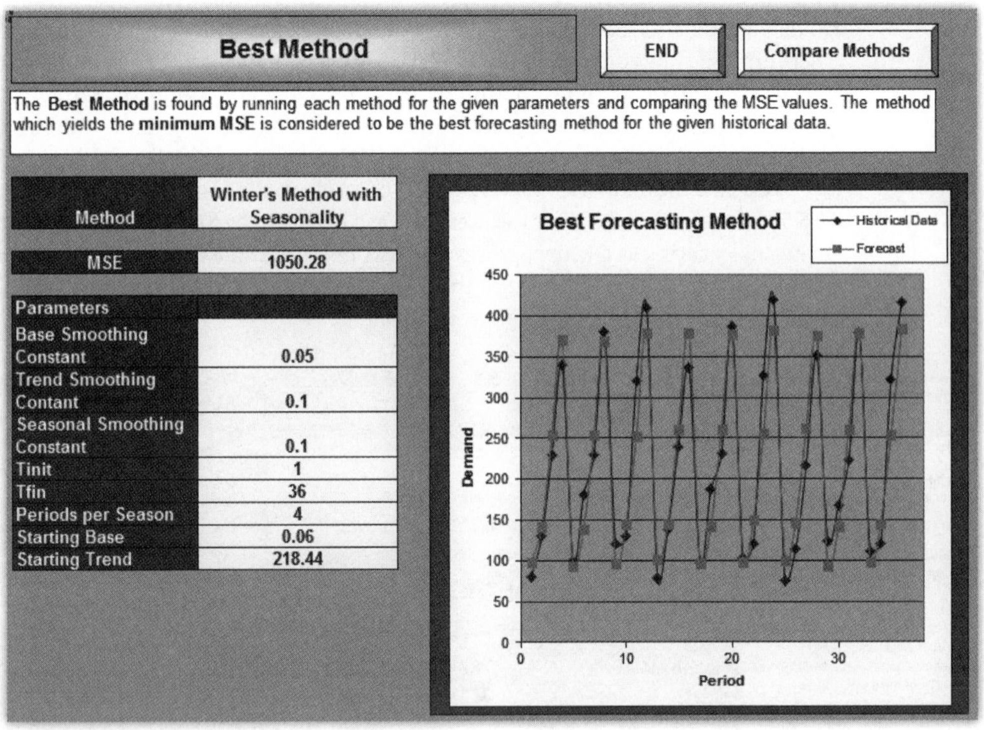

Figure CS5.4 The best method sheet.

Summary

Welcome sheet	Includes the application description and the "Run Demo" and "Start" buttons.
Historical data sheet	Stores the users' historical data of demand per period.
Compare methods sheet	Where the users can select a forecasting method, enter corresponding parameters, and forecast data using the selected method. Includes a chart of the historical data and the forecast data as well as the MSE values.
Best method sheet	Reveals the best method with the minimum MSE value and parameters. Includes a chart of the historical data and the best forecast.

CS5.3 *User Interface*

For this application's user interface, we include navigational and functional buttons as well as several controls on the worksheet. The welcome sheet contains the "Run Demo" and "Start" buttons, which both bring the users to the historical data sheet. The "Run Demo" button enters the historical data for the users, and the "Start" button allows the users to enter their own historical data. There are "End" buttons on all the other sheets that take the users back to the welcome sheet.

The "Compare Methods" button returns the users to the compare methods sheet from the best method sheet. The "Continue," "Forecast," and "Find Best Method" buttons are functional buttons that call procedures, which we will discuss later.

We create the main user interface using controls on the compare methods sheet. (See Figure CS5.5.) Four check boxes allow the users to select between the four available forecasting methods. A rectangle, acting as a frame, groups the text boxes and the labels for each set of parameters. Each group of controls is layered so that, depending on which method the users select, the corresponding parameter controls are at the front.

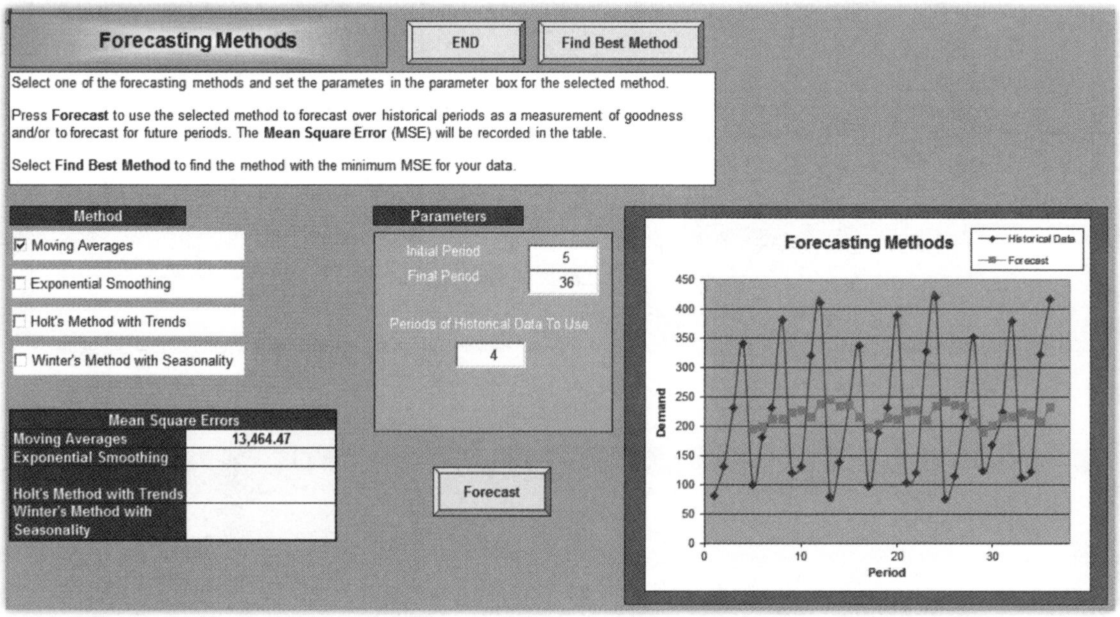

Figure CS5.5 Forecasting and the parameters for the Moving Average Method.

For example, in Figure CS5.5, the Moving Average check box is selected, and, therefore, the group of controls for the Moving Average parameters appears. In Figure CS5.6, the Winter's Method with Seasonality check box is selected, and the group of controls changes to display the parameters for the Winter's Method.

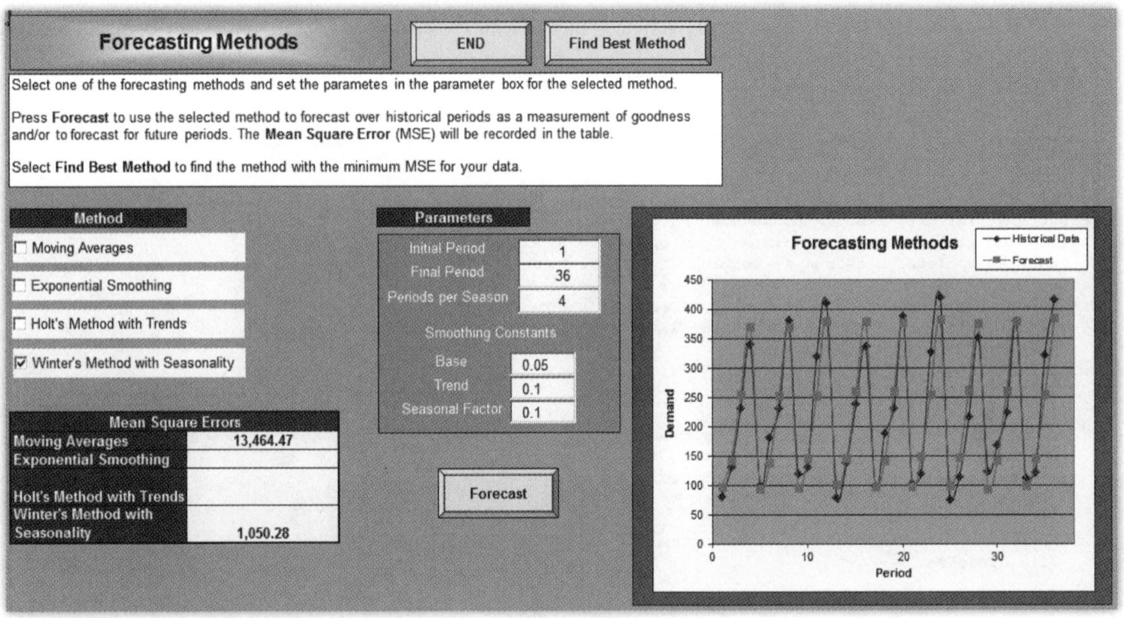

Figure CS5.6 Forecasting and the parameters for the Winter's Method.

Summary

Navigational buttons	"Run Demo" and "Start" on the welcome sheet; "End" on all the other sheets; "Compare Methods" on the best method sheet.
Functional buttons	"Continue" on the historical data sheet; "Forecast" and "Find Best Method" on the compare methods sheet.
Controls on the worksheet	Check boxes for method selection; rectangle shapes, text boxes, and labels for the parameters.

CS5.4 Procedures

We will now outline the procedures for this application, beginning with the initial sub procedures and the variable definitions. (See Figure CS5.7.) The "Start" button calls the "Main" procedure, which, in turn, calls the "ClearPrevious" procedure and takes the users to the historical data sheet. The "RunDemo" procedure, called from the "Run Demo" button, copies a set of historical data and takes the users to the historical data sheet. Finally, the "ClearPrevious" procedure clears the previous data on all the sheets.

```
Option Explicit

Public t As Integer, i As Integer, MeanDem As Double, TInit As Integer, TFin As Integer, _
NHistPer As Integer, ExAlpha As Double, HoltAlpha As Double, HoltBeta As Double, _
StartTrendH As Double, StartBaseH As Double, SumDem As Double, SumIDem As Double, _
Forecast As Boolean, WinAlpha As Double, WinBeta As Double, WinGAmma As Double, _
WinNSeas, StartTrendW As Double, StartBaseW As Double, Method As String, _
MinMSE As Double, BestMethod As String, NPerMA As Double, NPerReg As Double, _
BestMAPer As Double, WinDSum1 As Double, WinDSum2 As Double, WinDSum3 As Double

Sub Main()   'called from Start button
    Call ClearPrev

    Worksheets("HistData").Visible = True
    Worksheets("Welcome").Visible = False
    MsgBox "You may now enter your historical data."
End Sub

Sub RunDemo()    'called from Run Demo button
    Call ClearPrev

    'copy demo data
    Range("DemoData3").Copy
    Range("HistPer").Offset(1, 0).PasteSpecial

    Worksheets("HistData").Visible = True
    Worksheets("Welcome").Visible = False
    Range("A1").Select
    MsgBox "The demo historical data has been entered for you."
End Sub

Sub ClearPrev()
    Application.ScreenUpdating = False
    'clear hist data
    Range(Range("HistPer").Offset(1, 0), Range("HistDemand").End(xlDown)).ClearContents
    'clear chart data
    Range(Range("ParStart").Offset(1, 0), Range("ParStart").End(xlDown).Offset(0, 2)).ClearContents
    Range(Range("ParBase"), Range("ParBase").End(xlDown).Offset(0, 3)).ClearContents
    'clear MSE values
    Range(Range("MSEStart").Offset(0, 1), Range("MSEStart").Offset(3, 1)).ClearContents
    'clear all from Best sheet
    Range(Range("BestParameters").Offset(1, 0), Range("BestParameters").Offset(6, 1)).ClearContents
    Application.ScreenUpdating = True
End Sub
```

Figure CS5.7 The variable declarations and the "Main," "RunDemo," and "ClearPrev" procedures.

The "Continue" button on the historical data sheet calls the "Continue" procedure, which counts the number of periods of historical data the users have entered.(See Figure CS5.8.) It then initializes the controls on the compare methods sheet, where it takes the users.

```
Sub Continue()  'called from Continue button on Historical Data sheet
    Application.ScreenUpdating = False
    'check that enough values were entered
    If Application.WorksheetFunction.CountA(Range(Range("HistPer"), _
    Range("HistPer").End(xlDown))) < 6 Or _
    Application.WorksheetFunction.CountA(Range(Range("HistDemand"), _
    Range("HistDemand").End(xlDown))) < 6 Then
        MsgBox "Please enter at least 5 periods worth of data."
        Exit Sub
    End If

    'count number of periods for default values
    NHistPer = Range(Range("HistPer").Offset(1, 0), Range("HistPer").End(xlDown)).Count
    Range(Range("HistDemand").Offset(1, 0), Range("HistDemand").End(xlDown)).Name = "HistData"
    Range(Range("HistPer").Offset(1, 0), Range("HistDemand").End(xlDown)).Copy
    Range("ParStart").Offset(1, 0).PasteSpecial xlPasteValues
    Application.CutCopyMode = False

    'initialize textboxes on Method sheet
    With Worksheets("Method")
        .txtInitMA = 5
        .txtFinMA = NHistPer
        .txtHistMA = 4
        .txtInitEx = 2
        .txtFinEx = NHistPer
        .txtAlphaEx = 0.1
        .txtInitHolt = 1
        .txtFinHolt = NHistPer
        .txtAlphaH = 0.1
        .txtBetaH = 0.2
        .txtInitW = 1
        .txtFinW = NHistPer
        .txtSeasonW = 4
        .txtWAlpha = 0.05
        .txtWBeta = 0.1
        .txtWGamma = 0.1
        .txtSeasonW = 4
    End With

    Worksheets("Method").Visible = True
    Worksheets("HistData").Visible = False
    Application.ScreenUpdating = True
End Sub
```

Figure CS5.8 The "Continue" procedure.

The "Calc" procedure, called from the "Forecast" button, checks which method the users selected and records the corresponding parameters. (See Figures CS5.9 and CS5.10.) It then calls one of the following procedures to perform the calculations for this method: "MovAvg," "ExpSm," "Holt," or "Winter."

```
Sub Calc()  'determines which method the user wants to use and makes forecast
    Application.ScreenUpdating = False
    With Worksheets("Method")
        Range(Range("ParForc").Offset(1, 0), _
            Range("ParForc").Offset(NHistPer, 0).End(xlDown)).ClearContents
        Range(Range("DeSeas").Offset(1, 0), _
            Range("ParSFEst").Offset(NHistPer, 0).End(xlDown)).ClearContents

        Select Case Method
        'Moving Averages
            Case "MovAvg"
            If .txtHistMA > NHistPer Then
                MsgBox "The number of historical periods to use must be " & _
                "less than or equal to " & NHistPer
                Exit Sub
            Else
                NPerMA = .txtHistMA.Value
            End If
            If .txtInitMA < NPerMA Then
                MsgBox "For Moving Averages, the Initial Period to forecast for must " & _
                    "be greater than the Number of Historical Periods you are using."
                Exit Sub
            Else
                TInit = .txtInitMA
            End If
            TFin = .txtFinMA
            Call MovAvg
        'Exponential Smoothing
            Case "ExpSm"
            If .txtAlphaEx >= 1 Or .txtAlphaEx <= 0 Then
                MsgBox "The Smoothing Constant must be between 0 and 1."
                Exit Sub
            Else
                ExAlpha = .txtAlphaEx
            End If
            If .txtInitEx < 2 Or .txtInitEx > NHistPer + 1 Then
                MsgBox "For Exponential Smoothing, the Initial Period must be greater " & _
                    "than 1 and less than the total Number of Periods + 1."
                Exit Sub
            Else
                TInit = .txtInitEx
            End If
            TFin = .txtFinEx
            Call ExpSm
```

Figure CS5.9 The first half of the "Calc" procedure.

The "MovAg" procedure performs the calculations for the Moving Average method by using the initial period, the final period, and the number of historical periods for determining the average. (See Figure CS5.11.) The "ExpSm" procedure performs the calculations for the Exponential Smoothing method using the initial period, the final period, and the smoothing constant. (See Figure CS5.12.) The "Holt" procedure performs the calculations for Holt's Method with Trends. (See Figure CS5.13.) This method requires initialization of the base and trend values before it employs the users' parameters. These parameters include the initial period, the final period, and two smoothing constants. The "Winter" procedure performs the calculations for Winter's Method with Seasonality. (See Figures CS5.14 and CS5.15.) This method requires initialization of the base and trend values, which it calculates by first deseasonalizing the data. Next, it employs the initial period, the final period, the number of periods in a season, and three smoothing constants specified by the users. Each of these procedures ends by calculating the MSE.

```
        'Holt's Method
            Case "Holts"
            HoltAlpha = .txtAlphaH
            HoltBeta = .txtBetaH
            TInit = .txtInitHolt
            TFin = .txtFinHolt
            Call Holt
        'Winter's Method
            Case "Winter"
            WinNSeas = .txtSeasonW
            WinAlpha = .txtWAlpha
            WinBeta = .txtWBeta
            WinGAmma = .txtWGamma
            TInit = .txtInitW
            TFin = .txtFinW
            Call Winter
        'Find Best Method
            Case "FindBest"
                Method = "MovAvg"
                Call Calc
                Method = "ExpSm"
                Call Calc
                Method = "Holts"
                Call Calc
                Method = "Winter"
                Call Calc
        End Select
    End With

    Worksheets("Method").Activate
    Call UpdateChart
    Application.ScreenUpdating = True
End Sub
```

Figure CS5.10 The second half of the "Calc" procedure.

```
Sub MovAvg()    'Moving Average method
    Range("MADecVar").Value = NPerMA
    Range("MATFin").Value = TFin

    'perform calculations for all periods specified by user
    For t = TInit To TFin
        If t <= NHistPer Then
        SumDem = Application.WorksheetFunction.Sum(Range(Range("ParHist").Offset((t - NPerMA), 0), _
            Range("ParHist").Offset((t - 1), 0)))
        Range("ParForc").Offset(t, 0).Value = 1 / NPerMA * SumDem
        ElseIf t > NHistPer Then
            Range("ParHist").Offset(t, -1).Value = t
            Range("ParForc").Offset(t, 0).Value = Range("ParForc").Offset(NHistPer, 0).Value
        End If
    Next t

    'calculate forecasting error
    Range("MAObjFunc").Value = Application.WorksheetFunction.Average(Range(Range("ParSq").Offset(TInit, 0), _
        Range("ParSq").Offset(TFin, 0)))
    If TFin <= NHistPer Then
        Range("MSEStart").Offset(0, 1).Value = Range("MAObjFunc").Value
    End If
End Sub
```

Figure CS5.11 The "MovAvg" procedure.

```
Sub ExpSm()     'Exponential Smoothing method
    'initialize
    Range("ExDecVar").Value = ExAlpha
    Range("ExTFin").Value = TFin
    Range("ParBase").Value = Application.WorksheetFunction.Average(Range _
                (Range("ParHist").Offset(1, 0), Range("ParHist").Offset(NHistPer, 0)))
    Range("ParForc").Offset(TInit - 1, 0).Formula = "=" & Range("ParBase").Offset((TInit - 1) Mod NHistPer, 0).Address
    Range("ParBase").Offset(1, 0).FormulaR1C1 = "=ExDecVar*RC[-4] + (1-ExDecVar)*" & Range("ParBase").Value
    Range("ParForc").Offset(1, 0).FormulaR1C1 = "=R[-1]C[3]"

    'perform calculations for all periods specified by user
    For t = TInit To TFin
        Range("ParStart").Offset(t, 0).Value = t
        If t <> 1 Then
            Range("ParBase").Offset(t, 0).FormulaR1C1 = "=ExDecVar*RC[-4] + (1-ExDecVar)*R[-1]C"
            Range("ParForc").Offset(t, 0).FormulaR1C1 = "=R[-1]C[3]"
            If t > NHistPer Then
                Range("ParHist").Offset(t, -1).Value = t
                Range("ParForc").Offset(t, 0).FormulaR1C1 = "=OFFSET(ParBase, " & NHistPer & ",0,1,1)"
            End If
        End If
    Next t

    'calculate forecasting error
    Range("ExObjFunc").Formula = "=AVERAGE(" & Range("ParSq").Offset(TInit - 1, 0).Address & ":" & _
        Range("ParSq").Offset(TFin, 0).Address & ")"
    If TFin <= NHistPer Then
        Range("MSEStart").Offset(1, 1).Value = Range("ExObjFunc").Value
    End If
End Sub
```

Figure CS5.12 The "ExpSm" procedure.

```
Sub Holt()  'Holt's method for Trends
    'initialize
    Range("HAlpha").Value = HoltAlpha
    Range("HBeta").Value = HoltBeta
    Range("HoltTFin").Value = TFin

    'find trend and base
    StartBaseH = Application.WorksheetFunction.Intercept(Range("HistData"), Range("HistData").Offset(0, -1))
    Range("ParBase").Value = StartBaseH
    Range("HoltTFin").Offset(1, 0).Value = StartBaseH
    StartTrendH = Application.WorksheetFunction.Slope(Range("HistData"), Range("HistData").Offset(0, -1))
    Range("ParTrend").Value = StartTrendH
    Range("HoltTFin").Offset(1, 0).Value = StartTrendH

    'perform calculations for all periods specified by user
    For t = TInit To TFin
        If t <= NHistPer Then
            Range("ParBase").Offset(t, 0).Formula = "=HAlpha * RC[-4] + (1 - HAlpha) * (R[-1]C + R[-1]C[1])"
            Range("ParTrend").Offset(t, 0).FormulaR1C1 = "=HBeta*(RC[-1]-R[-1]C[-1])+(1-HBeta)*R[-1]C"
            Range("ParForc").Offset(t, 0).FormulaR1C1 = "=(R[-1]C[3] + R[-1]C[4])"
        ElseIf t > NHistPer Then
            Range("ParHist").Offset(t, -1).Value = t
            Range("ParForc").Offset(t, 0).Formula = "=" & Range("ParBase").Address & "+" & _
                t & "*" & Range("ParTrend").Address
        End If
    Next t

    'calculate forecasting error
    Range("HoltObjFunc").Formula = "=AVERAGE(" & Range("ParSq").Offset(TInit, 0).Address & ":" & _
        Range("ParSq").Offset(TFin, 0).Address & ")"
    If TFin <= NHistPer Then
        Range("MSEStart").Offset(2, 1).Value = Range("HoltObjFunc").Value
    End If
End Sub
```

Figure CS5.13 The "Holt" procedure.

```
Sub Winter()    'Winter's method for seasonality
    'initialize
    Range("WAlpha").Value = WinAlpha
    Range("WBeta").Value = WinBeta
    Range("WGamma").Value = WinGAmma
    Range("WinTFin").Value = TFin

    'deseasonalize demand to find initial base and trend values
    For t = (TInit + WinNSeas / 2) To (NHistPer - WinNSeas / 2)
        'if number of periods even
        If WinNSeas Mod 2 = 0 Then
            WinDSum1 = 0
            For i = t + 1 - WinNSeas / 2 To t - 1 + WinNSeas / 2
                WinDSum1 = WinDSum1 + 2 * Range("ParHist").Offset(i, 0).Value
            Next i
            Range("DeSeas").Offset(t, 0).Value = (Range("ParHist").Offset(t - WinNSeas / 2, 0).Value + _
                Range("ParHist").Offset(t + WinNSeas / 2, 0) + WinDSum1) / (2 * WinNSeas)
        Else
          'if number of periods odd
           WinDSum2 = 0
           For i = t - Rnd(WinNSeas / 2) To t + Rnd(WinNSeas / 2)
               WinDSum2 = WinDSum2 + Range("ParHist").Offset(i, 0).Value / WinNSeas
           Next i
           Range("DeSeas").Offset(t, 0).Value = WinDSum2
       End If
    Next t

    'find trend and base using regression on deseasonalized demand
    Range("WinPer").Value = WinNSeas
    StartTrendW = Application.WorksheetFunction.Slope(Range(Range("DeSeas").Offset(TInit + WinNSeas / 2, 0), _
        Range("DeSeas").Offset(NHistPer - WinNSeas / 2, 0)), _
        Range(Range("ParHist").Offset(TInit + WinNSeas / 2, -1), Range("ParHist").Offset(NHistPer - WinNSeas / 2, -1)))
    Range("ParTrend").Value = StartTrendW
    Range("WinPer").Offset(1, 0).Value = StartTrendW
    StartBaseW = Application.WorksheetFunction.Intercept(Range(Range("DeSeas").Offset(TInit + WinNSeas / 2, 0), _
        Range("DeSeas").Offset(NHistPer - WinNSeas / 2, 0)), _
        Range(Range("ParHist").Offset(TInit + WinNSeas / 2, -1), Range("ParHist").Offset(NHistPer - WinNSeas / 2, -1)))
    Range("ParBase").Value = StartBaseW
    Range("WinPer").Offset(2, 0).Value = StartBaseW
```

Figure CS5.14 The first half of the "Winter" procedure.

```
    're-evaluate deseasonalized demand with base and trend found from regression
    For t = 1 To NHistPer
        Range("DeSeas").Offset(t, 0).Value = StartBaseW + StartTrendW * t
        'find estimated seasonal factors
        Range("ParSFEst").Offset(t, 0).Value = Range("ParHist").Offset(t, 0).Value / Range("DeSeas").Offset(t, 0).Value
    Next t

    'find seasonal factors
    For t = 1 To WinNSeas
        WinDSum3 = 0
        For i = 0 To NHistPer / WinNSeas - 1
            WinDSum3 = WinDSum3 + Range("ParSFEst").Offset(i * WinNSeas + t, 0).Value
        Next i
        Range("ParSF").Offset(t, 0).Value = WinDSum3 / (NHistPer / WinNSeas)
    Next t

    'perform calculations for all periods specified by user
    For t = TInit To TFin
        If t <= NHistPer Then
            Range("ParBase").Offset(t, 0).FormulaR1C1 = "=WAlpha*(RC[-4] / RC[2]) + (1-WAlpha)*(R[-1]C + R[-1]C[1])"
            Range("ParTrend").Offset(t, 0).FormulaR1C1 = "=WBeta*(RC[-1]-R[-1]C[-1])+(1-WBeta)*R[-1]C"
            Range("ParSF").Offset(t + WinNSeas, 0).Formula = "=WGamma * (" & Range("ParHist").Offset(t, 0).Address & _
            "/ " & Range("ParBase").Offset(t, 0).Address & ") + (1 - WGAmma) * " & Range("ParSF").Offset(t, 0).Address & ""
            Range("ParForc").Offset(t, 0).FormulaR1C1 = "=(R[-1]C[3] + R[-1]C[4])*RC[5]"
        ElseIf t > NHistPer Then
            Range("ParHist").Offset(t, -1).Value = t
            Range("ParForc").Offset(t, 0).Formula = "=(" & Range("ParBase").Address & "+" & t & _
                "*" & Range("ParTrend").Address & ")*" & Range("ParSF").Offset(t Mod NHistPer, 0).Address
        End If
    Next t

    'calculate forecasting error
    Range("WinObjFunc").Formula = "=AVERAGE(" & Range("ParSq").Offset(TInit, 0).Address & ":" & _
        Range("ParSq").Offset(TFin - 1, 0).Address & ")"
    If TFin <= NHistPer Then
        Range("MSEStart").Offset(3, 1).Value = Range("WinObjFunc").Value
    End If
End Sub
```

Figure CS5.15 The second half of the "Winter" procedure.

Once the selected method calculations are performed, the application calls the "Update-Chart" procedure, which updates the chart on either the compare methods or best method sheet by resetting the source data to include the newly forecasted data values. (See Figure CS5.16.)

```
Sub UpdateChart()    'updates chart with forcast data for selected method
    ActiveSheet.ChartObjects(1).Activate
    With ActiveChart
        .SetSourceData Source:=Worksheets("Parameters").Range(Range("ParStart").Offset(1, 0), _
            Range("ParForc").Offset(TFin, 0))
        .SeriesCollection(1).Name = "Historical Data"
        .SeriesCollection(2).Name = "Forecast"
        .Axes(xlCategory).MinimumScale = 0
        .Axes(xlCategory).MaximumScale = TFin + 2
    End With
    Range("A1").Select
End Sub
```

Figure CS5.16 The "UpdateChart" procedure.

The "FindBest" procedure is called from the "Find Best Method" button on the compare methods sheet. (See Figure CS5.17.) This procedure begins by calling the "Calc" method to run each of the forecasting method procedures with the last parameters set by the users. It then evaluates the MSE values for each method to find the method with the minimum MSE. Once it finds the minimum MSE, it recalls the corresponding calculation procedure to produce the forecast data to graph. It then displays the minimum MSE value for this method, the method's name, and the method's parameters on the best method sheet.

```
Sub FindBest()
    Application.ScreenUpdating = False
    'run all methods again with TFin = NHistPer
    With Worksheets("Method")
        .txtFinMA = NHistPer
        .txtFinEx = NHistPer
        .txtFinHolt = NHistPer
        .txtFinW = NHistPer
    End With
    Method = "FindBest"
    Call Calc

    'compare all MSE to find method with Min MSE
    MinMSE = 999999999
    For i = 1 To 4
        If Range("MSEStart").Offset(i - 1, 1).Value < MinMSE Then
            MinMSE = Range("MSEStart").Offset(i - 1, 1).Value
            BestMethod = Range("MSEStart").Offset(i - 1, 0).Value
        End If
    Next i
    'report name and MSE
    Range("BestName").Value = BestMethod
    Range("BestMSE").Value = MinMSE

    'report parameters and update chart data by recalling procedure for best method
    Range(Range("ParForc").Offset(1, 0), _
        Range("ParForc").Offset(NHistPer, 0).End(xlDown)).ClearContents
    Select Case BestMethod
        Case "Moving Averages"
            Worksheets("Parameters").Range("MAParam").Copy
            Range("BestParameters").Offset(1, 0).PasteSpecial xlPasteValues
            Call MovAvg
        Case "Exponential Smoothing"
            Worksheets("Parameters").Range("ExSmParam").Copy
            Range("BestParameters").Offset(1, 0).PasteSpecial xlPasteValues
            Call ExpSm
        Case "Holt's Method with Trends"
            Worksheets("Parameters").Range("HoltParam").Copy
            Range("BestParameters").Offset(1, 0).PasteSpecial xlPasteValues
            Call Holt
        Case "Winter's Method with Seasonality"
            Worksheets("Parameters").Range("WintParam").Copy
            Range("BestParameters").Offset(1, 0).PasteSpecial xlPasteValues
            Call Winter
    End Select

    Worksheets("BestMethod").Activate
    Call UpdateChart
    Worksheets("BestMethod").Visible = True
    Worksheets("Method").Visible = False
    Application.ScreenUpdating = True
End Sub
```

Figure CS5.17 The "FindBest" procedure.

The navigational procedures are for the "End" buttons on all the sheets and for the "Compare Methods" button on the best method sheet. (See Figure CS5.18.)

```
Sub EndProg()
    Worksheets("Welcome").Visible = True
    ActiveSheet.Visible = False
End Sub

Sub ReturnCompare()
    Worksheets("Method").Visible = True
    ActiveSheet.Visible = False
End Sub
```

Figure CS5.18 The navigational procedures.

Summary

Main	Initializes the application and takes the users to the historical data sheet.
RunDemo	Copies the default historical data and takes the users to the historical data sheet.
ClearPrev	Clears the previous values on all the sheets.
Continue	Counts the number of periods of historical data and initializes the controls on the compare methods sheet.
Calc	Calls the procedure to perform the calculations for the selected method and then calls the "UpdateChart" procedure.
MovAvg	Performs the calculations for the Moving Average method.
ExpSm	Performs the calculations for the Exponential Smoothing method.
Holt	Performs the calculations for Holt's Method with Trends.
Winter	Performs the calculations for Winter's Method with Seasonality.
UpdateChart	Updates the chart with the forecast data just calculated.
FindBest	Finds the method with the minimum MSE and updates all the information on the best method sheet.
Navigational procedures	Apply to the "End" and "Compare Methods" buttons.

CS5.5 *Re-solve Options*

The users can re-solve this application by changing any of the parameters for the selected methods on the compare methods sheet and re-pressing the "Forecast" button. These parameters include changing the final period to forecast future periods. (See Figure CS5.19.) With the new parameters set, the users can press the "Find Best Method" button again to determine the updated best method for the data.

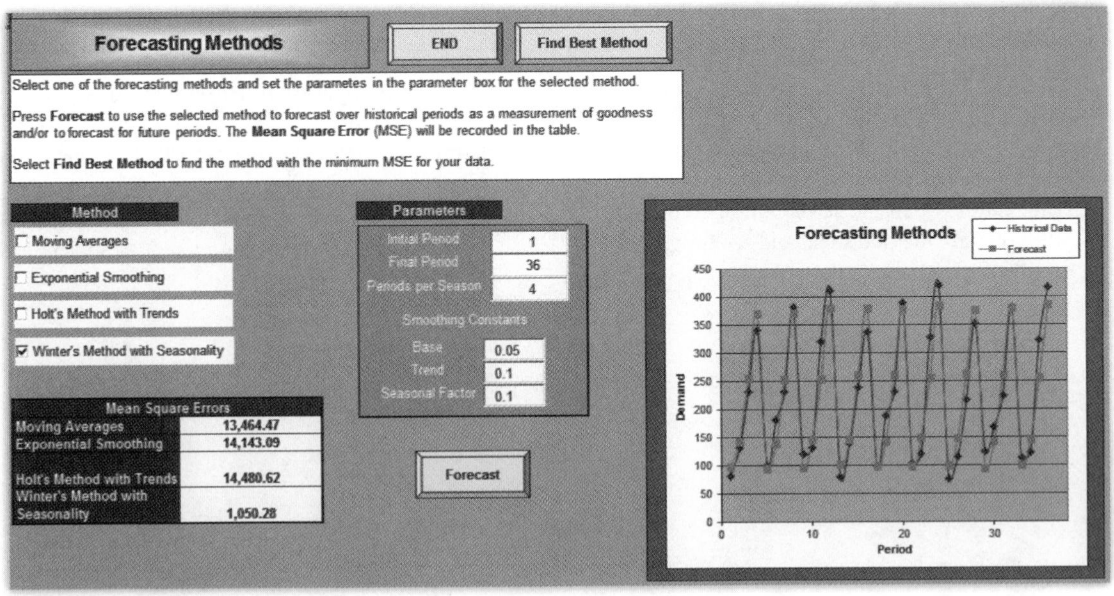

Figure CS5.19 Forecasting future periods on the compare methods sheet.

Summary

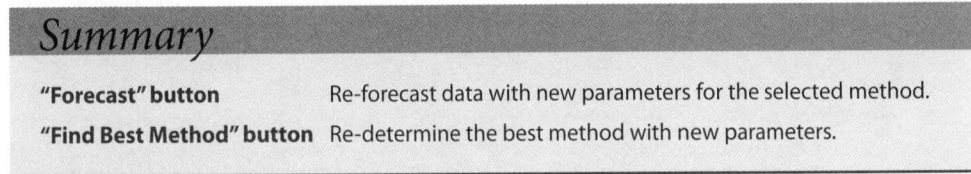

"Forecast" button	Re-forecast data with new parameters for the selected method.
"Find Best Method" button	Re-determine the best method with new parameters.

CS5.6 *Summary*

- The forecasting methods application allows the users to calculate forecasts using Moving Averages, Exponential Smoothing, Holt's Method with Trends, and Winter's Method with Seasonality. It also determines the best method for the given historical data by finding the method that yields the minimum MSE.
- This application requires four worksheets: the welcome sheet, the historical data sheet, the compare methods sheet, and the best method sheet.
- For this application's user interface, we use navigational and functional buttons as well as controls on the worksheet.
- Several procedures for this application initialize and perform the forecasting calculations for the selected methods.
- The users can re-solve the application by changing the method parameters and re-forecasting the data or re-determining the best method.

CS5.7 *Extensions*

1. Modify the application so more than one method can be calculated and graphed at a time. For example, if the users want to compare the forecast data for two methods at one time, they should be able to select both methods on the compare method sheet and see the graphed results for both methods.
2. Modify the application so users can compare forecasts for one method with different sets of parameters. How would you create this new interface?
3. Create a procedure to optimize the parameters for all of the methods. (*Hint:* Use Risk Solver Platform.)

CASE STUDY

six Facility Layout

chapter OVERVIEW

CS6.1 Application Overview and Model Development

In this application, we study a facility location problem that consists of placing n facilities at n locations to minimize the total handling cost. This problem is also known as the Quadratic Assignment Problem (QAP). It arises in many other applications, such as the allocation of plants to candidate locations, the backboard-wiring problem, the design of control panels and typewriter keyboards, and turbine balancing.

CS6.1.1 Model Definition and Assumptions

In this problem, we are given n departments, numbered 1, 2, °, n, and n facilities, also numbered 1, 2, … , n. Distances between locations are given by an $n \times n$ distance matrix $\{dij\}$. The interaction between departments is given by an $n \times n$ flow matrix $\{f_{ij}\}$, which represents the number of trips made between the departments per unit time. The objective in this problem is to assign each facility i to a location $s[i]$ so that the total distance traveled, given by

$$\sum_{i=1}^{n}\sum_{j=1}^{n} f_{ij} d(s[i]s[j]) \quad \text{is minimal.}$$

For simplicity, we assume the following: (i) the locations are arranged in a rectangular grid; (ii) a facility can be assigned to any location; (iii) the distances between locations are rectilinear distances; and (iv) the flow matrix is randomly generated. The users can, however, overwrite the distance and flow matrices.

We also allow the users to change the default numbering assigned to the facilities. In other words, they can begin with a specified layout to determine what improvements are possible from that starting point. We also allow the users to fix some facilities.

We include a local search method to solve the facility location problem. We start with a feasible assignment of facilities to locations and improve it repeatedly by performing pair-wise exchanges between facilities.

For more information on this facility location problem, please see *Facility Layout and Location* by Francis and White.

CS6.1.2 Input

The input for this application is the following:

- Number of facilities
- Renumbering of the facilities if the users choose this option
- Which facilities are fixed if the users choose this option

CS6.1.3 Output

The output for this application is the following:

- Final facility layout
- Chart and table of the change in cost for each iteration of the local search method

CS6.2 *Worksheets*

This application requires four worksheets: the welcome sheet, the layout sheet, the data sheet, and the report sheet. The welcome sheet contains the title, the description of the application, and the "Start" button. (See Figure CS6.1.) The "Start" button displays to the users an input form and then takes them to the layout sheet.

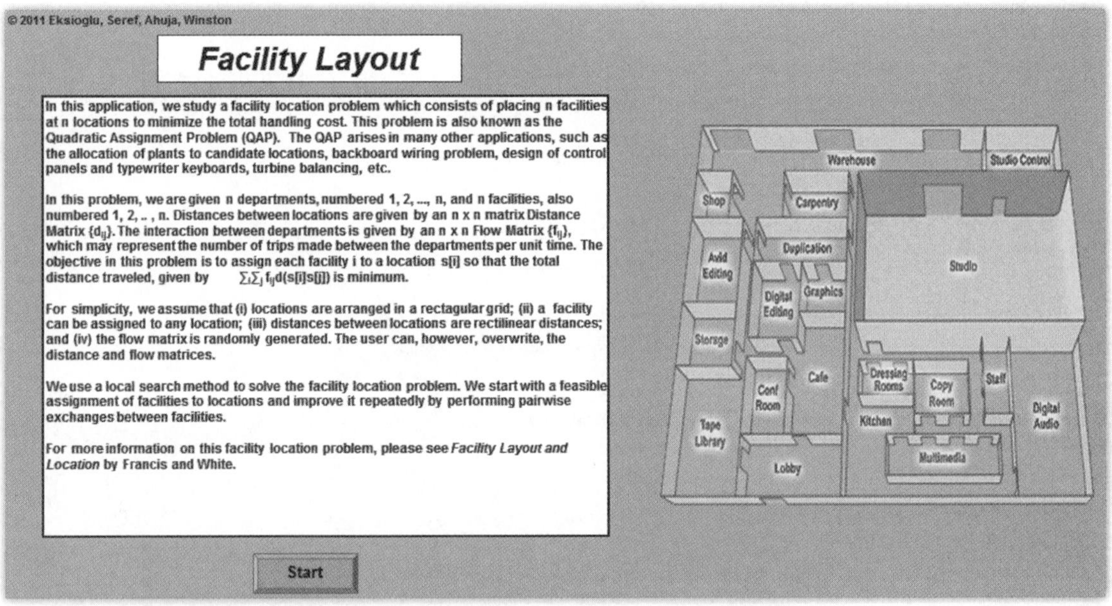

Figure CS6.1 The welcome sheet.

The layout sheet contains the initial layout, created using the facility size the users have provided. (See Figure CS6.2.) It has a detailed set of instructions to explain all of the users' options, which correspond to the buttons on the screen. The users can press the "Change Layout" button to change the default numbering of the initial layout. This option updates the layout sheet with a new set of instructions and buttons. (See Figure CS6.3.)

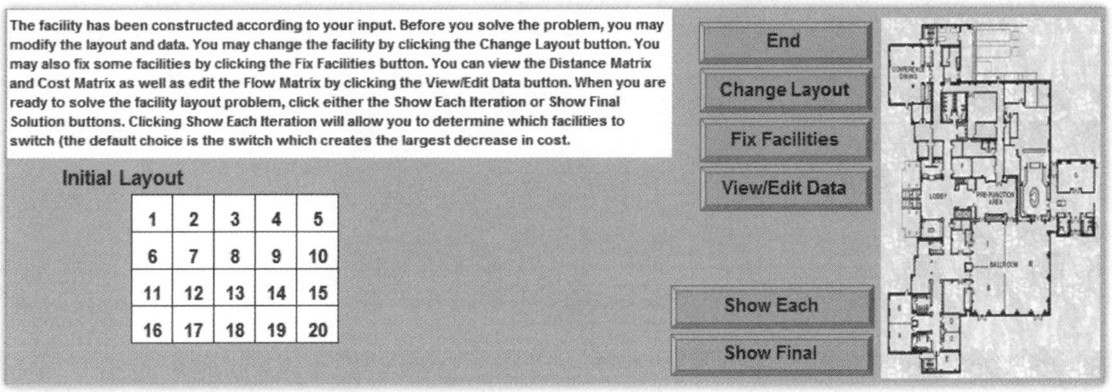

Figure CS6.2 Layout sheet.

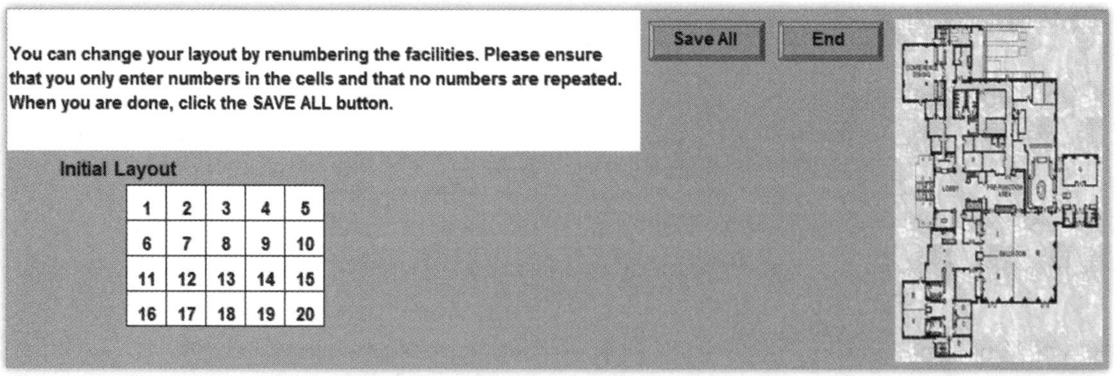

Figure CS6.3 The layout sheet for changing the layout option.

The users could also press the "Fix Facilities" button to amend some facilities before solving the problem. This option also updates the layout sheet with new instructions and buttons. (See Figure CS6.4.)

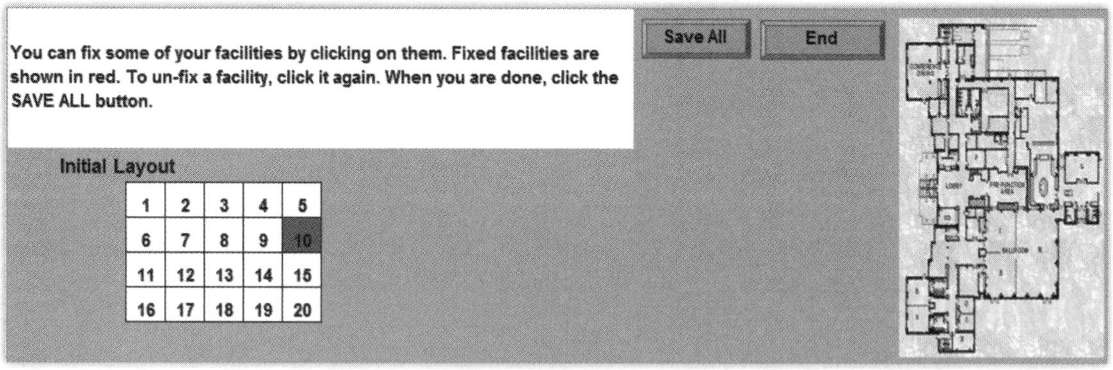

Figure CS6.4 The layout sheet for fixing the facilities option.

The users can also press the "View/Edit Data" button to proceed to the data sheet. The data sheet contains the distance matrix calculated from the facility, the flow matrix with the initial random values, and the cost matrix calculated from the distance and flow matrices. (See Figure CS6.5.) The users can modify the flow matrix if desired and return to the layout sheet.

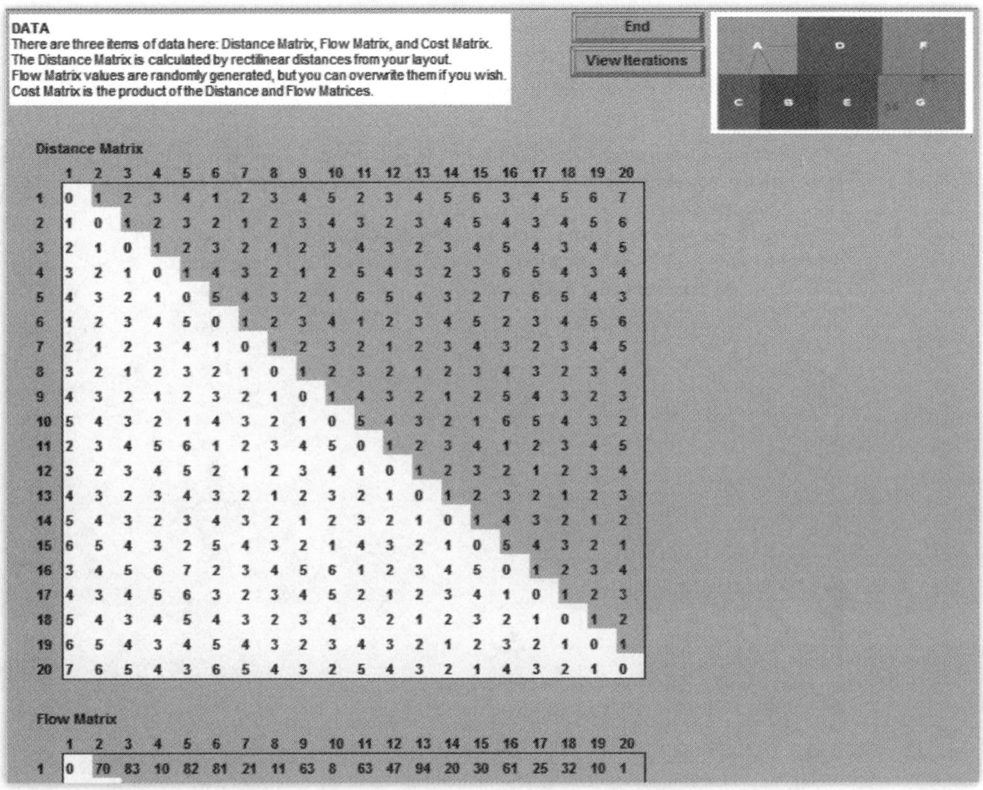

Figure CS6.5 The data sheet with the distance, flow, and cost matrices.

The users can then press the "Show Each Iteration" or "Show Final Solution" buttons to solve the problem. The "Show Each Iteration" button pauses each iteration by displaying a form that the users can refer to in order to decide which facilities to switch; the updated facility for each iteration is then shown. (See Figure CS6.6.)

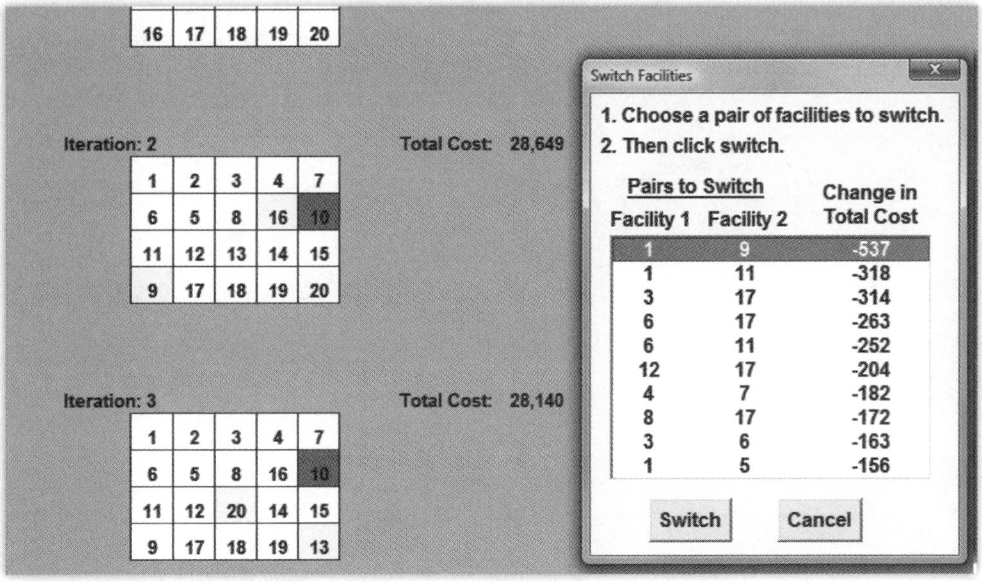

Figure CS6.6 The layout sheet during the iterations.

When the local optimal solution has been found, the layout sheet is updated with new buttons that allow the users to go to the report sheet. (See Figure CS6.7.) The "Show Final Solution" button simply generates all the iterations and updates the layout sheet in the same manner.

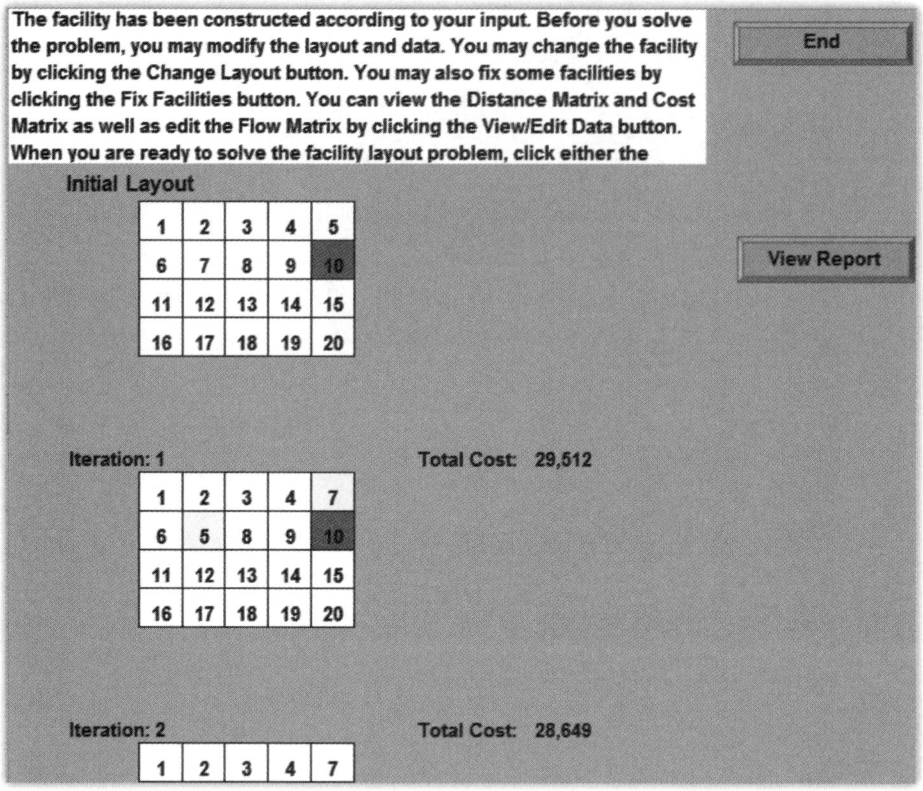

Figure CS6.7 The layout sheet after the local optimum has been determined.

The report sheet presents the final layout, a table, and a chart of the change in cost for each iteration. (See Figure CS6.8.) The users can review the data or iterations by clicking on the "View Data" or "View Iterations" buttons, respectively.

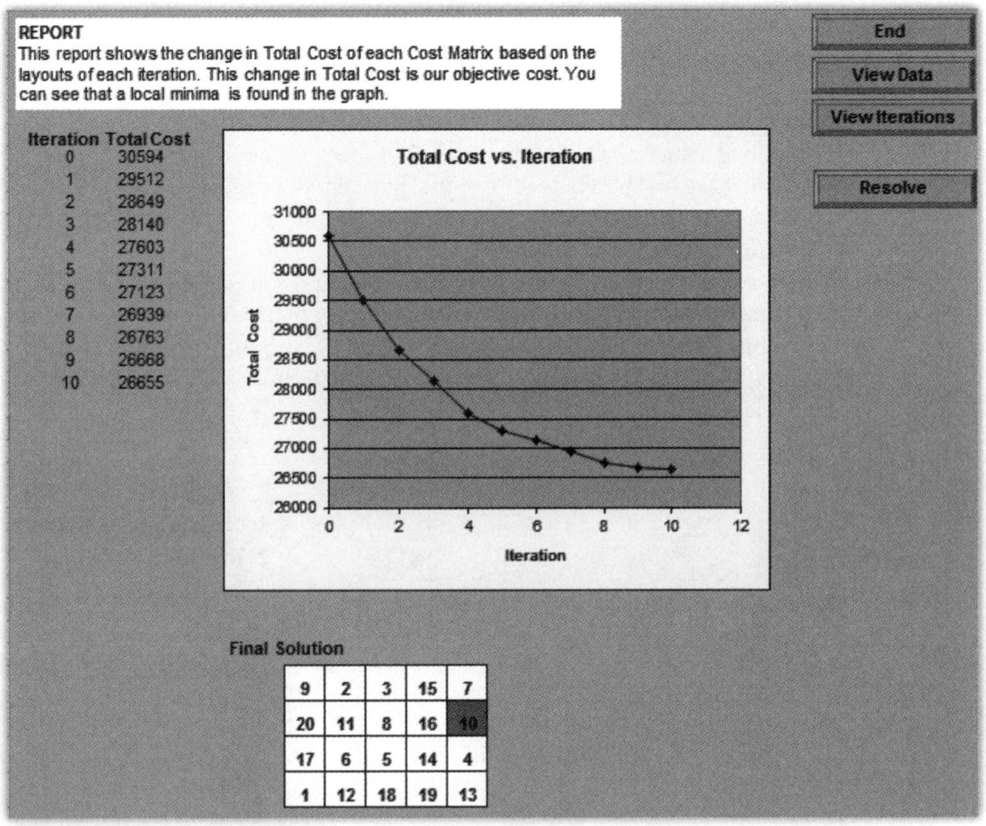

Figure CS6.8 The report sheet.

Summary

Welcome sheet	Contains the application description and the "Start" button.
Layout sheet	Contains the layout option, the change facilities option, the fix facilities option, the solv-ing options, and the iterations.
Data sheet	Stores the distance matrix, the flow matrix, and the cost matrix.
Report sheet	Contains the final facility, the chart, and the table of the change in cost for each iteration.

CS6.3 User Interface

For this application's user interface, we use navigational and functional buttons as well as two user forms. On the welcome sheet, the "Start" button brings the users to the layout sheet. The first user form, the input form, then appears.

This form prompts the users for the size of the facility. (See Figure CS6.9.) This size is represented by the number of rows and columns, such that one row by one column represents one facility. We assume that the number of rows and columns is less than ten each.

The layout sheet contains several navigational and functional buttons. The navigational buttons include "End," "Change Facilities," "Fix Facilities," and "View/Edit Data." The "View Iterations" button on the data sheet is another navigational button that brings the users back to the layout sheet. The functional buttons on the layout sheet are "Show Each Iteration" and "Show Final Solution." On the updated layout sheet for the change facilities and fix facilities options, the "Save All" button is a functional button that records any changes made to the facility. After the solution is found, the "View Report" button appears as another navigational button to take the users to the report sheet.

If the users view each iteration as the problem is solved, then they use the iteration form. (See Figure CS6.10.) This form lists the ten facility pairs with the largest change in cost from switching. The users can select any of these facility pairs and press the "Switch" button to perform the switch in the local search method. The default facilities are the first pair listed that has the largest change in cost.

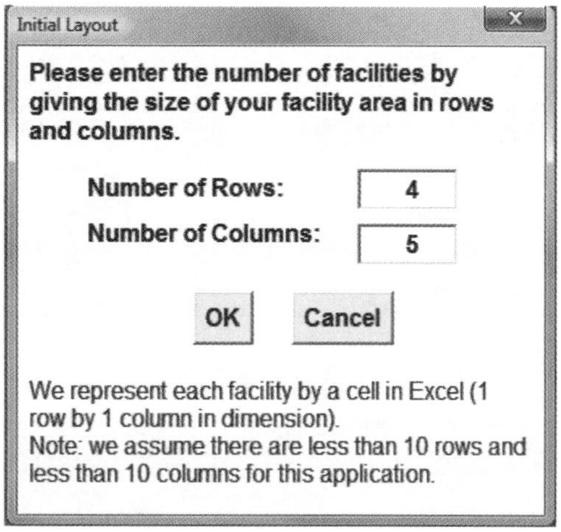

Figure CS6.9 The input form.

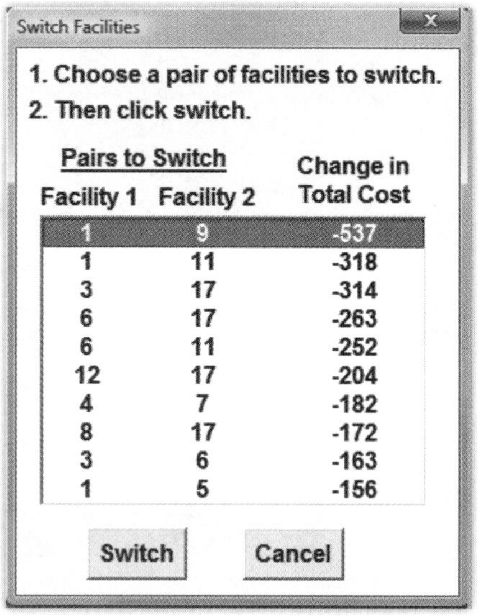

Figure CS6.10 The iteration form.

On the report sheet, the "View Data" and "View Iterations" buttons serve as two more navigational buttons. The "Re-solve" button is a functional button, which we discuss later.

Summary

Navigational buttons	"Start" on the welcome sheet; "End" on all the sheets; "Change Facilities," "Fix Facilities," and "View/Edit Data" on the layout sheet; "View Iterations" on the data sheet; "View Report" on the updated layout sheet; "View Data" and "View Iterations" on the report sheet.
Functional buttons	"Show Each Iteration" and "Show Final Solution" on the layout sheet; "Save All" on the updated layout sheet; "Re-solve" on the report sheet.
Input form	Receives the size of the facility by number of rows and columns.
Iteration form	Allows the users to select a pair of facilities to. switch for the iteration.

CS6.4 Procedures

We will now outline the procedures for this application beginning with the initial sub procedures and the variable definitions. (See Figure CS6.11.) The *Main* procedure is called from the "Start" button. It calls the *ClearPrevious* procedure and initializes the formatting of the layout sheet. It then displays the input form and calls the *CreateLayout* procedure to create the initial layout using the facility size the users have provided. It then calls the *CreateData* and *CreateDataMatrices* procedures to generate the data for this layout.

```
Option Explicit
Option Base 1

Public NRows As Integer, NCols As Integer, NFacilities As Integer, _
Totalcost As Double, k As Integer, i As Integer, j As Integer, _
n As Integer, P As Integer, Q As Integer, Dist() As Integer, _
Flow() As Integer, Cost() As Integer, ChangeCost() As Double, _
ShowIter As Boolean, NIterations As Integer, ChangeCostSize As Integer, _
XCoord() As Integer, YCoord() As Integer, StartCell As Range, _
TempStartCell As Range, ws As Worksheet, Solved As Boolean, _
Temp As Integer, Resolving As Boolean, DistStartCell As Range, _
FlowStartCell As Range, CostStartCell As Range, Changed As Boolean, _
Fixed As Boolean, FixFacA() As Boolean, row As Integer, col As Integer

Sub MAIN()  'called from Start button
    Application.ScreenUpdating = False
    Call ClearPrevious

    With Worksheets("Layout")
      .Activate
      .Shapes("ViewRep").Visible = False
      .Visible = True
    End With
    Range("Instruc") = Range("DefaultI").Value

    'initialize which buttons to show and hide
    Call Buttons2

    Worksheets("Welcome").Visible = False
    Worksheets("Data").Shapes("ViewRepSh").Visible = False
    Range("Instruc").Offset(1, 0).Select
    Application.ScreenUpdating = True

    'find facility size and initialize data
    If Resolving = False Then
        frmLayout.Show
    End If

    Application.ScreenUpdating = False
    Call CreateLayout
    Call CreateData
    Call CreateDataMatrices
    Application.ScreenUpdating = True
End Sub
```

Figure CS6.11 The variable declarations and the *Main* procedure.

The *ClearPrevious* procedure clears all the previous data values and the formatting for the all sheets. (See Figure CS6.12.) It also initializes some variables. The procedures for the input form receive the number of rows and columns the users have provided and, with these values, calculate the total number of facilities. (See Figure CS6.13.)

```
Sub ClearPrevious() 'clear previous values and formatting
    For Each ws In ActiveWorkbook.Worksheets
      If ws.Name <> "Welcome" And ws.Name <> "TempSheet" Then
            ws.Cells.ClearContents
      End If
    Next

    Worksheets("Layout").Cells.Borders.LineStyle = xlNone
    Worksheets("Layout").Cells.Interior.ColorIndex = xlNone
    Range("Instruc").Interior.ColorIndex = 2

    Worksheets("Data").Cells.Borders.LineStyle = xlNone
    Worksheets("Data").Cells.Interior.ColorIndex = xlNone

    Worksheets("Report").Cells.Borders.LineStyle = xlNone
    Worksheets("Report").Cells.Interior.ColorIndex = xlNone

    NIterations = 0
    Totalcost = 0
    Solved = False
    Changed = False
    Fixed = False
End Sub
```

Figure CS6.12 The *ClearPrevious* procedure.

```
Sub cmdCancel_Click()
    Worksheets("Welcome").Visible = True
    Worksheets("Layout").Visible = False
    Unload Me
    End
End Sub

Sub cmdOK_Click()
    Dim ctl As Control
    For Each ctl In Me.Controls
        If TypeName(ctl) = "TextBox" Then
            If ctl.Value = "" Then
                MsgBox "Please make sure all textboxes are filled in.", _
                    vbMsgBoxSetForeground = "yellow"
                ctl.SetFocus
                Exit Sub
            End If
        End If
    Next

    NRows = txtNumRows
    NCols = txtNumCols
    NFacilities = NRows * NCols
    Unload Me
End Sub
```

Figure CS6.13 The input form procedures.

The *CreateLayout* procedure formats each row and column of the facility according to the size the users have provided. (See Figure CS6.14.) It also numbers each facility sequentially as it is formatted. Then, it initializes an array for storing fixed facilities so that no facilities are fixed initially.

```
Sub CreateLayout()
'create initial layout and number facilities
    Worksheets("Layout").Activate
    Set StartCell = Range("C5")

    k = 1
    For i = 1 To NRows
        For j = 1 To NCols
            With StartCell.Offset(i, j)
                .Value = k
                .BorderAround Weight:=xlThin
                .Interior.ColorIndex = 2
            End With
            k = k + 1
        Next j
    Next i

    'reset fix facilities to none
    ReDim FixFacA(NFacilities)
    For k = 1 To NFacilities
        FixFacA(k) = False
    Next k
End Sub
```

Figure CS6.14 The *CreateLayout* procedure.

The *CreateData* procedure creates the data for the distance, flow, and cost matrices. (See Figure CS6.15.) The application first calculates each facility's x- and y-coordinates, which are used to find the Euclidian distance between each pair of facilities. The flow matrix values are generated randomly, and the cost matrix values are simply the product of the distance and flow for each facility pair.

```
Sub CreateData()    'calculate distance, flow, and cost data
    'calc x and y coord for all facilities
    ReDim XCoord(NFacilities), YCoord(NFacilities)
    k = 1
    For row = 1 To NRows
        For col = 1 To NCols
            XCoord(Range("LayoutEdge").Offset(row, col).Value) = (k - 1) Mod (NCols) + 1
            YCoord(Range("LayoutEdge").Offset(row, col).Value) = Fix((k - 1) / NCols) + 1
            k = k + 1
        Next col
    Next row

    'calc distance, flow, and costs for all facility pairs
    ReDim Dist(NFacilities, NFacilities), Flow(NFacilities, NFacilities), _
    Cost(NFacilities, NFacilities)
    For k = 1 To NFacilities
        For n = k + 1 To NFacilities
            Dist(k, n) = Abs(XCoord(k) - XCoord(n)) + Abs(YCoord(k) - YCoord(n))
            'flow created randomly
            Flow(k, n) = Round(1 + 99 * Rnd, 0)
            Totalcost = Totalcost + Dist(k, n) * Flow(k, n)
        Next n

        For n = 1 To k - 1
            Dist(k, n) = Dist(n, k)
            Flow(k, n) = Flow(n, k)
        Next n
    Next k
    Range("TotalCost") = Totalcost
    Range("Iteration") = NIterations
End Sub
```

Figure CS6.15 The *CreateData* procedure.

The *CreateDataMatrices* procedure places the matrix values in matrix form on the data sheet. (See Figures CS6.16 and CS6.17.) Each matrix is formatted as an upper-triangle matrix.

```
Sub CreateDataMatrices()    'create data matricies for distance, flow, and cost
    Worksheets("Data").Activate
    Set DistStartCell = Range("B7")
    Set FlowStartCell = DistStartCell.Offset(NFacilities + 3, 0)
    Set CostStartCell = FlowStartCell.Offset(NFacilities + 3, 0)

    'distance matrix
    DistStartCell.Offset(-1).Value = "Distance Matrix"
    For k = 1 To NFacilities
        For n = 1 To NFacilities
            DistStartCell.Offset(k, n) = Dist(k, n)
            DistStartCell.Offset(0, k).Value = k
            DistStartCell.Offset(k, 0).Value = k
        Next n
        If k <> 0 Then  'show upper-triangular matrix
         Range(DistStartCell.Offset(k, 1), _
            DistStartCell.Offset(k, k)).Interior.ColorIndex = 36
        End If
    Next k
    Range(DistStartCell.Offset(1, 1), DistStartCell.Offset(NFacilities, NFacilities)). _
        BorderAround Weight:=xlThin

    'flow matrix (only updated initially, so that user can change values)
    If Solved = False Then
        FlowStartCell.Offset(-1).Value = "Flow Matrix"
        For k = 1 To NFacilities
            For n = 1 To NFacilities
                FlowStartCell.Offset(k, n) = Flow(k, n)
                FlowStartCell.Offset(0, k).Value = k
                FlowStartCell.Offset(k, 0).Value = k
            Next n
            If k <> 0 Then  'show upper-triangular matrix
             Range(FlowStartCell.Offset(k, 1), _
                FlowStartCell.Offset(k, k)).Interior.ColorIndex = 36
            End If
        Next k
        Range(FlowStartCell.Offset(1, 1), FlowStartCell.Offset(NFacilities, NFacilities)). _
            BorderAround Weight:=xlThin
    End If
```

Figure CS6.16 The first part of *CreateDataMatrices* procedure.

```
    'cost matrix
    CostStartCell.Offset(-1).Value = "Cost Matrix"
    For k = 1 To NFacilities
        CostStartCell.Offset(k, 0) = k
        CostStartCell.Offset(0, k) = k
    Next k
    For k = 1 To NFacilities
        For n = 1 To NFacilities
            CostStartCell.Offset(k, n) = Dist(k, n) * Flow(k, n)
        Next n  'show upper-triangular matrix
        Range(CostStartCell.Offset(k, 1), _
            CostStartCell.Offset(k, k)).Interior.ColorIndex = 36
    Next k
    Range(CostStartCell.Offset(1, 1), _
        CostStartCell.Offset(NFacilities, NFacilities)).BorderAround Weight:=xlThin
End Sub
```

Figure CS6.17 The second part of *CreateDataMatrices* procedure.

The *ChangeLayout* and *FixFac* procedures simply update the layout sheet with new instructions and buttons for the change facilities and fix facilities options, respectively. (See Figure

CS6.18.) The *SaveAll* procedure records any changes the users have made for either of these options. (See Figure CS6.18.) If the users have changed the facility numbering, then the *CreateData* and *CreateDataMatrices* procedures must be called again to update the distance matrix. If the users have fixed some facilities, then these are recorded in an array and formatted on the layout. The layout sheet is then updated to display the initial instructions and buttons again.

```
Sub ChangeLayout()   'called from Change Layout button
    'change instructions
    Range("Instruc").Value = Range("ChangeI").Value
    Changed = True
    'hide and show different buttons
    Call Buttons
    Range("Instruc").Offset(1, 0).Select
End Sub

Sub FixFac()     'called from Fix Facilities button
    'change instructions
    Range("Instruc").Value = Range("FixedI").Value
    Fixed = True
    'hide and show different buttons
    Call Buttons
    Range("Instruc").Offset(1, 0).Select
End Sub

Sub SaveAll()    'called from Save All button
    'if user was changing facilities
    If Changed Then
        'recalc dist and cost matrices
        Call CreateData
        Call CreateDataMatrices
        Changed = False
    End If

    'if user was fixing facilities
    If Fixed Then
        'record fixed facilities
        For row = 1 To NRows
            For col = 1 To NCols
                If Range("LayoutEdge").Offset(row, col).Interior.Color = vbRed Then
                    FixFacA(Range("LayoutEdge").Offset(row, col).Value) = True
                End If
            Next col
        Next row
        Fixed = False
    End If

    'reset instructions
    Range("Instruc") = Range("DefaultI").Value
    Worksheets("Layout").Activate
    'reset buttons
    Call Buttons2
End Sub
```

Figure CS6.18 The *ChangeLayout*, *FixFac*, and *SaveAll* procedures.

The *ShowFinal* and *ShowEach* procedures set a Boolean variable and then call the *LocalSearch* procedure. (See Figure CS6.19.) The *LocalSearch* procedure is the main procedure of the application, as it performs the local search method to find the problem solution. (See Figures CS6.19 and CS6.20.)

```
Sub ShowFinal() 'called from Show Final Solution button
    ShowIter = False
    Call LocalSearch
End Sub

Sub ShowEach()  'called from Show Each Iteration button
    ShowIter = True
    Call LocalSearch
End Sub

Sub LocalSearch()   'perform local search algorithm
    'hide buttons
    Worksheets("Layout").Shapes("ShowEachIt").Visible = False
    Worksheets("Layout").Shapes("ShowFinalSol").Visible = False

    'initialize
    ReDim ChangeCost(NFacilities, NFacilities)
    Set TempStartCell = Worksheets("TempSheet").Range("B5")
    Range(TempStartCell, TempStartCell.End(xlDown).End(xlToRight)).ClearContents
    Application.ScreenUpdating = False
    Worksheets("TempSheet").Activate
    ChangeCostSize = 0

    For k = 1 To NFacilities
        'if facility k fixed then skip to examine next k
        If FixFacA(k) = False Then
            For n = k + 1 To NFacilities
                'if facility n fixed then skip to examine next n
                If FixFacA(n) = False Then
                    ChangeCost(k, n) = 0
                    'change in cost is difference in cost if facilities k and n were switched
                    For i = 1 To NFacilities
                        ChangeCost(k, n) = ChangeCost(k, n) - (Flow(i, k) - Flow(i, n)) _
                                * (Dist(i, k) - Dist(i, n))
                    Next i
                    ChangeCost(k, n) = ChangeCost(k, n) + 2 * Flow(k, n) * Dist(k, n)
                    'record switch only if change in cost is negative
                    If ChangeCost(k, n) < 0 Then
                        ChangeCostSize = ChangeCostSize + 1
                        TempStartCell.Offset(ChangeCostSize, 0) = k
                        TempStartCell.Offset(ChangeCostSize, 1) = n
                        TempStartCell.Offset(ChangeCostSize, 2) = ChangeCost(k, n)
                    End If
                End If
            Next n
        End If
    Next k
```

Figure CS6.19 The *ShowFinal* and *ShowEach* procedures and the first part of the *LocalSearch* procedure.

```
    'if no negative change in cost found, then local optimum reached
    If ChangeCostSize = 0 Then
        Worksheets("Layout").Activate
        Application.ScreenUpdating = True
        MsgBox ("Solution is locally optimal")
        'update buttons
        Worksheets("Layout").Shapes("ViewRep").Visible = True
        Worksheets("Data").Shapes("ViewRepSh").Visible = True
        Worksheets("Layout").Shapes("FixF").Visible = False
        Worksheets("Layout").Shapes("ChangeL").Visible = False
        Worksheets("Layout").Shapes("ViewDataSh").Visible = False
        'create the report sheet
        Call CreateReport
        Range("Instruc").Offset(1, 0).Select
        Exit Sub
    'otherwise, decide which pairs are best to switch
    Else
        Range(TempStartCell.Offset(1, 0), TempStartCell.Offset(ChangeCostSize, 2)).Name = "Pairs"
        'sort pairs from largest negative change in cost to smallest negative change in cost
        Range("Pairs").Sort Key1:=Range("D:D"), order1:=xlAscending
        'only show user top 10 choices
        Range(TempStartCell.Offset(1, 0), TempStartCell.Offset(10, 2)).Name = "Pairs"

        If ShowIter = True Then
            'give user the list of pairs which generate negative change in cost
            Worksheets("Layout").Activate
            frmIteration.lstIteration.RowSource = "Pairs"
            Application.ScreenUpdating = True
            frmIteration.Show
        ElseIf ShowIter = False Then
            'choose pair with largest negative change in cost
            P = Range("Pairs").Cells(1, 1)
            Q = Range("Pairs").Cells(1, 2)
            'update layout
            Call Update
            'recall LocalSearch procedure
            Call LocalSearch
        End If
    End If
End Sub
```

Figure CS6.20 The second part of the *LocalSearch* procedure.

LocalSearch calculates what the change in cost is if two facilities are switched. Notice that it does not perform this evaluation for any pair that includes a fixed facility. All pairs that cause a negative change in cost, that is a decrease in the cost, are listed and sorted. The top ten pairs from this list are displayed on the iteration form. If the users opt to just show the final solution, then the top item from this list, the pair with the largest decrease in cost, is selected. The *Update* procedure then updates the distance and cost matrices, and then the *LocalSearch* procedure is re-called. If there are no facilities that cause a decrease in the cost, then a local optimum has been reached and the *CreateReport* procedure is called.

The procedures for the iteration form record which pair of facilities the users select to switch. (See Figure CS6.21.) They then call the *Update* and *LocalSearch* procedures.

The *Update* procedure updates the distance and cost matrices and displays the new layout. (See Figures CS6.22 and CS6.23.) The x- and y-coordinates are updated, and the facilities are renumbered for the switched facilities. The switched facilities and any fixed facilities are also highlighted. The application displays the updated cost and the iteration number on the layout sheet and records them on the report sheet.

```
Option Explicit

Sub cmdCancel_Click()
    Worksheets("Welcome").Activate
    Worksheets("Welcome").Visible = True
    Worksheets("Layout").Visible = False
    End
End Sub

Sub cmdSwitch_Click()
    P = Range("Pairs").Cells(lstIteration.ListIndex + 1, 1)
    Q = Range("Pairs").Cells(lstIteration.ListIndex + 1, 2)
    Unload Me
    Call Update
    Call LocalSearch
End Sub

Sub UserForm_Initialize()
    lstIteration.Selected(0) = True
End Sub
```

Figure CS6.21 The iterations form procedures.

```
Sub Update()    'update facilities after switch is made
    Application.ScreenUpdating = False
    'update distance matrix
    For i = 1 To NFacilities
        Temp = Dist(P, i)
        Dist(P, i) = Dist(Q, i)
        Dist(Q, i) = Temp
    Next i
    For j = 1 To NFacilities
        Temp = Dist(j, P)
        Dist(j, P) = Dist(j, Q)
        Dist(j, Q) = Temp
    Next j

    'update cost and iterations on report sheet
    NIterations = NIterations + 1
    Totalcost = Totalcost + ChangeCost(P, Q)
    Range("TotalCost").Offset(NIterations) = Totalcost
    Range("Iteration").Offset(NIterations) = NIterations

    'update facility display
    Worksheets("Layout").Activate
    Range(StartCell, StartCell.Offset(NRows, NCols)).Copy
    Set StartCell = StartCell.Offset(NRows + 3)
    StartCell.PasteSpecial
    Range(StartCell.Offset(1, 1), _
        StartCell.Offset(NRows, NCols)).Interior.ColorIndex = 2
    For i = 1 To NRows
        For j = 1 To NCols
            'highlight the pair of facilities that was just switched
            If StartCell.Offset(i, j) = P Or StartCell.Offset(i, j) = Q Then
               StartCell.Offset(i, j).Interior.ColorIndex = 36
            End If
            'highlight any fixed facilities
            If FixFacA(StartCell.Offset(i, j).Value) = True Then
                StartCell.Offset(i, j).Interior.Color = vbRed
            End If
        Next j
    Next i
    StartCell.Value = "Iteration: " & NIterations
    StartCell.Offset(0, NCols + 4).Value = "Total Cost:  "
    StartCell.Offset(0, NCols + 5).Value = Totalcost
```

Figure CS6.22 The first part of the *Update* procedure.

```
    'update coordinates and facility numbers
    Dim XTemp As Integer, YTemp As Integer, _
    PValue As Integer, QValue As Integer

    PValue = StartCell.Offset(YCoord(P), XCoord(P))
    QValue = StartCell.Offset(YCoord(Q), XCoord(Q))

    XTemp = XCoord(P)
    XCoord(P) = XCoord(Q)
    XCoord(Q) = XTemp

    YTemp = YCoord(P)
    YCoord(P) = YCoord(Q)
    YCoord(Q) = YTemp

    StartCell.Offset(YCoord(P), XCoord(P)) = PValue
    StartCell.Offset(YCoord(Q), XCoord(Q)) = QValue

    Application.ScreenUpdating = True
    If ShowIter = True Then
      'keep screen shifting down
      StartCell.Offset(0, -2).Select
    End If
End Sub
```

```
Sub CreateReport()  'creates final report sheet
    Application.ScreenUpdating = False
    Solved = True
    'update matrices since Update procedure is not called
    Call CreateDataMatrices

    'copy and paste final layout to report sheet
    Range(StartCell.Offset(1, 1), StartCell.Offset(NRows, NCols)).Copy
    Worksheets("Report").Activate
    Range("G29").Offset(1, 1).PasteSpecial
    Range(Range("G29").Offset(1, 1), _
        Range("G29").Offset(NRows, NCols)).Interior.ColorIndex = 2
    For i = 1 To NRows
        For j = 1 To NCols
            'only highlight fixed facilities (not switched facilities)
            If FixFacA(Range("G29").Offset(i, j).Value) = True Then
                Range("G29").Offset(i, j).Interior.Color = vbRed
            End If
        Next j
    Next i

    Worksheets("Layout").Activate
    Application.ScreenUpdating = True
End Sub
```

Figure CS6.23 The second part of the *Update* procedure and the entire *CreateReport* procedure.

The *CreateReport* procedure displays the final solution on the report sheet. (See Figure CS6.23.) It updates the final matrices by calling the *CreateDataMatrices* procedure. It then copies and pastes the final layout to the report sheet and highlights the fixed facilities.

Figure CS6.24 presents the navigational procedures for the "View Data," "View Report," "View Iterations," "End," and "Re-solve" buttons, and it presents the procedures for showing and hiding the buttons on the layout sheet.

```
''''''''''''''''''''''''
'navigational procedures
''''''''''''''''''''''''
Sub ViewData()
    Worksheets("Data").Visible = True
    ActiveSheet.Visible = False
End Sub

Sub ViewReport()
    Worksheets("Report").Visible = True
    ActiveSheet.Visible = False
End Sub

Sub ViewIter()
    Worksheets("Layout").Visible = True
    ActiveSheet.Visible = False
End Sub

Sub EndProg()
    Worksheets("Welcome").Visible = True
    ActiveSheet.Visible = False
    Resolving = False
End Sub

Sub Resolve()
    Resolving = True
    Call MAIN
    Worksheets("Report").Visible = False
End Sub

'functions to show/hide buttons
Function Buttons()
    ActiveSheet.Shapes("SaveAll").Visible = True
    ActiveSheet.Shapes("FixF").Visible = False
    ActiveSheet.Shapes("ChangeL").Visible = False
    ActiveSheet.Shapes("ViewDataSh").Visible = False
    ActiveSheet.Shapes("ShowEachIt").Visible = False
    ActiveSheet.Shapes("ShowFinalSol").Visible = False
End Function

Function Buttons2()
    ActiveSheet.Shapes("SaveAll").Visible = False
    ActiveSheet.Shapes("FixF").Visible = True
    ActiveSheet.Shapes("ChangeL").Visible = True
    ActiveSheet.Shapes("ViewDataSh").Visible = True
    ActiveSheet.Shapes("ShowEachIt").Visible = True
    ActiveSheet.Shapes("ShowFinalSol").Visible = True
End Function
```

Figure CS6.24 The navigational procedures and buttons functions.

Summary

Main	Initializes the application and takes the users to the historical data sheet.
ClearPrevious	Clears the previous values on all the sheets.
Input form procedures	Record the number of rows and columns in order to calculate the number of facilities.
CreateLayout	Creates the initial layout for the provided dimensions and numbers of each facility.
CreateData	Calculates the data for the distance, flow, and cost matrices.
CreateDataMatrices	Displays the distance, flow, and cost matrices on the data sheet.
ChangeLayout	Updates the layout sheet for the change facilities option.
FixFac	Updates the layout sheet for the fix facilities option.
SaveAll	Records the changes made during the change facilities or fix facilities options.
ShowFinal	Sets the Boolean value and calls *LocalSearch*.
ShowEach	Sets the Boolean value and calls *LocalSearch*.
LocalSearch	Performs the local search method; creates a list of all the facility pairs that decrease the cost if switched; recalls *Update* and *LocalSearch* until the local optimum is found, and then calls *CreateReport*.
Iteration form procedures	Record which pair the user want to switch and call *Update* and *LocalSearch*.
Update	Updates the distance and cost matrices; displays the updated layout for the current iteration.
CreateReport	Updates the matrices and displays the final layout.
Navigational	Apply to the "View Data," "View Report," "View Iterations," "End," and "Re-solve"
procedures	buttons.

CS6.5 Re-solve Options

The users can re-solve this application by pressing the "Re-solve" button on the report sheet. This re-calls the *Main* procedure to clear the previous solution and bring the users back to the layout sheet for the same facility. The users can change the layout numbering, fix some facilities, and modify the flow matrix and then re-solve the problem for the same facility.

Summary

"Re-solve"	Brings the users back to the layout sheet to re-solve for the same facility with possibly different input.

CS6.6 Summary

- This application solves the facility location problem, which consists of placing n facilities at n locations to minimize the total handling cost. A local search method solves it.
- This application requires four worksheets: the welcome sheet, the layout sheet, the data sheet, and the report sheet.
- For this application's user interface, we use navigational and functional buttons as well as two user forms.
- Several procedures in this application initialize and perform local search methods by comparing changes in cost for the pair-wise switching of the facilities.
- The users can re-solve the application by pressing the "Re-solve" button on the report sheet to return to the layout sheet in order to modify the input and re-solve the problem for the same facility.

CS6.7 Extensions

1. Allow the users to stop the local search method before a local optimum is reached. In other words, the users should be able to stop the local search after any iteration.
2. How could you modify this application to allow the users to provide text names to the facilities? Instead of Facility 1, 2, etc., let the users name them "Jason's Office," "Marjorie's Office," or some other descriptive names.
3. What are some other re-solve options possible for this application?
4. Could other methods solve this problem? Try implementing one and begin the application by prompting the users to select which method they wantto use (for example, local search or genetic algorithms).

CASE STUDY

seven Portfolio Management and Optimization

chapter OVERVIEW

CS7.1 Application Overview and Model Development

In this application, we allow users to create and/or edit their portfolios as well as optimize their investments. To create a portfolio, the users can choose from a list of stocks in a database. Listed by name and category, these stocks can be compared to each other by their annual return and change in market price. Once the users have created their portfolios, they can also edit them and optimize their investments.

CS7.1.1 Model Definition and Assumptions

The underlying model for optimizing the portfolio investment plan minimizes risk subject to certain constraints. These constraints include the following: the amount of cash invested must be less than or equal to the amount of cash available for investing; the return on the portfolio must be greater than or equal to the minimum return desired for the entire portfolio; and the amount invested per stock must be less than or equal to a maximum amount to be invested in each stock.

We will now outline this model mathematically. Let x_i be the amount we invest per stock i in the portfolio. The index i varies from 1 to n, where n is equal to the number of stocks in the portfolio.

Let r_i represent the expected return on stock i. The expected returns are determined based on each stock's historical data of annual returns from the past five years.

Let v_i represent the variance of stock i. This variance is calculated based on historical data of quarterly market prices for the past four quarters and the current quarter. To calculate the variance, we first determine the quarterly variance for each stock by finding the difference between each quarter's market price and the mean market price. We then calculate the average variance for each stock.

Let σ_{ij} be the covariance between two stocks i and j. The covariance shows the relationship between two stocks. If the covariance is positive, then as one stock value increases so does the other stock value at a ratio equal to the covariance value. If the covariance is negative, then as one stock value increases, the other stock value decreases at a ratio equal to the covariance value. We define the covariance factor for each pair of stocks i and j as the following product:

$$\sigma_{ij}\,(v_i\,v_j)\,(x_i\,x_j)$$

We can now define the risk of the portfolio, z, as the sum of the product of the square of the investment and the variance over all stocks plus the total covariance factor for all stocks in the portfolio:

$$z = \sum_{i=1}^{n}\left(x_i^2 * v_i\right) + \sum_{i=1}^{n}\sum_{j=1}^{n}\sigma_{ij}\left(v_i v_j\right)\left(x_i x_j\right)$$

We define the return on the portfolio as the sum of the product of the investment amount and the expected return over all stocks:

$$\sum_{i=1}^{n} x_i r_i$$

Let us represent the optimization inputs from the users as follows: C = total cash available for investing; D = desired return on the portfolio; and M = maximum amount to invest per stock. We can now finalize the mathematical model representation:

$$\text{Minimize} \quad z = \sum_{i=1}^{n}\left(x_i^2 * v_i\right) + \sum_{i=1}^{n}\sum_{j=1}^{n}\sigma_{ij}\left(v_i v_j\right)\left(x_i x_j\right)$$

Subject to:

$$\sum_{i=1}^{n} x_i \leq C\frac{n!}{r!(n-r)!}$$

$$\sum_{i=1}^{n}(x_i r_i) \geq D$$

$$x_i \leq M \qquad \text{for } i = 1 \text{ to } n$$

$$x_i = \{0,1\} \qquad \text{for } i = 1 \text{ to } n.$$

We will use Risk Solver Platform to solve this nonlinear programming problem. To find out more about calculating risk by variance in market price, please refer to *Investment Science* by Luenberger.

CS7.1.2 Input

We require the users to create a portfolio as the first input:

- Portfolio = selected stocks

Each selected stock's annual return and market price change are recorded to calculate the expected return and price variance.

Before solving the optimization, we prompt the users for the following input:

- Total cash for investing
- Minimum return desired
- Maximum amount to invest per stock

CS7.1.3 Output

The output reported to the users after the optimization is complete consists of the following:

- Minimum return
- Cash used
- Portfolio return
- Amount to invest per stock
- Portfolio's efficient frontier

CS7.2 *Worksheets*

We use nine worksheets in this application: the welcome sheet, four data sheets, two information sheets, a model sheet, and an output sheet. The welcome sheet contains the application title, a description, and some images (see Figure CS7.1). The "Start" button calls the Main sub procedure and displays the Main Menu to the users.

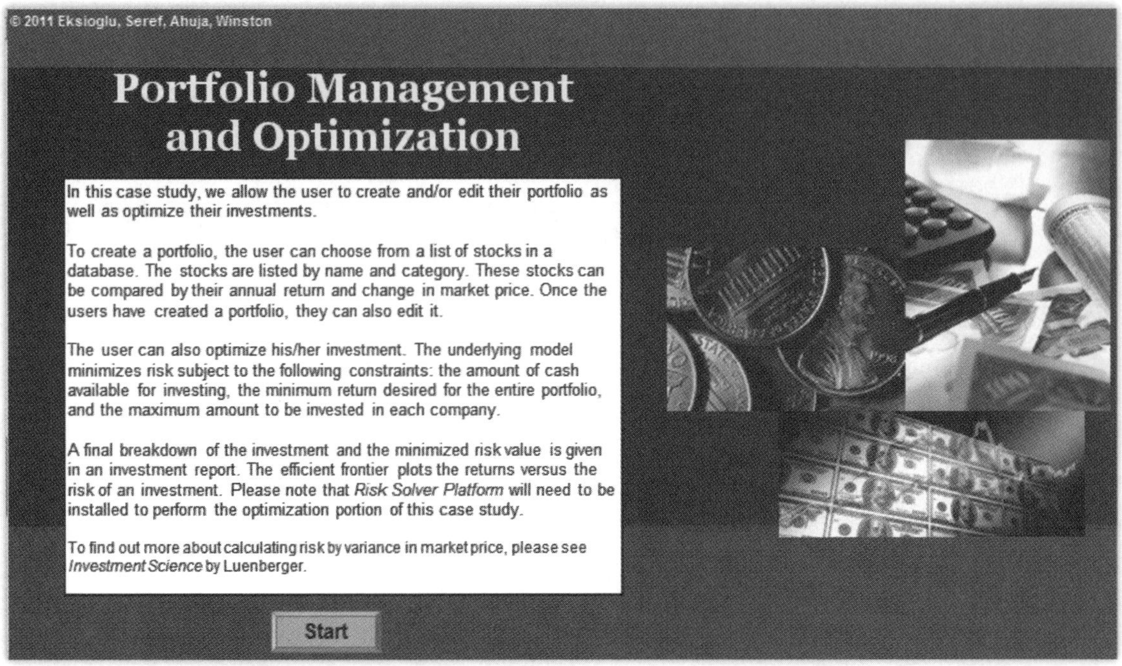

Figure CS7.1 The "Welcome" sheet.

Let us first discuss three of the four data sheets. The first data sheet, the "All Stocks" sheet (see Figure CS7.2), contains the complete list of stocks available for this application. The sheet lists each stock's name and category as well as its quarterly price for five quarters (including the current price) and the annual return for five years.

All Stocks

Company Name	Category	Price Quarter 1	Price Quarter 2	Price Quarter 3	Price Quarter 4	Current Market Price	Annual Return Year 1	Annual Return Year 2	Annual Return Year 3	Annual Return Year 4	Annual Return Year 5
Intel	Tech	53.6	44.0	44.0	44.9	23.0	0.62	0.42	0.17	0.17	0.92
Dell	Tech	53.3	42.6	33.5	31.1	21.8	0.03	0.24	0.09	0.53	0.48
MSFT	Tech	20.2	46.6	21.2	44.9	26.0	0.08	0.80	0.95	0.70	0.31
Toshiba	Tech	22.1	25.7	42.6	23.0	26.5	0.67	0.62	0.69	0.27	0.35
Compaq	Tech	53.8	52.4	51.8	38.9	40.7	0.05	0.38	0.59	0.76	0.08
Gas Inc.	Energy	39.8	58.5	54.6	38.8	26.2	0.96	0.97	0.51	0.58	0.56
BP	Energy	67.1	49.7	47.1	47.0	53.5	0.73	0.03	0.79	0.58	0.50
Nuclear Inc	Energy	62.4	52.4	22.0	39.4	70.2	0.11	0.29	0.93	0.25	0.82
Exxon	Energy	29.7	22.1	26.5	39.3	73.9	0.69	0.53	0.56	0.73	0.52
Mobile	Energy	49.8	30.3	24.4	55.5	68.6	0.76	0.83	0.59	0.95	0.02
Hydro Inc.	Energy	59.9	35.4	45.1	48.3	33.1	0.10	0.39	0.02	0.58	0.65
Citgo	Energy	29.6	45.3	43.8	60.5	69.7	0.88	0.13	0.38	0.33	0.35
Chevron	Energy	27.3	26.8	50.2	47.8	26.7	0.22	0.82	0.27	0.94	0.03
Ford	Auto	21.9	73.6	68.9	60.3	63.2	0.88	0.02	0.90	0.75	0.47
Saturn	Auto	39.6	67.5	63.9	51.5	21.1	1.00	0.22	0.31	0.08	0.54
Toyota	Auto	73.1	54.9	57.3	20.4	53.8	0.83	0.54	0.63	0.97	0.49
Honda	Auto	26.6	56.0	43.9	57.4	33.4	0.99	0.21	0.69	0.80	0.68
Isuzu	Auto	38.2	55.6	46.2	40.7	60.9	0.56	0.16	0.67	0.74	0.92
Mercedes	Auto	29.6	62.8	67.0	63.9	23.5	0.74	0.90	0.28	0.81	0.22
Aflac	Insurance	23.5	44.4	35.5	39.6	50.4	0.16	0.25	0.92	0.34	0.10
Nationwide	Insurance	39.7	43.1	54.3	46.9	40.0	0.11	0.63	0.88	0.40	0.03

Figure CS7.2 The "All Stocks" data sheet.

The second data sheet is the "Covariance" sheet (see Figure CS7.3). This sheet stores the covariance values (σ_{ij}) between all pairs of stocks. We will use this data in preparing the optimization model to calculate the total covariance factor for the portfolio.

All Stocks: Covariances

Company Name	Intel	Dell	MSFT	Toshiba	Compaq	Gas Inc.	BP	Nuclear Inc	Exxon	Mobile	Hydro Inc.	Citgo	Chevron	Ford	Saturn	Toyota	Hond
Intel	0.0	0.268	0.821	-0.936	0.121	0.270	-0.282	0.927	0.182	0.466	0.032	0.495	0.933	-0.839	0.483	-0.817	-0.081
Dell	0.268		-0.563	0.083	0.685	0.148	0.897	0.118	-0.754	0.602	-0.004	0.672	0.927	0.780	-0.881	-0.869	0.397
MSFT	0.821	-0.563		0.194	-0.039	-0.006	-0.372	0.097	0.077	0.194	0.027	0.982	0.940	0.524	-0.971	0.256	-0.783
Toshiba	-0.936	0.083	0.194		-0.036	0.324	0.385	0.119	-0.435	0.137	-0.318	0.207	0.826	-0.254	-0.776	0.896	-0.406
Compaq	0.121	0.685	-0.039	-0.036		0.767	-0.009	0.406	0.362	-0.477	-0.987	-0.188	-0.569	-0.537	-0.421	-0.708	-0.397
Gas Inc.	0.270	0.148	-0.006	0.324	0.767		-0.207	0.090	0.271	0.335	0.585	-0.289	-0.343	-0.678	-0.627	-0.320	-0.834
BP	0.000	0.897	-0.372	0.385	-0.009	-0.207		-0.630	-0.091	-0.969	-0.249	-0.239	0.191	0.458	-0.710	-0.608	0.619
Nuclear Inc	0.927	0.118	0.097	0.119	0.406	0.090	-0.630		-0.929	-0.144	0.519	0.618	0.365	0.672	0.589	0.820	0.384
Exxon	0.182	-0.754	0.077	-0.435	0.362	0.271	-0.091	-0.929		-0.138	-0.240	-0.379	-0.150	-0.435	-0.492	-0.029	0.595
Mobile	0.466	0.602	0.194	0.137	-0.477	0.335	-0.969	-0.144	-0.138		-0.091	0.532	0.459	-0.862	0.641	-0.053	-0.727
Hydro Inc.	0.032	-0.004	0.027	-0.318	-0.987	0.585	-0.249	0.519	-0.240	-0.091		-0.672	0.813	0.818	-0.701	-0.932	0.127
Citgo	0.495	0.672	0.982	0.207	-0.188	-0.289	-0.239	0.618	-0.379	0.532	-0.672		0.039	0.540	0.576	0.996	-0.843
Chevron	0.933	0.927	0.940	0.826	-0.569	-0.343	0.191	0.365	-0.150	0.459	0.813	0.039		-0.599	0.062	0.570	-0.846
Ford	0.000	0.780	0.524	-0.254	-0.537	-0.678	0.458	0.672	-0.435	-0.862	0.818	0.540	-0.599		-0.733	-0.725	0.222
Saturn	0.483	-0.881	-0.971	-0.776	-0.421	-0.627	-0.710	0.589	-0.492	0.641	-0.701	0.576	0.062	-0.733		0.021	0.889
Toyota	0.000	-0.869	0.256	0.896	-0.708	-0.320	-0.608	0.820	-0.029	-0.053	-0.932	0.996	0.570	-0.725	0.021		-0.789
Honda	0.000	0.397	-0.783	-0.406	-0.397	-0.834	0.619	0.384	0.595	-0.727	0.127	-0.843	-0.846	0.222	0.889	-0.789	

Figure CS7.3 The "Covariance" data sheet.

The third data sheet is the "Portfolio" sheet (see Figure CS7.4). It records the information from the "All Stocks" sheet for the stocks in the users' portfolios. We will also use this sheet later to perform some calculations for the optimization (see Figure CS7.5). These calculations are for the mean price over five quarters, the variance in price for each quarter, the sum of the variances, and the sum of the annual returns.

Portfolio

Company Name	Category	Price Quarter 1	Price Quarter 2	Price Quarter 3	Price Quarter 4	Current Market Price	Annual Return Year 1	Annual Return Year 2	Annual Return Year 3	Annual Return Year 4	Annual Return Year 5
Aflac	Insurance	23.5	44.4	35.5	39.6	50.4	0.16	0.25	0.92	0.34	0.10
Ann Taylor	Retail	29.0	14.9	13.1	29.1	10.0	0.09	0.12	0.82	0.92	0.76
ATT	ommunicati	48.9	27.8	34.4	27.1	46.9	0.70	0.06	0.98	0.92	0.91
Banana Rep	Retail	28.7	17.2	23.0	11.7	27.4	0.14	0.00	0.18	0.46	0.16
BP	Energy	67.1	49.7	47.1	47.0	53.5	0.73	0.03	0.79	0.58	0.50
Burdines	Retail	13.2	12.4	26.8	26.4	29.9	0.65	0.78	0.07	0.87	0.82

Figure CS7.4 The "Portfolio" data sheet.

Annual Return Year 2	Annual Return Year 3	Annual Return Year 4	Annual Return Year 5	Mean Price	Price Var Quarter 1	Price Var Quarter 2	Price Var Quarter 3	Price Var Quarter 4	Current Price Var	Var Sum	Ret Sum
0.25	0.92	0.34	0.10	38.7	15.1	5.7	3.1	0.9	11.7	36.58	1.77
0.12	0.82	0.92	0.76	19.2	9.8	4.3	6.1	9.9	9.2	39.39	2.71
0.06	0.98	0.92	0.91	37.0	11.9	9.2	2.6	9.9	9.9	43.49	3.57
0.00	0.18	0.46	0.16	21.6	7.1	4.4	1.4	9.9	5.8	28.57	0.94
0.03	0.79	0.58	0.50	52.9	14.2	3.2	5.8	5.9	0.6	29.61	2.63
0.78	0.07	0.87	0.82	21.8	8.6	9.3	5.1	4.7	8.2	35.78	3.18

Figure CS7.5 Calculations on the "Portfolio" data sheet.

The first sheet that the users visit is the "Create/Edit Portfolio" sheet (see Figure CS7.6); it is the first of two information sheets. In this sheet, the users can create or modify their portfolios by performing one of the two following actions: selecting several stocks from the "All Stocks" list and clicking the "Add" arrow button to add these stocks to their portfolios; or selecting several stocks from the "Portfolio" list and clicking the "Remove" arrow button to remove these stocks from their portfolios.

If the users are not sure which stocks are best to add or remove from their portfolios, they can click the "Compare All Stocks" button to proceed to the second information sheet: the "Compare Stocks" sheet (see Figure CS7.7). Otherwise, if they feel their portfolios are complete, they can click the "Save Portfolio and Return to Main Menu" button to return to the Main Menu. The "Exit" button allows the users to exit the application.

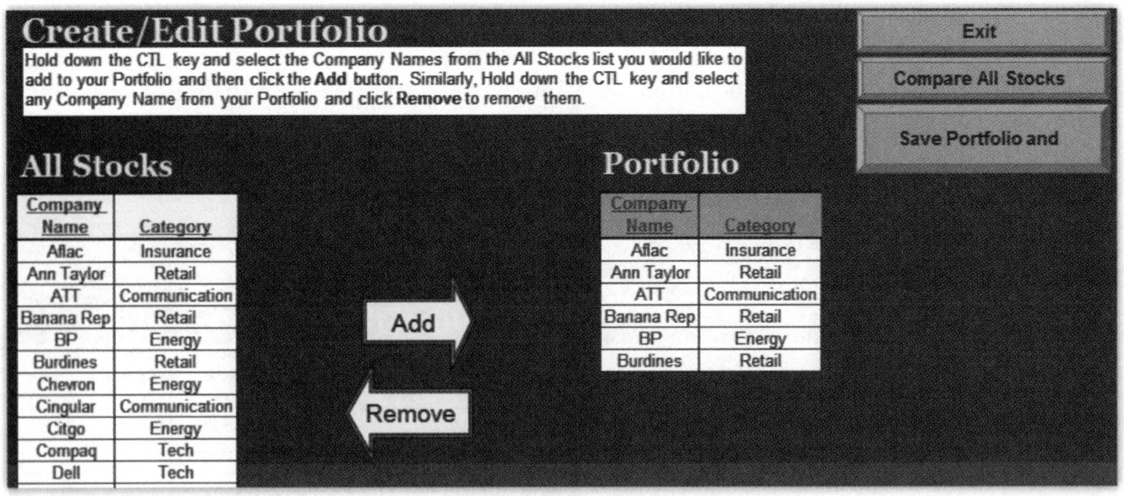

Figure CS7.6 "Create/Edit Portfolio" information sheet.

The "Compare Stocks" sheet allows the users to select several stocks from the "All Stocks" list and plot either their annual returns or the change in market price. The users select one of these options from the combo box on the worksheet and then press the "Show Plot" button. The corresponding chart then appears. The users can then return to the "Create/Edit Portfolio" sheet by clicking the "Return to Create/Edit Portfolio" button. The users can also exit the application at this point by clicking the "Exit" button.

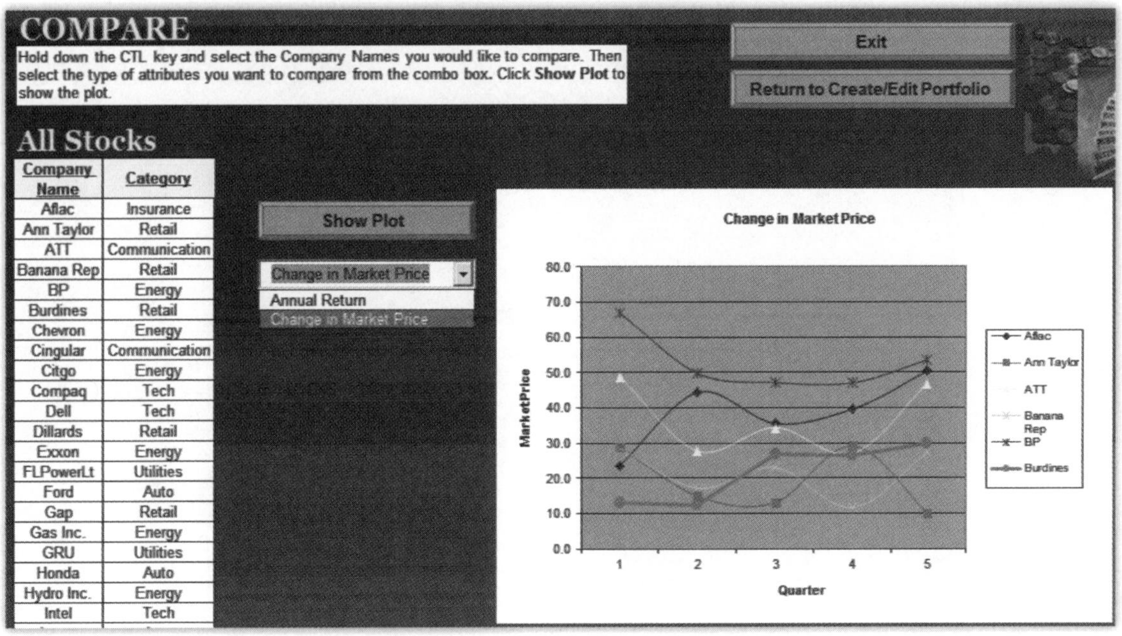

Figure CS7.7 "Compare Stocks" information sheet.

To create these charts, we use the fourth data sheet: the "Chart Data" sheet (see Figure CS7.8). If the users have selected to plot the change in market price, then we copy the quarterly prices for the selected stocks from the "All Stocks" sheet and paste them on the first table shown. If the users have selected to plot the annual returns, then we copy the annual returns from the "All Stocks" sheet and paste them on the second table shown. The two overlaying graphs on the "Compare Stocks" sheet refer to these tables as their source data.

Chart Data

Change in Market Price

Company Name	Current Market Price	Price Quarter 1	Price Quarter 2	Price Quarter 3	Price Quarter 4
Aflac	23.5	44.4	35.5	39.6	50.4
Ann Taylor	29.0	14.9	13.1	29.1	10.0
ATT	48.9	27.8	34.4	27.1	46.9
Banana Rep	28.7	17.2	23.0	11.7	27.4
BP	67.1	49.7	47.1	47.0	53.5
Burdines	13.2	12.4	26.8	26.4	29.9

Annual Return

Company Name	Annual Return Year 1	Annual Return Year 2	Annual Return Year 3	Annual Return Year 4	Annual Return Year 5
Aflac	0.16	0.25	0.92	0.34	0.10

Figure CS7.8 The "Chart Data" data sheet.

After the users have finalized their portfolios, they complete an input form and then come to the output sheet, which we call the "Investment Report" sheet (see Figure CS7.9). This output sheet graphs the investment amounts for each stock in the users' portfolios and displays the values in an adjacent table. The minimized risk, or variance, of the portfolio is also provided. The return and desired return are displayed as well as the cash used and the total cash available. The efficient frontier presents the relationship between the minimum risk and expected return for the selected portfolio.

The "Modify Input" and "Modify Portfolio" buttons correspond to two re-solve options, which we discuss later. The "View Model" button allows the users to view the model sheet, and the "Exit" button allows them to exit the application.

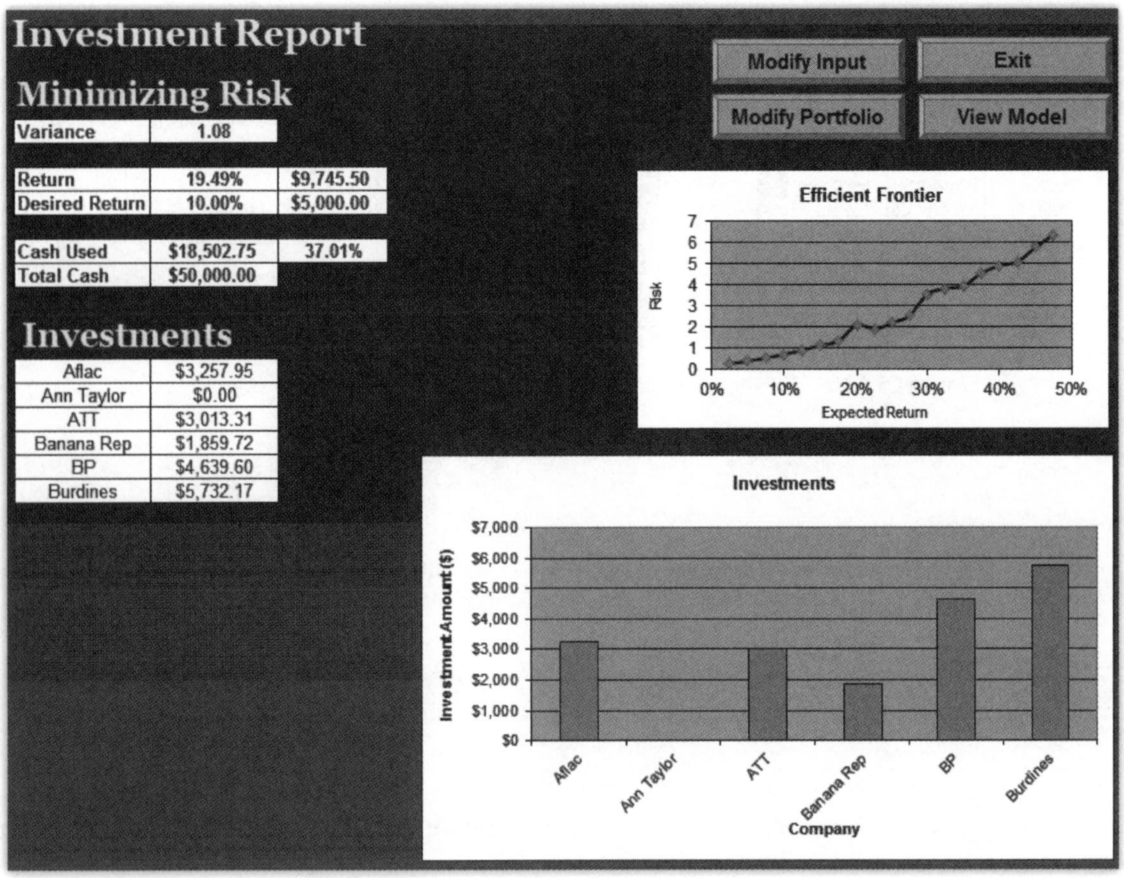

Figure CS7.9 The "Investment Report" output sheet.

The model sheet lists all of the stocks in the portfolio with adjacent cells for the investment amount (see Figure CS7.10). These are the changing cells whose values are determined when optimization is performed. These values, solved as percentages, are converted into dollar amounts in the next column. We refer to the dollar amounts to check the constraint that each stock receives less than or equal to the maximum investment amount per stock. The code then calculates the expected return and variance and displays these figures in the next two columns. We use these values in the third column; their sum is the risk value. This risk value, in the "Minimum Risk" cell at the top of the sheet, is the objective function cell. The code procedures also calculate the formulas for the fourth column: the covariance factors. These factors are calculated for all pairs of stocks in the portfolio using the stock in each row as the pivot. The total covariance factor is the sum of the values in this column. The "Min Return" and "Unit Constraint" columns capture the other two constraints.

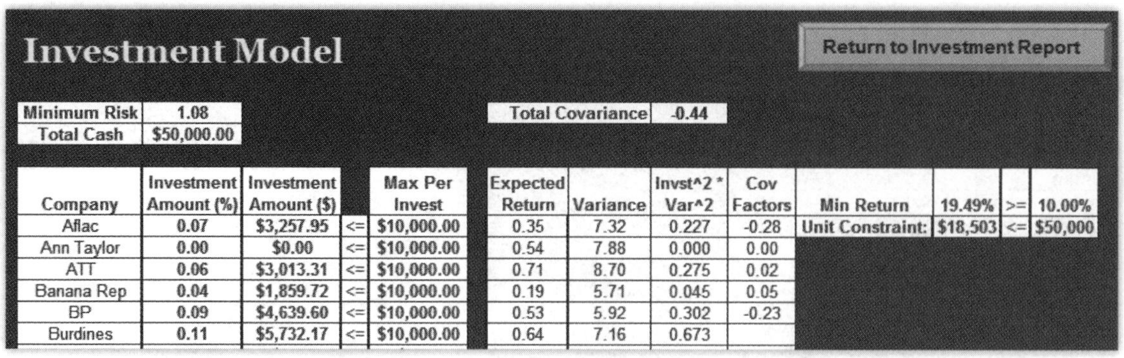

Minimum Risk	1.08
Total Cash	$50,000.00

Total Covariance	-0.44

Company	Investment Amount (%)	Investment Amount ($)		Max Per Invest	Expected Return	Variance	Invst^2 * Var^2	Cov Factors
Aflac	0.07	$3,257.95	<=	$10,000.00	0.35	7.32	0.227	-0.28
Ann Taylor	0.00	$0.00	<=	$10,000.00	0.54	7.88	0.000	0.00
ATT	0.06	$3,013.31	<=	$10,000.00	0.71	8.70	0.275	0.02
Banana Rep	0.04	$1,859.72	<=	$10,000.00	0.19	5.71	0.045	0.05
BP	0.09	$4,639.60	<=	$10,000.00	0.53	5.92	0.302	-0.23
Burdines	0.11	$5,732.17	<=	$10,000.00	0.64	7.16	0.673	

Min Return	19.49%	>=	10.00%
Unit Constraint:	$18,503	<=	$50,000

Figure CS7.10 The model sheet.

Summary

Welcome Sheet	Includes the application description and "Start" button.
"All Stocks" Data Sheet	Includes all stocks available for creating a portfolio; also records the quarterly market price and annual returns.
"Portfolio" Data Sheet	Stock information is copied for the stocks in the users' portfolios; some calculations are also made.
"Create/Edit Portfolio"	The users can create or modify their portfolios by selecting stocks from the
Information Sheet	"All Stocks" list and clicking the "Add" or "Remove" buttons.
"Compare Stocks"	The users can compare changes in market price or annual returns for selected
Information Sheet	Stocks from the "All Stocks" list.
"Chart Data" Data Sheet	Data is copied from the "All Stocks" sheet for the corresponding chart data.
"Investment Report"	Investment amounts per stock are reported in a table and chart; also reports
Output Sheet	Minimized risk, portfolio returns, and cash used.
Model Sheet	Contains the optimization model.

CS7.3 User Interface

For this application, we employ two user forms, one control on a worksheet, and several navigational and functional buttons. The first form that the users see is the Main Menu (see Figure CS7.11). It provides them with three navigational options: create a new portfolio, edit their current portfolio, or optimize their portfolio investment plan. We use a frame and option buttons to present these three options.

If the users select to create a new portfolio, then they are taken to the "Create/Edit Portfolio" sheet, which is cleared of past data. If the users select to edit their current portfolio, then they are taken to the same sheet, except no clearing is done. If the users select to optimize their portfolio investment plan, then the optimization code is run and the users are taken to the output sheet. We include some error checking, which assures that the users create a portfolio before optimizing.

The users can select the function buttons to "Add" and "Remove" stocks to and from their portfolio on the "Create/Edit Portfolio" sheet. If they use the navigational button to "Compare All Stocks," then they can use the control on the "Compare Stocks" worksheet. This control is a combo box that lists the two plot options: "Change in Market Price" and "Annual Return" (see Figure CS7.12). Once the users make a selection, they can use the "Show Plot" functional button to display the plot for the selected stocks.

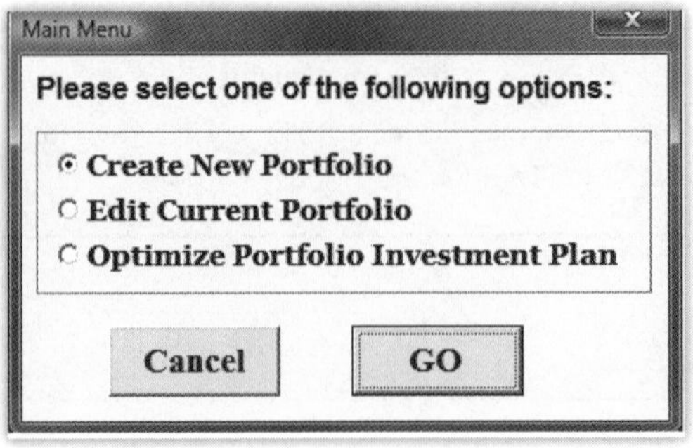

Figure CS7.11 The main menu.

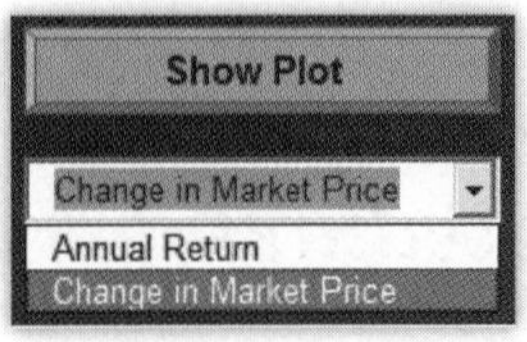

Figure CS7.12 The combo box control on the "Compare Stocks" worksheet.

Once the users save their portfolio with the "Save Portfolio and Return to Main Menu" functional button on the "Create/Edit Portfolio" sheet, they may then optimize their portfolio. When they make this selection from the Main Menu, they can observe the optimization input form: "Minimize Risk" (see Figure CS7.13). This form prompts the users for three optimization inputs: the total cash available to make the investment, the minimum desired return on the portfolio, and the maximum amount they can invest per stock. We employ text boxes and labels to clarify what input is needed.

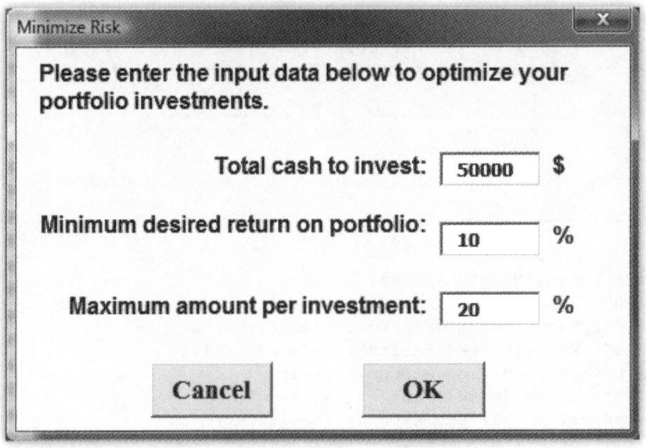

Figure CS7.13 Input form for optimization.

Summary

Main Menu Form	Gives the users three options: create new portfolio, edit current portfolio, or optimize portfolio investment plan.
Compare Stocks	Allows the users to select between change in market price plot and annual returns
Worksheet Control	Plot for comparing stocks.
Minimize Risk Input Form	Receives input that is used for the optimization model.
Navigational Buttons	Include "Exit," "View Model," "Compare All Stocks," "Return to Create/Edit Portfolio," and "Return to Investment Report."
Functional Buttons	Include "Add," "Remove," "Save Portfolio and Return to Main Menu," "Show Plot," "Modify Input," and "Modify Portfolio."

CS7.4 Procedures

We will now outline the procedures for this application, beginning with the initial sub procedures and variable definitions (see Figure CS7.14). The *Main* procedure informs the users that Risk Solver Platform is needed. This prompt only occurs the first time the users open the application. Some Boolean variables are set and the Main Menu appears. If the users select to create a new portfolio, the *ClearPrevious* procedure clears all previous portfolio data. We do not clear this data if the users want to edit the previously created portfolio.

```
Option Explicit
Public ws As Worksheet, TotalCash As Double, MinReturn As Double, _
MaxPerInvest As Double, FirstOpen As Boolean, i As Integer, j As Integer, _
ExpRet(100) As Double, Var(100) As Double, repeat As Boolean, CompName As String, _
PortExists As Boolean, SResult As Integer, PortfOptProb As New RSP.problem

Sub MAIN()
    If FirstOpen Then
     MsgBox "Please note that Risk Solver Platform will need to be installed" & _
          " to perform the optimization portion of this case study."
    End If
    FirstOpen = False
    PortExists = False

    frmMainMenu.Show
End Sub

Sub ClearPrevious()
  Worksheets("Portfolio").Range("B7:M43").ClearContents
  Worksheets("CEPortfolio").Range("H12:I12").ClearContents
  Worksheets("CEPortfolio").Range("H13:I48").Delete shift:=xlUp
  Worksheets("CEPortfolio").Range(Range("PerInv").Offset(1, 0), _
        Range("PerInv").Offset(1, 0).End(xlDown)).Clear
  Worksheets("CEPortfolio").Range(Range("PerInv").Offset(1, -1), _
        Range("PerInv").Offset(1, -1).End(xlDown)).ClearContents
  Worksheets("CEPortfolio").Range("H11").Name = "Portfolio1"
  Worksheets("Chart Data").Range("B10:O46").ClearContents
End Sub
```

Figure CS7.14 The variable declarations, the *Main* procedure, and the *ClearPrevious* procedure.

Once the Main Menu appears and the users make a selection, the Main Menu code performs the appropriate actions (see Figure CS7.15). If the users choose to create a new portfolio, the *ClearPrevious* procedure is called and they are taken to the "Create/Edit Portfolio" sheet. If the users choose to edit their portfolio, then they are taken directly to the "Create/Edit Portfolio" sheet without clearing any data. If the users select to optimize their portfolio investment plan, we first perform an error check to ensure that a portfolio has already been created. If there is a portfolio, then we display the optimization input form and call the optimization procedure.

```
Sub cmdCancel_Click()
    Unload Me
    Worksheets("Welcome").Visible = True
    Worksheets("Investment Report").Visible = False
    End
End Sub

Sub cmdGO_Click()
    If optCreatePortfolio Then
        Unload Me
        Call ClearPrevious
        Worksheets("CEPortfolio").Visible = True
        Worksheets("Welcome").Visible = False
        PortExists = True
    ElseIf optEditPortfolio Then
        Unload Me
        Worksheets("CEPortfolio").Visible = True
        Worksheets("Welcome").Visible = False
        PortExists = True
    ElseIf optOptInvest Then
        If PortExists = False Then
          MsgBox "Please note that you should have created" & _
                " a portfolio before continuing with this option."
          Exit Sub
        End If
        Unload Me
        frmMinRisk.Show
        Call Optimize
    End If
End Sub
```

Figure CS7.15 The Main Menu code.

If the users have already gone to the "Create/Edit Portfolio" sheet, they will have some additional sorting features for the "All Stocks" list and the "Portfolio" list of stocks. They can sort the list by the stock names or the stock categories. The sorting procedure is placed in the *SelectionChange* event procedure of the worksheet (see Figure CS7.16).

```
Private Sub Worksheet_SelectionChange(ByVal Target As Range)
    On Error GoTo last
    If ActiveCell.Value = "Company Name" Then
        'sort by company name
        Range(ActiveCell, ActiveCell.Offset(0, 1).End(xlDown)).Name = "SortRange"
        Range("SortRange").Sort key1:=Range("SortRange").Columns(1), _
                order1:=xlAscending, Header:=xlYes
    ElseIf ActiveCell.Value = "Category" Then
        'sort by category
        Range(ActiveCell, ActiveCell.Offset(0, -1).End(xlDown)).Name = "SortRange"
        Range("SortRange").Sort key1:=Range("SortRange").Columns(2), _
                order1:=xlAscending, Header:=xlYes
    End If
last:
End Sub
```

Figure CS7.16 The sorting procedure for the "Create/Edit Portfolio" sheet.

On the “Create/Edit Portfolio” sheet, the users can click on the “Add” and “Remove” buttons to create their portfolio. The “Add” button is associated with the *AddToPortfolio* procedure (see Figure CS7.17 and CS7.18), which includes much error checking to ensure that the button functionality works correctly. We must ensure that the users have selected a name from the list of “All Stocks” to add to the portfolio. We then add the selected stocks to the portfolio and format the new list. We must also check that no stocks were repeated.

We now assign the “Remove” button to the *RemoveFromPortfolio* procedure and perform some error checking to ensure that the users made appropriate selections (see Figure CS7.19). We then remove the stocks from the “Portfolio” list and shift the other stocks to reformat the list.

```
Sub AddToPortfolio()
    Application.ScreenUpdating = False
    'copy selected company and category and paste in Portfolio columns
    If Application.Union(Range("AllStocks1"), Range(Selection.Address)).Address _
            = Range("AllStocks1").Address Then
     On Error Resume Next
     Selection.Copy
     If Err.Number = 1004 Then
        MsgBox "Please make a smaller selection."
        Exit Sub
     End If

     i = 2
     Do Until Range("PortfolioName").Cells(i, 1) = ""
        i = i + 1
     Loop
     'find end of current list
     Range("PortfolioName").Cells(i, 1).PasteSpecial xlValues

     'check for repeats
     repeat = False
     j = i
     Do Until Range("PortfolioName").Cells(j, 1) = ""
     'Do While repeat = False
        Range("PortfolioName").Cells(j, 2).FormulaR1C1 = "=MATCH(RC[-1],Portfolio1,0)"
        If Not IsError(Range("PortfolioName").Cells(j, 2).Value) Then
            'Or Range("PortfolioName").Cells(j, 2).Value <> 1 Then
          Range("PortfolioName").Rows(j).Select
          Selection.Delete shift:=xlUp
          repeat = True
        Else
          'append new entries
          Range(Range("Portfolio1").Cells(1, 1), Range("Portfolio1").Offset(1, 0)).Name = "Portfolio1"
          Range(Range("Portfolio2").Cells(1, 1), Range("Portfolio2").Offset(1, 0)).Name = "Portfolio2"
          j = j + 1
        End If
        'j = j + 1
     Loop
```

Figure CS7.17 The first part of the *AddToPortfolio* procedure.

```
    'format new entries
    Do Until Range("PortfolioName").Cells(i, 1) = ""
       With Range("PortfolioName").Rows(i)
         .HorizontalAlignment = xlCenter
         .Interior.ColorIndex = 2
         .BorderAround Weight:=xlThin
         .Borders(xlInsideVertical).Weight = xlThin
       End With

       Range("PortfolioName").Cells(i, 2).Select
       ActiveCell.FormulaR1C1 = "=VLOOKUP(R[0]C[-1],AllStocksName,2, False)"
       i = i + 1
    Loop
    Application.CutCopyMode = False
    Application.ScreenUpdating = True

    If repeat = True Then
     MsgBox "Repeated stocks were not added to the portfolio."
    End If

    Range("AllStocksName").Cells(1, 1).Select
   Else
    MsgBox "This command can only be used on All Stocks names. " & _
           "Please make sure no other cells are selected."
   End If
End Sub
```

Figure CS7.18 The second part of the *AddToPortfolio* procedure.

```
Sub RemoveFromPortfolio()
    Application.ScreenUpdating = False
    'delete selected company and category from Portfolio columns
    If Application.Union(Range("Portfolio1"), Range(Selection.Address)).Address _
           = Range("Portfolio1").Address Then
     On Error Resume Next
     Selection.ClearContents
     If Err.Number = 1004 Then
        MsgBox "Please make a smaller selection."
        Exit Sub
     End If

     i = 2
     Do While Range("PortfolioName").Cells(i, 2).Interior.ColorIndex = 2
        If Range("PortfolioName").Cells(i, 1) = "" Then
            Range("PortfolioName").Rows(i).Select
            Selection.Delete shift:=xlUp
            Range(Range("PerInv").Offset(i - 1, 0), Range("PerInv"). _
                Offset(i - 1, -1)).Delete shift:=xlUp
        Else
            i = i + 1
        End If
     Loop

     Application.ScreenUpdating = True
     Range("AllStocksName").Cells(1, 1).Select
    Else
     MsgBox "This command can only be used on Portfolio names. " & _
            "Please make sure no other cells are selected."
    End If
End Sub
```

Figure CS7.19 The *RemoveFromPortfolio* procedure.

If the users go to the "Compare Stocks" sheet, they will also be given sorting features for the "All Stocks" list. They can sort the list by the stock names or by the stock categories. Again, we place the sorting procedure in the *SelectionChange* event procedure of the worksheet (see Figure CS7.20).

```
Private Sub Worksheet_SelectionChange(ByVal Target As Range)
    If ActiveCell.Value = "Company Name" Then
        'sort by company name
        Range(ActiveCell, ActiveCell.Offset(0, 1).End(xlDown)).Name = "SortRange"
        Range("SortRange").Sort key1:=Range("SortRange").Columns(1), _
                order1:=xlAscending, Header:=xlYes
    ElseIf ActiveCell.Value = "Category" Then
        'sort by category
        Range(ActiveCell, ActiveCell.Offset(0, -1).End(xlDown)).Name = "SortRange"
        Range("SortRange").Sort key1:=Range("SortRange").Columns(2), _
                order1:=xlAscending, Header:=xlYes
    End If

End Sub
```

Figure CS7.20 The sorting procedure for the "Compare Stocks" sheet.

Once the users make a selection from the combo box on the worksheet, they can press the "Show Plot" button to update the chart. This button is assigned to the *ShowPlot* procedure (see Figure CS7.21). Depending on which selection was made in the combo box, a corresponding procedure is called.

```
Sub ShowPlot()
    If Worksheets("Compare").cmbAttrib.Value = "Annual Return" Then
        Call PlotAnnualReturn
    ElseIf Worksheets("Compare").cmbAttrib.Value = _
            "Change in Market Price" Then
        Call PlotChangePrice
    End If
End Sub
```

Figure CS7.21 The *ShowPlot* procedure.

If the users select "Annual Return," then the application calls the *PlotAnnualReturn* procedure (see Figure CS7.22). This procedure copies the selected stocks' annual return records from the "All Stocks" worksheet in a table on the "Chart Data" sheet. There are already two charts created on the "Compare Stocks" sheet that have the corresponding tables on the "Chart Data" sheet set as their respective source data. Therefore, instead of refreshing the source data of a chart in the *PlotAnnualReturn* procedure, we simply change the appropriate chart object's position so it is in front of the other chart.

```
Sub PlotAnnualReturn()
    'record which companies have been selected and copy their data from
    'AllStocks sheet to ChartData sheet
    Worksheets("Chart Data").Range("B10:O46").ClearContents
    If Application.Union(Range("AllStocksC1"), Range(Selection.Address)).Address _
            = Range("AllStocksC1").Address Then
    On Error Resume Next
     Selection.Copy
     If Err.Number = 1004 Then
        MsgBox "Please make a smaller selection."
        Exit Sub
     End If
     Application.ScreenUpdating = False
     Range("ChartReturn").Cells(1, 1).PasteSpecial
     i = 1
     Do While Range("ChartReturn").Cells(i, 1) <> ""
        CompName = Range("ChartReturn").Cells(i, 1).Value
        Worksheets("All Stocks").Activate
        j = 1
        Do Until Range("AllStocksAll").Cells(j, 1).Value = CompName
            j = j + 1
            Range("AllStocksAll").Cells(j, 1).Select
        Loop
        Range(ActiveCell.Offset(0, 7), ActiveCell.Offset(0, 11)).Copy
        Worksheets("Chart Data").Activate
        Range("ChartReturn").Cells(i, 2).PasteSpecial
        i = i + 1
     Loop
     Application.ScreenUpdating = True
     Application.CutCopyMode = False

     Worksheets("Compare").Activate
     ActiveSheet.ChartObjects("Chart 19").Select
     ActiveChart.SetSourceData Source:=Range(Range("ChartReturn").Cells(1, 1), _
        Range("ChartReturn").Cells(1, 1).End(xlDown).End(xlToRight)), PlotBy:=xlRows
     ActiveSheet.ChartObjects("Chart 19").BringToFront
     Range("AllStocksC1").Cells(1, 1).Select
    Else
     MsgBox "This command can only be used on All Stocks names." & _
            " Please make sure no other cells are selected."
    End If
End Sub
```

Figure CS7.22 The *PlotAnnualReturn* procedure.

If the users select "Change in Market Price" in the combo box, then the *PlotChangePrice* procedure is called (see Figure CS7.23). This procedure performs the same error checking and copying actions as the *PlotAnnualReturn* procedure, but for the quarterly market price data instead of the annual returns. It also changes the appropriate chart object's position so it is in front of the other chart.

```
Sub PlotChangePrice()
    'record which companies have been selected
    Worksheets("Chart Data").Range("B10:O46").ClearContents
    If Application.Union(Range("AllStocksC1"), Range(Selection.Address)).Address _
            = Range("AllStocksC1").Address Then
     On Error Resume Next
     Selection.Copy
     If Err.Number = 1004 Then
        MsgBox "Please make a smaller selection."
        Exit Sub
     End If
     Application.ScreenUpdating = False
     Range("ChartPrice").Cells(1, 1).PasteSpecial
     i = 1
     Do While Range("ChartPrice").Cells(i, 1) <> ""
        CompName = Range("ChartPrice").Cells(i, 1).Value
        Worksheets("All Stocks").Activate
        j = 1
        Do Until Range("AllStocksAll").Cells(j, 1).Value = CompName
            j = j + 1
            Range("AllStocksAll").Cells(j, 1).Select
        Loop
        Range(ActiveCell.Offset(0, 2), ActiveCell.Offset(0, 6)).Copy
        Worksheets("Chart Data").Activate
        Range("ChartPrice").Cells(i, 2).PasteSpecial
        i = i + 1
     Loop
     Application.ScreenUpdating = True
     Application.CutCopyMode = False

     Worksheets("Compare").Activate
     ActiveSheet.ChartObjects("Chart 18").Select
     ActiveChart.SetSourceData Source:=Range(Range("ChartPrice").Cells(1, 1), _
        Range("ChartPrice").Cells(1, 1).End(xlDown).End(xlToRight)), PlotBy:=xlRows
     ActiveSheet.ChartObjects("Chart 18").BringToFront
     Range("AllStocksC1").Cells(1, 1).Select
    Else
     MsgBox "This command can only be used on All Stocks names. " & _
            "Please make sure no other cells are selected."
    End If
End Sub
```

Figure CS7.23 The *PlotChangePrice* procedure.

Once the users have finished creating the portfolio, they can click the "Save Portfolio and Return to Main Menu" button, which is assigned to the *SavePortfolio* procedure (see Figure CS7.24). This procedure simply copies all of the stock data from the "All Stocks" sheet and pastes it on the "Portfolio" sheet for the stocks in the portfolio. It then calls a navigational procedure to display the Main Menu again and return to the welcome sheet.

```
Sub SavePortfolio()
    'copy detailed info from AllStocks sheet to Portfolio
    'sheet based on info in CEPortfolio
    Application.ScreenUpdating = False
    Worksheets("Portfolio").Range("B7:M43").ClearContents
    i = 2
    Do While Range("PortfolioName").Cells(i, 1) <> ""
        CompName = Range("PortfolioName").Cells(i, 1).Value
        Worksheets("All Stocks").Activate
        j = 1
        Do Until Range("AllStocksAll").Cells(j, 1).Value = CompName
            j = j + 1
            Range("AllStocksAll").Cells(j, 1).Select
        Loop
        Range(ActiveCell, ActiveCell.Offset(0, 11)).Copy
        Worksheets("Portfolio").Activate
        Range("PortfolioAll").Cells(i - 1, 1).PasteSpecial
        i = i + 1
        Worksheets("CEPortfolio").Activate
    Loop
    Application.ScreenUpdating = True
    PortExists = True
    Call ReturntoMainMenu
End Sub
```

Figure CS7.24 The *SavePortfolio* procedure.

If the users now select to optimize the portfolio investment plan, the optimization input form will appear. The code for this form performs some error checking and then assigns the text box values to the corresponding variables (see Figure CS7.25). Note that the percentages for the last two inputs are converted into decimal values.

```
Sub cmdCancel_Click()
    Unload Me
    Worksheets("Welcome").Visible = True
    Worksheets("Investment Report").Visible = False
    frmMainMenu.Show
End Sub

Sub cmdOK_Click()
    'check that all text boxes have been filled
    Dim ctl As Control
    For Each ctl In Me.Controls
        If TypeName(ctl) = "TextBox" Then
          If ctl.Value = "" Or Not IsNumeric(ctl) Then
                MsgBox "Please enter positive numeric " & _
                        "values in all boxes."
                ctl.SetFocus
                Exit Sub
          End If
        End If
    Next

    Unload Me
    TotalCash = txtCash
    MinReturn = txtMinReturn / 100
    MaxPerInvest = txtMaxPerInvest / 100
End Sub
```

Figure CS7.25 The optimization input form.

The *Optimize* procedure is then called (see Figure CS7.26 and CS7.27). This procedure clears the model sheet and inserts the updated variance and expected return values along with the covariance factors. It also records the desired return and total cash inputs. Once the changing cells and constraint cells are prepared, we initiate an instance of the optimization problem object, set Standard GRG Nonlinear as the solution engine, and set value of the iterations parameter of this engine equal to 100. Next, we call the procedure that generates the data for the efficient frontier (see Figure CS7.28). The Optimize procedure then optimizes the problem using the *Solver.Optimize* method, and assigns the value of *Solver.OptimizeStatus* parameter to the *SResult* variable. We use this variable to communicate with the users if the problem is infeasible. This interaction allows the users a chance to modify their input values or portfolio selection and then to re-solve the problem. The procedure then updates the output sheet and creates a table with the decision variable results.

```
Sub Optimize()
    Application.ScreenUpdating = False
    Worksheets("Investment Report").Visible = True
    Worksheets("Investment Model").Visible = True
    Worksheets("Covariance").Visible = True
    Worksheets("Welcome").Visible = False
    Worksheets("Investment Model").Range("B11:C48").ClearContents
    Worksheets("Investment Model").Range("E11:I48").ClearContents
    Worksheets("Investment Model").Range("K11:K48").ClearContents
    Worksheets("Investment Report").Range("B17:C17").ClearContents
    Worksheets("Investment Report").Range("B18:C100").Delete shift:=xlUp

    'input data taken from form and portfolio data
    Dim PortSize As Integer
    PortSize = Range(Range("PortfolioAll").Cells(1, 1), Range("PortfolioAll"). _
            Cells(1, 1).End(xlDown)).Rows.Count
    For i = 1 To PortSize
        ExpRet(i) = Range("RetSum").Cells(i, 1).Value / 5
        Var(i) = Range("VarSum").Cells(i, 1).Value / 5
        Range("PortExpRet").Cells(i).Value = ExpRet(i)
        Range("Variance").Cells(i).Value = Var(i)
    Next i
    Range(Range("InvestAmnt").Cells(1, 1), Range("InvestAmnt"). _
            Cells(PortSize, 1)).Name = "ChangingCells"
    Range("PortfolioAll").Columns(1).Copy
    Range("PortInvestName").PasteSpecial
    Range("TotalCash").Value = TotalCash
    Range("MinReturn").Value = MinReturn

    Dim tempCov As Double
    For i = 1 To PortSize
        Range("MaxPerInvest").Cells(i).Value = MaxPerInvest * TotalCash
        Worksheets("Investment Model").Range("E10").Offset(i, 0).Value = "<="
        'calculate covariance factor for each pair of investments
        j = i + 1
        Do While Range("PortInvestName").Cells(j).Value <> ""
            tempCov = Round(Range("CovStart").Offset(Application.WorksheetFunction. _
                Match(Range("PortInvestName").Cells(i).Value, Range("CovLeft"), 0), _
                Application.WorksheetFunction.Match(Range("PortInvestName").Cells(j) _
                .Value, Range("CovTop"), 0)).Value, 2)
            If j = i + 1 Then 'first value entered
            Range("CovFacs").Offset(i, 0).Formula = "=" & tempCov * Range("Variance"). _
                Cells(i).Value * Range("Variance").Cells(j).Value & "*" & Range("ChangingCells"). _
                Cells(i).Address & "*" & Range("ChangingCells").Cells(j).Address
            Else
            Range("CovFacs").Offset(i, 0).Value = Range("CovFacs").Offset(i, 0).Formula & _
                " + " & tempCov * Range("Variance").Cells(i).Value * _
                Range("Variance").Cells(j).Value & "*" & Range("ChangingCells").Cells(i).Address & _
                "*" & Range("ChangingCells").Cells(j).Address
            End If
            j = j + 1
        Loop
    Next i
```

Figure CS7.26 The first part of the *Optimize* procedure.

```
    Range("CovFacSum").Formula = "=SUM(" & Range(Range("CovFacs").Offset(1, 0), _
            Range("CovFacs").End(xlDown)).Address & ")"

    'run Solver from Investment Model Sheet
    Worksheets("Investment Model").Activate
    PortfOptProb.Init Worksheets("Investment Model")
    PortfOptProb.Engine = PortfOptProb.Engines("Standard GRG Nonlinear")
    PortfOptProb.Engine.Params("Iterations").Value = 1000
    Call EfficientFrontier
    PortfOptProb.Solver.Optimize Solve_Type_Solve
    SResult = PortfOptProb.Solver.OptimizeStatus
    Set PortfOptProb = Nothing

    'modify Investment Report
    Range(Range("PortInvestName").Cells(1, 1), Range("PortInvestName").Cells(PortSize, 1)).Copy
    Worksheets("Investment Report").Range("B17").PasteSpecial
    Range(Range("InvstDoll").Cells(1, 1), Range("InvstDoll").Cells(PortSize, 1)).Copy
    Worksheets("Investment Report").Range("C17").PasteSpecial xlValues
    'Worksheets("Investment Model").Range("A1").Select

    Worksheets("Investment Report").Activate
    Range("C17").Copy
    Range(Range("C18"), Range("C18").Cells(PortSize - 1, 1)).PasteSpecial xlPasteFormats
    ActiveSheet.ChartObjects("Chart 30").Activate
    ActiveChart.SetSourceData Source:=Sheets("Investment Report").Range(Range("B17"), _
            Range("B17").Cells(PortSize, 2))
    Range("A1").Select

    Worksheets("Investment Model").Visible = False
    Worksheets("Covariance").Visible = False
    Application.ScreenUpdating = True
    Application.CutCopyMode = False

    If SResult = 5 Then
        MsgBox "The solution is infeasible for this portfolio. " & _
                "The input values are too constrained."
    End If
End Sub
```

Figure CS7.27 The second part of the *Optimize* procedure.

The *EfficientFrontier* procedure solves the same optimization problem for different values of expected return. We use the *PsiOptParam()* function to change the value of the expected return from 10% to 50% during each of the 20 optimization runs that are being performed. The optimal risk values found by Solver during these optimization runs are printed. Then, the source data for the efficient frontier graph of the Investment Report output sheet is updated using these values.

The navigational procedures are used for eight different buttons (see Figure CS7.29).

```
Sub EfficientFrontier()
Dim CurrentRet As Double
    CurrentRet = Range("MinReturn").Value
    'setup the model for parametric optmization
    Range("MinReturn").Formula = "=PsiOptParam(0.1,0.5,0.3)"
    PortfOptProb.Solver.NumOptimizations = 20

    'optimize and save the results to create the efficent frontier
    PortfOptProb.Solver.Optimize Solve_Type_Solve
    Range(Range("EfficFront").Offset(0, 2), Range("EfficFront"). _
            Offset(20, 2)).ClearContents
    Range("EfficFront").Copy
    Range("EfficFront").Offset(0, 2).PasteSpecial (xlPasteValues)

    'setup the model for the single portfolio optimization
    PortfOptProb.Solver.NumOptimizations = 1
    Range("MinReturn").Value = CurrentRet
End Sub
```

Figure CS7.28 The efficient frontier procedure.

```
Sub ModInput()
    frmMinRisk.Show
    Call Optimize
End Sub

Sub ModPortfolio()
    Worksheets("CEPortfolio").Visible = True
    Worksheets("Investment Report").Visible = False
End Sub

Sub ExitProgram()
    Worksheets("Welcome").Visible = True
    ActiveSheet.Visible = False
    PortExists = False
End Sub

Sub ReturnToPortfolio()
    Worksheets("CEPortfolio").Visible = True
    Worksheets("CEPortfolio").Activate
    Worksheets("Compare").Visible = False
End Sub

Sub Compare()
    Worksheets("Compare").Visible = True
    Worksheets("Compare").Activate
    Worksheets("CEPortfolio").Visible = False
End Sub

Sub ReturntoMainMenu()
    Worksheets("Welcome").Visible = True
    ActiveSheet.Visible = False
    frmMainMenu.Show
End Sub

Sub ViewInvestModel()
    Worksheets("Investment Model").Visible = True
    Worksheets("Investment Model").Activate
    Worksheets("Investment Report").Visible = False
End Sub

Sub ViewInvestReport()
    Worksheets("Investment Report").Visible = True
    Worksheets("Investment Report").Activate
    Worksheets("Investment Model").Visible = False
End Sub
```

Figure CS7.29 The navigational procedures.

Summary

Main	Initializes the application and retrieves the initial input from the users.
ClearPrev	Initializes the variables, clears previous values, and clears animation layout formatting.
Main Menu Code	Directs the users to the "Create/Edit Portfolio" sheet or to the optimization input form and output sheet.
Sorting for "Create/	Allows the users to sort the "All Stocks" list and the "Portfolio" list by stock name
Edit Portfolio"	or category.
AddToPortfolio	Adds stock(s) to the "Portfolio" list and performs error checking.
RemoveFromPortfolio	Removes stock(s) from the "Portfolio" list and performs error checking.
Sorting for	Allows the users to sort the "All Stocks" list by stock name or category.
"Compare Stocks"	
ShowPlot	Calls the *PlotAnnualReturn* or *PlotChangePrice* procedures, depending on the users' combo box selection.
PlotAnnualReturn	Copies the annual return data from the "All Stocks" sheet and brings the corresponding chart to front.
PlotChangePrice	Copies the market price data from the "All Stocks" sheet and brings the corresponding chart to front.
SavePortfolio	Copies all data from the "All Stocks" sheet and pastes it on the "Portfolio" sheet for portfolio stocks; re-shows the Main Menu.
Input Form Code	Records input values.
Optimization	Updates model sheet, runs Solver commands, calls the efficient frontier procedure, and updates output sheet.
Efficient Frontier	Finds the minimum risk for different values of expected return, and updates the source data of the efficient frontier graph.
Navigational	For navigational buttons.

CS7.5 *Re-solve Options*

This application consists of two re-solve options, which are associated with the "Modify Input" and "Modify Portfolio" buttons on the output sheet. If the users click "Modify Input," then the optimization input form is again displayed (see Figure CS7.30). The users can modify their input values and press "OK," and the optimization will be re-performed, and efficient frontier recalculated. If the users select the "Modify Portfolio" button, then they will return to the "Create/Edit Portfolio" sheet. They can then modify their portfolio and click the "Save Portfolio and Return to Main Menu" button to return to the Main Menu and select the optimization button again. The optimization will then be re-performed, and efficient frontier recalculated. Note that these re-solve options are also available to the users if their problem is infeasible.

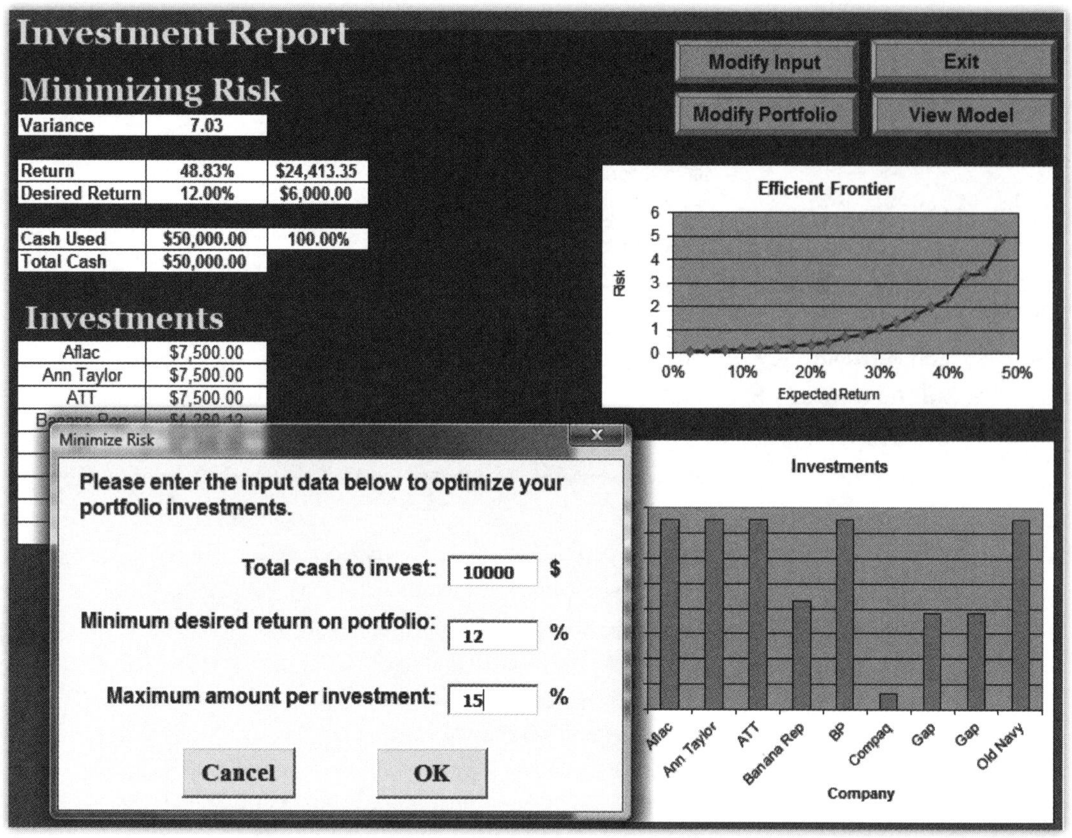

Figure CS7.30 Modify Input re-solve option.

Summary

Modify Input Re-solve Option	Re-displays the optimization input form; users can change values; optimization then runs again.
Modify Portfolio Re-solve Option	Users return to the "Create/Edit Portfolio" sheet; they can modify the portfolio then return to optimization; optimization is then re-run.

CS7.6 Summary

- The "Portfolio Management and Optimization" application allows users to create and/or edit a portfolio as well as optimize the portfolio investment plan. The efficient frontier graph presents the relationship between the expected return and minimum risk for an investment portfolio.
- This application consists of nine worksheets: the welcome sheet, four data sheets, two information sheets, a model sheet, and an output sheet.
- There are two user forms, one control on a worksheet, and several navigational and functional buttons.
- This application incorporates several procedures, which allow the users to create and modify their portfolio and then view the optimized investment plan.
- The output sheet offers two re-solve options: modify the optimization input or the portfolio; and re-run the optimization.

CS7.7 Extensions

1. Solve the optimization by maximizing returns instead of minimizing risk.
2. Allow the users to place unique upper and lower bounds on the amount to invest for each stock.
3. Allow the users to fix certain stock investments and optimize for the others.
4. Add more data to the "All Stocks" sheet and create more charts for the "Compare Stocks" sheet.
5. What is another re-solve option that can be added to the application? Implement this new option.

CASE STUDY

eight Reliability Analysis

chapter OVERVIEW

CS8.1 Application Overview and Model Development

This case study is a DSS application of the reliability analysis problem. This problem estimates the system failure time of a system of machines.

CS8.1.1 Model Definition and Assumptions

In this application, we consider a series-parallel system of machines in which there are three machine types, each working in parallel and connected serially (see Figure CS8.1).

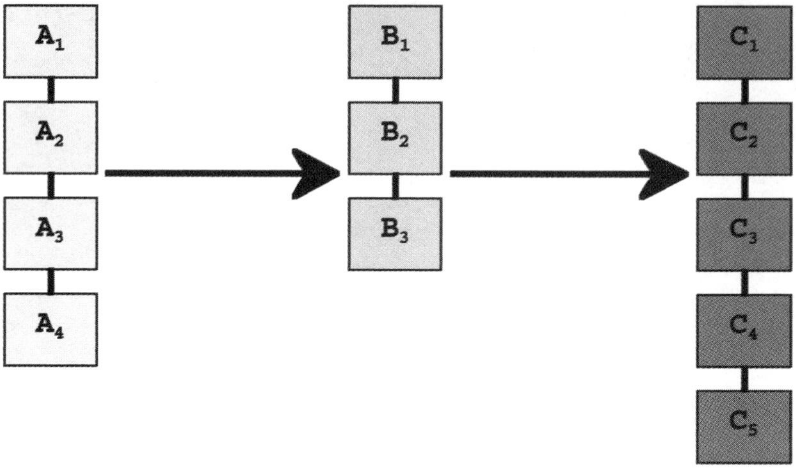

Figure CS8.1 An example of a parallel serial system made up of three machine types A, B, and C, each with a various number of machines.

To estimate failure time, we consider each machine type to be a ***k out of n*** system. That means, given there are n machines of a machine type, the entire machine type is considered to be working as long as k of those n machines are working. We then consider the entire system of all machine types to also be a *k out of n* system. In this application, we assume $n = 3$ machine types and $k = 3$. That is, any time one machine type fails, the entire system fails.

We use the Weibull distribution to estimate the failure times of the machines in each machine type (we actually use the "two-parameter Weibull"). Weibull random variables are the most common random variables used to model failure times of machines (see *Probability Models* by Winston for more details). The cumulative distribution function of the Weibull distribution is as follows:

$$F(t) = 1 - e \wedge ((-t / \beta) \wedge \alpha)$$

Therefore, the inverse function for the Weibull distribution, where p is the probability that X is in the Weibull distribution and X is the Weibull random variable, is as follows:

$$X = \beta * (\ln (1 / (1 - p)) \wedge \alpha$$

We could use this function to generate random Weibull values for the simulation. However, for this application we have created a spreadsheet simulation model and use the PsiWeibull() function of Risk Solver Platform (Figure CS8.2). This function takes two parameters, α and β. Therefore, we first need to determine the value of these parameters. We fit the Weibull parameters for each machine type based on its given means and standard deviations of time to failure. We simulate the system failure time using these Weibull parameters.

We create a spreadsheet model that randomly generates as many Weibull values as the total number of machines in the system. For each machine type we identify the time when the K-th machine failed by using the ***LARGE(Array, K)*** function of Excel. This function takes two parameters, *Array* and *K*. Array is the range of data for which we want to determine the K-th largest value. *K* is the position in the range of the value to return. For example, suppose that we have 5 type A machines, and this machine type is working as long as 3 machines are working. Then, the time of failure for machine type A is the third largest of failure times. The following are the formulas we use to identify failure time for each machine type.

Cell C12: = LARGE(C18:C1002, C10)
D12: = LARGE(D18:D1002, D10)
E12: = LARGE(E18:E1002, E10)

For this application, we analyze the distribution of the system failure time, which is the minimum of these three values. This minimum is calculated in cell C13. We use the ***PsiOutput()*** function to indicate that this is one of the output cells for the simulation model.

Cell C13: = MIN(C12:E12) + PsiOutput()

We also identify which machine type causes the most system failure. We wish to correct the bottleneck machine type and improve the overall performance of the system. To identify the type of machine that caused system failure we use three additional output cells, C11, D11 and E11. The following are the formulas typed in these cells.

Cell C11: = IF($C$13=C12,1,0) + PsiOutput()
E11: = IF($C$13=D12,1,0) + PsiOutput()
D11: = IF($C$13=E12,1,0) + PsiOutput()

We use the **IF** function of Excel to compare system's failure time (cell C13) with the failure time of a particular machine. If these values are equal, the IF function returns 1 indicating that this particular machine caused system's failure. We then use the ***PsiMean()*** function in the output sheet to calculate the mean value for these cells overall simulation trials, which presents the percentage of time the system failed due to machines A, B or C.

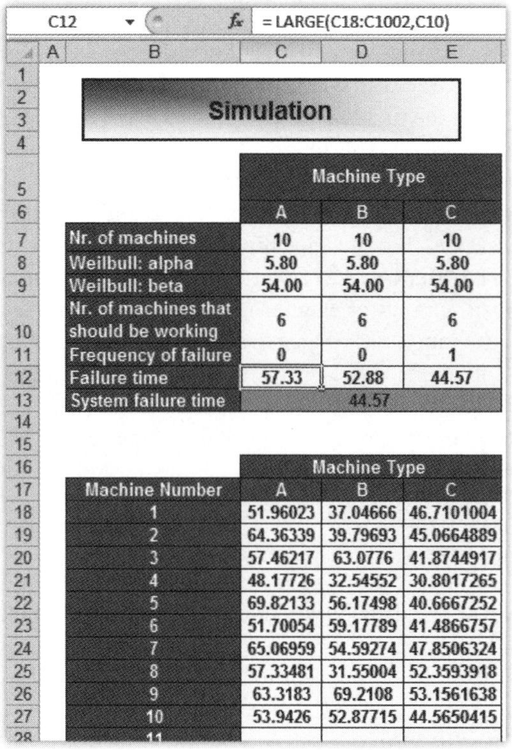
C12 = LARGE(C18:C1002,C10)

Simulation

	Machine Type		
	A	B	C
Nr. of machines	10	10	10
Weilbull: alpha	5.80	5.80	5.80
Weilbull: beta	54.00	54.00	54.00
Nr. of machines that should be working	6	6	6
Frequency of failure	0	0	1
Failure time	57.33	52.88	44.57
System failure time		44.57	

	Machine Type		
Machine Number	A	B	C
1	51.96023	37.04666	46.7101004
2	64.36339	39.79693	45.0664889
3	57.46217	63.0776	41.8744917
4	48.17726	32.54552	30.8017265
5	69.82133	56.17498	40.6667252
6	51.70054	59.17789	41.4866757
7	65.06959	54.59274	47.8506324
8	57.33481	31.55004	52.3593918
9	63.3183	69.2108	53.1561638
10	53.9426	52.87715	44.5650415

Figure CS8.2 Reliability spreadsheet simulation model.

The output sheet for this application summarizes these findings by using a histogram of the system failure time and a histogram of the frequency with which a particular machine type causes a system failure, and by displaying the overall mean system failure time.

CS8.1.2 Input

Using the model described in the above section, we can define the following input:

- The number of machines per machine type (n)
- The number of machines that should be working per machine type (k)
- The cost per machine for each machine type
- The mean and standard deviation of time to failure for each machine type
- The number of simulation trials to perform

We use one user form to receive the first four input values from the users. We also include one Input Box to record the number of simulation trials to perform. We keep the input values on a table in the main sheet to enable the users to modify them at any time.

CS8.1.3 Output

Our output is comprised of the following:

- The optimal Weibull parameters per machine type
- The mean system failure time
- The histogram of system failure times from simulation
- The histogram of frequency with which each machine type causes system failure from the simulation

The output appears on the output sheet. There are also some important resolve options, which we will discuss in a later section.

CS8.2 *Worksheets*

We use five worksheets in this application: the welcome sheet, a calculation sheet for optimizing the Weibull parameters, the user input sheet where user's input is displayed, a sheet for the simulation model, and the output sheet. The welcome sheet provides a description of the application and has a "Start" button assigned to the Main procedure (see Figure CS8.3).

The calculation sheet fits the Weibull parameters for each machine type (see Figure CS8.4). We perform the optimization using Risk Solver Platform; therefore, the sheet is organized with ranges for the decision variables, the constraints, and the objective function. The input cells for this optimization are the mean and standard deviation for time to failure for each machine type. Each machine type's Weibull parameters are fitted one at a time.

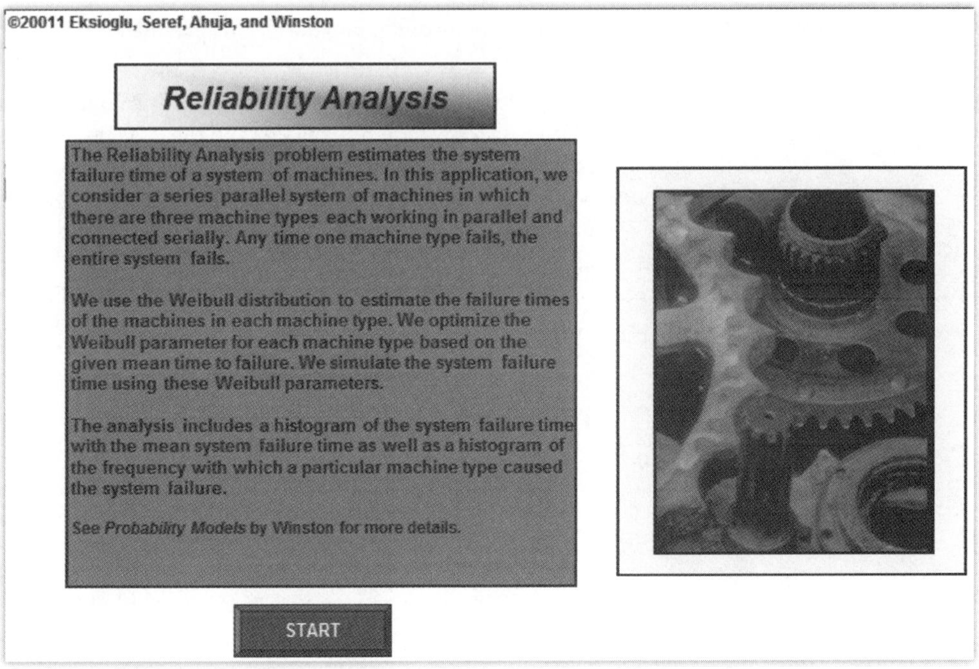

Figure CS8.3 The welcome sheet.

The decision variables are the Weibull parameters alpha and beta. Both of these have the upper and lower bounds shown adjacent to their cells. These bounds are the only constraints. We then calculate a mean and standard deviation time to failure using alpha and beta to find the square error compared to the users' input for these values. The objective function is therefore to minimize the sum of these square errors.

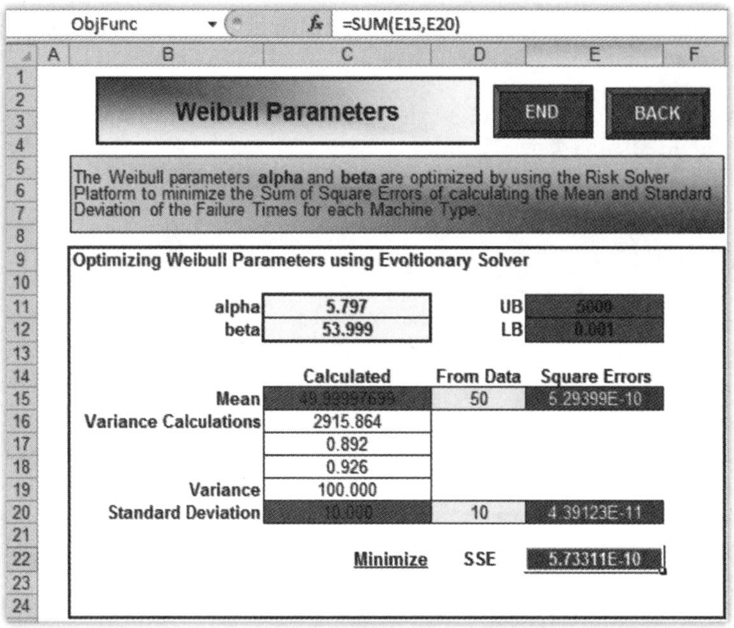

Figure CS8.4 The calculation sheet for optimizing the Weibull parameters.

There are two buttons on this sheet: "End" and "Back." The "End" button returns the users to the welcome sheet, and the "Back" button returns them to the user input sheet.

The user input sheet has a table that displays the input data entered by the user and the resulting values of alpha and beta for each machine type. There are four buttons on this sheet: "Start Simulation," "View Weibull Model," "Recalculate Weibull Parameters," and "End." The "Start Simulation" buttons simulates the system using the parameters entered by the user. The "View Weibull Model" takes the user to the Weibull sheet. "Recalculate Weibull Parameters" button recalculates the values of alpha and beta given user's input displayed in the user input sheet. The "End" button returns the users to the welcome sheet (Figure CS8.5).

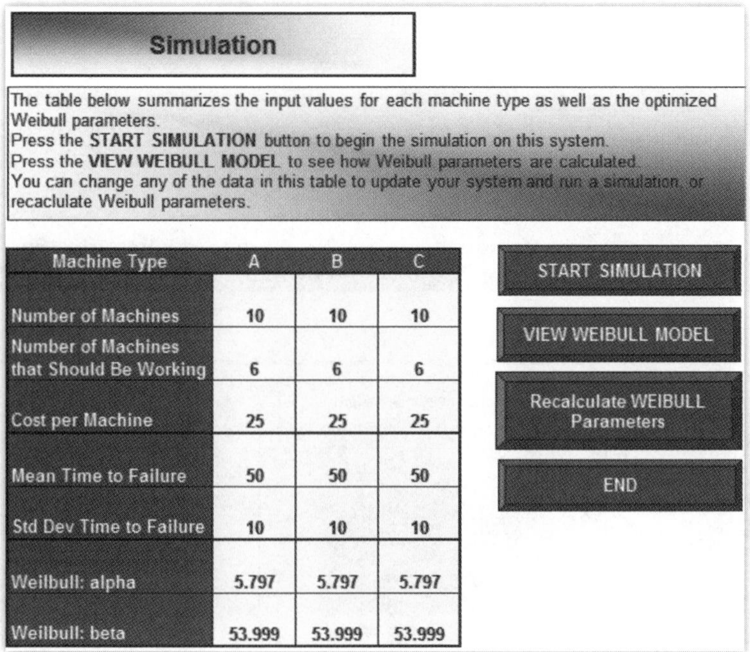
Simulation
The table below summarizes the input values for each machine type as well as the optimized Weibull parameters.
Press the START SIMULATION button to begin the simulation on this system.
Press the VIEW WEIBULL MODEL to see how Weibull parameters are calculated.
You can change any of the data in this table to update your system and run a simulation, or recaclulate Weibull parameters.
START SIMULATION
VIEW WEIBULL MODEL
Recalculate WEIBULL Parameters
END

Machine Type	A	B	C
Number of Machines	10	10	10
Number of Machines that Should Be Working	6	6	6
Cost per Machine	25	25	25
Mean Time to Failure	50	50	50
Std Dev Time to Failure	10	10	10
Weilbull: alpha	5.797	5.797	5.797
Weilbull: beta	53.999	53.999	53.999

Figure CS8.5 The user input sheet.

The next sheet that the users see is the simulation sheet, which contains an input table and the results of simulation (see Figure CS8.2). The input table presents input values that are used in the simulation model, and also presents failure time per machine type, system failure time and the machine type that caused the failure of the system. There are two buttons in this sheet, the "End" button that takes the user to the welcome sheet; and the "View Analysis" button that takes the user to the output sheet.

The final sheet, the output sheet (see Figure CS8.6), displays the mean system failure time, a histogram of the system time failures from the simulation, and a histogram of the frequencies with which each machine type caused the system failure. This is the most important information for the users to analyze in order to determine how the system is behaving. In this sheet, the mean failure time and the frequency of failure for different machine types are calculated using the *PsiMean()* function as follows:

Cell B18: **= PsiMean(Simulation!C13)**
C44: **= PsiMean(Simulation!C11)**
C45: **= PsiMean(Simulation!D11)**
C46: **= PsiMean(Simulation!E11)**

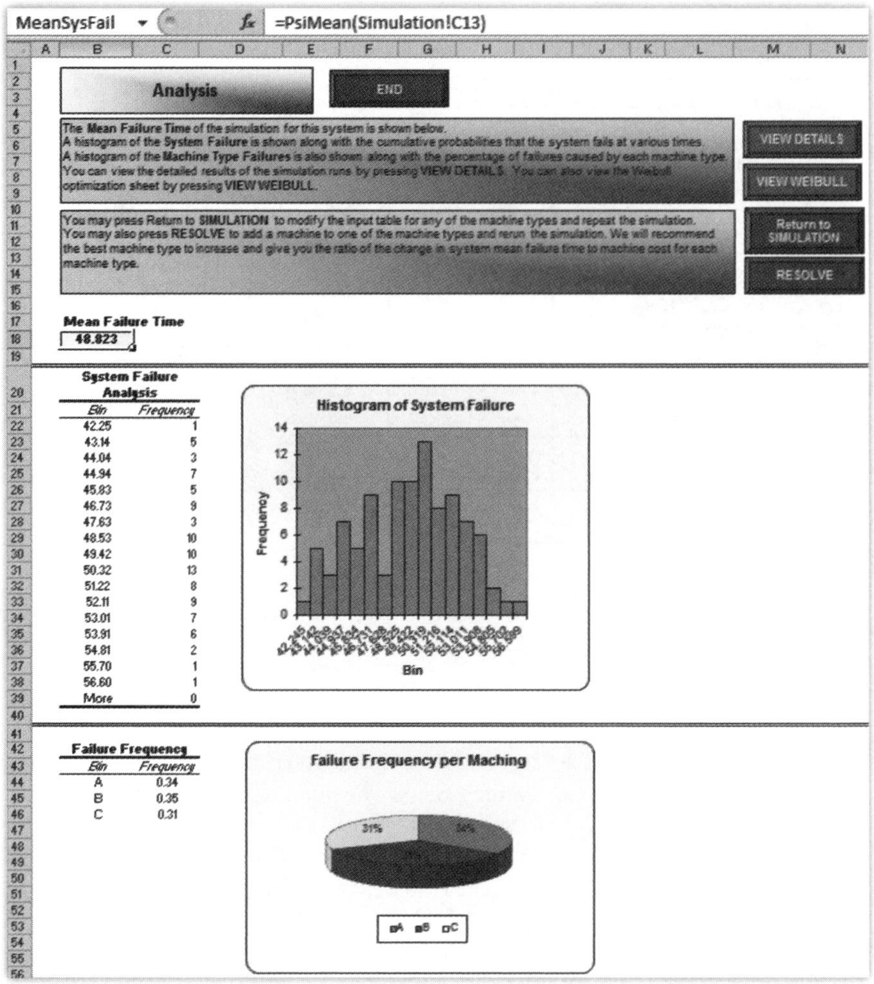

Figure CS8.6 The output sheet.

This sheet includes several buttons. The "End" button returns the users to the welcome sheet. The "View Details" button takes the users to the simulation sheet. The "View Weibull" button takes the users to the Weibull calculation sheet. The last two buttons, "Return to Simulation" and "Resolve," are used with the resolve options, which we will discuss in a later section.

Summary

Welcome sheet	Includes the application description and the "Start" button.
Weibull sheet	Fits the Weibull parameters using the Solver. Includes the "End" and "Back" buttons.
User input sheet	Displays user's input. The user can make changes to the input data, recalculate Weibull parameters, and run the simulation.
Simulation sheet	Contains the summary table of user's input and simulation results; the simulation spreadsheet model; and "End," and "View Analysis" buttons.
Output sheet	Contains the mean system failure time, the histogram for system failure times, and the histogram for machine type failures. Its buttons are: "End," "View Details," "View Weibull," "Return to Simulation," and "Resolve."

CS8.3 *User Interface*

This application possesses one user form, one input table, several navigational buttons, and a few functional buttons. We also employ one Input Box and a Message Box. The user form contains input for each machine type (see Figure CS8.7). It prompts the users for the number of machines, the number of machines that should be working, the cost per machine, and the mean and standard deviation of time to failure for the machine type. We use two frames to group similar text boxes. The "OK" button has an associated Click procedure, which we will describe later.

This form appears to the users three times in order to receive the input for each machine type. We include a dynamic label at the top of the sheet that displays the name of the current machine type with which the input is associated. Notice that we use a label and not a text box for this value since the users should never modify its value.

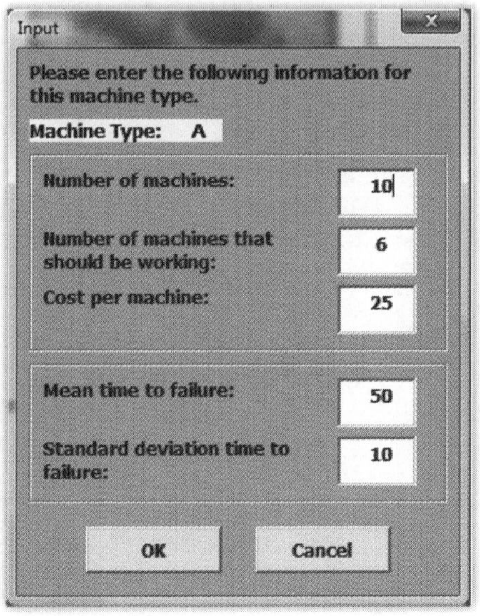

Figure CS8.7 The input form with the dynamic label value for machine type "A."

In the previous section, we described the input table on the user input sheet. It simply summarizes the users' input from the user form as well as the fitted Weibull parameters. The users can change this input before the simulation is run. The navigational buttons and functional buttons were also discussed in the previous section with each corresponding worksheet.

The Input Box prompts the users for the number of simulation trials (see Figure CS8.8). We give a title and a default value of 100 trials to the Input Box.

The Message Box informs the users that the Weibull parameter optimization has been completed (see Figure CS8.9). The corresponding calculation sheet appears behind the Message Box. We take the users directly to the simulation sheet, not allowing them to pause on the calculation sheet. However, the users can revisit the Weibull parameter optimization calculations.

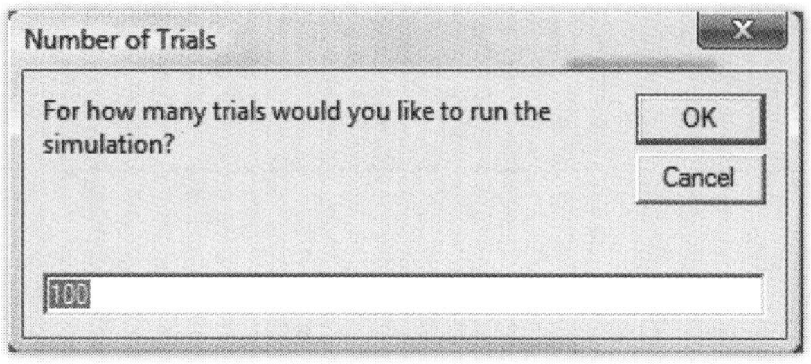

Figure CS8.8 The Input Box prompts the users for the number of simulation trials to perform.

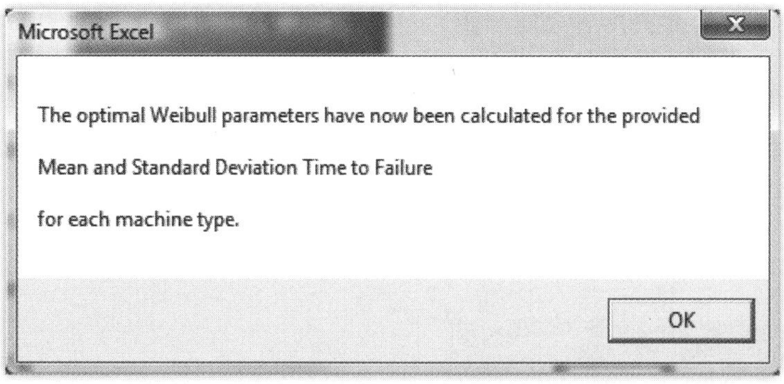

Figure CS8.9 The Message Box informs the users that the Weibull parameter optimization is complete.

Summary

Input Form	Receives the initial input from the users.
Input table on	Summarizes the user input and displays the fitted Weibull parameters for each
userinput sheet	machine type.
Input Box	Prompts the users for the number of simulation trials.
Message Box	Informs the users that the Weibull parameters have been fitted.
Navigational Buttons	"End," "Back," "View Details," "View Weibull," and "Return to Simulation."
Functional Buttons	"Start," "Start Simulation," "Recalculate Weibull Parameters," and "Resolve."

CS8.4 *Procedures*

Let us now outline the procedures for this application. We begin with the Main sub procedure and variable definitions (see Figure CS8.10). The public variables are used in multiple procedures. We define all other variables within the procedure in which they are used.

The Main procedure begins by calling the *ClearPrev* procedure, which initializes variables and clears previous worksheet values (see Figure CS8.11). Next, the Main procedure uses a loop to show the users the input form so one form is displayed for each machine type. The dynamic label is adjusted before the form appears so it displays the name of each machine type. The Click event procedure of the "OK" command button on the input form performs some error checking and then assigns the input values to the corresponding cells in the user input sheet (see Figure CS8.12).

```
Option Explicit
Option Base 1

Public i As Integer, j As Integer, temp As Variant, runs As Integer, _
MachName(3) As String, NumRuns As Integer, ws As Worksheet, _
RngValue As Double, BestChoice As Integer, ReliabilityProb As New RSP.Problem, _
Ratio(3) As Double, Resolving As Boolean, ChangeSysFail(3) As Double

Sub Main()
'Assigned to "Start" button on welcome sheet;
    Call ClearPrev

    'get input for all machine types
    For i = 1 To 3
        frmInput.lblType.Caption = MachName(i)
        frmInput.Show
    Next i

    'calc Weibull parameters for each machine type
    Worksheets("Weibull").Visible = True
    Worksheets("Welcome").Visible = False
    Call CalcWeibull
    MsgBox "The optimal Weibull parameters have now been calculated for the provided " _
    & vbCrLf & vbCrLf & "Mean and Standard Deviation Time to Failure " & vbCrLf & _
    vbCrLf & "for each machine type."

    Worksheets("UserInput").Visible = True
    Worksheets("Weibull").Visible = False
End Sub
```

Figure CS8.10 The Main procedure and variable declarations.

```
Sub ClearPrev()
'Called from Main procedure;
    'initializes variables and clears previous values and formatting
    MachName(1) = "A"
    MachName(2) = "B"
    MachName(3) = "C"

    'clear UserInput worksheet
    Range(Range("InputData").Offset(1, 1), Range("InputData").Offset(7, 3)).ClearContents

    'clear histogram related data
    Range(Range("HistDataStart").Offset(0, -1), Range("HistDataStart").End(xlDown)).Clear
    Range(Range("HistTime"), Range("HistTime").Offset(18, 3)).ClearContents
    Range(Range("HistFreqFail").Offset(1, 1), Range("HistFreqFail").Offset(3, 1)).ClearContents

    Resolving = False
End Sub
```

Figure CS8.11 The *ClearPrev* procedure.

```
Private Sub cmdCancel_Click()
    Unload Me
    End
End Sub

Private Sub cmdOK_Click()
    Dim ctl As Control
    For Each ctl In Me.Controls
        If TypeName(ctl) = "TextBox" Then
            If IsNumeric(ctl) = False Or ctl.Value = "" Then
                MsgBox "Please enter a numeric value for all input."
                Exit Sub
                ctl.SetFocus
            End If
        End If
    Next

    If Int(txtNumMach.Value) < Int(txtNumToFail.Value) Then
        MsgBox "The number of machines to casue a failure should be " & _
                "less than the number of machines.", vbCritical
        End
    End If

    With Range("InputData")
        .Offset(1, i).Value = Int(txtNumMach.Value)
        .Offset(2, i).Value = Int(txtNumToFail.Value)
        .Offset(3, i).Value = CDbl(txtCost.Value)
        .Offset(4, i).Value = CDbl(txtMean.Value)
        .Offset(5, i).Value = CDbl(txtStd.Value)
    End With
    Unload Me
End Sub
```

Figure CS8.12 The *cmdOK_Click* event procedure.

We then call the *CalcWeibull* procedure; it uses the Solver commands to find the optimum Weibull parameters for each machine type (see Figure CS8.13). We use the spreadsheet optimization model in Weibull sheet to initiate an instance of the optimization problem object. Then, we employ a loop to change the input cells that contain the mean and standard deviation of time to failure for each machine type. Within this loop, the problem is optimized using the *Solver.Optimize* method and the decision variable cell values, the alpha and beta values, are recorded for each machine type. Once we return to the Main procedure, the Message Box appears to inform the users that the optimal Weibull parameters have been found for each machine type. The Main procedure then takes the users to the user input spreadsheet.

```
Sub CalcWeibull()
Dim WeibProb As New RSP.Problem
'Called from Main procedure;
'uses mean failure time and standard deviation of failure time as input;
'uses Solver to optimize Weibull parameters

    Application.ScreenUpdating = False
    WeibProb.Init Worksheets("Weibull")

    'for each machine type, enter mean and stdev fail time to Solver sheet
    For i = 1 To 3
        Range("UserMean").Value = Range("InputData").Offset(4, i).Value
        Range("UserStd").Value = Range("InputData").Offset(5, i).Value

        'starting guess
        Range("Beta").Value = Range("InputData").Offset(4, i).Value
        Range("Alpha").Value = (Range("InputData").Offset(5, i).Value) / 10

        'run solver - do not need to reset changing cells, obj func, or constraints
        WeibProb.Solver.Optimize Solve_Type_Solve
        Range("InputData").Offset(6, i).Value = Range("alpha").Value
        Range("InputData").Offset(7, i).Value = Range("beta").Value
    Next i
    Set WeibProb = Nothing

    Application.ScreenUpdating = True
End Sub
```

Figure CS8.13 The *CalcWeibull* procedure.

On the user input sheet, the "Start Simulation" button calls the *Simulation* procedure. The *Simulation* procedure creates the simulation data, and performs the simulation (see Figure CS8.14). This procedure employs an Input Box for the number of trials to perform during the simulation. Some error checking is done to check if the users pressed the "Cancel" button on the Input Box. It then begins a loop to update the input data required in the simulation sheet. Next, updates the formulas that go to the simulation spreadsheet model. The spreadsheet model is now completed. An instance of the simulation problem object is initiated using this model. The Solver.Simulate method is used to simulate the problem. Finally, the Analysis procedure is called to create the histograms for the system failure and machine type failures (see Figure CS8.15). Analysis procedure also updates the spreadsheet formulas that report the mean system failure time and frequency of failure per machine type.

```
Sub Simulation()
'Assigned to "Run Simulation" button on Weibull and Output sheets;
    'find number of runs
    Application.ScreenUpdating = False
    Worksheets("Simulation").Activate
    If (Resolving = False) Then
        temp = InputBox("For how many trials would you like to run the simulation?", _
            "Number of Trials", 100)
        If temp = "" Then
            End
        Else
            NumRuns = temp
        End If
        ReliabilityProb.Solver.NumTrials = NumRuns
    End If

    'get the input data
    For j = 1 To 3
        With Range("SimTable")
            .Offset(1, j).Value = Range("InputData").Offset(1, j).Value
            .Offset(2, j).Value = Range("InputData").Offset(6, j).Value
            .Offset(3, j).Value = Range("InputData").Offset(7, j).Value
            .Offset(4, j).Value = Range("InputData").Offset(2, j).Value
        End With
    Next j

    'update spreadsheet simuation model using user's input
    Range(Range("SimStart").Offset(1, 1), Range("SimStart").Offset(100, 3)).ClearContents
    Range(Range("SimStart").Offset(1, 1), Range("SimStart").Offset(Range("C7").Value, 1)) _
        .Formula = "=PsiWeibull($C$8,$C$9)"
    Range(Range("SimStart").Offset(1, 2), Range("SimStart").Offset(Range("D7").Value, 2)) _
        .Formula = "=PsiWeibull($D$8,$D$9)"
    Range(Range("SimStart").Offset(1, 3), Range("SimStart").Offset(Range("E7").Value, 3)) _
        .Formula = "=PsiWeibull($E$8,$E$9)"
```

(a)

```
    'load and run the simulation model
    ReliabilityProb.Init ActiveWorkbook
    ReliabilityProb.Solver.Simulate

    If Resolving = False Then
        'only update output sheet if not resolving
        Call Analysis
        Set ws = Worksheets("Output")
        ws.Activate
        ws.Visible = True
        Worksheets("UserInput").Visible = False
    End If
    Range("A1").Select
    Application.ScreenUpdating = True
End Sub
```

(b)

Figure CS8.14 The *Simulation* procedure.

```
Sub Analysis()
'Called from Simulation procedure;
'Creates histograms and displays mean system failure time
    Application.ScreenUpdating = False
    Worksheets("Output").Activate

    'HISTOGRAM OF SYSTEM FAILURE TIME
        'collect the data generated during the simulation
    For runs = 1 To NumRuns
        Range("HistDataStart").Offset(runs - 1, 0).Value = _
                ReliabilityProb.Functions(1).AllTrials(0, runs - 1)
    Next runs

        'create the data ranges of the histogram
    Range(Range("HistDataStart"), Range("HistDataStart").Offset(runs, 0)).Name = "HistData"
    Range(Range("HistDataStart").Offset(0, -1), Range("HistDataStart").Offset(16, -1)).Name = "HistBin"
    Range("HistDataStart").Offset(16, -1).Value = ReliabilityProb.Functions(1).Statistics.Maximum(0)
    Range("HistDataStart").Offset(0, -1).Value = ReliabilityProb.Functions(1).Statistics.Minimum(0)
    RngValue = (Range("HistDataStart").Offset(16, -1).Value - Range("HistDataStart").Offset(0, -1).Value) / 16
    For i = 1 To 15
        Range("HistDataStart").Offset(i, -1).Value = Range("HistDataStart").Offset(i - 1, -1).Value + RngValue
    Next i

        'create the histogram
    Range(Range("HistTime"), Range("HistTime").Offset(18, 3)).ClearContents
    Application.Run "ATPVBAEN.XLAM!Histogram", Range("HistData"), Range("HistTime"), Range("HistBin") _
        , False, False, False, False
    With Range(Range("HistTime").Offset(1, 0), Range("HistTime").Offset(1, 0).End(xlDown))
        .NumberFormat = "##.00"
        .HorizontalAlignment = xlCenter
    End With

    'HISTOGRAM OF FREQUENCY OF FAILURES
        'update the source data of the histograms
    Range("HistFreqFail").Offset(1, 1).Formula = "=PsiMean(Simulation!C11)"
    Range("HistFreqFail").Offset(2, 1).Formula = "=PsiMean(Simulation!D11)"
    Range("HistFreqFail").Offset(3, 1).Formula = "=PsiMean(Simulation!E11)"

    'MEAN FAILURE TIME
    Range("MeanSysFail").Formula = "=PsiMean(Simulation!C13)"
    Range("Current_SystFail").Value = Range("MeanSysFail").Value

    Set ReliabilityProb = Nothing
    Application.ScreenUpdating = True
End Sub
```

Figure CS8.15 The *Analysis procedure.*

The remaining procedures are the navigational procedures (see Figure CS8.19). These are for the "End," "Back," "View Analysis," "View Details," "View Weibull," and "Rerun Simulation" buttons.

```
'navigational procedures
Sub EndProg()
    Worksheets("Welcome").Visible = True
    ActiveSheet.Visible = False
End Sub

Sub ViewSummary()
    Set ws = ActiveSheet
    Worksheets("Output").Visible = True
    ws.Visible = False
End Sub

Sub ViewDetails()
    Worksheets("Simulation").Visible = True
    ActiveSheet.Visible = False
End Sub

Sub GoBack()
    ws.Visible = True
    ActiveSheet.Visible = False
End Sub

Sub ViewWeibull()
    Set ws = ActiveSheet
    Worksheets("Weibull").Visible = True
    ws.Visible = False
End Sub

Sub RerunSim()
    Worksheets("UserInput").Visible = True
    ActiveSheet.Visible = False
End Sub
```

Figure CS8.16 The navigational procedures.

Summary

Main	Initializes the application and retrieves the initial input from the users.
ClearPrev	Initializes the variables, clears the previous values.
cmdOK_Click	Checks errors and assigns input values to corresponding cells in the user input sheet.
CalcWeibull	Invokes the Solver to determine optimal Weibull parameters for each machine type.
Simulation	Runs the simulation.
Analysis	Creates histograms and displays the mean system failure time.
Navigational	For navigational buttons.

CS8.5 *Re-solve Options*

This DSS presents two main re-solve options. The first allows the users to return to the user input sheet, modify the input table, and re-run the simulation by pressing the "Return to Simulation" button on the output sheet.

For example, in Figure CS8.17, we have returned to the simulation sheet after the initial simulation was run. We have changed the values for the "Number of Machines that Should be Working" in the input table from 6 for each machine type to 3, 6, and 9. We then press the

"Start Simulation" button again to restart the simulation. The simulation runs using new input that has been recorded.

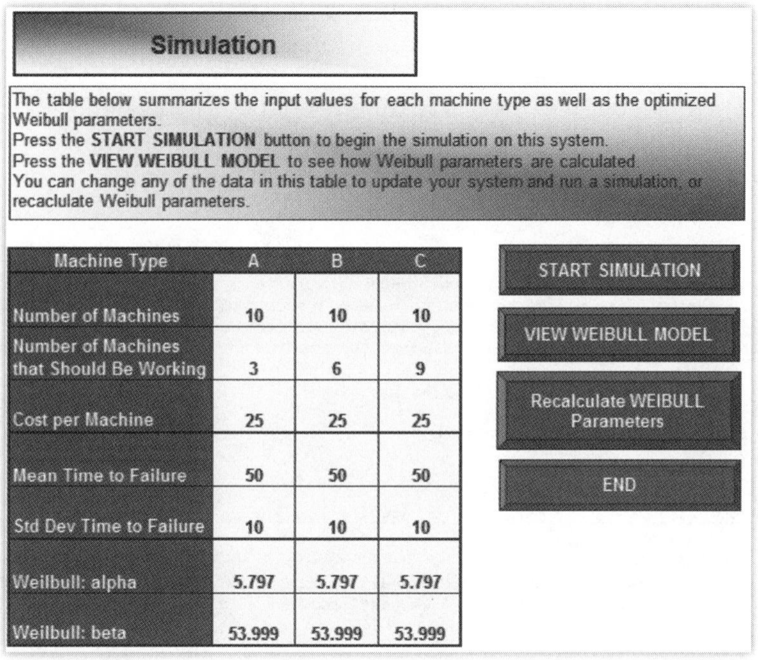

Figure CS8.17 An example of the first e-solve option.

We can then view the output sheet again by pressing the "View Analysis" button; we now can observe that the machine type C has, indeed, caused the majority of the system failures (see Figure CS8.18). This is due to the fact that this machine type now fails more frequently. The second machine type A to fail causes a system failure.

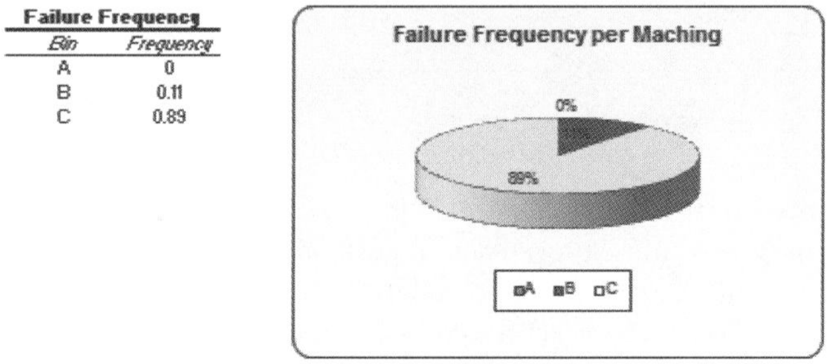

Figure CS8.18 Updated analysis from the first resolve option.

The second resolve option enables the users to determine the system bottleneck machine type and add one machine to this machine type to improve system performance, or, to increase the mean system failure time. We perform this option with a *Resolve* procedure that is called when the users press the "Resolve" button on the output sheet (see Figure CS8.19).

The *Resolve* procedure reveals a resolve form in which the users can choose which machine type to add a machine to. However, before doing that, we want to suggest to the users which machine type would be the best choice. To do so, the *Resolve* procedure begins by performing some trials to determine the optimum choice. For each machine type, one machine is added and the simulation is rerun. We then record the improvement in the mean system failure time. After this process is done for all three machine types, we compute a ratio of these improvements to each machine type's cost. The optimal machine type is the one with the highest ratio; in other words, it is most beneficial to add a machine that will cause the most improvement in system failure time at the least cost.

```
Sub Resolve()
'Assigned to "Resolve" button on output sheet;
'adds one machine to each machine time (sequentially) and
'reruns the simulation to record change in mean system failure time;
'compares ratio of this time change to the cost per machine of the machine type;
'suggests that the user adds one machine to the machine type with the largest ratio

    Dim MaxRatio As Double, k As Integer
    Resolving = True
    Application.ScreenUpdating = False

    For k = 1 To 3
        'add 1 machine of type i
        Range("InputData").Offset(1, k).Value = Range("InputData").Offset(1, k).Value + 1
        'repeat simulation
        Call Simulation
        ChangeSysFail(k) = Range("MeanSysFail").Value - Range("Current_SystFail").Value
        Ratio(k) = ChangeSysFail(k) / Range("InputData").Offset(3, k).Value

        'reset values
        Range("InputData").Offset(1, k).Value = Range("InputData").Offset(1, k).Value - 1
    Next

    'find max ratio
    MaxRatio = 0
    For i = 1 To 3
        If Ratio(i) > MaxRatio Then
            MaxRatio = Ratio(i)
            BestChoice = i
        End If
    Next i

    Application.ScreenUpdating = True
    frmResolve.Show
End Sub
```

Figure CS8.19 The *Re-solve* procedure.

The resolve form then appears (see Figure CS8.20). When the form is initialized, we display the improvements in system failure time, machine costs, and ratio values for each machine on a table in the form (see Figure CS8.21). We also update a dynamic label to display the best choice, which we suggest to the users, and select the corresponding option button.

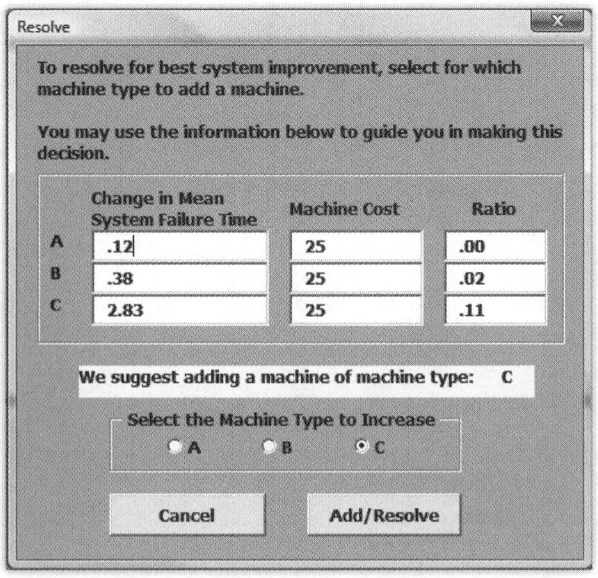

Figure CS8.20 The resolve form.

```
Private Sub UserForm_Initialize()
'enters values found in Resolve procedure on form;
'displays suggested machine type

    txtChangeSysA.Value = Format(ChangeSysFail(1), "##.00")
    txtChangeSysB.Value = Format(ChangeSysFail(2), "##.00")
    txtChangeSysC.Value = Format(ChangeSysFail(3), "##.00")

    txtMachCostA.Value = Range("InputData").Offset(3, 1).Value
    txtMachCostB.Value = Range("InputData").Offset(3, 2).Value
    txtMachCostC.Value = Range("InputData").Offset(3, 3).Value

    txtRatioA.Value = Format(Ratio(1), "##.00")
    txtRatioB.Value = Format(Ratio(2), "##.00")
    txtRatioC.Value = Format(Ratio(3), "##.00")

    If BestChoice = 1 Then
        optA = True
        lblBestChoice.Caption = "A"
    ElseIf BestChoice = 2 Then
        optB = True
        lblBestChoice.Caption = "B"
    ElseIf BestChoice = 3 Then
        optC = True
        lblBestChoice.Caption = "C"
    End If

End Sub
```

Figure CS8.21 The initialization event procedure for the resolve form.

A frame with these option buttons retrieves the users' machine type selection. The "Add/Resolve" button records this selection and increases the number of machines of this machine type by one (see Figure CS8.22). It then updates the input table and simulation input table and recalls the Simulation procedure.

```
Private Sub cmdCancel_Click()
    Unload Me
    Worksheets("Welcome").Visible = True
    ActiveSheet.Visible = False
    End
End Sub

Private Sub cmdAddResolve_Click()
'records user's selection on which machine type to increase;
'updates number of machines for this machine type;
'updates animation layout and input table on simulation sheet;
'Calls StartSim to rerun simulation

    If optA Then
        BestChoice = 1
    ElseIf optB Then
        BestChoice = 2
    ElseIf optC Then
        BestChoice = 3
    Else
        MsgBox "No selection was made! Try again!"
        End
    End If

    Range("SimTable").Offset(1, BestChoice).Value = _
            Range("InputData").Offset(1, BestChoice).Value + 1
    Range("InputData").Offset(1, BestChoice).Value = _
            Range("InputData").Offset(1, BestChoice).Value + 1

    Unload Me
    Resolving = False
    Call Simulation
End Sub
```

Figure CS8.22 The Click event procedure for the "Add/Resolve" button on the re-solve form.

The users can then observe the results from the new simulation run. For example, in Figure CS8.23, we have added one machine to the third machine type. Notice that this modification is reflected in the input table. The users can then review the analysis to determine if the mean system time has indeed improved. This process may be repeated as many times as the users desire.

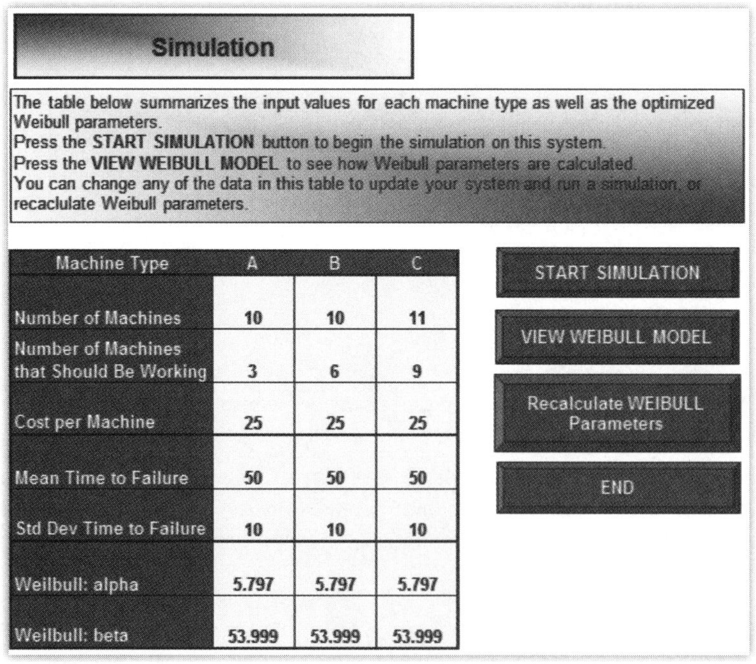
Simulation
The table below summarizes the input values for each machine type as well as the optimized Weibull parameters.
Press the START SIMULATION button to begin the simulation on this system.
Press the VIEW WEIBULL MODEL to see how Weibull parameters are calculated.
You can change any of the data in this table to update your system and run a simulation, or recaclulate Weibull parameters.
Machine Type | A | B | C
Number of Machines | 10 | 10 | 11
Number of Machines that Should Be Working | 3 | 6 | 9
Cost per Machine | 25 | 25 | 25
Mean Time to Failure | 50 | 50 | 50
Std Dev Time to Failure | 10 | 10 | 10
Weilbull: alpha | 5.797 | 5.797 | 5.797
Weilbull: beta | 53.999 | 53.999 | 53.999
START SIMULATION
VIEW WEIBULL MODEL
Recalculate WEIBULL Parameters
END

Figure CS8.23 An example of the second resolve option.

Summary

First resolve option	The users press the "Return to Simulation" button on an output sheet to return to the simulation sheet; they can modify the input table and rerun the simulation; the analysis is updated with the new simulation results.
Second resolve option	The users press the "Resolve" button on the output sheet to view the resolve form; the resolve form enables them to add one machine to one machine type; the best choice is suggested to the users after running trial simulations in the Resolve procedure.

CS8.6 *Summary*

- The reliability analysis problem estimates the failure time of a system of machines. A parallel serial system of machines is analyzed. This is considered to be a *k out of n* system of machines; in other words, for the system to be working k out of n machines should be working. The Weibull distribution models the machine failure times for the simulation.
- There are five worksheets for this application: the welcome sheet, the calculation sheet for Weibull parameter optimization, the user input sheet, the simulation sheet, and the output sheet.
- The initial input user form requests input that is summarized in an input table on the user input sheet; the users can modify this input at any time.
- This application has several procedures that walk the users through the Weibull parameter optimization, simulation, and analysis.
- The first resolve option allows the users to rerun the simulation after modifying the input table on the simulation sheet. The second option enables the users to improve the mean system failure time by adding one machine to a selected machine type. The most favorable choice is suggested to the users.

CS8.7 *Extensions*

1. Add an option to the output sheet in which the users can determine the probability that the system will survive past a specified system failure time.
2. Add an option that repeats the second resolve option until a desired system failure time is reached.
3. Make the application more dynamic by allowing the users to analyze more than three machine types.
4. Suppose that we do not have access to Risk Solver Platform. Update the existing procedures to complete the simulation of this problem, collect statistics, and build the histograms displayed in the output sheet. Similarly, update Weibull parameters optimization procedures to use the standard Solver of Excel instead.
5. What is a similar problem in which this application could be used with slight modifications?

CASE STUDY

nine Retirement Planning

chapter OVERVIEW

CS9.1 Application Overview and Model Development

In this application, we want to help the users answer the following questions: (i) At what age can I retire?; (ii) How much savings can I retire with?; and (iii) What is my best investment strategy? These questions are solved as separate options: options A, B, and C, respectively. We perform a simulation to determine the mean age, savings, and investment strategies for these three options.

CS9.1.1 Model Definition and Assumptions

Let us now describe the simulation calculations performed. We assume that the users know and provide the following input in the beginning of the application: current age, current savings, annual salary, annual percent increase in salary, and percent of users' salary to invest each year. For the investment strategy, we assume that the users distribute their funds between treasury (T.) bills, bonds, and stocks. This strategy is considered to be an asset allocation of the percentage of the users' savings they wish to invest. The users provide asset allocation as percentages (summing to 100 percent). The users record all of this input and place it on the sheet where we perform the simulation calculations.

We translate the users' percent values for the asset allocation into initial investment dollar amounts using the formula below. We perform this calculation for all investment types. (See Figure CS9.1.)

*Initial investment in T. Bills = (percent of salary to invest * current salary + current savings) * T. Bills asset allocation*

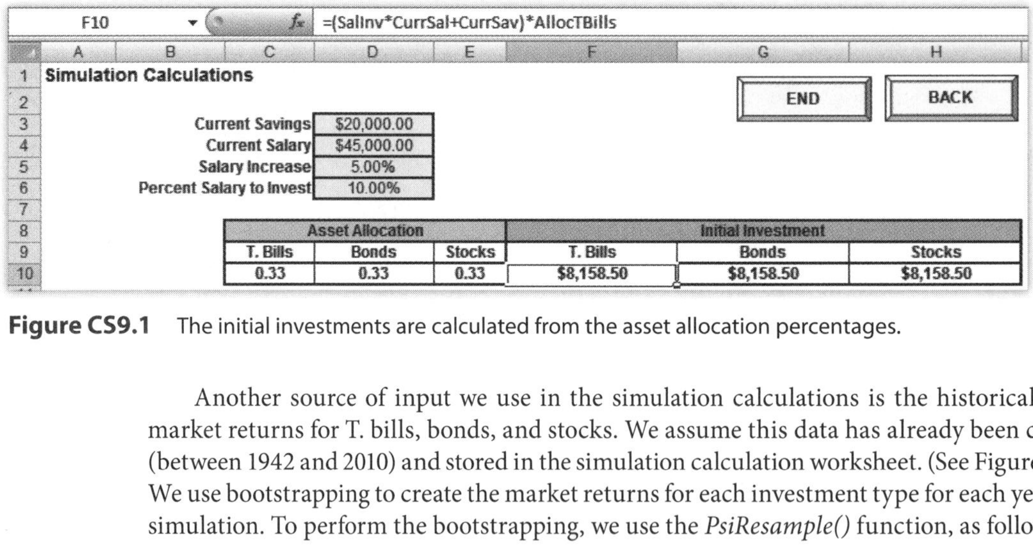

Figure CS9.1 The initial investments are calculated from the asset allocation percentages.

Another source of input we use in the simulation calculations is the historical data of market returns for T. bills, bonds, and stocks. We assume this data has already been collected (between 1942 and 2010) and stored in the simulation calculation worksheet. (See Figure CS9.2.) We use bootstrapping to create the market returns for each investment type for each year of the simulation. To perform the bootstrapping, we use the *PsiResample()* function, as follows:

Current market returns for T. Bills = PsiResample ($R$14:$R$82)

This function returns a random sample of the trial values in the range "$R$14:$R$82," which contain the historical data for T. Bills presented in Figure CS9.2. The formula is similar for bonds and stocks.

	Q	R	S	T
13	Year	Bills	Bonds	Stocks
14	1942	0.0327	0.0777	0.1162
15	1943	0.0312	0.0893	0.3749
16	1944	0.0324	0.001	0.4361
17	1945	0.0475	0.0342	-0.0842
18	1946	0.0241	0.0466	-0.249
75	2003	0.0547	-0.0269	0.0523
76	2004	0.0635	0.0967	0.1681
77	2005	0.0837	0.1811	0.3149
78	2006	0.0781	0.0618	-0.0317
79	2007	0.056	0.193	0.3055
80	2008	0.0351	0.0805	0.0767
81	2009	0.029	0.1824	0.0999
82	2010	0.039	-0.0777	0.0131

Figure CS9.2 The historical market returns used for bootstrapping.

Next, we use these bootstrapped returns to calculate the ending investment returns for the current year. (See Figure CS9.3.) For each investment type, we apply the following formula:

*Ending portfolio returns for T. Bills = Current investment in T. Bills * (1+ market returns for T Bills)*

F14 =F10*(1+C14)

	A	B	C	D	E	F	G	H	I
1	Simulation Calculations								
2							END	BACK	
3			Current Savings	$20,000.00					
4			Current Salary	$45,000.00					
5			Salary Increase	5.00%					
6			Percent Salary to Invest	10.00%					
7									
8			Asset Allocation			Initial Investment			
9			T. Bills	Bonds	Stocks	T. Bills	Bonds	Stocks	
10			0.33	0.33	0.33	$8,158.50	$8,158.50	$8,158.50	
11									
12			Market Returns (from Bootstrapping)			Ending Investment Returns			
13	Age	Year	T. Bills	Bonds	Stocks	T. Bills	Bonds	Stocks	Total Returns
14	50	1	0.0658	-0.0026	0.1847	$8,695.33	$8,137.29	$9,665.37	$26,497.99
15	51	2	0.0149	-0.0559	-0.0842	$10,552.18	$9,816.05	$9,521.81	$29,890.03
16	52	3	0.056	0.0073	0.1898	$12,255.38	$11,690.20	$13,808.20	$37,753.78

Figure CS9.3 Calculating the ending investment returns using the bootstrapped market returns.

We then calculate the current year salary, the current year addition to savings, and the updated investment dollar amount for each investment type. (See Figure CS9.4.) To calculate these values in their corresponding columns, we apply the following formulas:

*Current salary = (1+percent annual salary increase)*previous year's salary*

*Current addition to savings = percent of salary to invest * current salary*

*Current investment in T. Bills = (total returns + addition to savings) * T. Bills asset allocation*

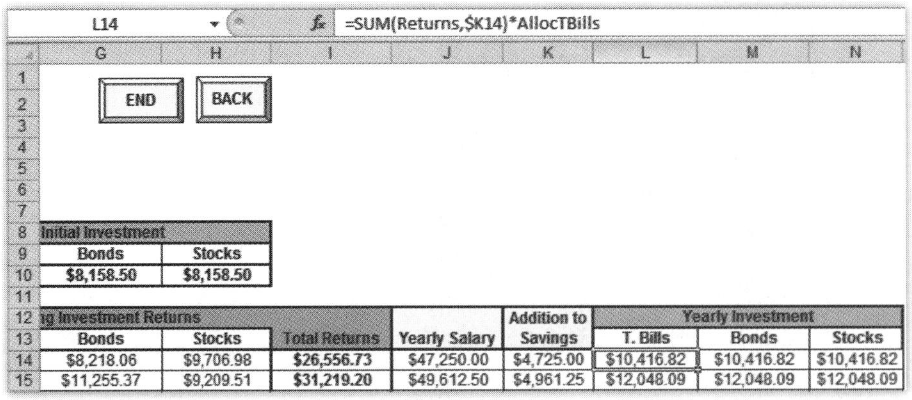

Figure CS9.4 Calculating the yearly salary, addition to savings, and investment amounts.

We perform these calculations (in each of the columns shown in the figures above) over several years (or rows). The number of years for which we make the calculations depends on which option the users are interested in solving. For each option, the first year matches the current age of the users. For option A, the last year matches the year when the users' desired savings at retirement is met. For options B and C, the last year matches the age at which the users wish to retire.

We use two different strategies to complete our simulations for options A and B, and option C. For options A and B, we use *For Next* loops to perform a spreadsheet simulation of the model described above. We realized that the VBA code to accomplish these simulations is shorter, and easy to understand. For option C we use Risk Solver Platform.

For options A and B, we use the data randomly generated in the spreadsheet we already setup to record the final age (option A) or savings (option B) at this final year. We consider this entire set of calculations to be one trial of the simulation. We repeat the simulation trials by updating the PsiResample() function used to generate market returns. We do so by typing the command "Calculate" in the VBA code, which is equivalent to the F9 manual calculation update function in the worksheet. The mean and standard deviation of the age (option A) or retirement savings (options B) are then calculated from the results recorded in each simulation trial.

For option C, we perform a sensitivity analyses to find the investment strategy that maximizes mean savings. We investigate 30 different investment strategies. For each strategy, we change the existing asset allocation, and perform 100 simulation trials using Risk Solver Platform. For each investment strategy we present the corresponding mean and standard deviation of Total Returns at the retirement age specified by the user. We sort the data based on mean savings (see Figure CS9.5). Note that, this worksheet is not protected. Therefore, the user can make changes to the strategies listed and re-run the application to identify better investment strategies.

Sensitivity Analysis Results					
Investment Strategy	Tbills	Bonds	Stocks	Mean Savings	Std Dev Savings
1	0	0	1	$1,668,050	$1,355,585
2	0	0.1	0.9	$1,331,199	$1,012,393
3	0.1	0	0.9	$1,216,204	$650,599
4	0	0.2	0.8	$1,196,017	$698,621
5	0.2	0	0.8	$1,194,319	$657,279
6	0.3	0	0.7	$1,009,842	$468,742
7	0	0.3	0.7	$991,708	$521,411
8	0	0.4	0.6	$979,820	$343,485
9	0.4	0	0.6	$839,597	$327,221
10	0	0.6	0.4	$823,186	$288,545
11	0	0.5	0.5	$819,120	$288,320
12	0.5	0	0.5	$744,534	$224,134
13	0	0.7	0.3	$695,668	$196,915
14	0.6	0	0.4	$673,193	$195,205
15	0	0.8	0.2	$622,553	$138,886
16	0.7	0	0.3	$585,656	$127,735
17	0	0.9	0.1	$546,510	$114,961
18	0.8	0	0.2	$516,134	$67,523
19	0.2	0.8	0	$496,267	$110,750
20	0.1	0.9	0	$480,960	$104,755
21	0	1	0	$477,024	$131,297
22	0.4	0.6	0	$461,141	$72,724
23	0.9	0	0.1	$454,416	$48,674
24	0.3	0.7	0	$445,814	$75,177
25	0.5	0.5	0	$444,893	$60,978
26	0.6	0.4	0	$439,845	$52,613
27	0.7	0.3	0	$427,962	$48,601
28	0.8	0.2	0	$420,278	$38,162
29	0.9	0.1	0	$406,406	$34,512
30	1	0	0	$405,424	$39,647

Figure CS9.5 The results of the sensitivity analysis for option C.

CS9.1.2 Input

The input for this application is the following:

- Current age
- Current savings
- Annual salary
- Annual percent increase in salary
- Percent of users' salary they wish to invest each year
- Desired salary at retirement with confidence interval (for option A)
- Desired age at retirement (for options B and C)
- Investment strategy (or asset allocation) (for options A and B)

CS9.1.3 Output

The output for this application is the following:

- Mean and standard deviation for age to retire (option A)
- Mean and standard deviation for savings at retirement (options B and C)
- Mean and standard deviation for 30 asset allocations strategies (option C)
- Histogram of age to retire (option A) or savings at retirement (options B and C)

CS9.2 *Worksheets*

This application requires four sheets: the welcome sheet, the simulation calculations sheet, the simulation runs sheet, and the results sheet. The welcome sheet contains the title, the description of the application, and the "Start" button. (See Figure CS9.6.) The "Start" button displays several forms to the users and then takes them directly to the results sheet.

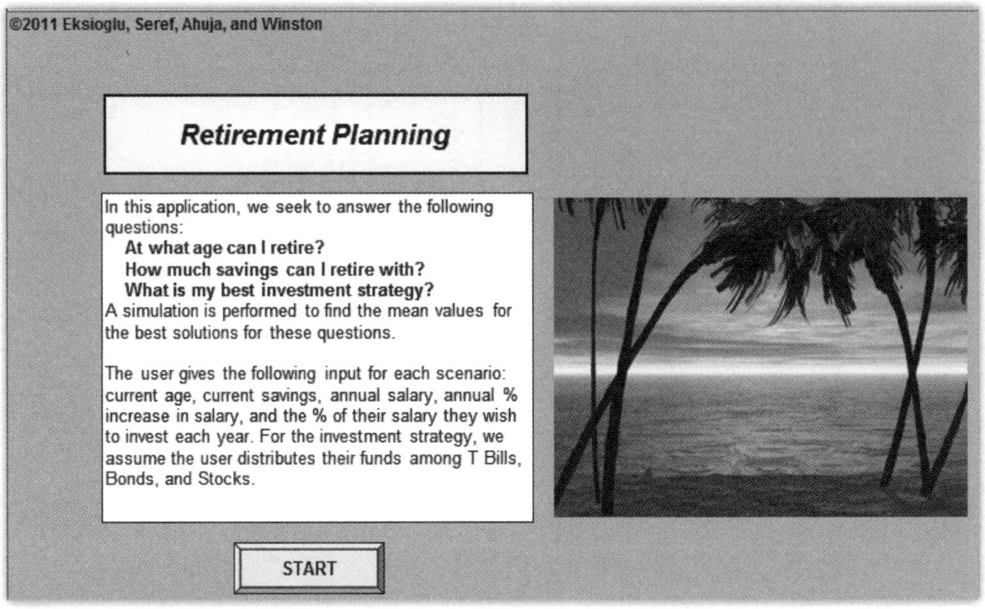

Figure CS9.6 The welcome sheet.

The simulation calculations sheet performs the calculations described in section CS9.1.1. (See Figure CS9.7.) This sheet is initially hidden from the users, although the users have the option to view this sheet by pressing a button on the results sheet.

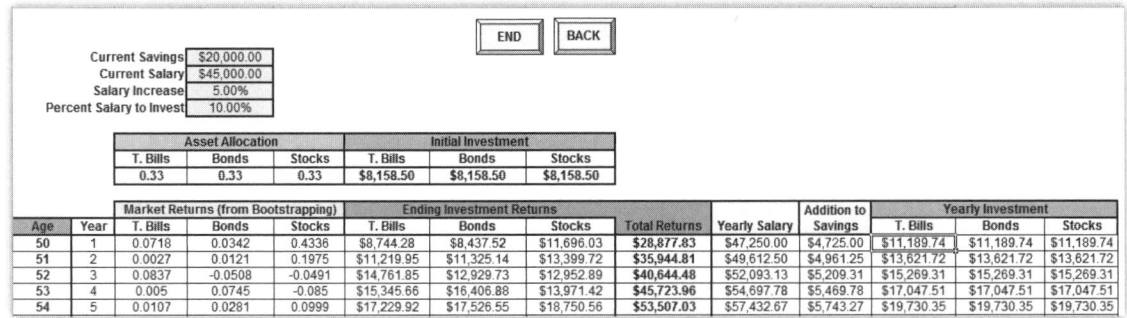

END BACK

Current Savings	$20,000.00
Current Salary	$45,000.00
Salary Increase	5.00%
Percent Salary to Invest	10.00%

Asset Allocation			Initial Investment		
T. Bills	Bonds	Stocks	T. Bills	Bonds	Stocks
0.33	0.33	0.33	$8,158.50	$8,158.50	$8,158.50

		Market Returns (from Bootstrapping)			Ending Investment Returns					Addition to	Yearly Investment		
Age	Year	T. Bills	Bonds	Stocks	T. Bills	Bonds	Stocks	Total Returns	Yearly Salary	Savings	T. Bills	Bonds	Stocks
50	1	0.0718	0.0342	0.4336	$8,744.28	$8,437.52	$11,696.03	**$28,877.83**	$47,250.00	$4,725.00	$11,189.74	$11,189.74	$11,189.74
51	2	0.0027	0.0121	0.1975	$11,219.95	$11,325.14	$13,399.72	**$35,944.81**	$49,612.50	$4,961.25	$13,621.72	$13,621.72	$13,621.72
52	3	0.0837	-0.0508	-0.0491	$14,761.85	$12,929.73	$12,952.89	**$40,644.48**	$52,093.13	$5,209.31	$15,269.31	$15,269.31	$15,269.31
53	4	0.005	0.0745	-0.085	$15,345.66	$16,406.88	$13,971.42	**$45,723.96**	$54,697.78	$5,469.78	$17,047.51	$17,047.51	$17,047.51
54	5	0.0107	0.0281	0.0999	$17,229.92	$17,526.55	$18,750.56	**$53,507.03**	$57,432.67	$5,743.27	$19,730.35	$19,730.35	$19,730.35

Figure CS9.7 The simulation calculations sheet.

The simulation runs sheet contains the outputs for each trial of the simulation. For option A, the age of retirement is recorded for each run. [See Figure CS9.8 (a).] For option B, the savings at retirement is recorded for each run. For option C, the savings at retirement is also recorded for each run for the best investment strategy identified by the sensitivity analysis. [See Figure CS9.8 (b).]

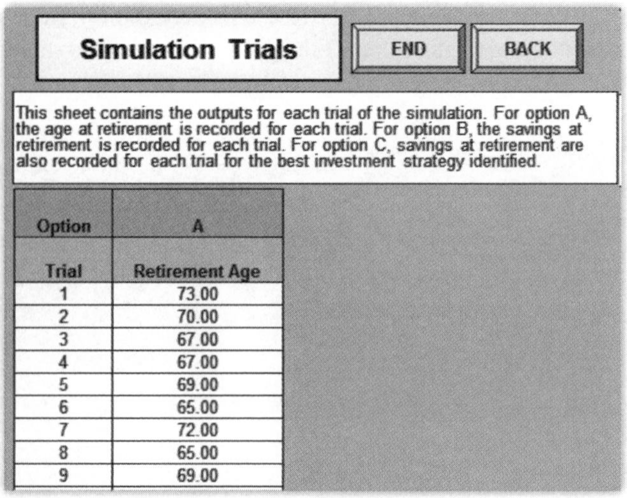

Option	A
Trial	Retirement Age
1	73.00
2	70.00
3	67.00
4	67.00
5	69.00
6	65.00
7	72.00
8	65.00
9	69.00

(a)

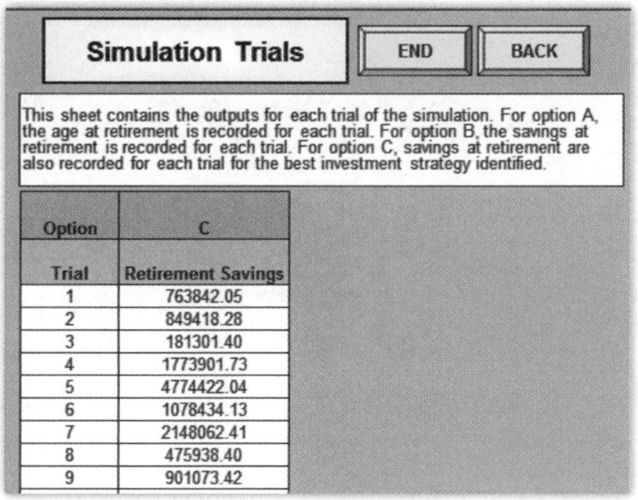

Option	C
Trial	Retirement Savings
1	763842.05
2	849418.28
3	181301.40
4	1773901.73
5	4774422.04
6	1078434.13
7	2148062.41
8	475938.40
9	901073.42

(b)

Figure CS9.8 The simulation runs sheet.

The results sheet displays the mean and standard deviation of the solutions for the selected option. It also shows a corresponding histogram of the values of the simulation runs. For option A, for the given desired returns and the confidence interval, the mean and standard deviation of the retirement age values are presented with the corresponding histogram. [See Figure CS9.9 (a).] For option B, for the given retirement age, the mean and standard deviation of the savings values are presented with the corresponding histogram. [See Figure CS9.9 (b).] For option C, the mean and standard deviation of the savings for the best asset allocation strategy are presented with the corresponding histogram (as in option B) along with the mean and standard deviation values for 30 asset allocation strategies. [See Figure CS9.5.]

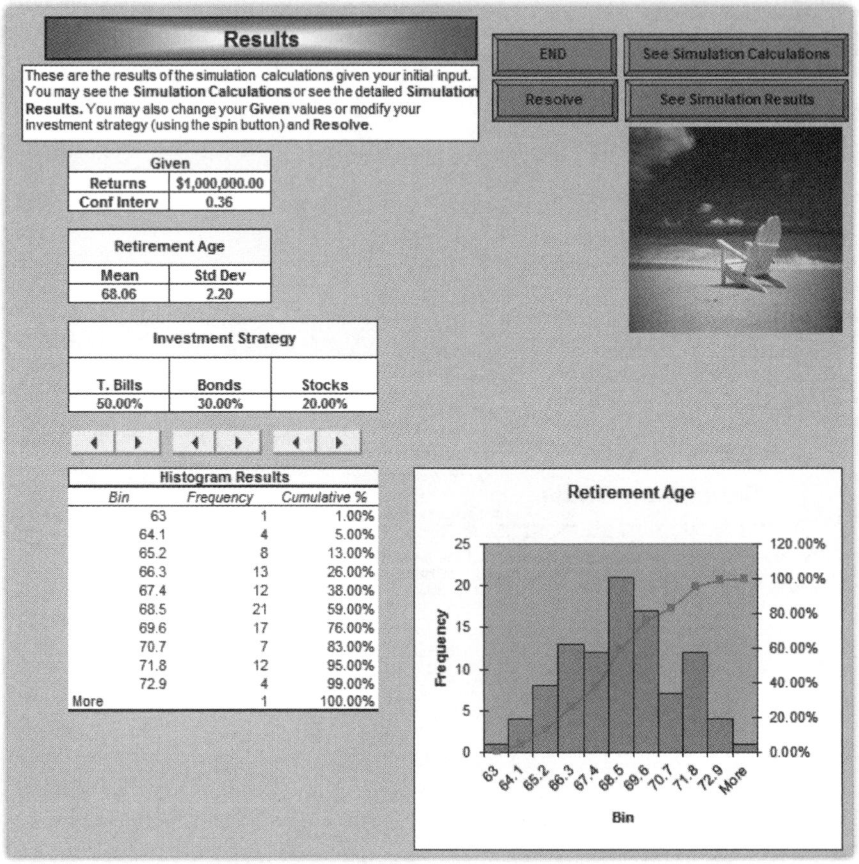

(a)

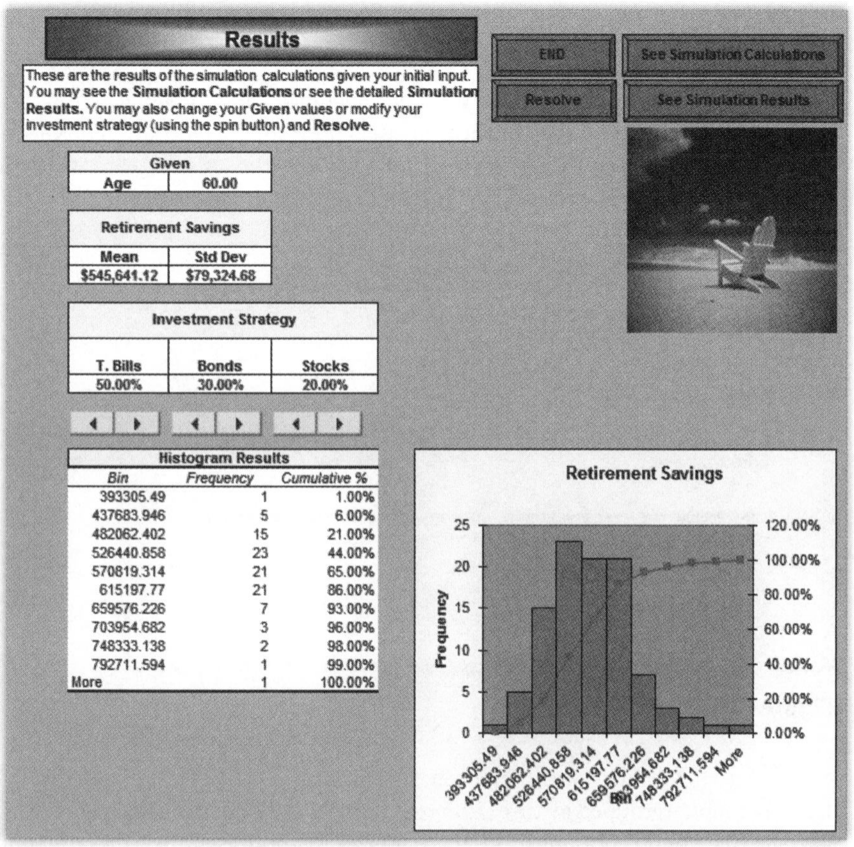

Given	
Age	60.00

Retirement Savings	
Mean	Std Dev
$545,641.12	$79,324.68

Investment Strategy		
T. Bills	Bonds	Stocks
50.00%	30.00%	20.00%

Histogram Results		
Bin	*Frequency*	*Cumulative %*
393305.49	1	1.00%
437683.946	5	6.00%
482062.402	15	21.00%
526440.858	23	44.00%
570819.314	21	65.00%
615197.77	21	86.00%
659576.226	7	93.00%
703954.682	3	96.00%
748333.138	2	98.00%
792711.594	1	99.00%
More	1	100.00%

(b)

Figure CS9.9 The results sheet.

Summary

Welcome sheet	Contains the application description and the "Start" button.
Simulation calculations sheet	Where the simulation calculations are performed for each run.
Simulation runs sheet	Where the simulation results are recorded for each simulation trial.
Results sheet	Displays the mean and standard deviation of the results from the simulation trials with a corresponding histogram of these values.

CS9.3 User Interface

For this application's user interface, we use navigational and functional buttons, two user forms, and controls on the worksheet. When the users press the "Start" button on the welcome sheet, the options form appears. (See Figure CS9.10.) It allows the users to select which option to solve (A, B, or C), and it requires a frame and three option buttons.

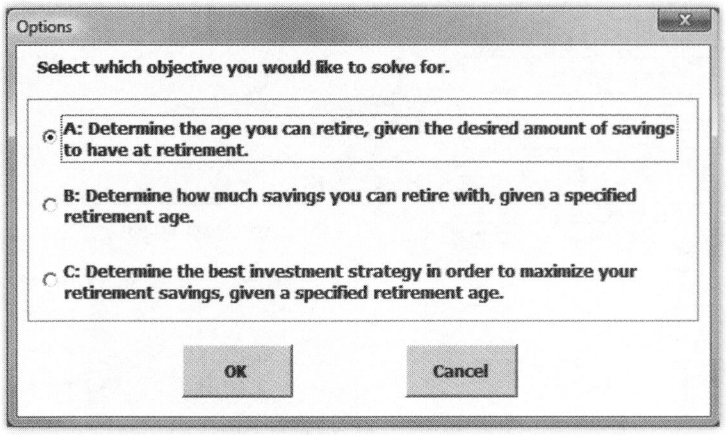

Figure CS9.10 The options form.

The users then view the input form. (See Figure CS9.11.) This is a dynamic form in that the last set of input (grouped by three different frames) is different depending on which option the users selected on the options form. If the users select option A, then they are prompted for the desired savings at retirement and the confidence interval. [See Figure CS9.11 (a).] If the users select option B, then the frame containing this input is replaced by a frame that prompts the users for the age at which they wish to retire. [See Figure CS9.11 (b).] If the users selects option C, then the last frame with the asset allocation becomes locked and grayed. [See Figure CS9.11 (c).]

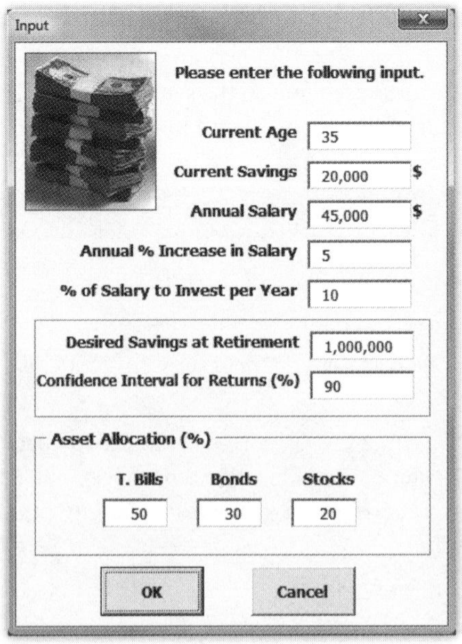

(a)

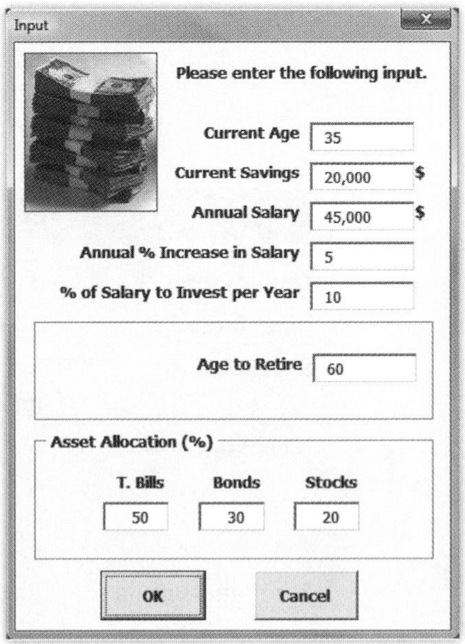

(b)

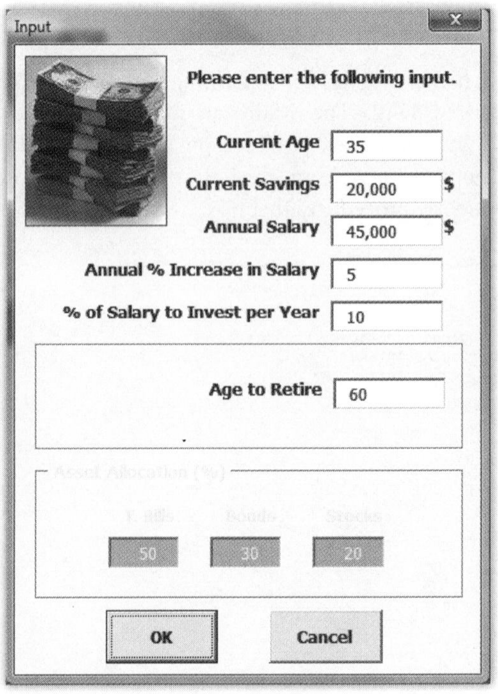

(c)

Figure CS9.11 The input forms.

On the results sheet, for options A and B, we use spin buttons to allow the users to modify their investment strategy and re-solve the application by pressing the "Re-solve" button. For option C, the user can change the asset allocation scheme on the sensitivity analysis results table and click "Re-solve" button. We will discuss this in more detail in Section CS9.5.

Summary

Options form	The users choose among options A, B, and C.
Input form	The users provide input for the selected option.
Spin buttons	Change the asset allocations on the results sheet for the re-solve option.
Navigational buttons	"Start" on the welcome sheet, "End" on all the sheets, "Back" on the simulation calculations and simulation runs sheets, and "See Simulation Calculations" and "See Simulation Results" buttons on the results sheet.
Functional button	"Re-solve" on the results sheet.

CS9.4 Procedures

We will now outline the procedures for this application beginning with the variable declarations and initial sub procedures. (See Figure CS9.12.) The "Main" procedure, which is called from the "Start" button, calls the "ClearPrev" procedure to clear the previous values from all the sheets. The "Main" procedure then displays the option form (from which the input form is shown). It ends by calling the "RunSim" and "CreateReport" procedures that takes the users to the results sheet.

```
Option Explicit
Option Base 1

Public SolveA As Boolean, SolveB As Boolean, SolveC As Boolean, _
RetSav As Double, RetAge As Integer, runs As Integer, _
strategyNr As Integer, row As Integer, OutputFormula As String

Sub Main()
    Call ClearPrev

    frmOptions.Show
    'frmInput.show from Options form

    Call RunSim
    Call CreateReport

    Worksheets("Results").Visible = True
    Worksheets("Welcome").Visible = False
    Range("A1").Select
End Sub

Sub ClearPrev()
    Worksheets("SimRuns").Range("SimResults").ClearContents
    Range(Range("Strategy").Offset(1, 5), Range("Strategy"). _
            Offset(1, 5).End(xlDown)).ClearContents

    SolveA = False
    SolveB = False
    SolveC = False
End Sub
```

Figure CS9.12 The variable declarations and the "Main" and "ClearPrev" procedures.

Using Boolean variables, the procedures for the option form record which option the users have selected. (See Figure CS9.13.) These procedures also perform dynamic formatting for the input form.

```
Private Sub cmdCancel_Click()
    Unload Me
    End
End Sub

Private Sub cmdOK_Click()
    If optA Then
        SolveA = True
        frmInput.fraA.Visible = True
    ElseIf optB Then
        SolveB = True
        frmInput.fraB.Visible = True
    ElseIf optC Then
        SolveC = True
        frmInput.fraB.Visible = True
        With frmInput.fraAsset  'grey and lock
            .ForeColor = &H8000000B
            .txtSBonds.BackColor = &H8000000B
            .txtSStocks.BackColor = &H8000000B
            .txtSTBills.BackColor = &H8000000B
            .lblTBills.ForeColor = &H8000000B
            .lblBonds.ForeColor = &H8000000B
            .lblStocks.ForeColor = &H8000000B
            .txtSBonds.Locked = True
            .txtSStocks.Locked = True
            .txtSTBills.Locked = True
        End With
        Range("StrategyTable").Copy
        Range("Strategy").Offset(1, 1).PasteSpecial xlPasteValues
    End If

    Unload Me
    frmInput.Show
End Sub

Private Sub UserForm_Initialize()
    With frmInput
        .fraA.Visible = False
        .fraB.Visible = False
        With .fraAsset  'white and unlock
            .ForeColor = &H80000012
            .txtSBonds.BackColor = &H80000005
            .txtSStocks.BackColor = &H80000005
            .txtSTBills.BackColor = &H80000005
            .lblTBills.ForeColor = &H80000012
            .lblBonds.ForeColor = &H80000012
            .lblStocks.ForeColor = &H80000012
            .txtSBonds.Locked = False
            .txtSStocks.Locked = False
            .txtSTBills.Locked = False
        End With
    End With
End Sub
```

Figure CS9.13 The option form procedures.

The procedures for the input form perform some error checking for the text boxes and then record the input for the selected option. (See Figure CS9.14.) Most input values are recorded directly to the simulation calculations sheet. Because they will be checked during the simulation code, the desired savings (for option A) and the retirement age (for options B and C) are stored in variables.

```
Private Sub cmdCancel_Click()
    Unload Me
    End
End Sub

Private Sub cmdOK_Click()
    'check that all text boxes filled
    Dim ctl As Control
    For Each ctl In Me.Controls
        If TypeName(ctl) = "TextBox" Then
            If IsNumeric(ctl.Value) = False Then
                MsgBox "Please enter a numeric value for all input."
                Exit Sub
                ctl.SetFocus
            End If
        End If
    Next

    With Worksheets("SimCalc")
        .Range("CurrAge").Value = txtCurrAge.Value
        .Range("CurrSav").Value = txtCurrSav.Value
        .Range("CurrSal").Value = txtAnnSal.Value
        .Range("SalInc").Value = txtSalInc.Value / 100
        .Range("SalInv").Value = txtPerInv.Value / 100

        If SolveA Then
            RetSav = txtRetSav.Value
            Worksheets("SimRuns").Range("Alpha").Value = 1 - txtCI.Value / 100
        ElseIf SolveB Or SolveC Then
            RetAge = txtRetAge.Value
        End If

        If SolveA Or SolveB Then
            .Range("Alloc").Cells(1).Value = txtSTBills.Value / 100
            .Range("Alloc").Cells(2).Value = txtSBonds.Value / 100
            .Range("Alloc").Cells(3).Value = txtSStocks.Value / 100
        End If
    End With

    Unload Me
End Sub
```

Figure CS9.14 The input form procedures.

The "RunSim" procedure performs the simulation. For options A and B, we simply loop for the 100 runs and update the formulas on the simulation calculations sheet by typing the command "Calculate." We record the results of each run by taking the values on the row specified by the users' input for the selected option. [See Figure CS9.15 (a).] For option C, we first initialize the simulation model. Next, we perform 30 simulation runs, one for each investment strategy identified. For each run we perform 100 simulation trials. The summary results from these simulation runs are sorted to identify the best strategy. For the best strategy, we re-run the simulation, and print the corresponding results [See Figure CS9.15 (b).] We need these results to build the corresponding histogram of retirement savings.

```
Sub RunSim()
    Dim MySimProb As New RSP.Problem

    Application.ScreenUpdating = False
    Worksheets("SimCalc").Activate

    If SolveA Then
        Worksheets("SimRuns").Range("RunVal").Offset(-1, 0).Value = "A"
        Worksheets("SimRuns").Range("RunVal").Value = "Retirement Age"
        Range(Range("BigRuns"), Range("BigRuns").Offset(0, 20)).Columns.Hidden = True
        For runs = 1 To 100
            'search for row with desired return
            row = Application.WorksheetFunction.Match(RetSav, Range("TotalReturns"), 1)
            Worksheets("SimRuns").Range("RunVal").Offset(runs, 0).Value = _
                    Range("Age").Cells(row + 1).Value
            Calculate
        Next

    ElseIf SolveB Then
        Worksheets("SimRuns").Range("RunVal").Offset(-1, 0).Value = "B"
        Worksheets("SimRuns").Range("RunVal").Value = "Retirement Savings"
        Range(Range("BigRuns"), Range("BigRuns").Offset(0, 20)).Columns.Hidden = True
        For runs = 1 To 100
            'search for row with retirement age
            row = Application.WorksheetFunction.Match(RetAge, Range("Age"), 0)
            Worksheets("SimRuns").Range("RunVal").Offset(runs, 0).Value = _
                    Range("TotalReturns").Cells(row).Value
            Calculate
        Next
    ElseIf SolveC Then 'using Risk solver platform
        Worksheets("SimRuns").Range("RunVal").Offset(-1, 0).Value = "C"
        Worksheets("SimRuns").Range("RunVal").Value = "Retirement Savings"
```

(a)

```
            Calculate
        Next
    ElseIf SolveC Then 'using Risk solver platform
        Worksheets("SimRuns").Range("RunVal").Offset(-1, 0).Value = "C"
        Worksheets("SimRuns").Range("RunVal").Value = "Retirement Savings"
        Range(Range("Strategy"), Range("Strategy").Offset(0, 20)).Columns.Hidden = False
        'setup simulation model in RSP
        row = Application.WorksheetFunction.Match(RetAge, Range("Age"), 0)
        OutputFormula = Range("TotalReturns").Cells(row).Formula
        Range("TotalReturns").Cells(row).Formula = _
                Range("TotalReturns").Cells(row).Formula + "+PsiOutput()"
        MySimProb.Init ActiveWorkbook
        MySimProb.Solver.NumTrials = 100
        MySimProb.Solver.NumSimulations = 1
        'run simulation for each investment strategy
        For strategyNr = 1 To 30
            On Error Resume Next
            Range("AllocTBills").Value = Range("Strategy").Offset(strategyNr, 1).Value
            Range("AllocBonds").Value = Range("Strategy").Offset(strategyNr, 2).Value
            Range("AllocStocks").Value = Range("Strategy").Offset(strategyNr, 3).Value
            MySimProb.Solver.Simulate
            Range("Strategy").Offset(strategyNr, 4).Value = MySimProb.Functions(0).Statistics.Mean(0)
            Range("Strategy").Offset(strategyNr, 5).Value = MySimProb.Functions(0).Statistics.StdDev(0)
        Next strategyNr
        Range("TotalReturns").Cells(row).Formula = OutputFormula
        'sort the results of simulation based on mean returns
        Range(Range("Strategy").Offset(1, 1), Range("Strategy").Offset(1, 5).End(xlDown)). _
                Sort Range("Strategy").Offset(1, 4), xlDescending
        're-run the simulation for the best investment strategy
        Range("AllocTBills").Value = Range("Strategy").Offset(1, 1).Value
        Range("AllocBonds").Value = Range("Strategy").Offset(1, 2).Value
        Range("AllocStocks").Value = Range("Strategy").Offset(1, 3).Value
        MySimProb.Solver.Simulate
        For runs = 1 To 100
            Worksheets("SimRuns").Range("RunVal").Offset(runs, 0).Value = _
                MySimProb.Functions(0).AllTrials(0, runs - 1)
        Next runs
        Set MySimProb = Nothing
    End If

    Application.ScreenUpdating = True
End Sub
```

(b)

Figure CS9.15 The "RunSim" procedure.

The "CreateReport" procedure displays the mean and standard deviation values for the selected option. (See Figure CS9.16.) Some rows are hidden and unhidden, and the spin buttons are made visible and invisible depending on which option is selected. The histogram of simulation run values is also created.

```
Sub CreateReport()
    Worksheets("Results").Activate

    If SolveA Then
        Range("Given").Value = "Desired Returns"
        Range("Given").Offset(0, 1).Value = RetSav
        Range("Given").Offset(0, 1).NumberFormat = "$#,##0.00"
        Range("ConInt").Rows.Hidden = False
        Range("Found").Value = "Retirement Age"
        Worksheets("SimCalc").Range("Alloc").Copy
        Range("Invest").Offset(2, 0).PasteSpecial xlPasteValues

        Range("UserInvest").Rows.Hidden = False
        With Worksheets("Results")
            .spnTBills.Visible = True
            .spnStocks.Visible = True
            .spnBonds.Visible = True
        End With
        'mean age, std dev age, CI
        With Range("FoundVal")
            .Offset(0, 0).NumberFormat = "##.00"
            .Offset(0, 1).NumberFormat = "##.00"
        End With

    ElseIf SolveB Then
        Range("Given").Value = "Retirement Age"
        Range("Given").Offset(0, 1).Value = RetAge
        Range("Given").Offset(0, 1).NumberFormat = "#,##0.00"
        Range("ConInt").Rows.Hidden = True
        Range("Found").Value = "Retirement Savings"
        Worksheets("SimCalc").Range("Alloc").Copy
        Range("Invest").Offset(2, 0).PasteSpecial xlPasteValues

        Range("UserInvest").Rows.Hidden = False
        With Worksheets("Results")
            .spnTBills.Visible = True
            .spnStocks.Visible = True
            .spnBonds.Visible = True
        End With
        'mean returns, std dev returns
        With Range("FoundVal")
            .Offset(0, 0).NumberFormat = "$#,##0.00"
            .Offset(0, 1).NumberFormat = "$#,##0.00"
        End With

    ElseIf SolveC Then
        Range("Given").Value = "Retirement Age"
        Range("Given").Offset(0, 1).Value = RetAge
```

(a)

```
        End With

    ElseIf SolveC Then
        Range("Given").Value = "Retirement Age"
        Range("Given").Offset(0, 1).Value = RetAge
        Range("Given").Offset(0, 1).NumberFormat = "#,##0.00"
        Range("ConInt").Rows.Hidden = True
        Range("Found").Value = "Retirement Savings"
        'optimal Values for x1, x2, x3
        With Range("FoundVal")
            .Offset(0, 0).NumberFormat = "$#,##0.00"
            .Offset(0, 1).NumberFormat = "$#,##0.00"
        End With
        Range("UserInvest").Rows.Hidden = False
        With Worksheets("Results")
            .spnTBills.Visible = False
            .spnStocks.Visible = False
            .spnBonds.Visible = False
        End With
        Range("TBills").Value = Range("Strategy").Offset(1, 1).Value
        Range("Bonds").Value = Range("Strategy").Offset(1, 2).Value
        Range("Stocks").Value = Range("Strategy").Offset(1, 3).Value
    End If

    'create histogram
    Range(Range("HistOutput"), Range("HistOutput").End(xlDown).End(xlToRight)).ClearContents
    Application.Run "ATPVBAEN.XLAM!Histogram", Worksheets("SimRuns").Range("SimResults"), _
        Worksheets("Results").Range("HistOutput"), , False, True, False, False
    Worksheets("Results").Activate
    ActiveSheet.ChartObjects(1).Select
    ActiveChart.ChartTitle.Characters.Text = Range("Found").Value
    Range(Range("HistOutput"), Range("HistOutput").End(xlDown). _
            End(xlToRight)).Interior.ColorIndex = 2
    Range("A1").Select
End Sub
```

(b)

Figure CS9.16 The "CreateReport" procedure.

Figure CS9.17 presents the navigational procedures.

```
Sub EndProg()
    Worksheets("Welcome").Visible = True
    ActiveSheet.Visible = False
End Sub

Sub SeeCalc()
    Worksheets("SimCalc").Visible = True
    Worksheets("Results").Visible = False
End Sub

Sub SeeRuns()
    Worksheets("SimRuns").Visible = True
    Worksheets("Results").Visible = False
End Sub

Sub GoBack()
    Worksheets("Results").Visible = True
    ActiveSheet.Visible = False
End Sub
```

Figure CS9.17 The navigational procedures.

Summary

Main	Initializes the application and shows the users the option form.
ClearPrev	Clears the previous values on all the sheets.
Option form procedures	Record the users' option.
Input form procedures	Record the users' input for the selected option.
RunSim	Performs the simulation calculations for the selected option.
CreateReport	Displays the results for the selected option.
Navigational procedures	Apply to the "End," "Back," "See Simulation Calculations," and "See Simulation Results" buttons.

CS9.5 Re-solve Options

The users can re-solve this application by pressing the "Re-solve" button on the results sheet. For options A and B, the users can change their asset allocation with the provided spin buttons (or by typing directly in these cells). [See Figures CS9.9 (a) and (b).] The users can also change the input values in the "Given" table by typing directly into these cells. For option C, the user can change the investment strategies listed in the corresponding table. We have set validation rules in the spreadsheet to ensure that the asset allocation inputs from the user are positive numbers between 0% and 100%.

When the users press the "Re-solve" button, the "Re-solve" procedure is called. (See Figure CS9.18.) This procedure begins by recording any changes to the input cells. Before changes to the investment strategy are recorded, the procedure ensures that the updated investment strategy still sums to 100%. Finally, the application re-calls the "RunSim" and "CreateReport" procedures.

```
Sub Resolve()
    'record new input and resolve
    With Worksheets("SimCalc")
        If SolveA Then
            RetSav = Range("Given").Offset(0, 1).Value
        ElseIf SolveB Or SolveC Then
            RetAge = Range("Given").Offset(0, 1).Value
        End If

        If SolveA Or SolveB Then
            'check that investment strategy still sums to 100%
            If Application.WorksheetFunction.Sum(Range("UserInvest")) <> 1 Then
                MsgBox "Investment strategy must sum to 100%.", _
                        vbExclamation, "Investment Strategy Error"
                Exit Sub
            End If
            'record new values
            .Range("Alloc").Cells(1).Value = Range("Tbills").Value
            .Range("Alloc").Cells(2).Value = Range("Bonds").Value
            .Range("Alloc").Cells(3).Value = Range("Stocks").Value
        ElseIf SolveC Then
           'check that investment strategy still sums to 100%
            For strategyNr = 1 To 30
                If Application.WorksheetFunction.Sum(Range(Range("Strategy"). _
                    Offset(strategyNr, 1), Range("Strategy").Offset(strategyNr, 3))) <> 1 Then
                    MsgBox "Investment strategy " & strategyNr & " must sum to 100%.", _
                            vbExclamation, "Investment Strategy Error"
                    Exit Sub
                End If
            Next strategyNr
        End If
    End With
    Call RunSim
    Call CreateReport
End Sub
```

Figure CS9.18 The "Re-solve" procedure.

Summary	
"Re-solve" button on the results sheet	Calls the "Re-solve" procedure to record the updated input values and to re-run the simulation calculations.

CS9.6 *Summary*

- This application helps the users answer the following questions: (i) At what age can I retire?; (ii) How much savings can I retire with?; and (iii) What is my best investment strategy? Simulation calculations for the selected option answer these questions.
- This application requires four worksheets: the welcome sheet, the simulation calculations sheet, the simulation runs sheet, and the results sheet.
- For this application's user interface, we use navigational and functional buttons, two user forms, and controls on the worksheet.
- Several application procedures perform the simulation calculations for the selected option. We use Risk Solver Platform to perform simulation runs and collect corresponding statistics.
- The users can re-solve this application by pressing the "Re-solve" button to re-run the simulation with updated input values.

CS9.7 *Extensions*

1. Recall the RunSim() procedure for option C (Figure CS9.15 (b)). We use a *For Next* loop to perform 30 simulation runs of different investment strategies. Alternatively, you can use the *PsiSimParam()* function to perform these 30 simulation runs. During each simulation run, asset allocation schema would change based on the investment strategies we have identified. Change this current procedure so that we can use the *PsiSimParam()* function instead of the loop.
2. Recall the RunSim() procedure (Figure CS9.15 (a) and (b)). Suppose that we cannot use Risk Solver Platform to perform the simulation runs required to identify the best investment strategy. How will you modify this procedure so that we can still randomly generate asset returns, and perform the simulations required by this application?
3. Figure CS9.5 presents the results of the sensitivity analyses. The user can change the allocation of assets in this table, and then resolve option C to identify better investment strategies. Suppose that we do not want the user to make changes to this table, in other words, we want this worksheet protected. How should you change the RunSim() procedure to take care of the fact that this worksheet is protected from the user, but still certain updates need to be performed when you run this code?
4. Give the users the option to re-solve the application by changing their option selection. What other re-solve options can be added?
5. Is there another option (aside from options A, B, and C) that can be considered in this application? How would you implement this to the simulation calculations sheet and procedures?

CASE STUDY

ten Queuing Simulation: Single Server and Multi Server

chapter OVERVIEW

CS10.1 *Single Server Queuing Model Simulation*

Queuing theory is an important branch of operation research that has numerous applications in service and manufacturing settings. This application simulates a queue of customers serviced by a single server. The application provides histograms of average waiting times in queue and average server utilization over a large number of simulation trials.

CS10.1.1 Model Definition and Assumptions

The application assumes exponentially distributed customer inter-arrival times and customer service times. The users provide the means of these density functions. We setup a simulation spreadsheet model that makes use of the information entered by the user to calculate waiting time in queue, time in the system for each customer and server utilization. Figure CS10.1 presents the Simulation spreadsheet model.

To complete this spreadsheet model we generate customer inter-arrival and service times using the *PsiExponential()* function. We use inter-arrival times to calculate customer arrival time in the system. Arrival time for customer i is the sum of inter-arrival times of customers 1 to $i-1$. The times at which each customer's service begins and ends are then calculated. The first customer begins service upon her arrival in the system. The time at which customer i service begins is the maximum value between her arrival time and the time at which the preceding customer's service ends. The time at which a customer's service ends is simply the sum of the time at which the service begins and the service time. The following formulas generate and store these values for the *2*-nd customer. These formulas are then copied and pasted to the remaining of the spreadsheet.

Cell B11: = PsiExponential($B$6)
C11: = C10 + B11
D11: = MAX(C11,F10)
E11: = PsiExponential($D$6)
F11: = D11 + E11
G11: = D11 − C11
H11: = F11 − C11

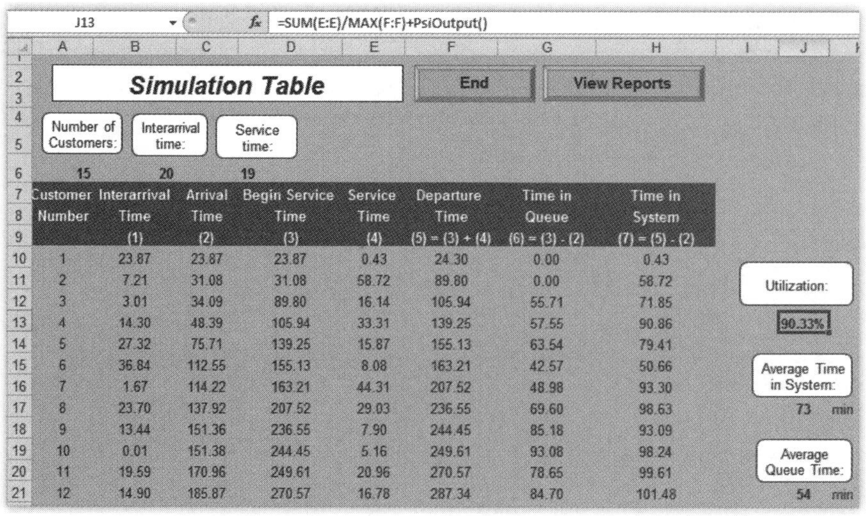

Customer Number	Interarrival Time (1)	Arrival Time (2)	Begin Service Time (3)	Service Time (4)	Departure Time (5) = (3) + (4)	Time in Queue (6) = (3) - (2)	Time in System (7) = (5) - (2)
1	23.87	23.87	23.87	0.43	24.30	0.00	0.43
2	7.21	31.08	31.08	58.72	89.80	0.00	58.72
3	3.01	34.09	89.80	16.14	105.94	55.71	71.85
4	14.30	48.39	105.94	33.31	139.25	57.55	90.86
5	27.32	75.71	139.25	15.87	155.13	63.54	79.41
6	36.84	112.55	155.13	8.08	163.21	42.57	50.66
7	1.67	114.22	163.21	44.31	207.52	48.98	93.30
8	23.70	137.92	207.52	29.03	236.55	69.60	98.63
9	13.44	151.36	236.55	7.90	244.45	85.18	93.09
10	0.01	151.38	244.45	5.16	249.61	93.08	98.24
11	19.59	170.96	249.61	20.96	270.57	78.65	99.61
12	14.90	185.87	270.57	16.78	287.34	84.70	101.48

Figure CS10.1 The Simulation spreadsheet setup.

In the Simulation spreadsheet we also calculate the average server utilization during a simulation trial, average time in the queue, and average time in the system. The following formulas are used to calculate these averages:

Server Utilization (J13):	*=SUM(E:E)/MAX(F:F) + PsiOutput()*
Average Time in System (J17):	*=AVERAGE(H:H)+PsiOutput()*
Average Queue Time (J21):	*=AVERAGE(G:G)+PsiOutput()*

The *PsiOutput()* function is used by Risk Solver Platform to indicate that these are output cells of the simulation. In the Report Summary spreadsheet we use then the *PsiMean()*, *PsiMax()* and *PsiMin()* functions to calculate the mean, maximum and minimum values of waiting time, time in system and utilization overall simulation trials. The only argument of these functions is the address of an output cell. For example, *PsiMean(J13)* calculates the mean utilization overall simulation runs.

We use the data from the table in the Simulation worksheet to create a timeline of simulation events. This timeline is located on a hidden data sheet (See Figure CS10.2.). Note that we are animating one single simulation trial. The main reason for animating one trial is to give the user a visual display of how the simulation works, without greatly impacting the computational time of this application. In this hidden spreadsheet we also store data we later use to create the charts displayed in the Report Summary spreadsheet.

Data

Time:	Activity:	Time:	Queue Length:	Customer:	Waiting Time:
44	Arrival	44.14	0.00	1.00	0.00
44	BeginServe	44.14	1.00	2.00	0.00
44	EndServe	44.29	0.00	3.00	5.08
63	Arrival	63.36	0.00	4.00	0.00
63	BeginServe	63.36	1.00	5.00	0.00
75	Arrival	74.86	0.00	6.00	0.00
80	EndServe	79.94	1.00	7.00	0.00
80	BeginServe	79.94	1.00	8.00	20.91

Figure CS10.2 The hidden data sheet with the simulation timeline and other data required to create charts.

In the Animation spreadsheet, the yellow cells represent customers moving through the queue. A customer initially arrives to a queue line; if the server is "Idle," then the customer moves to the server and begin service; if the server is "Busy," then the customer stays in the queue until the server becomes "Idle" again. (See Figure CS10.3.)

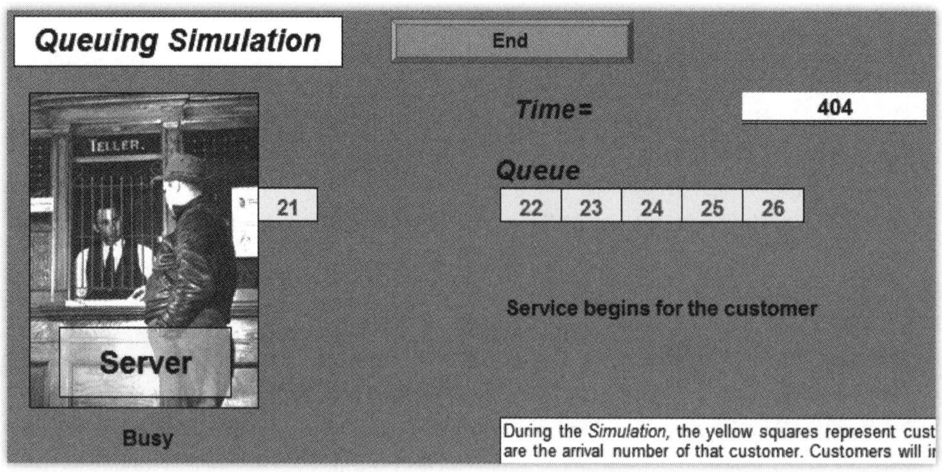

Figure CS10.3 Simulation animation on the animation sheet.

When the simulation is complete, the users can begin a new problem or view a report. This report contains histograms of average customer waiting times and server utilization overall simulation trials along with other statistics. We also chart the queue length and waiting time in queue for the last simulation trial. For more details on queuing models, please see *Introduction to Operations Research* by Winston.

CS10.1.2 Input

The input for this application is the following:

- Number of customers for which to perform the simulation
- Mean inter-arrival time per customer (assuming exponential distribution)
- Mean service time per customer (assuming exponential distribution)

CS10.1.3 Output

The output for this application is the following:

- Maximum, minimum, and average waiting time per customer
- Maximum, minimum, and average queue length per unit time
- Maximum, minimum, and average time in the system
- Maximum, minimum, and average server utilization
- Histogram of the average waiting times over all simulation trials
- Histogram of the average server utilization over all simulation trials
- Chart of the waiting time per customer in the last simulation trial
- Chart of the queue lengths over all the time units in the last simulation trial
- Detailed statistics of the waiting times, server utilization and the queue lengths

CS10.2 *Worksheets*

This application requires four sheets: the welcome sheet, the simulation sheet, the animation sheet and the report summary sheet. (There is also a fifth hidden sheet, which creates the timeline described in the previous section; see Figure CS10.2.) The welcome sheet contains the title, the description of the application, and the "Start" button. (See Figure CS10.4.) The "Start" button takes the users to the animation sheet.

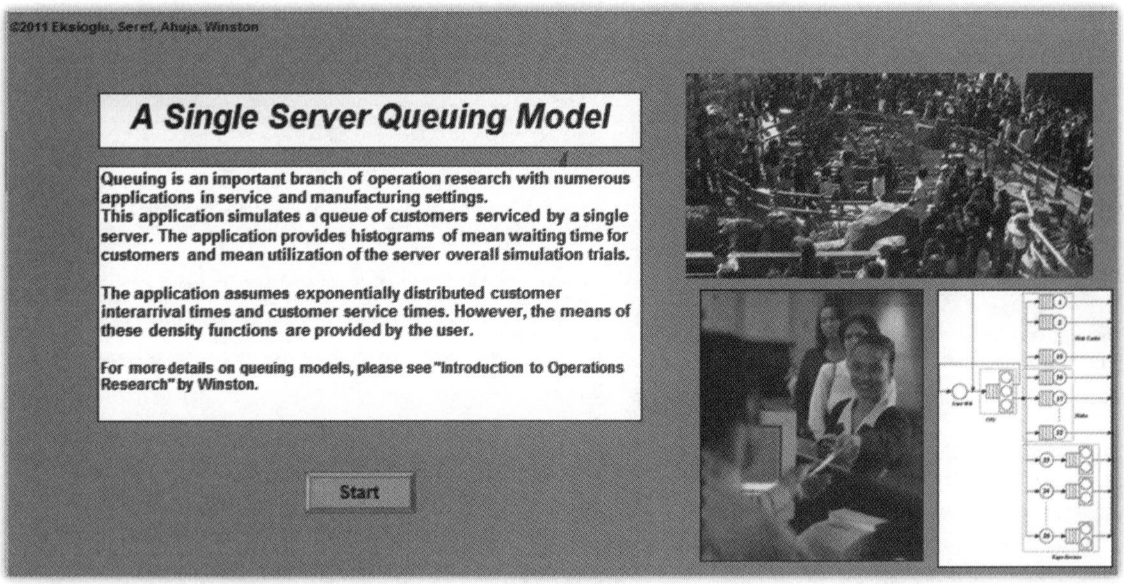

Figure CS10.4 The welcome sheet.

The animation is performed on the animation sheet. (See Figure CS10.5.) For the animation, we format cells to be yellow and with customer numbers to represent customers moving through the queue. The queue area is titled "Queue." A customer initially arrives to the "Queue." If the server is "Idle," then the customer moves to the server and begins service. If the server is "Busy," then the customer stays in the queue until the server becomes "Idle" again. The "Time" is also updated as the simulation is performed. A statement below the "Queue" describes to the users the current action at the given time. For example, in Figure CS10.5 (a), a customer (Customer 16) has just arrived to the queue; Customer 13 is currently being served. When the simulation is complete, two new buttons appear to allow the users to view the report or to solve a new problem. [See Figure CS10.5 (b).]

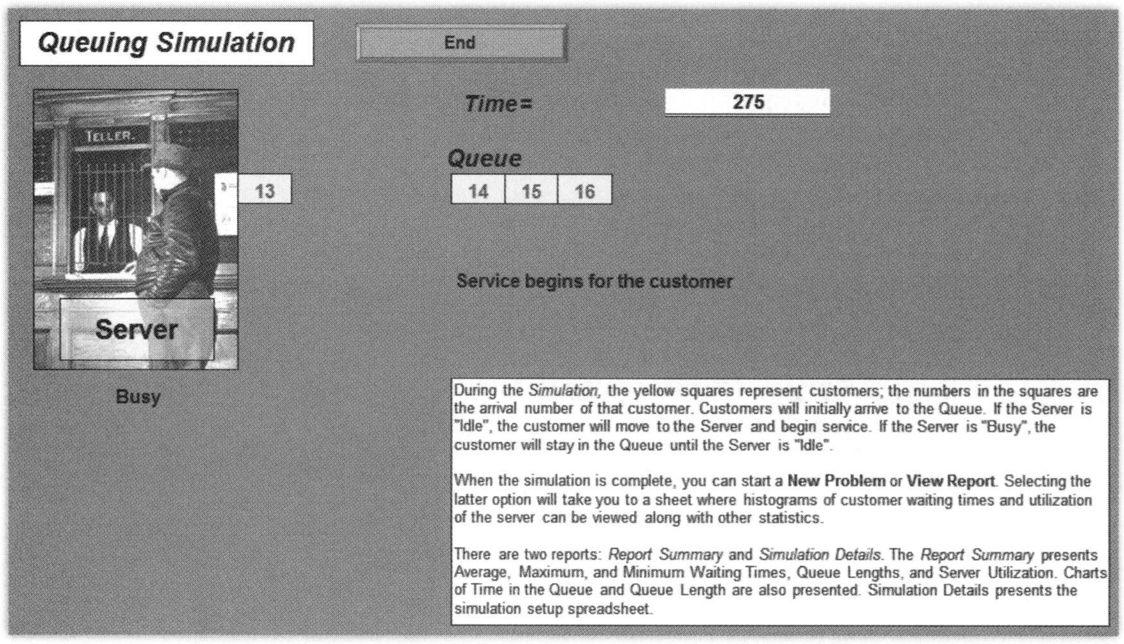

(a)

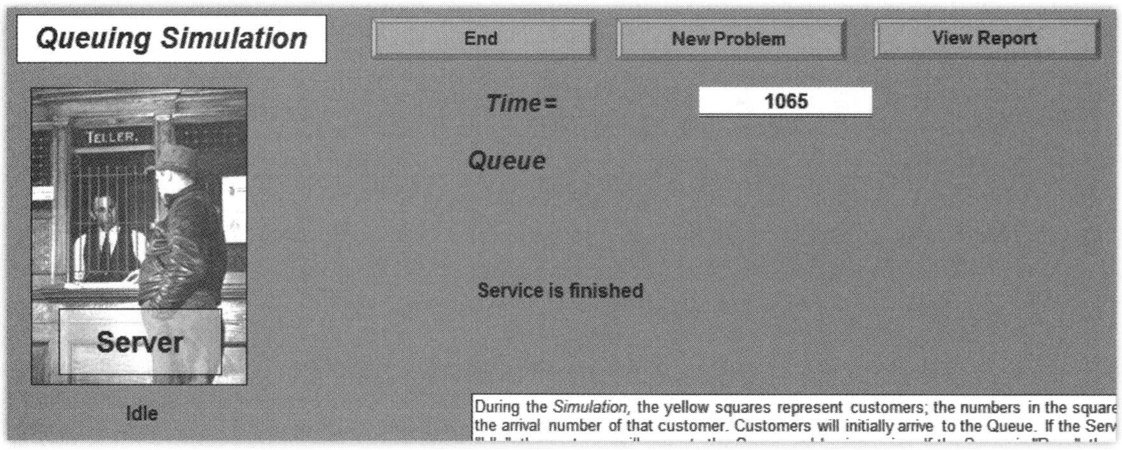

(b)

Figure CS10.5 The animation sheet.

If the users press the "View Report" button, then the report summary sheet appears. (See Figure CS10.6 (a) and (b).) This sheet summarizes the users' input values and the maximum, minimum, and average values of the mean waiting time and mean server utilization overall simulation trials. This spreadsheet also presents the maximum, minimum, and average values of queue length per unit time and waiting time per customer during the last simulation trial. There are also charts and histograms for the waiting times, utilization and queue lengths. From this sheet, the users can press the "View Details" button to proceed to the simulation details sheet.

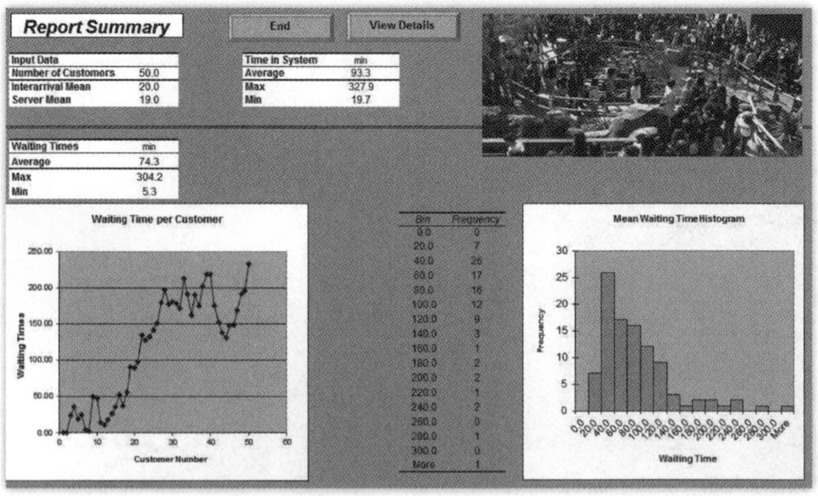

(a)

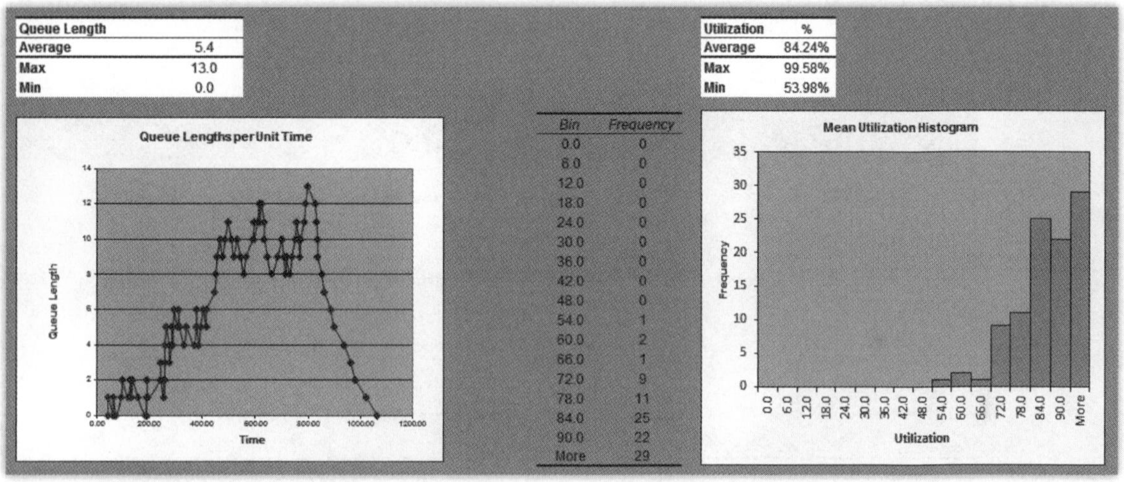

(b)

Figure CS10.6 The report summary sheet.

The Simulation sheet provides the detailed list of arrival time, time in queue, and time in the system per customer. This table is updated during each simulation trial. We calculate the average time in the system, the average time in the queue and the average server utilization for each simulation trial (See Figure CS10.7.). The users can return to the report summary sheet by pressing the "View Reports" button.

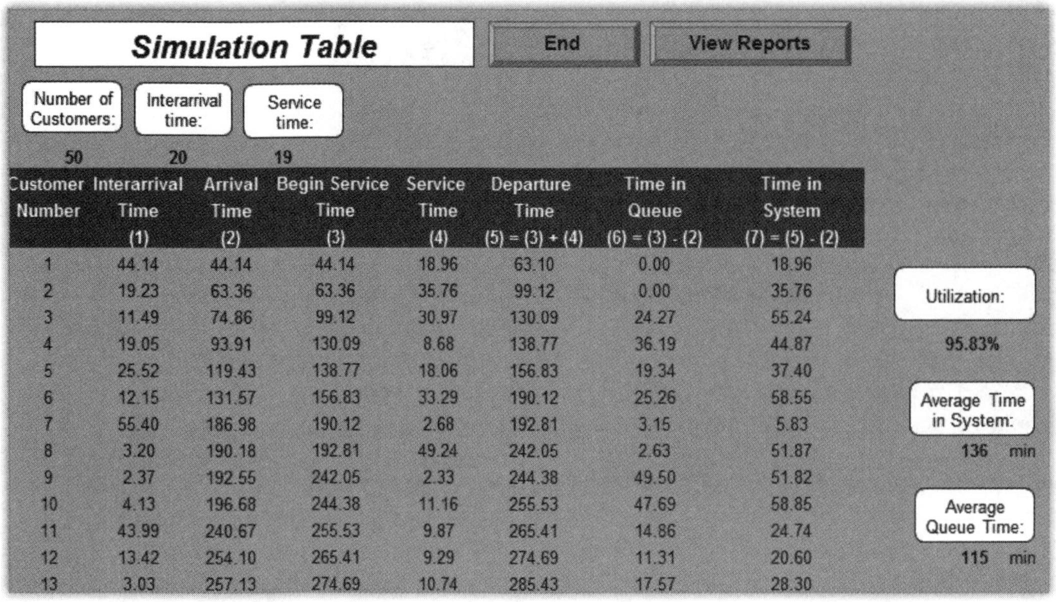

Simulation Table

End | View Reports

Number of Customers:	Interarrival time:	Service time:
50	20	19

Customer Number	Interarrival Time (1)	Arrival Time (2)	Begin Service Time (3)	Service Time (4)	Departure Time (5) = (3) + (4)	Time in Queue (6) = (3) - (2)	Time in System (7) = (5) - (2)
1	44.14	44.14	44.14	18.96	63.10	0.00	18.96
2	19.23	63.36	63.36	35.76	99.12	0.00	35.76
3	11.49	74.86	99.12	30.97	130.09	24.27	55.24
4	19.05	93.91	130.09	8.68	138.77	36.19	44.87
5	25.52	119.43	138.77	18.06	156.83	19.34	37.40
6	12.15	131.57	156.83	33.29	190.12	25.26	58.55
7	55.40	186.98	190.12	2.68	192.81	3.15	5.83
8	3.20	190.18	192.81	49.24	242.05	2.63	51.87
9	2.37	192.55	242.05	2.33	244.38	49.50	51.82
10	4.13	196.68	244.38	11.16	255.53	47.69	58.85
11	43.99	240.67	255.53	9.87	265.41	14.86	24.74
12	13.42	254.10	265.41	9.29	274.69	11.31	20.60
13	3.03	257.13	274.69	10.74	285.43	17.57	28.30

Utilization: 95.83%

Average Time in System: 136 min

Average Queue Time: 115 min

Figure CS10.7 The simulation sheet.

Summary

Welcome sheet	Contains the application description and the "Start" button.
Simulation sheet	Where the simulation animation is performed.
Report Summary sheet	Provides the summary of the input; the max, min, and average waiting times and queue lengths; and the chart and histogram of the waiting times and queue lengths.
Data sheet	Contains a detailed list of the waiting times per customer and the queue lengths per unit time. This sheet is hidden.

CS10.3 User Interface

For this application's user interface, we use navigational and functional buttons and one user form. When the users proceed to the animation sheet, a simulation input form appears. (See Figure CS10.8.) This form prompts the users for the application input: the number of customers for which to perform the simulation, the mean inter-arrival time per customer, and the mean service time per customer. This form requires three text boxes.

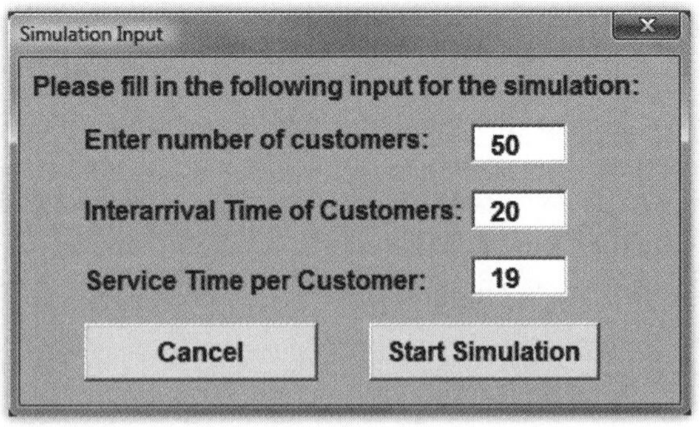

Figure CS10.8 The simulation input form.

Summary

Simulation input form	Receives the number of customers, the mean inter-arrival time per customer, and the mean service time per customer.
Navigational buttons	"Start" on the welcome sheet, "End" on all the sheets, "View Report" on the simulation sheet, "View Details" on the Report Summary sheet, and "View Report" on the report details sheet.
Functional button	"New Problem" on the simulation sheet.

CS10.4 Procedures

We will now outline the procedures for this application beginning with the variable declarations and the initial sub procedures. (See Figure CS10.9.) The *Main* procedure is called from the "Start" button. It calls the *ClearPrevious* procedure to clear the previous values from all the sheets. The *Main* procedure then shows the users the simulation input form and calls the *Simulation*, *Animation*, and *CreateReports* procedures.

```
Option Explicit
Option Base 1

Public i As Integer, NCust As Integer, InterArrivMean As Double, _
ServerMean As Double, QLength() As Integer, AvgQ As Double, _
QueueLength As Integer, Customer As Integer, WaitStart As Range, QueueStart As Range,
ws As Worksheet, EndRange As Range, FirstOpen As Boolean, SingleS As New RSP.Problem

Sub MAIN()      'this sub is called from the Start button on the Welcome sheet
    If FirstOpen Then
        MsgBox "NOTE: The Data Analysis Toolpack/Add-in is required to view" & _
                " histograms in the Report Summary."
    End If
    FirstOpen = False

    Call ClearPrevious
    With Worksheets("Animation")
       .Activate
       .Shapes("ViewReport").Visible = False
       .Shapes("NewProb").Visible = False
       .Visible = True
    End With
    Worksheets("Welcome").Visible = False

    frmInput.Show
    Call Simulation
    Call Animation
    Call CreateReports
End Sub

Sub ClearPrevious()      'clears previous data
    Application.ScreenUpdating = False
    'all table titles are written in text boxes to avoid clearing
    Worksheets("Animation").Cells.ClearContents
    Worksheets("Data").Cells.ClearContents

    'histogram data on report summary sheet
    With Worksheets("Report Summary")
        .Range("G17:H36").ClearContents
        .Range("G45:H78").ClearContents
        .Range("Input").ClearContents
        .Range("QueLenSum").ClearContents
    End With

    'the table created for simulation
    Range(Range("SimTable"), Range("SimTable").Offset(1, 6). _
            End(xlDown)).ClearContents
    Application.ScreenUpdating = True

End Sub
```

Figure CS10.9 The variable declarations and the *Main* and *ClearPrevious* procedures.

The procedures for the simulation input form simply record the input value the users have provided. (See Figure CS10.10.) Some error checking checks the values of the text boxes.

```
Sub cmdCancel_Click()
    Unload Me
    Worksheets("Welcome").Visible = True
    Worksheets("Simulation").Visible = False
    End
End Sub

Sub cmdOK_Click()
    'error checking for text boxes
    Dim ctl As Control
    For Each ctl In Me.Controls
        If TypeName(ctl) = "TextBox" Then
            If ctl.Value = "" Then
                MsgBox "Please make sure " & _
                    "all textboxes are filled in."
                ctl.SetFocus
                Exit Sub
            End If
        End If
    Next

    NCust = txtNumCust
    InterArrivMean = txtInterArriv
    ServerMean = txtServer
    Unload Me
End Sub
```

Figure CS10.10 The input form procedures.

The *Simulation* procedure updates the input data (from the user) in the Simulation spreadsheet (See Figure CS10.11.). Using this data, the cell values of the first two rows of the table are automatically updated. Note that the ClearPrevious procedure clears the data on this table, other than the first two rows. We copy the formulas of these two rows to the rest of the table. We believe that this approach is easy to use when populating the simulation table. There are other methods one can use to calculate the values that go into this table. We leave this as an exercise for the reader. In this procedure we initialize the SingleS problem object variable, set engine parameters, and call the *Simulate* method to run 100 simulation trials of our problem.

```
Sub Simulation()
    Application.ScreenUpdating = False
    'Create simulation table
    With Worksheets("Simulation")
        .Range("A6").Value = NCust
        .Range("B6").Value = InterArrivMean
        .Range("D6").Value = ServerMean

        .Range(Range("SimTable").Offset(-1, 0), Range("SimTable").Offset(-1, 6)).Copy
        .Range("SimTable", Range("SimTable").Offset(NCust - 3, 6)).PasteSpecial xlPasteAll
    End With
    Worksheets("Simulation").Activate

    'Initialize the Simulation Model
    SingleS.Init ActiveWorkbook
    SingleS.Engine.Params("SamplingMethod") = 2
    SingleS.Engine.Params("RandomSeed") = 12
    SingleS.Solver.NumTrials = 100
    SingleS.Solver.Simulate
    Range("W1").Select
    Application.ScreenUpdating = True
End Sub
```

Figure CS10.11 The *Simulation* procedure.

The *Animation* procedure performs the animation (see Figure CS10.12.) of a simulation trial. From this procedure we call the *Timeline* procedure which uses the results from the Simulation table to create a timeline of the simulation events (see Figure CS10.13.). This timeline is printed in the hidden Data spreadsheet. We step through the timeline, and for each time value, we check the corresponding event description: "Arrival," "BeginServe," or "EndServe." Depending on the event, the corresponding animation actions are taken. The queue length is also recorded for each time period.

```
Sub Animation()     'perform the simulation
    ReDim QLength(3 * NCust)
    QueueLength = 0
    Customer = 0

    Call CreateTimeTable
    'step through "timeline" data
    'perform animation and record queue length
    Worksheets("Animation").Activate
    For i = 1 To 3 * NCust
        Application.ScreenUpdating = False
        With Range("TimeLine")
            QLength(i) = QueueLength
            Select Case .Cells(i, 2)
                'arrival: customer number inc, queue length inc
                Case "Arrival"
                    Customer = Customer + 1
                    Range("Action") = "Customer arrives in the queue"
                    QueueLength = QueueLength + 1
                    Range("Queue").Offset(0, QueueLength) = Customer
                'begin serve: customer moves to server, queue length dec
                Case "BeginServe"
                    Range("Status") = "Busy"
                    Range("Action") = "Service begins for the customer"
                    Range("BeingServed") = Range("Queue").Offset(0, 1)
                    Range("Queue").Offset(0, 1).Delete (xlToLeft)
                    QueueLength = QueueLength - 1
                'end serve: server free, customer leaves
                Case "EndServe"
                    If QueueLength = 0 Then
                        Range("Status") = "Idle"
                    End If
                    Range("Action") = "Service is finished"
                    Range("BeingServed").ClearContents
            End Select
            Range("Time") = .Cells(i, 1)     'update system time
        End With
        Application.Wait (Now + TimeValue("0:0:01") / 2)
        Application.ScreenUpdating = True
    Next i

    Worksheets("Animation").Shapes("ViewReport").Visible = True
    Worksheets("Animation").Shapes("NewProb").Visible = True
End Sub
```

Figure CS10.12 The *Animation* procedure.

```
Sub CreateTimeTable()
    Application.ScreenUpdating = False

    Worksheets("Simulation").Activate
    Range(Range("CustomerNr").Offset(0, 2), Range("CustomerNr").Offset(NCust, 5)).Copy
    Range(Range("SimData").Offset(0, 2), Range("SimData").Offset(NCust, 2)).PasteSpecial xlPasteValues

    Range(Range("SimData"), Range("SimData").Offset(3 * NCust - 1, 1)).Name = "TimeLine"
    For i = 1 To NCust
        Range("TimeLine").Cells(i, 1) = Range("SimData").Offset(i - 1, 2).Value
        Range("TimeLine").Cells(i, 2) = "Arrival"
    Next i
    For i = i To 2 * NCust
        Range("TimeLine").Cells(i, 1) = Range("SimData").Offset(i - 1 - NCust, 5).Value
        Range("TimeLine").Cells(i, 2) = "EndServe"
    Next i
    For i = i To 3 * NCust
        Range("TimeLine").Cells(i, 1) = Range("SimData").Offset(i - 1 - 2 * NCust, 3).Value
        Range("TimeLine").Cells(i, 2) = "BeginServe"
    Next i

    'sort the timeline by times
    Range("TimeLine").Sort Key1:=Range("TimeLine").Columns(1), Order1:=xlAscending
    Application.ScreenUpdating = True
End Sub
```

Figure CS10.13 The *Timeline* procedure.

Finally, the *CreateReports* procedure is called. This procedure updates the simulation summary outputs, charts and histograms displayed on the Report Summary spreadsheet. The procedure begins by printing user's input on the spreadsheet. Next, it uses a *For Next* loop to calculate the time-weighted average queue length, and it uses the *Application.WorksheetFunction.Max* and *Application.WorksheetFunction.Min* to identify the minimum and maximum queue lengths.

In the Report Summary spreadsheet there are two histograms, one that presents the frequency of average server utilizations, and one that presents the frequency of average customer waiting time in the queue during all simulation trials. We use the *AllTrials()* property of *Functions()* object to identify the average utilization and average time in the queue during each simulation trial. These values are then used to calculate bin values, and update the source data for the histograms (Figure CS10.14(a) and (b)). We use the *CreateReports* procedure to also update the source data of two charts: waiting time per customer and queue length. The data for these charts comes from the Simulation spreadsheet. Figure CS10.2 presents the source data for the charts.

```
Sub CreateReports() 'create report sheet
    Application.Calculation = xlCalculationManual
    'display user input
    With Range("Input")
      .Cells(1) = NCust
      .Cells(2) = InterArrivMean
      .Cells(3) = ServerMean
    End With

    'display min, max, avg queue lengths
    For i = 1 To 3 * NCust
        Range("TimeLine").Cells(i, 4) = QLength(i)
    Next i
    AvgQ = 0
    With Range("SimData")
        For i = 2 To 3 * NCust
            AvgQ = AvgQ + (.Cells(i, 1) - .Cells(i - 1, 1)) * .Cells(i, 4) / .Cells(3 * NCust, 1)
        Next i
    End With

    With Range("QueLenSum")
      .Cells(1) = AvgQ
      .Cells(2) = Application.WorksheetFunction.Max(Range(Range("TimeLine").Cells(1, 4), _
                Range("TimeLine").Cells(NCust * 3, 4)))
      .Cells(3) = Application.WorksheetFunction.Min(Range(Range("TimeLine").Cells(1, 4), _
                Range("TimeLine").Cells(NCust * 3, 4)))
    End With

'HISTOGRAM OF MEAN UTILIZATION DURING SIMULATION
    'Extract utilization per trial
    Worksheets("Simulation").Activate
    For i = 0 To SingleS.Solver.NumTrials - 1
        Worksheets("Simulation").Range("AY15").Offset(i, 1).Value = SingleS.Functions(0). _
                AllTrials(0, i) * 100
    Next i
    'Create bins and histogram for utilization
    Range("AY15").Name = "BinStart"
    Range("AZ15", Range("AZ33").End(xlDown)).Name = "HistData"
    Range("BinStart").Value = 0
    For i = 1 To 15
        Range("BinStart").Offset(i, 0).Value = _
           Int(Range("BinStart").Offset(i - 1, 0).Value + 6.667)
    Next i
    Range(Range("BinStart"), Range("BinStart").End(xlDown)).Name = "Bins"
    Application.AlertBeforeOverwriting = False
    Application.Run "ATPVBAEN.XLAM!Histogram", Range("HistData"), Range("UHist"), _
            Range("Bins"), False, False, False, False
```

(a)

```
'HISTOGRAM OF MEAN WAITING TIME DURING SIMULATION
    'Extract waiting time per trial
    For i = 0 To SingleS.Solver.NumTrials - 1
        Worksheets("Simulation").Range("AY15").Offset(i, 1).Value = SingleS.Functions(2). _
                AllTrials(0, i)
    Next i
    Set SingleS = Nothing
    'Create bins and histogram for wait times
    Range("BinStart").Value = 0
    For i = 1 To 15
        Range("BinStart").Offset(i, 0).Value = _
            Int(Range("BinStart").Offset(i - 1, 0).Value + (Range("WaitTimeSum").Cells(2).Value / 15))
    Next i
    Application.AlertBeforeOverwriting = False
    Application.Run "ATPVBAEN.XLAM!Histogram", Range("HistData"), Range("WaitingHist"), _
            Range("Bins"), False, False, False, False

'CHART OF WAITING TIME DURING SIMULATION
    Application.ScreenUpdating = False
    Worksheets("Report Summary").ChartObjects("Chart 1").Activate
    Range(Range("CustomerNR"), Range("CustomerNr").Offset(NCust - 1, 0)).Copy
    Range("SimData").Offset(0, 4).PasteSpecial (xlPasteValues)
    Range(Range("WaitingTime"), Range("WaitingTime").Offset(NCust - 1, 0)).Copy
    Range("SimData").Offset(0, 5).PasteSpecial (xlPasteValues)
    Range(Range("SimData").Offset(0, 4), Range("SimData").Offset(NCust - 1, 5)).Name = "WTChartData"
    ActiveChart.SetSourceData Source:=Range("WTChartData")

'CHART OF QUEUE LENGTH DURING SIMULATION
    Application.ScreenUpdating = False
    Worksheets("Report Summary").ChartObjects("Chart 73").Activate
    Range(Range("SimData"), Range("SimData").Offset(3 * NCust - 1, 0)).Copy
    Range("SimData").Offset(0, 2).PasteSpecial (xlPasteValues)
    Range(Range("SimData").Offset(0, 2), Range("SimData").Offset(3 * NCust - 1, 3)).Name = "QueueLengths"
    Worksheets("Report Summary").ChartObjects("Chart 73").Activate
    ActiveChart.SetSourceData Source:=Range("QueueLengths")

    Range("G18:H78").HorizontalAlignment = xlCenter
    Range("G18:G78").NumberFormat = "0.0"
    Worksheets("Report Summary").Visible = False
    Worksheets("Animation").Visible = True
    Worksheets("Animation").Activate

    Application.Calculation = xlCalculationAutomatic
End Sub
```

(b)

Figure CS10.14 The *CreateDetails* procedure.

The navigational procedures appear in Figure CS10.15.

```
Sub EndProg()
    Worksheets("Welcome").Visible = True
    ActiveSheet.Visible = False

    Worksheets("Animation").Shapes("ViewReport").Visible = True
    Worksheets("Animation").Shapes("NewProb").Visible = True
End Sub

Sub ViewRepSum()
    Set ws = ActiveWorkbook.ActiveSheet
    Worksheets("Report Summary").Activate
    Worksheets("Report Summary").Visible = True
    ws.Visible = False
    Range("A1").Select
End Sub

Sub ViewRepDet()
    Set ws = ActiveWorkbook.ActiveSheet
    Worksheets("Simulation").Activate
    Worksheets("Simulation").Visible = True
    ws.Visible = False
    Range("A1").Select
End Sub
```

Figure CS10.15 The navigational procedures.

Summary

Main	Initializes the application and prompts the users with the simulation input form.
Simulation input form procedures	Record the users' input for the simulation.
Simulation	Updates the data in the Simulation worksheet, and uses Risk Solver Platform to simulate the model.
Animation	Performs the animation by stepping through the timeline.
Timeline	Creates a timeline of simulation events, such as, customer arrivals, customer being served and customer leaving the system.
CreateReports	Displays the summary values; creates the charts and histograms.
Navigational procedures	For the "End," "View Report" and "View Details" buttons.

CS10.5 *Re-solve Options*

The users can re-solve this application by pressing the "New Problem" button on the simulation sheet. This button recalls the *Main* procedure to again prompt the users with the simulation input form and repeat the simulation and animation.

Summary

"New Problem" button on the simulation sheet	Recalls the *Main* procedure and repeats the simulation.

CS10.6 *Multi Server Queuing Model Simulation and Optimization*

The multi server queuing model application simulates a queue of customers serviced by multiple servers. This application also provides histograms of mean waiting times and mean utilization when the simulation is over. This application has an additional functionality. It performs a simulation of the queuing model, and it also performs an optimization to determine the best number of servers that the system should have.

CS10.6.1 New Assumptions

This application also assumes exponentially distributed customer inter-arrival times and customer service times. Each server is assumed to have equal service times. The users provide the means of these density functions.

We again setup an Excel spreadsheet model in order to simulate this problem. The spreadsheet model is very similar to the model we set up for the single server problem. We randomly generate customer arrivals in the system, and service time. We then calculate the begin service time, departure time, and time in the queue for each customer. However, now we also need to identify which server will be seized by the user. We will be using the first available rule. In order to identify which server has been available for the longest time, we are adding to the simulation spreadsheet model in Figure CS10.1 additional columns (see Figure CS10.16). Columns J to N present the earliest finish time for each server. Column F identifies which server should be used by a customer. We assume that the very first customer will use server 1. The following are the formulas we use in these columns:

```
Cell J13: =IF($J$11=$F13,G13,J12)
     K13: =IF($K$11=$F13,G13,K12)
     L13: =IF($L$11=$F13,G13,L12)
     M13: =IF($M$11=$F13,G13,M12)
     N13: =IF($N$11=$F13,G13,N12)
     F13: =MATCH(MIN(J12:N12),J12:N12,0)
```

This simulation model uses circular referencing (cell F and cells J through N). Excel does not consider this circular referencing, but PSI Interpreter of Risk Solver Platform does. PSI Interpreter does not work well with circular referencing, therefore we should instead use the Excel Interpreter. To make the change we add the following line in our code in the *Simulation()* procedure. MultipleS is the problem object variable created for this simulation.

```
MultipleS.Model.Params("Interpreter") = 2
```

Note: the PSI Interpreter is much faster than Excel Interpreter; therefore, it will take longer to simulate this model. We are limiting this application to using up to 5 servers. However, this spreadsheet model can easily be extended to include additional servers.

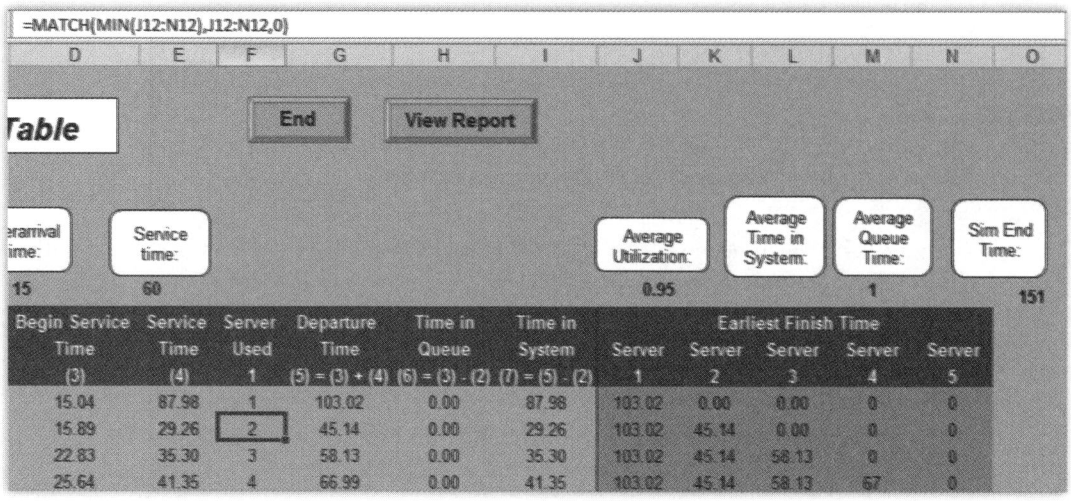

Figure CS10.16 The Excel simulation model setup.

The animation for this simulation is again similar to the single server application. The created timeline is examined for each time value, and the corresponding event is animated.

For the optimization option, the users provide some new input: the customer waiting cost per time unit, the server cost per time unit, and trial values for the optimal number of servers. The users define an interval for the trial number of servers by providing a minimum, maximum value. The following loop then performs the simulation part of the application for each trial number of servers:

For *SIter = MinServ* **To** *MaxServ*
    Call *Simulation(SIter)*
    Call *CreateOptReport(SIter)*
Next *SIter*

The total costs are calculated, and the optimal number of servers is considered to be the scenario with the minimum total costs. The application calculates these costs as follows:

*Total customer waiting cost = customer waiting cost per time unit * average waiting time * total number of customers*

*Total server cost = server cost per time unit * number of servers * sum of service times over all servers*

Total cost = total customer waiting cost + total server cost

We use VBA to calculate these costs, and use the MIN function of Excel on the optimization report summary sheet to identify the minimum total costs. We next use the MATCH function on the spreadsheet to identify the number of servers that gives the minimum costs, and use conditional formatting to highlight the minimum costs and corresponding number of servers.

CS10.6.2 Additional Input

The additional input for this application is the following:

- Number of servers (for the simulation option)
- Maximum and minimum number of servers (for the optimization option)
- Customer waiting cost per time unit
- Server cost per time unit

CS10.6.3 Additional Output

The additional output for this application is the following:

- Summary of waiting times, queue lengths, and costs per trial server number (for the optimization option)
- Optimal number of servers and minimum total cost (for the optimization option)

CS10.7 *Additional Worksheets*

This application requires one new worksheet: the optimization report summary sheet. It displays a summary of waiting times, queue lengths, and costs per trial server number and tells the users the optimal number of servers and the minimum total cost. (See Figure CS10.17.)

Report Summary: Optimization

End

Input Values	
Number of Customers	50
Mean Interarrival Time	15
Mean Server Time	60
Waiting Time Cost per Customer per Unit Time	$2.00
Cost per Server per Unit Time	$10.00

Optimization Results	
Optimal Number of Servers	5
Minimum Total Cost	$31,732.95

Number of Servers:	1	2	3	4	5
Waiting Times					
Average	1109.91	359.18	132.59	45.23	14.85
Max	1651.16	628.09	292.17	135.45	54.55
Min	552.28	83.38	16.48	4.49	0.59
Server Utilization					
Average	99.22%	95.42%	89.20%	78.95%	67.26%
Max	99.96%	99.37%	98.17%	94.96%	90.36%
Min	96.66%	88.01%	63.94%	47.95%	38.36%
Costs					
Total Customer Wait Cost	$110,991.10	$35,918.46	$13,258.91	$4,523.27	$1,485.18
Total Server Cost	$29,948.85	$29,925.53	$30,003.66	$30,111.78	$30,247.77
Total Cost	$140,939.94	$65,843.98	$43,262.58	$34,635.05	$31,732.95

Figure CS10.17 The optimization report summary sheet.

The animation sheet is now updated to show multiple servers for the animation. (See Figure CS10.18.)

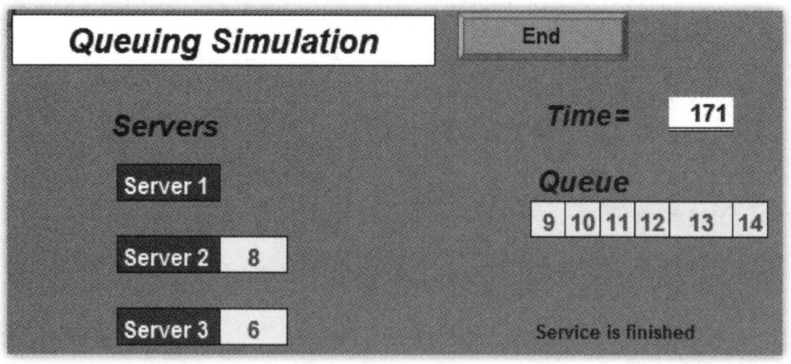

Figure CS10.18 The updated animation sheet.

Summary

Optimization Summary Report	Displays a summary of customer waiting times, server utilization, costs per trial server number, the optimal number of servers, and the minimum total cost.
Updated animation sheet	Now shows the multiple servers for the simulation animation.
Updated data sheet	Now also displays the server used by a customer.

CS10.8 Additional User Interface

For this application's user interface, we use navigational buttons, two new user forms, and modify the simulated input form. From the "Start" button on the welcome sheet, the users now first view a main menu form. (See Figure CS10.19.) This form asks the users if they want to perform the simulation option or the optimization option. This form requires two option buttons and a frame.

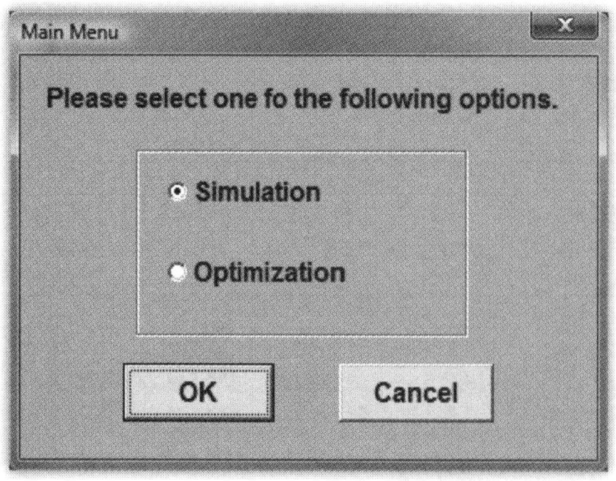

Figure CS10.19 The main menu form.

If the users choose the simulation option, then the simulation input form appears. [See Figure CS10.20 (a).] This form has a new text box to ask the users for the number of servers in the queuing system. Also, two frames now group the server and the customer input. If the users choose the optimization option on the main menu form, then the simulation input form appears. [See Figure CS10.20 (b).] However, the users do not specify the number of servers for this option since a trial number of servers is used.

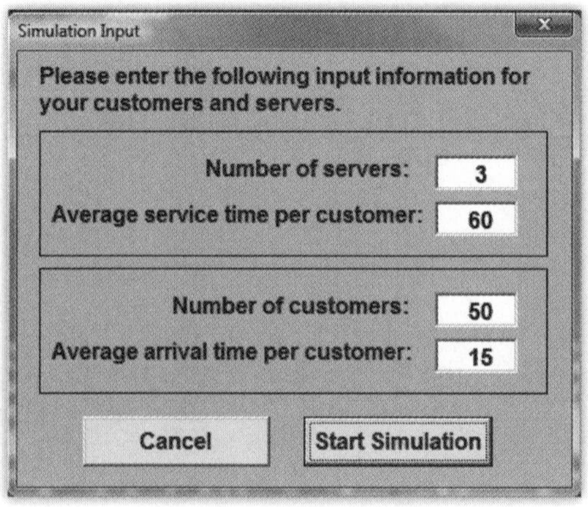

(a)

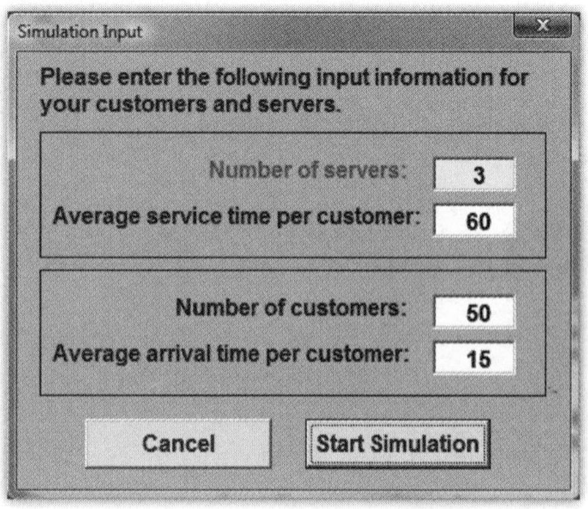

(b)

Figure CS10.20 The updated simulation input form.

The optimization option has a new input form: the optimization input form. (See Figure CS10.21.) This form prompts the users for the maximum and minimum number of servers for the trials, the customer waiting cost per time unit, and the server cost per time unit. This form requires two frames and several text boxes.

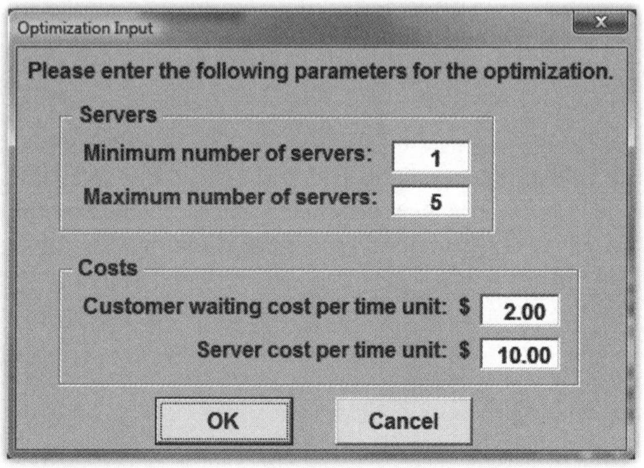

Figure CS10.21 The optimization input form.

Summary

Main menu form	Prompts the users to perform the simulation or the optimization option.
Updated simulation input form	Now also asks the users for the number of servers.
Optimization input form	Prompts the users for the maximum and minimum number of servers for the trials, the customer waiting cost per time unit, and the server cost per time unit.

CS10.9 Additional Procedures

There are a few additional procedures for this application, and several from the single server application have been updated. In the *Main* procedure, the optimization option now has an addition. (See Figure CS10.22.) A loop performs the simulation over all the trial values for the number of servers.

```
 'optimization
If PerformOpt Then
    'perform simulation for each trial number of servers
    Application.ScreenUpdating = False
    For SIter = MinServ To MaxServ
        Call Simulation(SIter)
        Call CreateOptReport(SIter)
    Next SIter
    Application.ScreenUpdating = True
    Worksheets("Opt Report Summary").Visible = True

    Worksheets("Welcome").Visible = False
    Range("A1").Select
End If
```

Figure CS10.22 The addition to the *Main* procedure.

The two new user forms also now have new procedures. The procedures for the main menu form take the users to the sheet that corresponds to the selected option, and the procedures display the simulation input form. (See Figure CS10.23.) The procedures for the optimization input form record the users' input and perform some error checking. (See Figure CS10.24.)

```
Sub cmdCancel_Click()
    Unload Me
    End
End Sub

Private Sub cmdOK_Click()
    If optSim Then
        'perform sim
        PerformSim = True

        With Worksheets("Animation")
          .Activate
          .Shapes("ViewReport").Visible = False
          .Shapes("NewProb").Visible = False
          .Visible = True
        End With
        Worksheets("Welcome").Visible = False

        With frmInput   'allow user to input number of servers
            .lblServ.ForeColor = &H800000
            .txtNServ.BackColor = &H80000005
        End With
    ElseIf optOptim Then
        'perform opt
        PerformOpt = True

        With frmInput   'do not allow user to input number of servers
            .lblServ.ForeColor = &H808080
            .txtNServ.BackColor = &H8000000B
        End With
        frmOptInput.Show
    End If

    'return to main code and show Input form
    Unload Me
End Sub
```

Figure CS10.23 The new procedures for the main menu form.

```
Sub cmdCancel_Click()
    Unload Me
    End
End Sub

Private Sub cmdOK_Click()
    Dim ctl As Control
    For Each ctl In Me.Controls
        If TypeName(ctl) = "TextBox" Then
            If ctl.Value = "" Then
                MsgBox "Please make sure all textboxes are filled in."
                ctl.SetFocus
                Exit Sub
            ElseIf ctl.Value <= 0 Or Not IsNumeric(ctl.Value) Then
                MsgBox "Please enter a number greater than 0 for all values."
                ctl.SetFocus
                Exit Sub
            End If
        End If
    Next

    MinServ = txtMinServ
    MaxServ = txtMaxServ
    SCost = txtSCost
    CustCost = txtCustCost

    Unload Me
End Sub
```

Figure CS10.24 The new procedures for the optimization input form.

The *Simulation* procedure has changed only slightly (see Figure CS10.25). This procedure now takes as an argument the number of servers in the system. By doing this, we are able to call and run the same procedure for different number of servers.

```
Sub Simulation(ServNum)
    'Create simulation table
    Application.ScreenUpdating = False
    Worksheets("Simulation").Activate
    With Worksheets("Simulation")
        .Range("C8").Value = ServNum
        .Range("J12").Name = "EFTime"
    End With

    Range(Range("SimTable").Offset(-1, 0), Range("SimTable"). _
        Offset(-1, 12)).Copy
    Range("SimTable", Range("SimTable").Offset(NCust - 3, 12)) _
        .PasteSpecial xlPasteAll

     'Initialize the Simulation Model
    MultipleS.Init ActiveWorkbook
    MultipleS.Model.Params("Interpreter") = 2
    MultipleS.Solver.NumTrials = 30
    MultipleS.Solver.Simulate
    Range("W1").Select
    Application.ScreenUpdating = True
End Sub
```

Figure CS10.25 The updated *Simulation* procedure.

The *Timeline* procedure (Figure CS10.26) in addition to generating the timeline of the events, it also records the ID of the server that a customer seizes, and eventually releases when departing the system. The animation employs this server ID to bring the customer to the correct server.

```
Sub CreateTimeTable()
    Application.ScreenUpdating = False

    Range(Range("CustomerNr").Offset(0, 2), Range("CustomerNr").Offset(NCust, 6)).Copy
    Range(Range("SimData").Offset(0, 3), Range("SimData").Offset(NCust, 3)).PasteSpecial xlPasteValues

    Range(Range("SimData"), Range("SimData").Offset(3 * NCust - 1, 2)).Name = "TimeLine"
    For i = 1 To NCust
        Range("TimeLine").Cells(i, 1) = Range("SimData").Offset(i - 1, 3).Value
        Range("TimeLine").Cells(i, 2) = "Arrival"
        Range("TimeLine").Cells(i, 3) = "Arrival"
    Next i
    For i = i To 2 * NCust
        Range("TimeLine").Cells(i, 1) = Range("SimData").Offset(i - 1 - NCust, 7).Value
        Range("TimeLine").Cells(i, 2) = "AEndServe"
        Range("TimeLine").Cells(i, 3) = Range("SimData").Offset(i - 1 - NCust, 6).Value
    Next i
    For i = i To 3 * NCust
        Range("TimeLine").Cells(i, 1) = Range("SimData").Offset(i - 1 - 2 * NCust, 4).Value
        Range("TimeLine").Cells(i, 2) = "BBeginServe"
        Range("TimeLine").Cells(i, 3) = Range("SimData").Offset(i - 1 - 2 * NCust, 6).Value
    Next i

    'sort the timeline by times
    Worksheets("Data").Activate
    Range("TimeLine").Sort Key1:=Range("SimData"), Order1:=xlAscending, _
        Key2:=Range("SimData").Offset(0, 1), Order2:=xlAscending, _
        OrderCustom:=1, MatchCase:=False, Orientation:=xlTopToBottom
    Range("I:I").ClearContents
    Application.ScreenUpdating = True
End Sub
```

Figure CS10.26 The updated *Timeline* procedure.

We add a new procedure called *CreateOptReport* for the optimization option. (See Figure CS10.27.) This procedure takes as an argument the number of servers in the system. We call this procedure during optimization to record the summary waiting time, server utilization, and the cost values for each trial number of servers.

```
Sub CreateOptReport(ServNum) 'create report sheet
    'Waiting time stats
    Range("W_Time_Stat").Offset(1, ServNum).Value = MultipleS.Functions(1).Statistics.Mean(0)
    Range("W_Time_Stat").Offset(2, ServNum).Value = MultipleS.Functions(1).Statistics.Maximum(0)
    Range("W_Time_Stat").Offset(3, ServNum).Value = MultipleS.Functions(1).Statistics.Minimum(0)

    'Utilization stats
    Range("S_Util_Stat").Offset(1, ServNum).Value = MultipleS.Functions(0).Statistics.Mean(0)
    Range("S_Util_Stat").Offset(2, ServNum).Value = MultipleS.Functions(0).Statistics.Maximum(0)
    Range("S_Util_Stat").Offset(3, ServNum).Value = MultipleS.Functions(0).Statistics.Minimum(0)

    'Costs stats
    Range("Costs_Stat").Offset(1, ServNum).Value = NCust * _
            Range("W_Time_Stat").Offset(1, ServNum).Value * CustCost
    Range("Costs_Stat").Offset(2, ServNum).Value = ServNum * Range("S_Util_Stat").Offset(1, ServNum).Value _
            * SCost * MultipleS.Functions(2).Statistics.Mean(0)
    Range("Costs_Stat").Offset(3, ServNum).Value = Range("Costs_Stat").Offset(1, ServNum).Value _
            + Range("Costs_Stat").Offset(2, ServNum).Value

    Set MultipleS = Nothing
    If ServNum = MaxServ Then
        With Worksheets("Opt Report Summary")
            .Range("D6").Value = NCust
            .Range("D7").Value = InterArrivMean
            .Range("D8").Value = ServerMean
            .Range("D9").Value = CustCost
            .Range("D10").Value = SCost
        End With
    End If
End Sub
```

Figure CS10.27 The new *CreateOptReport* procedure.

Summary

Updated Main procedure	Now includes a loop over the trial number of servers for the optimization option.
New main menu form procedures	Direct the users depending on the option selected.
New optimization input form procedures	Record the new input for the optimization option.
Updated Timeline procedure	Now creates new data to determine which server each customer is serviced by.
Updated Simulation procedure	Now takes as an argument the total number of servers in the system.
New CreateOptReport procedure	Outputs statistics about mean server utilization, waiting time in queue, and related costs for the optimization option.

CS10.10 New Re-solve Options

The users can now use the results of the optimization option to return to the simulation option and input the optimal number of servers. To do so, the users first choose the optimization option and then press the "End" button on the report summary optimization sheet to return to the welcome sheet. There, the users choose the simulation option from the main menu form. For the simulation option, users can still select the "New Problem" button as a re-solve option.

Summary

Main menu form The users can first choose the optimization option, determine the optimal number of servers, and then return to the main menu form to choose the simulation option. This optimal number of servers can now be inputted into the simulation option.

CS10.11 Summary

- The single server queuing application simulates a queue of customers serviced by a single server. The multi server queuing application simulates a queue of customers serviced by multiple servers and also contains an optimization option to determine the optimal number of servers.
- This application requires five worksheets: the welcome sheet, the animation sheet, the simulation sheet, the report summary sheet, and the hidden data sheet.
- For this application's user interface, we use navigational buttons and user forms. For the single server application, there is one user form; for the multiple server application, there are three user forms.
- Several procedures for this application perform the simulation and/or optimization. We create Excel spreadsheet models for the single and multi-server queuing problem, and use Risk Solver Platform to simulate these models. The spreadsheet model randomly generates customer arrivals and service time, and uses formulas to calculate customer begin service time and departure time. We use this data to create a timeline of events to perform the animation.
- The users can re-solve this application by pressing the "New Problem" button on the simulation sheet. For the multiple server application, the users can also use the results of the optimization option to return to the simulation option and input the optimal number of servers.

CS10.12 Extensions

1. Allow the users to choose between a "fast" and "slow" simulation speed. Add this option to the simulation input form.
2. Add error checking to input forms so that only numbers can be entered.
3. Improve the "New Problem" re-solve option by updating the simulation input form with the users' last values instead of the default values.
4. Allow the users to change the distribution for the inter-arrival and server times.
5. Perform the simulation over a period of time instead of for a certain number of customers. (For example, run a one-day or one-week scenario.)
6. For the multi server application, create a histogram that can compare a server's utilization. The user should be able to enter different mean

server times for each server and then compare the server utilization according to the new histogram.

7. For the multiple server application, allow the users to consider a cost for lost customers. Customers are assumed to be lost or to have left the queue if a given amount of waiting time occurs while the customers are in the queue. Count the number of lost customers and include the cost in the optimization analysis.
8. We use Risk Solver Platform to simulate both, the single and multi-server problems. Suppose that you do not have access to Risk Solver Platform. Update the VBA procedure of this application to complete the simulations without using Risk Solver Platform.
9. The multi-server spreadsheet model uses the MATCH function of Excel. This is one of the reasons why we use the Excel Interpreter instead of PSI Interpreter to simulate the model. Modify the spreadsheet simulation model to complete the simulation without using MATCH or LOOKUP function of Excel so that you can solve the multi-server model using the PSI Interpreter.

APPENDIX

A Excel Add-Ins

appendix **OVERVIEW**

A.1 *Introduction*

This appendix chapter is intended to present an overview of some of Excel's *Add-Ins* which are useful tools for building a DSS in Excel. An Add-In is an accessory software program that extends the capabilities of the existing Excel application. We have discussed the Risk Solver Platform in several chapters of this book. This Add-In is a useful tool for solving optimization and simulation problems. One of the most well-known Add-Ins is the Excel Solver, which is used to solve mathematical programs using optimization techniques. In this appendix chapter, we will review the Data Analysis ToolPak, which includes commonly used statistical tools; the Solver, including the Premium Solver; CPLEX, an optimization tool; @RISK, a statistics and simulation tool; Crystall Ball, a simulation tool; and StatTools, a statistical analysis tool. Again, this chapter is intended only as an overview of these Add-Ins. For more information, refer to each program's individual website or other references.

A.2 *Including Add-Ins and References using VBA*

Although various *Add-Ins* are available in Excel, they can only be used after they have been included or referenced. To include an *Add-In* in Excel, users must select *File > Options* from the Ribbon to activate the *Excel Options* dialog box. In this dialog box, select the *Add-Ins* category on the left. Select the *Excel Add-Ins* from *Manage* combo box on the bottom of the dialog box (see Figure A.1) and then click *Go*. The *Add-Ins* dialog box in Figure A.2 appears. From this dialog box select the Add-Ins that you want to use. For example, users may select "Risk *Solver Add-in*," "Solver Add-in" or "*Analysis ToolPak*." To use an *Add-In* that is not shown on the menu list, users can click the *Browse* button to select an *Add-In* file from their computer. Once the *Add-In* has been included, the related features will become available in Excel, and the corresponding user interface may be integrated in the *Ribbon*. For example, the *Analysis ToolPak* and *Solver* commands are located in the *Data > Analysis* group on the *Ribbon*. There is a new tab on the Ribbon *called Risk Solver Platform* which contains all related groups of commands. (*Note:* Sometimes this requires closing and re-opening the Excel file.)

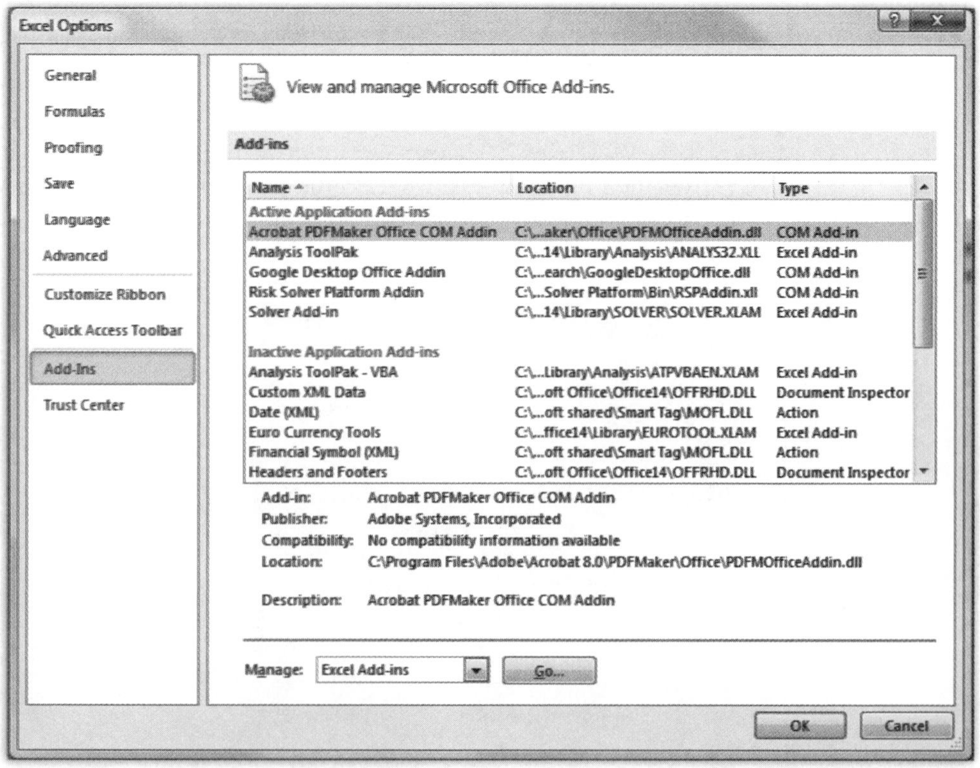

Figure A.1 The Excel Options dialog box.

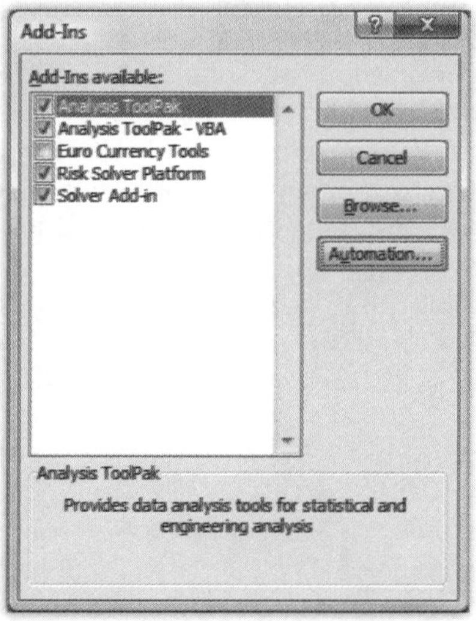

Figure A.2 The Add-Ins dialog box in Excel.

Likewise, some sets of VBA functions are associated with particular libraries that must be referenced in the Visual Basic Editor (VBE) before they can be used. For example, in order to use Object-Oriented API in Risk Solver Platform to manipulate an optimization problem through procedures created in VBA, developers must reference the Risk Solver Platform xx Type Library in the VBE. To add a library reference in the VBE, programmers must go to *Tools > References* from the VBE menu and then select the library they wish to reference (see Figure A.3). To reference a library that is not on the list, programmers can click the *Browse* button and select a library file from their computer.

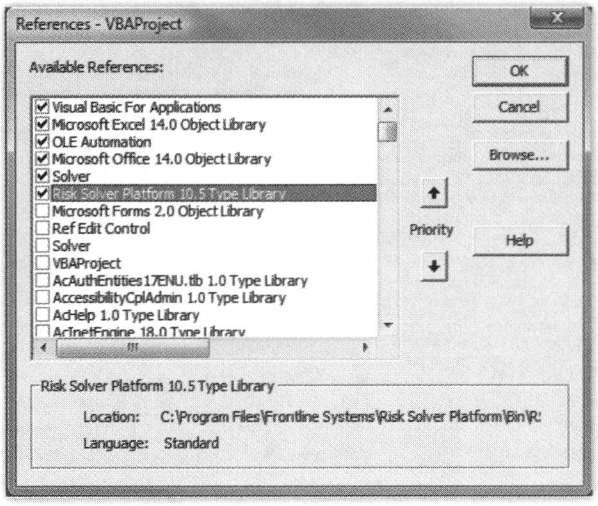

Figure A.3 The VBA Library reference window in the VBE.

Since it is necessary to have an Add-In included in Excel or a VBA Library referenced in the VBE in order for their related functions to be available, we must ensure these settings are made for any DSS application that relies on such functions. There are two ways to do this: either we instruct users to select the necessary Add-Ins and/or VBA references, or we update these settings automatically using VBA. We suggest using the following code to automatically include an Add-In or reference a VBA Library.

To automatically include an Add-In using VBA, we use the ***AddIns*** object and set the ***Installed*** property to True. To use the AddIns object, we must name a specific Add-In. Below is the code that automatically installs the "Analysis *ToolPak*," "Analysis *ToolPak* – VBA," and "Solver" Add-Ins.

```
AddIns("Analysis Toolpak").Installed = True
AddIns("Analysis Toolpak - VBA").Installed = True
AddIns("Rspaddin").Installed = True
AddIns("Solver Add-in").Installed = True
```

To automatically reference a VBA Library using VBA, we use the ***ThisWorkbook*** object and the Application object. For the ThisWorkbook object, we want to change the ***VBProject*** property's ***References*** subproperty by using the ***AddFromFile*** method. That is, we want to add a reference to the VBA project of the current workbook by referring to a particular file. The file we want to add as a reference is the ".xlam" library file corresponding to the Add-In or reference we want to use. We add this file by naming the path, or location, of this file. (This is equivalent to using the *Browse* button in *Tools > References* dialog box in the VBE.) To find the unique location of any file on the users' computer, we use the ***LibraryPath*** property of the Application object. This property represents the path on the users' computer to the Microsoft "Library" folder. Below is the code to automatically reference the Risk Solver Platform xx Type Library ("RSPAddin.xll"), Solver Library ("Solver.xlam") and the Analysis Library ("ATPVBAEN.xlam").

```
ThisWorkbook.VBProject.References.AddFromFile "C:\Program Files\Frontline Systems\Risk Solver Platform\Bin\RSPAddin.xll"
ThisWorkbook.VBProject.References.AddFromFile Application.LibraryPath & "\Solver\Solver.xlam"
ThisWorkbook.VBProject.References.AddFromFile Application.LibraryPath & "\Analysis\ATPVBAEN.xlam"
```

Note that in order to change the *VBProject* property of the ThisWorkbook object, users must have their security settings such that access to the Visual Basic Project is allowed. To change this security setting, users must select *File > Options* from the Ribbon to activate the *Excel Options* dialog box. In this dialog box, select the *Trust Center* category on the left. Click on the *Trust Center Settings…* command on the right side of the dialog box. On the *Trust Center* dialog box that appears select *Macro Settings* category on the left, and check the box that reads, "Trust access to VBA project object model" (see Figure A.4).

Note: Users should, of course, also have the "Disable all Application Add-ins" box unchecked. This is usually unchecked by default in Excel, but it is advisable to inform users of this security setting. To access this check box you should click on the *Add-ins* category in the *Trust Center* dialog box. Likewise, under the *Macro Settings* category of *Trust Center* dialog box, users must have "Enable all macros" option selected in order for any VBA code to be performed.

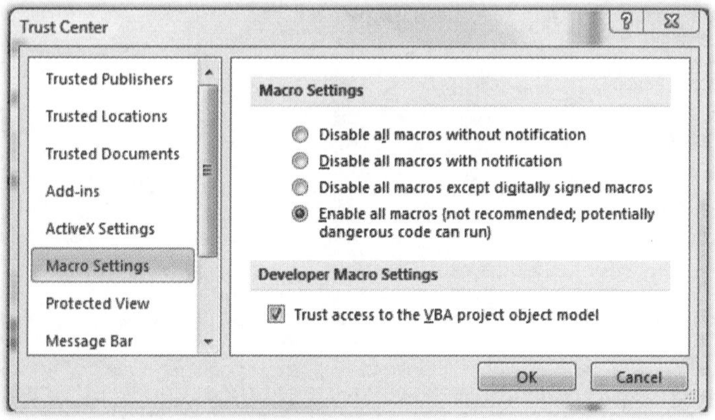

Figure A.4 The Trust Setting dialog box.

If this security setting is not made, then the above code aimed at changing the *References* of the *VBProject* of *ThisWorkbook* will not work. Therefore, we recommend prompting users to change their security settings and using the *On Error Resume Next* code to avoid errors.

In Figure A.5, we show the Add-In installation and Library reference code in a Workbook_Open event procedure. This procedure includes a message box to inform users about the necessary security settings.

```
Private Sub Workbook_Open()
'change add ins in Excel window ... must know name of add in
AddIns("Analysis Toolpak").Installed = True
AddIns("Analysis Toolpak - VBA").Installed = True
AddIns("Rspaddin").Installed = True
AddIns("Solver Add-in").Installed = True

'change refernce in VBE for Solver VBA code and/or Simulation/Analysis code
MsgBox "Please update your Excel security settings." & vbLf & vbLf & _
"Go to File > Options" & vbLf & vbLf & _
"In the Excel Options dialog box select Trust Center category" & vbLf & vbLf & _
"Click Trust Center Settings…command." & vbLf & vbLf & _
"Select Macro Setting category on the left." & vbLf & vbLf & _
"Check the box that reads: Trust access to VBA project object model."

On Error Resume Next
ThisWorkbook.VBProject.References.AddFromFile Application.LibraryPath & "\Solver\Solver.xlam"
ThisWorkbook.VBProject.References.AddFromFile Application.LibraryPath & "\Analysis\ATPVBAEN.xlam"
ThisWorkbook.VBProject.References.AddFromFile _
    "C:\Program Files\Frontline Systems\Risk Solver Platform\Bin\RSPAddin.xll"
End Sub
```

Figure A.5 The complete Add-In and reference code in a Workbook_Open event procedure.

A.3 *Data Analysis ToolPak*

The *Analysis ToolPak* is an Add-In program which provides methods we can use to perform statistical analysis. This Excel Add-In includes statistical analysis techniques such as *Descriptive Statistics*, *Histograms*, *Exponential Smoothing*, *Correlation*, *Covariance*, *Moving Average*, and others (see Figure A.6). These tools automate a sequence of calculations in Excel that require much data manipulation. We will now discuss how to use *Descriptive Statistics* and *Histograms* in the *Analysis ToolPak*.

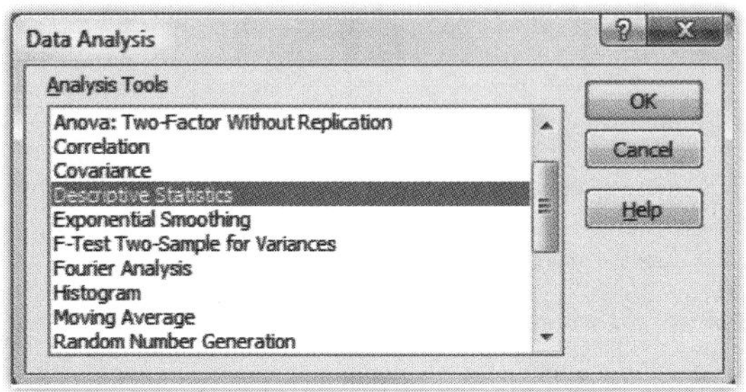

Figure A.6 The Data Analysis dialog box provides a list of analytical tools.

Recall the Single Server Queuing problem discussed in Section 9.5.2. Figure A.7 presents the data about customer interarrival time in the system. Suppose that we want to learn about statistical properties of this data set, such as, mean, median, standard deviation, etc. To accomplish this, we click on the *Data > Analysis > Data Analysis* command on the *Ribbon*. From the *Data Analysis* dialog box we select the *Descriptive Statistics* option. In the Descriptive Statistics dialog box that appears we identify the *Input Range* where our data is located, the *Output Range* where the results of this analysis will be displayed, and the type of statistics to calculate. Figure A.7 presents the results from this analysis.

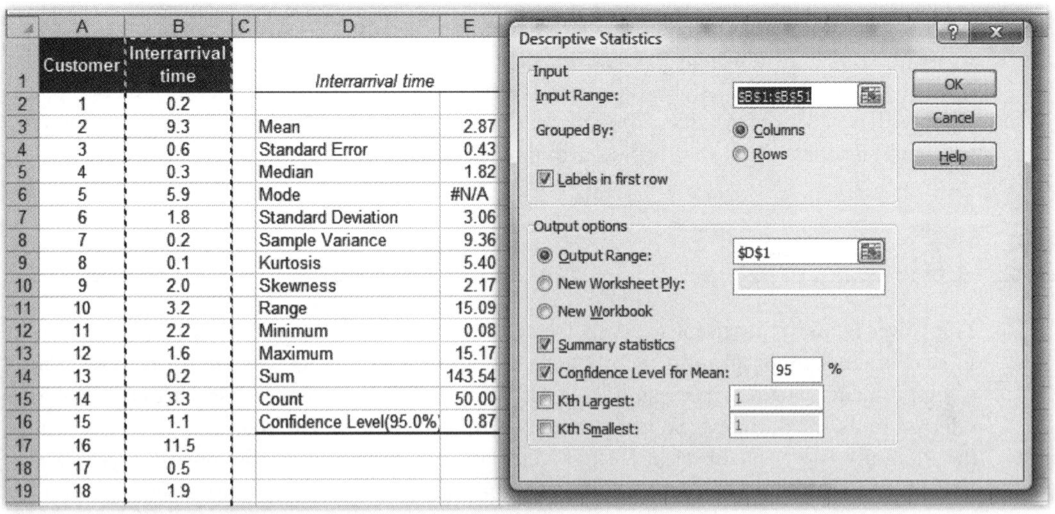

Figure A.7 Using the Descriptive Statistics data analysis tool.

Suppose that we now want to build a histogram of the customer interarrival time in the system. To accomplish this, we click on the *Data > Analysis > Data Analysis* command on the *Ribbon*. From the *Data Analysis* dialog box we select the *Histogram* option. In the Histogram dialog box that appears we identify the *Input Range* where our data is located, the *Output Range* where the results of this analysis will be displayed, and the type of charts to present in the spreadsheet. Note that we are not identifying a *Bin Range* for our data. Excel will automatically identify the Bin Range for us. Figure A.8 presents the results from this analysis.

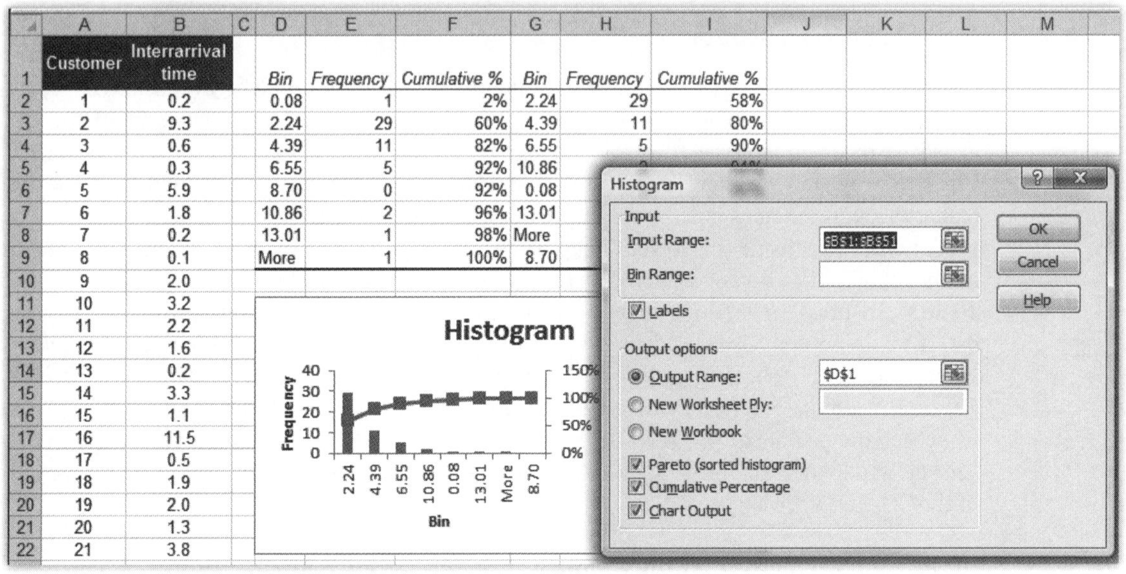

Figure A.8 Using the Histogram data analysis tool.

(Note: Before using the *Analysis ToolPak*, we must ensure that it is an active Add-in. To do so, we press *Alt + TI* to display the Add-Ins dialog box, and select *Analysis ToolPak* from the list. If we do not see it on the list, we may need to update the installation of Excel on the computer. After we have checked *Analysis ToolPak* on the *Add-ins* list, we should find the *Data Analysis* command under the *Data > Analysis* group on the Ribbon.)

A.4 The Solver

The Solver is an optimization Add-In created by Frontline Systems in 1991. It is designed to solve mathematical programming problems including linear, integer, and non-linear programming problems. The Solver version included in most Microsoft Excel installation packages is referred to as the Standard Solver. Frontline's other products, the Risk Solver Platform and the Premium Solver (a subset of Risk Solver Platform) can handle problems of larger size, as well as smooth and non-smooth nonlinear programs. In Chapter 8 we discussed how to solve linear and non-linear problems by using different solver engines of Risk Solver Platform, such as, the *Standard LP/Quadratic, the Standard Evolutionary Engine,* and the *Standard GRG Nonlinear Engine.* In this section, we will discuss how to use the Standard Solver of Excel and the Premium Solver.

In Chapter 19 we discuss how to use Object Oriented API in VBA to build and solve an optimization problem using Risk Solver Platform. In this section we discuss how to use VBA commands to build and solve an optimization problem using Excel's Standard Solver.

We conclude this section by discussing some of the limitations of Excel's Standard Solver. These limitations were the main motivation for introducing Risk Solver Platform in this new edition of the book.

A.4.1 Excel Standard Solver

In Chapter 8 we discuss in detail how to build an optimization problem, and use Risk Solver Platform to solve the problem. In order to use the Standard Solver, similar steps should be followed: we read and interpret the problem, prepare the spreadsheet and then solve the problem. The two tools however have different user interface. Therefore, in this section we walk the reader through the steps one should take when using the Standard Solver of Excel.

In order to activate the Solver dialog box, we click on *Data > Analysis > Solver* command on the Ribbon. If we do not see *Solver* in the *Analysis* group, we must first add the *Solver Add-In.* To do so, we press *Alt + TI* to display the Add-Ins dialog box, and select *Solver Add-In* from the list. If we do not see *Solver Add-In* in the *Add-In* list, we click *Browse* and look for the *Solver.xlam* file from the following directory: *C Drive > Program Files > Microsoft Office > Office (or Office12) > Library > Solver.* Double-click on this file. Now we should find *Solver Add-In* in the list; check the box next to it. Restart Excel. If we do not find the *Solver.xlam* file, we go to the *Add-Ins* window as explained above; select *Solver Add-in* and press *OK.* Insert the MS Office CD in the CD-ROM drive when asked.

STEP 1: Read and Interpret the Problem

Determine the type of problem (linear programming, integer programming, or nonlinear programming) and outline the model parts. Write these mathematically, with the objective function and constraints in terms of the decision variables.

STEP 2: Prepare the spreadsheet

Transfer these parts of the model to the Excel spreadsheet, clearly defining each part of the model in the spreadsheet.

STEP 2.1: **Place the Input Table**

Place all input values on the spreadsheet in the form of a table. We will reference this input when forming the constraint and objective function formulas.

STEP 2.2: **Set the Decision Variables Cells**

List the decision variables in individual cells with an empty cell next to each one. The *Solver* places values in these cells for each decision variable as it solves the model.

STEP 2.3: **Enter the Constraint Formulas**

Place the constraint equations in the spreadsheet; enter them separately using formulas in terms of the decision variable cells already defined.

STEP 2.4: **Enter the Objective Function Formula**

Place the objective function in a cell by transforming this equation into a formula in terms of the decision variables.

STEP 3: Solve the Model with the *Solver*

The Solver can now interpret this information and use one of its optimization algorithms to solve the model. To run Solver, we click on *Data > Analysis > Solver* command on the Ribbon; the dialog box in Figure A.9 then appears.

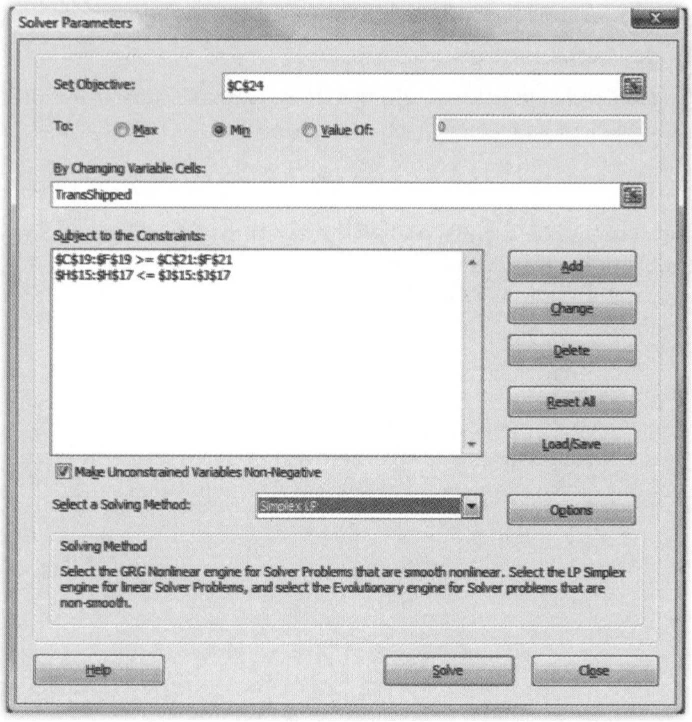

Figure A.9 The Solver Parameters dialog box for the Transportation Problem application of Section 8.4.1. This window reads the decision variables, constraints, and objective function as parameters of the model.

STEP 3.1: Set Objective

The *Set Objective* refers to the location of the formula for the objective function. Determine if we are maximizing or minimizing the objective function. Specify this by selecting the *Max* or *Min* options below the *Set Objective* textbox. We also have the option of solving the objective function to reach a particular value. In that case, we select *Value Of* and enter the value that we want the objective function to achieve.

STEP 3.2: Select *Changing Variable Cells*

Select the decision variables, called *Changing Variable Cells*. We click on the button to the right of the text box and highlight the decision variable cells, or we can enter the cell reference or a range name directly.

STEP 3.3: Add Constraints

Specify the constraints. To do so, we press the *Add* button next to the large *Constraint* textbox. The smaller window shown in Figure A.10 then appears. We must include the following three pieces of information in each added constraint: the cell with the constraint formula; the inequality sign; and the cell with the *RHS* value or a directly entered numerical value. We click *Add* to define the next constraints.

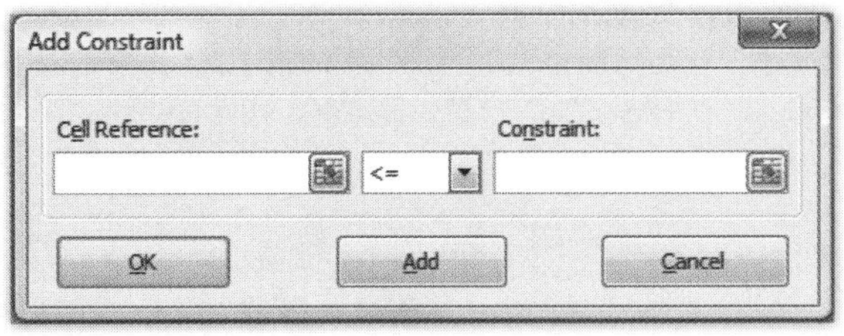

Figure A.10 *Adding Constraints* involves selecting the cell with the equation formula, choosing the inequality or equality sign, and selecting the cell with the RHS value. *Comment* and *Report* are optional.

After adding all of the constraints, press *OK* and return to the *Solver* dialog box. Observe all of the constraints in the *Constraint* textbox. Note that we can press the *Change* button to edit any of the constraints and the *Delete* button to erase them.

STEP 3.4: Select an Engine and *Set Solver Options*

From the *Solving Method* drop-down list select *Simplex LP* to solve linear programs, *GRG Nonlinear* to solve smooth nonlinear programs, and *Evolutionary* to solve non-smooth problems. Next, click the *Options* button to access the *Options* dialog box (see Figure A.11). We can change any of these options or leave them at their default values.

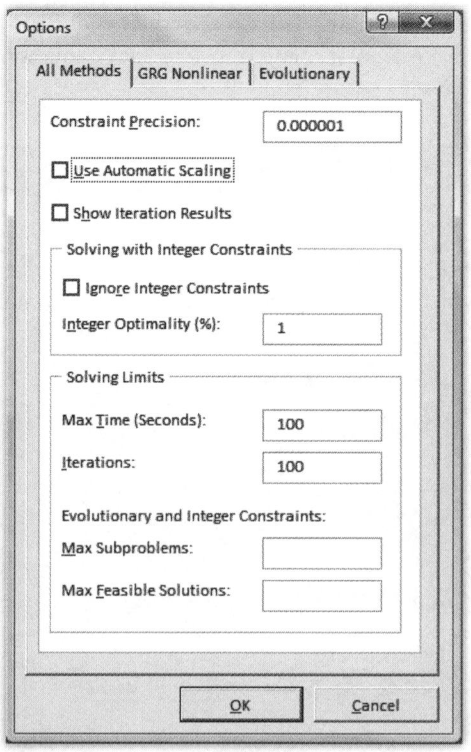

Figure A.11 The Options dialog box allows users to specify how Solver will work with a model.

STEP 3.5: Solve the *Model and Review the Results*

We now press *Solve* to run the *Solver*. After the *Solver* has found a solution, the window in Figure A.12 appears, and we are able to observe the *Solver* solution in the background on the spreadsheet.

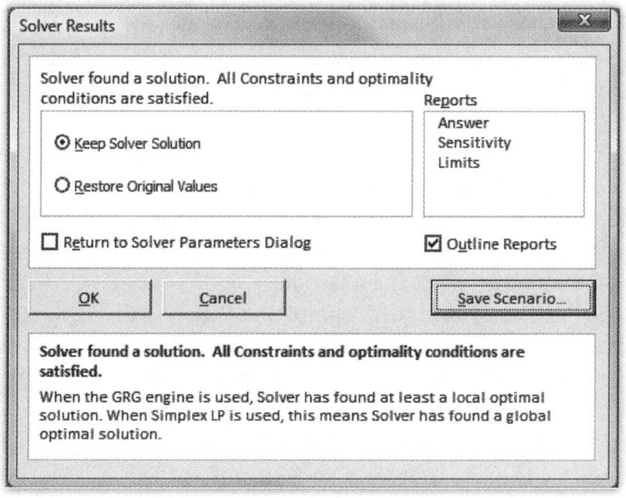

Figure A.12 Excel displays this window after we run Solver and find a solution.

After reviewing this solution, we can choose to *Keep the Solver Solution* or *Restore the Original Values*. We can also opt to have reports made from the *Solver* solution: the *Answer* report, the *Sensitivity* report, and the *Limits* report.

Summary

Steps for using the Standard Solver

Step 1: Read and Interpret the Problem.

- **1.1:** Decision Variables.
- **1.2:** Objective Function.
- **1.3:** Constraints.

Step 2: Prepare the Spreadsheet.

- **2.1:** Place the Input Table.
- **2.2:** Set the Decision Variables Cells.
- **2.3:** Enter the Constraint Formulas.
- **2.4:** Enter the Objective Function Formula.

Step 3: Solve the model with *Solver.*

- **3.1:** Set the Target Cell.
- **3.2:** Select the Changing Cells.
- **3.3:** Add the Constraints.
- **3.4:** Select a Solution Engine and Set the Solver Options.
- **3.5:** Solve the Model and Review the Results.

A.4.2 Frontline's Premium Solver

The *Premium Solver* is a subset product of *Risk Solver Platform. Risk Solver Platform* combines the capabilities of *Premium Solver* for optimization, *Risk Solver* for simulation, and other tools for optimization of *uncertain* models. Note that, you can use the Standard Solver and Premium Solver to work with a model that you have already created using Risk Solver Platform, and vice-versa.

The *Premium Solver* is located in the *Add-Ins* tab on the Ribbon. Note that, the Solver Parameters dialog box of the Premium Solver has similarities and differences with the Solver dialog box of the Standard Solver. However, a reader that is familiar with Chapter 8 should find it easy to navigate this dialog box. Steps 1 and 2 are exactly the same when using the Premium Solver as when using the standard Solver. Even the sub-steps 3.1, 3.2, and 3.3 are no different. However, depending on which algorithm we decide to use, there is a different set of Solver Options for sub-step 3.4.

The Solver Parameters dialog box has a drop-down list to select which Solving Method, or which set of algorithms, we want to use to solve the problem (see Figure A.13). The options listed are the Standard GRG Nonlinear, Standard LP/Quadratic, Standard Evolutionary, Standard Interval Global and Standard SOCP Barrier. These algorithms can solve linear and non-linear (smooth and non-smooth) problems.

The *Evolutionary Solver* is a hybrid of *genetic and evolutionary algorithms and classical optimization models* to solve non-smooth problems. Once we select this algorithm, we click on the *Options* button to access the dialog box shown in Figure A.14.

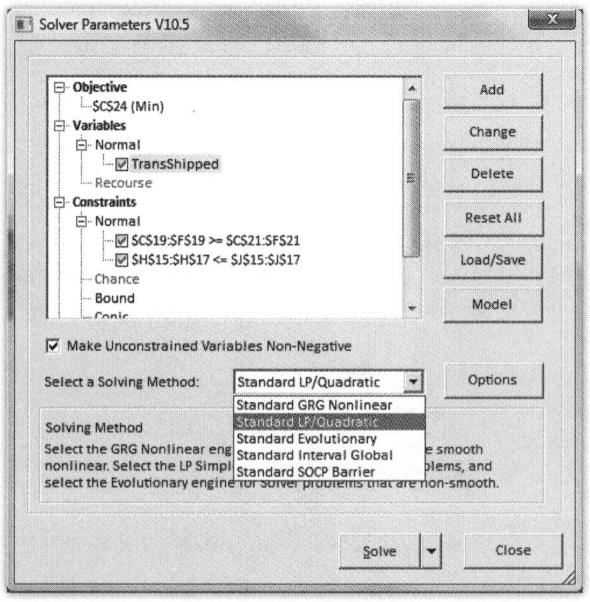

Figure A.13 The Premium Solver offers three different Solver methods.

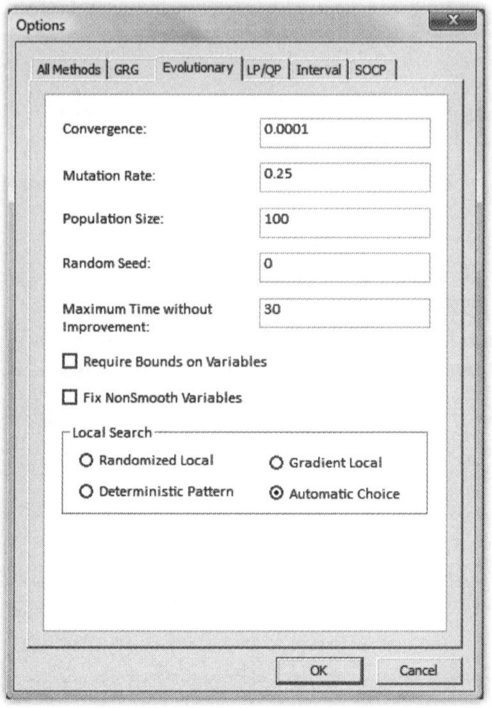

Figure A.14 The Options for the Standard Evolutionary Solver.

The *Population Size* and *Mutation Rate* are parameters associated with the *Genetic Algorithm*. The *Population Size* basically sets the initial number of feasible solutions. The *Mutation Rate* determines how often the "Mutation" part of the *Genetic Algorithm* is performed. We recommend setting the *Population Size* to at least 50; if there are several variables and constraints, it may be wiser to have a *Population Size* of 100 or 1,000. The *Mutation Rate* can be small, but it usually performs better at 0.25 than at 0.075. The Local Search options can be specified to further determine the behavior of the Genetic Algorithm. At this point, we will not further discuss this algorithm.

After we have specified these options, we can press *Solve* to run the Solver. The Solver Results window as shown in Figure A.15 then appears. We may see "Solver has converged to the current solution ..." or "Stop chosen when ..." as possible messages in this window. We also have a different list of available Solver Reports, including the Population Report. This report provides the best, mean, maximum, and minimum values along with the standard deviation of the *Changing Variable Cells*, or decision variable, values across all iterations.

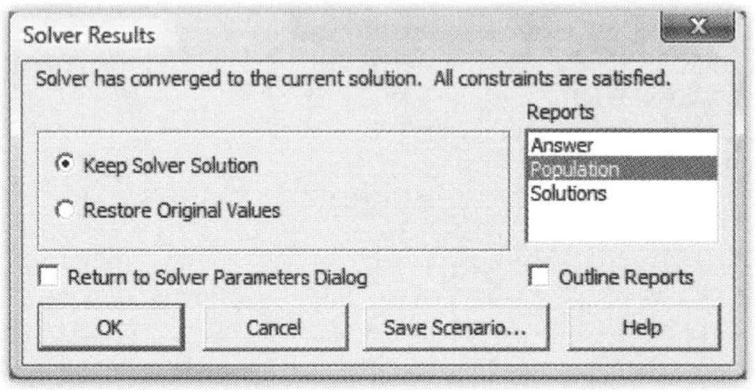

Figure A.15 The Solver Reports for the Evolutionary Solver include a Population Report.

A.4.3 Solver Commands in VBA

We will now learn how to identify the ranges which contain the decision variables, objective function, and constraints as input to the Solver using VBA code. We also learn how to set Solver options and run the Solver in VBA. We then see what VBA commands will generate Solver reports.

The first Solver function we use is the ***SolverReset*** function. This function resets all Solver parameters. All previous objective functions, decision variables, and constraint settings will be empty, and all Solver options will be set to their default values.

There are two main Solver functions used to input the Solver parameters in VBA. These are *SolverOK* and *SolverAdd*. We use ***SolverOK*** to set the objective function and decision variables. The format of this function and argument titles are as follows:

SolverOK(SetCell, MaxMinVal, ValueOf, ByChange)

We use the ***SetCell*** argument to specify the range of the objective function. The ***MaxMinVal*** argument specifies if this objective function will be maximized, minimized, or solved to a particular value. The values this argument can take are 1 (= maximize), 2 (= minimize), and 3 (= value). If this argument value is 3, then we use the ***ValueOf*** argument to set this value; if the objective function will be maximized or minimized, then this argument is ignored. The ***ByChange*** argument specifies the range which contains the decision variables.

We use the second main Solver function to input constraints; this is the ***SolverAdd*** function. We should use this function to add each individual constraint or each group of similar constraints. The *SolverAdd* function has three arguments:

SolverAdd(CellRef, Relation, FormulaText)

The ***CellRef*** argument specifies the range which contains a constraint equation. This equation should reference the decision variable cells. The ***Relation*** argument can take one of five values which specify the inequality of the constraint: 1 is <=, 2 is =, 3 is >=, 4 is *int* (integer values), and 5 is *bin* (binary, 0/1, values). The ***FormulaText*** argument specifies the range which contains the RHS value of the constraint.

There are two more functions which we can use to modify constraints: ***SolverChange*** and ***SolverDelete***. These functions will allow us to modify or delete constraints, respectively. They both have the same arguments as the *SolverAdd* function.

To set the Solver options in VBA, we use the ***SolverOptions*** function. This function has many arguments for each of the options we have seen previously in the Solver Options dialog box. There are two arguments which we will use more frequently, which are ***AssumeLinear*** and ***AssumeNonNeg***. Both of these arguments take *True/False* values; *True* makes the corresponding assumption. For most of our models, we will set both of these arguments to true as follows:

SolverOptions AssumeLinear:=True, AssumeNonNeg:=True

The other option arguments include ***MaxTime, Iterations, Precision, StepThru, Estimates, Derivatives, Search, IntTol, Scaling***, and ***Convergence***. We normally ignore these option arguments; however, we can explore these options in more detail using the *Help* menu option.

After we have entered the Solver input and have set any options, we are ready to run the Solver. To run the Solver in VBA, we use the function ***SolverSolve***. This function has two arguments and is written as follows:

SolverSolve(UserFinish, ShowRef)

The ***UserFinish*** argument uses a *True/False* value to determine whether to return the Solver results with or without showing the Solver Results dialog box. We will usually set this argument value to *True*; if the value is *False* then the Solver Results dialog box will appear after the Solver has run the model. We use the ***ShowRef*** argument with the *StepThru* option. The *StepThru* option causes the Solver to pause at each trial solution when it is set to *True*; *False* is the default value. Since we usually do not use this option, we will also usually omit the *ShowRef* argument of the *SolverSolve* function.

SolverSolve UserFinish:=True

The *SolverSolve* function also returns an integer value classifying the result. The values 0, 1, or 2 signify a successful run in which a solution has been found. The value 4 implies that there was no convergence, and the value 5 implies that no feasible solution could be found.

When the Solver has finished running, we can decide whether or not we want to keep the results and if we want to generate any reports. We specify this using the ***SolverFinish*** function. This function has two arguments and is written as follows:

SolverFinish(KeepFinal, ReportArray)

The ***KeepFinal*** argument takes the value 1 if we want to keep the Solver solution and the value 2 if we want to keep the previous values (if this is the first time running the Solver, then the previous values are null). The default value of this argument is 1, which is the value which we usually want; therefore, this argument does not need to be specified if we want to use the default value.

We use the ***ReportArray*** argument to specify which reports, if any, we want to generate. We enter the value of this argument using the *Array* function. The array values can be 1 (to generate an Answer Report), 2 (to generate a Sensitivity Analysis Report), and/or 3 (to generate a Limits Report). We can enter any or all of these values in the array. For example, if we want to keep our final solution and generate a Sensitivity Analysis Report and Limits Report for the above problem, we would type the following:

SolverFinish KeepFinal:=1, ReportArray:=Array(2, 3)

There are three functions that correspond to saving a set of Solver parameters: *SolverSave*, *SolverLoad*, and *SolverGet*. The ***SolverSave*** function will save a certain set of Solver parameters that have been summarized in a range on any worksheet. This range is the value of the one function argument ***SaveArea***. The ***SolverLoad*** function will load a set of Solver parameters that have been saved. The argument for this function, ***LoadArea***, will take the same value entered as the *SaveArea* argument in the *SolverSave* function. We can use the third function, ***SolverGet***, to find information about a set of Solver parameters. We can find more detailed information on its two arguments, ***TypeNum*** and ***SheetName***, using the *Help* menu option.

Summary

Function	**Description**	**Arguments**	**Values**
SolverOK	Input objective function and decision variables	**SetCell**	range
		MaxMinVal	1 (max), 2 (min), 3 (value)
		ValueOf	value
		ByChange	range
SolverAdd	Input constraints	**CellRef**	range
		Relation	1 (<=), 2(=), 3(>=), 4 (int), 5 (bin)
		FormulaText	range
SolverOptions	Set Solver options	**AssumeLinear**	True/False
		AssumeNonNeg	True/False
SolverSolve	Run the Solver	**UserFinish**	True/False
		ShowRef	
SolverFinish	Keeping results and generating reports	**KeepFinal**	1 (keep), 2 (ignore)
		ReportArray	Array(1, 2, and/or 3), where 1 (Answer Report), 2 (Sensitivity Analysis), 3 (Limits Report)

A.4.4 Limitations and Manipulations of the Standard Solver

Since the beginning of the Excel Solver in 1991, several improvements and modifications have been made to this optimization software. The software developers and users discovered some of the Standard Solver's limitations, which we will now discuss briefly. Note that we can overcome these limitations by using recent releases of Solver, or other Add-Ins available for use in Excel.

Let us first discuss problem size limitations. We are referring to the summarized table in Figure A.16 (from *www.solver.com*). The Standard Solver cannot solve linear and nonlinear programming problems with more than 200 variables. The Premium Solver, on the other hand, has a limit of 2,000 variables for linear programming problems, and 500 variables for nonlinear programming problems. However, Risk Solver Platform supports plug-in large-scale Solver Engines such as KNITRO, MOSEK, Gurobi, XPRESS, and OptQuest. These plug-in engines can solve problems with millions of variables.

We have also noted that it takes a long time for IP problems to be solved with the Standard Solver. The time for solving IP problems with the Premium Solver is 10 times faster than with the Standard Solver, and 20 to 40 times faster with Risk Solver Platform. It is clear that in order to solve larger problems, we should products such as Premium Solver, or plug-in large-scale Solver Engines offered by Risk Solver Platform.

Problem Size:	**Standard Solver**	**Premium Solver**	**Risk Solver Platform**
Linear Variables	200	2,000	8,000
Nonlinear Variables	200	500	1,000
Non-smooth variables	200	500	1,000
Speed (approximate):			
Linear Problems	1X	3X	40X
Mixed-Integer Problems	1X	10X	40X
Nonlinear Problems	1X	1X	7–15X
Non-Smooth Problems	1X	1–10X	2–20X

Figure A.16 A summary of the size and speed comparisons between the Standard Solver and Premium Solver.

Another potential problem with Solver and other mathematical software is poor scaling of related model parameters and variables. For optimization problem with a mixture of small and large coefficient values in the constraints or the objective function and the possible values that the decision variable can take, rescaling is necessary. For example, suppose we are solving a binary IP problem whose decision variable values can only be 0 or 1 and whose constraint coefficients are in the hundreds of thousands. When solving such a problem, Solver performs many calculations that require quantities derived from the objective function and constraints be divided or subtracted from one another. When these calculations are performed, due to manipulating numbers of different magnitudes, round-off errors build up to the point where Solver solutions are not reliable. To correct this error, we select *Use Automatic Scaling* box in the *Solver Options* dialog box. Solver will scale the values of the objective function and constraints internally to minimize the effect of poor scaling. However, since scaling is performed on the initial values of the variables, problems may arise when the final value of such a variable is different from its initial value by several orders of magnitude. Therefore, it is suggested that we must first re-scale the problem parameters by dividing the constraint coefficients by some large number and adjusting the costs to maintain proportionality. The Standard Solver is then able to find a solution, which should then be re-scaled again to find a solution proportional to the initial coefficient values.

There are also technical benefits to using the Premium Solver, including the algorithms. The algorithms available with the Standard Solver are Simplex LP, GRG Nonlinear and Evolutionary. These algorithms are used to solve linear programming, mixed-integer programming, and nonlinear smooth and non-smooth problems. In addition to these algorithms, the Premium Solver uses Standard LP/Quadratic, Standard Interval Global and Standard SOCP Barrier. These are algorithms specialized to solving quadratic programming, quadratically constrained, and second order cone programming problems. This is one of the main reason reasons why the Premium Solver manages to solve larger optimization problems faster than the Standard Solver.

We also would like to stress that Risk Solver Platform, the "super-product" of Frontline Systems Inc. supports plug-in large-scale solver engines capable of solving optimization problems of large size in a short amount of time. The plug-in solver engines are: KNITRO, a trademark of Ziena Optimization Inc.; MOSEK, a trademark of MOSEK ApS.; OptQuest, a trademark of OptTek Systems Inc.; and XpressMP, a trademark of FICO, Inc.

A.5 *CPLEX*

IBM® ILOG CPLEX Optimizer is a powerful tool for solving linear programming, network flow, quadratic programming, quadratic constrained programming, and mixed-integer programming problems. This tool is now available for use in Excel through a CPLEX solver Add-in. In order to use this Add-in to solve an optimization problem, we need to setup our spreadsheet by defining the data section, the decision variable section, objective function section, and constraint section. This spreadsheet setup is the same to spreadsheet setup for Risk Solver Platform discussed in Chapter 8. The Model Information dialog box (the equivalent of Solver Parameter dialog box of Risk Solver Platform) allows us to define the objective function, the sense of our objective function, the decision variables, and the problem constraints.

For more details, refer to the IBM website: *http://www.ibm.com/*.

A.6 *@RISK*

@RISK is a statistics and simulation Add-In program developed by Palisade. As an add-in, @ RISK is integrated with the Excel spreadsheet, enabling us to add risk analysis to our existing models. @RISK's risk analysis features allow us to see all possible outcomes in a given situation and tells us how likely they are to occur. @RISK uses Monte Carlo simulation to show us these outcomes. Running an analysis with @RISK involves three steps: defining uncertainty parameters, determining desired output, and running a simulation.

The newest version of @RISK, @RISK 5.7, lets us write our own custom applications using VBA functions created for @RISK. These allow us to dynamically use the @RISK reporting options, sensitivity analysis, scenario analysis, distribution fitting, and others. For a list of these functions, see: *http://www.palisade.com/risk/risk_vba_macros.asp*.

For more details, refer to the Palisade website: *http://www.palisade.com/*.

A.7 Crystal Ball

Crystal Ball is a simulation Add-In program developed by Decisioneering. Crystal Ball can help us create dynamic forecasting tools, manage risk, reduce variability, and make more informed business and strategic decisions. Crystal Ball performs two tasks: defining uncertainty and running a simulation. First, it lets us define the uncertain inputs in our spreadsheet as probability distributions. Second, it uses the defined distributions and Monte Carlo simulation to create thousands of possible alternative outcomes for our model. Beyond those two functions, Crystal Ball includes a set of statistical and graphing tools to create and present risk models.

For more details, refer to the Decisioneering Crystal Ball website: *http://www.crystalball.com/*.

A.8 StatTools

StatTools is another statistical Add-In program developed by Palisade. StatTools provides a very powerful statistical toolset within Excel, so you can analyze data and work in the familiar Microsoft Office environment. This add-in replaces several of Excel's worksheet statistics functions, with its own, robust StatTools versions. For example, Excel's AVERAGE function is replaced with StatMean() function. StatTools calculations meet the highest tests for accuracy, with performance optimized through the use of C++ .DLLs, not macro calculations.

For more details, refer to the Palisade website: *http://www.palisade.com/*.

A.9 Summary

- The Analysis ToolPak is an Add-In program that provides tools one can use to perform statistical analysis. This Excel Add-In includes statistical analysis techniques such as *Descriptive Statistics*, *Histograms*, *Exponential Smoothing*, *Correlation*, *Covariance*, *Moving Average*, and others.
- The Solver is an optimization Add-In designed to solve mathematical programming problems including linear, integer, and non-linear programming problems. Frontline Systems provides a Standard Solver and Premium Solver version of the Solver Add-In; the Premium Solver can solve large-size optimization problems faster mainly due to using a wider variety of algorithms that are specialized to better address specific problem characteristics.
- The Standard Solver has a limit of 200 variables for LP and NLP problems. The Premium Solver, on the other hand, has a limit of 2,000 variables for LP problems, and 1,000 variables for NLP problems.
- IBM® ILOG CPLEX Optimizer is a powerful tool for solving linear programming, network flow, quadratic programming, quadratic constrained programming, and mixed-integer programming problems.
- @RISK is a statistics and simulation Add-In program developed by Palisade. As an add-in, @RISK is integrated with the Excel spreadsheet, enabling us to add risk analysis to our existing models.
- Crystal Ball is a simulation Add-In program developed by Decisioneering. Crystal Ball can help us create dynamic forecasting tools, manage risk, reduce variability, and make more informed business and strategic decisions.
- StatTools is another statistical Add-In program developed by Palisade. StatTools replaces Excel's built-in statistics with its own statistical functions.

APPENDIX B

B Debugging and Error Checking

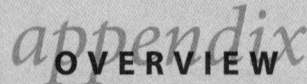

appendix OVERVIEW

B.1 *Introduction*

In this appendix chapter, we offer help to the reader in understanding possible errors that may be encountered in VBA. We describe the types of errors that may be found and some tools to identify the cause of these errors. We also give some suggestions for avoiding errors in the VBA code.

B.2 *Types of Errors*

After designing and coding an application, we will usually encounter some "bugs" or errors when running our program for the first or first several times. These errors can be simple or more complicated. Some simple errors may include misspelling words in variables or range references, misnaming User Form objects, and forgetting to declare variables, dimension arrays before using them, or initialize counting variable values or range variables. These are simple in that they do not take long to correct and are usually easy to identify.

Summary

Some possible simple errors:

- Misspelling words in variables or range references
- Forgetting to declare variables
- Forgetting to initialize counting variable values or range variables
- Forgetting to dimension arrays before using them
- Misnaming User Form objects

Some of the more complicated errors may be ***logical errors***—improper use of properties or methods—or ***user-created errors***. Property and Method misuse requires us to review our knowledge of various properties and methods; the Help file can be useful for this. However, logical errors and user-created errors will require the use of some extra debugging tools and error-checking commands.

Logical errors are usually found in loop structures, especially nested loops, but may also be found in other structures, such as complex conditional structures. For these errors, the code runs without a problem, but the results are inaccurate. These errors are complicated because they are usually hard to identify. Since the code will not display an error and bring us to the problem point in the code, we will have to use the debugging techniques described below to "walk through" our code and determine where the logical error may be. Once we have identified the error, we will have to return to any mathematical modeling or outline of our application to ensure that the appropriate calculations or actions are being performed in the correct order.

User-created errors can also be complicated and hard to determine. Users may delete cells whose names are referenced in the code, input data incorrectly, or press buttons in a different order than we intended. These errors will not be found in our code but should be prevented by placing extra commands or structures in our code. These error checking, or preventing, methods are discussed below.

Summary

Logical errors:	To identify these, use the *debugging* tools described below.
User-created errors:	To prevent these, use the *error checking* commands below.

B.3 The Debug Toolbar

The Debug Toolbar contains helpful debugging tools to search through our code and identify possible errors. To view this toolbar, go to *View > Toolbars > Debug* in the VBE (see Figure B.1). The first icon on the toolbar is the ***Design Mode*** icon, which allows us to modify shapes, buttons, control toolbox objects, or other objects in Excel. The next three icons are ***Run***, ***Pause***, and ***Stop***, which are used to perform the respective actions with the code. The next several icons are the primary debugging icons.

There is a breakpoint tool icon and three main stepping tool icons that we will use to debug our code. We discuss these debugging features in the next section. Stepping through a program allows us to execute the code in steps; these steps can be one line at a time, one loop at a time, one procedure at a time, etc. We can use these tools throughout the entire code or in a particular procedure or segment of code. There are also some debugging window options available on the toolbar, which we will discuss in a later section.

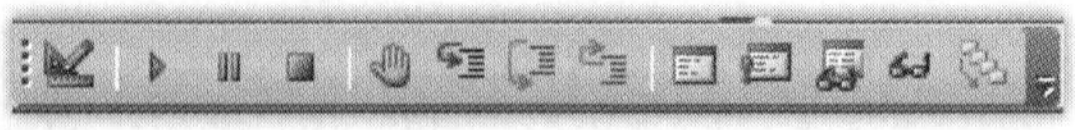

Figure B.1 The Debug Toolbar.

We can also find these tools plus others listed under the Debug menu in the VBE (see Figure B.2). The first option in this menu is ***Compile VBAProject***. This tool checks our code for any syntax errors, usually simple errors, without executing the code. There is one extra stepping tool, called *Run To Cursor*, which we describe below. There is also an extra breakpoint tool given here; again we describe this in more detail below.

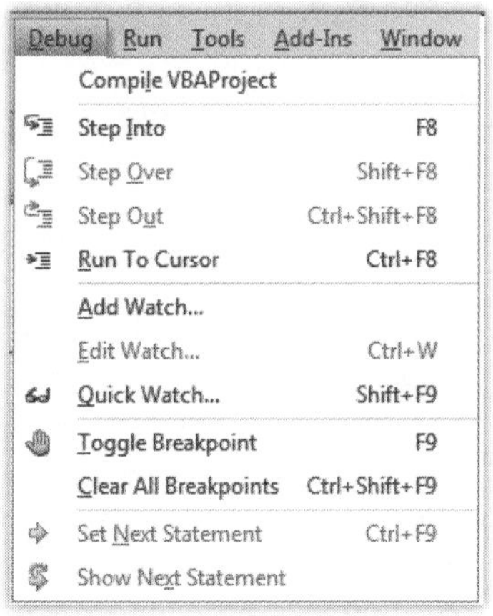

Figure B.2 The Debugging tools listed in the Debug menu.

B.3.1 Step-Into

The ***Step-Into*** stepping code is used to execute every line of code one line at a time. To use Step-Into, use the  icon from the Debug Toolbar, the *Step Into* option from the Debug menu, or the shortcut key *F8*. This tool is the most common stepping tool; it is used to initiate stepping through code in which all stepping tools can be used. It is also used to find the exact line in which a bug exists. That is, the other stepping tools can be used to step through larger segments of code, but once we arrive at an area in the code where we guess or know the bug is, we will always use the Step-Into tool to find the exact line or exact moment when the bug occurs. When the code is in run mode, we can place and hold our cursor over any variable to see its current value. This is especially helpful when debugging for logical errors.

B.3.2 Step-Over

The ***Step-Over*** tool will skip over code called procedures. That is, if we are stepping through code in a sub procedure that calls another sub procedure or a function procedure, when the *Call* statement is read, the Step-Into tool would move to the called procedure and continue executing code one line at a time, whereas the Step-Over tool will skip the called procedure (executing it in normal run time, not one line at a time) and move on to the next line of code in the main procedure. To use Step-Over, use the  icon from the Debug Toolbar, the *Step Over* option from the Debug menu, or the shortcut key *Shift+F8*.

B.3.3 Step-Out

The ***Step-Out*** tool is also used primarily with called procedures. If we are stepping through a procedure in which another procedure is called, and instead of using the Step-Over tool to skip this called procedure code we continue using Step-Into, we may find ourselves in a long loop or sequence of actions in this called procedure in which we do not believe a bug will be found. To finish executing all of the code in this called procedure at once and return to the main procedure, use the Step-Out tool. To use Step-Out, use the  icon from the Debug Toolbar, the *Step Out* option from the Debug menu, or the shortcut key *Ctl+Shift+F8*.

B.3.4 Run To Cursor

The ***Run To Cursor*** tool allows us to execute code in normal run time until the point at which our cursor is located in the code; at this point the code is paused, and we can step through the code using the other stepping tools. The Run To Cursor tool is found in the Debug menu, not the Debug Toolbar; it has the shortcut key *Ctl+F8*.

B.3.5 Breakpoints

Breakpoints are used like the *Run To Cursor* tool. A breakpoint is set on a particular line of code (seen as a highlighted line across the code), and when the program is run, execution occurs in normal run time for every line of code before the breakpoint and pauses at the breakpoint. Debugging a particular part of a large program may be easier if all previous lines of code are executed quickly and then the step through tool is used to slowly narrow the search for the bug. The main difference between *Run To Cursor* and breakpoints is that multiple breakpoints can be placed in our code. This can be advantageous if there is more than one place where we suspect the bug to be. We can execute code to the first breakpoint, use a few step through tools to analyze some lines of code, then execute until the next breakpoint, and so on; use the *Run* option to execute code in normal run time until each breakpoint.

To place breakpoints in the code, select a line of code and use the ***Toggle Breakpoint*** tool. To use this tool, choose the icon from the Debug Toolbar, the Toggle Breakpoint option from the Debug menu, or the shortcut key *F9*; we can also simply click on the left-hand margin of the code window next to the line where we want to insert the breakpoint. To remove a breakpoint from our code, use the Toggle Breakpoint again on the same line of code where the breakpoint currently is. We can also use the ***Clear All Breakpoints*** option from the Debug menu to clear all breakpoints added to the code; the shortcut for this tool is *Ctl+Shift+F9*. There are other debugging tools available, but these are the ones we will use most often.

Summary

Step through tools

- **Step-Into:** execute each line of code
- **Step-Over:** skip over called procedures
- **Step-Out:** exit current procedure

Executing and pausing

- **Run To Cursor:** execute until point where cursor is
- **Toggle Breakpoint:** place or remove breakpoints
- **Clear All Breakpoints:** remove all placed breakpoints

B.4 *The Debug Windows*

As mentioned in Chapter 11, there are two debug windows available in the VBE: the *Watch Window* and the *Immediate Window*. These are useful tools in keeping track of what is happening to variable values, properties and methods, and possible bug locations.

B.4.1 Watch Window

In the Watch window, we type variable names to be "watched" by VBE and displayed whenever their values change. To view the *Watch Window*, choose *View > Watch Window* in the VBE, or use the icon from the Debug Toolbar.

To enter a variable into the Watch Window, use the ***Add Watch*** option from the Debug menu; we can also right-click in the Watch Window and select *Add Watch* from the drop-down options or simply highlight a variable in the Code Window and drag it to the Watch Window. If we use the Add Watch tool, we will see the window shown in Figure B.3; here we can enter the name of the variable and the location of the variable: procedure and module names.

Note that the location of the variable is very important. If we choose a private variable, for example, we will not be able to view its value once we have moved to another procedure. Likewise, if we want to watch a public variable that is used in different modules, we will need to add a watch for each variable location. Any time the code is executed in a location different from the watched variable location, we will see an *<Out of Context>* message instead of the variable value.

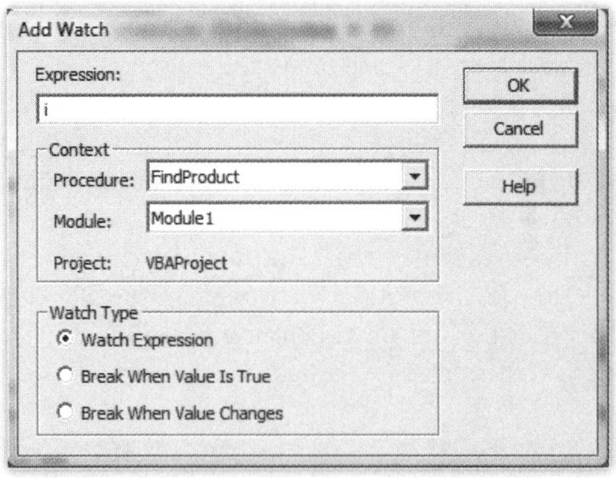

Figure B.3 Add Watch places variables in the Watch Window.

There are also three ***Watch Types*** available: ***Watch Expression***, ***Break When Value Is True***, and ***Break When Value Changes***. The Watch Expression will be the most commonly used Watch Type; this simply allows us to view the variable value as it changes. The break options will pause the code when the specified action occurs.

The Watch Window is very useful for checking for logical errors. It can also help us keep track of counting variables in loop structures and input values from the user (see Figure B.4).

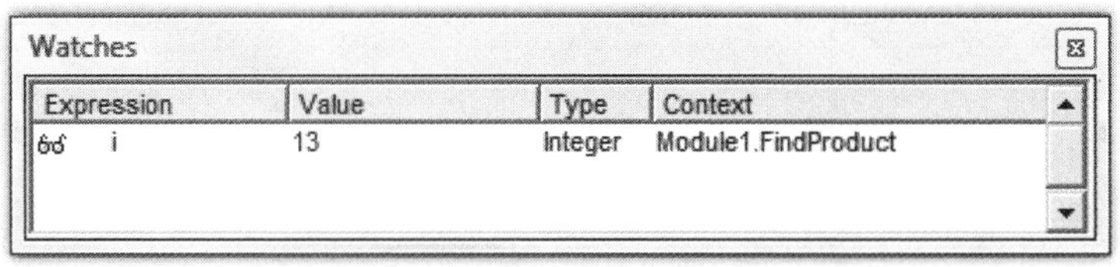

Figure B.4 The Watch Window is tracking the value of the counting variable i.

To check the current value of a variable while using the step through tools, we can use the ***Quick Watch*** tool. To do this, we highlight a variable in our code and use the icon from the Debug Toolbar or select the *Quick Watch* option from the Debug menu. The Quick Watch window will tell us the value and location of the selected variable (see Figure B.5). We can press the ***Add*** button in the Quick Watch dialog box to add this variable to the Watch Window. We can also hold our cursor over a particular variable in the Code Window to see its value. This is a useful tool when we do not wish to populate the Watch Window with too many variables, but rather just to check while running the code some other variables that are not as much of a concern as those in the Watch Window.

Figure B.5 Quick Watch shows the value and location of the selected variable.

B.4.2 Immediate Window

Whatever is typed in the Immediate Window is executed as soon as it is entered. To view the Immediate Window, choose *View > Immediate Window* from the VBE toolbar, or use the icon from the Debug Toolbar. We can use this window to check particular actions before entering them into our code, to test certain procedures that may be called in the code, or perform other sets of actions. To use the Immediate Window, simply type directly in it as we would in the Code Window (see Figure B.6). This can be a useful tool for checking if code will work before we insert it into our program and for narrowing the bug search to a particular set of actions in the middle of our code.

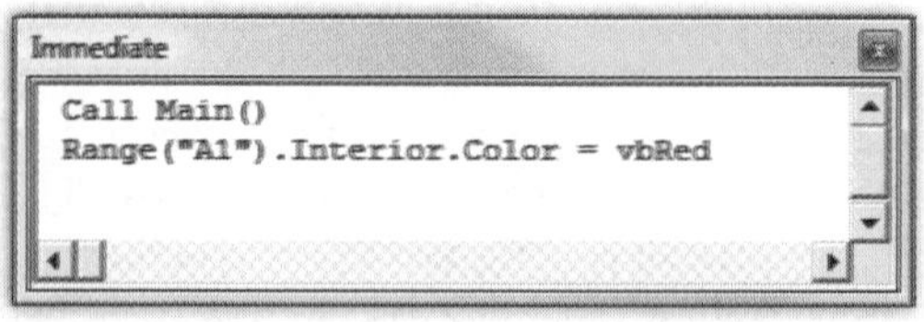

Figure B.6 The Immediate Window executes a line of code as soon as it is entered.

Summary

Watch Window:	Variable names are typed to be "watched" by VBE and displayed whenever their values change.
Add Watch:	Used to enter a variable into the Watch Window.
Quick Watch:	Used to check the current value of a variable while using the step through tools.
Immediate Window:	Whatever is typed in the Immediate Window is executed as soon as it is entered.

B.5 *Debugging Tips*

There are some ideas to keep in mind while coding and debugging to reduce the search for bugs. First of all, as mentioned earlier, check for simple errors first, such as misspellings. These are the most common errors and, fortunately, the easiest to correct. Another good idea is to keep our code organized. If we have several smaller procedures instead of large procedures, then debugging can be performed much more easily. It will be easier to identify segments of code that run correctly and those that generate errors.

Another important idea to remember is making sure that necessary References have been added to our project in the VBE. For example, if we are trying to use Solver functions, we must first reference the Solver using *Tools > References* in the VBE. Similarly, if we are trying to call functions from the Analysis ToolPak, we will need to ensure that the necessary Add-Ins has been installed.

B.6 *Error Checking*

The above debugging techniques are used to check already-written code. These error checking techniques, however, will be additional code added to our program to prevent user-created errors and to keep the program running without too many VBA error messages.

B.6.1 Review of some techniques

We have discussed some error checking techniques in previous chapters. For example, to check whether a user has entered a numerical value with an Input Box, we use a *Variant* data type temporary variable and the *IsNumeric* function (see Chapter 16). Another error checking technique we saw was with User Form objects. To ensure that all text box values were filled when an OK command button was clicked, we used the *Control* data type, *TypeName* function, and *SetFocus* method (see Chapter 18). We also used error checking techniques with the Solver functions. To prevent VBA error messages for infeasibility, we get the status of the solution using the *OptimizeStatus* property of *Solver*, and assigned this value to a variable (see Chapter 19). With all of these techniques, we always use an If, Then statement to check whether an error condition is true or not. We then use Message Boxes to communicate possible errors to the user.

Communication with the user is very important and can prevent several errors from happening. It is important to make Input Box and User Form statements clear. We should also specify any necessary instructions on the spreadsheets in the program to help guide the user. We have seen in previous chapters how to hide and show various buttons, or shapes, on the spreadsheet at different times during the program. This is another good preventative method to keep the user from choosing options or actions at an inappropriate time.

There are some other helpful techniques to prevent user-created errors and to keep the program running if these errors occur.

B.6.2 Is Functions

Aside from the *IsNumeric* function used previously, there are some other ***IsFunctions*** available for error checking. The ***IsNull*** function checks whether or not a variable has a valid value. This is useful with Input Boxes or Text Boxes to ensure that the user has entered some valid value. Similar to this function is the ***IsEmpty*** function. This function checks whether or not a variable has been initialized or whether or not a *String* variable contains any value or is an empty string "". This can be important if we are depending on the user to give some value to variables which will be used in later references or calculations.

There are two useful *Is Functions* used to check data types: ***IsArray*** and ***IsDate***. The *IsArray* function checks whether or not a particular variable is being used as an array. For example, if a variable is declared with the intention of becoming an array, it may not be given a particular size or data type but be declared as a *Variant*. Then, later in the code, we may assign this variable some user-defined values using an *Array* function. To check whether this assignment was performed correctly, we would use the *IsArray* function with this variable. The *IsDate* function checks whether or not a variable has a value that can be converted to a date. If the variable was declared as a *Date* data type, it would check that the values assigned are valid. If the variable was declared as a *String*, it would check that the format of the string value can be converted to a date. This is useful since most users enter dates using a variety of string formats and not *Date* data type values.

Summary

Is Functions

IsNumeric:	Checks whether or not a variable has a numeric value.
IsNull:	Checks whether or not a variable has a valid value.
IsEmpty:	Checks whether or not a variable has been initialized.
IsArray:	Checks whether or not a particular variable is being used as an array.
IsDate:	Checks whether or not a variable has a value that can be converted to a date.

B.6.3 On Error Resume Next

The ***On Error Resume Next*** statement is used to skip an error and continue running the program. This statement should be placed before a line of code in which an error may occur; to identify these areas, consider sections where users are affecting the variable values or actions of the code. Note that if we resume running the code after an error has possibly occurred, there may be some incorrect calculations or reports made if the user has provided bad input. Therefore, we recommend using this statement when there is a possible user-created error that may generate a VBA error message that we want to avoid but will not directly affect the value of any variables or other insignificant object properties. For example, in the following code we have initialized an integer variable value so that if the user enters a non-integer input value, we can ignore the error and continue with the code.

```
Sub CopyPaste()
    Dim size As Integer
    size = 1

    On Error Resume Next
    size = InputBox("How many values do you want to copy?")

    Range("A1").Offset(size,0).Copy
    Range("B1").PasteSpecial
End Sub
```

B.6.4 On Error GoTo

The ***On Error GoTo*** statement is also used to avoid seeing the VBA error messages. This statement should also be placed before a line of code in which an error may occur. The difference with this statement is that there should be a line number or procedure name after the statement *GoTo*. Line numbers are not automatically given in VBA code; rather, we have to insert our own for specific areas of code if desired. To insert a ***line number***, simply enter any number in the first column of the VBE Code Window (do not tab) and place a colon (:) at the end of the line. These numbers do not have to be relative to the location of the procedure in our module; that is, the line numbers are independent for each procedure. For example, in the following code, we have numbered the lines 1 through 4. In this example, if the user does not enter a positive number for the integer variable, the Log function cannot be performed. Therefore, we return to the Input Box statement on line 2 of the code.

```
Sub Division()
1: Dim UserVal As Integer

2: UserVal = InputBox("Please enter a positive number.")

3: On Error GoTo 2
4: MsgBox "The log base 2 of your number is: " & Log(UserVal)

End Sub
```

We can also use ***line labels***; these are entered into the code in the same manner as line numbers, but they can be any word instead of a number. (Note that we can enter line numbers and line labels either on the same line of code or on the line above the relative code.) In the following example, we use the *On Error GoTo* statement to ensure that we do not try to take the square root of a negative number.

```
Sub CalcSqRt()
  Dim UserVal As Integer

InputLine:
  UserVal = InputBox("Please enter a number.")

  On Error GoTo InputLine
  MsgBox "The square root of this number is: " & Sqr(UserVal)

End Sub
```

Note that we can only "go to" a line within the current procedure. For example, we may want to redirect the user to perform a different set of actions, or we may simply move to a new loop or line of statements in the code if an error occurs. We can also use the ***GoTo*** statement by itself to return to any line of code after we have found an error and reacted to it.

B.6.5 Err Object

There is also an ***Err*** object that can be used to understand what error is occurring and to redirect the user accordingly. The Err object will be used most often with the ***Number*** property. Each VBA error has a number associated with it; notice the number at the top of the VBA error message when an error occurs (see Figure B.7).

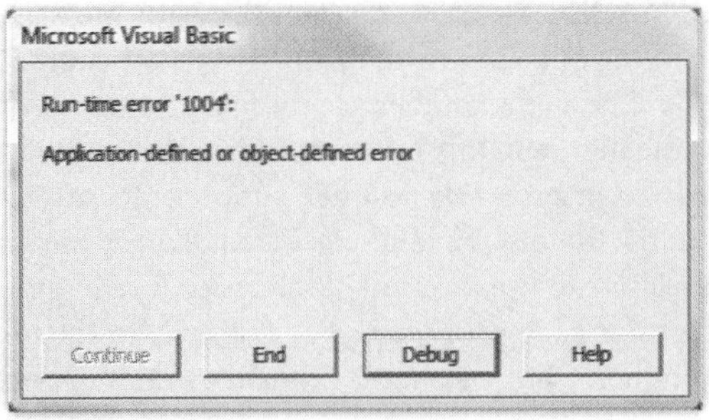

Figure B.7 The number of this VBA error is '1004.'

This can be a useful error checking technique in that we can immediately redirect the user in a specific manner. For example, if we are using range names in our code and the user has deleted the cell that contained the range name, we can identify this error by the Err *Number* property and specifically instruct the user to rename the cell in Excel. This check is usually done with an *If, Then* statement in combination with the *On Error Resume Next* statement. We will need to ignore the error first and then analyze it. The code below would generate the error message shown in Figure B.7 if there were no such ranges named in Excel:

```
Sub Test3()
    Range("Input").Copy
    Range("Result").PasteSpecial
End Sub
```

If we use the error checking techniques below, however, then the user will only see our Message Boxes and no VBA error messages:

```
Sub Test3()
    On Error Resume Next
    Range("Input").Copy
    If Err.Number = "1004" Then
        MsgBox "Please select cell A2 and name it 'Input'."
        Exit Sub
    End If
    On Error Resume Next
    Range("Result").PasteSpecial
    If Err.Number = "1004" Then
        MsgBox "Please select cell B2 and name it 'Result'."
        Exit Sub
    End If
End Sub
```

There are other properties of the Err object; however, we feel the *Number* property will be the most useful.

Summary

On Error Resume Next:	Used to skip an error and continue running the program.
On Error GoTo:	Used to skip to a line number or procedure name after the words Go To.
Err.Number:	Used to understand what error is occurring and to redirect the user accordingly.

B.7 *Summary*

- Some simple errors may include misspelling words in variables or range references, misnaming User Form objects, and forgetting to declare variables, dimension arrays before using them, or initialize counting variable values or range variables.
- Logical errors are usually found in loop structures, especially nested loops. For these errors, the code runs without a problem, but the results are inaccurate. Use debugging tools to identify these errors.
- User-created errors can also be complicated and hard to determine. Users may delete cells whose names are referenced in the code, input data incorrectly, or press buttons in a different order than we intended. Use error checking techniques to identify and prevent these errors.
- The Debug Toolbar and Debug menu provide debugging tools to search for simple errors or logical errors.
- The *Step-Into* stepping code is used to execute every line of code. It is used to initiate stepping through code in which all stepping tools can be used. It is also used to find the exact line in which a bug exists.
- The *Step-Over* tool will skip over code-called procedures (executing it in normal run time not one line at a time) and move on to the next line of code in the main procedure.
- The *Step-Out* tool is also used primarily to finish executing all of the code in a called procedure at once and return to the main procedure.
- The *Run To Cursor* tool allows us to execute code in normal run time until the point at which our cursor is located in the code; at this point the code is paused and we can step through the code using the other stepping tools.
- A breakpoint is set on a particular line of code, and when the program is run, execution occurs in normal run time for every line of code before the breakpoint and pauses at the breakpoint. The main difference between *Run To Cursor* and breakpoints is that multiple breakpoints can be placed in our code. Use the tools *Toggle Breakpoint* and *Clear All Breakpoints*.
- There are two debugging windows: Watch Window and Immediate Window.
- In the Watch window, we type variable names to be "watched" by VBE and displayed whenever their values change. Use *Add Watch* to add a variable to the watch window.
- Whatever is typed in the Immediate Window is executed as soon as it is entered.
- Error Checking techniques from past chapters include using the *Variant* data type, *IsNumeric* function, *Control* data type, *TypeName* function, and *SetFocus* method.
- Other useful *Is Functions* include: *IsNull*, *IsEmpty*, *IsArray*, and *IsDate*.
- Two useful error checking statements are *On Error Resume Next* and *On Error Go To*. The *On Error Resume Next* statement is used to skip an error and continue running the program. The difference with this statement and the On *Error Go To* statement is that there should be a line number or procedure name after the words *Go To*.
- Line numbers and line labels can be added to our code to use with *Go To* statements.
- The Err object can be used to understand what error is occurring and to redirect the user accordingly. The Err object will be used most often with the Number property.

APPENDIX C

C Advanced Programming Topics

OVERVIEW

C.1 *Introduction*

This appendix chapter is intended to give the reader an idea of the advanced programming that can be done using VBA for Excel. The VBA topics covered in Part II of the text present an overview of how to use VBA to create procedures and some GUI in order to develop a DSS application. However, there are other advanced programming features available in VBA that can enable a developer to create a more sophisticated DSS. In this appendix chapter, we discuss object-oriented programming in VBA using class modules. We also discuss how to call outside applications from within VBA code to allow another program to aid in the DSS operations. More details on these and other advanced programming topics are discussed in texts devoted solely to VBA.

C.2 *Object-Oriented Programming in VBA for Excel*

We have already introduced VBA for Excel as an object-oriented programming language in the sense that it is used to manipulate Excel objects. In Chapter 11, we explain how properties, methods, and events are the three ways in which an Excel object can be manipulated using VBA. A property changes a descriptive value, a method performs an action, and an event reacts to a user's action. Object-oriented programming in the general sense implies that objects can be defined in the code along with their descriptive values and functions. Such programming features are also found in languages such as C++, Java, and VB .Net. In this section, we describe how to go beyond the available list of objects, properties, methods, and events in VBA for Excel and define a new custom list of objects.

C.2.1 Class Modules

To define a new object in VBA, we use class modules. To use a class module, we simply insert one into our project as we have done when inserting modules and user forms: in the VBE, click *Insert > Class Module* from the main menu or use the insert icon. A new class module will then appear in the Project Explorer (see Figure C.1).

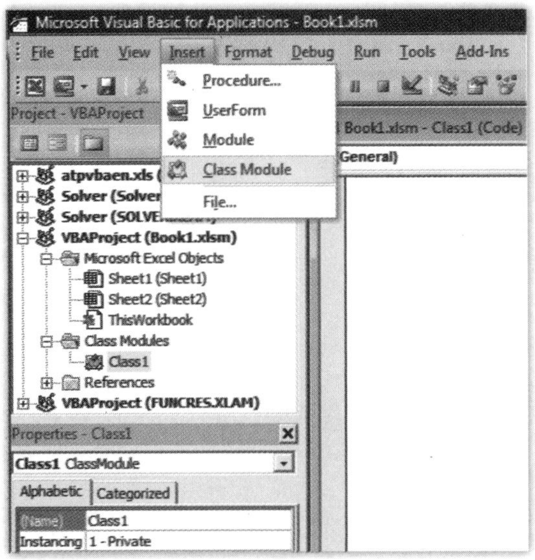

Figure C.1 A class module has been inserted.

Once we have inserted a class module, we should change its name property. In Figure C.1, the default name given to a new class module is "Class#," where # refers to the number of the class module we have added. Use the Properties window to change the selected class module's name to reflect the type of object we are going to create. This class module name will, in fact, be the new object's name.

Let us create an object as an example of using class modules. Suppose that we want to create a portfolio object that we may use in a portfolio DSS. We may want to create such an object so that we could create and manipulate portfolios directly with the new portfolio object's properties and methods. That is, the code used to create these features and functions of the portfolio (in the class module) would be called indirectly in repeated situations, which would alleviate the need for us to repeat this code in our main module. To begin creating this new portfolio object, we would first insert a class module and rename it "Portfolio" (see Figure C.2).

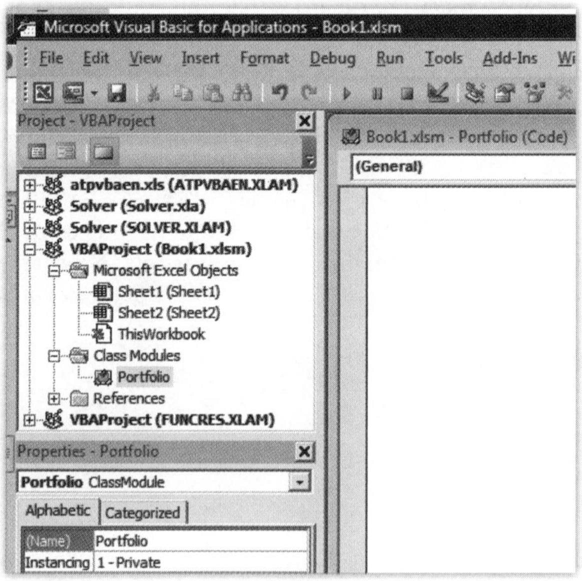

Figure C.2 A new class module is inserted and named "Portfolio" to create the new portfolio object.

C.2.2 Defining Properties

There are two different types of property definitions that we can use to define a new object: ***Get*** and ***Let***. The *Get* property definition allows a user to get a property value for the object. The *Let* property definition allows a user to set a property value for the object.

The format for the *Get* definition is as follows:

```
Property Get property_name1() As property_data_type
        property_name = some_value
End Property
```

The property definition procedure is similar to a function procedure in that a value is returned for the property name. Note that we may pass some variables or values to the property procedure if needed. Note also that we must define the data type of the property.

The *Get* definition can be used alone, however, if the *Let* definition is used, it must also have a corresponding *Get* definition. The format for the *Let* definition is as follows:

Property Let property_name2(set_value) As data_type
some_value = set_value
End Property

Here, we see that the *Let* procedure depends on the value to which the object property is being set (above, *set_value*). Notice that the property name (which is different from the property name used in the *Get* procedure) is not returned with a value. Instead, the variable that is used as the property value in the *Get* procedure (here, *some_value*) is assigned the new value in the *Let* procedure (*some_value = set_value*).

Let us return to our portfolio object example and create two properties. We will use both of these property definition types to create properties that find and change the value of the name of the portfolio. To write the *Get* procedure, we will use the property name "PortName." We could assign this variable to any value for the portfolio name, but we will use a variable "UserName" to hold this name value. This variable may be initialized to some value, such as "Portfolio1"; we discuss this in section C.2.4 on defining events. We will also use this variable in creating the *Let* procedure.

For the *Let* procedure, we will use the property name "SetName." We will use a variable, "NewName," to receive the new property value that is passed to the procedure. We will then assign the name value variable "UserName" to this new value variable "NewName," See Figure C.3 for the *Get* and *Let* property procedures for the name property of the portfolio object.

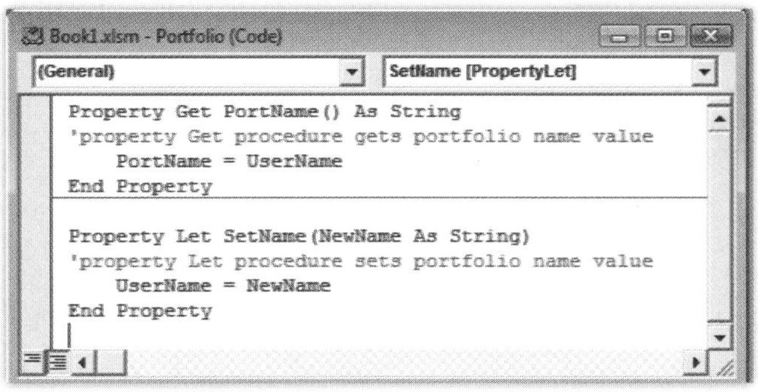

Figure C.3 The *Get* and *Let* procedures for finding and changing the name of the portfolio object.

In a procedure in our main module, we could now use these new object properties to find and change the portfolio name. For example, in the following code we display the current, or default, portfolio name and then change it and display the new name.

```
MsgBox Portfolio.PortName              'display current portfolio name
Portfolio.SetName = "MyPortfolio"      'change name to "MyPortfolio"
MsgBox Portfolio.PortName              'display new name
```

(*Note:* we would not actually use "Portfolio" as the object name in the code, but would create a variable instance of this object. We discuss this more in section C.2.5 on how to use new class objects.) We may consider other properties as well. How would we define a property that reports the size of the portfolio? (Hint: Read section C.2.3 to learn about the array variable used to store the portfolio information.)

C.2.3 Defining Methods

To define a new method, we use standard sub or function procedures. We would use a function procedure if we wished to return a value for our method, such as in the *MsgBox* function, which can be used to return a value indicating the user's button choice. If there are any arguments required for the method, list them as parameters in the method procedure with their respective data types. For example, a general method format may be as follows:

Sub method_name(argument1 As data_type)

Actions to perform, using argument1 value

End Sub

For our portfolio object example, let us consider two methods to create: adding a stock to the portfolio and printing the portfolio stocks and values. We will call the first method the "AddStock" method. To add a stock to our portfolio object, we want to record the stock name and value. Thus, we will need two arguments for our method, which we will call "StockName" and "StockVal." The outline of this method procedure will be as follows:

Sub AddStock(StockName As String, StockVal As Double)

...

End Sub

We will store all stocks and values for the portfolio in an array that we will update in this method procedure. For now, let us assume this portfolio array, "PortArray," has already been defined (we discuss initializing variables in Section C.2.4). We use a variable "PortSize" to store the number of stocks in the portfolio. Therefore, the "PortArray" array is a two-dimensional array of size two by "PortSize," with the first dimension value equal to the stock name and the second dimension value equal to the stock price. That is, for some stock *i* (*i* = 1 to "PortSize"):

PortArray(1, i) = stock_name_i

PortArray(2, i) = stock_value_i

When we add a new stock to our portfolio object, we will first need to update the "PortSize" variable value, then re-dimension the "PortArray" array variable, and then record the new stock name and stock value to the array. The resulting "AddStock" method procedure is shown in Figure C.4.

```
(General)                                AddStock

Sub AddStock(StockName As String, StockVal As Double)
'method to add stock to portfolio using given name and value

'increase portfolio size
    PortSize = PortSize + 1
    ReDim Preserve PortArray(2, PortSize)

'input new value
    PortArray(1, PortSize) = StockName
    PortArray(2, PortSize) = StockVal
End Sub

Sub PrintPort()
'method to display current portfolio
'output portfolio array elements to worksheet
    For i = 1 To PortSize
        Range("A1").Offset(i, 0).Value = PortArray(1, i)
        Range("B1").Offset(i, 0).Value = PortArray(2, i)
    Next i
End Sub
```

Figure C.4 The "AddStock" and "PrintPort" method procedures.

For the second method we want to define, we will create a procedure called "PrintPort." To print the portfolio, we will simply output to the spreadsheet all of the current stock names and values stored to our portfolio object array. We therefore do not need any input parameters, or arguments, for this method procedure. We will simply loop through the array, using the "PortSize" dimension variable, and output both the stock name and stock value to the spreadsheet. The complete "PrintPort" method procedure is shown in Figure C.4.

We may consider other methods that modify the "PortArray" array variable. How would we create a method for removing a stock from the portfolio? How would we create a method for changing the stock value of a particular stock in the portfolio? What other methods may be useful for our portfolio object?

C.2.4 Defining Events

There are two events that can be defined for a new object: *Initialize* and *Terminate*. The *Initialize* event is automatically called whenever a new instance of the object is created, and the *Terminate* event is automatically called whenever the object instance is deleted. The formats for these events are as follows:

Sub Class_Initialize()
    . . .
End Sub
Sub Class_Terminate()
    . . .
End Sub

Notice that the word "Class" is used as the general object name for this event, not the object name that was created (such as "Portfolio"). The *Initialize* event can be used to initialize variable values and perform any preliminary actions associated with the new object. Similarly, the *Terminate* event can be used to reset any variable values and clear variable memory storage.

In our portfolio object example, we use the *Initialize* event to initialize all of our variable values. We would like to also note that we have declared our variables at the top of the class module, namely the "UserName," "PortSize," and "PortArray" variables. Since we assign the "PortName" variable, in the "PortName" property, to the "UserName" variable, we want to ensure that there is a default value for "UserName" in case the "PortName" property is used before the name has been set with the "SetName" property. We set this default value in this event procedure. We also want to set the default portfolio dimension to 1 (that is, one stock). We then give an initial stock name and value to store in the "PortArray" array. The complete *Initialize* event procedure is shown in Figure C.5.

```
Class                    Initialize
Option Base 1
Public PortSize As Integer, UserName As String
Dim PortArray() As Variant

Sub Class_Initialize()
'the initialize event for the procedure

'set default values
    UserName = "MyPortfolio"
    PortSize = 1

'initialize portfolio with default stock
    ReDim PortArray(2, 1)
    PortArray(1, 1) = "Stock1"
    PortArray(2, 1) = 50
End Sub
```

Figure C.5 The *Initialize* event is defined for the portfolio object.

C.2.5 Using New Class Objects

Once the object has been created with its corresponding properties, methods, and/or events, we can now use it in our main module procedure. To use a new object, we must first declare a variable of that object type and then create an instance of that object using the ***Set*** and ***New*** statements. The general format for performing these tasks is as follows:

Dim variable_name As object_name
Set variable_name = New object_name

We could also achieve this in one line of code as follows:

Dim variable_name As New object_name

Once we have done this declaration and object instance creation, we are free to use the object with its corresponding properties, methods, and/or events in the remainder of our module procedures. That is, now, when we type our new object variable name followed by a period, we should see a list of the properties, methods, and events created in our class module.

For our portfolio object example, we would create a new portfolio object variable in our main module as follows:

Dim MyPort As Portfolio
Set MyPort = New Portfolio

Here, "MyPort" is the name of the new object variable, and "Portfolio" is the name of the object that was created in the name property of the class module. Now, when we type "MyPort" in the remainder of the procedure, we should see the list of properties, methods, and events we created as shown in Figure C.6. Note that as soon as an instance of the object variable is declared, the *Initialize* event procedure is called automatically.

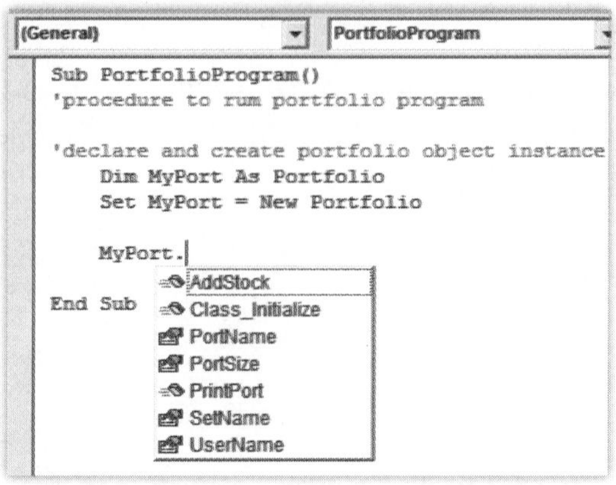

Figure C.6 The new portfolio object variable is created with corresponding object properties, methods, and events available.

Let us now use our new portfolio object variable to begin creating a specific portfolio. We can start by giving our portfolio a name, and then we can add a stock to it. To give our portfolio a name, we will use the *SetName* method we created earlier. We will simply type the following:

MyPort.SetName = "My New Portfolio"

This statement will automatically call the *SetName* procedure with the "NewName" parameter equal to "My New Portfolio." This string value will then be set to the "UserName" variable. We can output the portfolio name to the spreadsheet using the *PortName* property we created as follows:

Range("A1").Value = MyPort.PortName

This statement automatically calls the *PortName* procedure, which assigns the "PortName" value to the "UserName" variable. Now, let us add a stock to our portfolio. To do this, we will use the *AddStock* method we created with a given stock name and value. For example, we could type the following:

MyPort.AddStock StockName:="Stock2", StockVal:=35

The argument names and required data types will automatically appear as we are writing the method (see Figure C.7). This method will add this stock name and value to the "PortArray" array used in the class module. It will also increase the count for the total number of stocks in the portfolio using the "PortSize" variable in the class module. Note that neither of these variables is declared nor used in the main module as they are part of the class module procedures.

```
'add new stock to portfolio
    MyPort.AddStock StockName:="Stock2", StockVal:=35
                    AddStock(StockName As String, StockVal As Double)
```

Figure C.7 The method arguments and data types are given when using the method.

We can then print all of the stocks currently in our portfolio by using the *PrintPort* method we created as follows:

MyPort.PrintPort

This method will list the stocks with their corresponding values on the spreadsheet. The complete procedure for using the portfolio object is shown in Figure C.8. The output generated in the procedure is shown in Figure C.9.

```
(General)                                  PortfolioProgram

Sub PortfolioProgram()
'procedure to rum portfolio program

'declare and create portfolio object instance
    Dim MyPort As Portfolio
    Set MyPort = New Portfolio

'give a name to portfolio and display its value
    MyPort.SetName = "My New Portfolio"
    Range("A1").Value = MyPort.PortName

'add new stock to portfolio
    MyPort.AddStock StockName:="Stock2", StockVal:=35

'print entire portfolio
    MyPort.PrintPort

'clear portfolio object instance
    Set MyPort = Nothing
End Sub
```

Figure C.8 The complete procedure in the main module that uses the portfolio object.

	A	B
1	My New Portfolio	
2	Stock1	50
3	Stock2	35

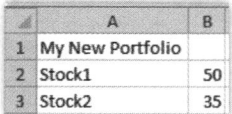

Figure C.9 The output from the *PortfolioProgram* procedure.

Thus, we have created and used a new object in VBA. We may think of other properties, methods, and events that could be created for the portfolio object. What are some other objects that may be useful to create for a DSS application?

C.3 *Opening Other Applications From VBA*

In this section, we describe how external programs or files can be opened from VBA. We will discuss how to open an executable program, a file, and a Microsoft application. There may be many situations in which calling another application from VBA may enhance the performance of our spreadsheet-based DSS.

C.3.1 Starting an Executable Program

It may be useful to open an executable program in VBA for several reasons. Suppose we have created a simulation application in VBA but would like to perform a more advanced simulation analysis using the Arena software; we may like to open the Arena application at some point in our code to perform the simulation or generate analysis reports. Suppose that we want to perform an advanced optimization using C++ or CPLEX; we may want to create our interface for inputs and output in Excel but call an executable file to perform the optimization.

To start an executable program from VBA, we will use the ***Shell*** function. The *Shell* function has two parameters: *PathName* and *WindowStyle*. The *PathName* parameter should be set to the path location of the program we want to open; it is a string value and should either be written using quotations or assigned to a string variable. The *WindowStyle* parameter determines how the program will be displayed. The table below gives a list of these parameter names and values along with a description of how the opened program will appear.

vbHide	0	Window is hidden and focus is passed to the hidden window. The **vbHide** constant is not applicable on Macintosh platforms.
vbNormalFocus	1	Window has focus and is restored to its original size and position.
vbMinimizedFocus	2	Window is displayed as an icon with focus.
vbMaximizedFocus	3	Window is maximized with focus.
vbNormalNoFocus	4	Window is restored to its most recent size and position. The currently active window remains active.
vbMinimizedNoFocus	6	Window is displayed as an icon. The currently active window remains active.

The format of the *Shell* function is then as follows:

Shell PathName:="...path_name...", WindowStyle:=vb...

We can also use the *Shell* function with its return value, called ***TaskID***. If the *Shell* function is able to successfully open the executable program, it will return the task ID, or unique program number, of the program. The format for using the *Shell* function in this manner is simply as follows:

TaskID = Shell("...path_name...", vb...)

Let us consider a simple example. Suppose we wish to open Adobe Acrobat. To open this executable program in a window of normal size and focus, we would type the following:

Shell PathName:="C:\Program Files\Adobe \Acrobat 8.0\Acrobat \Acrobat.exe ", _
WindowStyle:=vbNormalFocus

We recommend adding some error-checking code when using this function in case there is a problem when opening the program. That is, we may use the statement *On Error Resume Next* before using the *Shell* function. We could also check whether an error occurred using the *Err* object so that we could report an error message to the user if necessary. (Refer to Appendix B for more on error checking.) A completed procedure using the *Shell* function with error checking for opening Adobe Acrobat is shown in Figure C.10.

```
(General)                                    OutsideApp

Sub OutsideApp()
'procedure to run an outside application

'open Adobe Acrobat with Shell function ... used with executable files
    On Error Resume Next

    Shell PathName:="C:\Program Files\Adobe\Acrobat 8.0\Acrobat\Acrobat.exe", _
        WindowStyle:=vbNormalFocus

'or equivalently
    'TaskID = Shell("C:\Program Files\Adobe\Acrobat 8.0\Acrobat\Acrobat.exe", _
            vbNormalFocus)

    If Err <> 0 Then
        MsgBox "The application could not be opened.", vbCritical
    End If
End Sub
```

Figure C.10 The *Shell* function is used to open Adobe Acrobat.

Remember that the *Shell* function is only used to call an executable program; that is, the file in the path name must end with ".exe." Once the program is opened, it will run simultaneously with our VBA code. Therefore, the remainder of our VBA procedure should not depend on this application as it may finish executing before the opened program finishes.

C.3.2 Writing, Appending to, and Reading a File

There may be various reasons to access a file from VBA. We may need to input data from a text file or write output to a new file. We described in Chapter 21 how to input data from a text file to a spreadsheet using VBA. This required the use of the *ActiveSheet.QueryTables.Add* method, which reads and delimits the text file information in order to record it to the spreadsheet.

We may also wish to open an entire workbook in order to access information on its worksheets. To open a workbook, we can simply type the following:

Workbooks.Open ("...file_name...")

Here, the file name should end with ".xlsx." We may, for example, have a workbook with several sheets of information that we want to refer to in our procedures. We could open this workbook and then access its sheets by making the opened file active. To do this, we would type the following:

Windows("...file_name...").Activate

We could then use Worksheet and Range objects referring to this active workbook.

In addition to inputting information from a text file, we may also wish to access text files in order to record output. We will now discuss how to create a new file and write to it as well as how to open an existing file and append to or read from it. First, let us have a general discussion of the objects needed to perform these tasks.

When working with new or existing file objects, we use the ***FileSystemObject*** object type. To create this object, we define a variable, say "fileObject," and set it to this object type using the ***CreateObject*** function as follows:

Dim fileObject
Set fileObject = CreateObject("Scripting.FileSystemObject")

We can use any name for this object variable; here we have used "fileObject." Once the object is created, we will define an instance of this object depending on our objective of reading, writing, or appending. The general format for creating an instance of a file object is as follows:

Dim myFile
Set myFile = fileObject.OpenTextFile("...file_name...", IOmode, Format)

Here, we have defined the variable "myFile" to be the instance of the file object. Notice that we are using the "fileObject" FileSystemObject variable in order to create the instance. We specify that the object we are using is a text file by using the method ***OpenTextFile***. The arguments for this method are the file name, which must end with ".txt," the *IOmode*, and the *Format*. The *IOmode* refers to the input-output mode; that is, whether we are reading, writing, or appending to this text file object. These three parameter values are shown in the table below.

ForReading	1	To read a text file.
ForWriting	2	To write a new text file.
ForAppending	8	To append to an existing text file.

The *Format* argument determines the format in which the file will be opened. There are three parameter values for this format, which are shown in the table below.

TristateUseDefault	–2	Opens the file using the system default.
TristateTrue	–1	Opens the file as Unicode.
TristateFalse	0	Opens the file as ASCII.

For example, if we wish to create a new file, we would type the following (using the "myFile" and "fileObject" variables previously defined):

Set myFile = fileObject.OpenTextFile("NewFile.txt", 2, –2)

Here, we have created a new file called "NewFile.txt," which we can now write to. To write to a file, we use the ***Write*** method followed by a string of text. For example, we may write the following string to our new file:

myFile.Write "This is a new file."

Notice that we are using the "myFile" object variable, which has been set to this newly created file. We can write using text strings directly or string variables. We can also use the *vbCrLf* statement to create a new line in our file. When we are done writing to our new file, we should close the file by typing the following:

myFile.Close

Now let us suppose that we want to append text to an existing file. We should first create a new instance of our file object as follows:

Set myFile = fileObject.OpenTextFile("UserData.txt", 8, –2)

Here, we are opening a file called "UserData.txt" to append to it (*IOmode* = 8). Once we have opened the file, we can append to it using the *Write* method as shown above. We should again close the file when we are done appending to it.

To read a file, we again create an instance of the file object, this time with the *IOmode* parameter equal to 1.

Set myFile = fileObject.OpenTextFile("UserData.txt", 1, –2)

Here, we have opened the file "UserData.txt." There are then two options for reading from this file. We can read an entire line using the ***Readline*** method, or we can read the entire file using the ***Readall*** method. The *Readline* method may be used as follows:

MsgBox myFile.Readline

This would display the current line to the user in a Message Box. As we write this code repeatedly, the *Readline* method will move on to the next line in our file to read. The *Readall* method is used similarly, as follows:

MsgBox myFile.Readall

Here, all of the text in the file is displayed in a Message Box. (Note that we do not have to use a Message Box to display the text using these methods. We could store the text to a string variable or output to the spreadsheet.)

An example procedure using all of the techniques discussed in this section is shown in Figure C.11. The Message Boxes displayed for reading a line from the "NewFile.txt" file and for reading all of the text from the "UserData.txt" file are shown in Figure C.12.

```
(General)                                   OpenReadWriteFile

Sub OpenReadWriteFile()
'open another Excel file ... workbook
    Workbooks.Open ("Testing.xlsx")
    Windows("Testing.xlsx").Activate

'ForReading = 1, ForWriting = 2, ForAppending = 8
'Default = -2, Unicode = -1, ASCII = 0
    Dim fileObject, myFile
    Set fileObject = CreateObject("Scripting.FileSystemObject")

'write new file
    fileObject.createTextFile "NewFile.txt"
    Set myFile = fileObject.openTextFile("NewFile.txt", 2, -2)
    myFile.Write "This is a new file."
    myFile.Close

'append to file
    Set myFile = fileObject.openTextFile("UserData.txt", 8, -2)
    myFile.Write vbCrLf & "New data."
    myFile.Close

'read file
    Set myFile = fileObject.openTextFile("NewFile.txt", 1, -2)
   MsgBox myFile.readline, , "New File"

    Set myFile = fileObject.openTextFile("UserData.txt", 1, -2)
    MsgBox myFile.readall, , "User Data"
    myFile.Close
End Sub
```

Figure C.11 The *OpenReadWriteFile* procedure illustrates opening a workbook and creating a file object for writing, appending, and reading.

(a) **(b)**

Figure C.12 The Message Boxes displayed for the *Readline* method and *Readall* methods applied to the "NewFile.txt" and "UserData.txt" files, respectively.

C.3.3 Starting a Microsoft Application

One last useful way to open an outside application is to open another Microsoft application. This may be beneficial if we need to open a Microsoft Access database to display to a user who may want to view reports or table information. We may also want to open Microsoft Word to show a document or allow the user to write a document. We may also want to open Microsoft Outlook to allow the user to send an email related to the application.

To open a Microsoft application, we use the Application object with the ***ActivateMicrosoftApp*** method as follows:

Application.ActivateMicrosoftApp (xl...)

Here, the *xl* argument value should specify which Microsoft application we wish to open. For example, in Figure C.13, we write the code to open Microsoft Access.

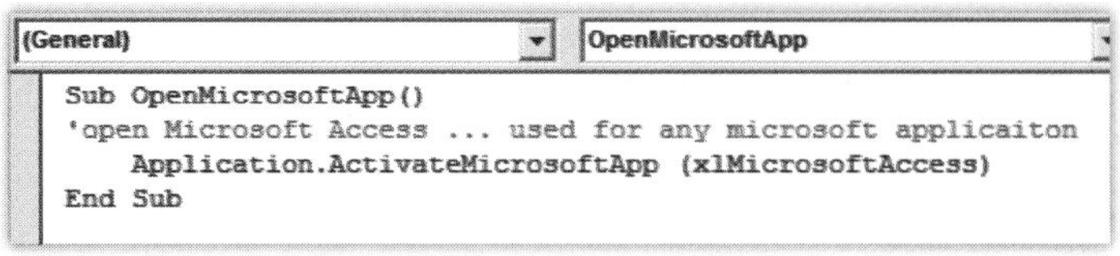
(General)
OpenMicrosoftApp
Sub OpenMicrosoftApp()
'open Microsoft Access ... used for any microsoft applicaiton
Application.ActivateMicrosoftApp (xlMicrosoftAccess)
End Sub

Figure C.13 Opening Microsoft Access.

C.4 *Summary*

- Object-oriented programming in the general sense implies that objects can be defined in the code along with their descriptive values and functions.
- To define a new object in VBA, we use class modules.
- There are two different types of property definitions that we can use to define for a new object: *Get* and *Let*. The *Get* property definition allows a user to get a property value for the object. The *Let* property definition allows a user to set a property value for the object.
- To define a new method, we use standard sub or function procedures.
- There are two events that can be defined for a new object: *Initialize* and *Terminate*. The *Initialize* event is automatically called whenever a new instance of the object is created, and the *Terminate* event is automatically called whenever the object instance is deleted.
- To use a new object, we must first declare a variable of that object type and then create an instance of that object using the *Set* and *New* statements.
- To start an executable program from VBA, we will use the *Shell* function. The *Shell* function has two parameters: *PathName* and *WindowStyle*.
- To open a workbook, we can simply type *Workbooks.Open*.
- When working with new or existing file objects, we use the *FileSystemObject* object type. To create this object, we define a variable and set it to this object type using the *CreateObject* function. We then specify that the object we are using is a text file by using the method *OpenTextFile*.
- To write to a file, we use the *Write* method followed by a string of text. There are then two options for reading from this file. We can read an entire line using the ***Readline*** method, or we can read the entire file using the *Readall* method.
- To open a Microsoft application, we use the Application object with the *ActivateMicrosoftApp* method.

References

We have composed a list of references for each part of the text. These references provide some, but not all, of the materials used to compose the book text, example files, exercise files, and case studies. The reader may refer to these sources to learn more details about Excel, VBA (including databases and SQL), or any of the specific case studies. We also list several general references which discuss decision support systems, GUI design, and programming principles.

Part I: Excel Essentials

Jelen, B. Microsoft *Excel 2010 In Depth*. Que Publishing, 2010.

Ragsdale, C.T. Spreadsheet Modeling & Decision Analysis: A Practical Introduction to Management Science. 6th Edition. South-Western Cengage Learning, 2011.

Risk Solver Platform Reference Guide. Frontline Solvers, 2010.

Risk Solver Platform User Guide. Frontline Solvers, 2010.

Walkenbach, J. Microsoft *Excel 2010 Bible*. Wiley Publishing Inc., 2010.

Walkenbach, J. Microsoft *Excel 2010 Formulas*. Wiley Publishing Inc., 2010.

Winston, W. *Microsoft Excel 2010 Data Analysis and Business Modeling*. Microsoft Press, 2011.

Part II: VBA for Excel

Albright, S.C. *VBA for Modelers*. 3rd Edition. South-Western Cengage Learning, 2010.

Chapra, S.C. VBA for Excel. 2nd Edition. Prentice Hall, 2010.

Connolly, T. and Begg, C. *Database Systems: A Practical Approach to Design, Implementation, and Management*. 5th Edition. Addison-Wesley Publishing Co., 2009.

Elmasri, R. and Navathe, S. *Fundamentals of Database Systems*. 6th Edition. Addison-Wesley Publishing Co., 2011.

Groff, J., Weinberg, P., Oppel, A. *SQL: The Complete Reference*. 3rd Edition. McGraw Hill, 2010.

Jelen, B. Syrstad, T. *VBA and Macros: Microsoft Excel 2010*. Que Publishing, 2010.

Risk Solver Platform Reference Guide. Frontline Solvers, 2010.

Risk Solver Platform User Guide. Frontline Solvers, 2010.

Walkenbach, J. *Excel 2010 Power Programming with VBA*. Wiley Publishing Inc., 2010.

Webb, J. and Saunders, S. Programming *Excel with VBA and .NET*. O'Reilly Media, Inc., 2006.

Part III: Case Studies

Ahuja, R., Magnanti, T. and Orlin, J. *Network Flows: Theory, Algorithms and Applications.* Prentice Hall, 1993.

Albright, S.C., Winston, W. and Zappe, C. *Data Analysis and Decision Making with Microsoft Excel.* 3rd Edition. South-Western Educational Publishing, 2008.

Chopra, S., and Miendl, S. *Supply Chain Management: Strategy, Planning, and Operations.* 4th Edition. Prentice Hall, 2010.

Francis, R., McGinnis, L. and White, J. *Facilities Layout and Location.* Prentice Hall, 1992.

Halliday, D., Walker, J. and Resnick, R. and *Fundamentals of Physics.* 9th Edition. John Wiley & Sons, Inc., 2010.

Luenberger, D. *Investment Science.* Oxford University Press, 1998.

Mirchandani, P. and Francis, R. (Eds.), *Discrete Location Theory,* Wiley, 1991.

Nahmias, S. *Production and Operations Analysis. 6th Edition.* McGraw Hill, 2008.

Winston, W. and Albright, S.C. *Practical Management Science.* 4th Edition. South-Western Cengage Learning, 2011.

Winston, W. and Venkataramanan, M. *Introduction to Mathematical Programming.* 4th Edition. Brooks/Cole, 2003.

Winston, W. *Decision Making Under Uncertainty with Risk Optimizer.* Palisade Corp., 1999.

Winston, W. *Introduction to Operations Research: Applications and Algorithms.* 4th Edition. Duxbury Press, 2003.

Winston, W. *Introduction to Probability Models.* 4th Edition. Brooks/Cole, 2004.

General References

Ahuja, R. and (Şeref) Hanna, M. Decision Support Systems Development: An Essential Part of OR Education. *Operations Research Letters* **31**, 2004, pp. 12–13.

Ahuja, R. and Pol, A. *Developing Web-Enabled Decision Support Systems.* Dynamic Ideas, 2007.

Caron, R. Microsoft Corporation: Coding Techniques and Programming Practices. http://msdn.microsoft.com/library/default.asp?url=/library/en-us/dnvsgen/html/cfr.asp, Feb 2000.

Chan, Y. and Storey, V. The use of spreadsheets in organizations: Determinants and consequences. *Information & Management* **31**, 1996.

Cragg, P. and King, M. Spreadsheet Modeling Abuse: An Opportunity for OR? *Journal of Operational Research Society* **44**, 1993.

Galitz, W. *The Essential Guide to User Interface Design: An Introduction to GUI Design Principles and Techniques.* 3rd Edition. Wiley Publishing, 2007.

Gass, S., Hirshfeld, D. and Wasil, E. Model world: The spreadsheeting of OR/MS. *Interfaces* **30**, 2000.

Geoffrion, A. and Krishnan, R. Prospects for operations research in the e-business era. *Interfaces* **31(2)**, 2001, pp. 6–36.

Hess, R. and Scerno, D. How Electronic Spreadsheets Changed the World. *Interfaces* **39(2)**, 2009, pp. 159–167.

Johnson, J. *GUI Bloopers 2.0.* Morgan Kaufmann, 2008.

LeBlanc, L. and Galberth, M. Implementing Large-Scale Optimization Models in Excel via VBA. *Interfaces* **37(4)**, 2007, pp. 370–382.

Mandel, T. *Elements of User Interface Design.* John Wiley & Sons, 1997.

Olavson, T. and Fry, C. Spreadsheet Decision-Support Tools: Lessons Learned at Hewlett-Packard. *Interfaces* **38(4)**, 2008, pp. 300–310.

Power, D. and Sharda, R. Model-Driven DSS: Concepts and Research Directions. *Decision Support Systems* **43(3)**, 2007, pp. 1044–1061.

Power, D. *Decision Support Systems: Concepts and Resources for Managers*. Quorum Books, 2002.

Power, D. *DSS Resources*, 2011. URL = http://www.dssresources.com

Ragsdale, C. Teaching management science with spreadsheets: From decision models to decision support. *INFORMS Transactions on Education* **1(2)**, 2001, pp. 68–74.

Şeref, M. and Ahuja, R. Spreadsheet-Based Decision Support Systems. In: *International Handbook on Information Systems*. Bernus, P., Blazewicz, J., Schmidt, G. and Shaw, M. Eds. Springer, 2007, pp. 277–297.

Turban, E. Sharda, R. and Delen, D. *Decision Support and Business Intelligent Systems*. 9th Edition. Prentice-Hall, 2010.

About the Authors

Sandra D. Ekşioğlu

Sandra Ekşioğlu is an Assistant Professor at Mississippi State University (MSU), in the Department of Industrial and Systems Engineering. Her research is focused in the area of Operations Research (OR). She uses OR tools to model and solve large scale supply chain design and management, logistics management and transportation-related problems. Sandra's research on biomass-to-biofuel supply chain has resulted on a number of innovative models and solution algorithms that improve the performance of this supply chain. She received the NSF CAREER Award in support of this research. Sandra has taught the Information Systems for Industrial Engineers class at MSU for several semesters. This class teaches students how to build Spreadsheet-Based Decision Support Systems. Sandra used the feedback and comments from students to make valuable additions and modifications to this new edition of the book.

Michelle M.H. Şeref

Michelle Şeref has a Ph.D. in Operations Management from the University of Florida and a Master's and Bachelor's degree in Industrial and Systems Engineering from the same university. Michelle wrote her Master's thesis on decision support system development and design while simultaneously working on the first edition of this book and the creation of educational materials for a course in DSS. Michelle's Ph.D. dissertation focused on supply chain management decisions under various marketing strategies, including advance sales inventory management and new product development pricing and timing decisions. Using her advanced education and research experience in optimizing operations decisions, Michelle is now pursuing a second Ph.D. in rhetoric and communication to study the relationship between social behavior and language. Michelle's new dissertation focus is on causes and remedies of miscommunication in intercultural and interdisciplinary communication. She plans to complete her new Ph.D. at Virginia Tech and continue her career in academia.

Ravindra K. Ahuja

Ravindra Ahuja is a Professor in Industrial and Systems Engineering at the University of Florida, Gainesville, and also the founding President & CEO of Innovative Scheduling, Inc., a company focused on developing business intelligence solutions for large-scale and complex problems arising in logistics and transportation. Professor Ahuja has contributed both to the theory and applications of Operations Research and his contributions have received highly competitive awards from INFORMS, including 1993 Lanchester Prize, 2003 Pierskalla Award, 2006 Wagner Prize, 2007 Koopman Prize, and INFORMS Fellowship in 2008. He is a coauthor of the widely used text and reference book, "Network Flows: Theory, Algorithms, and Applications." He is also a coauthor of the companion book, "Developing Web-Enabled Decision Support Systems," which describes how to build web applications using VB .NET and ASP .NET. Professor Ahuja consults for several Fortune 500 companies.

Wayne L. Winston

Wayne Winston is a professor at the Kelly School of Business at Indiana University, Bloomington, in the Department of Operation & Decision Technologies. He has a Masters degree from MIT in mathematics and a Ph.D. from Yale University in operations research. Professor Winston has written several widely used textbooks on spreadsheet modeling and operations research, including *Introduction to Mathematical Programming, Introduction to Probability Models*, and *Practical Management Science*. His primary research areas are spreadsheet models, applied probability, dynamic programming, quality control, and math and sports. He teaches various spreadsheet modeling courses in the MBA program at Indiana University and has been the recipient of the Lilly Award for Teaching Excellence four times. Professor Winston is also involved in several consulting projects with companies including Eli Lilly, Bristol Myers Squibb, Microsoft, Intel, Cisco, the Dallas Mavericks, and the Department of Defense and US Army. He is also a two-time Jeopardy! champion.

Index

B

S